"This rollicking western about a woman who'll do anything to save her family is based on the true tale of one of the country's first female deputy sheriffs."

—*People,* **Best Books of the Fall**

"Stars an unforgettable, not-to-be-messed-with heroine . . . The rest is kick-ass history."

—*Marie Claire*

"*Girl Waits with Gun* might sometimes be a story in which truth is stranger than fiction, but it also makes for pretty charming fiction."

—**NPR**

"Fans of strong female characters will find their new favorite heroine in Constance Kopp . . . *Girl Waits with Gun* is a historical thrill ride, racing through funny, tragic, and terrifying scenes."

—*Cosmopolitan,* **24 New Books to Read This Fall**

"[Stewart's] created several memorable characters here, in particular Constance, who, enterprising and independent but with a closely guarded sorrow in her past, seems like an American answer to Maisie Dobbs."

—*USA Today,* **New and Noteworthy**

"[A] confident, charming, sure-footed debut—a fresh, winning and delightful mystery with a warm heart, impish humor and a heroine who quietly shatters convention."

—*Dallas Morning News*

"You will be cheering Constance Kopp on through every page. The race to catch a murderer is thrilling in itself, but the powerful woman driving the book is what will really keep readers turning pages!"—*Bustle,* **11 Smart Books to Read If You Love Thrillers**

"How could you not fall in love with a book about one of the first female deputy sheriffs and her sisters—especially when it's written by the enthralling Amy Stewart? Full of long-held secrets, kicked-up dust, simmering danger, and, oh yes, that gun—this gritty romp illuminates one of history's strongest women with a hold-your-breath panache."

—Caroline Leavitt, *New York Times* best-selling author of
Is This Tomorrow and *Pictures of You*

"*Girl Waits with Gun* makes excellent use of history to put a fresh spin on classic cop-and-crook types. Amy Stewart's true-life protagonist is a 'rough and tumble' version of the early twentieth century's New Woman. She is witty, sharply drawn, and suffers no fools!" —Suzanne Rindell, author of *The Other Typist*

"*Girl Waits with Gun* is fresh, funny, and utterly compelling—and Constance Kopp and her sisters are not just great investigators, but completely original women. It was a blast from start to finish and I can't wait to see what Deputy Kopp gets up to next."

—Lisa Lutz, author of *The Spellman Files,*
How to Start a Fire, and others

"Amy Stewart has crafted the best kind of historical novel; she uncovers an intriguing, all-but-forgotten historical nugget and spins it into a wildly entertaining tale with an engaging, tough-minded heroine. *Girl Waits with Gun* hits the bull's-eye."

—Daniel Stashower, author of *The Hour of Peril: The Secret Plot*
to Murder Lincoln Before the Civil War

"Amy Stewart's debut novel, *Girl Waits with Gun,* is an irresistible and thoroughly enjoyable book, a suspenseful historical mystery spiced with marvelous characters, wit, and humor. Is it too soon to beg for a sequel?"

—Jennifer Chiaverini, author of *Mrs. Grant and Madame Jule*

"Engaging, lively, and substantive, *Girl Waits with Gun* is a perfect mystery, and the Kopp sisters are my new best friends. Amy Stewart writes about crime as well as she writes about plants and poisons. I loved this book, and will be first in line for the next installment."

—Sara Gran, author of *Claire DeWitt and the Bohemian Highway*

"Yowza! Amy Stewart's debut boasts pomaded gangsters, pistol-packin' dames, kidnappings, shots in the dark, and everything from Girls Gone Wrong to carrier pigeons finding their way home. You might want to stay up all night reading, you might want to lie down on your fainting couch with a cool cloth on your forehead. Either way, you'll have the time of your life."

—Robert Goolrick, *New York Times* best-selling author of *A Reliable Wife*

"A smart, romping adventure, featuring some of the most memorable and powerful female characters I've seen in print for a long time. I loved every page as I followed the Kopp sisters through a too-good-to-be-true (but mostly true!) tale of violence, courage, stubbornness, and resourcefulness." —Elizabeth Gilbert

GIRL WAITS
WITH GUN

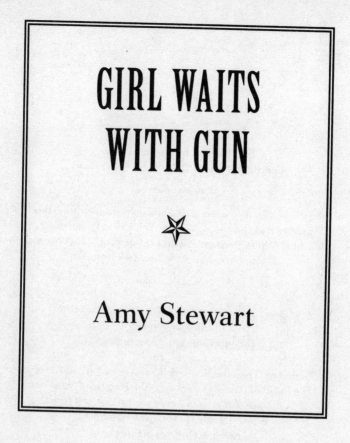

GIRL WAITS
WITH GUN

Amy Stewart

Mariner Books
Houghton Mifflin Harcourt
Boston   New York

First Mariner Books edition 2016
Copyright © 2015 by the Stewart-Brown Trust

www.hmhco.com

Library of Congress Cataloging-in-Publication Data
Stewart, Amy.
Girl waits with gun / Amy Stewart.
pages ; cm
Summary: "From the New York Times best-selling author of
The Drunken Botanist comes an enthralling novel based on
the forgotten true story of one of the nation's first female
deputy sheriffs"—Provided by publisher.
ISBN 978-1-328-79921-0 (pbk)
1. Sheriffs—New Jersey—Paterson—Fiction. 2. Policewomen—
New Jersey—Hackensack—Fiction. 3. Silk Workers' Strike, Paterson,
N.J., 1913—Fiction. 4. Black Hand (United States)—History—20th
century—Fiction. 5. Organized crime—New Jersey—Fiction.
6. New Jersey—History—20th century—Fiction. I. Title.
PS3619.T49343G57 2015
813'.6—dc23   2014045223

Book design by Greta D. Sibley

Printed in the United States of America
DOC 10 9 8 7 6 5 4 3 2 1
4500640146

To John Birgel and Dennis O'Dell

"I got a revolver to protect us," said Miss Constance,
"and I soon had use for it."

— *New York Times*, June 3, 1915

1

OUR TROUBLES BEGAN in the summer of 1914, the year I turned thirty-five. The Archduke of Austria had just been assassinated, the Mexicans were revolting, and absolutely nothing was happening at our house, which explains why all three of us were riding to Paterson on the most trivial of errands. Never had a larger committee been convened to make a decision about the purchase of mustard powder and the replacement of a claw hammer whose handle had split from age and misuse.

Against my better judgment I allowed Fleurette to drive. Norma was reading to us from the newspaper as she always did.

"'Man's Trousers Cause Death,'" Norma called out.

"It doesn't say that." Fleurette snorted and turned around to get a look at the paper. The reins slid out of her hands.

"It does," Norma said. "It says that a Teamster was in the habit of hanging his trousers over the gas jet at night but, being under the influence of liquor, didn't notice that the trousers smothered the flame."

"Then he died of gas poisoning, not of trousers."

"Well, the trousers—"

The low, goosey cry of a horn interrupted Norma. I turned just in time to see a black motor car barreling toward us, tearing down Hamilton and picking up speed as it crossed the intersection. Fleurette jumped up on the footboard to wave the driver off.

"Get down!" I shouted, but it was too late.

The automobile hit us broadside, its brakes shrieking. The sound of our buggy shattering was like a firecracker going off in our ears. We tumbled over in a mess of splintered wood and bent metal. Our harness mare, Dolley, faltered and went down with us. She let out a high scream, the likes of which I had never heard from a horse.

Something heavy pinned my shoulder. I reached around and found it was Norma's foot. "You're standing on me!"

"I am not. I can't even see you," Norma said.

Our wagon rocked back and forth as the motor car reversed its engine and broke free of the wreckage. I was trapped under the overturned rear seat. It was as dark as a coffin, but there was a dim shape below me that I believed to be Fleurette's arm. I didn't dare move for fear of crushing her.

From the clamor around us, I gathered that someone was trying to rock the wagon and get it upright. "Don't!" I yelled. "My sister's under the wheel." If the wheel started to turn, she'd be caught up in it.

A pair of arms the size of tree branches reached into the rubble and got hold of Norma. "Take your hands off me!" she shouted.

"He's trying to get you out," I called. With a grunt, she accepted the man's help. Norma hated to be manhandled.

Once she was free, I climbed out behind her. The man attached to the enormous arms wore an apron covered in blood. For one terrible second, I thought it was ours, then I realized he was a butcher at the meat counter across the street.

He wasn't the only one who had come running out when the automobile hit us. We were surrounded by store clerks, locksmiths, grocers, delivery boys, shoppers—in fact, most of the stores on Market Street had emptied, their occupants drawn to the spectacle we were now providing. Most of them watched from the sidewalk, but a sizable contingent surrounded the motor car, preventing its escape.

The butcher and a couple of men from the print shop, their hands black with ink, helped us raise the wagon just enough to allow Fleurette to slide clear of the wheel. As we lifted the broken panels off her, Fleurette stared up at us with wild dark eyes. She wore a dress sheathed in pink taffeta. Against the dusty road she looked like a trampled bed of roses.

"Don't move," I whispered, bending over her, but she got her arms underneath herself and sat up.

"No, no, no," said one of the printers. "We'll call for a doctor."

I looked up at the men standing in a circle around us. "She'll be fine," I said, sliding a hand over her ankle. "Go on." Some of those men looked a little too eager to help with the examination of Fleurette's legs.

They shuffled off to help two livery drivers, who had disembarked from their own wagons to tend to our mare. They freed her from the harness and she struggled to stand. The poor creature groaned and tossed her head and blew steam from her nostrils. The drivers fed her something from their pockets and that seemed to settle her.

I gave Fleurette's calf a squeeze. She howled and jerked away from me.

"Is it broken?" she asked.

I couldn't say. "Try to move it."

She screwed her face into a knot, held her breath, and gingerly bent one leg and then the other. When she was finished she let her breath go all at once and looked up at me, panting.

"That's good," I said. "Now move your ankles and your toes."

We both looked down at her feet. She was wearing the most ridiculous white calfskin boots with pink ribbons for laces.

"Are they all right?" she asked.

I put my hand on her back to steady her. "Just try to move them. First your ankle."

"I meant the boots."

That's when I knew Fleurette would survive. I unlaced the boots and promised to look after them. A much larger crowd had gathered, and Fleurette wiggled her pale-stockinged toes for her new audience.

"You'll have quite a bruise tomorrow, miss," said a lady behind us.

The seat that had trapped me a few moments ago was resting on the ground. I helped Fleurette into it and took another look at her legs. Her stockings were torn and she was scratched and bruised, but not broken to bits as I'd feared. I offered my handkerchief to press against one long and shallow cut along her ankle, but she'd already lost interest in her own injuries.

"Look at Norma," she whispered with a wicked little smile. My sister had planted herself directly in the path of the motor car to prevent the men from driving away. She did make a comical sight, a small but stocky figure in her split riding skirt of drab cotton. Norma had the broad Slavic face and thick nose of our father and our mother's sour disposition. Her mouth was set in a permanent frown and she looked on everyone with suspicion. She stared down the driver of the motor car with the kind of flat-footed resolve that came naturally to her in times of calamity.

The automobilist was a short but solidly built young man who had an overfed look about him, hinting at a privileged life. He would have been handsome if not for an indolent and spoiled aspect about his eyes and the tough set of his mouth, which suggested he was accustomed to getting his way. His face was puffy and red from the heat, but also, I suspected, from a habit of putting away a quart of beer at breakfast and a bottle of wine at night. He was dressed exceedingly well, in striped linen trousers, a silk waistcoat with polished brass buttons, and a tie as red as the blood seeping through Fleurette's stockings.

His companions tumbled out of the car and gathered around him as if standing guard. They wore the plain broadcloth suits of working men and carried themselves like rats who weren't accustomed to being spotted in the daylight. Each of them was unkempt and unshaven, and a few kept their hands in their pockets in a manner that suggested they might be reaching for their knives. I couldn't imagine where this gang of ruffians had been off to in such a hurry, but I was already beginning to regret that we had been the ones to get in their way.

The driver waved his arms and shouted for the crowd to clear the road. The other men took up his command and started yelling at the onlookers and pushing at them like drunks in a barroom brawl—all but one of them, who backed away and tried to run. He stumbled and the men in the crowd easily took hold of him. With twenty or so people blocking the way, the motor car's engine sputtered and died, but the shouting and shoving went on.

I couldn't catch Norma's eye. She was taking them in, too, the outrage draining from her face as she realized that this gang was trouble.

The shopkeepers, clerks, and drivers of other automobiles now stalled along the curb were all barking orders and pointing fingers at once.

"You're going to pay these ladies for what you did!" one yelled.

"Their horse spooked!" the driver shouted back. "They ran right in front of us!"

A ripple of dissent rose up. Everyone knew that the horse was never to blame in these collisions. A horse could watch where it was going, but an automobile with an inattentive driver could not. These boys had obviously had something on their minds besides the traffic when they roared into town.

I couldn't leave Norma to face them by herself. I gave Fleurette a firm pat to keep her planted on the buggy seat and ran around to stand next to Norma. All eyes traveled over to me. As the tallest and the oldest, I must have looked like the responsible party.

There was no one to introduce us, but it was the only way I knew to begin.

"I am Constance Kopp," I said, "and these are my sisters."

I addressed the men with all the dignity I could muster, considering that I'd just been upside down in an overturned buggy. The driver of the motor car looked pointedly away as if he couldn't be bothered to listen to me, and in fact made a great show of behaving as if I weren't standing right in front of him. I took a breath and spoke louder. "As soon as we settle on the damages, you may be on your way."

The one who had tried to run away—a tall, thin man with droopy eyes and a prominent front tooth—leaned over and whispered something to the rest of them. They appeared to be making some kind of plan. As he hobbled around to discuss the situation, I saw that his limp was caused by a wooden leg.

The driver of the automobile nodded at his friends and reached for the door handle. He was going to push through the crowd and drive off without a word! Norma started to say something but I held her back.

He pried the door open. Seeing no alternative, I ran over and slammed it shut.

This elicited a satisfied little gasp from the bystanders, who were clearly enjoying themselves. I saw no choice but to press my advantage. I stepped up and stood as tall as I possibly could, which meant that I towered above him considerably. He was about to address my collarbone, but thought better of it and lifted his chin to stare me in the face. His mouth hung open slightly, and as I watched, perfectly round beads of sweat bloomed in even rows above his lip.

"I suppose we may require a new buggy, as you seem to have smashed this one beyond repair," I said. A pin sprung loose from my hat at that moment and rang like a tiny bell as it hit the gravel. I had to force myself not to look down at it and hoped there were no other pins or fasteners working their way loose, as they could in moments of great agitation like these.

"Get offa my car, lady," he said between clenched teeth.

I glared down at him. Neither of us moved. "If you refuse to pay, then I must see your license plate," I declared.

He lifted one brow as if issuing a challenge. At that I marched around to write the plate number in a little notebook I carried in my handbag.

"Don't bother with this," Norma said from just behind me. "I don't like them looking at us."

"I don't either, but we need his name," I said in a low hiss.

"I don't care to know his name."

"But I do."

People were starting to crane their necks to hear us argue. I walked back around to the man and said, "Perhaps you'll save me the trouble of asking the state of New Jersey for your name and address."

He looked around at the crowd and, seeing no alternative, leaned toward me. He smelled of hair tonic and (as I'd suspected) liquor and the hard, metallic stench that leaked out of all the factories in town. He spat the particulars at me, releasing a wave of abdominal breath that forced me to take a step back as I wrote them down: Henry Kaufman of Kaufman Silk Dyeing Company on Putnam.

"That will do, Mr. Kaufman," I said, in a voice loud enough for the others to hear. "You'll have our invoice in a few days."

He made no answer but swung back into the driver's seat. One of his friends gave the engine a hard crank and the motor roared to life. They all climbed aboard and the car lurched ahead, clearing a path through the mob of shoppers. Men held their horses back and mothers pulled their children to the sidewalks as the motor car careened away.

Norma and I watched the dust rise up behind Henry Kaufman's tires and settle back down again.

"You let them go?" Fleurette said from her perch on our buggy's broken seat. She had assumed the pose of an audience member at a play and seemed very disappointed in our performance.

"I didn't want to spend another minute with them," Norma said. "They're the worst people I've ever seen. And look what they've done to your leg."

"Is it broken?" asked Fleurette, who knew it wasn't but loved to elicit from Norma one of her gloomy predictions.

"Oh, probably, but we can set the bone ourselves if we have to."

"I suppose my dancing career is at an end."

"Yes, I believe it is."

The livery drivers led a shaky but intact Dolley back to us. What remained of our buggy had been moved to the sidewalk, where it lay in a dozen or so pieces.

"I'm not sure it can be repaired," one of the liverymen said, "but I could send my stable boy around to the carriage shops to inquire."

"Oh, there's no need for that," Norma said. "Our brother will come and fetch it. He drives a wagon for work."

"But let's not involve Francis!" Fleurette protested. "He'll blame it on my driving."

I stepped between them, not wanting the liveryman to withdraw his offer of help while we squabbled. "Sir, if you could send your boy to my brother's place of business, I'd be very grateful." I wrote down the address of the basket importer where Francis worked.

"I'll take care of it," he said. "But how are you girls getting home?"

"Constance and I can walk," Norma said quickly, "and our little sister will ride."

I wasn't sure I could walk. I was already stiff and sore from the crash and it would be past dark by the time we got home. But I was in no mood to debate Norma, so I accepted the man's offer of a saddle for Dolley. We lifted Fleurette into place and wrapped her injured foot in a flour sack before sliding it into the stirrup. Norma took hold of Dolley's reins and we shuffled down Market, looking more like refugees from a war than three sisters out shopping for an afternoon.

Ordinarily, I would have considered getting run down by an automobile to be the worst sort of catastrophe that could befall the three of us. But this was not to be an ordinary year.

❧ 2 ❧

THE NEXT MORNING the sun worked past the half-curtained windows and hit the mirror on the wall opposite, casting a blinding light across my bed. Even at that early hour, the air was heavy and unbearably hot. I kicked the blanket away and tried to sit up. As soon as my feet touched the floor I knew I'd been hurt worse than I had realized. My right arm was useless, the shoulder red and hot and bruised so badly that I could hardly bear to move it. With some difficulty I opened the top buttons of my nightgown and slid out of it. I was hardly able to stand, but after a few attempts, I forced myself upright and struggled into the first dress I could find that didn't require me to raise my arm above my head.

Walking was nearly impossible. My hip felt like it had been pushed out of joint. I couldn't quite hold myself upright, and every time I put weight on my left leg, my knee cried out in pain.

This was not the soreness of a hard day's work. It felt more like the aftermath of a beating. I made my way to the hall and kept one hand on the rail as I shuffled downstairs.

I found Fleurette in the kitchen, eating a boiled egg with a spoon.

"Bonjour," she said. After Mother died last year, Fleurette took to imitating her speech mannerisms. Mother, having grown up in Vienna with a French father and an Austrian mother, spoke French and two distinct styles of German. Fleurette preferred the French for its romantic flourishes. Norma and I found the affectation tiresome, but we had conferred on it and decided to ignore it.

"Let me see your foot."

She lifted her skirt and presented a badly bandaged ankle. The cloth was stained a rusted brown. I am sorry to admit that it was a stagnation of dried blood, and not our poorly situated pins, that held the bandage in place.

"Ach. We did not take very good care of you last night."

"Je pense que c'est cassé."

"Surely not. Can't you move it? Stand up."

Fleurette didn't move. She picked at her egg cup and kept her eyes down. "Norma said to tell you that Francis—" But before she could finish, there was a rattle at the kitchen door and my brother let himself in.

"Which one of you was driving?" he said. With Mother gone, Francis had taken on the proprietary air of the man of the house, even though he'd been married and living in Hawthorne for years.

Fleurette—who looks people square in the face when she lies to them—turned to Francis and said, "Constance, of course. I'm too young to drive, and Norma was reading the paper."

"It doesn't matter who was driving," I said. "That man aimed his machine directly at us. Dolley could have been killed."

"*I* could have been killed," Fleurette said with a dramatic roll of her eyes. She shifted around in her chair to give Francis a look at the purple bruise emerging just above her knee. He turned away, embarrassed.

"She'll be fine, won't she?" he asked, and I nodded. He held the door open and gestured for me to come along for a private scolding and an examination of the wreckage he'd just delivered.

Outside was a wide and airy barn that housed Dolley, an occasional goat or pig, and a dozen or so chickens. The eaves had been extended on one side to accommodate Norma's pigeon loft. The imbalance between the two sides of the building made it seem in constant danger of losing its footing. Next to it, facing the drive, was the entrance to our root cellar. A few summers ago, Francis had laid the stone walk that led us there.

He spoke in a low voice so Fleurette couldn't listen in from the kitchen door. "Who is this man, this Harry—what was it?"

"Henry Kaufman," I said, "of Kaufman Silk Dyeing Company."

That brought him to a stop as surely as if he'd walked into a wall. He planted his feet and looked down at them with a long and loud exhale. This was a mannerism of our father's, one I had almost forgotten until Francis reached the age at which exasperation became an everyday emotion. Francis had our father's light brown hair and his pale Czech features, but where our father had managed to take a high forehead and light, intelligent eyes and make himself into something of a ruffian, Francis took the same features and composed them into those of a serious gentleman, with perfectly slicked and combed hair and a mustache that turned up neatly at the ends.

"He's a silk man? Are you sure?"

"One can hardly picture him running a factory, but that's the address he gave. He's on Putnam with all the others."

He shook his head and squinted at Norma, who had heard us coming and backed out of her pigeon loft. She took her time locking it behind her. Norma had cut her hair short this spring, insisting on doing it herself and chopping at it until her brown curls framed her face unevenly. In the last few years, she'd taken to wearing riding boots and a split skirt that fell to just above her ankles. In this costume she would climb ladders to repair a gutter or traipse down to the creek to trap a rabbit. Fleurette used to sing a little song to her that went, "Pants are made for men and not for women. Women are made for men and not for pants." Norma took offense at the song but nonetheless insisted that what she wore could not be considered pants in the least.

"You aren't hurt," I said, as she walked up. At least one of us could still move.

"My head aches terribly," she said, "from listening to Fleurette go on about how she was nearly killed yesterday. She talks too much for a girl who is almost dead."

"I wondered why she was up so early. She's been rehearsing her story for Francis."

"Listen to me, both of you," Francis said. He put a hand on each of us and led us down the drive to his wagon. "This man Kaufman. What exactly did he say?"

"As little as he could before roaring off in that machine with all his hoodlum friends," I said, as I reached up with my good arm to help Francis pull the tarpaulin off the back of his wagon. "But I let him know that he should expect—Oh."

The buggy was a horror of splintered wood and twisted metal. Until now I hadn't thought about exactly how it had looked when we left it in Paterson, but here it was, this fragile veneer of wood panels and leather and brass fittings that had done so little to shelter us from the force of Henry Kaufman's automobile.

Norma and I stared at it. It was a wonder we'd survived.

Francis removed his hat and ran a hand through his hair. "I can't be out here all the time looking after you girls."

"We haven't asked you to look after us," I said. "We only needed our buggy brought here, and that wasn't too much of a bother, was it?"

"No, but without a man around the place—"

"We haven't had a man around the place since you married!" I interrupted. "And what difference would it have made? He hit us broadside with his automobile. There was nothing you could have done."

"It doesn't matter. You shouldn't be out here by yourselves," Francis said, "especially now that you've lost your buggy. Wouldn't you rather stay in town with us?"

"I prefer not to live in a town," Norma said. "Going to town nearly got us killed yesterday, in case you've forgotten. We're much safer here."

Francis looked down at his feet again—this had been our father's way of stopping himself from saying something he didn't want to say—and worked his jaw back and forth for a minute before giving in. "All right. I'll take care of the repairs. I know a man in Hackensack who can do it. It looks bad, but

I think it can be rebuilt. The gears are fine, and most of the panels came apart at their seams."

"We can arrange for the repairs," I said, "and Henry Kaufman will pay for it."

"You can't make him pay, and you shouldn't have anything to do with him," Francis said. "You know what these men are like. Didn't you see what they did to the strikers last year?"

Francis didn't have to remind me. Everyone had seen what happened to the strikers. The mill owners got it into their heads that a worker could operate four looms at a time, instead of two, and do it for ten hours a day instead of eight. Three hundred mills shut down. Factory workers in New York City walked off the job in solidarity. The streets in Paterson were choked with outraged strikers. Even the children who worked as pickers and twisters in the mills took up their placards and marched.

The mill owners used their considerable influence to have the police turn up at rallies and arrest as many people as the jails would hold. When the police were overwhelmed, the silk men hired their own private force. That's when houses started burning down. That's when speeches were interrupted by gunshots. That's when bakeries and butchers were warned not to sell food to the strikers. Eventually the workers were too starved and defeated to do anything but return to their looms.

The silk men behaved as if they owned Paterson. But none of them had the right to run us down in the street and get away with it.

"Mr. Kaufman doesn't frighten me," I said. "He will pay what he owes."

⤐ 3 ⤏

THAT BUSINESS about us moving in with Francis began on the evening of our mother's funeral, after a supper of ham sandwiches and pickles and Bessie's lemon cake. While Norma and Fleurette washed the dishes, I sat with Francis on his back porch and watched him fill his pipe. From the lane behind the house came the sound of his children playing some game whose rules were known only to them, but which seemed to involve tossing a stick through a large metal hoop. I settled into a reed chair next to him and breathed my first calm breath of the day. It did not last.

"You know Bessie and I would love to have you girls come live with us," Francis said once he'd gotten his tobacco to smolder.

I groaned and kicked my feet up on the porch rail. "That was very unconvincing. Besides, you don't have room for the brood you've already got."

"Well, the uncles don't have room for you back in Brooklyn, either. I don't know where else you'd go."

There had been a sudden shower after the burial, but the sky had cleared while we were eating our supper. Against the gathering dark the first few stars appeared. I looked up at them and realized that on that night, and forever after, my mother would be sleeping outdoors, under the stars, under her blanket of earth. She despised dirt and rarely went outdoors, and would have been horrified by her new circumstances if she'd given any thought to it at all before buying that burial plot.

"Why do we have to go anywhere?" I said.

"You can't stay on the farm by yourselves. Three girls, all alone out there?"

"How is that so different from when Mother was alive? Are four girls any better than three?"

If Francis understood that I was teasing him, he didn't show it. He tapped his pipe and thought seriously about it for a minute. "Well, the only reason you were out there in the first place—"

I leaned over and shushed him when I heard Fleurette in the kitchen. We waited with our heads inclined toward the window, but we couldn't tell where she'd gone.

Francis lowered his voice. "All I mean to say is that she's nearly grown now. What are you going to do when she's ready to go off and get married? Live out there like a couple of old spinsters?"

The idea of Fleurette as a bride sent a jolt through my rib cage. "Marriage? She's only fourteen! Besides—" Before I could finish, Fleurette's voice sailed through the window screen.

"I'm fifteen!"

Francis rubbed his eyes and shifted around in his chair to

face me. "You girls are my responsibility now, and you should be with us. You could help Bessie around the house, and you could . . ." He trailed off, having exhausted the list of things he thought the three of us could do.

I rose to my feet, shaking out the gray-and-black tweed Fleurette had chosen as my mourning costume, and bent over Francis's chair.

"We can manage on our own," I whispered. "And if Bessie needs as much help as you say, we'll hire out Fleurette for the summer. She needs something to occupy her time."

"I'm not for hire!" Fleurette shouted.

AFTER THAT, Francis turned up every few months with another well-intentioned scheme to guarantee some sort of future for the three of us. The fact that we were unmarried and lacking an income that would keep us for life had not bothered him as much while Mother was alive. But he seemed to feel that he had inherited us when she died. He had grown into the sort of man who worried constantly over his small responsibilities: his snug little house in Hawthorne, his generous and resourceful wife, his secure employment, and his two healthy and well-behaved children. It did not seem to me that he should have any worries at all, but Francis was a man who brooded. Lacking any troubles of a more serious nature, he took to brooding over us.

Most men of his age had an unencumbered female relative or two tucked in an attic bedroom, so he must have seen it as inevitable that he would eventually take on a few as well. He did understand that we would have to be kept occupied, so his schemes always included tedious domestic employment for the three of us.

The house next door to his was put up for sale, and he suggested buying it and having us run it as a boarding house — on his behalf, of course, with the rents going to pay the mortgage. We refused, as we had no interest in becoming boarders in our own boarding house.

He then offered to hire me and Norma to tutor his children, even though they were learning their letters and numbers in school and didn't require the services of two grown women. Fleurette, he suggested, could take in work as a seamstress. When Francis talked about bringing in other people's torn and rotten clothing for repair, I just looked at him as if I'd never seen him before and wondered aloud if he remembered anything about the woman who raised him.

That's not to say that I didn't worry about what would become of us. We'd tried to find a few tenant farmers, but there was enough land for sale that no one particularly needed to rent from us. We had been forced to sell off a lot every few years just to keep going and were left with an oddly shaped thirty-acre parcel not accessible by any road but Sicomac, where the house was situated. It would be difficult to sell any more of it without building a new road right through our land, and, besides, I thought it best to keep what little land we still owned, as property seemed to be the best insurance against penury in old age.

Norma was terribly attached to the farm and refused to consider going anywhere else. She found rustic living more agreeable and, like many people who prefer the countryside, possessed a disposition that lent itself to living quite a distance from the nearest neighbor. She was distrustful of strangers, impatient of polite talk and frivolous society, indifferent to shops, theaters, and other diversions of city life, and unreasonably devoted to the few things that did interest her: her pigeons, her newspapers, and her family. She wouldn't leave the farm unless we carried her off. But Francis was right—if Fleurette was to have a future, it surely wouldn't be out in the countryside, stitching buttonholes and tossing corn to the chickens.

Something would have to be done about the three of us. I was tired of hearing my brother's ideas, but I hadn't any of my own. I did know this: a run-in with an automobile was not to be taken as evidence of our inability to look after ourselves. It was nothing but a mundane business matter and I would manage it without any assistance from Francis.

4

July 16, 1914

Misses Constance, Norma, and Fleurette Kopp
Sicomac Road
Wyckoff, New Jersey

Dear Mr. Kaufman,

I write to supply you with an accounting of
the damages inflicted upon our buggy by you and
your automobile on the afternoon of July 14. The
damages visited upon my sisters and I are considerable as well. Dear Fleurette is but fifteen
years of age and now suffers from a badly broken
foot and a dread of motor carriages which will
no doubt impede her advancement into the coming engine-powered age. But I confine myself at
present to the harm done to our buggy.

4 (four) hickory spokes @ $1 each,
    cracked: $4
1 (one) carriage lamp, smashed: $3
1 (one) whip socket, dislodged and lost in
    the commotion: $1
1 (one) oak panel, splintered to bits: $8
1 (one) complete hood assembly, bent beyond
    repair: $10
Assembly and re-attachment of disparate
    pieces: $24
Total (due in full promptly upon receipt, as
    we are at present without a buggy): $50

We appreciate your prompt payment by return
post. We remain,

> Yours in a state of caution along our town's
> > ever more crowded avenues,
> Misses Constance, Norma, and Fleurette Kopp

"I am not afraid of automobiles," said Fleurette from the divan.

"Of course you are," I said. "Now, be quiet and rest your foot."

"I can rest my foot without being quiet."

"Those figures are too high," said Norma. "He won't take it seriously and he'll throw it in the trash."

"I'm including the time for a hired man to work on it," I said.

"I don't recall anything about a hired man. Read it again," said Norma.

"Don't," said Fleurette. "I'm tired of Mr. Kaufman."

"Then I'll post it."

"I'm not fifteen, either," said Fleurette.

I thought it should've been obvious to her that fifteen was a more tender age than sixteen and the violation therefore more grievous.

Fleurette grumbled and shifted in the silk peignoir she'd chosen for her convalescence. A pattern of peacock feathers ran along the collar, which she thought made her look glamorous. We'd been overindulging her since Mother's death, and I realized I would have to put a stop to that. Her taste for luxurious fabrics alone was going to ruin us.

I rose with some difficulty to get a stamp. My shoulder had calmed considerably since the collision, but every morning brought a fresh insult: an ankle that couldn't take my weight, a rib that cried out when I took a breath. Fleurette couldn't get her foot into a shoe, which made her something of an invalid. It fell to Norma to look after both of us and go out for whatever supplies we needed. Without our buggy, she had the choice of taking a long walk in hot weather to the trolley in Wyckoff, or saddling Dolley and riding her in. Naturally, she chose the latter. She'd already been as far as Paterson and back twice in the last few days, balancing a basket of pigeons on Dolley's rump and releasing them along the way.

For years Norma had been entranced with the idea of carrier pigeons and their utility in transmitting messages between people living in the countryside, or soldiers at war, or doctors wishing to monitor the progress of far-flung patients (the idea being that a doctor would leave several pigeons with his patient, to be dispatched at intervals with reports of the patient's progress). Telegraph and telephone wires would never stretch far enough to reach everyone who needed to send a message, she reasoned, and could not be trusted for the transmission of private information anyway, because the operator was privy to every word. But a properly trained and equipped pigeon, released hundreds of miles away, would fly a direct course at great speed, through storms or enemy fire, to bring a message home.

To prove this point, Norma was in the habit of taking her pigeons as far away from home as she could and sending them back with tiny missives strapped to their legs. Having no news of any importance to relate to us so soon after leaving the house, she sent us newspaper clippings instead. Norma read half a dozen papers every day and took it as her moral obligation to have an opinion on all the doings in northern New Jersey, not to mention New York and the rest of the world. She spent the better part of every evening with her newspapers, stashing clippings in drawers all over the house for future use. It was not unusual for one of us to go looking for the sugar or a pincushion and instead find an announcement titled "Diplomat's Wife Impaled on Fence."

She rigged up a tripwire in the pigeon loft so that a bell would ring near our front door when a bird arrived carrying the news of the day, as selected by Norma for its dramatic nature or the instruction it might offer. Variations on "Girl Fined for Disorderly Housekeeping" arrived any time I failed to do my part of the washing up. "Large Percentage of Women Recklessly Follow Prevailing Fashions Without Knowing Why" was delivered after Norma objected to Fleurette's silk tunic embroidered with birds of paradise, her attempt to copy the fashions of Paris. "The Morals of a Woman Are Read in Her Gowns" came the next ominous message.

Fleurette devised a way to get revenge by replacing each objectionable headline with one of her own and leaving it for Norma to find. Norma would discover "Piles Quickly Cured at Home" tied to her pigeon's leg band, or "Imbecile Sister Reported Missing."

Although Mother hated the birds and wouldn't go near the pigeon loft, she had encouraged Norma's interest in them, believing that girls should have hobbies that kept them entertained and close to home. She made no secret of the fact that she hoped raising baby birds would encourage a mothering instinct in Norma that would lead her to marriage and children. Exactly how Norma would find a husband, living out in the countryside as we did, was never explained. And Mother seemed oblivious to the fact that Norma was so opinionated, so argumentative, and so set in her ways that no man would ever dare take up with her. It didn't help that Norma had all the girlish charm of a boulder and had never shown the slightest interest in romantic love or child rearing. Mother had been right that pigeons made a good pastime, but Norma was in no danger of becoming engaged as a result.

At least Norma had some satisfactory means of occupying herself. I found the demands of farm life to be dull and unnecessarily difficult. When Francis married and moved into town several years ago, Norma happily took charge of the barn and its occupants. Fleurette kept up with the sewing and the washing, and the three of us took turns at cooking. I was left with the disagreeable task of weeding and watering the vegetable garden. I hated spending all that time bent over in the dirt for a basket of wormy cabbages. All I ever wished for was a good clean job in an office and a salary that would allow me to purchase a cabbage if I wanted one, which I didn't think I would.

There was a time when I tried to find a life for myself away from the farm. First I sent away for a course to study to be a nurse, but Mother, with her dread of filth and disease, was so horrified by the idea that I had to put it aside. Then I took up a course in law, having heard that there was a woman lawyer in New Brunswick and thinking I could petition to join her firm. Believing this line of work would force me into close quarters with criminals and drunks, Mother was even less pleased. I completed my coursework nonetheless, but when the time came to send it back to New York and request the next lesson, my papers were gone. Mother would not admit to it, but I knew she took them.

Now I was starting to wonder if I would live my whole life out here. I worried that I was destined to die in the same bed my mother had died in, leaving behind nothing but a cellar full of parsnips and uneven rows of stitches along cuffs and collars that nobody even remembered me making.

WE WAITED A WEEK for a response to our letter. There was enough nursing to keep me occupied, and to make me wish I'd taken that medical course. Twice a day I washed and bandaged Fleurette's foot, hardly daring to press too hard against it to feel for broken bones. She insisted that we not send for Dr. Winter, a musty old man with watery eyes and hands that shook as they reached for his patients' unclothed limbs. I didn't blame her for wanting to keep him away. But all I could do was clean her scrapes and scratches and require her to rest. This meant that I also had to bring her meals on a tray and answer a little bell she'd found in our sewing basket and kept on hand to ring whenever she was thirsty or tired or bored, which was most of the time.

The only place I could go to escape the sound of that bell was Mother's old room, which stood exactly as it had on the day she died, with her robe still hanging on the closet door and her hairbrush still on the dresser, a few wiry white hairs rising from it.

For months I couldn't go into her room at all. But lately I'd taken to slipping in when I wouldn't be noticed, and sitting on the edge of her bed the way I did when she was sick. During the last few days of her life her eyes would often flutter open, seeing nothing, and remain locked in a gaze that never shifted. I had to put a mirror to her mouth to make sure she was still breathing. I spent hours on the edge of that bed, watching her drift close to death and rise away from it, over and over.

The bed, which had belonged to her mother, was an old-fashioned heavy antique brought over from Austria, with rosettes of carved walnut along the headboard that served no purpose other than to gather dust. As I sat gingerly on the edge, the sheets crackling with starch, I realized that no one had been in to clean in months. It was Fleurette's job to dust, which explains why it accumulated in our house the way it did.

The walls were papered in a pale green and white pattern of chrysanthemums that had faded terribly and started to lift away, revealing cracked plaster and horsehair. Something would have to be done about this room. Even Mother—with her dread of change and her attachment to tradition and the heavy dark rituals of grief—would surely not object to me dismantling this shrine to her final years and making something useful of it. But I couldn't bring myself to do it yet. For years I just wanted to be free of her, and now I found myself clinging to the only traces of her that remained.

Fleurette always addressed Mother in French, but I knew that Mother preferred the German of her girlhood in Austria. I would never hear the language spoken in this house again if I didn't continue to whisper it to her.

"Mama, wär es nicht endlich Zeit, dass wir was mit Deinem Zimmer machen?"

I received no answer. Perhaps Mother didn't care what happened to her room. I took a deep breath. Her violet-scented powder still hung in the air. From somewhere downstairs a door slammed, and Fleurette, having given up on her bell, hollered my name.

It had always been Mother's responsibility to answer to Fleurette's demands. *"Geh amal nachschaun, was sie will?"* I asked her.

But Mother didn't volunteer to go. I rose and closed the door quietly behind me.

⊰ 5 ⊱

"TRY THE PLUMS," Fleurette said at breakfast a few days later.

Norma ignored her and kept her eyes on her newspaper.

"Just one. Just a bite." Fleurette took her butter knife and cut out a perfect triangle of toast and plum preserves. She slid it onto Norma's plate.

"Look," she whispered. *"C'est tout violet."*

Norma rattled her newspaper and put it between herself and the offending toast.

"That's more red than purple," I said, sitting down across from them. "You'll never win at this."

Fleurette giggled and took her toast back.

The long-standing and largely one-sided feud between Norma and Fleurette over the regal hue of their breakfast condiments began years ago, when Norma absentmindedly reached for a jar of pickled red cabbage and spooned it onto her toast. After the initial shock, she found that she liked it a great deal and continued to eat it, every morning, for the rest of her life thus far. Fleurette was only seven or eight when this began and couldn't understand how anyone could eat such a disagreeable food for breakfast. She asked Norma about it so often that one day Norma finally said, "Because it's purple, of course. Didn't you know that eating purple food at breakfast increases one's height by two inches over a lifetime? It's why we're all so much taller than you."

She waved her newspaper around as if to suggest that she'd read it from a place of authority, adding, "If only there was anything more purple than pickled cabbage, I'd eat that instead."

Fleurette didn't know how to tell when Norma was making a joke—none of us did, really, even all these years later—and took the challenge seriously, presenting Norma with any purple food she could find in the morning: jams and preserves, violet pastilles, blueberries and grapes. Every now and then, she resumed the old feud again out of habit. But so far, she'd failed. Not even plum preserves could match the brilliance of Norma's cabbage.

That's just how it was with Norma: once she approved of a thing, she adopted it to the exclusion of everything else. If she believed pickled cabbage and toast to be the best breakfast, it would be a betrayal of her principles to eat jam and porridge. If a pair of boots suited her, they became the only style she wore. I'd only ever seen one book on her nightstand (*The Practical Pigeon: A Complete Treatise on Training, Breeding, Flying and Uses of Winged Messengers*) and suspected that she had read it hundreds of times, having found none better.

At breakfast I read aloud my second letter to Henry Kaufman. Before I got past the salutation, Norma interrupted.

"I don't like this Kaufman," she said.

"Well, of course you don't like him," Fleurette said. "None of us do."

"What I mean to say is that I don't like us writing letters to him," Norma said. "We shouldn't be carrying on a correspondence with a man like that."

"It's an invoice, not a correspondence," I said. "And this will be the last one. I'll go and collect from him myself if he doesn't reply."

"But do you not agree with me that we shouldn't . . ."

"Norma! He owes us the money." Fifty dollars was no small sum to us. We lived on about six hundred a year, and because we were relying mostly on savings, that fifty dollars took one month of independence away from our dwindling funds. I rattled the paper and began again.

July 23, 1914

Misses Constance, Norma, and Fleurette Kopp
Sicomac Road
Wyckoff, New Jersey

Dear Mr. Kaufman,

I trust you have received our invoice for the damages inflicted upon our buggy as a result of the collision with your automobile on July 14. The amount owed remains the same. The buggy remains in a state of disrepair. Anticipating that you are a busy man whose bookkeeper undoubtedly falls behind in his work when business is brisk, I will present myself at your place of business next Tuesday

to collect in full if we have not yet received the
fifty dollars owed. Until then, I remain,

> Yours in a state of cautious expectation,
> Miss Constance Kopp

"It's best not to criticize a man's bookkeeper," Norma said
without looking up from her newspaper.

"I was only offering an explanation for his failure to respond."

"You wouldn't like that, if you were his bookkeeper." She
noticed a strand of pickled cabbage on the back of her hand
and flicked it onto her plate.

"I wouldn't like much of anything if I were Mr. Kaufman's
bookkeeper," I said, signing my name to the letter.

I MAILED THE LETTER on a Thursday. When no reply arrived by the morning post on Tuesday, I readied myself for a
visit to Paterson.

"Are we going to town?" Fleurette said when she saw me
in my hat.

"I am," I said. "I have business to do. You're not well
enough yet."

"But I haven't left the house in ages." She flopped into a
stuffed chair in our sitting room. She'd wrapped herself in a
Japanese shawl and pinned her hair into a complex arrangement of cascading glossy curls, held together somehow by an
enormous red silk poppy. The bandage had just come off her
foot, and to celebrate her newly liberated appendage, she was
wearing ballet slippers.

"Read a book," I said. "Help Norma in the kitchen if you're feeling so much better."

More moaning. More flopping about on the chair. I wished for the hundredth time that we had treated Fleurette less like a curiosity, an exotic bird nesting in our chimney, and more like a child in need of instruction.

I left her to issue her protests to an empty room and went outside to saddle Dolley for the trip into town. Dolley was not happy to see me coming. I was built like a farmer, even taller and broader than my brother. I looked ridiculous on a horse. But there would be no other way to get around until our buggy was repaired.

Norma had been in the barn all morning, mucking out the chicken coop and spreading fresh straw in the horse stall. It smelled of sweet, dry grass. She'd given Dolley a good brushing and was checking her hooves when I walked in. She ran a hand down the mare's leg until the hoof lifted off the ground for inspection. Animals instinctively trusted Norma. She'd held every sort of claw or hoof or paw.

"I spoke to that boy at the dairy who fixes their wagons," Norma said when she saw me. "He says it can be put back together. He'll come over in the evenings and do the job."

I didn't say anything. I pulled the saddle off the wall and Norma helped me cinch it into place.

"Mr. Kaufman isn't going to pay, and we'll still have to get our buggy repaired," Norma said. "That boy has all the tools, and he's just down the road."

There was no point in arguing over it. Living this far out of town was dull enough without a means of escape. We couldn't all ride Dolley. "All right. Have him keep a record of his expenses," I said, "and make sure it comes to fifty dollars."

Norma finished her inspection of Dolley's hooves and walked her out of the barn. "We don't go around demanding money from strange men," she said, as she watched me hoist myself up.

"This is an exception," I said.

"Well, then we shouldn't make exceptions," Norma replied, and trudged off to pump water for the chickens.

THE KAUFMAN SILK DYEING COMPANY sat along the railroad tracks among a string of other dyers, warpers, and winders, bleach works, jacquard card cutters, and suppliers of dyestuffs and intermediates—all housed in low brick buildings that turned their backs to the street. The windows sat high enough off the ground to prevent anyone from looking in, but I could hear the sounds of industry from within: the clattering of machines, the sloshing of dye in tubs, and voices calling to one another in German, Italian, French, Polish—every language but English.

Delivery wagons had worn deep ruts in the street. Dolley picked her way around them, and I watched the small signs stenciled across the metal doors at each factory until we came to Henry Kaufman's. I heaved myself out of the saddle without any finesse and lashed Dolley to a post. She tossed her head and snorted to let me know she was happy to see me go.

Inside, the coppery sulfuric stench of the dyes hit me with such force that I had to close my eyes and grope blindly for a handkerchief. I coughed and choked and fought the urge to take a deep breath, not wanting to draw any more of it into my lungs. I couldn't swallow and my vision was so clouded with tears that I could hardly make out the dim figures around me. I almost backed out the door and went home.

Finally I composed myself and saw that I was standing at the edge of a factory floor, looking down a row of enormous troughs, with two or three men attending to each of them. Steam rose up from the troughs and floated to the broad wooden beams overhead. The dye lay in bright pools at the workers' feet, and to protect their feet they wore wooden clogs stained in shades of deep midnight blue and a bright pink the color of peppermint candy. Everywhere the dye met another color it turned a blackish gray. It took two men to hoist the skeins of silk out of the troughs on their metal poles, and when they did, the dye ran down their arms and into their shirtsleeves. A troupe of girls and young boys pushed brooms around the edges of the room, sloshing the runoff into drains, and a few of them wheeled carts piled high with raw silk. Off to one side, a row of wringers were in constant motion, clattering and groaning as the workers fed the wet skeins through them.

A few men looked up at me through the steam but no one said anything. To my right was a long, windowed wall dividing the office from the factory floor. I lifted my skirt and walked over to try the door but it was locked. Through one of the windows, a secretary looked up from her desk and seemed to be considering what to do with me. Finally she rose and led me in.

"I'm sorry to bother you," I said. "I'm here to see Mr. Henry Kaufman."

She ushered me through the door and closed it quickly behind us, which seemed to have more to do with keeping the malicious odor out than an eagerness to invite me in.

"Your name?" She spoke with a brisk efficiency. She wore a smartly tailored navy suit with a long plain skirt and a trim jacket, and her hair was tied in a tight bun. After resuming her post behind the desk, she looked at me over the top of delicate gold spectacles and waited for me to explain myself.

I said my name and told her that I had come to deliver an invoice for damages to our buggy. She held her hand out as if she was in the habit of receiving such invoices daily. I gave it to her and she laid it across her blotter, smoothed the folds, and read it slowly. Then she looked up at me with an expression that I could not read. It might have been sorrow or shock or deep skepticism.

"Henry did this," she said, mostly to herself.

"He claimed that our horse ran in front of him, but everyone along Market saw the accident, and he is most certainly the one who ran into us."

She waved her hand to silence me. "I don't doubt your story. Are you sure this took place on the fourteenth?"

She glanced up at me and I nodded.

With a sigh she handed the letter back to me. "He was supposed to meet with our banker. He told me a tire burst."

She dropped her head into her hands and muttered something I couldn't hear.

"Forgive me for saying—"

"Oh," she interrupted, "you're forgiven. What is it?"

"With the company he was keeping, I don't believe he was on his way to visit a banker."

She gave another long, aggrieved exhalation and pushed herself to her feet. "Have you any brothers, Miss Kopp?"

"Just one," I said.

"Is yours as much trouble as mine?"

"Henry Kaufman is your brother?" I said. "I'm sorry. I thought you were the secretary."

"I am, according to the letterhead. Marion Garfinkel. My husband's Ed Garfinkel. We're in town from Pittsburgh to try to sort out the mess Henry's made of our factory." Before I could say another word, she turned and yelled in the direction of a closed door across the room.

"Henry!"

In addition to her desk, there were three others, all occupied by young women working at typewriters and ledger books. The girls ducked down when she shouted. The door didn't open.

Through gritted teeth she muttered, "If he ignores me one more time—" and marched over to his office. Without turning around to look at me again, she called, "Stay there."

She rapped at the door and rattled the knob. When it didn't open, she fumbled around for a ring of keys at her waist and let herself in. "Henry, there's a girl out here who says—" Then the door slammed behind her, and I heard nothing but muffled shouting.

I fidgeted with my handbag and tried to ignore the curious glances of the other girls. Dolley had been waiting unattended long enough, and I just wanted to hand him my invoice and leave. The shouting had ceased from inside Henry Kaufman's office. I picked up my letter from Mrs. Garfinkel's desk and crossed the room, giving the door a quiet knock.

It swung open. Marion appeared to be on her way out, but she stepped aside and swept her arm into the room, inviting me to enter, her lips pinched together in a kind of forced smile.

"My brother doesn't recall the incident," she said crisply.

"But I—"

"Tell him yourself, then."

I had the uneasy feeling that I was being sent in to prove a point, although I couldn't imagine what that point might be. I took one hesitant step inside and Marion slammed the door behind me. I could hear her shoes clicking across the floor as she hurried to her station.

Behind an enormous oak desk sat Henry Kaufman in yet another elegant suit, his hair slicked back the way men wore it if they were going out for the evening. But with that round, soft face, he looked more like a child trying to dress like his father. He couldn't have been much younger than me — thirty, perhaps — but he had the pampered manner of a boy who had been too long at boarding school. He would've seemed entirely harmless if there hadn't been a cold distance in his eyes and an angry set to his mouth. Here in this factory, he seemed like a man who didn't want what he had, but also didn't have exactly what he wanted.

And in leather chairs all around the room were his friends, his unsavory, no-good friends. There was the droopy-eyed man with the wooden leg, slumped over in a brown suit that was two sizes too big for him, and a beefy character with arms like stovepipes and the broadest set of chins I'd ever seen. The rest were lean and angular types who each seemed to have lost something in a fight: one lacked a third finger on his left hand, one was missing a patch of hair above his ear, and another wore a milky glass eye. They all held cards in their hands, and a bottle of whiskey sat on the table between them.

I wanted out of that room.

"Oh, you're the one," Henry Kaufman said. "She came in here talking about a girl wanting money and I told her it could have been half of New Jersey."

The other men snickered and drew on their cigarettes.

I stood a little straighter and looked down at him with what I hoped was a calm and dignified air. "Then you remember me. I am Constance Kopp, and—"

"And these are your sisters," he sneered. "Or haven't you brought them along? Who is the youngest one? Fleurette?"

I felt a little sick when he said her name. "We haven't had a reply to our letters," I said, "so I've brought you another one. You owe us fifty dollars for the damages to our buggy, and I will take payment now."

He didn't accept the letter I held out for him, so I stepped forward and dropped it on his desk.

"I'll just speak to your father about this," he said. "Is his business here in Paterson? Or does he . . ." He picked up the envelope and examined our return address. "Or does he work on your farm in Wyckoff?"

He had our address. I should have asked him to make payment at our bank. In spite of the heat, I went very cold.

"You live on Sicomac Road? Down by the dairy?"

He came around the desk and stood right in front of me, easing his shoulder between me and the doorway, drawing a low whistle from one of the men. Henry Kaufman may have been a head shorter than me, but he was stout and powerfully built. He smelled of whiskey, and again of hair tonic and his own factory.

"I'm sure I can find it," he said in a low voice. "When I get there, tell me, through which window may I find Miss Fleurette's bedroom?"

He looked over at his friends and they laughed. There was a roar in my ears and suddenly he was very small and far away. I grabbed his shoulders and threw him against the wall, hard enough that the back of his skull cracked the plaster.

"Don't you dare," I said. I'd gathered his lapels up in my fists without realizing I'd done it. From the corner of my eye, I could see the other men rising to their feet.

A thin trickle of blood smeared the wall. There was a shuffle behind me and I could feel someone breathing over my shoulder.

"If you'd like to pick a fight with a man your own size," he said quietly, "I'll send one over."

My hands flew away from him as if they'd touched a hot pan. Before the other men could get hold of me I was out the door and running past the secretaries. Marion rose from her desk and called out to me, but I didn't answer.

I pushed the door open and fell out onto the factory floor, running straight into a slender red-haired girl carrying a steaming tray of fabric. She dropped the tray and emerald-green dye ran down the front of her apron. We slid around in a puddle of it, and then someone shouted in Polish and the girl grabbed my arm to stay upright, but I shook her off and ran for the door without once looking back.

Outside, I grabbed Dolley's bridle and dragged her a few blocks away before stopping to catch my breath. My palms were slick with sweat and my head floated away from my neck like a balloon tethered by a string. Little pinpricks of light swam in front of me. I swallowed to push down the bile rising up in my throat, and then forced myself to focus on the shop across the street, a place called Gurney's that sold boilers and ranges. "WE MAKE IT HOT FOR YOU" read the sign in the window, next to another sign announcing that the shop was closed for vacation because Paterson was hot enough already.

An engine rattled around the corner and I pulled Dolley toward me. Would they come after me? I held my breath and waited, but the machine rumbled past and its driver didn't even turn to look at me.

I tried to imagine how I would tell Norma and Fleurette what had happened.

He said your name, I would say to Fleurette. *He asked about your bedroom.*

And to Norma: *He said he wanted to speak to our father.*

I could still feel the men in that room coming up behind me and a hand reaching for my shoulder.

⊰ 6 ⊱

HAD MY MOTHER BEEN ALIVE, none of this would have happened. We didn't go marching into factories to demand payment from strange men. In fact, we hardly ever went anywhere. Mother didn't even like to go out shopping. When we lived in Brooklyn, she had almost everything delivered, and when we moved to the countryside, it became Francis's responsibility to ride into town and get things for us.

My mother named me after her, but I was never like her. She was Constance Clementine Kopp and I was Constance Amélie, my middle name being her mother's name. Francis was her firstborn, but having grown up with four brothers, a boy was unremarkable to her. She was waiting for a girl: a girl she could wrap inside her cloistered world, a girl who would sit next to her and work at needlepoint and keep her secrets and pretend not to hear the door when someone knocked.

She lived most of her life in this country, but she was never an American and she didn't trust Americans or American ways. Her parents left Vienna when she was sixteen, like so many of the middle class did in the wake of the revolution of

1848. My grandfather—an educated man, a chemist—liked to say that he brought his family here to give them a more stable and certain future, and to keep his boys out of the endless wars with France and Italy, but my grandmother once whispered that they moved to get away from the Jews. "After they got to leave the ghettos they could live anywhere," she hissed, and glanced out the window as if she suspected they were moving to Brooklyn, too, which of course they were.

My mother married my father, Frank Kopp, at the age of twenty. He was what my grandparents called Bohemian, which meant that he was Czech, but in some convoluted way having to do with the outcomes of wars still being fought in those distant countries, they had decided that he was practically Austrian. They were relieved he wasn't a Jew, and even though my mother had met him in New York, he wasn't an American. On the grounds of what he was not, my grandparents allowed him to marry their daughter.

He was a wine merchant when they married, but he failed at that and became a bartender, and when that occupation didn't agree with him, he was only a drunk. My mother forced him out of the house many times, but he didn't leave for good until I was about ten. After that we saw him so infrequently that people began to think that Mother was a widow, an idea she encouraged. When we left Brooklyn she didn't tell him where we'd gone, and as far as I knew, he'd never tried to find out.

Secrets and deception were my mother's specialty. She invented new birth dates for herself whenever it suited her to lie about her age. She mistrusted authorities and never quite believed she had a right to live here. There must have been some record of her entrance to this country, but she knew nothing about it and claimed not to be a citizen. She possessed no identification, no marriage license, and no birth certificates for any of us, having birthed us at home and breathed not a word of it to any official. She had a dread of doctors, tax collectors, census-takers, inspectors, newspaper reporters, and the police—particularly the police.

She believed that Americans were crude and uncivilized, and tried instead to raise us as good Austrians, insisting that we speak her own peculiar blend of French and German, and engaging us in the tedious practices of lace-making and decorative painting in an effort to keep us indoors and away from the other children in the neighborhood.

As a result, there was not a bread tin or a sewing box in our Brooklyn apartment that hadn't been painted with a spray of roses and then covered with a doily. Our home was a dark and crowded museum of our mother's Viennese girlhood. Her faded needlepoint hung on the wall alongside oil portraits of unnamed ancestors and a china doll in a glass case that wore the hair of her long-dead grandmother. A miniature porcelain tea set—each dish edged in gold and hand-painted with delicate toadflax and fern—sat inside a mahogany breakfront alongside a collection of miniature glass animals: elephants and lions, fish and sea monsters. We were forbidden to touch them.

She never opened the door for strangers. She read salacious newspaper stories to me and Norma as we worked at our sewing, hoping, I suppose, that with each stitch her shocking morality tales would teach us the dangers that a knock at the door could bring. I can't look at our childhood samplers without remembering the disgraceful fate of Laura Smith, age seventeen, who was lured away from her home by the grocer and ruined by him, or that of thirteen-year-old Lena Luefschuetz, found dead for reasons having to do with her "undesirable companions." A girl named Amelia was arrested for "going into a hallway with an Italian" and was detained as a witness for two weeks, which prevented her from boarding a steamship that would have carried her back to the bosom of her family in Germany and away from the horrors that a city like New York could visit upon a young girl. *"Arme Amelia, so weit weg von ihrer Familie,"* Mother would say under her breath. Amelia lived constantly in her prayers.

For weeks we followed the story of a girl arrested for waywardness after her mother called the police and demanded that they take her away. Her own mother! The girl had been out past her curfew, which, we were shocked to learn, was ten o'clock. The girl claimed that the door was locked and her mother would not let her in, so she had no choice but to ride her bicycle all night long. A trial was held in which her cyclometer was presented as evidence. It showed that she had traveled fifty miles. A church pastor testified on her behalf, as did a Sunday school teacher. The magistrate seemed inclined to let the girl go until her mother held up a letter the girl had written to "a young physician in Manhattan." (Mother read this in a grim tone, suggesting that nothing good could come of correspondence with physicians.) The magistrate read the letter, gave the girl a shocked and stern look, and committed her to the Wayside Home until she turned twenty-one.

If Mother knew what that letter contained, she wouldn't tell us. All she wanted us to understand was that in America, letters were dangerous, as were hallways, bicycles, doctors, and Italians. We could be locked up for any of it, and ruined.

She would have been terrified by our accident, not just because of our injuries and the damage to the buggy, but because it left us so exposed. The thought of the three of us thrown into a heap on Market Street, a crowd gathered around us, everyone watching, everyone wondering who we were—Mother dedicated her life to avoiding that very thing.

And now I had gotten into a fistfight with a factory owner. If my mother had nightmares, this would have been one of them.

⪥ 7 ⪥

FLEURETTE AND NORMA didn't look up when I walked in. They were engaged in a game of preference, with Fleurette holding two of the three hands.

"Oh, good," Fleurette said when she saw me. "Come and take Mother's place."

"You're bidding for Mother?" I said, dropping into a chair across from them. Fleurette was on the divan with a pillow propped up next to her in the place of a third player. Norma was seated across from her with her own hand, wearing a look of high skepticism.

"No, she's bidding for a pillow," Norma said, "and I have begun to suspect that the pillow is cheating."

"Constance wasn't here," Fleurette said. "We'll never have a threesome if you're always running off by yourself like that."

"I'm not always running off," I said.

"Did Mr. Kaufman pay?" Fleurette asked.

I had decided that Fleurette shouldn't know what had happened. She was an excitable girl, prone to vivid dreams and wild ideas. If she thought we had an enemy, she'd keep me up half the night with elaborate cloak-and-dagger schemes.

"Mr. Kaufman has received the invoice," was all I said.

Norma raised an eyebrow at me and put down her cards. "It's nearly dinnertime. Constance and I will finish the noodles."

"Don't cut them into squares!" Fleurette called as we left for the kitchen. "They taste better as triangles."

On the kitchen table Norma had rolled out the noodles for *Krautfleckerl* and laid a wet towel across the dough. When we were girls in Brooklyn the entire building knew what the Kopp family was having for dinner when the odor of onions, vinegar, caraway, and cabbage filled the hallway.

"It's what Fleurette wanted," Norma said, before I could ask why she was making a hot cabbage dish on a sweltering summer evening. "She was missing Mother all day, and you weren't here to do anything about it."

"It was good of you to play cards with her." I took a knife and began cutting the noodles. Norma watched me warily from the stove.

"What are you doing?" she asked when I made the first cut.

"Triangles."

"You're making a mess of them. Just cut them the way we always do and let Fleurette make her own triangles."

"But she doesn't want it that way. I thought we were making this for her."

Norma reached for the knife. "I'll cut the noodles. You do the cabbage."

I pushed her away and sliced a row of perfect squares. "Well, you're right about Henry Kaufman," I said. "He is the most ill-mannered young man I've ever met. And that gang of thugs he runs around with! What's a businessman doing with a crowd like that?"

Norma dropped the noodles into the pot, and a cloud of steam rose up around her. The curls at the back of her neck were slick against her skin. Without turning around, she said, "He was not so happy to see you?"

"No, he was not. I don't expect we'll be getting any money out of him."

She banged her spoon against the pot and turned around, waving it at me. "It's just as well that we forget about Henry Kaufman. I've got that boy working on the buggy. He brought over an old runabout the dairy isn't using. We can ride that until ours is finished."

I took a breath and tried to summon the nerve to tell her what had happened. But the air sailed right back out of my mouth the way it came in, and no words followed. What was the point in revisiting the entire awful encounter?

"That's just fine," I said at last. "I'd like to forget about it."

Through the kitchen window I could see the neighbor's pigs pacing in their pen. I tossed our kitchen scraps to them, a small service that earned us a flitch of bacon in the fall. The pigs were still some weeks away from slaughter, but already their bellies dragged in the mud as they staggered around, calling out in their guttural pig language.

I dropped the pitted stalk of the cabbage into a bowl and looked around for something else to feed them.

"Take the potato peelings," Norma said, and I did, walking them across the road in the unrelenting heat. The cicadas whined from some distant grove, and the crickets in the tall grass around the dairy pond raised their own chorus, which was not a song at all but just the dull scraping of a hundred blades against each other.

The pigs grunted and shuffled toward the fence when they saw me coming with my bowl of scraps. With the drone of the countryside all around me, I didn't notice Henry Kaufman's motor car until it was nearly on top of me.

He was driving and there were three men with him. The setting sun kept me from making out their faces, but I thought I could see the young man with the droopy eyes gaping at me, his mouth half open, his front tooth jutting out in a look of perpetual, confounded surprise, and the great hulking figure of the man with the stovepipe arms next to him. The car fired and coughed as if it was about to die, then roared again and swerved right at me. I fell back into the weeds. One of the men leaned out and yelled, "Take your pick, Henry! Which one of these girls do you want?"

Another one laughed and said something I couldn't hear.

"The French girl. What was she—"

Another mutter, and then he did the most intolerable thing. He shouted her name down our drive, as if he knew her, as if he knew anything about us at all.

"Fleurette! That's the one! Here, girly!" and then there was nothing but rough and drunken laughter and the thunder of the engine and dust everywhere. A bottle flew out the back of the car and hit a rock, shattering to pieces as the men disappeared down Sicomac Road.

The bowl slipped out of my hand. I watched the sand-colored cloud of dust settle back into the road, and then the air was still. Even the crickets had been shocked into silence. I stood and tried to pick the burrs and foxtails out of my skirt, but my fingers trembled and wouldn't take hold of them.

Across the way Norma stood in the half-opened front door, Mother's old kitchen apron tied crookedly over her riding clothes. Fleurette perched on her toes and peered around her to get a better view. They looked like those fuzzy figures in a picture postcard, frozen in place, staring out from some world that no longer existed.

⊰ 8 ⊱

THE THREE OF US retreated to my bedroom. Our dinner was forgotten and the noodles were a sticky mess in their pot. Fleurette was red-cheeked and wild-eyed. Norma was as grim as I'd ever seen her. She kept her eyes on the floor, and her breath came out noisily as she worked up to whatever she was going to say.

"How did he find us?" Fleurette asked, bouncing on my bed.

"I wish you'd stop fidgeting," Norma said.

"I can't. How does he know my name?"

They both looked up at me expectantly, Fleurette eager for the rest of the story, and Norma dreading it.

"Well—the letters. I put our address on them and our names."

Norma tied a knot in a loose piece of piping around her knees. Fleurette considered it a waste of her talents to make undergarments for us, when a complete set could be purchased so inexpensively from the catalogs, but Norma had grown attached to a particular style of nainsook chemise that was no longer offered. She wore them until they frayed at the hems and then had to bribe Fleurette to make her a new one.

"Don't pull on it," Fleurette whispered. Norma pulled her hands away but kept her eyes on the fraying edge.

"I'll go to the police tomorrow," I said.

Norma snorted. "I take a dim view of the police in this county."

"What do you know about them? We've never so much as spoken to a police officer."

"I read the papers. They can't even catch a pickpocket. Do you remember just last week, at the train station—"

"Norma," I said, giving a great sigh of exasperation, which was what I so often did after saying her name. "It's a simple matter for the police. He has wrecked our buggy and refuses to pay, and now he's harassing us."

"And why is that?" Norma said.

"Why is he harassing us? You saw the crowd of hooligans he runs around with. They probably have nothing better to do. They—"

Norma raised one eyebrow at me, a particular talent of hers that she deployed whenever she wanted to assign blame.

"You don't think I'm at fault!" I cried. "If he'd been any kind of gentleman, he would have paid the damages straight-away. All I've done is to try to collect what we were owed."

Fleurette had been looking back and forth between the two of us like a spectator at a tennis match. But she couldn't stay silent any longer. "Where does Mr. Kaufman live? Let's go to his house tonight. We can all wear disguises, and we'll wait until he's gone to bed, and—"

Norma shushed her and put her hand over mine. "I don't think you know how you look sometimes," she said, patting me in a show of sympathy.

I pulled my hand away. "How I look?"

"At the accident. You towered over him, and you shoved that car door closed so he couldn't get in. How do you think that made him appear to his friends?"

"Like a fool," I said.

"He is a fool," Fleurette added.

"And what about today? Were his friends with him again?"

"Oh, they run in a pack," I said. "They're like wild dogs."

"And by any chance did you make Henry Kaufman look like a fool again today?" Norma asked, her voice still quiet and steady. "In front of all those wild dogs?"

I closed my eyes and pictured his head hitting the plaster, a detail I was now glad I hadn't shared with Norma. "But that's no reason to come after us. He's the one who ran us down."

"I don't believe he sees it that way."

"Well, it's nice of you to take his side," I snapped, and tugged at my bedcovers, dislodging Norma. Hunger got the better of Fleurette, and she persuaded Norma to go downstairs with her to see what they could salvage from our ruined dinner. I stayed in bed, feeling that I deserved to be sent upstairs without my supper. The very idea of food turned my stomach anyway. I was made nauseous by the idea of drunken lunatics charging at us in motor cars and strange men hurling threats at Fleurette.

Fleurette, who had seen so little of the world, who Mother kept even more carefully hidden away than her other girls.

Fleurette was like a little jewel, small and bright and easy to steal. And now, with me in charge of her welfare for only a year, these men were driving by the house and shouting at her.

What was I to do? Mother would have wanted me to put up the storm shutters and bar the doors and hide in the root cellar every time an automobile drove by. Norma, who saw the farm as some sort of fortress designed to keep the rest of the world at bay, would have agreed. But I was tired of hiding out here in the country.

Francis would have wanted me to sell the farm and move in with him, where we could all be properly supervised. But I wasn't about to become one of those women who serves out a life term as her brother's housekeeper.

The only way I could fall asleep was to tell myself that I was making too much of the situation. I had made one small miscalculation in confronting Mr. Kaufman and had brought a little trouble our way as a result. It would not happen again.

THE NEXT MORNING, Norma and I sat down with Fleurette and warned her to be wary of automobiles driving past our house and to stay away from unfamiliar men in all circumstances.

"You two sound like Mother," Fleurette said, rolling her eyes. She still had the long dark lashes that some children are born with, and she had a habit of fluttering them at us dismissively.

"This time it's real," I said. "This time it's serious."

"Mother thought everything was serious."

I didn't appreciate being compared to my mother, but Mr. Kaufman did seem to pose a fresh new danger. "Promise me,"

I said. "No automobiles. No strange men. We must stay away from him until he forgets all about us."

She promised. "But we're still going to Paterson next week, aren't we?"

I looked over at Norma for an explanation. She reached into the basket next to her chair and pulled out yesterday's newspaper.

"I might have seen something about a moving picture concern coming to town," she said, thumbing through the pages. "They're going to film a motor car running into a trolley as part of a safety campaign."

"I think we've had enough of motor cars running into things," I said.

"Oh, we have to go," Fleurette said, jumping up from her chair. She wore an outlandishly large pale pink dahlia in her hair. It seemed to be placed purposefully next to her face as if to offer a comparison. "Norma promised you'd take me."

Norma kept her face behind the paper. "I would go myself, but I couldn't possibly. You know I take my pigeons out on Thursdays."

"You take them out on Wednesday and Friday, too," I said, "and on Monday and Saturday. Tuesdays are—"

"They dislike any change to their routine," Norma said. "It would put them out of joint."

"Well, I can't go, either," I said, although I didn't have a reason.

Fleurette tugged at my arm the way she used to when she was a little girl. "But what if they're looking for actresses?"

"It's a crash," I said. "What use would they have for an actress?"

"I have experience with crashes," she said.

"I don't think they'd want you for a safety campaign."

"Please," she said. "Norma said you would. She said you had nothing else to do but keep me entertained."

"Norma!" I tried to snatch the paper away from her, but she wouldn't let it go.

"And after that terrible fright I had yesterday," Fleurette said, working her eyebrows into a sorrowful little knot. "Wouldn't an afternoon out do me good?"

She leaned over and pursed her lips at me in that droll, beguiling way she had. The girl was unbearably pretty and knew it. Sometimes I wanted to pick her up and squeeze her until she could hardly breathe. Whether that impulse grew out of love or rage I could not say.

THE ACCIDENT was to be staged at the corner of Main Street and Market. Norma helped us hitch Dolley to the runabout we had on loan from the dairy. Its seat was only just wide enough for the two of us.

"You see, I couldn't have gone anyway," Norma said with evident relief.

The questions began as soon as we rolled onto Sicomac Road.

"What sort of part do you think they'd have for a young girl?" Fleurette asked.

"We're only going to watch."

"I could play the part of the victim with her leg crushed under the wheel."

"You are not going to be in the pictures."

"You don't know that."

I kept pointedly quiet, but it didn't matter since she hadn't been listening to me anyway.

"At least let me drive."

"After what happened last time?"

We continued in this fashion until we reached Paterson and rode over the river and past the great hulking Lambert Castle, one of those foolish medieval follies built by American industrialists after their first trip abroad. This particular industrialist, a silk man named Catholina Lambert, was still occupying his folly, after having seen his wife and all but one of their eight children off to the graveyard, most of them lost to consumption or childhood fevers or a kick to the head by a horse. I heard that he married his wife's sister, herself a widow, and that they spent their days in the marble atrium gazing up at the enormous dark oil portraits of other, more distant castles, and of moldy forests, and of the Lambert ancestors. The terrace offered an expansive view of New York City, but apparently the occupants of the castle didn't care to look at the view, for no one ever saw them outdoors.

Fleurette fell silent as we rode under the shadow of the castle. When she was a child and misbehaved, we used to threaten to send her there to work in the kitchen. She believed us. She believed everything we told her until she turned fourteen. The castle held enormous power over Fleurette—and over everyone in town, really. No one could stand to go near the place.

"Who lives over here?" Fleurette said, once we had put the castle behind us.

"All the silk men do," I said.

From our vantage point on the hill, we could see the mills and factories clustered together at the edge of Paterson's downtown, casting their shadows into the Passaic River. Narrow brick stacks discharged coal smoke into the air, where it formed a permanent gray cloud. The river dwindled to a trickle this time of year, leaving nothing but mud and boulders and puddles visited by mosquitoes. The mill owners preferred to live a comfortable distance away from their red-bricked empire, so they retreated to this cool, quiet neighborhood with its canopy of elms and wide, sloping streets.

"You're taking a very roundabout way into town," Fleurette said, fidgeting with her hat.

"We're early," I said. "I thought we could ride around the park."

"Well, I wanted to get there early!" Fleurette protested. "I wanted to have a chance to meet the director!"

"I know you did," I said, slowing Dolley to a leisurely walk under the elms.

PATERSON was a city of industry. Every schoolchild read the story about Alexander Hamilton and his Society for Establishing Useful Manufactures, conceived for the purpose of harnessing the powers of the Great Falls of the Passaic River and building along its banks a national manufactory. Although things did not go as Hamilton had planned at first, Paterson did eventually grow into a city of steel mills and, later, silk mills. The factories produced locomotives, Colt revolvers, and, most recently, hair ribbons and yardage. But all industry ceased when a motion picture concern came to town.

As Fleurette rushed to the intersection of Market and Main, dragging me behind her, we passed banks that had closed for the afternoon, grocers who had locked their fruit stands, and jewelry stores with shutters over their windows. Businessmen in pinstriped suits stood on the sidewalk as if they had no business to attend to. Schoolteachers crowded into the street with their young charges. Police officers pushed the crowd aside, only to get a better look for themselves.

Fleurette couldn't see above anyone's head, so I let her climb the stairs of the library (closed until further notice) and perch atop a lamppost pedestal. She wrapped her arm around the post and craned her neck to see. In a peach-colored afternoon dress that flowed and swirled around her and her hair in dark glossy waves around her shoulders, she looked like Liberty with her torch. I stood below and watched with alarm as young men took their eyes off the proceedings down the street and grinned up at her instead. She kept her chin high, but I saw her glancing down at her admirers and wished I'd taken the post with her to discourage their interest.

The intersection had been cleared as if for a duel. One of Paterson's older trolley cars sat on the tracks, awaiting its fate. An enormous black motor car lurked on the other side of the intersection, half a block away, its engine growling. A wooden platform had been built for the camera, which stood all alone on its three-legged stand.

Finally the motor car's engine roared and a conductor jumped into the trolley and waved to the crowd. Everyone yelled back and fluttered their handkerchiefs at him. The driver of the motor car stood and waved to even more applause. Then they both settled down and a hush fell over the crowd.

The cameraman gave a nod. Someone raised a megaphone and counted down.

"Three. Two. One. Go!"

Over gasps and screams from the audience, the trolley rolled along its tracks and the motor car came at it broadside, picking up speed, just as Henry Kaufman had. The conductor looked out with an exaggerated expression of fear, which drew a laugh from the audience just as the car plowed into the trolley. It rocked back and forth. The conductor's expression grew more alarmed, and finally, with one last push from the motor car, it collapsed on its side, its wheels spinning.

Cheers erupted from the crowd. Fleurette was jumping up and down and clapping madly. Policemen, firemen, and a doctor with his medical bag all ran to the trolley, but the conductor emerged, victorious, shaking his fists in the air. All around me, people were congratulating one another as if they'd had some role in the outcome.

I turned to look for Fleurette, but at that moment I felt a hand on my sleeve. It was the red-haired girl from the factory.

"You don't remember me," she shouted, straining to be heard over the crowd. She was younger than I'd first realized—not much older than Fleurette—and would have been pretty if she hadn't spent her life in a dye shop. Her hair was thin and dull, her mouth pinched, and there was a burn mark on her neck and another one like it on the back of her hand, both of them quite brown, suggesting an accident that occurred years ago. Her fingers bore the gray stains that accumulated from the dye.

"I do," I said. "I made you spill all that dye. I'm sorry." I stepped back and took my arm away from her. There was nothing on the library's pedestal but a lamppost. Fleurette had left her spot.

"It's nothing to be sorry for," she said. "We can't help but spill dye. Every day my apron's a different color."

The people in the crowd were pushing past me like a school of fish.

"Please excuse me," I said. "I'm looking for my sister."

I broke away from the crowd and backed into the street

so I could get a better look at the library steps. It was nothing but a sea of hats, and all of a sudden I couldn't remember which hat Fleurette had worn. Now I was thinking about Henry Kaufman, too, and watching the side streets to make sure I didn't see a black motor car roll away with a young girl in the passenger's seat.

By the time I saw Fleurette, she was almost upon me, still smiling, still glowing, still bouncing on her toes. I grabbed her and pulled her roughly to me, looking over the top of her head as I did. She tried to push away from me but I wouldn't let her.

A voice behind me whispered, "Is she the one?"

I spun around but kept one arm wrapped around Fleurette's neck. It was the girl from the factory again.

"Is this her?" she asked. "I knew it couldn't have been you."

Fleurette wriggled away from me to get a better look at her. "Who are you?"

She took a deep breath and settled her shoulders. "I'm Lucy Blake. I work in Henry Kaufman's factory. Is there another child? You can tell me."

"Another child?" Fleurette screwed up her face and looked back and forth between the two of us. The girl's meaning was starting to dawn on me.

"I had a boy," Lucy said. "Bobby. But he's gone."

"I beg your pardon, Miss Blake," I said, pulling Fleurette away from her. "There's been a misunderstanding. I went to see Mr. Kaufman about the payment of an invoice."

Lucy gave Fleurette another quick glance. "Do you mean that she isn't—"

I shook my head, horrified by the idea of Fleurette having anyone's child, much less Henry Kaufman's.

"What boy?" Fleurette asked breathlessly. "Where has he gone?"

Lucy looked at Fleurette with teary eyes. The story tumbled out before I could think to stop it. "I don't know," she said, her voice wavering. "I never asked Henry for anything until we went out on strike. I just wanted enough money to feed Bobby. Nothing for me! I only needed milk and bread. But Henry was furious. He thought I was trying to trick him into giving me a share of the family business."

"That sounds like him," I said in spite of myself. I didn't want Fleurette to hear any of this, but I was growing outraged on the girl's behalf.

She sniffed and nodded. "He knew there was a baby. I mean, I hid it as long as I could, but he saw me every day. He knew. I told him all I wanted was to keep my job—nothing from him! He's not fit to be a father."

"Of course not," I said quickly.

"But when I asked him for help through the strike, he acted as if I were threatening extortion! He wouldn't give me a dime. So I had to send Bobby away in the children's evacuation."

"You sent your baby away?" Fleurette said. "How could you?"

"Fleurette! What choice did she have?" The strikers' children left Paterson by the wagonload last year, bound for New York City, where families sympathetic to the strike had agreed to take care of them until their parents were back at work and could afford to feed them again. We had all seen the pictures in the paper of them leaving, those doleful children with notes pinned to their collars.

"All the other children came back, except mine," Lucy

said, grabbing at my hands. "I think Henry had something to do with it, don't you?"

I shook her hands off, tripping over my skirt as I fell away from her. I felt as though I'd been pushed out of a window. Henry Kaufman was a sluggard and a scoundrel, but a kidnapper?

"I couldn't possibly know," I said. "Haven't you been to the police?"

A man carrying a stack of hatboxes jostled me as he walked by. I jumped and pulled Fleurette back to the library steps. Lucy Blake looked nervously around and followed.

"I can't," she whispered, grabbing my wrist and leaning up to my ear. "If I go to the police, he'll make sure I disappear, too. That's what he told me."

Why was she was telling me this? I could hardly look at her, but I couldn't move, either. Fleurette, crushed against me, watched her with wide, dark eyes.

"He's getting so much worse," she continued. "When he first took over the factory, he wasn't so terrible. He could be nice when he wanted to, especially with the girls."

I put a hand over Fleurette's ear. "Lots of men can be nice to girls."

Fleurette pulled away. "I can hear you!"

"But he's horrible now," Lucy said. "He'd rather run with that gang of his than run the factory. They do nothing but drink whiskey and plot their little schemes. They're always going out to get revenge or to teach someone a lesson. You wouldn't believe the fights they get into, even with each other."

"What about his sister?" I said. "She seems sensible enough."

Lucy shook her head. "She's disgusted with the whole mess. Her family has all sorts of mills, and this is the only one that's in trouble. She and Mr. Garfinkel have been sent in to get Henry straightened out, but she can't do anything with him either."

"But surely she could help you?"

"I tried. Mrs. Garfinkel wants nothing to do with my situation. And it isn't that she doesn't believe me. I had a few things of Henry's — some notes he left me and . . ." She glanced at Fleurette, who had never listened so carefully to anyone in her life. "Well, some personal things of his. She knows Bobby is her nephew. But I'm just one more problem as far as she's concerned—" Her voice broke again, and she brought a handkerchief up to her eyes. "She told me not to mention it again and not to involve the police in her family's affairs."

"Why would you work for those people?" Fleurette said.

"Hush," I told her.

"I can't go anywhere else," Lucy said. "All the mills keep blacklists. I'm to stay quiet if I want any job in town. And I keep hoping I'll hear something about Bobby. When you walked in last week, I thought you might know of a similar situation. I thought we could help each other. I've been looking for you."

All at once it came to me that if this girl was in so much trouble with Henry Kaufman, Fleurette and I shouldn't be seen on the streets with her. "I'm sorry, Miss Blake, but our situation is quite different. I hope you . . . I mean . . . just look after yourself." I took Fleurette's arm and turned to walk away.

"Watch out for him," she called after us. "He won't stop. Once you cross him, he doesn't forget."

Something about her story was bothering me. I halted in the middle of the sidewalk and turned around. She was standing all alone in front of the library, watching us go.

"Lucy, what about the people in New York who were keeping your baby? What do they say?"

"That's just it," Lucy said. "They're gone, too."

⊰ 9 ⊱

FLEURETTE GOT TO DRIVE HOME. She nosed the runabout along Paterson's crowded streets while I stared straight
ahead, trying to shake off the peculiar feeling that had taken
hold of me since we broke free of Lucy Blake.

Something had shifted, in some subtle way I couldn't put
a name to. The everyday rush of shoppers and carriages and
motor cars and shopkeepers and delivery boys, once so familiar to me, now seemed foreign and vaguely threatening. I
watched three men push a wagon with an enormous wooden
crate perched atop it. They had to hold it on all sides to keep it
from crashing over as it rolled by. What it contained I couldn't
see, but all at once I was suspicious of it. What were they hiding: Ammunition? A bank vault? A missing person? Across the
street, a woman walked out of her shop with a bucket that she
discharged into the gutter. I shuddered and wondered what
foul mess she was trying to scrub away. A girl about Fleurette's age stepped in front of our horse with a baby-shaped
bundle pressed against her chest, and all I could think was:
Whose child is that? Where are you taking it?

Fleurette pushed Dolley onward, keeping quiet until we reached the edge of town. Then she said, "Did Mr. Kaufman really do all those things?"

"I don't know."

"Do you think she was lying?"

"It doesn't seem that way."

"Shouldn't she go to the police?"

"Fleurette! Please." I was exhausted and irritated. I wanted nothing more than to lie down in a cool dark room and close my eyes. Fleurette was holding Dolley back, making her plod along, dragging out our journey. A milk truck passed us, then a wagon overloaded with traveling trunks and furniture.

"Are we ever going to get home?" I asked her.

"Not until you tell me what this is all about."

"I don't know anything more than you do."

"Why would she take up with a man like that?"

I sighed and shook my head. "All the usual reasons."

"Because she was in love?"

"Maybe."

"And she thought he would marry her?"

"Quite possibly."

"I don't see how anyone could marry a man like that."

I thought about that for a minute. "Maybe he wasn't always that bad. Maybe he used to be different."

"Did you used to be different?" Fleurette asked.

I didn't answer that.

WE RETURNED HOME to find Bessie in the sitting room with Norma. She had dropped by, she declared, to deliver a strawberry cake she'd won in an auction to benefit the library, but I suspected that Francis wanted a woman's opinion on how we were managing. Norma appeared to have passed the inspection because Bessie was getting ready to leave when we arrived. She rose from her chair when she saw me and pulled me affectionately to her. She was a cheerful, plump woman with a wide, generous smile and the kind of brown hair that turned red in the summer. As she leaned toward me, she murmured, "Your brother worries about you. He just doesn't know how to show it."

"Sending over a strawberry cake is a fine start," I said, giving her shoulder a squeeze.

"You know that was my idea." Turning to Fleurette, she said, "Have you really been watching a picture get made all day?"

Fleurette began a lively and elaborate report in which she not only managed to keep our meeting with Lucy Blake a secret, but invented an afternoon's worth of activities to explain the length of our absence, including an actual derailed streetcar that forced a lengthy detour, an impromptu turn through the piano shop to hear a demonstration of new sheet music, and an encounter with a street vendor selling green African parrots from an enormous brass cage. The parrots spoke French, she said, and a little Dutch, but when asked their nationality would reply in a chorus, "We're Spanish!" The man selling them could offer no explanation for that. He merely laughed and shrugged and offered Fleurette a good price if she would take two.

The ease with which these small, meaningless lies unraveled from her tongue astonished me. Who taught her to fabricate such stories? I could hardly look at Norma while Fleurette spun those outlandish tales. For once Norma seemed not at all suspicious of the story being told to her, and Bessie was completely taken in by it, leaving us with a wave of her hand and shaking her head over the idea of parrots with French accents. It made me wonder how often I, too, had let Fleurette fool me.

ALL EVENING I tried to push Lucy out of my mind, but her predicament tugged at me. I couldn't stop thinking about the possibility that somewhere, at the center of this mess, that girl's child was missing.

Norma knocked at my bedroom door that night just as I was getting into bed. She sat on the edge of the mattress, one leg tucked under her and the other stretched out alongside me. She smelled of milk soap from her bath, and rice powder, and her hair was all wet curls, each one lifting individually as it dried in the warm night air.

She had a way of pursing her lips when she had something serious to say. I knew better than to ask directly and just waited to hear what it was.

"Green African parrots?" she asked.

"What about them?"

"Where did Fleurette get the story about the man selling green parrots on the street? You didn't expect me to believe that, did you?"

I had to smile. "No. I was surprised that you did."

"Well, I didn't." Norma looked down and smoothed the wrinkles out of the bedspread. "This has to do with Henry Kaufman, doesn't it?"

"Well—in a way, yes. It does."

"I can't believe you would take Fleurette to see that man. We hardly let her out of the house for years, and now you're parading her in front of a criminal. Why would you—"

"But it wasn't Mr. Kaufman. It was a girl from the factory."

"We don't know any girls from factories."

"I saw her when I went to Mr. Kaufman's office, and we ran into her on the sidewalk today. She . . . she thought I was in a different sort of trouble with him."

"Different sort of trouble?" she said, looking up and fixing those sharp eyes on me. "How many different sorts of trouble does Mr. Kaufman have to offer?"

"The girl, whose name is Lucy—"

"Don't tell me her name."

"I don't have to tell you any of this."

"No, tell me. What about her?"

"She had a baby."

"Oh. And she asked for your expertise?" Norma raised an eyebrow at me.

"Norma! The baby's gone missing. Lucy thinks Mr. Kaufman had something to do with it."

"Why would he care about a factory girl and her baby?"

"It's his child."

Norma ran her fingers through her wet hair. "Mr. Kaufman's morals sink lower with every passing day. By Wednesday, he'll be a murderer."

"Lucy thinks he's kidnapped the boy, so I suppose—"

"Do you not agree with me," Norma said, stretching out on my coverlet and putting her (blessedly clean) feet against my pillow, "that a man who carries on with factory girls and then kidnaps their children is the sort of man with whom the Kopp sisters would rather not become better acquainted?"

"I do," I said, "but don't you think it's terrible what happened to that girl?"

Norma propped herself up on an elbow to get a better look at me. "I do think it's terrible what happens to girls who get themselves into trouble. But we've had enough trouble already."

"I just feel that someone should try to help her."

"That feeling will pass." She rolled off my bed and stood over me, her arms crossed. "Francis and Bessie are having us over for a roast. I told her you'd do the peas."

"Nobody likes my peas," I said.

"But we like having you *do* them," she said. "Now, go to sleep and don't think about that girl anymore and I won't either." This seemed to be a satisfactory conclusion to her, so she slipped out and closed the door gently, leaving me alone in the dark, willing myself not to think about Lucy Blake.

❧ 10 ❧

IN BROOKLYN our only excursions out of the house, apart from school, were to dancing lessons at the Rivers' Academy, where our uncle Charles worked as an accompanist. Because he was willing to keep an eye on us, Norma, Francis, and I were made to spend most of our afternoons there, enduring minuets and fancy dress tableaux, lumbering through polkas and tarantellas, memorizing marches, and sitting in the corner folding crepe flowers for headdresses while the younger children had their turn in front of the mirrors.

Francis also took lessons on the zither from our uncle. On recital days he would stand, shaking, on the stage, and pick out a solo while Norma and I danced a wooden duet next to him. Being the tallest girl in the class, I was once dressed as Uncle Sam and placed in the center of the stage while forty-five girls, each portraying a different state, danced around me. Norma refused to choose a state. Wyoming was forced upon her. She wore a linen dress the color of sand and spread her arms wide to convey the vastness and futility of a place she could not imagine and did not wish to.

It was after one of those dancing lessons that I met the Singer man for the first time. In those days we lived on the top floor of a building with a rear entrance for delivery men and a front entrance for everyone else. Salesmen used to ring the bell in spite of the signs telling them not to. They sold silver polish and washing powder, pencils and notions, books by subscription and even fruit tree saplings. I used to watch the man with the bundle of twigs over his shoulder going up and down our street, finding no takers for his black cherries and Cox's apples. Only the most unlucky fruit tree peddler would be assigned Brooklyn as a territory. But a sewing machine salesman had an easier time of it.

The salesmen would ring the bell until someone let them in. Eventually their footsteps would approach our door, and then the knock would come, and my mother's hands would descend upon the heads of her daughters, a signal to remain quiet and perfectly still until the threat had passed.

Salesmen were dirty, she told us. They sold inferior goods that no store would offer. They preyed on lonely shut-ins and the feeble-minded. They only wanted in so they could come back and burgle our home while we were away. And they carried fleas.

I knew that couldn't be right. I went to school with girls who got their hair ribbons from a traveling salesman, and their kid shoes. I'd seen the sheet music man stop in at the dance academy to offer new songs for sale. A man selling tonics and remedies poured me a sample one winter when he heard me coughing on the sidewalk. (I ran away, but only because I was afraid my mother would catch me talking to him.) So I understood that salesmen were not as dangerous as my mother believed, but I didn't dare contradict her, and Norma didn't either.

This is why we were so astonished to come home from the dance academy one day and find a Singer salesman in our mother's parlor, demonstrating a new electric motor. Mother looked at us like one of the terrified kidnapping victims she read about in the newspaper. The Singer man just rose to his feet and smiled.

Having only just turned eighteen, I was too old for dancing lessons, but Norma, at the age of fourteen, was finishing her last year and had convinced me to go along and help with the younger children so that she wouldn't have to face it alone. She was embarrassed to be seen in her pleated skirt and bloomers, so she ran past the Singer man and slammed the door to our bedroom. That left me face-to-face with him.

"*Sholem aleykhem,*" he said quietly, as if my mother weren't in the room. "I am here on behalf of the Singer Sewing Machine Company. How do you do?"

He was a Jew. I had heard Yiddish spoken on the street, but never under our own roof. I stared past him at my mother, who sat frozen on the divan. How had she allowed this to happen?

He spoke to me again in that soft voice. "And you must be one of Mrs. Kopp's lovely daughters."

From his accent, I could tell he'd only been in the country a short while, but already he'd learned good English.

When I didn't say anything, he added, "I met your mother just as she was stepping out the door to hang her washing. I'd been next door showing Mrs. Fritz the benefits of our newest model. Your mother was kind enough to let me demonstrate it again here in your parlor."

My mother? Kind? He must have put a spell on her.

"I am Constance Kopp," I said at last. "Please excuse my sister. I'm afraid she's overly tired from her exertions at dancing class."

The Singer man was half a head taller than I was, which was already a rarity for me at that age. He had chocolate-brown eyes and a head of thick black hair that parted in the middle and flopped across his forehead. He looked down at me through gold-rimmed spectacles that gave him the appearance of a scholar.

"You are not tired from dancing class?"

"I don't take the class anymore. I'm too old for it."

"A girl is never too old to dance."

He was one of those men who perpetually smiled and whose face had become agreeably lined because of it. I knew I shouldn't smile back at him, but I did.

At last my mother found her voice. "My daughter does not like to dance."

Without turning away from me, he said, "But she took the lessons."

"Dancing lessons are good for girls." Mother rose and marched between us to the door and held it open. Seeing that he hadn't moved, she added, "She does not like to sew, either."

At last he turned around to retrieve his sample bag and the model of the electric motor. He gave me a polite nod and something more—a wink?—as he walked to the door.

"Perhaps she would like a lesson," the Singer man said, deploying one of his warm and generous grins on my mother from the hallway. "I offer instruction on all of our machines."

My mother closed the door on him and I turned so she

couldn't see the rush of blood to my face. At that moment I wondered if she had been right all along. Maybe young girls really did face threats to their virtue every day in America, even in their own homes, even from traveling salesmen carrying nothing but order books and sample cases.

THE NEXT TIME the Singer man knocked on our door, I was the one who let him in.

I'd refused to take Norma to dancing lessons any longer. Mother wouldn't let her go alone, so every Wednesday and Saturday the two of them rode the trolley to the dance academy, leaving me at home to start supper. Francis was working as a stock clerk for a hardware store, which meant that I found myself with the unexpected luxury of an empty apartment twice a week.

That afternoon I'd been very lazy, reading a book on the divan and neglecting the roast I was supposed to cook for dinner. It was an unusually mild day for November, and I had opened all the windows, pushing aside the heavy tapestry curtains to let in the high, clear breeze.

I had adopted Mother's habit of never answering a knock at the door—all of us had—but this one came so softly that it seemed harmless. I was at the door before I had time to think about what I was doing.

The Singer man's eyes crinkled when he smiled. "I hoped I'd find you at home, Miss Kopp."

Something happened to my limbs. They were frozen in place but also fully charged, as if a great river were rushing through them. He was inside with the door closed behind him before I could move. Now I knew how he'd gotten past my mother on his first visit. He had a way of gliding through a door as if every home were his own and he'd been expected for hours.

The Singer man put his case on the table and released its latches. The sides fell open to reveal a polished black machine.

"It's our newest model. I wanted you to see it first. I thought it might persuade you to take more of an interest in your sewing."

Nothing could make me take an interest in sewing, but for reasons I didn't understand, I nodded anyway and sat next to him and watched as he unrolled his fabric samples and bobbins. Each length of cloth had been stitched before, hemmed and pleated and taken apart again, exhibiting the traces of every sewing lesson he'd ever given.

I have a vivid memory of a piece of gingham rolling under the machine, and of a feeling just below my heart like a bird had hatched and was struggling to get out. It rose up into my throat and I swallowed to keep it down. Some part of me was aware that time was passing and that Mother and Norma were due home, but I could hardly breathe, much less rouse myself to look at the clock.

The Singer man possessed the long, thin fingers of a musician. He could handle the slimmest grade of thread and make the most minute adjustments to his machine the way one tunes an instrument. Those fingers brushed across mine to guide a piece of fresh silk under the needle, leaving a row of fine blue stitches more perfect and precise than anything my mother had ever attempted.

The lesson went on for an hour, ending just ten minutes before Norma and Mother returned. He left as silently as he came and our flat showed no sign that he'd been there. When he was gone, I stood in the middle of the empty room, wondering if I'd only imagined him.

I can't say that I learned anything. I was in no position to purchase one of his machines and he must have known it. That night, as we waited for the roast to finish, I said nothing about how I'd spent the afternoon. It was the first secret I'd ever kept from my family.

OVER THE NEXT FEW DAYS, Norma and I did not speak of Henry Kaufman or Lucy Blake. But Fleurette could think of little else, and she took any opportunity to pull me aside and tell her outlandish ideas to me.

"What if the boy is to be the heir to the Kaufman fortune, and he has been smuggled off to Russia, where he will never know his true heritage?" she asked one day in the languid hours of late afternoon, when Norma was out with her pigeons and we had retreated to our cool, dim sitting room to read. "He could be another *dauphin perdu*."

"We don't have princes in America," I said. "And why would he be taken to Russia?"

She put a finger purposefully on her pointed little chin as she thought about it. "The Bolsheviks. They took him to New York in the evacuation, and then they found out he was a silk man's son, and they put him on a ship to Russia to be raised as a revolutionary."

I put my book down, as Fleurette's story was vastly more interesting. "And will he return someday?"

"Yes," she said, stretching her arms above her head and yawning. "At eighteen, when he becomes a man, he'll claim his fortune from his father, who will be very old by then—"

"Not so terribly old," I corrected her.

"Oh yes, very old, fifty or so, and the *dauphin* will return to Paterson—"

"I'd like to think Mr. Kaufman will have been run out of Paterson by then."

She cleared her throat theatrically to discourage further interruptions. "He'll return and find his father, *wherever he may be,* and claim his fortune, and then hand his money out to all the workers in the factory, and Mr. Kaufman will scream and shout, but he'll be penniless and his workers will all go home in the middle of the day with their pockets full."

"But what about Lucy? Shouldn't she get something?"

"He'll have a palace built in Russia for her, and they'll return together so she can be queen of the Bolsheviks." Fleurette slapped her own book shut to signal the end of the story.

"I'm fairly certain the Bolsheviks don't want a queen."

"Well, she should get to be queen of *something* in the end."

ALL OF FLEURETTE'S STORIES about Lucy Blake involved hidden treasures, dramatic rescues, and glorious escapes to exotic locales, which were always populated with peacocks and black swans, those being, in her mind, the *accoutrements* of the royal class.

But Lucy Blake wasn't a character in a fairy tale. And her baby was not a *dauphin perdu,* but the illegitimate child of a factory girl, lost in a city of millions.

Although I worried over her predicament and wondered about the mess Henry Kaufman had made of her life and his own, those matters were, in some ways, still an abstraction to me. To my way of thinking, I'd had an accidental encounter with a man who was certainly not a fine citizen and possibly a criminal—but the entire affair was on its way to becoming a memory, a bizarre story that Fleurette would embroider and Norma would file away as a cautionary tale, but that would have no bearing on our lives henceforth. I didn't even think of Henry Kaufman as a man who went out and did things every day—who combed his hair and ate his lunch and drank in saloons with his friends and quarreled with his sister. In my mind, Henry Kaufman existed only in those moments when I had seen him, and the rest of the time he was still and quiet, like a marionette hung backstage by his strings, motionless until someone took him up and sent him skittering back to life.

What I couldn't fathom—what I hadn't considered, really—was that we continued to exist in his mind. He wasn't a marionette on a post, and he hadn't forgotten about us. He was always out there, doing whatever it was that Henry Kaufman did, and I had failed to appreciate the fact that sometimes what Henry Kaufman did was think about us.

This was at last made clear to me late one Tuesday night, when I found myself inexplicably awake, jolted out of a bizarre dream about Lucy and a bright green swan swimming in the dye tubs at Mr. Kaufman's factory. The sound that had awoken me was an engine rattling outside my bedroom window.

I sat up and clutched a pillow to me, having nothing else to protect me from whatever was coming. There was a flash of light through the window and then the glass shattered, sending shards flying around me. Something heavy hit the bed and I screamed.

From outside the window came the sound of tires spinning in the gravel and a motor car roaring away.

I had the shaky, nauseated feeling that comes from being thrown so suddenly from sleep. I gathered my blankets around me as protection against whatever had hit my bed. My fingers skipped around, past the broken glass, and there it was.

A brick. There was a piece of string around it, and paper tucked underneath.

Then Fleurette was in the room, and Norma's footsteps were close behind. The window with its mouth of jagged glass gaped at us.

"Get down on the floor," I whispered. I rolled out of bed and risked a step across the shattered remains of my window, which clinked and glittered across the floor. I peeked outside, but the road was dark and vacant, as if nothing had happened.

Norma and Fleurette were crouched down in their nightgowns, staring up at me, their arms wrapped across their knees.

"It was him, wasn't it?" Fleurette said. "He's back."

I nodded. "I think so."

We waited a second and then Norma rose and lit a lamp. She lifted the paper away from the brick and unfolded it gingerly, as if something might fly out of it.

```
Madam:
    Stay away from H. Kaufman and his place of
business. This time we warn you. Soon we shoot.
We use gun on you, we use more bullets, we
get you.
                                H. K. friend
```

She passed it to me and then to Fleurette. The note was written in childish block letters, like a right-handed man writing with his left hand.

"Shoot?" Fleurette said. "Does he really mean to shoot at us?"

I looked out the window again. The trees whispered in the dark and an owl made a muffled cry. I was still half inside that dream of the factory and the swan, and I had the strangest feeling that Mr. Kaufman had come after me because I had dared to dream about him. "Surely not," I said. "He hardly knows us."

A breeze rose and lifted the curtain away from the broken window. All three of us jumped.

"I thought it was a man climbing in," Fleurette said, her hand over her throat.

"You can't sleep in here," Norma said to me. "Not with the window like that."

I took the brick and knocked the rest of the glass out of the pane. Outside was nothing but the dark barn and the empty lane. "I'll be fine," I said, although I wasn't at all sure I would be. "It's only a prank, meant to frighten us and nothing more."

"Let me read the note again," Fleurette said, reaching for it.

"I don't want you brooding over it all night long and having nightmares."

"Just let me see it."

I held it above my head. "No! We should all go back to our beds, and we'll talk about it in the morning."

She leaned against me. "What would Mother make of all this?"

I smoothed Fleurette's hair, not daring to look at Norma over the top of her head. "I don't know what she would have done," I said. "Nothing like this ever happened to her. But I know what she would say to you."

"Really? What?"

"*Geh ins Bett.*"

"All right! I'm going."

Norma leaned against the door frame and watched Fleurette return to her bedroom. Then she slipped back into my room and closed the door behind her.

"How can you be so certain that Mr. Kaufman does not intend to shoot us," she began, "when he wrote a letter stating exactly the opposite and went to the trouble to break a window to deliver it?"

"I'm not certain of anything," I said. "I just didn't want Fleurette to work herself into a pitch in the middle of the night."

Norma sat down next to me on the bed and picked up bits of broken glass, dropping them into her cupped hand. "I suppose this is how we'll live now, behind boarded windows with strange men throwing bricks at us. If only we had a basement, we could move into it and never go out at all."

"It was only a prank, and I don't think they'll do it again," I said. "We've given them no cause to." Next to my pillow I found a chip of window glass the size of a penny with a little white paint on it.

"Well, of course *we* haven't given them cause," Norma said, "but you have. Men don't like to admit when they've done something wrong, and they particularly don't like strange ladies coming around demanding payment in compensation for their wrongdoing."

"That's not a reason to shoot at us."

"It's not a reason for a sensible person to shoot at us," she said. "If Mr. Kaufman were sensible, he wouldn't have run us down in the first place. In fact, he never would have bought one of those machines." The auto industry had a formidable foe in Norma, who believed self-propelled vehicles to be a path to lawlessness and social chaos. Mr. Kaufman was only strengthening her argument.

"Well, it's a matter for the police now. I'll go and see them in the morning."

"You won't find the police to be any help at all. They won't arrest him, and if they go and ask him questions, he'll only get more agitated, and I don't want to know what he'll do then."

There was a footstep in the hall. Fleurette pushed open the door and flopped down on my bed. Norma leapt up so as not to spill her handful of glass. "Go back to sleep," I said.

"But, Constance. I just realized."

"What?"

"Lucy was telling the truth. He goes after anyone who crosses him and he doesn't stop."

"I would hardly say that we're the ones who crossed him." But I remembered the way I'd pushed him against the wall. He'd looked like a trapped animal. And what do animals do when they're cornered?

"If this is how he treats us, what has he done to Lucy?" She put her head on my pillow and looked at me pleadingly.

I shook my head. "I don't know. I can't imagine."

"What are you going to do about that girl and her baby?"

"Well, there's nothing at all I can do, especially now that we're having bricks thrown at us."

"But if you don't, who will?"

I leaned over and put my chin on Fleurette's head. Norma looked down at the two of us and drew in her breath as if in preparation for another speech on the inadvisability of having anything to do with the matter, but the words wouldn't come or she decided not to say them. She opened her hand above my waste bin and the slivers of glass fell down like rain.

⪧ 12 ⪕

A LATE SUMMER STORM blew through Hackensack the next morning and washed the dust off the buildings. By the time I got to town, the sun had pushed away the clouds and the city smelled of clean hay and wet stone. The sour, ripe heat of summer had lifted. I climbed the courthouse steps under the heady influence of this shift in the season, and stood just inside the door to let the perspiration dry behind my collar before I approached the girl at the receptionist's desk.

"I am here to file charges against a man," I said. "It's a criminal matter."

"Is this man your—" She pursed her rosebud lips and I suppose she thought about the word "husband" in relation to me and decided against it.

"He is a man who committed a crime," I said. "Have I come to the right place?"

She gave me a look of prim disapproval but directed me to an office and told me to speak to whatever detective I found there. I marched past her desk and through the high and bright rotunda, where the muffled noises from the court-rooms met in the center and circulated, lifting a contentious and quarrelsome murmur to the stained-glass dome above. The door to the prosecutor's office was closed. I pushed my way in without knocking.

Seated at the desk was a slump-shouldered man with a face the exact shape and texture of an egg. His eyes were a jaundiced yellow, and his lips pointed down in a deep V shape, giving the impression of a permanent and immovable frown. The plate on his desk read simply "DETECTIVE."

He was talking to a man in a brown suit. I couldn't see the other man—his back was turned—but the detective regarded him with an expression of profound disgust, the way one might look at a tramp carrying a colony of fleas under his coat. He jumped to his feet when he saw me, clearly relieved by the interruption.

"Good morning, miss," he said. "I am Detective Courter. How may I—"

"I'd like to file a criminal complaint," I said.

The other man rose and turned to face me. He was not a tramp, just a man in a plain suit and a bow tie. He wore a mustache that seemed too wide for his face, bringing to mind a boy in his father's clothes. He looked at me through mourn-fully dark and deep-set eyes.

"Sheriff Robert Heath," he said. "How do you do?"

I introduced myself and explained the purpose of my visit. As I did so, Sheriff Heath stepped aside to yield the floor to Detective Courter. I addressed my concerns to the detective but could not help glancing at the sheriff, who watched the exchange with a half-suppressed smile.

Upon hearing my account, Detective Courter glanced at the sheriff and then sat down at his desk and squinted at the threatening note I'd presented to him.

"Miss, did you say the accident took place over in Paterson? Isn't that a matter for Passaic County?"

"Yes," I said, "but I live here in Bergen County, and he's harassed us twice at our house." The truth was that I'd chosen Hackensack over Paterson because I hoped that the police in Hackensack would be less sympathetic to the silk men than those in Paterson, a city dominated by the industry.

"It appears, Miss Kopp," he said, not moving his eyes from the paper, "that this is a matter for you to settle directly with him. If he's damaged your buggy, simply write out the charges and send them to him." He raised his eyes to me at last, elevating one eyebrow in a manner that suggested that he'd just brought the matter to an entirely satisfying conclusion.

I took a seat across from the detective, leaned toward him, and spoke slowly and quietly.

"After Henry Kaufman plowed his automobile through a crowd of people on Market Street and destroyed our buggy, he drove past our house with three other men and shouted vulgarities at my younger sister. He then hurled a brick and this letter through my bedroom window in the middle of the night." I paused to give him time to write this down, as would be the custom when a citizen comes to the courthouse to make a complaint. He did not write anything down, and in fact did not appear to possess a pen or any writing paper. But I continued.

"I have sent Mr. Kaufman an invoice, which he refuses to pay. Now I wish to file a complaint. He has committed a series of criminal actions against us with no provocation whatsoever."

Mr. Courter looked up at the sheriff, who gave him a nod of acknowledgment but said nothing. He looked back at the letter and then up at the ceiling. Discovering no answer stamped in tin above him, his glance fell back to me. At last another idea came to him.

"Now, Miss Kopp," he said. "With whom did you file the report?"

"I have come to file the report with you," I said.

"Well—ah—yes. But the officer at the scene. What officer took down a report of the damages to your buggy?"

"There was no officer. I was surprised that not a single constable came to our aid. But a few men from the shops helped us right our horse, and I took down Mr. Kaufman's name and address so that I might forward him a bill for the damages."

He seemed to consider my reply. "Well, we only investigate the accident reports that come to us from the officers, Miss Kopp. If no report was taken, there's nothing I can do."

It was my turn to consider him. I rose from my chair and looked down at him. His head was covered in thick black strands glistening with oil. It reminded me of Mr. Kaufman's. They seemed, all at once, like the same man.

"My sister Fleurette is but thirteen years of age," I said, loud enough to cause him to jerk his neck back and look up at me. "She has been threatened twice by a dangerous criminal." I grabbed the letter and snapped it once again under his nose. "You know as well as I do what can happen to young girls. It is your duty to stop this man."

Detective Courter, I am sad to say, reacted to my speech

with a fit of giggles. He leaned back, his shoulders shaking and his eyes wet. At last he seemed to come out of it and realize that I was still standing over him.

"Are you suggesting," he said, "that this man might run off with your sister rather than pay a fifty-dollar bill for damages? A silk man?"

"I don't see what difference his profession could make. Are you prepared to take my complaint?"

The sheriff coughed quietly in the corner. Detective Courter glared at him. After a few more delays and equivocations, the detective managed to find a pen and I returned to my seat. I repeated the entire story and watched him copy it down. I left out the most unpleasant bits of my encounter with Henry Kaufman in his office, and did not mention Lucy Blake and her claims about the kidnapped child. I didn't trust Detective Courter to handle the girl's situation with any sensitivity.

While he wrote, I looked around the office. It was a fine room, lined with good oak panels and lit by brass lamps with milk-glass shades suspended from the ceiling, clearly designed for pursuits more honorable than those that were at present taking place within it. Along one wall ran a bank of cabinets fitted with bookshelves, drawers for files, and cubbyholes for messages, all empty. The room had been furnished with two desks for the detectives and a secretarial stand equipped with a typewriter and a telephone, but from the accumulation of dust I could see there was no secretary to operate them. I couldn't imagine they could keep a woman in that position for long. I certainly wouldn't have wanted to work for a man like Mr. Courter.

At the end of my recitation, I glanced at the page he had filled with notes and satisfied myself that it was accurate.

"Well," he said, closing the book and brushing off his hands as if he'd just completed a long day's work. "That takes care of it. Thank you for bringing this to our attention." He stood to see me out.

I kept my seat. He sank uncertainly back to his. "When can I expect to hear from you, Detective?" I asked.

He opened the ledger again as if he hoped to find the answer written there. "Ah—yes. Well, we have your case on file, and if any other incidents should arise—"

"I expect that there will be no more incidents. I expect you to pursue charges against Mr. Kaufman and put a stop to this unwarranted harassment of my family!" I said, rising to my feet at last.

Some change came over Detective Courter when I spoke to him like that. He looked up at me coldly. A vein throbbed on his temple and his eye twitched slightly. "I will speak to the prosecutor," he said slowly.

"And what are we to do if he comes back?"

He looked over at Sheriff Heath, who was staring at his feet. "Haven't you anyone to look after the three of you?" Mr. Courter said with mock concern. "A father or an uncle? A brother, even?"

It had grown very stifling and I decided I couldn't stay in that room another minute. I spun around and left without another glance at either of them.

I WAS STANDING on the courthouse steps trying to catch my breath when I heard—or rather felt—Sheriff Heath behind me. I spun around to face him. He was a tall man, tall enough to look me squarely in the eye.

"I take it this is your first visit to the prosecutor's office," he said.

"It is," I said. "I won't waste my time here again."

He smiled. The sun had been gaining strength all morning and now it struck his face, highlighting the composition of lines and angles around his eyes. There was a kindness about him and a sort of sober warmth and decency, which struck me as unusual for a man in public service in New Jersey.

"I'll speak to Mr. Kaufman. If he gives you any more trouble, come see me."

"I didn't realize your duties extended beyond running the prison and chasing down poultry thieves."

"Poultry thieves do fall under my jurisdiction, Miss Kopp, but so do gangs throwing bricks through windows. Besides, I've had trouble with Kaufman before. May I see the note?"

I offered it to him. "What kind of trouble?"

"During the strikes. The silk men had their own ideas about how to keep order. He had his friends following my men around to make sure we didn't go too easy on the strikers. I didn't appreciate it."

He squinted at the letter and shook his head. "I wouldn't mind a chance to go after that bunch. I suspect they're up to more than just chasing you and your sisters around."

"What do you mean?"

"The usual things. Smuggling liquor. Gambling. Blackmail. They're all thugs and con men, that crowd. A note like this is just the kind of thing they do. Has he tried to shake you down for money?"

"No! Why would he? He's the one who owes us money!"

"You must understand that this is just a game for them."

"Well, it's a cruel game," I said. "And why didn't you say anything back there?"

He shrugged. "You saw what Courter was like. He's not going to take on that gang. The prosecutor's office can be very friendly with the factory owners. But don't worry. Mr. Kaufman doesn't have any friends in the Sheriff's Department."

"Well, that isn't all he's done. I talked to one of the girls who works for him—"

"One of the girls?" He gave me another one of those amused half-smiles. "When did you talk to the girls?"

"It was one particular girl. I just bumped into her. This girl got into some trouble, and it was Mr. Kaufman who . . ." I wasn't sure how to say it, but Sheriff Heath seemed to catch my meaning.

"I'm afraid that is outside my jurisdiction, Miss Kopp."

"But now the child has gone missing, and she thinks Mr. Kaufman is behind it."

The sheriff frowned and cocked his head to the side. "Who's the girl?"

"Well . . ." I took a step back. "What are you going to do if I tell you? I don't want to get her into any more trouble."

Just then a man in a deputy's uniform came running around the corner from the jailhouse, calling the sheriff.

"I can't do anything unless I know who she is," he said. "Have her come and talk to me herself if she wants help."

"But I—"

The deputy ran up to us, wheezing, and said, "They just brought him in."

Sheriff Heath looked at him in surprise. "Already? Well, Miss Kopp," he said, extending his hand. I almost never shook hands with a man, but I removed my glove and slid my palm into his. His hand was warm and dry and I gripped it rather tightly. He laughed a little as he released me. "Not to worry. Mr. Kaufman is no longer your concern. If he bothers you again, come tell me right away. You can telephone me at the Hackensack jail any time of the day or night. And tell that girl to come see me. Will you do that?"

Before I could answer he was gone, trotting down the courthouse steps with his deputy. They spoke excitedly as they walked away from me, already caught up in some far more important matter. I watched them disappear into the side entrance to the jail, and the most inexplicable sorrow and longing settled in around me.

A train rattled in the distance and its whistle announced the next stop. It was leaving for Paterson, where Lucy Blake was working her morning shift at the factory.

I should have gone home. It was nearly time for lunch, and Norma didn't like it when one of us was not present at a meal. I hesitated for just a minute, then I picked up my skirts and ran for the train.

❧ 13 ❧

I ARRIVED IN PATERSON an hour before the noon whistle. Along Broadway a group of boys were taking down bunting left over from a parade to honor the mayor's birthday. In their wake came a troupe of girls selling buttons to raise money to aid victims of the fire in Salem. Three of the girls took hold of me at once, spotting an easy mark. I couldn't imagine what Fleurette would do with a set of white buttons that had been stamped with the words "SALEM SUFFERERS, 1914" in red, but I handed over fifty cents anyway and put a few in my pocketbook. The girls wandered on and I lingered outside a druggist, accepting a sample of a digestive tonic that tasted suspiciously like sugar syrup and wine. I passed the rest of the time staring into shop windows, a little queasy over what I was about to do.

Henry Kaufman's factory was just a short walk away. I paced up and down Putnam, getting close to the address and then turning back again. I was standing across the street from the ramshackle brick building as every dyer in his employment emerged for lunch, all dressed in their gray smocks.

The break was nearly over by the time Lucy Blake walked out and stood in the sun, her face turned upward and her eyes closed.

"Lucy?" I called, as quietly as possible. Still, three or four men turned around and watched me approach her. Lucy took a step back and shook her head very slightly to warn me away, but it was too late. I'd made up my mind.

"Lucy, I think I can help," I said when I got closer. "About the matter we discussed."

She looked up at a row of windows at the opposite end of the building where the offices were housed. "Over here," she said, leading me around the corner.

Once we were out of sight, she said, "You shouldn't be here. What is it?"

The whistle blew and she jumped. "I've found someone who wants to talk to you," I said quickly. "About your baby. I'll go with you."

The whistle blew again. "I have to go before they lock us out," she said. "Don't come back here. You can meet me at home to-night." She gave me her address, and then she was gone.

IF I'D RETURNED HOME, Norma would have tried to talk me out of visiting Lucy, and Fleurette would have insisted on coming with me. Being unable to face either possibility, I spent the afternoon in the library and left a little after six o'clock to go see her.

Lucy lived in a neighborhood of narrow clapboard-covered row houses a few blocks off Broadway. I'd ridden past it but never had reason to stop there, as it was inhabited entirely by people who worked in the mills. Paterson was not a company town, but the factory owners had been buying boarding houses and corner markets around here for years. The people who lived there paid rent to their boss, bought groceries from their boss, and went into debt to their boss if their money ran short.

I could find no house numbers along her street, so I started at the corner and counted until I found hers, an old flat-fronted two-story house whose front porch had recently gone missing. Either it had fallen off or burned, and no one had bothered to build another one. I lifted my skirt and climbed atop a pair of concrete blocks that had been placed there to allow entrance. A directory next to the door had been painted the same dull maroon as the rest of the building, as if the painter could not be bothered to stop long enough to paint around the list of people who lived inside. But someone had glued a card to the metal plate and written out the names of the occupants and their room numbers.

Lucy lived on the second floor. Finding no bell to ring and the door unlocked, I entered the dim hall and started up the stairs.

There was a crash overhead and the sound of glass breaking, then a girl's cry. I backed down and into the hall. Upstairs a door slammed and then opened again.

"Where is she?" came a man's voice.

"I don't know," a girl said. "I told you I don't know." There was another thud and I could hear her crying.

"She had no business talking to you!"

I jumped. How could I have failed to recognize that voice? I had no time to gather my thoughts before I heard his footsteps on the landing.

"You tell that Kopp girl to leave you alone," he shouted, his voice booming in the stairwell. "If I see you with her again, you'll be out on the street."

I had to move. Behind me was a door to what I hoped was a kitchen or a storeroom. It was unlocked so I opened it and backed in. Henry Kaufman pounded down the stairs just as I closed the door behind me. I looked around and realized I wasn't in a kitchen, but a lodger's room. Fortunately for me it was empty. There was an iron bed topped with a thin mattress and a ratty blanket, an oil lamp on a low table, and dingy striped wallpaper peeling off in long strips. A man's Sunday shoes sat in the corner. A yellowing newspaper wilted on a chair. My own reflection in a mirror on the wall opposite startled me—in my gray felt hat with the veil across it and my navy traveling suit, I looked like a society matron at an afternoon recital. I wished I'd worn a plainer suit of clothes. My size made me conspicuous enough.

A clock ticked somewhere nearby. There was an odor in the room, something foul and unwashed. I wanted out desperately. I waited until the footsteps passed and the front door opened and closed again, then I turned the knob quietly and I was free.

At the top of the stairs she stood like she'd been waiting for me.

"Lucy," I said. "I'm sorry."

"You shouldn't be here," she whispered. She looked tiny in her percale housedress, covered by an apron that was much too large for her and nearly wrapped around her twice. She held one corner of it in her fist and twisted the fabric around her fingers. Her cheek bore the mark of Henry Kaufman's hand, and her nose was swollen from crying.

I didn't make a move up the stairs. I wasn't sure what to do. "Is he your landlord?"

She looked surprised. "Well, yes. Of course. He owns this building and the two next door. Or his family does. He manages them now, if you call this managing."

I stood for a moment and considered that.

Lucy continued. "Mrs. Garfinkel said we could stay, even after she found out—" She looked down the stairs nervously as if she thought someone might hear.

"All right," I said. "Lucy, may I come up and talk to you? I'm sure he's gone, and if he does return, I'll take care of it. I can handle him."

She looked me over. "I suppose you could. You're bigger than he is, aren't you?"

Once again that sound came to me, the sharp crack when his head hit the plaster. I wasn't sorry I'd shoved him, and I thought I might like to do it again, after the way he treated this poor girl.

Lucy seemed to have calmed down, so I kept climbing and followed her to the door.

Her room was larger than that of the absent lodger downstairs, but it held two of the same type of narrow iron bed and a wardrobe as well as a dresser. The wallpaper depicted silhouettes of children rolling hoops across a lawn. There was a gold filigree border around each scene, but the gold had mostly cracked and flaked away, revealing the once-white underlay of the paper. There was no kitchen, just a wood stove topped by a hot plate and a chafing dish. The only chair was piled high with mending. Seeing nowhere to sit, I put my handbag on the edge of the nearest bed.

"That's my mother's bed," she said. "She cleans for a lady across the river. You can sit there. I'm sorry, I—" She looked around nervously, then scooped up the mending and sat in the chair, holding the bundle in her lap. She looked at me expectantly.

"I take it Mr. Kaufman saw me talking to you," I said at last.

She nodded. "I stopped for groceries on the way home, and when I got here, he was waiting. He has a passkey to the rooms."

I wondered how many other young girls lived in rooms he had passkeys to. "Well," I said, "I only came to tell you that I think something ought to be done about your son."

"I know," she said, and lapsed into tears again. "I should never have let him go with the strike mothers. I didn't know what else to do. We hadn't been paid in months, and the relief tents were always running out of food. I couldn't let him starve, could I? But you don't know what it was like, having to let him go."

I let her cry and clutch her bundle of clothes and rock back and forth as if she were soothing a baby. At that moment I could picture her pulling away from the strike mothers, not wanting to let go of her boy.

After a few minutes, she sniffed and wiped her eyes and looked at me. "I've tried to find him but it's hopeless. Everyone is gone. Everyone who had anything to do with the evacuation just disappeared."

"And you never went to the police?" I asked.

Her eyes flew open. "Oh, no! Henry would kill me if I sent the police after him."

"Well, he wouldn't—"

"No, I mean it. He would send his men after me in the middle of the night. He would burn this building right down, and me in it. You send the police after those men, and you're as good as dead."

She said it so matter-of-factly. I'm sure my heart stopped cold for two or three beats. What had I done?

"Are you sure? I know someone who would be willing to help, if only—"

She looked at me as if I were an imbecile. "Miss Kopp! If Henry has my boy—if he's put him somewhere—what do you think he will do to him when he finds out I've called in the police?"

My face must have been frozen, because she leaned over and peered at me. "Did you hear me?"

I nodded numbly.

"I don't know why you're here," she said, "but if all you have to offer is a call to the police, then I'm afraid you don't do me much good."

I coughed and tried to find my voice. "Well. I don't know what else I could do."

"I don't, either," she said, blinking back furious tears.

There didn't seem to be anything else to say, so I stood to leave. She made a sad sight, with her head down and her arms still wrapped around her heap of clothes to be mended.

"Before I go," I said, "why don't you just tell me what you know? Just in case I do think of something."

She raised her eyes to me and sniffed. She wasn't finished being angry at me, but in a flat voice she told me what I wanted to know. I took down the address of Regina Doyle, in whose care little Bobby had been placed. She told me that two women had taken responsibility for evacuating the children during the strike. They'd been in the papers every day last year, and I recognized their names, Sanger and Flynn. She also furnished me with a description of the baby, although it had been over a year since she'd seen him. He would be almost two years old by now. I asked her if she remembered anything from her trips to the city to try to fetch him, but she shook her head and her tears started again.

"It's no use," Lucy said. "Regina Doyle is gone. I walked up and down the street asking after her, but no one even remembers seeing her."

"She didn't leave an address with the landlord?" I asked.

She shook her head. "Nothing. One day she was just gone, along with everyone who knew her. The strike leaders who lived in that building disappeared all at once."

I heard a noise on the stairs and we both froze. The footsteps went past her door and up to the next floor. I took a long and shaky breath and told Lucy, somewhat dispiritedly, that there had to be a way to get some help for her. She shook her head and made me promise once again not to go to the police.

Having nothing else to offer, I said my goodbyes and stumbled down the narrow stairs into the glare of the setting sun. The street was strangely empty and silent but for the snap of laundry on the lines and the call of a man selling fish scraps from a wagon. It was the end of his route, so he had nothing left but porgie and the severed heads of sea bass that the housewives in the better neighborhoods hadn't wanted.

❧ 14 ❧

I COULD HAVE TOLD THE SINGER MAN to stop coming around. Our door had a lock. He couldn't get in unless I let him.

And I kept letting him in.

Within a few weeks it became apparent that the Singer man's long, fine fingers could handle buttons and clasps as well as a needle and thread. No man was more familiar with the ways that fabric could be bound up and taken apart than a sewing machine salesman. The first time he reached out to my neck and separated my collar from my dress I held perfectly still, surprised by how nimble and quick he could be. In the perpetual dusk of my mother's parlor, he worked at my dress like a tailor at a fitting, insisting that I stand in the middle of the room while he moved in a circle around me, releasing hooks and pushing pearl buttons through the loops my mother had stitched to hold them. He touched them lightly, as if he were merely testing their strength or checking for flaws in their design. On every visit he released another of the countless ties and latches with which we girls bound ourselves according to the fashions of 1897. It was a few weeks before he made it past the last one, but the Singer man was patient, smiling down on me as he released them. He closed his eyes like a man at prayer when he kissed me.

My mother had impressed upon me the idea that a girl should never sit alone on a divan with a man. And so we never sat on the divan. The Singer man made sure I always stood.

My knees gave out just once, but he pulled me up again.

THE SINGER MAN KNEW BEFORE I DID. He was precisely attuned to the fit of my dresses, having opened and closed them so many times that winter, even adding his own darts and pleats to make them fit better. When he saw my waist straining against his own stitches, he knew.

There was a place in New Jersey for girls like me, he said. One of the other Singer men told him about it.

Other Singer men? All at once I understood that there must have been other girls in Brooklyn taking sewing lessons from Singer men. Whatever bank of fog had been clouding my mind for the last few months cleared at the mention of other salesmen giving sewing lessons to other girls. The room came into very sharp and cold focus when he said it, and my situation was suddenly apparent to me in a way that it hadn't been before. The words describing my predicament dropped into place like type in a newspaper column.

Still I let him slip his fingers under my skirt to judge whether there was enough fabric to take it out a few inches.

I never once considered telling my mother. There was the fact of the child, and there was the fact that I'd let that man into her house again. A Jew going door-to-door, peddling the machinery of the coming century, taking her daughter apart stitch by stitch, right inside the creaky and cloistered preserve she'd built to hold us.

I didn't know what else to do but let the Singer man take me to Wyckoff and deposit me at Mrs. Florence's Country Home for Friendless and Erring Women. There was never any discussion of seeing a doctor or drinking a syrup or tossing myself down the stairs. I didn't know about any of that. I wouldn't know about it until I got to Wyckoff and the other girls told me.

So without a word, I disappeared. One summer morning I awoke in my own bed in Brooklyn as I always had, with Norma sleeping fitfully beside me, and the next morning I awoke on a wool mattress in Wyckoff, having registered under a false name the night before, presented as the unfortunate cousin of the Singer man.

I left no note behind. I took nothing with me, not even a change of clothes. In Wyckoff I would make myself a new wardrobe. As a parting gift the Singer man left me his sample machine.

⚜ 15 ⚜

THE POTATOES were heaving out of the soil. The leafy tops
had already bloomed and wilted. They'd have to be scrubbed
and packed in straw for the cellar before they turned green. I
kicked at a few of them and they lifted right out of the earth,
scattering the colonies of sow bugs hidden underneath.

Norma was brushing Dolley as I walked into the barn.
When she saw me she gave the horse a pat on the rump,
nudging her back into the stall.

"Why don't you time the pigeons today," she said, "as long
as you're out here and have so little to do."

I did have something to do, but I hadn't yet told Norma
about it. Instead I helped her saddle Dolley and led the horse
around front while she took the pigeon basket and went to
get some birds. She'd installed a pigeon clock in the loft recently, a box containing a special timer that could be stopped
when a pigeon's leg band was dropped into it. At competitions the judges would open each box, start the clocks as the
birds were released, and then lock them shut. Each competi-
tor would carry the box home and wait for their pigeons to

arrive. When they flew into the loft, the band would be re-moved and pushed through a slot in the box to mark the time. The boxes would have to be returned to the judges to be opened, the flight times recorded, and the velocities cal-culated.

Norma didn't race her birds, as it would have required her to join a pigeon club and she didn't believe in associating with people on any organized basis, but she liked to keep track of their flying speeds regardless. It had become my responsibil-ity to stand at the loft and mark the time of their return.

She gave me a starting time and I agreed to wait in her dusty and feather-lined loft with a pocket watch in my hand, while she rode to town with a watch of her own. When the hour struck, I was to start the clock and lock the box, know-ing that somewhere, a few miles away, she was releasing the birds.

"I'll just go as far as Ridgewood and get my papers," Norma said. She hoisted her pigeon basket and strapped it to Dolley's saddle. From inside the basket came the shuffling of feathers and claws in what I took to be an expression of excitement on the part of the birds.

We checked our watches and conferred on the time I'd start the clock. Then she was gone, down the drive and out of sight, leaving me alone with a half-empty pigeon loft and a plot of potatoes.

I HAD JUST GONE INSIDE when Norma's pigeon bell rang.

"Ach. I've got to go get that bird."

"Go ahead," Fleurette said. She was making her favorite lunch, buttered bread with sugar, and was eager to get me out of the kitchen before I told her she shouldn't waste sugar like that. I'd been threatening to send our sugar to the Belgian soldiers if she kept spooning it onto everything she ate.

But I left her alone with the sugar bowl and ran out to stop the clock. The first pigeon to arrive had disappeared into the farthest corner of the loft, where he picked at his leg band but wouldn't let me remove it. He sat up very straight on his perch, a little opalescent feathered man, eyeing me with an expression of affront and suspicion that was uncannily similar to Norma's. I couldn't stand up straight in the loft, so after I flailed around and got my hair caught in the chicken wire and cursed the bird for its stubbornness, I backed out and stood next to the door as the next ones arrived.

Two more pigeons landed. This time I managed to wrestle the bands off their skinny legs and push them into their slots on the clock. The rest of the flock descended a few minutes later. I was back inside, trying to get the sugar bowl away from Fleurette, when Norma returned.

"How'd they do?" she said.

"The first one wouldn't come to me. He landed about a minute ahead of the others."

Norma dropped a newspaper on the table. "Your friend's in the paper," she said.

Fleurette read the headline: "Chicken Thief Goes to Bergen for Trial?"

"Let me see it." I read just enough to see that it involved Sheriff Heath. This was Norma's way of letting me know that we didn't need a chicken enforcement man involved in our affairs.

"What's the sheriff doing for us?" Fleurette asked.

"He's just going to talk a little sense into Henry Kaufman," I said.

"But Norma doesn't like him?"

"Norma doesn't know him," I said.

"Oh, but I know who he is," Norma said. "He's the one who's always begging the Board of Freeholders for more money for the prisoners."

"What do you mean, money for the prisoners?" Fleurette asked.

"The Freeholders are elected to see to it that the county is run in a businesslike manner, but Sheriff Heath is extravagant with the taxpayers' money," Norma said. "He wants to buy each of his inmates a new suit of clothes and offer them a library of books to read and give them a nice shave and a haircut, too. I'm glad the board won't let him. If he got his way, the criminals in this town would get better treatment than guests at a hotel."

"Can't you find a single polite thing to say about the man who has offered to come to our rescue?" I said.

"He hasn't rescued us yet," Norma said.

MY POTATOES had been slightly damp when I pulled them out and they were drying in the sun. As I was turning them over and brushing the dirt off them, I felt Norma come up behind me.

"You're still thinking about that girl," she said.

I didn't answer. I kept my eyes on the ground.

"We mustn't have anything more to do with Mr. Kaufman," she said. "I've told you so, and Francis agrees."

"When did you talk to Francis?"

"He stopped in yesterday when you were gone."

I stood up and brushed my hands against each other. "And you told him? About the brick? About—"

She shrugged. "Fleurette did. She couldn't resist. And I wasn't going to lie to him. He, of course, feels the whole situation is further proof that we cannot manage on our own."

"It's a bit late for that," I said. "We've been managing just fine."

Norma folded her arms and squinted at the vegetable garden and the giant stands of dandelions casting their shadows. She'd threatened many times to take over the management of the garden if I couldn't keep it tidy. I always told her she was welcome to it and that I would take any chore of hers in exchange. She hadn't accepted the offer yet, but I could tell the weeds were offending her sense of order.

"Some people eat dandelions," I said.

She sniffed. "You didn't tell me what happened with the girl."

"I thought you didn't want anything to do with it," I said.

"I don't, and you shouldn't have gone. But what did she say?"

I tried not to smile. Norma had an endless curiosity about other people's misfortunes. It was why she read so many newspapers. Something terrible was always happening to someone, somewhere, and Norma made it her business to know about it.

"There's not much to tell," I said. "Mr. Kaufman is a brute, but we already knew that. He rents his boarding houses out to young girls, and he goes around to collect rent personally every month. Which is to say—"

"Oh, please don't say it," Norma put in. "I know what that means."

"Lucy sent her boy off in the children's evacuation last year. He never returned, and the lady who was keeping him is gone. She really doesn't know anything more than that."

"She knows not to get the police involved."

"Only because she's afraid for her life," I said.

"As are we all, with Mr. Kaufman making plain his intention to shoot at us."

Dolley knocked over her bucket of oats and Norma retreated to the barn to set it upright. I trailed inside behind her. Dolley blinked calmly at us both. I put a hand on the warm flat patch between her eyes, then thumped her on the rib cage the way Norma always did. It calmed me to put my hands on her. She had a powerful heartbeat and a deep, steadfast breath like something from another time, some calmer era. I leaned against her, this enormous vanilla-colored creature who was so much sturdier than I was.

"I should do something for Lucy," I said, keeping my eyes on the horse.

"No, you shouldn't."

"I think I will. I'll just go into New York and see what I can find out. There's no harm in asking a few questions."

"No harm? After those men came to our house? And called out Fleurette's name like she's a common—"

"I know what they did," I interrupted. "But someone has to go looking for that child."

"I don't see why it has to be you," Norma said.

"Because—" I turned at last to face her. It took everything I had to look her in the eyes. "Because what if no one had gone looking for me?"

❧ 16 ❧

AT MRS. FLORENCE'S HOME I never spoke of my family. Most of the girls didn't. A few had run away like I had, and the rest had been deposited there by a tight-lipped, terrified mother or sister, to whom they would return some months later, having agreed upon a story about a semester in board-ing school or a visit to an aunt in the distant countryside. One time an infant was left on the doorstep with no mother at all, just an envelope stuffed with money and a note promising that an aunt or uncle would come and claim it as soon as one could be persuaded to do so. No one ever did.

I tried not to think of my own mother. She'd become such an authority on the fates of wayward and vanished girls. Now I was a girl ruined by a traveling salesman and then taken away to a home in New Jersey without a word to her family. Surely that headline had already been written.

Sometimes at night I would dream of my mother at the bottom of a well, darkness all around her, the stars too dis-tant to see. No sound but the rippling of water and the echo of her own voice against the walls. She waited for help, but none came. Week after week I returned to her in my dreams, and she was still there, so far down the well that even the sun never found her.

Did she go to the police? Did she write to our father? Did she walk the streets and ask every grocer and fruit peddler if they'd seen me? I wondered about it every night while I was away. She never spoke to me about that time, and Francis has always been too embarrassed to say much of anything about it, but eventually I got the truth from Norma. It came in scraps of whispered conversation over the years, in those rare moments when we were alone and Norma was in the mood for confidences.

I know that when they woke up and found me gone, they told themselves that I must have had a good reason to go out early in the morning, and that I would return later in the day with an explanation that, although difficult to imagine, would make sense. That night they sat up well past dark around the dim flame of a single gas lamp, knowing, I suppose, that going to bed would be an admission that there was no ordinary, everyday explanation for my disappearance, and that when they awoke in the morning, they would have passed into some new era in their lives—the era that began with the unexplained loss of one of their own, and whatever that might mean next for them. They slept in their chairs to forestall the arrival of that new day, but one by one they stole off to bed in the middle of the night, and then I was well and truly gone.

I can picture Mother in her old stuffed chair in the corner the next morning, stabbing at a piece of embroidery, her lips moving but no sound coming out. She had a way of stopping all conversation with her own grim silence. Poor Francis must've been stunned to realize that it would fall to him, as the man of the house, to bring up the delicate subject of his sister's sudden departure. (And they always thought of it as a departure, seeing no way that I could have been snatched from my bed and carried off against my will.)

Francis offered to make the usual inquiries—to the police, to the shopkeepers in the neighborhood, to the agents at the train station, and to our uncles and their wives, in case I had confided in one of them. But Mother wouldn't allow it. Her refusal told him that she had already passed judgment and decided that whatever the reason for my disappearance, it had to be something shameful, something not to be spoken of, even with the rest of the family. (She always kept my disappearance a secret from her brothers, and later they would refer to the time I enrolled in a secretarial college in Philadelphia. I learned to smile and agree that it had been an interesting course but that secretarial work was not for me.)

Norma agreed with Francis that they should go to the police and speak to anyone in the neighborhood and do whatever else was in their power to bring about my return. Mother was absolute in her opposition, and it was this, I believe, that caused something to break between the two of them. Norma realized, with a sudden cold shock, that if she herself disappeared, Mother would not go looking for her, either. And Norma was bold enough to say this out loud.

"You would do nothing? You would just let me go?"

This was the only part of the story Norma ever told me in any detail. She was still hurt by it years later. Mother had taken Norma's chin forcefully in her hand and said, "You would never disappear. You would never treat me like that."

That's when Norma understood what Mother had really intended with her newspaper stories of disgraced girls. They were a warning of not just what could happen to us out in the wide and unruly world, but also of what would happen if we tried to come home again.

Then my brother heard about another girl who had been visited by a sewing machine salesman. She had vanished, too, but had come home on her own before the baby was born and confessed it all.

Francis whispered his suspicion to Norma, thinking she would deny that her sister would do any such thing. But she turned pale and reached into her sewing basket to show him an unfamiliar bobbin she'd found just a few days earlier under the china cabinet, one that didn't fit Mother's machine. They both realized at once what it meant.

Still they weren't ready to tell Mother until they could be certain. Francis had been unable to learn the name of the home to which the other girl had been sent, so it fell to Norma to write letters to every girls' home in New York, New Jersey, and Pennsylvania, and that is what she did, night after night, writing out a new copy of the letter with a description of me and the date of my disappearance and posting it every morning to a different address.

By the time her letter reached Wyckoff, the baby had been born.

⊰ 17 ⊱

THE TRAIN TO NEW YORK was so crowded that I could find no seat except one next to an old woman carrying a bag of rabbit pelts. It quickly became evident why no one else was seated next to her. A cloud of ammonia hung around the bag, as did a colony of something tiny and dreadful: gnats or, worse, lice. She didn't get off in Rutherford or any of the other stops just outside Paterson. She was bound for the city, probably aiming to deliver her rancid bundle to one of those dingy furriers at the edge of the garment district that dealt in snakeskin and small game. As soon as the train stopped for a minute, I moved to another car. Finally a boy saw me looking for a seat and gave me his.

It was a relief to get off that train and out of the station. I realized that I couldn't remember the last time I'd been to New York alone. My uncles still lived in Brooklyn with their wives and children, and sometimes they'd have us to dinner on a Sunday. Once or twice we'd taken Fleurette to a play. But it never occurred to me that I could come on my own, and I had never once been confronted by the entirety of the city, by the enormity of it, by the possibility that I could go anywhere and do anything.

I knew what I had to do at that moment. I set out for the building on East Thirtieth where Regina Doyle was believed to have lived with Lucy's baby. I rushed past the shops selling buttons and shoe leather, past the lunch counters and the grocers with their cartons of soft apples in the street, past the office buildings with gold lettering across their windows.

In a short while I arrived at the address I'd been given. It was just an ordinary brownstone in the middle of a row of similarly ordinary four-story buildings. The third-floor windows had been outfitted with flower boxes that held the russet stubs of neglected geraniums.

A woman passed me on the sidewalk and climbed the stairs. "Pardon me," I said, running up behind her. "I'm looking for someone who used to live here."

"I don't know him," she said, never turning back to look at me.

"No, I was wondering—" and then she was gone, the door slamming shut behind her before I could get hold of it.

I tried the door and found it locked. There was a row of door-bells, but I didn't recognize any of the names on the plate.

From around the corner came a delivery boy carrying packages from the butcher. I asked him if he remembered a woman named Regina Doyle living in the building and he shook his head. "Don't recall, miss," he said, never slowing down.

"But you must make deliveries here," I called, addressing his back as he walked away.

Nothing.

It hadn't occurred to me that people would refuse to answer a question put to them directly. It must have been apparent to everyone I approached that I had no real authority. I had no card, no credential, no letter of introduction. And so I stood on the street and waited for something to come to me—a witness, a clue, a better idea. Nothing did.

For lack of another plan, I took a walk around the block and stopped in a corner market, then a shoe shop, and then a bookstore, to ask after Regina Doyle and the baby. No one had heard of her. It didn't help that I had so little by way of a description of the two of them. I stopped a man peddling flowers and a girl carrying her baby brother. They didn't have a single word for me.

Down the street I located a photographer's studio, situated in a basement apartment and identified by a brass plaque on the railing. "LAMOTTE STUDIOS," it read. "PHOTOGRAPHY. ALL SUBJECTS." There was no bell to ring. I pushed the door open and found myself not in a portrait studio, as I had expected, but in a cramped office littered with paperwork and stacks upon stacks of the same kind of large brown envelope. Affixed to each one was a clasp with a red string. The strings seemed to be alive, as if they were crawling over the mess and not merely dangling from it.

If there was a lamp anywhere in the room, I couldn't find it. The only light came from the front window, which was half covered with the sort of greenish-brown moss that grew on the steps of all basement apartments out of reach of the sun.

From behind a low door a man's voice called, "Two more minutes!" I replied that I'd wait, although I wasn't sure what I was waiting for. There came the sound of water sloshing around and a switch clicking on and off again. I guessed that he was developing photographs and I was proven right when he emerged from a room with an entirely black interior. He wore the sort of rubber apron that a butcher would wear, and he smelled of a mixture of sulfur and gas. He was a short, pudgy man with thick spectacles and a badly made wig of brown hair that failed to cover his silver sideburns.

"Oh!" he said, looking up at me in surprise. "I was expecting the boy."

"What boy?"

He pushed his spectacles up his nose and leaned forward on his toes to give me a better look. "An errand boy," he said. "You are not—no, never mind. Forgive me. I am Henri La-Motte. How do you do?"

"Constance Kopp," I said. "I know the name LaMotte. *Votre famille vient-elle des Côtes-d'Armor?*"

He laughed. "Oh, no, no. I forgot my French as fast as my mother tried to teach it to me. Girls listen to their mothers. Boys don't."

"You may be right about that," I said. "My brother never spoke a word that wasn't good Brooklyn English. My mother was heartbroken that her grandchildren sounded like New Yorkers." I surprised myself. I couldn't remember the last time I'd spoken about my family to a stranger. But there was something so jovial and relaxed about Mr. LaMotte. He seemed to invite confidences.

"Well," he said. "Miss Kopp, who, judging from her name, speaks German as well as she does French—"

"Die Familie meiner Mutter stammt aus Österreich."

"Oui. Or *ja.* Are we here for language lessons, or do I have an envelope for you?"

"An envelope?" I asked, looking around at the piles of them. "No, I just wanted to ask you something. You see, I'm looking for someone . . ."

"Oh, yes," he said. "I understand. But you don't start with me."

"What?"

"The investigator calls me once you've made your arrangements."

"Investigator?"

He took a step closer to me and looked up, bemused, over the tops of his lenses.

"Yes. A detective," he said. "You wish to find someone? We take the photographs, but we only ride along with the investigators. We don't go running around on our own. They call us when they are ready for us."

"You work for detectives?" I said. "I thought this was a portrait studio."

He laughed. "Oh, I gave that up years ago. Everyone with a camera and a set of draperies runs a portrait studio. Miss Kopp, I am in the business of collecting evidence. My photographers take pictures to be furnished as exhibits at court proceedings. Or, more frequently, they take pictures that persuade people to stay out of the courts. If you'd like a portrait, I could send you—"

"Oh, no," I said, still trying to follow what he was telling me. "No, my question is about the neighborhood. I'm looking for a boy who lived on the next block."

"He didn't work for me," Mr. LaMotte said.

"No, he was—he is—a baby. A lady who lived around the corner took him in and now we can't find her." I gave her name and address.

Mr. LaMotte pursed his lips and drew in a long breath. "Oh, *mademoiselle*, you've found trouble. Did you go looking for it, or did it come to you?"

"I . . . well, I suppose it came to me."

"Then send it back!" Mr. LaMotte said, turning to pull off his rubber apron and hang it on a hook. He sat down at his desk and nearly disappeared behind the clutter. "Send it back, Miss Kopp, and go back to Brooklyn yourself. That's my advice." He picked up a pen to indicate that our conversation was over.

"I don't live in Brooklyn anymore," I said. "I live just outside Paterson now. I'm only here for the day to—"

"Paterson?" he said, looking up at me again and pushing that ridiculous hairpiece higher up his forehead so he could see past it. "Does this have something to do with the silk strikes?"

"Yes!" I said, a little too loudly. "It might. The baby was evacuated during the strikes."

He shook his head. "There were all kinds of Bolsheviks living over there during the strikes. You used to be able to hear them arguing from a block away. The police could stand right out on the sidewalk and learn every one of their plans. But they've all moved on now."

At that moment, the door opened and a boy entered. "There you are!" said Mr. LaMotte, clearly relieved by the interruption. "We have three cases for you, is that right?" The boy nodded and looked at me suspiciously.

"That's all right. Miss Kopp was just leaving. *Veuillez m'excuser, mademoiselle.* I have nothing more for you. Good day." He turned to dig through his empire of envelopes.

There was nothing to do but nod and take my leave. I wrote down my name and address and left it among the papers on his desk in case he remembered anything that might help. Then I was back on the street, puzzling over the slim bit of information the photographer had given me. I walked around the block again and stood facing Regina Doyle's building, looking up at its windows, every one of them curtained and closed.

Finally the door opened and a little boy ran out. This time I was up the stairs quick enough to catch it. I turned to say something to the child, but he was across the street and out of earshot before I could.

The door closed behind me and I stood facing a row of mailboxes in the vestibule. None of them bore the name Doyle, or any name that looked familiar to me. I could see no alternative but to go from one apartment to the next.

I rapped on the first door and got no answer. At the second apartment a girl of about ten opened the door. She held a baby on her hip. I asked if her mother was home, and the girl shook her head and gently closed the door and locked it.

I heard the music of a flute behind the next door. As I raised my hand to knock, a voice came from the stairs behind me.

"Miss! Didn't you see the sign?"

I spun around and faced an older, heavyset man in workman's clothes. He lumbered down the stairs, keeping his eyes on his feet and huffing loudly.

"A sign? No, I—"

He stopped on the bottommost step, panting.

"No solicitation. Take your pamphlets or your samples or what have you, and go on down the street. No one in this building wants to be bothered."

The flute music stopped. I supposed the flautist was listening.

"I'm not here to sell anything. I'm looking for a lady who

used to live here. Regina Doyle. She had a baby with her, but it didn't belong to her."

He stopped to consider that, then said, "Didn't belong to her? Then what was it doing here?"

"Sir, I—"

"Never mind. Don't know her. Go tell it to someone else." He waved me toward the door again. Seeing no way to get past the man and up the stairs, I wished him a good day and let myself out.

I was still standing on the steps a few minutes later when the door opened and a young man stepped out. He was so thin that his collarbone protruded through his shirt. He closed the door quietly behind him and said in a near-whisper, "Are you the one looking for Mrs. Doyle?"

"Yes. Was that you I heard playing the flute?"

He nodded and took my arm, leading me down the front steps. "I don't know where she is," he said in the same low voice, "but she was in with a whole gang of unionists. They started getting Black Hand threats and they all moved out at once."

"What kind of threats?"

He turned to look back at the building as if he was afraid someone was listening. "Usual things. Fire. Kidnapping. Then they snuck away in the middle of the night."

"Have you any idea where Mrs. Doyle might be?"

He shook his head. "Run off by the Black Hand men. That's all I know."

I thanked him and he darted back upstairs.

Was Henry Kaufman a Black Hander? The papers had been filled with stories of Black Hand crime for the last few years, most of it conducted by Italians who engaged in a trade that consisted primarily of making threats against anyone who might be in a position to pay to make the threats stop. The demands were simple and crudely worded. The usual method was to send a note promising a fire or a kidnapping unless a sum of money was paid, customarily a thousand dollars.

If the threat was kidnapping, it was usually aimed at a pretty young girl, the inference being that the girl would be sold into white slavery. A notion like that always made a father open his checkbook, no matter how much the police advised against paying them off. Any man would gladly pay a thousand dollars just to rid his mind of the idea of his child forced into prostitution.

Norma read these stories aloud to us, just like Mother used to. She was fond of shuffling between the crime page and the society page to point out that many girls, shortly after being the subject of such a threat, found themselves suddenly engaged to be married, often to an associate of the fathers who had been pressed into service. Let her husband keep her from harm, the poor father must have thought. A man can only take so much.

A wind had come up along Sixth Avenue and I had to lean into it and fight my way back to the train station. Having spent a day in the crowds and confusion of New York City, I could see the futility of this sort of search. Finding one small boy in a city of five million seemed impossible. It wasn't hard to disappear. I'd done it myself.

❧ 18 ❧

FLEURETTE HAD A KNACK for overhearing everything. She was small and crafty, able to slide behind a door or duck under a window without anyone noticing. She was possessed of especially fine hearing and had a musical ear that could follow the cadences of two hushed voices and pick out their meanings. There was no way to keep a secret from her in our house: she would peer through keyholes, run outside and lean against doorjambs, or climb into the attic and press her ear against the gaps in the floorboards. Even the chicken coop was not safe, as she would steal into the pigeon loft and listen through the wide planks. In fact, the only way for Norma and I to have a private conversation was to walk out to the middle of our meadow, where we could speak quietly to one another while looking in all directions to be assured that Fleurette was not creeping up on us—though as soon as she realized what we were doing, she would come running at us, and we'd have to finish our conversation in rapid-fire monosyllables to get it over with before she flopped, panting, at our feet.

When I returned home from the city, it was dark and windy and I didn't feel like walking through the meadow, so I allowed Fleurette to hear my account of the day. Norma insisted that I keep it brief, seeking only reassurance that I hadn't gotten us into any more trouble. Once she was satisfied that I had learned nothing of value and met no one who knew anything about Lucy Blake's child, she refused to allow another word to be spoken about it in her presence. Fleurette listened, wide-eyed, but didn't say anything until Norma went upstairs to bed.

"I think the flautist knows more than he let on," she said darkly. "He hears everything that goes on in that building. He seems so innocent with his music and that little blue parrot that goes everywhere with him . . ."

"He doesn't have a parrot," I said.

She cocked her head and looked at me thoughtfully. "You just didn't see it," she said. "You should've had me along. I could have snuck into his room while you were talking to him on the street. He might even have the baby. It could've been right there, under your nose, and you missed it."

"Don't imagine things," I said. "This isn't a fairy tale. It's a real baby and his mother wants him back."

Fleurette nodded. "But does Lucy really think she can keep a baby all by herself?"

"What do you mean?" I said, although I knew exactly what she meant and there was a pounding in my head as I tried to come up with an answer.

"She doesn't have a husband. She can't keep a baby. People will know."

She was stretched out on the divan and I was in the armchair next to her. Her feet were perched atop my knees, her black-stockinged toes wiggling in the air. This was nothing but a diversion to her.

I took one of those squirming feet in my hand. "I don't know how she thought she'd manage," I said, "but that is not our concern. If she won't speak to the sheriff, there's nothing more I can do for her."

"You're not going to see her again?" Fleurette sounded crushed.

"I don't know why I would," I said.

"Do you mean it's over?"

"I hope so."

"Well, what will we do now?"

ONE OF THE STRANGER EFFECTS of this business with Henry Kaufman was the way it dislodged us from our daily routines. It was as if the brick had shattered not just a window, but the carefully structured order we'd once had in our lives. Over the next few weeks Norma and Fleurette devoted themselves entirely to their own amusements, turning our household into a sort of half carnival, half menagerie. Fleurette converted the parlor into a theater, complete with a stage concealed behind a curtain of scandalous vermilion, three rows of plush seats, and an ingenious but dangerous arrangement of footlights cobbled together from all the old oil lamps placed in dark corners about the house. She put on performances nightly, most of which were attended by no one at all, but once I was horrified to walk in and find the young man from the dairy seated in the audience as if he had purchased a ticket. Fleurette was performing an Oriental dance of her own invention, accompanied by a fan of ostrich feathers she'd purchased from a street vendor in Paterson and colored a dull, vegetal pink using some sort of berry that fruited around our property. I sent the boy running out the kitchen door, warning him to make his exit quietly lest Norma hear him. I truly believe she would have gone after him with a fire iron.

Norma herself was no less of a problem. One of her pigeons had been injured on a long flight and she was nursing it back to health in her bedroom. Its foot was crushed and she kept what was left of it (the foot) in a bandage. Although she couldn't be sure, she thought that one of the toothpick-thin bones in its wing had also snapped during whatever sort of mishap had ensnared it and caused it to lose its message. ("Girl Is Sent to Reformatory" was the lost message, which she recited later to Fleurette, to no effect.) She fashioned a splint for it, but the splint kept the wing from folding back into its place, so the pigeon had a constant lopsided appearance, one wing half extended off the edge of the little tufted pillow it slept on.

She thought it might distress the pigeon to be kept locked in a room all day, far away from its customary perch in the loft, so she installed an old brass birdcage at the foot of her bed and brought in a fresh batch of pigeons every day to keep their injured flock-mate company. It didn't seem to do much good. The poor fellow slept most of the day and only occasionally opened an eye to peer at his feathered friends through the polished bars. Then, feeling that the other pigeons might be bored, Norma began conducting training exercises in her room, entreating them to fly over to a lampshade and back in exchange for a handful of bread crumbs.

She kept the birds clean — Norma was always ruthlessly sanitary when it came to her birds — so there was no odor, but there was a sound produced by their activities. One would not think that the burbling and rustling of feathers emanating from two or three captive pigeons would amount to much, but I heard it all over the house. There was a distinctly avian character about our place. I would not have been surprised if one came flying at me in the stairwell. I took to walking very carefully past her room, always prepared to duck.

Meals had become irregular events. We still had vegetables coming in from the garden, so some manner of soup was always on the stove, but Norma and Fleurette had decided to dip into it whenever they walked by rather than sit down together. Francis stopped in from time to time with one of Bessie's overloaded dinner baskets ("I don't know how that woman accidentally makes five extra pies, when I'm doing everything I can to put them away," he said), so in addition to the soup, we survived on twelve o'clock pie, Bessie's name for a dish made of leftover roast and potatoes, and her fine apple turnovers.

Washing up had also fallen out of favor. A pot got scrubbed when it was needed for something else, books and papers and other such clutter were only put away when the space was about to be used for some other activity, and the silver was never polished. Where once we had a day for airing out the beds and a day for scrubbing the floors and a day for washing clothes, now we weren't devoting any time at all to cleaning. I wouldn't have guessed that such a carefully ordered household could come apart so easily.

It had always been my responsibility to look after the money, and I continued those duties, as simple as they were. I paid the bills, watched our dwindling savings, and tried to find a way to carve off another plot of land to sell. I wondered if I could persuade Norma to take an interest in a small dairy operation of her own or to expand our flock of chickens and sell the eggs. But I knew we couldn't sell enough eggs to see us through.

In the evenings Fleurette sat with her sewing and Norma read her papers while I looked over the ledgers at my desk. There had been no sign of Henry Kaufman. Whatever Sheriff Heath had done must have worked.

ONE TUESDAY AT BREAKFAST, I decided I'd had enough of our slipshod ways and announced that we would spend the morning canning green beans and tomatoes, starting immediately and concluding at lunch, when the heat would make it too unpleasant to continue. Fleurette pouted and protested until I offered her a string of Mother's old cut-glass beads, meant to look like diamonds and emeralds, and told her that she could wear them one day for each jar of preserves we finished.

Norma disappeared early in the morning, sending a message by pigeon post that she must have been saving for this occasion: "Girl Scalded in Kitchen." Without her help the work went slowly, and we only managed three dozen jars by lunchtime. I left Fleurette to clean up and ducked out to pick up a few things in Hackensack. On the way home, I stopped in a bakery and bought a box of macaroons.

I was walking back to the trolley just as a dancing class was dismissed for the day. As the children rushed past me, the girls twirling around to hear the rustle of their skirts and the boys picking at their high, stiff collars, I wondered at the futility of teaching children to dance. What did we hope to accomplish by forcing them into those awkward pairings? They would find their way to each other on their own, without any help from their parents and their dancing teachers. And just as easily as they came together, they would come apart again.

As I was distracted by those thoughts, I didn't notice that an automobile had driven past and circled the block, rolling slowly by and coming to a stop just ahead of me. My whole body went cold at once when I saw it. I couldn't take a breath.

The passenger door opened and I looked quickly around, hoping to see someone standing nearby who could witness whatever was about to happen. It was a busy afternoon downtown, but no one seemed to be watching me.

"Miss Kopp," a voice said. "Wouldn't you like to ride with us?"

Sheriff Heath. At last I could breathe again.

He came toward me, wearing a funny crooked smile. "Were you expecting someone else?" His voice was warm and quiet.

"I do seem to run into him at the oddest times," I said.

"Maybe it would help if you stayed away from him," he said.

"I have! I haven't seen him at all!" I didn't mention the visit to Lucy's flat.

"That's good." Another one of those friendly half-smiles. He was looking at me very intently, the way you might peer into a bird's nest, hoping to find something fine and miraculous inside. I didn't know what to make of it.

"Now, won't you let us drive you home? We can talk about our friend Mr. Kaufman along the way."

We were attracting attention on the street. A mother was standing on the sidewalk with a baby on her hip, and four or five boys had gathered around the automobile. A deputy, looking rather embarrassed, emerged from the driver's seat and let the boys have a look inside.

"I suppose I'd better," I said. "Only I don't know what my sisters will make of me being driven home by the sheriff."

"I would like to speak to your sisters," he said, opening the door for me.

I wondered what performance Fleurette had rehearsed for the evening and what state of mind Norma might possibly be in.

"I'm not at all certain they're in any condition to receive visitors."

I SETTLED INTO THE BACK SEAT and started to direct the deputy to my house, but Sheriff Heath waved me away. "We know the way," he said.

"You've been there?"

"I'm keeping an eye out, that's all."

We rode along in silence for a minute.

"Whatever happened with that girl?" Sheriff Heath said. "I thought you were going to send her to me."

"She's afraid," I said. "She thinks he'll come after her if she goes to the police."

The sheriff and his deputy exchanged glances but said nothing. We were out of Hackensack by this time. The country road that led to our farm was always busy in the late afternoon as people and animals concluded their business for the day. It was not unusual to have to stop for a herd of slow-moving Guernsey cows. We passed a bakery truck headed back to the city after making its deliveries, and I realized quite abruptly that I should have thought to bring home something more substantial for dinner, as we had depleted the last basket from Bessie. We would probably be reduced to eating macaroons and boiled eggs and last summer's pickles.

"Well, I haven't forgotten your troubles with Kaufman," he said, "and I hope this takes care of it. We have a judge who will accept a complaint about the damages to your buggy. We just need you to sign a statement and appear at the courthouse to swear to its accuracy. Then the judge will order the fine and require Mr. Kaufman to stay away from you. We'll go collect the fine. You don't even have to see him. I can't say what effect any of this will have on him, but it's the best I can do."

"You . . . you filed charges? Against Henry Kaufman?"

Sheriff Heath looked at me quizzically. "Isn't that what you wanted?"

"I thought you were just going to talk to him."

"Well, I did talk to him, Miss Kopp. I told him to stay away from you and your sisters and to pay for the damage he did. Has he stayed away?"

"I think so."

"You think so?"

"Yes. He's stayed away."

"And now he's going to pay for the damages. This is how we prosecute criminals in Bergen County. Is that all right with you?"

I sighed and sat back in my seat. It didn't seem like I could refuse.

• • •

WHEN WE ARRIVED AT THE HOUSE, I led the men inside, realizing that there was a time, not long ago, when riding in a car with the sheriff, much less bringing him home with me, would have been a shocking and outrageous act. But since the collapse of the general order of our household, I thought little of it.

Norma heard me come in and walked down the stairs carrying her injured pigeon on a pillow. Her stockinged feet appeared first, and then the pillow in her arms.

"It's a good thing you're home. This requires two sets of hands. If you could just hold him while I—"

At last her face emerged from behind the banister. She stopped upon seeing the men in our front parlor. She must have recognized Sheriff Heath from the papers, because she frowned at him with the kind of deep-seated resolve that could not be summoned upon first impression. As with most people Norma disapproved of, she'd already put a great deal of effort into it and had no trouble in recalling her position.

The sheriff must have been accustomed to such treatment, because he simply introduced himself and his deputy.

Silence. Finally I said, "This is Norma. One of her carrier pigeons has been injured, and she has seen fit to move it indoors for its convalescence and to treat it like a member of the household."

The sheriff lit up at the mention of the pigeons. "One of my deputies has been asking about keeping pigeons," he said. "He thought it would be a good activity for the inmates, but my superiors don't want them at the prison. They're concerned about prisoners sending messages to their criminal associates."

I could tell that Norma was trying not to speak to the sheriff, but she couldn't help herself. "They only fly home," she said. "They're not postmen. They don't deliver along a route."

A wide grin emerged from under Heath's mustache. "I told them that myself, but . . ." and he shrugged at the pointlessness of arguing with one's superiors.

I had to admire the way he handled that. I didn't suspect for a minute that his deputy had been asking about keeping pigeons. But he said the one thing that he knew would draw her into conversation.

Norma snorted and turned to go back upstairs. "If you're looking for Fleurette," she called over her shoulder, "she went out to get some frogs."

The deputy and the sheriff looked at me with bemused astonishment. What sort of sideshow were we running here?

"When my sister was a little girl," I said, "a lady down the road used to pay her to catch frogs. Fleurette liked having an excuse to splash around in the creek. Frogs didn't bother her the way they did other girls. She'd catch a dozen in an afternoon and earn herself a little bit of money. The lady moved away a few years ago, but Fleurette still likes to go down there and get those frogs."

"You don't eat them, do you?" asked the deputy.

"I'm afraid we do," I said. "Would you like me to go down to the creek and get her? Maybe she'll sell you a frog for your dinner."

"That's all right, Miss Kopp," Sheriff Heath said, ushering his deputy out the door before he could say another word. "We've met the youngest Miss Kopp already."

"What? When was that?"

He opened the door and turned to smile at me. "We attended a matinee here in your living room recently. I believe it was the day you went to New York." He closed the door very gently in my face.

DINNER THAT NIGHT consisted of my mother's *ragoût de grenouilles,* the one dish Fleurette ever bothered to learn how to make, and only because she so loved to eat her prey. It was accompanied by a watercress salad and a lengthy scolding from me about the dangers of letting strange men into the house.

"They weren't strange men," Fleurette said between loud slurps of the sauce. "They weren't strange at all. They sat very quietly in the third row and applauded at all the right moments. I only wish they hadn't left before my encore."

I looked to Norma for reinforcement, but she'd been silent all evening. "What goes on around here when I'm away?" I said at last. "Do you just leave the front door open and let anyone walk in?"

"They aren't just anyone," said Fleurette. She pushed a strand of hair under a hat of blackish-green ravens' feathers she'd taken from Mother's closet and fixed in place with her old amber pins. I tried not to imagine what the frogs must have thought when they saw her coming in that hat. "They are sworn public officers. And apparently they are friends of yours. If you can invite them in, I don't see why I can't. Besides, they spend so much time sitting out there along the road in that stuffy automobile. They deserve to be entertained."

"You don't mean to say you saw them on our road?" Norma said, breaking her silence at last. "Right outside our house?"

Fleurette shrugged. "I thought Constance invited them," she said.

Norma stood up and dropped her bowl into the sink. "One doesn't *invite* the sheriff to sit outside with a man and a gun. If he's here, it can only mean that we are in more danger than we realized, and it's all because Constance persists in bothering Henry Kaufman."

"I haven't bothered him in some time," I said.

"You've sent the sheriff over to bother him, and that's the same thing."

"The sheriff seems to feel the danger has passed," I said. "Mr. Kaufman will be made to pay a fine and that should settle him down. We haven't seen him once since the sheriff took up the case, isn't that true?"

"You're very trusting of him," Norma said, putting on water for coffee, which she always drank after dinner. "I've said that I take a dim view of the police, and I think I'll extend that line of thinking to the sheriff, who seems not to know the most rudimentary fact about a carrier pigeon, suggesting an incurious mind. I don't think he has much to offer us, do you?"

Without waiting for an answer, she brushed her hands briskly on her skirt and went out the kitchen door to lock up the chickens. I scraped my spoon around the bottom of the bowl. Fleurette stood up, adjusting her ridiculous hat. "I've been working on a new dancing frock," she said. "Would you help me pin up the hem?"

I looked up at her, this little girl who started twirling as soon as she could walk. "Yes, of course. Go and try it on."

⪜ 19 ⪛

I DIDN'T KNOW I'd had a girl at first. All I saw was a head of black hair and the white apron of the nurse carrying her away. I had agreed to give up the child, but at that moment the wildest craving came over me. In my delirium I dreamt of mother cats biting and licking their kittens, and I imagine I would have nearly devoured that infant if only they would have given her back to me.

The doctor attending to me suspected a hemorrhage and was about to go after me with a curette. The ether cone descended but I kicked and fought it. There was a clatter of metal across the floor and a man shouting and then nothing but whiteness all around me.

I awoke hours later in the most fantastic purple darkness. It could have been the effects of the ether, but I felt weightless and clear-headed, and rose from my bed in the recovery room as lightly as steam lifting out of water. Somewhere under that roof was a child who belonged to me. The only thing in the world for me to do was to go and get it.

The night nurse dozed in her chair and didn't stir as I glided past. Not a single lamp had been left burning in the hall, but I knew the way to the nursery as if I'd walked it all my life. No squeak of the floorboard, no shuffle across the rug, no groan of the hinges alerted the nurses to my presence. I was inside the nursery with the door closed behind me, and the black-haired baby was in my arms, and the other babies—there were three more of them—wriggled and sighed and chortled up at me as if they knew exactly what I was doing.

And what did I do? I walked right out the front door with her. I took her down the long drive, which was dense with the overgrowth of climbing roses, and down the road into the cool October night, wearing only my nightgown and a pair of knitted slippers. The baby was wrapped in flannel and didn't seem to mind at all. She had a tiny pinched face like a flower that hadn't yet bloomed and lips that worked back and forth even though her eyes weren't open. Along that road I gave her a name. Fleurette Eugenie Kopp.

Eugenie for her father, Eugene. The Singer man.

In the months of my confinement, I had felt only shame when I thought of him and of what I'd allowed him to do to me. But now I was walking under a velvet-dark sky so filled with stars that I couldn't pick them apart, and the air was alive with the scent of grass and wood smoke and the sweet yeasty baby. Adding his name to hers seemed at that moment like putting a period at the end of a sentence. It was where he ended and she began.

The nurses found us in a hay barn the next morning. Of course they did. I was not the first girl to disappear in the night, and none of us, in our condition, could get far. Perhaps that's why they didn't take better precautions against us running away.

Fleurette was well and fed. She was a hungry girl, and although I'd had no instruction, there were enough natural forces at work on both of us to bring it about. The nurses sent for the wagon and brought us back to Mrs. Florence's, where Fleurette surely would have been taken from me again were it not for a letter that had arrived from Brooklyn that very morning.

October 9, 1897

Miss Norma Kopp
92 South 8th Street
Brooklyn, New York

Dear Mrs. Florence,

I write to inquire after the whereabouts of my sister, whose name is Constance Amélie Kopp, although she may not have given that name to you, who left a loving family on the 17 of July to seek the care of a home such as yours. Her mother wishes every day for her safe return and is prepared to adopt the child, if there is one, and raise it as the youngest member of a respectable family. Any expenses incurred by her care will be gladly repaid. She is a tall girl of nearly six feet in height and eighteen years, with hair more auburn than brown, eyes a light

hazel, a firm and decisive mouth and a tongue
that speaks French and German as well as her
native English.

With a word from you that such a girl is
under your care, we will come promptly to collect her and express to you our endless and
abiding gratitude for offering refuge to someone
who must have been rendered so insensible with
fright over her condition that she forgot that
the most suitable home for a child of hers was
the one in which she already lived.

Hoping for a joyful outcome to this most
difficult trial, I am

Yours very truly,
Norma Charlotte Kopp

⇥ 20 ⇤

September 15, 1914

BY MY OATH I, Constance Amélie Kopp of Wyckoff,
New Jersey, swear that one Henry Kaufman, of
Paterson, New Jersey, was the owner and driver
of a certain automobile which negligently collided with a buggy in which I was seated along
with my sisters Norma Charlotte Kopp and
Fleurette Eugenie Kopp, resulting in damages to
said buggy in the amount of fifty dollars, which
Mr. Henry Kaufman has refused to pay in spite of
numerous attempts to collect the amount owed.

Sworn before the Honorable Court of
Passaic County, New Jersey,
Constance Amélie Kopp

• • •

IT HAD RAINED that morning and there were steaming brown puddles on the sidewalk. I lifted my skirt, which left me without a hand to put over my nose. Paterson had never smelled so foul after a rain. I didn't want to imagine what must have overflowed and leaked out into the gutters.

If I hadn't looked up before we began climbing the courthouse steps, I would have run right into Henry Kaufman. He had his feet planted on the top step, and he stood with his hands in his pockets and his hat pushed back on his forehead, with all the lazy confidence of the idle rich. With him were two of his men: the one with the glass eye, and the enormous one with shoulders as broad as snowplows. A third man stood nearby, puffing desperately on a pipe. He was tall and thin, with curly hair that tended toward red, and gold spectacles.

Sheriff Heath saw them just after I did. He took my arm and steered me away from them.

"John," he said to the curly-haired man as we passed.

"Sheriff," the man said.

Those two words were enough to catch Henry Kaufman's attention. "Is she under arrest, Sheriff?" he called after us. "Because she's been harassing me at my place of business. Let the record show . . ."

Sheriff Heath pushed me through the courthouse door amid the laughter and back-slapping of Mr. Kaufman and his friends. I was relieved to feel the door close behind me. Inside, the courthouse lobby was cool and quiet.

"I thought he wouldn't be here," I said.

"I didn't think he would. He's up to something. I don't know how he roped a lawyer into this."

"That was his lawyer?" I asked.

The sheriff nodded and led me down a corridor lined on

both sides with men in shabby worsted suits or overalls. There was hardly enough room for us to get past.

Someone bumped into me and I nearly fell against the sheriff. "What is this?"

"It's the last of the charges against the silk strikers."

"A year later?"

"They were charged with unlawful assemblage and sentenced to hard labor, but never served their sentences," he said in a low voice. "Now there are rumors of another strike, and the police chief issued new warrants for all of them, just to discourage them from striking again. Today they had to appear or be arrested. Fortunately for them, they're going before one of the only judges who is at all sympathetic to their cause."

"You mean that he's not a friend of the silk men. Which is why we're going to see him."

He smiled. "That's the general idea." He took me down a side corridor away from the crowd. At an unmarked door he stopped and said, "Remember, this isn't a trial. Just swear to your statement and sign when the judge asks you to. That's all we're here to do."

I nodded and he held the door open. Just inside was a row of men, their backs to us. The sheriff cleared his throat and they turned and parted. The courtroom was as noisy as a carnival, with a clerk barking orders and spectators shouting and grumbling. Every seat in the gallery was taken, and there was hardly a spot around the edge of the room that wasn't occupied by a mill worker leaning against a wall and waiting his turn.

"I didn't know I'd have to do this in front of anyone," I whispered to the sheriff.

"It's a full docket," he said. "You'll be next." He gave a salute to the clerk, who nodded and whispered to the judge. The judge—a jowly, watery-eyed old man with white whiskers sprouting from his cheeks and ears—called out, "All right, Bob, bring her here."

The sheriff took my arm and led me to the front of the room. He handed the paper to the judge, who fumbled with his spectacles and read it to himself in a low mumble. Then he looked up at me.

"Is this all true?"

I looked at Sheriff Heath, who just nodded. "Yes, Your Honor," I said.

"And this man—Henry Kaufman—he's been given ample opportunity to pay the charges?"

"He has," said the sheriff.

"And is he here today?" The judge looked around the courtroom.

There was a shuffling sound from across the room and the curly-headed man stepped out of the crowd. He pulled a pipe out of his mouth to speak.

"Your Honor."

The judge looked around and found him. "John? You're not involved in this mess, are you?"

"I'm afraid I am." He seemed sad to admit it. "I have represented the Kaufman family's business interests for many years, and recently Mr. Henry Kaufman has engaged me to handle his personal affairs as well."

Sheriff Heath sighed and shook his head. The attorney stepped forward and the two of them exchanged polite nods.

"If Your Honor will permit it, my client begs the court to hear his statement."

"Where is your client?" the judge said.

The attorney cleared his throat. "My client prefers to wait outside due to the—ah—due to the interests of the parties—ah—other proceedings taking place today in Your Honor's court that might—"

"Never mind," said the judge. "Quickly. I was promised this was a simple matter."

"May it please the court," the lawyer said, pulling a piece of paper from his coat pocket and unfolding it. "The statement"—and here he glanced meaningfully at Sheriff Heath—"which I am obligated to read on my client's behalf in spite of counsel to the contrary offered as a matter of—"

The judge groaned. "Read it."

The lawyer rattled the paper, adjusted his stance, and began. "Mr. Henry Kaufman, of Kaufman Silk Dyeing Company of Paterson, New Jersey—"

The chatter in the room got louder as the mill workers realized that the man in question was a factory owner. No wonder Henry Kaufman didn't want to show his face.

"That's enough!" shouted the judge. The room quieted. "Go on, John."

The lawyer looked nervously around and repeated the opening line to himself before continuing in a monotone. "Hereby refutes all charges leveled against him pertaining to an incident on the fourteenth day of July, in the year 1914, in which a buggy under the control of the three Kopp sisters did willfully collide with Mr. Kaufman's automobile, inflicting substantial damage on said automobile, and, further, Mr. Kaufman alleges that Miss Constance Kopp is a unionist and anarchist sympathizer who has harassed him at his place of business and spoken to his workers with the intention of inciting strikes and riots among a peaceable workforce, and that said harassment has disrupted production at his factory and inflicted—"

At the mention of strikes and disruption of peaceable workplaces, another rumble went through the crowd, with several men standing to get a better look at me.

The judge rapped his gavel and a bailiff walked among the rows of benches, urging the men back to their seats.

"That's enough, John," the judge said. "Bring it here."

The lawyer handed it over and leapt quickly back as if he were afraid of getting hit with the gavel himself. After reading it, the judge looked up at me. "Miss Kopp. Are you a unionist?"

I was too surprised to say anything. He leaned closer and squinted at me.

"Are you one of those Wobblies? An anarchist sympathizer? A Bolshevik? That's what it says here."

This brought a round of laughter from the crowd. When it died down, I said, "No, sir. I only went to see Mr. Kaufman to collect on the amount owed. And we did not willfully collide—"

"That's fine, thank you," the judge said. He turned to the lawyer. "She doesn't look like much of an anarchist sympathizer to me, John."

"No, Your Honor."

"Is the statement made up entirely of fabricated nonsense, or just that bit?"

The lawyer opened his mouth to answer but then seemed to think better of it and closed it again.

"I thought as much. Now, Miss Kopp. Come here and sign your statement." He passed the paper across to me. I climbed the steps into the witness stand. He handed me his pen and

I signed my name. His hand trembled and his fingers had a bluish cast to them. I wondered how a man his age withstood the chaos and tumult of the courtroom every day.

"Thank you," I said quietly, sliding the paper back across his desk.

"Don't thank me for any of this," the judge said. "Looks like a whole lot of trouble to me." Then he leaned over again to address the sheriff.

"I'm ordering a fifty-dollar fine. It's up to you to collect it, Bob. And keep Miss Kopp and Mr. Kaufman away from each other. It appears they don't get along."

Sheriff Heath nodded grimly. "Yes, Your Honor."

"And next time, take your routine matters to another courtroom."

The mill workers laughed and some of them applauded. The judge pounded his gavel until they stopped.

WE STEPPED OUT into the bright noonday light and confronted the usual lunchtime rush on Main Street. "I'm sorry about that nonsense," the sheriff shouted above the rumble of traffic. "Mr. Kaufman might not know better, but his attorney should have. He's probably wishing he'd never heard of the Kaufman family."

"It's all right," I said. "I'm just glad it's over."

An automobile had stalled at the corner and its driver was standing over it, using his hat to fan the smoke billowing from the engine. No one could get around him, and the other drivers were honking and yelling. A large wagon pulled by two draft horses was trapped in the middle of the street, and the horses were trying without success to back away from the noise.

"What a mess," the sheriff said. "Wait here, Miss Kopp. I'll just go find a constable."

He ran into the crowd and I backed under the awning of a shoe shop until he reappeared, his coat over his arm, his shirt-sleeves rolled up. "Forgive me, Miss Kopp," he said, panting a little. "We just had to push him out of the way. Now, listen." He took my arm and led me down the street. "Don't pay any attention to those ridiculous claims. They weren't formal charges and they never will be. I saw this sort of thing during the strikes last year. These men call everyone they don't like a Bolshevik and an anarchist. They get their lawyers to write up all manner of absurd accusations in hopes of confusing the matter and tying up the courts. But it won't work. Not this time."

We crossed at the corner of Grand and a swarm of school-children, all running after an ice cart, separated us in the middle of the street. I reached the other side first and felt an arm at my elbow. Thinking it was the sheriff, I turned around and found myself staring into a milky glass eye.

"No more police."

He gave my arm a sharp twist that threw me off my balance, and by the time I regained my footing, I was face-to-face with Sheriff Heath and the man was gone.

⇥ 21 ⇤

THE SENSATION of that man's fingers digging into my elbow stayed with me all evening. I couldn't bring myself to tell Norma and Fleurette about it. I'd promised them that this day in court would put an end to our troubles with Mr. Kaufman, and I didn't know how to admit how wrong I'd been.

Sheriff Heath tried to tell me not to worry. He said that Henry Kaufman wouldn't be foolish enough to bother us again now that a judge had ordered him to stay away. I told him it would be a mistake to underestimate Mr. Kaufman's capacity for foolish and reckless behavior.

It didn't take long to find out which of us was right. I'd just settled down to sleep when a window shattered down the hall. I thought I heard a man laugh, but I might have dreamed it.

The three of us staggered out of bed toward one another. There was no moon and it was impossibly dark. I could barely see their faces in front of me.

"Whose window did they break?" Norma said. "It wasn't mine."

It took a minute for each of us to understand that none of our bedroom windows had been broken. Once we realized that, we all ran for Mother's room, half forgetting that she didn't occupy it anymore.

Norma was the first to find a lamp and light it. She made Fleurette go back to her room and put on shoes before she walked in. I found it very irritating that Norma had taken charge of the situation. Bricks coming through windows were my responsibility.

By the time Fleurette returned, Norma had the letter in her hand. She looked at me with an expression that I cannot properly describe. It was as if she had never met me, as if I were a complete stranger, standing in her mother's bedroom in the middle of the night.

"Is this how Sheriff Heath protects us?"

I didn't say a word. Norma read the letter to herself and handed it to me.

Madam:

You are here given warning not to sue H. K. for if you do you will suffer for we his friends will get square with you, we watched you in court house, if you make him spend any more money we will trap you or burn you. Don't give letter to police if you do you be sorry.

H. K. friends

We each read it twice, passing it around in the small circle where we stood among the broken glass. The brick had landed on the bureau, shattered a mirror, and knocked off a lacquered box of straight pins. They were splayed around us on the floor like slivers of ice.

Before any of us could say a word, we heard a motor in the distance. The roar grew louder and I yelled, "Get down!" just before another window shattered and a second brick barreled to the floor, breaking in half when it hit. Fleurette screamed that she was cut and I ran to her, crouching low in case the men were still outside. But the tires skidded in the drive and the motor car rumbled away. Fleurette fell against me.

"Are you hurt?" I said.

"I . . . I don't know. I felt something hit my head."

Norma moved the lamp closer, and I looked her over but found no cuts and only a few shards of glass in her hair. I reached for the brush on the dresser, but Fleurette said no.

"Not Mother's brush. Just leave it the way it was."

I set the brush down and smoothed Fleurette's hair with my fingers. "I don't think you're hurt," I said. "I think you're all right."

Norma pulled the lamp away and it was only then that I saw the note tied to the second brick. She read it and held it out to me without a word.

Dear Miss Florette,
     Have you ever been to Chicago? We believe a girl of your talents would find a nice place for herself with no trouble at all. Maybe we bring you with us next time we go. Are you ready for an adventure? Ha! Ha!
                                        —H. K. & Co

Fleurette, still leaning on my shoulder, took hold of the letter and read it under her breath.

"Chicago? Why am I going to Chicago?"

Norma raised an eyebrow, waiting for me to explain it.

"'A girl of your talents,'" she read. "What do they mean by that? They don't know me. Do they mean my dancing, or singing, or . . ."

I took a deep breath, looking to Norma for help. Finding none, I blurted it out. "This is a kidnapping threat. They're not talking about putting you on the stage in Chicago. They're talking about taking you to Chicago and selling you."

She scrunched her face up in that childish way she had. "Sell? What do you mean, sell? How would you—" and then she stopped. She sat up and wrapped her arms around her chest. We'd all read about white slavery in the papers, but I didn't know how much of it she understood.

"They drug you," I said quietly. "They grab you and cover your nose with chloroform and take you somewhere. There are men who will pay . . . who, ah, will pay for . . . that. For you."

Fleurette pulled away from me and stood with her fists tucked under her arms, looking down at her feet and the irregular pattern that the broken bits of Mother's mirror made on the floor. She was possessed of the kind of fine, pouty features that could be so easily shattered, and I watched the corners of her lips drop and tremble as the truth came to her. "But that's not what this is," she said in a whisper. "They're not serious, are they?"

I shook my head. "I don't know. I think Henry Kaufman is very dangerous. I think our buggy collided with the wrong man."

For a minute we just stood where we were and considered that. In the dark Mother's old room was quite beautiful. The chrysanthemums on the wallpaper glowed like distant jelly-fish in the sea. Near the window was a lamp fringed in glass beads that she'd brought with her from Vienna. A breeze came in and pushed them against each other, making the faintly musical sound of bells ringing someplace far away. Her filmy dressing gown still hung on the closet door and it lifted and swayed like a woman dancing. At that moment it looked like a stage set, not a home where ordinary people lived. I could imagine stagehands wheeling it all away, leaving us with nothing but a black floor and a backdrop.

"Well," I said at last. "You can't sleep alone tonight. I've got the biggest bed. You'll sleep with me."

"What about Norma?" Fleurette said.

Norma hadn't said a word since she read the letter. I wasn't sure she'd taken a breath. Her voice came out in a croak.

"I suppose we have no choice but to hunker down like soldiers in a trench. I'll make a bed for myself on the floor."

And that's what we did. Fleurette climbed straight into my bed. Norma went to get some blankets and while she was gone, I went looking for Francis's old hunting rifle. It had been years since I'd fired it, and I'd been aiming at rabbits, not at strange men in automobiles.

"What do you intend to do with that?" Norma asked when she returned.

"It does us no good in the back of a closet," I said. I leaned it against the window.

Norma settled down on her pile of blankets. "Why don't you put yourself in front of Fleurette so she doesn't catch the next round of flying glass?"

She was already half asleep in the middle of my bed. I rolled her to the side away from the window. She moaned and kicked but moved over.

I settled in next to her. Fleurette was so small that my body made a wall around her. Her rib cage rose and fell against me.

Norma nodded in the darkness. "You'll be the one they hit. That seems fair."

This time I had to agree with Norma. She turned to look again at the rifle, and then she put her head down, but I don't think she slept. I didn't either.

❧ 22 ❧

IT WAS NORMA who decided that we should live in Wyck-off. Mother was unable to make a plan of any kind. She was so astonished to learn that Francis and Norma had not only found me, but had made a commitment on her behalf to raise her newly discovered granddaughter as her own child, that she was rendered speechless and nearly paralyzed. Upon arriving in Wyckoff she stood on the porch at Mrs. Florence's, with Norma next to her (while Francis waited in the carriage at the end of the drive, as they were all unsure as to whether a man should even approach the house), but she could not raise her hand to knock. It fell again to Norma to take charge of the situation, gaining entrance to the house and asking to see her sisters.

Already Fleurette was her sister. There would not be a single moment in Fleurette's life in which she was to be treated as my daughter. Norma had arranged for Mother to sign adoption papers making Fleurette hers, and great care was taken to make sure that my name would never be found in Mrs. Florence's files—only the false name I'd given when I arrived.

The letter Norma had written was returned to her. Only a few nurses knew our secret, and they were accustomed to forgetting any details not written in the files, to best protect the interests of the child. An illegitimate girl might never marry, might never have a family of her own, might be cast out of any social circle she attempted to enter. The nurses understood this better than the families did. They assured Norma that no one would ever be told the circumstances of the child's birth, not even Fleurette herself.

Once my mother signed the papers, Fleurette was taken directly from the nursery and handed to her. A few minutes later a nurse came for me, and that's how I found her: seated in an armchair in Mrs. Florence's office, baby in her arms, Norma looking over her shoulder. When I walked in, they both looked up at me with identical expressions of curiosity and shock, but then Fleurette made some sound and their eyes went back to her. I perched on a high-backed chair and watched while they fussed over her.

I'd been so relieved when I learned that Norma had found me and that I'd be keeping my child, but now a stone sank to the bottom of my stomach. I wasn't really keeping her. They were keeping me, that was all.

We couldn't go back to Brooklyn. Girls of eighteen could not disappear for months and return at the same time that a baby was brought into the family without attracting suspicion and gossip. Francis rented a suite of rooms for us in Paterson and planned to return to Brooklyn for our things as soon as we settled on a place to live. Philadelphia was under consideration, as was Boston, with the idea that Francis could easily find work and Norma could finish school. Mother had her inheritance, so we were not without resources.

I believe we would have gone to Philadelphia or Boston had Norma not overheard, as we were leaving, a conversation between two of the nurses about a farm nearby. The man had moved out west and was eager to complete a sale. Norma made a note of the location and as we rode past Sicomac Road, asked Francis to turn and take a look at it.

There it was: the wide and gabled farmhouse, the barn, the pen for animals, the meadow that led to a creek lined in willows. Across the road the neighbor's cows moaned amiably. The drive was overgrown in weeds and the paint had flaked off the house, but Norma saw something there. She got out and took a walk around the barn and then around the house, and stood looking over the fields at the trees in the distance. When she returned to us—Mother, cradling Fleurette, with me sitting alongside, and Francis at the reins—she had already made up her mind.

"No one would know us here," she said to Mother. "And we'd be away from that filthy, crowded city." She glanced meaningfully at me, as if to suggest that filthy cities themselves were to blame for what had happened.

Mother nodded slowly. "When you children were small, I always wanted to bring you to the country. Your father would never agree to it."

Before Francis could object, she added, "Francis, you could fix up the farmhouse, and once that was done, I'm sure you could find work in Paterson."

"And what would you do?" I asked Norma. Everyone turned to look at me as if they'd forgotten I was there.

Norma smiled and looked back at the barn. "I'd get a goat and maybe some pigs. And I believe I might like to keep birds of some sort."

~ 23 ~

I MUST HAVE DOZED OFF around sunrise. I had been dreaming about a flock of messenger pigeons circling the roof in the early gray light before dawn, carrying slips of paper in their beaks and dropping them down on us. "Chicken Thieves Send Kidnapping Threat" arrived first, then "Police on Lookout for Brother's Hunting Rifle." Fleurette caught one in the air and held it out to me. "Sisters on War Footing," it read.

By the time I awoke the morning was half over. I sat up in bed and wondered if it had all been a nightmare—the brick shattering the window, the note threatening to take Fleurette from us. Then I saw the rifle leaning against the wall and knew I hadn't dreamed it.

A door opened downstairs and I followed the sound into our kitchen. Sheriff Heath had apparently just arrived and was holding his hat in his hand in the manner of a man about to deliver a speech. Norma and Fleurette were standing next to the kitchen table, each with a hand on the back of her chair. No one was saying a word. They were holding their postures as models do in a tableau. "Sisters Awaiting Rescue," it could have been called.

I leaned around the tableau in hopes that someone had left some coffee on the stove for me. They hadn't.

The sheriff's eyes were even darker and more deeply sunk into their sockets. His hair was matted to the side of his head and, as far as I could tell, he was wearing the same brown suit I'd last seen him in.

"You look like you've had even less sleep than we have," I said.

He grimaced and reached up to smooth his hair. "I suppose so," he said. "I was called out in the middle of the night to pull Henry Kaufman's automobile out of a ditch just up the road."

"I don't know why you didn't just leave it there," Norma said.

"Where was Mr. Kaufman?" Fleurette asked.

"He must have run off. We counted four men's footprints in the mud. I sent one of my men to watch your house, but we never saw him."

"That's because he visited us first," Norma said, "and treated us to his latest literary efforts."

"I was afraid of that. How was it delivered?"

"Again by brick," I said, "but this time he aimed for our mother's old room."

Sheriff Heath looked disappointed. "Smart man," he said. Then he saw our surprised expressions and apologized. "I mean that he's avoided using the post. If he mailed them we'd be able to charge him with a federal crime. He knows what he's doing. Could I see the letter?"

"There were two of them," I said. I thought I'd left them upstairs, but Norma pulled the letters out of her pocket. He gestured for her to set them on the table, then he sat down. We took our seats around him as he bent over the crumpled papers.

"Ladies, I'm going to teach you a little detective work." Fleurette sat straighter in her chair. This was precisely the wrong sort of excitement for a girl of her temperament. Without taking his eyes off the letters, he continued. "The first rule of crime scene investigation is to keep your hands off the evidence. If we're lucky we can take up a fingerprint, but not if yours are on top of it."

Norma was not a woman who appreciated having her mistakes pointed out to her. "You wished us to leave the letter on the floor and go peacefully back to bed, having no idea of its contents?" she said stiffly.

"Not at all," he answered, still scrutinizing the letters. "Just use a pair of gloves, a handkerchief, a corner of your skirt to pick it up. Anything will do."

After he finished reading, he slid a finger underneath and lifted both of the letters with calm and steady hands to make sure nothing was written on the back.

"I don't like it," he said, looking up at us at last. "It's got all the marks of a Black Hand letter."

"Black Hand?" Norma and I said at once.

"This is what they do," he said. "They start small, with vague threats. Maybe they break a window or fire a shot in the air, to let their victims know they're serious. Then the threats get more specific as to kidnapping and arson. There's always a warning not to go to the police."

"How clever we were to ignore their advice," Norma declared.

"Your sister was right to call for me and to stand up for herself," he said. "Most people wouldn't. That's why we don't see many of these early letters. But then comes a demand for money, and by that time the victims are too scared to do anything but pay."

"Are you saying that Henry Kaufman is a Black Hander?" I asked. "He's not even Italian."

"Not necessarily," the sheriff said. "These letters have been in the papers so much that anyone can copy their style. They're just imitating what they read. When did this happen?"

I shook my head. "I'm so sorry, Mr. Heath, but I don't think any of us thought to look at a clock. It was the dark of night and we were all so deeply asleep when it happened. There was a bit of confusion because—"

"It was a quarter past two," Norma said.

We all looked at her in surprise.

"I checked the clock when I went to get my blankets. Constance was too busy messing around with that rifle to notice what time it was."

Sheriff Heath sat back in his chair to regard Norma from a distance. "A rifle? What were you girls planning to do with a rifle?"

Norma sniffed. "She was planning to protect her sisters. What were you doing?"

He looked at me and back at Norma, perhaps trying to figure out where he stood with each of us. Then he pushed his chair back and asked if he could go upstairs to view the crime scene. Norma told him he could not, and I told him he could.

She shoved her chair away from the table and went out the kitchen door without a word. I took the sheriff upstairs and Fleurette followed.

Norma had knocked the glass out of the windows in our mother's room, swept up the broken mirror and the pins, and wedged boards into the empty panes. The bricks sat carefully in the center of the dresser, like trinkets put on display, the way one might exhibit a starfish taken from the beach.

Sheriff Heath looked around for a minute, glanced out the window, and tested the boards to be sure they were secure. His hat brushed against a little chandelier above the bed and made him duck. I was embarrassed for him to see Mother's things, the way we'd left them. There was a faint smell of gasoline about him that seemed to take up all the air in the room.

"I'll take the bricks," he said, wrapping a handkerchief around them. Then he looked down at Fleurette.

"Did they let you read that letter?" he asked.

I started to defend myself. "Had I known what it said—"

He held out a hand to stop me. "It's all right. It was directed at her. She should know."

Fleurette was leaning in the doorway. He put his hands on her shoulders, the way a father might, and she straightened up in surprise. It startled me, too, to see a man handle her like that. She bit her lip and looked up at him with wide, wet eyes.

"These men are serious," he said in a low voice. "They're not playing a game. I'm going to do everything I can to keep them away from you, and you're going to stay away from them. Understand?"

She nodded and took a deep gulp of air. He kept hold of her shoulders. I was standing behind him and found myself

166

watching the way the back of his neck lifted away from his collar as he bent to speak to her. "I don't want you to leave the front door unlocked. I don't want you to sleep with the windows open. I don't want you going down to the creek by yourself, and for that matter I don't want you to even go to the barn by yourself. If you're going to town, you take someone with you, and you watch out. All right?"

She could barely answer. "All right."

I thought he was finished, but he wasn't. He kept talking to her with that same mixture of paternal warmth and sternness that Fleurette had so rarely heard from anyone. Even Francis had never spoken to her quite like that.

"Keep your eyes down around strangers. Don't talk to anyone you don't know. Don't open the door for salesmen or delivery boys, unless you're expecting them. Can you do that?"

Fleurette was staring at him, mesmerized.

"Can you?"

She nodded. "Yes."

"You will stay off streetcars and trains. Don't have lunch or stop for any reason in a hotel. No hotels."

"No hotels," she whispered.

"And listen to your sisters and do what they say. If I'm going to put my men in harm's way for you, you mustn't do anything that makes their job more difficult or dangerous."

She took it all in with tremulous, wide-eyed surprise. At last he let go of her shoulders and said, "I'm going to take a walk outside and speak to your sisters now. I want you to keep yourself busy in here and don't try to follow us."

We left her in Mother's room and walked downstairs together. He let himself out through the kitchen door and I followed him. Norma was in the pigeon loft feeding her birds.

She took her time, enjoying making us wait. Sheriff Heath tried to ask a few polite questions about carrier pigeons, but she gave him disgruntled silence in response. When she was finished with her work, she shook a canvas apron off her neck and hung it on a nail outside the loft. She looked at us expectantly, but still she refused to speak.

"All right," Sheriff Heath said. "Come with me."

We followed him out to his car, which was parked near the end of our drive. He reached in the back seat and took out a wooden case. Then he straightened and looked around him, surveying the house with its shuttered windows, the old misshapen barn, the neighbor's hogs in their pen across the way, and our unmowed pasture with the river and the willow trees beyond it. Down the road the dairy cows lowed and slapped their tails against their flanks.

"Would you ladies mind a walk to the creek?" he said.

Norma and I followed him across the pasture, matching his long strides. In a few minutes we were standing under a copse of willow trees, their branches whip-thin and starting to shed leaves. Sheriff Heath scrambled down to the creek bed and set his case down. He straightened up to look back toward the house. "You can't see much of the house from down here," he said, mostly to himself.

Then he unlocked the case and we saw that he had two dark blue revolvers with him.

"Do both of you know how to shoot that rifle?" he asked.

"It belongs to our brother," I said. "We can fire it, but just to scare something off. I don't think I could hit anything."

"We could hit Mr. Kaufman, if it came to that," Norma said. That made the sheriff laugh.

"I hope you won't have to," he said. "Now, why don't you come try this one?"

Norma stood next to him and looked down the length of the creek. With the leaves coming off the trees, we could see all the way down to the end of our property line and into the woods beyond.

"Now, listen," Sheriff Heath said, with the same stern tenderness he'd shown to Fleurette. "You see the one red tree down there? The maple coming out right where the creek makes that bend?"

Norma nodded.

"Just below that is a big rock. A big white boulder really shining in the sun. Do you see it?"

Again she nodded.

He lifted a revolver from the case and opened the chamber to check the ammunition. Then he swung it closed and pressed the butt of it into her hand. He kept his hand over hers and raised it to the white rock.

"Use the notch on the top to get it in your sights," he said in a low voice. He was standing so close that he could talk right in her ear. "See the blade at the end of the barrel? Like a half a penny. Use that to line it up."

She nodded and aimed.

"That's good," he said. "Put one foot behind the other like this. Steady feet. Steady hand. Strong arm. Bend your elbow just a little. That's it."

Without turning her head, Norma shifted her eyes just enough to meet his. He brought his hand up to pull back the hammer, but before he could, she cocked it with her thumb, looked back at the rock, and fired a shot.

The explosion echoed up and down the length of the creek. I felt it hammer my chest, like another heart beating next to mine. There was the smell of something burning and a ringing in my ears. I couldn't tell if she'd hit the rock, but she'd fired it to Sheriff Heath's satisfaction.

She was still aiming the gun straight up the creek when he reached around and took it out of her hand. "That's good," he said. "Thank you." Then, turning to me, "Miss Kopp?"

Norma took a few steps back and folded her arms. I'd never seen her fire a revolver before and she seemed awfully satisfied with herself for having pulled it off.

It was my turn next. The sheriff took my right hand by the wrist and raised it. My fingers curled instinctively around his. He smiled and said, "Don't hold on to me. Hold on to the gun."

When he pressed the revolver into my palm, it was heavier than I expected and warm from having just been fired. I tried to keep my hand from shaking.

He stepped back and gave me the same instructions he had given to Norma. "Aim straight for that white rock. Plant your feet first. Strong arms. Steady hands. When you're ready—"

Before he could say another word I pulled the hammer back and squeezed the trigger. I must've hit the treetops, not the rock, because a flock of starlings raised a cry and circled in the sky before landing some distance away.

"That's all right," he said quickly. "That's just fine. Now you know what to expect. Fire it once more, and this time think about holding steady when it kicks. Use your sights."

I squared my stance and aimed the barrel straight at that rock, squinting at the notch and the narrow half-moon at the end of the barrel that were my guides, and fired. I don't think

I hit the rock, but I managed to keep the gun level. Then I stood holding the revolver straight out until Sheriff Heath took it from me.

He pulled three bullets out of his pocket and reloaded it, then bent down to lock it back in its case. After that he stood and offered the case to me.

"There's one for each of you," he said. "Don't let Miss Fleurette handle them. I'd rather she didn't even see them. Keep them near you at night, but don't put them under your pillows, and don't tuck them into your clothing. You're not to fire directly at anyone. If those men come back, aim in their general direction but shoot into the trees. You're just trying to scare them off. Understand?"

Norma nodded and climbed up and out of the creek bed. Sheriff Heath followed, then leaned down to offer his hand to me.

I didn't need it, but I took it.

ᴤ 24 ᴤ

AFTER THAT, Fleurette ceased her theatrical performances, and Norma returned her injured bird to the loft. Its wing had mostly healed but its delivery career was at an end. Fleurette, who hated chores and usually refused to do them, became remarkably obedient following her talk with the sheriff. She patched a hole in the coop where mice were getting in to steal the chickens' feed, and she painted the fence around the vegetable garden and cleared a patch for spring peas.

Sheriff Heath had his men watching the house, but they weren't there all the time. They would stop late at night on their way home from tending to some other criminal matter. I grew accustomed to the sound of an automobile idling in the road after midnight. This was why the sheriff warned us not to fire directly at anyone. He was afraid we'd shoot his own deputies. They seemed to understand that too, because they never stopped in front of our house. They always rolled a few yards past our driveway and parked in a wide, bare spot under an oak tree.

I thought a lot about Lucy going to work every day in the

dye factory and taking the wages she earned and handing them back to Mr. Kaufman in rent. And I pictured that baby, wherever he was. He'd be learning to talk by now. Someone would be calling to him with their hands outstretched the way people do with little children, but what name they called him I didn't know.

I did wish there was something I could do for Lucy. But it seemed like every advance I made against Henry Kaufman invited another brick through our window.

"WHO IS HENRI LAMOTTE?" Fleurette said one afternoon as she brought in the mail.

"Let me see it," I said.

"Not until you tell me who he is."

"Is the letter addressed to me?"

"I don't know. It's addressed to Miss Kopp. It might be for me."

She stood over my chair with the envelope in her hand. "You've already opened it, haven't you?" I said.

She held it out to me reluctantly. "It could've been for any one of us."

"You know better," I said.

October 1, 1914

Henri LaMotte, Proprietor
LaMotte Studios

Dear Miss Kopp,

I have found some photographs that may be of interest to you. They were taken last year at the building that was the subject of your inquiry.

One of my men had been engaged to photograph the goings-on at that address for several weeks, but the attorney who hired us never paid for his pictures. I had forgotten that we had them until they reappeared just now. If you want them, I will hold them for you until Tuesday. After that I must destroy them. We prefer not to become a repository for unclaimed photographic evidence, although I have apparently let my standards slip. I shall right the ship and sail on!

Au revoir,
Henri LaMotte

"What does it mean? Photographic evidence of what?"

I looked around to see if Norma was within earshot. She must have been outside. I read the letter again.

"It has to do with Lucy," I said at last.

Fleurette gasped and slid into my armchair, half perching on the arm and half sitting in my lap. She hadn't done that in years.

"We've found a clue, haven't we?" Fleurette breathed into my ear.

There was a sugary smell that hung around Fleurette, like the crumb tarts we used to bake when she was a little girl. I closed my eyes and the memory of it came over me. I used to tell her that she was good enough to eat, and she would shriek and run to Mother in mock horror.

She twisted around to look at me directly. "Would these pictures help her get her baby back?"

"I don't know," I said. "I'll forward the letter to her. She can decide what to do about it."

Fleurette jumped out of my lap. "But there's no time! He said you have to come and get them Tuesday. That's tomorrow. We have to take this to her now."

I shook my head. "You heard what the sheriff said. We have to be very careful around strangers."

"But she isn't a stranger," Fleurette said. "Just go over there and drop it in her mailbox."

I turned the envelope over in my hands. "I don't think I should," I said. "I believe Norma's right this time. We need to stay out of Henry Kaufman's business."

"But don't you care about that poor girl?" Fleurette said, a little desperation in her voice. "Try to imagine for one minute what it would be like to be a young mother and lose your baby like that. How would you feel?"

I bit the inside of my lip. She'd never come this close to the truth, and I didn't want her getting any closer. I'd made my own kind of peace with the past and was not eager to reckon with it again.

But Fleurette was right. Lucy was living with a kind of loss I had never known.

"Don't tell Norma where I'm going," I said.

⊱ 25 ⊰

ALONG LUCY'S STREET the windows of the old boarding houses were smudged with smoke and steam. Someone was boiling coffee, someone was scorching the bottom of a pot of soup, and someone was frying a fish. In front of one house, a woman in a brown dress bent over a patch of overgrown greens, searching among the tough stalks and seed heads for a few leaves that were still tender enough to eat.

I had put Mr. LaMotte's letter into an envelope of my own with a note of explanation, hoping to leave it in Lucy's mailbox and run off before anyone saw me. But when I tried to open the front door to Lucy's building, it wobbled and fell down, landing in the dark hallway with a bang. It had been torn off its hinges and propped up to cover the entrance.

I backed into the weedy front yard and looked up. One of the windows on the second floor had been boarded over. There were no signs of life in the building—no washing on the clothesline, no lights or curtains in the windows, no clatter of dishes or smell of dinner on the stove. Then, as I leaned closer to risk a peek through the gaping doorway, the odor hit me. Fire.

I jumped back as if the building were still burning. A woman across the street swept her porch and watched me. Three boys played with a ball on the corner, and when it bounced against the street it gave an eerie and empty echo.

A low fence between Lucy's building and the one next door had been knocked down. I stepped over it and walked around to the rear of the house, which was entirely scorched. Blackened timbers had begun to disintegrate in the autumn wind and rain, and the windows were nothing but holes offering admittance to birds and squirrels.

Where a back door might have once stood, there was nothing but a cement threshold and the burnt end of a wooden post. I took a step inside and kicked away a cracked glass doorknob and the blistered lid of an enameled pot. The rattle they made echoed around the hollow and charred interior. Even the staircase was gone. The remains of the bannister hung uselessly from the second floor.

If Lucy had been home, I didn't see how she could have made it out alive. Everyone on the upper floors would have been trapped.

I don't remember running to the trolley, but I was on board and halfway to Hackensack before I could hold my hands steady again. At the courthouse I asked to speak to Sheriff Heath.

"He just left," the girl at the reception desk said.

"A deputy, then," I said, pushing my hair back under my hat. I was still sweating from my race away from Lucy's. "I was to come here if—if something happened. Give them my name. It's Constance Kopp."

With as bored and indifferent an air as she could muster, the girl went and whispered something to the guard standing on the courthouse steps. "Wait here," she said, and the guard walked down the steps and around to the jail.

A few minutes later, a gray-haired man in a deputy's uniform walked in. "Deputy Morris, miss," he said. He looked at the receptionist, who was watching us curiously. "This way, please."

He took my arm and we walked down the corridor, where no one could hear us. "Sheriff Heath has been helping me and my sisters with some trouble we had," I said.

"Yes, miss. I've been by on patrol a few times. Has he bothered you again?"

I shook my head. "It's something else. It's about a fire over in Paterson. Sometime in the last few weeks. A boarding house on Summer. Did you hear about it?"

He thought for a minute. "I might have. What about it?"

"A friend of mine could have been there. Did everyone get out?"

He shook his head. "I don't know, miss. It wouldn't be a matter for the sheriff over here in Bergen County."

"But can't you find out?"

He looked down the hall at the receptionist. "I'd have to ask her to telephone."

"Couldn't you, Mr. Morris? Please?"

He laughed, but not unkindly. "Begging doesn't suit you, Miss Kopp."

FLEURETTE WAS SURPRISED to see me come downstairs the next morning in a hat and a traveling coat. She was sitting on the floor in the parlor, sorting through a box of buttons to find a matched set for a dress she was working on.

"Where are we going?" she said, jumping to her feet.

"You're staying here," I said. "I'm going into the city. I'll be back by suppertime."

"The city! Without me?" She stamped her foot and the buttons scattered across the rug. What a child she could be when she didn't get her way! I swallowed my irritation and bent down to speak to her in a low voice.

"You know I can't take you. You heard what the sheriff said. No train stations, no strangers, no strange places."

She pushed the buttons around with her toe. "You're going to go and get those pictures yourself, aren't you?" she said.

"I'm going to try. Now, I wish you'd be a good girl and stay here and do what we ask you to do."

"I've done everything you've asked me to do!" she cried. "You and Norma and the sheriff. When do I get to do anything for myself again?" She threw herself on the divan and buried her face in the cushion, sobbing.

What now? I only needed a few hours away, but I managed to set off a full-blown tantrum just by walking past Fleurette. I sighed and looked out the window. Norma was out there raking leaves. I knew she wanted to get away, too. It was unpleasant to be confined to the house for so long. We were living such queer and isolated lives out here by ourselves.

I sat down next to Fleurette and put my hand on her back the way I used to when she was a little girl. Into the pillow she said, "And next week is my birthday and what are we going to do about that?"

"It is? Are you going to be fifteen or sixteen?"

She gave me a little punch in the leg. "Seventeen. You know that."

"Already? Well, you're right. We should take you somewhere."

She sniffed and sat up. Her eyes looked like the clear night sky when she cried. "Where?" she asked.

"Anywhere you want to go. As long as the sheriff agrees."

"You'll ask him?"

"I will."

LUCY DIDN'T DIE IN THE FIRE. No one did. It started in the rear corner of the house—I could picture Henry Kaufman and his friends sneaking around with a bucket of kerosene—but the man living downstairs smelled it right away and ran upstairs to wake the others. He must have been the one whose room I'd backed into when I went to see Lucy. It had seemed like such a drab and miserable little room, but the man who lived in it had done something heroic. I wondered where he'd gone. I wondered where any of them had gone. Deputy Morris hadn't been able to tell me that. With Lucy's whereabouts unknown, I had no choice but to go to Mr. LaMotte's myself before he threw the pictures away.

The train got me into New York by noon. There was a tearoom near the station where ladies could have lunch, so I stopped there first and ate a ham salad sandwich and a pineapple ring with a cherry on top. There was coconut cake for dessert. I wasn't hungry anymore, but I'd grown tired of our farm cooking and couldn't resist something as exotic as coconut. I ordered a slice and drank a cup of coffee with it. The buttons on my dress were about to pop, I'd stuffed myself so. I was glad for the long walk to Mr. LaMotte's studio.

He was sitting at his desk, looking as if he'd been waiting for me. "Miss Kopp!" he exclaimed, jumping to his feet as I walked in. "Just in time."

I took a step forward and knocked a pile of envelopes off a

chair. "Pardon me," I said, crouching down to retrieve them. The envelopes were blank except for a name written in light pencil on the front of each one: *Wapole, Dowd, Kurtz, Wood.* They didn't seem to be in any particular order, so I scooped them up and returned them to the chair.

"Not to worry," he said. "They have a tendency to leap out at a person. Can't be helped." I thought that it could be helped with the employment of a filing cabinet and a secretary to file them, but I didn't say so.

"I hope I haven't kept you waiting," I said. "Your letter only just arrived yesterday, so I didn't have time to reply."

He cocked his head to the left and looked at me over the tops of his spectacles. "Oh, yes, the photographs. I have them here, and I would be most happy to let you look through them. But first I have a favor to ask of you."

Before he could continue, the door opened and a mountain of a man pushed his way into the tiny office. He wore the largest wool overcoat I'd ever seen on a person, and a black hat that a small child could have hidden inside. A shadow fell across his face, but I could see an enormous mustache above lips the size of sausages, and two bulging chins. "Is this her?" he asked in a growl that could only come from the Bronx.

Mr. LaMotte rushed around to stand between us. "Mr. Hopper! I wasn't expecting you so soon. Please let me introduce you to Miss Kopp."

I extended my hand and found it gripped roughly by something that felt like a catcher's mitt.

"How do you do?" I said. "I didn't realize I was expected."

"You're not here about the job?" the man grunted.

Mr. LaMotte waved his hands to silence us. "I was just getting around to that," he said. "Miss Kopp, I wonder if you might do a favor for my associate Mr. Hopper. You see, from time to time, we have need of a girl photographer, and—"

"A photographer?" I said, taking a step back and overturning yet another pile of envelopes. "I don't know a thing about photography. I'm only here because you said—"

"I said I'd be willing to do you a favor," Mr. LaMotte said, having regained his calm. "Now I'm asking you to do a favor for me. This gentleman would like you to pay a visit to a hotel for ladies just off Fifth Avenue."

"Pay a visit to a hotel?" Sheriff Heath had only just warned us to stay away from hotels. "I couldn't possibly."

"We only want you to inquire about the rooms and ask to see one with a rear-facing window on an upper floor. They'll give you a key and send you up by yourself. Just go and take a photograph of the room, and get a picture of whatever you can see from the window. Then return the key to the desk and bring the camera back here to me. I'll have your photographs waiting."

Before I could compose an answer, Mr. LaMotte added, "You look like a woman who can handle herself, Miss Kopp."

"Well, I—"

"Please be assured that we are not asking you to be involved in anything disreputable. The matter we are investigating concerns only a witness to a crime. We must confirm certain details of her story by attesting to the layout of the room and the view from the window. Nothing more. We would go ourselves, but they will only permit ladies upstairs, and I have none in my employment at present."

Mr. Hopper was breathing in that way that large men breathed, as if fueled by a boiler room instead of a pair of lungs. He still hadn't removed his hat. I couldn't get a good look at his face.

"Is Mr. Hopper one of your—"

"Associates. He handles investigations for several of the better attorneys in Manhattan. His reputation is beyond question. He enjoys the high regard of both the police and officers of the court."

Mr. Hopper made a sound that could have been a grunt of agreement. We both looked at him, but when he said nothing, Mr. LaMotte continued.

"He will accompany you to the hotel and bring you back here as soon as your work is completed. I assure you it won't take but an hour, and that is only if you enjoy a leisurely stroll up Fifth Avenue and visit some of our fine shops along the way."

Now Mr. Hopper chortled—a noise that sounded more like the eruption of a minor volcano—at the idea of enjoying a leisurely stroll with me.

I was too astonished to take offense. Never in my life had I been thrown into so many unexpected situations in such a short time. Mr. LaMotte took my silence for acquiescence and wasted no time in getting a camera in my hands. It was a little box camera that had been rigged to resemble a ladies' handbag. I admired the soft Italian leather handle and the fine tweed covering the box. This was a well-made instrument. As soon as it was in my hands, I decided that I should have one of my own someday.

"Hold it against yourself, just like that," Mr. LaMotte said. "There's nothing to it. This little lever slides across to open the shutter. Just go slowly, until you feel it engage on the other side. Then wind the key until the next number appears. You have eight pictures. Please do use them all. I must develop the film immediately, so a half-used roll doesn't save me anything. Get as much light as you can in the room and hold the camera perfectly still. Is that all clear? You can do that, can't you?"

He smiled up at me with genuine fondness, the way one might regard a niece one was bringing into the family business. I couldn't help but return the smile.

"It is, Mr. LaMotte. It's perfectly clear. But why are you asking me to do this? Surely if you need a girl photographer, you can find one in this city."

He stepped back and studied me for a minute. "You look capable, Miss Kopp. You are — forgive me for saying — substantial."

I saw no reason to take offense at that.

"And serious," he added quickly. "You seem like you could handle any sort of trouble that might — not that there will be any trouble, it's just . . . well —"

"It's all right," I said. "I'll be fine." With that I slid the camera's strap over my wrist and looked in the direction of the towering figure that was Mr. Hopper. He hadn't made a move. He was just waiting. I had a feeling that in his line of work, he spent a good deal of time waiting. "Shall we go?"

Mr. Hopper opened the door and pressed himself against it to make room for me to pass. He smelled of tobacco and wintergreen. Soon we were out in the pale October sunlight, marching toward Fifth Avenue like two soldiers.

He was not a man for conversation, but that suited me just fine. I made a point of not looking in a single shop window so he would not think I was the kind of girl who wanted to fritter away time trying on hats or squealing over bracelets. I don't know why it mattered to me what Mr. Hopper thought. I had not gone looking for a job as a girl photographer, but now that I had it, I intended to do it right.

When we rounded the corner on Fifth Avenue, a gust of wind caught us and made the going more difficult. The avenues were like canyons, the buildings funneling wind straight through them. I tucked the camera under my coat and buttoned up the collar.

Mr. Hopper only looked back once to make sure that I could keep up. I could.

The hotel for ladies, called the Mandarin, was located across the avenue, along a shabby block in the Thirties. It was just an ordinary six-story building with a pair of glass doors and a green canopy above them. A doorman stood outside under a brass gas lamp.

We walked swiftly past the hotel to the next corner. There Mr. Hopper stopped and told me he would wait for me. He pushed his hat back and looked down at me.

"All right, miss?"

His disposition was not unkind. He had deep brown eyes and a younger, softer face than I had first realized. He was probably the sort of man who terrified people without meaning to.

"I'm just fine," I said, and I meant it. I strode confidently back to the hotel. The doorman tipped his hat and opened the door.

The lobby was about what I'd have expected for a small hotel catering to a female clientele. The tiled floor was covered in red Oriental rugs. The walls were paneled along the lower half and papered in a pattern of green and gold ferns along the upper half. There were old gas lamps on the wall that matched the one outside, and a mahogany desk staffed by a porter and a prim older woman dressed in a smart blue velvet dress with brass buttons down the front. To the right was a sitting room where the guests could meet their male visitors.

I presented myself at the desk and did what Mr. LaMotte asked. He was right. There was no trouble about getting a key to go and inspect a room before reserving it. There was a room available on the sixth floor with rear-facing windows, the woman told me, and one on the fifth floor with a view to Fifth Avenue. I didn't need that one but she seemed to want me to consider it, so I took the keys for both.

The porter came around the desk to accompany me upstairs. I tried to make some excuse as to why I preferred to go on my own, but just then I was rescued by a mother and her three daughters emerging from the elevator and demanding the porter's assistance with their luggage. I smiled, ever the gracious guest.

"Please don't worry about me," I said. "I won't be but a minute." Before he could say anything I dashed up the stairs and out of sight.

I took a look at every floor as I went, and they were all the same—red carpets, oak paneling, and gold-striped wallpaper. It looked like a clean and decent hotel. On the sixth floor I found the room and let myself in. There was not much to see, just a brass bed topped with a white coverlet, a nightstand outfitted with a mirror and washbasin, and a small desk furnished with an ink blotter and writing paper. In one corner was a stand for luggage and a coat rack.

The layout of the room seemed not at all unusual to me, but I stood in the corner and took a picture. Then I pointed it at the window and took another one while I looked across the alley at the blackened brick coated with decades of coal dust. The gap between the hotel and the building across from it was nothing more than an empty space where people might have tossed their garbage or the contents of their chamber pots. I wondered what the mysterious witness had seen, and what had been hurled into that dark place.

There were only a few windows on the building opposite, just the sort of small utilitarian windows that would be placed in a stairway to illuminate it. I didn't know what about that view might have interested Mr. LaMotte. I had six pictures left, so I took two looking down, one to the left and one to the right. Then I held it straight out at eye level and did the same thing, and then I pointed it up at the rooftops and once again took a picture in each direction.

I stopped on the fifth floor to see that room, too, even though I had no particular reason to. I could see why the lady at the desk offered it to me. It was a much larger room, more like a suite, and it must have fetched a higher price. It was furnished with a larger desk and two overstuffed chairs arranged around a small tiled fireplace. A pair of wide floor-to-ceiling windows looked across to Fifth Avenue. I went to the windows and the sight of the avenue from above made something catch in my throat. If I wasn't looking down on the busiest place in the world, I was a few blocks from it. A river of people moved below me, identifiable only by their hats and scarves. An endless parade of buildings marched up to Central Park and down in the other direction to Wall Street. New buildings were going up all around, each in a race to get closer to the clouds, with their scaffolding silhouetted like bare tree limbs against the October sky.

There, in that room, I felt like I was at the center of something. I was someplace that mattered. And that made me feel like I was someone who mattered.

I liked that room very much. I wanted to rent it on the spot.

I returned the key and inquired about the rates for the room on the fifth floor. The woman behind the desk smiled and handed me a rate card. "I thought that one would suit you," she said.

Mr. Hopper was waiting where he said he would be. I assured him that I'd had no trouble getting the pictures, and we walked back to the studio in silence. When we arrived, he opened the door for me, but he did not go inside.

"Good day, Miss Kopp. I'm on to my next job. I'll leave you to yours."

With that he disappeared into the street.

Mr. LaMotte took the camera from me and set it in his darkroom. He returned with a fat envelope in his hands. "Your wages, miss," he said. "Take them with you. I've got to close shop and attend to matters of my own." He turned and started rummaging through a desk drawer.

I thanked him and tucked the envelope under my coat. I started to leave, but I couldn't resist asking him. "Mr. La-Motte?"

He looked up as if he was surprised that I was still there. "Yes?"

"What did the lady see?"

"Lady? What lady?"

"The one in the hotel."

He shook his head and came around the desk, peering up at me kindly. "Miss Kopp. I'm going to give you a piece of advice that will serve you well if you continue in this line of work."

"Line of work?"

"Whatever you want to call this little investigation you're conducting."

I reddened. "All right."

"The less anyone knows, the better. If you have nothing to tell, you won't have to worry about being questioned."

"I see."

"I mean it. Put up a barrier between your witnesses, your victims, your investigators, your prosecutors, your attorneys, and your friends and enemies at the newspaper. Don't let anyone know a single thing they don't have to know. And do your best to keep them from talking to each other." He made a series of chopping motions with his hands. "You see? Walls. I am putting a wall between you and the lady in the hotel. If you don't know about her, you can't tell anyone if they ask."

He turned back to his desk. Without looking up at me again, he said, "The fewer people who know what that lady saw, the better. My girl photographer in particular does not need to know."

I'm not your girl photographer, I thought. But I didn't say it. I took my pictures and left for the train station. Mr. La-Motte followed and locked the door behind us, hurrying off in the other direction with still more envelopes under his arm.

⊰ 26 ⊱

I COULDN'T LOOK at the photographs on the train. There were far too many people on board, all jostling for seats and all rushing to get home in time for supper, just as I was. I clutched the package and held on as we roared out of the city and back into Paterson. The train rattled and shook and swayed on its tracks, racing toward the station like a runaway horse.

In Paterson all the passengers had to get off and switch cars. I stepped out in the middle of the crowd and waited for it to disperse. Once the platform was empty, I took a seat on a bench and opened the envelope. Inside was a stack of over a hundred prints. Mr. LaMotte's name was printed nowhere on the prints or on the envelope. The only mark was the name *Ward* in light pencil.

The pictures had been taken over several weeks in the summer, from a vantage point just across the street from the address in question. I could see time passing on the face of the building. As the weeks wore on, the geraniums in the window boxes on the third floor leafed out and bloomed.

Then the windows opened, and bed sheets came outside to dry.

I was near the bottom of the pile when I heard a muffled cough behind me and jumped up. Sheriff Heath had been looking over my shoulder.

"What are you doing here?" I felt like I'd been caught doing something wrong.

"I'm an officer of the law, Miss Kopp," he said. "I don't have to account for my whereabouts. But you do. I thought you were home looking after your sisters. Fleurette told me where you'd gone. She said she was frightened to be left alone."

I pushed the photographs back in their envelope and tucked it under my arm. "She wasn't frightened—she just wanted to come along. Norma is perfectly capable of watching Fleurette for an afternoon. I had business in the city."

"What kind of business?"

"It doesn't concern you."

He frowned, but it was the false frown of someone who was only pretending to be hurt. "I have something for you," he said, reaching into his vest pocket. "Mr. Kaufman has paid his fine."

He handed me a roll of bills. I put the money in my handbag and dropped down to the bench again, suddenly exhausted. "Well. His debt is paid. This takes care of it."

He sat next to me. The train had pulled out of the station and we were alone on the platform. "I hope so. He wasn't happy about paying the fine, but he had little choice. It was due and I could have arrested him."

"That must have been a pleasant visit."

"It was not. His sister was there this time."

"So you've met Mrs. Garfinkel?"

He nodded. "She was not at all pleased to see me. She wants to keep her family's name out of the papers. She handed me two hundred dollars and said that she hoped this would be the end to Henry's legal troubles."

"Two hundred! But the fine was only fifty. You don't mean—"

He nodded. I stared at him, then reached for the roll in my handbag.

"Miss Kopp! I didn't take it."

"Of course you didn't."

He smiled and put his head down, then looked over at me from under the brim of his hat. "A sheriff can always find a way to put extra money in his pocket. I'm not that type of sheriff. Now, let's have a look at those pictures."

I thought about what Mr. LaMotte had said about putting up walls between the parties in an investigation. But I didn't want to argue about it, and I was fairly certain that the photographs held no clues anyway. I handed the envelope to Sheriff Heath and told him where I'd gotten them.

He thumbed through the pictures. In one of them an old woman with a cane stopped at the entrance but did not go inside, in another two boys ran upstairs for dinner, and several showed the same man returning home from work in a bellman's uniform.

"I don't recognize any of them," he said. "This doesn't have anything to do with that boarding house fire you were asking Morris about, does it?"

"I shouldn't say."

The sheriff sat still for a minute, looking at the empty train tracks. A piece of waxed paper from the delicatessen next to the station had rolled onto the tracks, and a gray rat ran out from under the platform to inspect it.

Finally he handed the envelope to me. "Well, may I drive you home, Miss Kopp?"

THE SHOPS IN PATERSON were due to close at any minute. Shoppers were dashing across the street with parcels in their arms, ignoring the line of motor cars shuddering and wheezing as they lurched in a slow and unsteady line. Green window shades came down at the bank as we rode past, and the grocer brought in his cart of onions from the sidewalk. A newsboy pushed the last of the evening edition into the hands of men rushing from their offices to catch the trolley home. The windows in the library went dim. Darkness chased us out of town.

The sheriff drove along in silence, his lips moving but no sound coming out. I stayed quiet as he seemed to be puzzling something out. By now it was almost completely dark. He said he wanted to pull over and check the headlamps before we drove into the country.

I got out of the car when he did. It felt good to stand along the side of the road with grass under my feet and breathe in the sharp, cold night air. I felt as though I had lived someone else's life all day, and now I was returning to my own.

Sheriff Heath bent down and squinted at the headlamps, then walked around to my side of the car and leaned against it, his hands in his pockets.

"This girl's afraid of the police, but she'll speak to you," he said. "A stranger."

"You're a stranger too," I said.

He looked out along the tops of the trees. "We always have trouble getting women to talk to us."

"They don't have any trouble talking to me."

"But that does us no good if you won't tell me about it," the sheriff said.

A black motor car took a bend in the road a little too fast and kicked gravel and dust at us. It was enough to spook me and I stumbled back into the grass. He took my elbow.

"It just caught me by surprise," I said, brushing off my dress. "But that reminds me. It's Fleurette's birthday soon. Do you think we could take her to town for the day?"

He thought about it for a minute. "Just keep an eye on her, and take your revolver. Don't go to Paterson. I don't want you running into him."

I agreed.

"Then go ahead. We'll drive by the house while you're gone."

"Doesn't the sheriff have better things to do than watch for prowlers in the countryside?"

He looked at me in surprise. "My mother always said things like that."

"I don't suppose I know your mother."

"She passed away last year."

He opened the door and I took my seat. "I'm sorry," I said. "Mine did too. I didn't know we had that in common."

He started the engine again and drove us a ways down the road, then said, "She had very definite ideas about a sheriff's duties, as did my father, although he didn't live long enough to see me in office."

"What was he like?"

"Oh, just ask any old-timer about Doc Heath. Twenty or thirty years ago, he ran Hackensack. He was the fire chief and the town druggist and the dentist."

"All at once?"

"My mother always wanted him to pick one and quit the others, but he never would. She's a Gamewell—the fire alarm company."

"That's her family's business?"

"Oh, yes. And every man who marries a Gamewell girl becomes a fire chief in some city or another so he can go around having fire alarms installed. But my father learned a little dentistry in the War between the States and couldn't help but do that, too. Then he became a justice of the peace—"

"A fourth profession!"

The sheriff nodded. "He used to brag about how he sent more people to jail, married more couples, and pulled more teeth than any man in New Jersey."

"You take after him, then," I said. "And are there more sheriffs and fire chiefs in the family?"

"Oh, no. My brothers are company men."

"I suspect you have sisters, too."

He nodded. "There were ten of us."

"Ten!"

"Only five lived. I was the first one to live."

I turned to the window and watched the trunks of the trees and the fence posts roll past us and disappear from view. "Your poor mother."

"She was . . ." He faltered, and then said, "Yes, she had a trying time."

"Well, I suspect your father would have liked to have seen you in office."

He shook his head and said, "I don't know what he would have thought. He was a lock-them-up-and-throw-away-the-key man. He didn't like any of my ideas about reforming the jails. If he were alive, he'd be down at the Board of Freehold-ers meeting every Tuesday night, complaining about my ex-penses like the rest of them do."

"Then you're still arguing with him, aren't you?" I said.

"I suppose I'm still arguing with his ideas." After a pause he added, "I know one thing he would've liked."

"What's that?"

"To see Henry Kaufman arrested. Doc Heath despised drunkenness and laziness, and he couldn't tolerate anyone harassing a lady."

"Well. Neither can I."

❦ 27 ❧

WHEN I PROMISED FLEURETTE I'd take her anywhere for her birthday, I meant that I would take her to her choice of shops in some nearby city. But she wanted to go to the seashore. "We didn't go at all this summer," she said. "Everyone says it's going to be the coldest winter in years. We should go just once before it gets too dreadful."

On the morning of her birthday, the sun streamed into our windows and got us all out of bed early. Even though there was a chill in the air, it was the sort of day meant to be spent outdoors. Norma rushed outside to get the buggy ready. Fleurette packed a blanket and three Chinese parasols, along with a bundle of silk scarves whose purpose I could not determine. I made chopped liver sandwiches and potato salad, and packed an apple for each of us and six hard-boiled eggs. We drank our coffee and ate our toast standing around the kitchen table. It seemed a waste of time to sit when we had somewhere to go.

We left Dolley at the stables next to the train station. We'd decided to go to the bathing beach at New Rochelle, where our uncle Frederick used to run a beer garden in the summer. It was nothing more than a tent in a gravel lot, but that was all the beach-going crowd wanted anyway. He'd set out benches and folding chairs and serve Austrian beer and sausages. The beer was his own recipe. "I make one kind," he used to tell his customers. "Cold."

When Francis, Norma, and I were children, we weren't allowed inside the beer garden. Mother would sit at a table nearest the beach with her knitting bag or a piece of embroidery and talk with her brother's wife and a few of our other female relations. We would run back and forth in the sand, collecting bits of driftwood and broken shells and arranging them around her feet like some kind of offering.

By the time Fleurette was a little girl, Norma and I were too old to play at the beach, but we went back occasionally for her sake. She talked about it as if we had a tradition of going every summer, but I couldn't remember the last time we'd taken her there. Our uncle had long ago given up the beer garden, being too old to manage it himself and having no sons to help him.

The train was nearly empty on the way to New Rochelle. From the station it was only a short walk to the beach. Fleurette ran on ahead while Norma and I lagged behind, carrying our lunch and the bag of parasols and scarves.

"It's odd to be here without Mother," Norma said under her breath.

At the water's edge, Fleurette kicked off her shoes and, before Norma or I could tell her not to, reached under her skirt to roll her stockings down. She stuffed them in her shoes and ran into the waves. We watched her from the edge of the

boardwalk, not sure if we should follow or set a more dignified example.

From a distance, she still looked like a little girl. She
dashed into the water with her skirt lifted to her knees and
shrieked when the waves leapt up at her.

"She's going to ruin that silk," I said.

"It isn't silk," Norma said. "It's one of those new fabrics
meant to be worn in the water. She's been working on it all
week."

"She has? I didn't notice."

"She works fast," Norma said. "She has a natural talent."

FLEURETTE'S INTEREST IN SEWING never struck any of
us as unusual until the day, when she was about eight years
old, that she found the Singer man's sample machine in my
closet and carried it down, sitting on the stairs and dragging
it in her lap.

"Can't I use this one, *maman*?" she asked, pulling it across
the floor like a puppy she wanted to adopt.

Mother looked up from the lace collar she was adding to a
pinafore. "Where did you find another—" she said, then her
face went blank.

Norma put her newspaper down and stared at the machine. They both very deliberately did not look at me.

She ran to Mother, throwing herself across her lap. "Constance had it," she said. "But Constance hates to sew. I want
to make you an apron. *S'il te plait, laisse-moi essayer.*"

Mother smoothed Fleurette's hair absently and looked
over at the machine.

"It's the wrong kind for a little girl," she said, her voice even and tightly controlled. "We will take it to Paterson and trade it for one that suits you. A Franklin, maybe. Not a Singer."

Without a glance at me, she pushed Fleurette off her lap, picked up the Singer man's machine, and walked outside with it. The next day, she and Fleurette went to town and returned with a new black Franklin decorated with an Egyptian phoenix and scarab motif and mounted in an oak cabinet. Francis had just married and moved to Hawthorne, so his bedroom became Fleurette's sewing room.

Within a year she was making her own play clothes, copying the styles in the ladies' pages of the newspaper. By the time she was twelve she'd moved on to fancy frocks and nightgowns. And now, it appeared, she was stitching bathing costumes as soon as the idea for a visit to the seashore occurred to her.

NORMA SPREAD OUT THE BLANKET along the short wall between the sand and the boardwalk and we sat down together. Fleurette yelled for us to come and join her but we waved her on and looked out at the expanse of flat slate-blue water. The waves had subsided and Fleurette took to kicking the ocean to get it moving again. A trio of seagulls circled and landed next to her. Finding herself with an audience, she splashed even more vigorously, which excited the gulls and prompted them to do a dance, shaking out their wings in the droplets of water she made rain down on them.

The sun warmed the little rock wall and we leaned against it. Norma closed her eyes and tilted her face up to the sky. "Isn't it nice to be on our own, without any armed deputies watching over us?" She sat up and looked around. "Or has Sheriff Heath followed us here and concealed himself inside

a bathing tent? I thought I saw one of them move a minute ago."

"We're perfectly safe," I said, "and I take it as a good sign
that we've seen nothing of Henry Kaufman lately."

Norma frowned. She rarely took anything as a good sign.
"Don't you agree," she said, in the lilting musical voice that
she used for her most sweeping proclamations, "that it would
be best if the three of us stayed entirely away from that business with the factory girl and made no more secret trips to
New York City that we don't tell the others about? Meaning,
of course, that you in particular—"

"Yes, I realize that you're speaking of me in particular. I
suppose Fleurette told you all about it, which means that I
don't need to." A pinch of sand had worked its way under my
collar and I sat up to brush it away.

"Fleurette loves secrets because she enjoys telling people
things they aren't supposed to know. I prefer to tell people the
things they *are* supposed to know," Norma said.

"You're very good at it," I answered.

"I have always thought so."

I felt something on my neck again and sat up to brush it
off. When I did, I realized that a colony of tiny black ants
resided inside a crevice in the rock wall and had organized
themselves to make an advance upon our dinner basket.
Norma and I stood up and shook the ants off our blanket,
and found a better place for ourselves a few yards away.

"This hasn't been good for Fleurette," Norma continued
when we'd settled back down. "She talks of nothing else. All
those mysterious trips and secret letters. She's far too excitable for something like this."

"We should find something more substantial to occupy her

time," I said. "Then she won't think about it so much. I don't want her working as a common seamstress. Maybe we could find a stenography course, or . . ." I realized I hadn't any ideas about an occupation for Fleurette.

"She'd never do the lessons," Norma said, "and even if she did, what then? We can't let her go off to an office every day. I can only imagine what she'd get up to."

I turned to look Norma squarely in the face. There was sand all over us, and some of it had landed on her eyelashes and the fine hair above her lip. "She'll have to go off on her own someday," I said. "Won't she?"

Norma shook her head. "I'd rather not think about it."

"But surely she's thinking about it," I said. "She's seventeen now. She's almost as old as I was when—"

"All the more reason to keep her at home," Norma said briskly, "if only we can keep strange men from driving by and calling after her. Do you think we can do that?"

I was tired of being lectured about Henry Kaufman. I stood up to get a better look at the ocean. At the end of the beach a group of girls about Fleurette's age sat on their wide striped blankets. They wore the sort of bathing costume we wouldn't let Fleurette have, the kind with divided skirts and a drawstring that lifted the hem up into bloomers for swimming. The idea was that girls would wait until they'd gone in the water to lift their skirts, but these girls hadn't and we knew Fleurette wouldn't either. Instead they drew them up as high as they would go and splayed their legs in the sunshine. Their blankets were arrayed in a starfish pattern so that their heads met in the middle. They were leaning in close, whispering to one another, their legs wiggling like a pale multi-limbed sea creature washed up onshore.

"We've come all this way. We should dip our toes in the water," I said.

The beach was almost silver, shimmering in the sunlight like a mirror. It had grown unexpectedly warm since our arrival, and all at once it felt more like August than October. I pulled the laces out of my shoes and—after looking around to make sure no one was watching—rolled off my stockings. The pleasure of immersing my bare feet in the warm sand made me shiver. Norma gave a little half-smile of surrender and soon she was barefoot, too. Once Fleurette saw us, she ran up and took us both by the hands, dragging us to the water. For an hour we splashed and kicked at the sand and chased the seagulls like any ordinary family at the beach.

We spread out our picnic and two boys came around selling lemonade and pretzels. Fleurette wanted us to buy something in honor of her birthday, so we did. We ate our pretzels in the sand and then stretched out on our backs to look up at the sky. The little waves barely made a sound at all when they patted the shore. The gulls whooshed down next to us to inspect our empty lemonade bottles and lifted off again. I must have fallen asleep, because the next time I looked around, Fleurette had left us and gone to stand by herself and look across Long Island Sound toward the distant and endless Atlantic.

❧ 28 ❧

AT FIRST, there was no point in pretending that the baby wasn't mine. Fleurette's bassinet stayed in my bedroom for the first year so that I could nurse her and get up with her in the middle of the night. But during the day, Mother took her from me.

"She has to learn to come to me," she said.

I knew she was right. I knew that, years later, Fleurette couldn't have an inexplicable bond with one sister that she didn't have with the other. The girl needed to grow up with one mother, and it had already been decided who that mother would be. So my mother was the one who held her and fussed over her and decided how to dress her and when to bathe her.

She only handed the baby to me when it was feeding time. I would take her into the pantry and crouch down on a little stool we'd put there for that purpose. It was just the two of us in the dark, surrounded by tins of baking soda and breakfast tea. Fleurette would look up at me through enormous black, uncomprehending eyes as she fed. She was looking at her mother, as any baby would when it nursed. With her eyes open but her mind unformed, she was witnessing the great secret of her life, one that she was supposed to forget, and would forget.

In those moments I felt like I'd stolen her. If she fell asleep I would sit and hold her, matching my breath to hers there among the preserves and pickled beans, counting the minutes until my mother's footsteps would come across the floor and the door would open.

"You know better," she would say, and take her from me.

Norma wasn't particularly interested in the baby. She was a teenager, still finishing school in Ridgewood, and happily occupied with farm chores in her spare time. She and Francis bought a pair of goats, they built a chicken coop and figured out how to raise a flock, and they put up a fence to keep the deer away from the vegetable garden. The two of them kept so busy that no one even noticed that they'd built a pigeon loft as well. It wasn't until an incubator appeared in the kitchen that we realized what Norma had in mind.

Baby pigeons were far more interesting to her than baby humans, but she took her turns with Fleurette anyway, sitting with her on the kitchen floor and watching the gray fledglings hop around in their crate of wood and straw. Sometimes Norma would take one of the baby birds firmly in her hand and hold it out to Fleurette, its legs splayed and its wings pinned behind it. Fleurette would reach one finger out to the bird's downy undercarriage and laugh uproariously.

Everything made Fleurette laugh. She was at the very center of a world created just for her, and she knew it.

❧ 29 ❧

NIGHT CLOUDS OBSCURED THE MOON over our house. We maneuvered down the drive in total darkness. Fleurette had fallen asleep on the ride home and slumped over against me, warm and heavy. Norma brought Dolley to a stop and was about to jump out and check on her birds when I saw it.

Our front door was open.

We both reached for Fleurette at the same time, which made her squeal.

"Shhhhh." I felt around under her feet for the picnic basket, where I'd hidden the revolvers. Fleurette caught a glimpse of them and gasped.

"What are those?"

I backed out of the buggy and took her chin in my hand. Her eyes were wide open now and frantic. "Be very quiet," I whispered. "If anything happens, go straight for the dairy and pound on the door until they let you in." She nodded. I pressed Dolley's reins into her hands.

Norma had stepped out on the other side of the buggy. I

tilted my head in the direction of the open door. We advanced toward it and she took a gun from me. We were almost to the porch when, from the other side of the house, the kitchen door burst open and half a dozen men scrambled out into the black night.

I chased after them, stopping just long enough to get them in my sights and fire.

The shot exploded across the meadow and sent a flock of crows screeching into the sky. By now the men had reached a bank of trees along the road and I could hardly see them. I took up my skirts and ran, but then came the kick of an automobile starting and the sound of tires grinding in the dirt.

By the time I reached the road, the black bulk had sputtered and motored away. I fired again and again into the darkness it left behind.

Gunpowder smoke and dust drifted around me in a cloud. It took a minute to clear, but once it did I took a deep breath and willed my hands to stop shaking. Only then did I turn to look back at our darkened house, and the dim figure of our horse in front. I couldn't see Norma or Fleurette.

I'd left them alone.

I ran back down the drive and Norma met me at the buggy. Both of us reached for Fleurette at once, as if we needed to feel her pulse.

"I didn't dare shoot once you started to run," Norma said.

"That's fine," I said. "I think they're gone."

We started to lift Fleurette out of the buggy, but she shook her head and stayed planted on her seat.

"We can't go in," she whispered. "What if he's waiting for us?"

"Who?" I asked.

"H-Henry Kaufman."

Norma and I both laughed at once, but it was a nervous, trembling laugh. "He never goes anywhere without that gang of his," I said. "If he was here, he ran out with the rest of them."

I turned to the open front door and shouted. "Did you hear that, Henry Kaufman? If you were here, you're gone now!" I fired my gun in the air, high over the house, to make my point. Norma flinched and Fleurette covered her ears, but I didn't care. I'd had enough of Henry Kaufman and I refused to be afraid of walking into my own house.

"Let's go." I stepped inside, feeling bold from the gunfire still ringing in my ears. Norma picked up our porch lamp and lit it as we went in.

Our grandfather clock was overturned in the foyer, surrounded by a mess of broken glass. We picked our way across it, stumbling over magazines splayed open and scarves and hats that should have been on our coat rack. Norma lifted the lamp, and it was only then that we understood. The house had been ransacked. Every piece of furniture in the parlor was piled in the middle of the room: upended chairs, overturned tables, desks with the drawers knocked out of them, and the divan, standing awkwardly on its end. Pictures had been torn from the walls and thrown into the pile, the glass broken out of the frames. Vases and lamps and even the contents of a knitting basket were strewn about.

The occasional table near the door, where we kept our mail, had been thrown into the drawing room, atop another pile of furniture. Books had been pulled from their shelves, and a potted rubber tree that I would have thought too heavy to move was on its side, surrounded by dirt and broken ceramic. Even the rug was rolled up into the rough, uneven pyramid made by our things.

"Did they take anything?" Fleurette asked at last.

I shook my head. "I don't think so. I think they were only trying to—"

By then we'd reached the sitting room, and all three of us smelled it at once. Smoke.

This time Norma ran on ahead, reaching the kitchen first and shouting for us to bring a blanket. Seeing nothing we could readily extract from the mess around us, we followed her in. They had started a fire on our kitchen table, setting flame to the newspapers we'd left there that morning. There was nothing left of them but dry and drifting ashes, and a few corners still curling and flickering. Now the lace table-cloth was giving way, each filament glowing orange before crumbling to black. The flames cast a weird light around the kitchen and the smoke drifted to the ceiling like a miniature storm cloud.

I pulled my coat off and Norma and I slammed it down on the table and beat at it while Fleurette drew a bucket of water. Soon there was nothing but a soggy pile of tweed and ashes on the table, along with the broken remains of the crumb-covered plates we'd left there that morning.

The three of us dropped into our chairs, panting and coughing a little, staring at the mess in front of us. The intruders had left the kitchen door open when they'd fled. It had a tendency to close on its own, but it was still open just enough to let in a draft of cold air. Our eyes wandered over to it.

There was a metal can just outside the kitchen door. Fleurette started to ask what it was, but I already knew.

"Kerosene. They were building a bonfire."

SOMEONE HAD TO CHECK THE BEDROOMS UPSTAIRS. After a moment of indecision over who should go—we were too exhausted and confused to think clearly—we walked through the downstairs rooms together, locking doors and windows as we went. Norma and I each kept a revolver pointed in a different direction.

"Where did you get those?" Fleurette asked.

"Sheriff Heath," I said quietly, out of the side of my mouth.

"Why would he give you . . ." And she trailed off as the answer occurred to her.

"Because of this," Norma said grimly. "Because he knew something like this might happen."

Once I was sure no one was hidden downstairs, I left them standing by the front door and ran up, pounding the stairs as loud as I could to announce my arrival, rapping my gun on each door before I entered. But our bedrooms were empty and untouched. Fleurette's chemise still dangled from the bedpost where she'd left it. Norma's treatise on pigeons was open on her nightstand. The thought of those men running through our rooms, touching our things, sent another jolt through me and my knees almost buckled.

Downstairs, Norma and Fleurette had already begun to sort through the mess and try to make sense of what happened. "Norma found a box of matches outside the kitchen door," Fleurette called to me, "and they're not the kind we use. She thinks they heard us ride up and didn't have time for the kerosene, but threw a match on the table before they left anyway."

I nodded, my arms crossed over my chest. "It must've been something like that."

Norma came in from the parlor with a man's overcoat hooked over one finger. She held it out at arm's length. "They left this behind."

Fleurette reached for it. "Can a coat have fingerprints?"

"I don't think so," I said. "Maybe the buttons. But let's be careful."

Fleurette took it from Norma and held it up in the dim light of the porch lamp. It was a thick wool coat, navy blue, lined in silk the color of rhubarb. There were leather tabs at the cuffs and collar, and buttons that must have been made of brass but looked like gold. It might have been hand sewn: as we leaned in, we saw no label advertising a department store or even the city of manufacture.

It was a beautiful piece of work, something worn by a man who appreciated fine tailoring. But it was also quietly terrifying to have the shape of the man who had been in our house suspended there from Fleurette's arms. I took it from her and found a place for it on our coat rack. We all stepped back and watched it like it might turn on us.

Something on the coat gleamed and caught the light. It was a gold stick pin topped by a diamond.

"Just the sort of thing a vain man would wear," Norma said.

We took up the lantern and made another turn around the wreckage. We found a handkerchief that didn't belong to us, and a man's gold ring. I couldn't see a jeweler's mark, but I held it carefully by the edges, hoping it might yield a fingerprint.

"We'll take this to the sheriff tomorrow," I said. "There's nothing more we can do tonight."

"We can't possibly stay here!" Norma said.

"Where do you expect us to go? I'm not about to wake up Francis at this hour. He'll never let us move back in here if he finds out about this."

Fleurette shuffled across the floor, kicking away the pieces of a ruby cut-glass bowl we'd always believed unbreakable. When she reached the stairs, she called over her shoulder, "I can't look at this mess any longer. If they come back, you two can just shoot at them and we'll clean it all up tomorrow."

"Get in my bed," I said.

When she was gone, Norma whispered, "I won't sleep in this house."

"I don't intend to sleep. But there's nowhere to go, unless you'd like to ride into Hackensack and ask the sheriff to take us into the jail for the night."

Norma deliberated over that for a minute. "If it's to be a choice between Francis and the Hackensack jail, I suppose we'll manage for one night."

We made one more check of the doors and windows together, then climbed the stairs and took up the same positions we'd occupied before. I wrapped myself around Fleurette, and Norma spread out her blankets under the window. The rifle leaned against the wall again, but this time Norma settled down with a revolver next to her, and I did too. Fleurette curled into a tight ball and stared at the wall. At some point in the early morning, her eyes closed. I listened to her breathe for hours.

❧ 30 ❧

THIS TIME WHEN I WENT TO TOWN, no one stayed at
home. We were up at the first light and packed a few valuables and keepsakes into the buggy in case the men returned
while we were gone. I rolled the intruder's coat into a pillowcase, along with the ring, stickpin, and the matches we'd
found. It made me queasy to touch all of it, but no one else
would.

Fleurette tried to take the reins but I wouldn't let her on
the grounds that I didn't know who we might be passing on
the road. So Norma drove and I sat with my arm around Fleurette and my hand over my handbag with the revolver tucked
inside. Along the way every black automobile looked suspicious to me. An engine misfired and I pushed Fleurette to the
floor, eliciting a yelp of protest.

"Stop it!" she said. "He's not going to come after us on the
street in front of everybody."

"He has before," I said.

"Stop it anyway," Norma said over her shoulder. "You'll
give me a nervous fit if you keep jumping around like that."

I didn't say anything for the rest of the drive, but I slid my hand in my bag anyway. I found the cold weight of the revolver calming.

We arrived at the jail in Hackensack before nine o'clock. It was a new building and a decidedly odd one, designed, according to the Board of Freeholders' wishes, to look like a medieval fortress with turrets and tiny windows of the sort one might use to shoot a cannon at attacking armies. The Hackensack River ran alongside it like a moat. The edifice had been mocked in the papers as being a waste of taxpayers' money and looking more like a playhouse for schoolboys than a serious building with a public purpose.

And like most medieval fortresses (I supposed, not having visited any others), it did not feature an expansive and welcoming entrance. We walked around the building once, unsure which of the locked, windowless doors were intended for our use. At last I shrugged, climbed some stairs, and pounded on the door that looked most promising.

A harried, red-cheeked woman in a yellow apron answered the door. A perfect angel of a baby sat on her hip, its face framed in blond curls. I took a step back in surprise.

"Oh," I said. "We meant to go to the prison. We're here to see Sheriff Heath. Did I . . ." and I trailed off, looking up at the building for some clue as to where I might have gone wrong.

"This is the prison," she said brusquely. "And it also happens to be my home."

She looked so affronted by this that I thought she expected an apology from me, but I wasn't sure what I'd done.

Fleurette started to say something. Before she got us into

even more trouble, I said, "I'm so sorry to disturb you. We're here on an urgent matter for the sheriff."

The baby was starting to squirm in the cold air. She closed the door slightly so that he was behind the door and out of the wind. "I know," she said. "He saw you coming from the third floor and called down. He'll be here soon as he can."

Again she stared at us. Her mouth was a hard blank line.

Realizing that we weren't going to be invited in, I said, "Where would you like us to wait?"

At that she exhaled a tired and exasperated sigh, looked out at the empty drive that ringed the prison, and pushed the door open. "I suppose you'll come in. The great minds who designed this building seemed to have forgotten about a public entrance or a waiting room."

We followed her inside. To my surprise, the room was furnished like an ordinary living room, with overstuffed chairs and a fireplace and children's toys strewn about.

"It looks like someone lives here!" Fleurette said.

I turned to tell her to be quiet, but the woman said sharply, "A lot of people live here, most of them thieves and murderers. But you're in the sheriff's living quarters. I am Mrs. Heath."

Mrs. Heath? I hadn't given any thought at all to the sheriff's wife, but if I had, I would not have pictured such an unpleasant and disagreeable woman. Although I couldn't imagine what sort of woman would want to keep up a home and children on the ground floor of this cold, stone structure.

"Pleased to meet you," I said, trying out a smile that wasn't returned. "I am Constance Kopp, and these are my sisters, Norma and Fleurette."

The baby squirmed out of her grasp. She set him down and gave me a long look as she stood up. Then she glanced at Norma and scrutinized Fleurette, who was especially pretty in a black velvet riding coat trimmed in rabbit fur. I should have told her to wear something more somber. We were going to a prison, not the opera.

"Bob hasn't mentioned any sisters to me," she said.

Just then I heard footsteps. To my relief, the sheriff rushed into the room. "I'm sorry about this, Cordelia," he said to his wife. She gave him no reply.

"Miss Kopp," he said, nodding at me. "This way, please."

I looked uncertainly at Norma, who was wearing a forced and unpleasant smile and clinging to Fleurette's sleeve.

"I'm sure Mrs. Heath would enjoy some company this morning," he said. It was more of an order than an invitation. We seemed to be just another disagreeable duty imposed by the sheriff upon his wife. It couldn't have been easy for her.

I followed him into a bleak corridor. He turned around to slide a metal gate in place behind us and lock it from a key on a large ring he wore on his belt. At the end of the corridor was another gate.

"David." A deputy appeared to let us in.

We stood in a tiny windowless room with a metal door opposite. It smelled of rust and turpentine wax. The deputy locked the gate behind us and then opened the door. This led us to Sheriff Heath's office.

It was a pleasant room, lined with glass-fronted bookcases and warmed by a small fireplace. I must have been holding my breath, because I let it out all at once as I sank into a chair opposite the sheriff's desk.

He didn't sit at his desk but instead took a chair next to me.

"Are you girls all right? What happened?"

I gave him the most straightforward account I could and presented him with the coat and jewelry. He lifted them out of the pillowcase and examined them slowly. "I wonder what stopped them."

"I think they heard us. If we'd come home even a few minutes later, they would have had time to pour kerosene all over everything and light quite a bonfire."

"My deputy rode past yesterday, but he didn't see anything. They must have come after he left." He sat back in his chair and looked up at the ceiling. "I wish we'd caught him," he said, mostly to himself. "That was our chance. Well, just be sure—"

"Wait," I said. "That isn't all he's done." A prickly sort of fear came over me as I realized that the fire at Lucy's had to be connected to what had happened at our house. "You remember the girl I told you about?"

He sighed. "Miss Kopp, I wish you would—"

"Listen! That was the boarding house in Paterson. He set that fire. He went after her first, then he came after us."

"What makes you think he set that one?"

"He'd already threatened to. She told me herself. She was terrified of him."

"But Kaufman's family owns that building. Are you telling me he burned down his own building just to scare off a girl?"

"He might have," I said. It sounded preposterous when he said it like that, but I knew it to be true.

"But you still won't give me the girl's name."

"I mustn't. I promised her."

Sheriff Heath stood and paced around the room. He put his hands in his pockets and kept his head down, as if the answers were written on the leather uppers of his boots. "I'll talk to the fire chief. And I'll work on the evidence we've got. I'll send my men around to the jewelers in town, and I know a tailor who might be able to help with the coat. Maybe the matchbox has a fingerprint. Then we'll have a case for the prosecutor."

"But what are we to do while you're out speaking to tailors? Turn our home into a bunker? Guard it in shifts? Keep one revolver pointed at the road at all times?"

He squeezed his eyes shut and ran a hand through his hair. "No. I'll do that. Take your sisters home and I'll be there as soon as I can."

Just then the door opened and a guard looked in. "They're ready for you, sir."

Sheriff Heath nodded and the guard backed out silently.

"Ready for what?" I asked.

"I'm sorry, Miss Kopp. It's a bad day at the prison. We found a man dead in his cell after Sunday services. I've got to speak to the inmates."

"Oh! I—"

"There isn't anything to say about it. Go home and look after your sisters."

There was something lost and uncertain in his face. He opened the door and the guard took me away.

❧ 31 ❧

WE TOOK OUR TIME putting the rooms back together, having decided to polish the floors and wash down the walls first.
Fleurette read about a way to take the bruises out of furniture by covering them in damp brown paper and applying a
hot iron until the dent rose to the surface. It seemed hopeless to try—every table and chair and breakfront was pitted
and scratched—but she had a new iron and was eager to put
it to use. Norma and I shoved the heaviest pieces back into
place, and she ministered to the upholstery and wood. We
dusted the books and put away the pictures whose frames had
broken, having decided that we'd grown tired of looking at
them anyway. The glass globes had been smashed out of every
lamp, but they'd grown too stained with smoke to clean, and
we were glad to replace them. When we were finished, the
rooms were brighter and airier than they'd ever been.

That week the charred body of a magazine illustrator was
found in what remained of a home in Harrington Park. A bur-
glar was suspected until the dead man's wife confessed to
Sheriff Heath that she'd run off to New York and her husband

had threatened to burn the house down if she didn't return. A few days later a woman drank poison on the courthouse steps because her employer would not give her the time off to see her children. The prisoners in Sheriff Heath's jail saw her collapse from their windows and shouted to him to save her. He carried her to his office and she died there, asking the sheriff to take care of her children when she was gone. The next day he resumed more mundane duties, arresting a girl for unlawful cohabitation and serving a foreclosure notice to a widow.

All of this was diligently cataloged in the newspaper. Reporters must have followed the sheriff everywhere. I wondered why they didn't follow him to our house. Perhaps they thought nothing of interest happened this far out in the country.

He drove down Sicomac Road twice a day to pick up a deputy and deposit another one. Sometimes he would park his automobile in our drive and wait for me to join him for a walk around the property. We would circle the barn, then make a wider loop around the house, and he would show me how to look for footprints and tire impressions. We'd walk out to the end of the drive and look up and down the road. If there was any news, he'd give it.

"You were right," he said one day, after about a week of this.

"About what?" We had just finished making our rounds of the house and barn.

"The boarding house. The fire chief in Paterson believes it was arson. Didn't you say you'd met Mr. Kaufman's sister?"

"Yes, Marion Garfinkel. She mostly runs the place, I think."

"Then I want you to come with me."

• • •

SHERIFF HEATH TELEPHONED IN ADVANCE and persuaded Mrs. Garfinkel to arrange a meeting with the two of us. He wanted me along on the grounds that she'd met me before and might be more willing to cooperate in an investigation if one of Henry Kaufman's victims was sitting across from her. She was reluctant to see us but agreed after Sheriff Heath said that he would only offer a private, quiet meeting once, and after that he would simply turn up unannounced with a full force of deputies and wouldn't be able to help it if a few reporters followed along.

"Come first thing in the morning," she'd said. "Henry never gets in before noon anymore."

Deputy Morris drove us to the factory but left us at the corner. "It's a friendly visit," Sheriff Heath said. "I don't want her to see the sheriff's wagon in front of her factory." He put his badge in his pocket.

Work had already begun for the day. The floor was still dry, but the first skeins were going into the dye troughs, and there would be a lake of pigment sloshing down the drains by the time we left. I was prepared this time with a handkerchief for my nose, but the odor wasn't as strong this early in the morning.

Marion Garfinkel was waiting for us at the door to the offices. "We can use Henry's office," she said, and led us there, past the clerks at their typewriters. With their eyes on us, she called out, "Girls, I'll be in a sales meeting."

The odor of stale cigarette smoke and spilled whiskey was even worse than that of the dye vats. Marion groaned and asked the sheriff to help work one of the levers that would open the tall windows.

"He keeps these windows closed because he's convinced someone is listening in on him," Marion said. "If he'd spend half as much time thinking about the factory as he spends scheming with those friends of his, I wouldn't be here."

She dropped into the wide leather chair behind his desk and gestured for us to sit. There were playing cards and ashtrays all over the table in the middle of the room, along with brass cartridge casings, which Sheriff Heath regarded with interest but did not touch. He pulled two chairs away from the table for us and turned them to face the desk.

"All right," Marion said when we were settled. "You've got your meeting. Let's do this quickly."

"Will your husband be joining us?" the sheriff said.

"He had business at our mill in Pittsburgh. Honestly, he'd rather I took care of this place. He hates dye shops, and he's not too fond of Henry."

"Will you be taking over for your brother?" he asked.

She made a dismissive little shrug and said, "I hope not. My father thought that Henry would shape up if he was put in charge of a factory and given control of its finances. But to be honest, the elder Mr. Kaufman has grown quite feeble, and the rest of us have been taking over the family's operations. I drew the short straw and was sent here to do something about Henry."

"What do you plan to do?"

"Well, Henry's got to go, and the only way to get him to leave is to cut off the money. But I need my father's signature for that. We're still working on it," she said with a tight smile. "Is that why you're here? To hear about our family's difficulties?"

Sheriff Heath held his hat in his lap and fingered the brim. "I don't mean to pry, Mrs. Garfinkel," he said. "This concerns a criminal matter. We'd like your help."

She glanced at me over the top of her glasses. "Henry paid his fine. Didn't that take care of it?"

"I'm afraid he has continued to harass Miss Kopp and her sisters. But today we—"

"Forgive me, Sheriff, but I can't be responsible for anything my brother does outside of these four walls. My husband and I are only interested in getting this factory back on a profitable footing and getting Henry—well, finding some solution to the problem of Henry, which, to be honest, has been this family's most pressing problem for longer than I care to remember." She looked up at the patch of sky just visible through the open window. "Since his fifth birthday, now that I think about it," she said, mostly to herself.

Seeing an opportunity, I leaned forward and said, "How much trouble can a boy get into on his fifth birthday?"

She turned sharply back to me. "He can set a fire in the cellar and try to push his brother down an air shaft."

"All in one day," the sheriff said quietly.

"All in one day. He should have been sent off to reform school, but oh, no. We can't have the Kaufman name associated with a school for troubled boys. No, it's always been so much better to just—"

She seemed all at once to remember to whom she was talking, and she stopped. "What is it, Sheriff? I'm sure we all have work to do this morning."

The sheriff was still considering the hat in his lap. "The matter I'm investigating," he said, "concerns a fire."

She groaned and leaned back in her chair. "The boarding house. I know. Our family's owned a whole row of them for years, and they've been nothing but trouble. I'm surprised we haven't had a grease fire before now. My husband's planning to sell them all off."

"Who told you it was a grease fire?" Sheriff Heath said.

"Well, Henry said he spoke to the fire chief and . . ." She stopped in midsentence, her mouth hanging open. "Henry."

With a sharp look from the sheriff, I stayed quiet. After a minute she began straightening the papers on the desk and said, "But there's no evidence of that, is there? And who would set fire to his own property?" She said it with the contemplative air of a lawyer considering a legal defense.

"I understand your brother had trouble with a girl who lived in that building. Miss Kopp said she worked here. Will she be here today?"

I froze. What was he doing?

Marion looked back and forth between the two of us, but before she said a word, I could tell our interview was over.

"I don't know what Miss Kopp thinks she knows, or what business it is of hers," she said crisply. "Lucy Blake is no longer in our employ. She left without notice and will not receive a reference. She'd been harassing my brother and, frankly, it's better that she's gone."

I cringed. I'd kept my promise and never given the sheriff Lucy's name, but I'd given him too much other information. Now he knew.

"I've been told a child is missing," the sheriff continued.

At that Marion rose to her feet and we reluctantly followed suit. "That girl only wanted our family's money. It was extortion, that was all. If there ever was a child—and I never saw one—it's probably better off wherever it is now."

She marched to the door and held it open. Sheriff Heath

followed and took hold of it gently, closing it again. He spoke so softly that even I had to lean over to hear.

"Someone attempted a bonfire at the home of the Kopp sisters last week. I came by only to ask your brother's whereabouts on that evening and the evening the boarding house burned. Your cooperation would let us handle this matter quietly."

There was a twitch at the corner of her mouth and I thought she might be considering it. But then she opened the door again.

"Thank you so much for your visit," she sang out for the benefit of the typists. "We won't be needing any."

❧ 32 ❧

"I WISH YOU WOULDN'T have brought Lucy Blake into this," I said as Deputy Morris drove us back to Wyckoff.

"I needed the girl's name," the sheriff said calmly. "She's a part of this mess. I can't help any of you if I don't know what's going on."

"She made me swear I wouldn't go to the police."

"But we can help her if she'll let us," the sheriff said. "If she'd only come to us when the baby was born, we could have petitioned a judge to have Kaufman declared the father. He would have been made to pay. We've done it before."

"I don't think a scared young factory girl would have gone running to the sheriff in the middle of the strikes, even if she had known," I said.

"Well. She shouldn't be so afraid of us," he said. "And you wanted me to know her name. You always did."

He was right, but I wasn't going to say it.

"Now she's a missing person," he continued. "Doesn't that change things? Wouldn't she have wanted you to do something if she turned up missing?"

"What are you going to do?" I asked.

"We'll take a description from you and we'll start looking," he said. "And we'll bring Henry Kaufman in as soon as I can get the prosecutor to agree on some charges."

"Do you mean you have to ask that man for permission before you bring an arsonist and kidnapper in for questioning? What was his name? Courter?"

"No," said the sheriff. "It's worse than that. I have to ask his boss."

When we rolled into the drive, Norma and Fleurette were standing outside with one of the deputies. "We have a letter," Fleurette called to us before we were even out of the car. She was bouncing up and down on her toes the way she did when she was excited. I was beginning to think Norma was right. Fleurette did see this as another installment in a Sunday serial.

Sheriff Heath rushed over and took the envelope from his deputy. "Did he mail it?" he said, holding it lightly by the edges.

He had, which the sheriff considered good news, because it meant that he could take it to a man at the post office assigned to work on Black Hand letters and other such threats sent through the mail.

I read it over his shoulder.

Madam,

You make mistake to bring police in. We settle this ourselves. If you insist on prosecuting Henry Kaufman you will be sorry, for we will blow up your home.

This time we get you, when you run, us shoot you before you pass us in field or street.

—H. K. & Friends

Sheriff Heath looked out at the road and my eyes followed his. Anything could come hurling down that road at us. I'd always felt so secluded in the countryside, so isolated. This is where we'd gone to hide. But we weren't hidden anymore.

Fleurette crossed her arms over her chest and hopped up and down to get warm. The day had grown gray and damp, and the chill was getting into our bones. Norma put an arm around her and rubbed her shoulders.

"I'll put a guard here around the clock," the sheriff said, his eyes still on the empty road. "We'll be able to see them coming. I don't want you to worry. The next time they turn up out here, they'll all be arrested."

But he also told us to stay away from windows, and to keep buckets of water around the house in case we had to put out a fire, and to keep our revolvers nearby, even during the day.

So that's the way it would be. We were under siege.

WINTER WAS CLOSING IN ON US. By the first week of November, we'd already had a few snow flurries. In the morning we had to sprinkle salt on the porch stoop to keep from slipping, and every day we chipped the ice out of Dolley's water trough. Our chickens went through an early molt, shedding their feathers so rapidly that in the morning we'd find the floor of their pen covered in them and think that one of them had been slaughtered by a fox in the night. Francis arranged for a boy to bring us a cord of firewood, knowing that we wouldn't make it to Christmas if it stayed this cold.

The willow trees down by the creek were encased in ice at sunrise. When I walked out to the meadow, I could hear those thin, whip-like branches jangling against each other like the glass on a chandelier. I worried about the deputies stationed out there in the cold, and finally got them to accept a camp stove to furnish some small measure of heat.

It was a few weeks before Henry Kaufman made good on his threat. I awoke to the sound of ice cracking under some-one's feet, but I had been so deeply asleep that at first I didn't understand what was happening. But then a twig snapped and I heard a man's soft cursing. In a second I was out of bed and crouched under the window. The revolver was so cold that it was a shock to wrap my hand around it.

I raised my eyes to the windowsill. The glass was covered in a fine, crystalline lacework of ice. I had to stand a little taller to find a spot that was clear enough to see through. From my bedroom I had a view of the meadow and the dead, dry vegetable garden. I could see only a corner of the barn. No light came from its window. I didn't know if the deputy was watching or not.

Seeing no one in the yard, I lowered myself back to the floor and wondered if I should wake Norma and Fleurette. We had only just started sleeping in our own bedrooms again a few nights ago. Now I wish we'd rigged up a bell to signal one another.

I slid my window open a few inches, and as I did, I again heard the crack of ice under someone's feet. I risked another look through the glass. He saw me just as I saw him. His gun was already drawn. I pushed my revolver through the narrow opening and fired.

The bullet hit a tree and he shot up at me. There was a small shudder when the bullet hit the house. A second later I heard the groan of the barn door swinging open. I couldn't shoot again without endangering the deputy. I dropped below the window and waited.

When the man didn't return fire, I stood alongside the window and peeked out. He was running down the drive, a short and stocky figure in a coat and hat. I couldn't say for certain that it was Henry Kaufman, but nothing about his appearance gave me reason to believe it wasn't.

A car met him at the end of our drive and roared away. It was only after the road was empty that I saw the deputy chasing after him, fast but not fast enough.

SHERIFF HEATH WAS ANGRY with his deputy for letting the man get away, but I forgave him. We could see from the footprints in the ice that our intruder had approached the house from the other side, staying away from the barn so as not to alert the deputy stationed there. Even if he had dozed off for a few minutes (an accusation from Sheriff Heath that he denied), it would have been difficult to get up and out of the barn in time to react. The entire confrontation only took a minute.

"Wouldn't this be a very good time to arrest the man and put an end to all this?" Norma said when the sheriff stopped in the next morning.

"We're still trying to make the case to the prosecutor," he said.

"But Constance saw him!" Fleurette said. She was sitting at the kitchen table spooning sugar on her toast. The sheriff, Norma, and I were standing in an awkward half-circle around her.

"She thinks she saw him," Sheriff Heath said. "And I think she did, too. But we have no proof."

"If only she'd shot him," Norma said, "we'd have excellent proof in the form of a frozen corpse in the drive."

"What about the coat and the stickpin and the ring? All those things they left behind?" I asked.

He shook his head. "I've sent my men around to every tailor and jeweler in town. No one recognizes them. The coat was made by a very good private tailor, and the jewelry has no marks. We couldn't get a print from the matchbox."

"And the letters?" I said.

"I've got someone at the post office working on that. I know it isn't any comfort, but we're doing everything we can."

"So is Henry Kaufman," Norma said.

After that, there were two deputies on duty, and the three of us went back to sleeping in the same room. We chose Mother's room because it squarely faced the barn and the road, making it more difficult for someone to sneak up to it. The bullet that had been fired at the house remained lodged in the siding. The wood was sturdy enough to protect us, so we weren't worried about anyone shooting at us through the walls. Our house was powerfully built of wide, thick timbers. It wasn't meant to withstand the ammunition of gangsters, but it seemed to be serving that purpose just fine.

All the same, we moved every piece of furniture in Mother's room to the outside wall. Any bullets coming at us would have to get through the shingles, the crossbeams, and Mother's oak chiffonier.

❧ 33 ❧

WE TRULY HAD GONE BACK INTO HIDING. There was the same sense of dread, of fear, of an ever-present danger pressing in from the outside world, that had hung about the house when we first moved to Wyckoff. I remembered the weight of it from last time, and the sense that I had brought this down upon us all.

Except that then we had a baby to distract us. Now we had a bored seventeen-year-old and a platoon of deputies stationed in our barn on twelve-hour shifts.

Norma scoured the newspaper every day for hints about what Kaufman and his gang might be up to. "There was a raid on a gambling parlor last night," she would say. "Maybe he got swept up in that." Any story about an automobile running someone down got her attention, for we knew him to be a dangerous driver. And if there was a fire—any kind of fire at all, even a kitchen fire started accidentally by a maid—Norma cut it out and left it for the sheriff to see.

"Not knowing his whereabouts is the worst of it," she said one morning. "What's he doing right now? When he's not going after us, who else do you suppose he's bothering?" Norma imagined that he had a long list of similarly situated women to harass and threaten. I said that I didn't think Henry Kaufman was capable of something as methodical as a list.

"No, I'm certain he doesn't keep a list," Norma said. "But I do wonder if he doesn't have a whole string of us he goes around and torments. I've half a mind to place an advertisement in the papers and form some kind of league."

"The Henry Kaufman Protection League," Fleurette said. Norma wrote it down.

"I want to know what he's done with Lucy Blake," said Fleurette. "Maybe he's got her and the baby hidden in the basement. Has anyone gone to look?"

Norma rattled her newspaper to signal her displeasure with the subject of Lucy Blake. But the girl's story played like a moving picture in Fleurette's head, and it was impossible to get her to stop talking about it.

"Why can't the sheriff find her?" Fleurette continued. "Wouldn't someone have seen her? They should ask at the train stations. Or we could put a notice in the paper about her. Haven't they done any of that? A girl can't just vanish."

"Oh, girls can vanish," Norma said without looking up at us.

IT WAS A WEEK before the next letter arrived. What prompted him to send it I couldn't imagine. We had hardly stepped foot outside, much less gone anywhere near him or his factory. I imagined Henry Kaufman's mind working like one of those swirling, sucking whirlpools that formed without warning at the bottom of the Passaic Falls. They'd arise from nothing and then spin around until something flew out of them—a piece of driftwood, a rubber ball, an old shoe. This was Henry Kaufman, spinning like a dervish until another demented letter came hurling out at us.

This one arrived once again by mail. It was delivered in the afternoon just before Sheriff Heath stopped in to pick up a deputy.

Madam: This is a last warning to you. We git this time the whole bunch of you, we lay for you. We know you and when we get you be sorry for we finish you.

    Good-by

                    Your time has come soon
                            -H. K. & Friends

"Last warning?" I said. "What does he want from us? Warning before what?"

Sheriff Heath sat down on the divan and closed his eyes for a minute. He looked terrible. His eyes were bloodshot and rimmed in dark veins the color of a bruise. As he held the letter, his hands trembled. He looked smaller somehow, as if he'd shrunk inside his overcoat.

"Sheriff Heath," I said, suddenly worried. "You don't look well." Why hadn't I noticed it before?

He gave a shuddering, chesty laugh that sent him into a coughing fit.

"Strange men are firing guns at your house and you're asking after my health?"

I was about to offer him coffee when we heard a bang and a scream from the meadow. The sheriff dropped the letter and was out the door before I could even make sense of what I'd heard.

Norma had been in the pigeon loft. I saw her running to the creek and Fleurette struggling across the meadow, where none of us should have been alone.

Norma got to her first. Fleurette was crying and pushing at her. Norma tried to hold her but then realized that she only wanted to get to the house. They turned and ran together, slipping in the mud and half-melted snow. Sheriff Heath reached her before I did. He pointed his two deputies in the direction of the creek bed and corralled us into the house.

Fleurette wore a black wool skirt that was soaked through with water and splattered with mud. If she had been wearing a hat, it was gone. She kept covering her face and turning away from us. It was impossible to get a word out of her.

Sheriff Heath saw that he could do nothing for a girl in this condition. He told us to take her upstairs and get her settled down. He would watch the house and wait for word from his deputies.

We took Fleurette to Mother's fortress-like bedroom, where at last she started to calm down. She let us pull off her wet clothes and wash her face and dress her in a nightgown and a flannel robe of Mother's. I found no scratches on her, just mud and grass. Once she was propped up in bed with us on either side of her, she was finally able to speak.

"Two men," she said. "I could barely see them through the trees. They were standing in the creek bed, like they were waiting for me."

"What did they do to you?" I said.

She wrapped her arms around her chest. "They fired at me and I ran."

"And you're sure you're not hurt?" I wanted to pull up her nightgown and check every part of her, her knees and elbows and the tiny dip between her shoulders, but she held tightly to the blankets and wouldn't let me.

"What were you doing down at the creek?" Norma asked.

Fleurette looked from Norma to me and back again, her chin trembling. "The water pump was stuck. I just went to get water for the washing. I thought everyone could see me."

The water pump did have a tendency to stick in the winter. We resorted to melting buckets of snow or bringing up water from the creek when we couldn't get it moving.

"But there were three men standing about with nothing to do," Norma said, "and one of us could have given it a try as well. You know we can usually get it going again. Why didn't you just ask someone for help?"

"That's enough," I said. "Sheriff Heath is waiting downstairs for a word from you. Can you describe these men?"

She shook her head and sunk deeper under the covers. "They wore long overcoats and hats with the brims turned down. They were tall men, taller than Mr. Kaufman, I think."

"And they were standing right in the creek? In the water?"

"They were on the flat rock I use to get across."

I ran my hand along her forehead and she closed her eyes. Her hair formed a perfect half-circle of brilliant inky black on the pillow. "Stay here and rest. We'll be downstairs with the sheriff."

Sheriff Heath and his deputies were standing outside in a tight circle, stamping their feet and talking in low voices. The men had parked an automobile in our neighbor's field on the other side of the creek and driven off in it. There was nothing but the ruts of tires in the dirt by the time the deputies got there.

We told them what little we had learned from Fleurette. It seemed most likely that the men had been crossing the creek to get closer to the house when she surprised them.

The sky had cleared a little that afternoon and lit up the frozen ground. Sheriff Heath raised a hand to shield his eyes from the glare and squinted at me. "They're getting bolder," he said. "They'll slip up soon enough. This is almost at an end. But I can't have the three of you running around in the woods and splashing in the creek. You have to do as we ask and stay where we can protect you."

Norma and I just nodded. We were going to have to take turns watching Fleurette.

"Is your sister asleep?" Sheriff Heath asked.

We said that she was.

He reached under his overcoat and consulted his watch. "That's fine. Let her sleep, and then see to it that she has a good supper. I'll be back at six."

"I'm not sure it's worth the trip," I said. "I don't think she'll have anything more to say."

He squinted up at the house and back down the road and then said, "I'm coming back to give her a shooting lesson. The three of you will all carry revolvers until this is over."

And that's how we came to be standing in a meadow on a bracingly cold November night, struggling to see our fence-post targets against the gathering dark, taking one shot after another as the sheriff braced us by the shoulders and spoke steadily in our ears, slipping the revolvers out of our pale and frozen hands to reload them so that we could fire again and again and again at the menace that waited somewhere out there beyond the creek bed.

❧ 34 ❧

HENRY KAUFMAN AND HIS FRIENDS had been toying with us the way a barn cat teases a fledgling fallen from its nest: viciously, but unhurriedly. So it was with some relief that we received, in the middle of November, his most serious and specific threat against us.

Now, at last, we had a date and a place.

```
Madam—We demand $1000 or we will kill you. Give
Monee to girl dressed in black at the corner of
Broadway and Carroll street, Paterson, Saturday
night at eight o'clock. If you don't pay we will
fire your house and take that girl of yours. We
know your horse and wagon. We live in Paterson.
Ha ha!
                                        —H. K. & Co.
```

I read it and pushed it to the middle of the table. We all looked at Deputy Morris, who happened to be on duty the afternoon it arrived. When he didn't say anything, each of us spoke at once.

"Well," I said. "This time we'll catch him."

"A thousand dollars!" Fleurette said. "Is that what I'm worth?"

"Stop that," Norma said. "And we won't pay it."

The deputy reacted to our chorus of voices by standing up and announcing, "This is a matter for Sheriff Heath to decide. You ladies go about your business. He'll be here soon enough."

But a storm came on that night, pushing hail and freezing rain across the fields in waves. Every time we thought it had let up, another icy draft blew through. The weather must have delayed the sheriff, and there was nothing to do but wait. The deputies had been on duty for over twelve hours. I finally convinced them to come in for a bowl of soup and a hot bun. Ordinarily it was forbidden for them to dine with us, but these men had expected to be home for supper and weren't. They had to have something.

Around ten Norma and Fleurette gave up and went to bed. I stayed up and walked the dark house for another hour until at last I heard the tires of Sheriff Heath's automobile in our gravel drive.

His deputies ran out to tell him about the letter, and soon he was standing in the parlor with four of his men around him, the two that were going off duty and the two that were starting the night shift. The room was filled with the smell of wet wool and smoke from the camp stove in our barn. Sheriff Heath took a seat on the divan, placed his hat on his knees, and read the letter to himself. When he was finished, he looked up at me, searching my face for something, then read it again.

"Take a walk around back," he told his men. "Carry a lamp and check the bushes and the outbuildings. Then wait for me in the barn."

When they were gone, he said, "Sit down. I have something to ask you."

"What is it?"

"Just—sit."

I dropped down next to him and waited. He rubbed his eyes and held his forehead in his hands, breathing so quietly that I thought he had fallen asleep right in front of me. At last he pulled his hands away and turned to look at me, his eyes watery and red.

He swallowed hard. "Miss Kopp. I've tried everything in my power to stop this man. I've followed him around town, I've watched his house, I've spoken to his sister and his business associates, and, for that matter, I've spoken to him. I've tried to build a case for the prosecutor but they fight me on it. They've never charged a factory owner with any kind of crime and they're not inclined to start now. The Kaufmans are a powerful family. They own mills in three states. They can get all the silk men behind them."

He waited to make sure I understood. I nodded, and he continued.

"I've also devoted more deputies to your protection than the sheriff's office can readily afford. The Freeholders fight with me over every invoice I submit to them. They make it nearly impossible for me to get my men paid. So far I've been able to hide the expense, but if they find out how much they are spending on this one case, I'll be held to account."

"I'm so sorry," I said. "I didn't realize—"

He held up his hand to silence me. "That's not your concern. What does concern you is the fact that we need to bring this matter to a resolution quickly. We cannot spend the rest of the winter lying in wait."

Once again he paused and waited for my agreement. I nodded and he went on.

"This letter gives us an opportunity. I would like you to go to Paterson on Saturday night as the letter instructs. You will carry your revolver and I will post men all around you. We will make sure nothing happens to you. But we must try to catch this girl in black or whoever might be with her."

"Of course," I blurted out. "We have to. I can do it. I've become quite practiced with the revolver." I might have sounded a little too eager to get a shot at Henry Kaufman. The sheriff looked over at me worriedly and seemed to take a minute to make up his mind.

"All right. That's fine," he said at last. "But that's not all I want you to do."

What else could there be? I squared my shoulders and waited.

"I think we should go to the papers," he said.

"The papers? Do you mean that we should let them write about us?" Norma would not like this idea. Other people's troubles belonged in the paper for the world to read about, not ours.

"Yes. I want to let them write a story about your vigil on the street corner. You will give them a full account of what has happened, going all the way back to July. Let them report on the events of Saturday night, whatever they may be, and run their stories in the papers on Monday."

"But why would you want reporters meddling in this?"

He leaned back and rested his head against the divan. "It

will force the prosecutor to take notice," he said, his voice a little hoarse. "The Freeholders don't like to see unsolved crimes in the paper. They complain about the bills from the prosecutor's office as much as they complain about mine. They want to see that they are getting their money's worth. If the papers run this story, the prosecutor will be made to answer for his lack of action." He looked over at me. "What do you think, Miss Kopp?"

I could feel my face flush. "We've always been a very private family."

"I know. You stay out here on this country road, with acres between you and the nearest neighbor. None of you seem to belong to any social clubs. I've never seen you entertain friends or school chums or gentlemen. For whatever reason, the three of you have made up your mind to stay out of sight. I know this won't be easy for you. But I think the only way to bring these men to trial is to begin with a trial in the papers, as distasteful as that is."

The decision was mine to make, really. Norma would be opposed to it, Fleurette would beg to sit for an interview, and it would be up to me to cast the deciding vote.

"Don't you think that drawing attention to him in the papers will only provoke him?"

"I don't think Henry Kaufman could be more provoked than he is right now." Sheriff Heath pulled out his watch. "It's almost midnight. Get some sleep. You can tell me in the morning."

I nodded and he rose to leave. In spite of his fatigue, he always stood very straight. He walked stiffly to the door and then he was gone, leaving me alone in the dark with my decision.

❦ 35 ❧

FLEURETTE NEVER ASKED why she was schooled at home. There were no other children on Sicomac Road, and it might not have occurred to her that there was a school in town she could have attended. She simply accepted the idea that little girls do lessons under the supervision of their families. She didn't know that Mother insisted on keeping her hidden, that Mother's fear of scandal and her mistrust of paperwork and government and organizations of any kind made it impossible for her to consider sending Fleurette out of the house.

We used to argue that the school would not question a woman in her late forties with a young daughter, but Mother was convinced that someone would put the puzzle together. Although we had adoption papers, which should have made these matters easier, we had never told Fleurette that she was adopted, so the papers did us no good. This left us in a difficult position. It seemed easier—at least in Mother's mind—not to discuss it at all and to just keep the child on the farm.

To explain Fleurette's birth to the family, my uncles were given the impression that our father had returned briefly to our lives and then left again. Fleurette must have had the same general idea, although we almost never spoke of our father.

Nothing about the situation seemed odd to her, until one day when she was about nine and had been told to read aloud from a book of pioneer stories for children. She was reading about Daniel Boone. None of us were paying much attention, as the sound of Fleurette reading her lessons aloud was such a familiar part of our day that we only pretended to listen as we went about our work.

I was balancing our ledger books and had my back to Fleurette as she read, "'At last they turned to go home, when suddenly two fierce-looking Indians sprang out of the woods and seized the boat.'" I looked over at Mother, alarmed, but she was intent on her needlepoint and didn't seem to hear. Mother thought nothing of letting children read the most terrifying tales of ogres and witches and adventures gone terribly wrong. It was one of our points of disagreement about Fleurette's upbringing.

"'Betsey fought with her own oar,'" Fleurette was saying, "'but it did no good: the Indians carried them off through the woods.'"

I put down my pencil and made ready to say something. Fleurette was a sensitive and imaginative child. She'd be up half the night after a story like this.

"'Betsey reached up and broke the bushes as she passed along. She knew that her father would look for her, and she hoped that he might follow her by seeing the broken bushes.'"

That was enough. "Mother, don't you think—"

Mother looked up, but before I could finish, Fleurette had closed her book and was standing in front of her. "Where is our father, *maman*?"

"What have you been reading?" she said, fumbling with her needlepoint.

"Pioneer stories," I said. "I was about to say that they're too much for a little girl."

"Don't we have a father?" Fleurette said, climbing into Mother's lap. "Doesn't Francis have a father?"

Mother pushed her back to the floor and smoothed her skirt. "Of course," she said. "Everyone has a father."

"Where is he?"

Mother looked at me for help. But she was the one who refused to speak of our father, and who seemed determined to make sure that he never heard about Fleurette and never knew where we lived.

"I'm afraid he's . . ."

I shook my head. It seemed unfair to Frank Kopp to say that he was dead. She'd called herself a widow before, but never in front of Fleurette. Besides, the man could appear at our front door someday, and what a shock that would be!

"Gone?" Fleurette said. "Gone to fight the Indians?"

Mother smiled and patted her hand. "That's right, *chéri*. He's very brave."

I couldn't believe how easily she lied to the child. Then again, what else would she have said?

"Is he coming back?"

"I'm afraid not. He's gone very far."

IN SOME WAYS, we all raised Fleurette. She was a wild and unpredictable child who was as happy stomping through the creek in search of frogs as she was in a dancing frock on a make-believe stage. It required the attention of all three of us—and Francis, before he married—just to keep her working at her lessons and her chores. As she got older, Mother couldn't match Fleurette's energy and abdicated more and more of the responsibility for bringing her up to me and Norma.

But for the first ten or twelve years of the girl's life, I stood by and watched my mother raise her. When she had a fever, Mother took care of her. On her birthday, Mother planned the party. And if she skinned her knee or got chased by one of the roosters, it was Mother she ran to with her tears.

It was never me. Fleurette never needed a thing from me—until now. I would stand on the corner with a gun all night if that's what it took to keep those men away from her.

❧ 36 ❧

"MISS KOPP, is it your assertion that the attack was entirely unprovoked?"

I sat at a table placed in Sheriff Heath's office for my use. He had wanted the reporters to come to the courthouse so he could parade them right past the prosecutor's office. But every room at the courthouse was occupied. The reporters milled around in the hall until the sheriff was satisfied that they'd attracted enough attention, and then he walked them across the lawn to the prison.

After a brief introduction from Sheriff Heath, I told my story in as straightforward a manner as possible. Every small newspaper in Passaic and Bergen County had sent a reporter. Many of the larger papers had news bureaus nearby, so reporters from New York, Philadelphia, Newark, and Trenton papers were present too.

The men sat quietly and scribbled notes as I gave a short and carefully rehearsed account of the events. But as soon as I finished, they unleashed a volley of questions that I was entirely unprepared to answer.

"Miss, had you ever fired a gun before Sheriff Heath gave you lessons?"

"How do three girls manage the running of a household on their own? Is there not an uncle or some other male relation who could take you in?"

"Haven't any of you received a proposal of marriage in all these years?"

I looked to Sheriff Heath for help. He'd been reclining in a chair behind his own desk, appearing entirely relaxed, as if he spent every afternoon being questioned by twenty reporters. But when I caught his eye, he jumped to his feet and took over.

"The Kopp sisters do just fine on their own," he said. "They live in the countryside and already knew how to handle a hunting rifle, and have proven quite competent with a revolver. And of course the attack was unprovoked, Simon. How would three girls in a buggy incite an oncoming automobile to plow directly into them?"

A rumble of laughter went through the room, then it fell silent as the reporters scribbled in their notebooks.

"I believe that answers your questions," Sheriff Heath said, returning to his seat.

A brawny Italian man in the back of the room said, "No, sir, I didn't get an answer to my question about marriage proposals."

I jumped up before Sheriff Heath could. These reporters needed to see that I could speak for myself. "The presence or absence of suitors in the lives of the Kopp sisters has no bearing on this matter," I told them, "and I see no men here today who would stand a chance with any one of us."

That got loud, appreciative guffaws from the men and a grin from the sheriff.

The questions lasted only a few more minutes, and then Sheriff Heath briefed the reporters on his role in the investigation and the lack of cooperation from the prosecutor's office. He gave them the particulars about the meeting with the woman in black planned for the following night, and distributed handwritten copies of the threatening letter so that they could reproduce it in full in their papers. He had arranged for any reporters who wished to be present on Saturday night to assemble in a garage on Broadway just a few blocks away from the meeting place. They were warned to arrive early and remain hidden until released by the sheriff or one of his deputies.

Every man in the room seemed eager to go along. There was a current of excitement in the air. It was the anticipation of a pack of hunting dogs waiting to be turned loose on their prey, or the nervous excitement of a posse rounded up in the night to go after a horse thief. Even I felt it.

But as soon as the reporters left, Sheriff Heath turned somber again. "This is only a game to them," he said. "I'll need to station a deputy at the garage to keep them from rushing out and bungling the whole operation." He stood to open the door for me. "But that's not your concern. Get some rest and be ready for tomorrow. Dress warmly and wear sturdy shoes. Bring a handbag for your weapon. I'll call for you at seven."

He'd polished his badge and put on a fresh collar. When I stood at the door, I could smell the dry, chalky laundry starch his wife used. "Thank you for coming to my aid. With the reporters, I mean. I'm not used to being interrogated like that."

He gave me the briefest of smiles and then said, "You did just fine, Miss Kopp. You gave it right back to them. They just wanted to see if you can handle yourself, and you can."

❧ 37 ☙

"SHOULDN'T I BE THE ONE to meet the girl and give her the money?" Fleurette said.

"No one is giving anyone money," I answered. "We are not about to take their demands seriously. The only item of value I'll be carrying is a revolver."

I was sitting on Fleurette's bed, watching her search her wardrobe for the proper ensemble in which to rendezvous with a blackmailer. She produced a cape with a fur collar and red velvet lining, and a hat that had a hidden pocket in the band.

"That cape would look ridiculous on me," I said, "and, besides, the sheriff wants me in dark, sensible clothes. It's going to be freezing tonight, and who knows how long I'll be standing out there."

Fleurette wrapped the cape around her own shoulders. I had to admit that it suited her. She looked like a woman of mystery, someone who might carry a thousand dollars to a lady in black and live to tell about it. She fixed her bright and lively eyes on me.

"Would you shoot her?" she asked.

"Who?"

"The girl in black. The one who's coming to collect the money. Would you fire at her?"

"No! I'm not going to shoot a girl who's been roped into this mess. Besides, the sheriff and his deputies will be all around me. All I have to do is stand in a conspicuous location and wait."

Fleurette twirled around and the cape flew about like a wild bird coming to land on her shoulders. "I would do a much better job of standing in a conspicuous location," she said.

I smiled. "I know you would."

Norma walked in, eyeing the frivolous garments Fleurette had thrown on the bed.

"You aren't wearing any of that," she said.

"Of course not," I said.

"I don't see why we bother employing deputies if the women of this community have to go out and catch their own criminals."

"They can't do this without me. You know that."

Norma frowned and crossed the room to look through a pile of handbags that Fleurette had tossed on a chair. She discarded a fringed teardrop-shaped bag of yellow silk, a beaded purse made to look like a butterfly, and a velvet pouch meant to hold binoculars at the theater. "These won't do for carrying a revolver," she said. "You'd get all tangled up in these frills if you needed to fire it."

"I won't need to fire it. Why are you two so convinced that I'm going out to gun down an innocent girl tonight?"

Norma looked at me sorrowfully, as if it pained her to see how little I understood about my own situation.

"He wouldn't have you carry it if he didn't think you might need it."

I'D BEEN PACING THE HOUSE for an hour by the time I heard the sheriff's tires in the drive. There were two deputies riding along, and two more would stay with Norma and Fleurette. Before he let me in the car, Sheriff Heath asked to have a look at my shoes to make sure I could run in them. I lifted my skirt and he looked down, then gave me a half-smile when he saw that I was wearing the boots I usually wear to muck out the barn.

"Good girl," he said quietly.

He reached for my handbag—a sensible leather traveling bag we'd found in Mother's closet—and inspected its contents. It was empty save for the revolver, which he pulled out and checked for bullets.

"You have nothing else of value? No jewelry around your neck or combs in your hair? No money tucked away?"

He was standing so close to me that I thought he might start rifling through my coat pockets.

"Nothing at all."

We gave each other a level stare. I had the feeling he was sizing me up one last time.

"All right," he said. "Then let's go."

No one said a word on the drive to Paterson. We parked at City Hall, several blocks away from the meeting place. We disembarked and I stood shivering in the garage, looking around at the ghostly old timbers and wondering what these walls had seen over the years. Had they ever watched anyone do what I was about to do?

"We can't get too close without attracting attention," Sheriff Heath explained. "You'll walk from here."

"From here!" Never in my life had I walked down a city street at night unaccompanied. But I regretted saying it. Sheriff Heath looked worried suddenly, as if he just realized he'd made a mistake in asking me to do this.

"I'll be fine," I said quickly.

He shook his head. "No. You're right. Someone should be with you. Here's what I'll do. I'll send my men with you, but they'll each walk one block over. Morris will stay a block to the east, on Fair, and English will walk a block to the west on Van Houten. I've got a deputy stationed on Auburn in front of the garage where the reporters are. He knows to watch out for you. You'll pass him on the way, but you'll walk on the opposite side of the street, and you won't look at him or signal to him unless you're in trouble."

I agreed to that and the three of us set out for Broadway. Deputy Morris went first and cut to the left, which would take him down a narrow street occupied mostly by cobblers and tailors and other such shops whose doors had closed hours ago. Deputy English waited a few minutes and then followed him, cutting over to the right to walk down a street populated with small churches and a girls' school. When Sheriff Heath gave me the nod, I left too, but he called after me in a whisper.

"Miss Kopp!"

I turned around. He was standing by himself in the entrance to the garage, his hands stuffed in his overcoat.

"You won't know where I am tonight. You won't be able to see me. But I'll be watching every minute. I won't take my eyes off you."

I swallowed the mixture of dread and apprehension well-ing up inside of me, then nodded and set off for Broadway.

The streets were dark, but not entirely empty. Four young couples went running past me, laughing and calling out to one another, maybe on their way to a dance. A few workmen walked silently along, the ends of their cigarettes glowing and bobbing like fireflies.

Paterson's downtown ended just past Straight Street, giv-ing way to three-story apartment buildings meant mostly for people who worked in the shops. Each one had an identical patch of grass in the front and a little flower bed that held ge-raniums in the summer and mounds of dirty snow in the win-ter. Smoke rose from the chimneys, and sometimes I could catch the smell of someone's dinner: a pork chop in a pan, onions and sausage stewing over a burner.

Sheriff Heath's men stayed just ahead of me. Every time I reached an intersection, I caught a glimpse of them cross-ing the same street one block away. As I approached Auburn, the deputy stationed there ducked into a doorway's shadows. I was careful not to look directly at him, and I made a point of not looking up at any of the windows around him to see if the reporters were watching me.

I arrived at Broadway and Carroll sooner than I'd expected and stood for a few minutes on each corner, studying the lay-out of the streets and the walkways, looking for an escape route, or a place to hide, should I require one.

On one corner stood a nondescript brick building that might have housed small offices. There were very few win-dows facing the street, and no lights in any of them. Across the street was a flower shop, also dark and shuttered. The corner opposite was a vacant lot, which was mowed and cleared, but strangely frightening to me for its emptiness. A vision came to me of a girl in black standing in the middle of the lot, her arms reaching out for the money she'd been promised, the dry stubble of last summer's grass and what remained of the snow all around her. It made me shiver to think about it.

I crossed the street to stand in front of a dilapidated wooden building that might have once been used as a workshop for a furniture maker or a blacksmith. It occurred to me that Sheriff Heath must have been hidden away somewhere, perhaps behind one of the building's boarded windows.

It had to be eight o'clock by now. There was no sign of a girl in black. In fact, no one had passed me on the street, and only two automobiles had driven by. I wondered what Norma and Fleurette were doing at home. Were they thinking of me this very minute? I tried to picture them, moving from window to window, watching for signs of trouble.

I'd been clutching the handbag under my arm for so long that I'd forgotten it was there. I reached in to make sure the revolver was aimed out in front of me. Just then I heard a loud bang that made me jump and nearly drop the bag. Down the street I could see one of the deputies leap out into the intersection to check on me.

It must have been a motor misfiring. I stepped out into a pool of light cast by the moon's reflection so that whoever was watching could see me.

A figure came striding up Carroll Street. In the darkness I couldn't tell if it was a man or a woman. Finally I made out the shape of a long skirt and a broad-brimmed hat.

Was that her? I couldn't tell if she was wearing black. Everything was black.

I shifted my handbag so I could feel the butt of the revolver through the leather. In spite of the cold, I was hot under my collar. A trickle of sweat ran down my chest, and another followed the same course along my spine.

As she got closer, she slowed down. Had she seen me?

I took a quick look around to make sure no one else was approaching. Several blocks away I saw two men cross the street. Somewhere a motor rattled and stalled. I noticed all the sounds I hadn't heard before: the guard dogs barking from behind the mills down on the river, the basement vents releasing hissing steam from the boilers, the distant wail of a baby who could not be comforted.

The girl got within a block of me and turned down Van Houten. She must have walked right past Deputy English. Was I expected to follow her? She'd given me no indication that I should, so I stayed at my post. Another automobile rolled by a few blocks away. There was the sound of a train whistle, then the ragged cough of a phlegmatic old man.

Finally a trio of men approached from the garage on Auburn. I recognized Sheriff Heath from the outline of his hat and his overcoat. I could also make out the figure of Deputy Morris and one of the reporters I'd met yesterday.

When they reached me, Sheriff Heath said in a low voice, "It's nine o'clock. We've waited long enough. Either they're not coming, or they spotted us and ran off."

"What about that girl on Carroll?" I asked.

He shook his head. "That wasn't her. English followed her home and talked to her. She didn't know anything about it."

I hadn't realized that I'd been holding my breath. I let it out at last. Sheriff Heath reached over and took the revolver from my handbag. "Let me carry this," he said. "You've done your job."

On the way back to the garage, he introduced me to the reporter, a man named George Pieters who worked for the Paterson paper. "George is a good friend of mine," Sheriff Heath said. "You can count on him to get the story right. I told him he could ride along with us and ask some questions on the way. You tell him whatever he wants to know. Tomorrow a bunch of them are going to come out to the house to get their interviews. They all wanted to talk to you tonight, but I told them to let you get some rest. Nobody's filing a story until tomorrow night anyway."

On the way home, the reporter asked me to explain again, in my own words, how this mess got started and what we'd done to try to stop it. He wanted to know what our house looked like when we returned home from the beach and found it in a state of preparation for a bonfire, and how I'd learned to handle a gun, and what would make a woman take the unusual step of arming herself with a revolver to protect her sisters from harm.

I looked out the window at the black night and the dim outlines of dairy barns and trees in the distance.

"My sisters and I have no one but each other," I said at last, "and if anyone should take up a handgun in their defense, I will be the one to do it."

⚜ 38 ⚜

THE PAPER WAS FOLDED on the kitchen table when I got up Monday morning. I lifted it up and saw an empty square where the headline should have been. The missing headline was returned by pigeon post a few hours later and I pasted it back in place.

GIRL WAITS WITH GUN
Miss Kopp, Annoyed for Months,
Goes to Place Named in Letter—
Home Guarded at Night

MISS CONSTANCE KOPP, who spent a large part of Saturday night under police guard waiting for the writer of Black Hand letters to appear to claim $1000 that had been demanded, said today that threatening letters were the least of the troubles that have placed the home of herself and her sisters in a virtual state of siege.

For weeks the house has been guarded night and day by armed men, but despite this the women on the place have been shot at by unknown prowlers whom Miss Kopp says come to the place in an automobile.

"One evening just after dusk I happened to look out of my bedroom window and saw a man standing near a tree not 50 feet from the house," said Constance Kopp. "He was on our property and I asked him what he wanted. There was no response, so I fired a shot through the window screen. Immediately he fired several shots back at me and I fainted from fright.

"On another occasion when Florette had gone down to the stream that runs through our land to get a pail of water, a man who was hiding in the brush nearby fired two shots at her.

"And yet, one, at least, of the County officials pooh-poohed our stories and refused to credit them.

"Why, these desperate but cowardly individuals even broke into our home one afternoon during our absence and piled up our best furniture in one room.

"None of us dare to go away from the house after dark without our revolvers, and we have a dandy magazine gun that we would love to turn loose on one of the skulking night prowlers, for that's all they are."

In response to the Black Hand letter sent to her home, Miss Kopp waited at the corner in Paterson until nine o'clock on a Saturday night but no girl dressed in black approached seeking $1000. Miss Kopp then left for her home. She had a revolver concealed in her muff and was ready to use it.

Sheriff Heath and some of his deputies patrolled the neighborhood of Broadway and Carroll Street in an automobile for an hour, closely watching Miss Kopp and all women dressed in black who passed this corner.

The Misses Kopp are attractive young women. The family is well to do. The authorities have granted the young women permission to carry revolvers.

"If we ever catch a strange man sneaking around our house after dark we will use the revolvers," said Miss Constance Kopp.

"YOU'VE NEVER FAINTED IN YOUR LIFE," Fleurette said, slapping the paper down on her sewing table. "And I'm going to write in and tell them how to spell my name."

Accounts of our ordeal ran in the *New York Tribune*, the *Sun*, the *New York Herald*, the *Philadelphia Evening Ledger*, and all the New Jersey papers. They got quite a bit wrong. One claimed that I stood on a street corner in Newark, several misspelled Fleurette's name, and all of them appended my quotes with more fanciful language. "Oh, for a Chance to Shoot at the Nasty Prowlers!" read one headline, which sent Fleurette into a fit of giggles.

"The papers have made a joke of our situation, which I knew they would do," Norma said. "I wish you would have told me you were thinking of speaking to them so I could have told you not to."

"You don't suppose Constance kept it from you intentionally, do you?" Fleurette asked, a look of mock surprise in her eyes.

Norma stirred her coffee to cool it and held the paper up again, tucking her chin down in a way that pushed the smallest roll of fat out from under her neck. It was a gesture of double-chinned disapproval that old ladies employed to great effect. I sometimes thought that Norma could not wait to reach a very elderly age and make full use of the gravity that one acquires later in life.

"There will, of course, be terrible consequences for exposing us in this manner," she said, "and I can hardly imagine what Francis will say, or poor Bessie, who has been nothing but kind to us and will have quite a shock today when she reads her paper."

"I'm surprised we haven't seen Francis already this morning," Fleurette said. "He must be saving it for Thanksgiving."

I had taken quite a chill on Saturday night and sat sniveling under an afghan reading the other papers while Fleurette let down the hem on a dress she'd outgrown. Norma finished her coffee and laced up her boots to take another batch of pigeons out for a ride. It was bitingly cold out, but the sun was shining and the roads were clear. Dolley had hardly left the barn in the last few weeks, and Norma had decided that both the horse and the pigeons needed some fresh air.

"Are you going to be well enough to travel on Thursday?" Fleurette asked as she snipped at the threads on her dress. "Because if you aren't, we're leaving you here with your own guard. I am not missing Thanksgiving."

"I'll be fine," I said, "and I certainly hope the deputies will get the day off."

"Oh, no, I'd like to bring a pair of them to dinner. Can you imagine Francis's face if we brought a police escort?"

IN FACT, Sheriff Heath was not at all willing to leave us unguarded on Thanksgiving. "I'll bet Kaufman and his gang won't take a holiday," he grumbled when he stopped by on Tuesday to deliver another deputy to our barn. We were taking our customary walk around the property. "They'll drink whiskey all day and drive around all night making a mess for my men to clean up. The holidays are the worst days of the year for us."

The wind picked up and lifted my hat. I pushed it back down over my ears.

"You shouldn't even be out in this cold," he said.

"I'm fine. I just caught a little chill. But surely your men want a day to spend with their families."

We passed the barn, where Deputy English was watching the chickens peck at the frozen stubble in their yard. He touched his hat and nodded.

"Oh, I'll give them the day off," the sheriff said. "But they'll be called in if there's a shooting or robbery, which I guarantee will happen before sundown. I'll be the one on patrol on Thursday."

"What will Mrs. Heath say to that?"

"Mrs. Heath—" He stopped and looked at me, that curious searching look that I couldn't decipher. There was something sorrowful about him all at once, but as soon as it came over him it went away again.

"Mrs. Heath is married to the Sheriff of Bergen County," he said briskly, "and she knows the sacrifice required."

❧ 39 ❧

I AWOKE ON THANKSGIVING MORNING to a world frozen in place. A northern storm had blown through the day before, leaving behind an unusually cold, clear sky. Every window in the house was entombed under a plate of ice. Icicles hung like daggers from the roof. There was no hope of moving the water pump, and none of us wanted to brave the frozen meadow to see if there was still water flowing in the creek. We broke icicles off the porch and melted them in the kitchen so we could wash up before we left for Francis and Bessie's. There were two jars of plum preserves left in the pantry and a nice package of salted pork from our neighbor, so we wrapped those in a tea towel and brought them along.

Sheriff Heath arrived just as we were getting ready to leave. "I wish you'd let me drive you," he said. Norma just grunted and pushed past him to harness Dolley.

"We're afraid of what Francis might think," Fleurette said.

"We are not afraid of Francis," I said. "We'll be fine. The crooks don't come out until tonight, right?"

The sheriff watched as Fleurette went to join Norma in the barn. She wore a stylish dress of reseda-green silk, gathered a little more tightly at the waist than I would have allowed had I any idea what she'd been working on.

"That girl has grown up in the time I've known her," he said.

I sighed and shook my head. "And I'm afraid the kidnapping threats have only gone to her head. She thinks she's quite the desirable little prize. I don't know what we're going to do with her."

"Keep her on the farm as long as you can," he said.

"I don't know how much longer that will be. But for today—"

"Today you should ride alongside her and keep an eye on the road. Pull down the storm curtains so no one can see you. Are you taking your revolver?"

"I am. But you don't think I'll need it?"

"I hope not."

Norma and Fleurette rode around front in the carriage. Dolley stamped at the ice and great clouds of steam came from her nostrils. I climbed up and squeezed in next to Fleurette.

"I'll drive past your brother's house a few times later today," the sheriff shouted as we turned to ride away.

I nodded and watched as he strode to the barn, a small figure in a gray and empty landscape.

FRANCIS AND BESSIE lived in a neighborhood of modest but thoroughly modern bungalows in Hawthorne. The homes were snugly built and outfitted with good plumbing and gas and new electrical wires. Each home sat next to a driveway and a garage built more for automobiles than carriages, although as we drove down the street, I saw that a few people still kept a horse stabled.

They were the first to occupy their home. After they moved in, the smell of sawdust and varnish hung about them for months. At Bessie's urging, Francis painted the house a cheerful cornflower blue and installed window boxes that sported primroses or geraniums, depending on the season. Every room blazed with electric lamps, even the children's room, and all the furniture came from Rafner's on Grand Street. Mother had been shocked to walk into their house for the first time and see that they had purchased a complete living room set, exactly as advertised in the newspaper. She'd been even more shocked when Norma pointed out that it had been listed for $195, with a charge account that offered a year to pay.

They purchased the walnut dining room set as well, which came with a china cabinet, a velvet seamless rug, and a buffet mirror. "I suppose I don't have to go down the hall to see that you bought the bedroom outfit, too," Mother had sniffed, "when we have a farmhouse full of furniture you could have taken."

But Francis and Bessie didn't want the furniture from the farmhouse, and for that I couldn't blame them. Their house was entirely new and, as Francis liked to say, "free of defects," by which he meant that it was free of gas leaks and drafts and the dark, hulking cabinets and monstrous carved chairs that represented our mother's Austrian girlhood. Theirs was an American house, a house of the twentieth century, and her old things had no place there.

Francis met us outside, unhitched Dolley, and walked her around back where she could get some water. The three of us stood on the front lawn, feeling too uncivilized to go inside. Had we really been sleeping with revolvers at our bedsides and shooting at strange men in the dark? Were we really in so much danger that the sheriff himself had to follow us around? It didn't seem like we belonged in Francis's cheerful cottage, this tidy place giving off warmth and light and the rich fragrance of Thanksgiving dinner.

The children spotted us and ran outside. The boy—whom we called Frankie to distinguish him from his father, Francis, and his grandfather, Frank—ran straight into Norma and almost knocked her over. The two of them shared a love of animals understood by no one else in the family. He led her indoors to ask her opinion about a nest of baby mice he'd uncovered in the garden. Lorraine, the older of the two, wore a dress she'd helped her mother make, and she and Fleurette fell into a conversation about collars and hemlines.

That left me on the porch by myself, taking a deep breath before I followed them inside and subjected myself to my brother's harangue.

Fortunately, it was Bessie who got to me first. She ran to me before I'd even closed the door and reached up to wrap her arms around my neck. We'd always had an unexpected sort of kinship. She was kind and infinitely patient with my brother, and she ran a good household and raised two well-behaved children. For that I admired her even if I didn't want to live the same kind of life she did. And in turn, for reasons I couldn't fathom, she treated me as if I led an adventurous and exciting life out in Wyckoff, worthy of envy and approbation.

"I'm glad to see you in one piece," she said, almost in a

whisper. "You gave us both a terrible scare. We didn't tell the children."

"Of course not," I said. "I'm sorry that you had to read it in the paper. That was thoughtless of us."

She stood back and smiled up at me, gripping my arms by the shoulders, and then leaned in again. "I've forbidden any talk of the newspapers in this house until after dinner."

Then she turned to lead me to the kitchen, adding in a low voice, "I only wish I could've taken a revolver and stood out there with you on Saturday night."

I laughed, imagining Bessie with a hand mixer in one hand and a gun in the other. "Come with me next time."

Bessie was rolling out dough on the drain board for another of what Francis called her "illustrious pies." For the next hour we worked side by side, talking of little other than the children and the weather and Bessie's volunteer work at the library. I marveled at how good it felt to be in a warm, well-appointed kitchen, enjoying such easygoing company. Maybe my life had been too rough lately. I was more relaxed in that kitchen than I had been in months.

"If you enjoy this so much, Constance, you can take over the cooking at Christmas," she said, grinning at me. "But you'll have to wait until next year. We're going to my aunt's in Boston this year. Why don't you all come with us?"

"It's too hard to leave the farm in the winter," I said. "We'll be fine on our own."

We ate our dinner in peace, with Bessie, Fleurette, and the children keeping up most of the conversation while Francis carved the birds and I passed the platters. It was a traditional Kopp family meal. Mother never did develop a taste for turkey, preferring a roasted goose or duck at the holidays. In keeping with her tradition, Bessie found a fine, fat duck and roasted a chicken as well. There were green beans and corn that she had canned last summer, pickled onions, and dinner rolls that exhaled steam when we broke them apart. The rolls were made according to a recipe of Mother's that no one other than Bessie had ever mastered. Little chips of butter, as cold as ice, had to be cut into the dough at the last possible minute, and no one else seemed to have a knack for it.

After dinner Norma and Fleurette stood to clear the table, and Francis and I stepped out on the back porch, where we could see Dolley nibbling at patches of thawed grass in the lawn. She pawed at the ground and slapped her tail around the way a person might hop up and down to keep warm.

Francis closed the door behind us and said, "I wasn't expecting to read about my sisters in the paper."

"Which paper?"

"There was more than one?" He groaned, his breath like smoke in the air.

"We made the news in New York and Philadelphia."

"No," he said sharply. "I didn't know about that."

For a minute we stood side by side in silence and let the sounds from inside the house settle in around us—the rattle of china and silver, the rush of water into a pan, the children's footsteps through every room. Francis lit his pipe and the sweet tobacco smoke drifted over to me.

I wasn't about to apologize or offer up any sort of explanation. I waited for him to say his piece.

"I didn't know you had armed men guarding the house. Most of those things in the paper—you never told me about any of that."

"I know. I should have. But what would you have done?

Bring us all here to live? What if Kaufman and his gang had followed us over here?"

He leaned on his porch railing. "Well, I should have done more. You're my responsibility."

"We are responsible for ourselves."

"And look at what a fine job you've done. What if those men at the creek had shot Fleurette?"

"But they didn't."

The door opened behind us. It was little Lorraine, sent by Bessie to ask us if we wanted coffee. We told her yes.

When she was gone, he said, "I knew it was a bad idea to leave you girls out there by yourselves. It's time to sell the farm."

I stared at him. "What do you mean? Mother meant it for us!"

"But you girls won't last out there much longer," he said. "I've been down to the bank and had a look at your account."

"You did what?" I shouted.

"Shhhhh," he said. "Listen to me. You can't keep selling off plots of land to pay the bills. What are you going to do? Mother didn't leave enough to support three girls for the rest of their lives. Within a year you're going to need some other income. And unless one of you has a husband in the wings I'm not aware of . . ."

"A husband? Now you're trying to pawn us off on a husband?"

He laughed. "I've never heard marriage described that way."

I leaned back and looked out into the approaching darkness. "Can't this wait? They're about to arrest him, and then we can put all this behind us. We'll sit down and figure something out."

Francis tilted his head and looked over at me, considering it. "All right. After Christmas. But no later than spring. That's a good time to sell a farm. It's the best thing for you. You'll see."

We sat together in uneasy silence. I heard the rattle of an automobile in the street and wondered if it was the sheriff. I didn't dare lean around the porch to look.

⇥ 40 ⇥

ARREST IN BLACK HAND LETTERS CASE
Harry Kaufman, Silk Dyer, of Paterson,
Indicted By Federal Grand Jury
for Threatening the
Misses Constance and Florette Kopp, of Wyckoff.

Dec. 3 — HARRY KAUFMAN, conducting a silk dyeing establishment in Paterson, is under arrest on a Federal indictment found in Newark, charging him with improper use of the mails. He was released subject to bail posted by his sister, Mrs. Marion Garfinkel of Pittsburgh.

Detective Francis A. Butler, who investigated the case upon receiving the sensational story of Miss Constance Kopp, of Wyckoff, made the arrest, and the indictment was the outcome of his inquiry.

The *Evening Record* last week told of the lively experiences of the Misses Kopp, all of which followed their encounter with Kaufman in Paterson nearly six months ago, when his auto crashed into their buggy. Kaufman refused to pay $50 for the damage done, and the suit was instituted.

Constance Kopp says anonymous letters began to arrive, threatening all sorts of disaster if they continued the suit against Kaufman. Armed men began to prowl around the house after dark, and shots were fired to terrorize the family and even at members of the family.

County Detectives Blauvelt and Courter, Prosecutor Wright, Assistant Prosecutor Zabriskie, Judge Seufert, and the Franklin Township Committee have all been working on this unusual case and the trial will no doubt prove particularly interesting.

Sheriff Heath has provided an armed guard at the Kopp home for some time past.

"WHO ARE ALL THESE PEOPLE?" I asked, setting down the newspaper and looking up at Sheriff Heath, who stood beaming at me along with Deputy Morris and Deputy English. Fleurette and Norma sat next to me on the divan, reading over my shoulder. Norma reached out with her scissors for the headline, but I batted her hand away. "Detective Blauvelt and Prosecutor Zabriskie and Detective Butler? I've never seen any of those men in my life. And since when has the Franklin Township Committee been involved? I thought they went after horse thieves."

Sheriff Heath grinned and pulled up a chair. "I believe you just learned an important lesson about law enforcement in Bergen County. My men do the hard work of chasing after thieves and shooting at intruders in the middle of the night. Then, as soon as a reporter turns up with a pencil and a notepad, the detectives and prosecutors leap from their desks long enough to make the arrest, serve the indictment, and make sure the papers spell their names right. That's their job, as they see it. We pay no attention to it and go about our business."

"That's no way to win reelection," Norma said. "It's no wonder you're so unpopular in the papers. All anyone ever hears are your complaints about prison conditions."

Sheriff Heath was in high spirits and couldn't be bothered by Norma's opinions. "I speak up for the people under my care," he said. "It's my duty. The voters in Bergen County can make their decision based on my actions, not the words of a reporter who can't spell the name of either the criminal or his victim."

"I'd vote for you," Fleurette said.

He nodded and rose to leave. "You ladies might just get your chance."

He reminded us that Mr. Kaufman would be free until the trial. "He's been warned that if anyone comes near your house, sends you a letter, or threatens you in any way, we will arrest him again and hold him this time. His lawyer is advising him to do as we say, and so is his sister. I don't think you need us patrolling at night anymore. But we'll drive by as often as we can."

We followed the men to the door, and I opened it, letting in a blast of freezing wind. "Thank you, Sheriff. I'm sure we'll be fine. But what about Lucy Blake? Haven't you turned up anything? Hasn't anyone reported her missing?"

"We've made inquiries, but I suspect she's just run off. There's not much we can do about that."

Fleurette clung to my arm and bounced up and down on her toes. "But what about the child?" she said. "We're quite convinced Mr. Kaufman was involved."

"You don't know that," Norma said.

Sheriff Heath pulled his collar around his neck. "He claims not to know a thing about it. I'm sorry, ladies, but we've just got nothing to go on."

Norma said, "I suppose the trial will be postponed until after Christmas?"

"Christmas? Oh, no. The trial won't commence for several months. The courts are terribly behind, and Mr. Kaufman's attorney will do everything he can to delay. He has no chance of winning, so his only hope is to put it off and send his client a nice high bill every month."

"You mean he'll be free for months before he goes to jail?" I said. I couldn't imagine living in a state of uncertainty for that long.

Sheriff Heath looked at his deputies and reached around us to close the door again. In a careful, somber voice, he said, "I beg your forgiveness if I've given you the wrong impression. We don't expect him to be sentenced to any time in prison. He'll get a good steep fine, but I believe his sister will pay it. And if she does, he'll stay out of jail unless he bothers you again. That's how these cases go."

Norma put her hands on her hips, jabbing me with her elbow as she did. "Why on earth wouldn't he go to jail? Are men in this country at liberty to shoot at windows and traipse through houses starting fires with no fear of punishment?"

The sheriff started to answer. "Miss Kopp, I —"

But I cut him off. "Do you mean that you're not ever going to lock him up? He'll just be out there, doing as he pleases?

Forever? And what are we to do?" I looked down at Fleurette and tried to imagine letting her go to town by herself while Henry Kaufman remained free. How would I possibly keep her safe?

"You may feel that we can go about without any sort of protection," I said, "but I don't see how. I intend to keep my revolver, and don't be surprised if I have reason to use it."

The sheriff gave me a long and steady look. "That's fine. Keep the gun."

Was he really leaving this to me? "I'd rather put Henry Kaufman in prison and go back to sleeping through the night," I said.

"Miss Kopp. You're asking for something I can't give you. I'd hold him under my roof for the rest of his days if I could. But the truth is that I can't prove anything except threats and intimidation, misuse of the mail, and a few shots that did nothing more than break a window and scare everybody."

"And that's not enough to put him in jail?"

"He'll pay for what he did. His name will be dragged through the papers. Between the fines and the fees his attorney will charge, this will hit his family in the pocketbook. And he'll go straight to jail if he so much as looks at the three of you ever again. That's the best I can do."

There was nothing else to say. We mumbled our thanks to the men and they pushed the door open and ran against the wind to their automobile.

❧ 41 ❧

THE NEXT FEW WEEKS brought one of the worst ice storms in New Jersey's history. A motor car slid off an icy bridge and tumbled into the Hackensack River, sending a newly married couple to their death. A wagon taking children to a church concert got stuck in a drift of snow, and two of the boys walked five miles to get help. Their feet froze along the way. One of them lost two toes and the other lost three. The schools in Paterson closed and so did the courthouse, because so few people could get to work.

Only the mills kept going, fueled by enormous boilers and the sweat of workers who could not afford to miss a day's pay at Christmas. The sky was perpetually gray above them from the steam and smoke belched into the air at all hours. This was the busiest season, when New York demanded all the ribbon and tassels and brightly colored fabric for party dresses that the mills could produce. Even when every road in Paterson was impassable, one route from the mills to the train station remained open. They didn't miss a single shipment.

The dyers and their helpers suffered more than any other silk worker in the winter. At least the weavers could stay dry. In the unheated dye shops, the steam and drippings from the tubs froze, making the floors slick with ice. Even the workers' clothes, soaked through with dye, would freeze on the way home. That used to be Lucy, running through the icy streets after sundown, her clammy apron stuck to her skin.

If we never found her, what would become of her and her child? Sometimes at night I stood at my window and looked out at the ice on the meadow and the barn roof and thought not just of Henry Kaufman and the torment he'd brought upon us, and Lucy, and who knows how many others, but of all the madness and malfeasance in the world beyond our rutted road. I understood the haunted look Sheriff Heath so often wore. To take a stand against it—to try to save one wronged girl or put one thief or murderer behind bars—would have been like trying to stop a locomotive with a patent leather bridle. I wondered what made the sheriff think he should even try. Most men would leave it to someone else and pursue a more comfortable occupation. But Sheriff Heath sought out his office. He campaigned for it. I understood why Mrs. Heath seemed so unhappy. It could not have been an easy life.

We saw very little of him or his deputies as the year drew to an end. It was too difficult for them to get down our road. We took comfort in the fact that if the sheriff couldn't get to us, neither could any other automobile. Even the milk wagon came only twice a week. The boy driving it seemed lonely, too. He stopped to talk to us every time he went by and always accepted our invitation to come inside and get warm.

Norma and I took up our own sort of patrol, circling our

house and grounds with our revolvers plainly drawn every few hours. We went even in the hail and the snow. It was probably an unnecessary exercise, but we both needed something to do. Life was very dull without the deputies around. We had a resolution of sorts to our case, but not the satisfaction of catching Henry Kaufman in the act of any crime. I did wish he would turn up once more so I could take a shot at him.

Still, we felt freer than we had in months. I read books in bed and slept late. We played cards and took on little projects around the house. Fleurette made a new set of curtains for the kitchen, and I began to scrape off the wallpaper in Mother's bedroom.

Then another letter arrived. The envelope was typed this time, not written out by hand, so I assumed it was a bill. I didn't even open it until I sat down at my desk that night. When I saw the first line I gasped. Norma and Fleurette ran across the room to read it over my shoulder.

December 21, 1914

George Ewing
78 Albion St.
Paterson, NJ

Dear Miss Kopp,

I overheard a deep laid conspiracy to abduct Florette. You have in some way been able to obtain the abhorrence of a dirty gang of Italians. For the time being all is O.K. Tell your girl not to answer any fake wire or phone calls to hospitals or other places. This can be settled,

and you and I and the gang the only ones to know
it. Keep your head. Don't go and publish anything in the newspapers, or it will spoil our
plans.

Write to me at this address if you are in
agreement. Do not send the authorities because
they will not find me. After I get word from you
I will arrange a meeting place.

Remember! We will settle this ourselves.

Sincerely,
George Ewing

"Who is George Ewing?" Norma asked.

I shook my head. "I've never heard of him. And this is the
first typewritten letter we've received. I believe we're dealing
with a new criminal."

Fleurette took the letter and read it again. "Not one of
these crooks can spell my name."

"The less they know about you, the better," I said. "And
this isn't an invitation to a dance, so stop complaining."

"Then what is it?"

"I don't know. I'll talk to Sheriff Heath tomorrow."

"Are we to have deputies in the barn for another year?"

EVERY TIME I closed my eyes that night, I dreamed of Fleurette as a little girl, sitting alone on our parlor floor with a
box of buttons. The room was dark save a lamp that cast a
pool of light across her. A knock came at the door and somehow I knew, in the way one knows things in dreams that one
shouldn't know, that she was being summoned to a hospital.

She jumped up, spilling her buttons across the floor. I tried to call out to her, but my mouth felt like it had been stuffed with cotton and I choked on the words. I reached for her, but my arms were so heavy I couldn't move them. She opened the door and disappeared into an explosion of light, blazing as bright as a house on fire.

I awoke choking and coughing in my dark room, a slick of sweat down my chest. I mopped it up with a sheet and untangled my legs from the covers, the heat pulsing off my skin into the frigid night air. I wanted to go check on Fleurette and Norma in their beds, but before I could move, the nightmares rose up and pulled me down again.

I remember little about the days that followed. A fever had come over me, and it seemed to rest on top of me like an enormous slumbering animal, something wild and menacing and unmoving. In my delirious state I knew that as long as I didn't wake the animal, it wouldn't hurt me. Once or twice Norma came into my room and tried to lift the blankets off to cool my skin. She told me later that I clutched at them and begged her not to disturb it, it being the creature I had imagined. She wasn't feeling well herself and lacked the strength to fight me.

Fleurette was the last to succumb. She had been nursing us both. She cooked the thinnest possible broth, nothing but hot water and salt and a chicken bone. I remember her forcing a spoon between my lips, but it made me cough and sputter, and I pushed her away.

She took to her bed before either of us were up again. There is a day or two that I cannot account for. The whole house was still and dark, the three of us each wrestling against our own fever-creatures.

Mine was the first to break. I awoke one morning with a ferocious appetite. I craved the most outlandish, impossible breakfast: a plate of fresh yellow eggs the likes of which we hadn't seen since the hens stopped laying in November, Mother's light, buttery rolls, the cherry preserves we'd not gotten around to canning last summer, and a sweet warm melon from the garden. My throat was so sore I could hardly swallow, and when I coughed I spat blood in the linen. But in spite of the pain, I would have devoured a meal like that without hesitation.

Instead I wrapped a blanket around my shoulders and made my way downstairs, keeping one shaky hand on the wall. The house must have been entirely unheated since Fleurette had taken to her bed. Even the stair rail was too cold to touch. I reached the kitchen and found that we were down to twigs and bark in the kindling basket, but I lit a fire in the stove anyway.

I found little to eat except tea and toast and the last jar of applesauce. I didn't know toast could taste that good. I thought surely the smell would wake Norma and Fleurette and lure them downstairs, but their appetites had not yet returned. I took them each a cup of tea. Norma was able to sit up and drink a little of it. But Fleurette's fever was working at her furiously. I'd never felt a face as hot as hers. I forced her covers down, but she fought for them just as I had done.

On the way downstairs a wave of dizziness came over me. I sat on the steps to steady myself. I knew I shouldn't be up yet, but I needed to get out to the barn to check on the animals and see if there was anything to eat in our root cellar. I wrapped a coat around my nightgown and pushed my bare feet into the rubber boots I'd left standing in the washing room.

But when I tried the kitchen door it wouldn't move. A drift of snow had blown against the house and frozen there, forming a wedge of ice.

I tried the front door and found it unyielding as well. Only the back door was clear of snow, though it too was frozen shut. I leaned into it and pushed it and kicked it until the stars of the nighttime sky swum around before me. It opened with a great crack and I stood panting in the thin, icy air.

Before I lost my nerve, I marched around the house to the barn. As I'd feared, Dolley and the chickens had been without water, as had Norma's pigeons. I put all my weight against the cistern pump and by some miracle got it moving. Dolley bent her enormous head to the water trough as I filled it, blinking at me through one coal-colored eye. The chickens cawed and moaned and flapped their wings until they got a drink, too. The pigeons cooed and warbled and showed no gratitude at all.

By this time, any residual warmth from my fever had dissipated and I felt distressingly light, as if I might float away or melt into the snow. I took hold of the handle to the cellar door but couldn't muster the effort to pull it open. I don't remember getting back to the house, except that there remained in my mind a picture of two bottles of cream the boy from the dairy must have just left on our porch, each of them buried in snow until only their red paper caps showed.

I slept all afternoon on the divan in my coat and boots. It wasn't until I roused myself to go to bed that I realized we had missed Christmas entirely.

⇥ 42 ⇤

THE DAY AFTER CHRISTMAS, a worker at a paper mill beat the night watchman and stole his pay. Sheriff Heath arrested five men and had to take into custody the eight-month-old infant belonging to one of them. I read the story to Fleurette on the first day she was able to sit up and talk.

"I wonder what Mrs. Heath thought of having a baby brought into the jail," she said.

"I can't imagine she would've liked it. She has her own children to look after."

"Some people like babies."

"I know. Only I wonder where its mother was."

An image of Lucy rose suddenly before me and I flinched. The fever had left me with the distinct impression that I was being haunted. Lucy was one of the ghosts, Henry Kaufman was another, along with this new man, George Ewing. I was not yet in my right mind.

And now there was the poor night watchman at the paper mill, beaten to death for his weekly pay. The stories in the papers were like the old Austrian fairy tales my mother used to whisper to us at night, populated by ogres and trolls and the weak-limbed mortals who could not fight them off.

WE HADN'T REALIZED IT AT FIRST, but Norma had been the sickest of all of us. She was left with a barking cough she could not shake. Fleurette kept a pot of water on the stove and carried it to her every few hours so she could breathe the steam. She could not be left alone. I didn't dare go to see Sheriff Heath until I knew Fleurette was well enough to look after Norma for the day.

Finally on New Year's Eve, I thought the two of them would be fine on their own. The road had been cleared by then and Dolley had an easy time of it. I think she was as eager to get outside and breathe the clean air as I was. The pastures along our lane were blanketed in white, punctuated only by a few bare tree trunks reaching out of the snow as if they were gasping for breath. Black cows hunkered down between them, as cold and unmoving as rocks.

When I arrived at the jail I went directly to the door of the sheriff's residence and rang the bell. There was no answer. I rang again and gave a sharp knock. I heard no sound from within. Finally the door swung open to reveal Sheriff Heath in trousers, bare feet, his shirt untucked, and a blanket wrapped around his shoulders. His chin was ridden with stubble and his hair hung in strands from his forehead. I recognized the glassy look in his eyes.

"You're ill," I said.

He coughed and stepped aside to let me in. There were dolls and toys scattered about, and a plate with what looked like last night's dinner. It was not a sight intended for company to see. I didn't know where to look. I kept my eyes on my feet.

"We've been sick, too."

Sheriff Heath coughed and nodded in response. "Everyone has."

"We got another letter." I offered him the envelope.

He raised his eyebrows at me and took it, then stumbled backward into a chair. I sat across from him and watched him read it twice. He dabbed at his nose with a handkerchief.

Finally he put it back into the envelope and handed it to me. He tried to speak but lapsed into another coughing fit. I waited while he pushed himself out of his chair and went into the kitchen. I heard the sound of water running. He returned with a glass of water and struggled to get it down. Why wasn't his wife looking after him?

"Do you have any help? Are the children unwell too? What about Mrs. Heath?"

"All sick."

"Won't you let me look in on them?"

He waved my questions away and pointed to the letter. "Arrange a meeting."

"Are you sure? After what happened last time?"

"Different man," he croaked. "We can get this one."

I WROTE TO GEORGE EWING and a week later, I had my response. He asked to meet at the train station in Somerville. Sheriff Heath didn't like it. "A train station," he muttered when he stopped by to see the letter. "Too many escape routes. He's done this before."

"Should I ask him for another meeting place?"

"No, it's fine," he said. "I'll have men on both platforms.

Just come prepared, as you did before. Don't bring any valuables, and wear something you can run in if you have to. Oh, and I need to be able to spot you in a crowd. Wear that hat with the veil across it. You're tall enough, it'll stand out even among the men's hats."

I shifted uncomfortably in my chair.

"Forgive me," he said, stifling a ragged cough. "Mrs. Heath is always reminding me that I should never comment upon a lady's appearance. It's a hazard of the job. I'm trained to notice details."

"About women's heights or their hats?" I asked. I didn't like the idea of him noticing either.

"You wore it on Broadway that night," he said. "Don't you remember? I promised I wouldn't take my eyes off you. What else was there to do but study your hat?"

I smiled. "That must have been very dull for you."

He slid his overcoat on and opened the front door, letting in a blast of arctic air. He pulled the brim of his hat down low over his eyes.

"None of my dealings with the Kopp sisters have been dull."

❧ 43 ❧

ON THE MORNING OF MY MEETING with George Ewing, I paced and fretted and watched the clock. I had on the very same get-up I'd worn before, except for the work boots. No one saw them in the dark on Broadway, but they'd be spotted in a train station. So I wore a sensible old pair of leather shoes with buttons across the top. I carried the same handbag, but now it held fifty dollars in marked bills supplied to me by Sheriff Heath. There would be no revolver this time, he'd instructed me, on the grounds that a train station was no place for a gun fight.

Fleurette was so intent upon coming along that I made Norma promise to keep her under constant watch after I left. "Sit on her if you have to," I told Norma. "I don't want her sneaking off to the train station."

"In this weather? You think she would walk to town?" Norma's voice had only just returned. She still spoke in a croak.

"Just watch her."

At last the sheriff's wagon arrived. He brought along Deputy Morris, whom we all missed seeing in our foyer in the afternoons, as well as his man English, who had shadowed me that night on Broadway, and another deputy, Richards. They were to take me to the train station and drive on from there. I would have a bit of a wait for the train, but they needed to get a good start for Somerville so they would be in place before I arrived. If all went as expected, they would arrest George Ewing and take him back in the wagon, and I would return by train to Ridgewood. The sheriff didn't want me to ride alongside the man who had been threatening me, even after he was under arrest, and I assured him I could make my way home on my own.

The station was surprisingly crowded that afternoon. It was the first clear day in some time. People who had been confined to their homes were getting out at last. Children raced around the platform as if it were a summer's day, and their mothers stood by indulgently, relieved to see them wearing themselves out in the fresh air. Groups of men stood about in their long black coats, stamping their feet in the cold and exhaling a mixture of steam and cigarette smoke.

Seeing all of this, Sheriff Heath turned down a side street and drove me two blocks away. He stopped in front of a newsstand.

"I don't want anyone to see you with us," he said. "Buy yourself a newspaper and circle around a few times. We'll be waiting for you in Somerville."

I stepped out and did as he asked. With a newspaper tucked under my arm, I paced the streets closest to the station and pretended to browse the shop windows. There was a hairdresser showcasing wigs she'd made from her customers' hair, and a locksmith's window with brass and iron locks gleaming like jewelry. At the pharmacy, someone had made a snowman out of rolled white bandages.

I glanced into the shop and there was Lucy Blake, standing in the doorway, staring at me. She wore a smock meant for housekeeping and a knobby red scarf of the sort an elderly aunt might knit for Christmas. When she saw me, she tried to dart out the door, but I took her elbow and pulled her back.

"Lucy? What happened to you?"

In a low voice she said, "We shouldn't talk here. I can't be seen with you."

"But you're all right," I said. "We've been looking for you. No one could find you after the fire."

"I'm fine."

"But the fire. Was it aimed at you?"

She bit her lip and blinked. Strands of hair flew about her face and she tucked them inside her hat. "I think so," she said. "He kept asking me why I'd been talking to you. And one night he just let himself in, very late, and stumbled across my mother's bed. I broke a plate over his head and he ran out. Later that night the fire started. It had to have been him."

"And everyone got out?"

"I think so. I'm fine, really. I'm taking care of some ladies now."

"What ladies?"

"Sisters. Both shut-ins. They share a house and I live downstairs and do for them. We live just up Dover Street." She pointed up the hill behind her. The homes had once been quite stately, with fish-scale shingles and widow's walks on the roof that probably gave a view all the way to New York on a clear day. Now most of them were boarding houses.

"What about your mother?"

"She took a position nearby. She does washing and mending, mostly."

I heard the rumble of the train in the distance. "I have to go," I said quickly. "Let me come back and talk to you. I've been wanting to show you some photographs I found of Regina Doyle's building. Can I bring them to you?"

She grabbed my arm. "Pictures of Bobby?"

"I don't think so," I said. "But maybe someone who was involved."

Now she was eager to see me. "When can you come?"

"Soon. And let me bring the sheriff, too. He's arrested Mr. Kaufman. I think he'd be able to help."

She shook her head. "I don't know."

The train had almost reached the station. "Think about it. Tell me, which house is yours?"

She gave me the number. The train whistled and screeched as it approached.

"I'll come and see you as soon as I can." She nodded and scurried down the street.

The train to Somerville was crowded, but the ride was blessedly brief. I squeezed into a seat and pulled out the newspaper, grateful for a distraction. As the train jerked and rocked along the tracks, I pretended to read the front page, but my thoughts were on Lucy. She'd been nearby all along. Maybe it wasn't too late to do something for her.

I put the paper down and looked out the window at the gray snow along the tracks. The telegraph wires wobbled and wove as the train rushed past. The landscape beyond them rolled by like a panorama in a theater: rows of houses turned away from the tracks, with only their laundry lines and burn barrels showing, then a stand of warehouses clad in rusted tin, then the open fields of brown stubble under snow.

I realized with a start that the next stop was Somerville and I'd hardly given George Ewing a single thought. A vein leapt up and throbbed against my collarbone and I had to put a hand over it to quiet it. I reminded myself that Sheriff Heath and his men would be waiting and watching. The station would be filled with people. I didn't know what sort of man I was looking for, but I only hoped I could outrun him or fight him if I had to.

Soon the brakes screamed, the engine exhaled a head of steam, and the conductor barked out the name of the Somerville station. I got off with a crowd of passengers and walked toward the ticket counter as if I had business to attend to, then stood around waiting for everyone to disperse.

The platform was entirely exposed to the north and the wind whistled as it went past the posts and the tin roof above me. It was nearly dark and a man was walking around lighting the old gas lamps. A few people gathered around them as if they were hoping for warmth, but the flames flickered behind glass and gave out only a thin pool of light.

I sat on a bench with my ankles crossed and my handbag in my lap. A few solitary men approached the bench, but each walked right past it. The clock in the station had just struck five. I tried not to watch it as I didn't want to look nervous. My feet bounced against the brick and I willed them to stay still.

I was staring at the ties on the tracks when a hand gripped my shoulder roughly from behind.

"Not here, Miss Kopp," a man muttered in my ear, his to-bacco-stained breath on my neck. I jerked my shoulder away and rose to face him, but just as I did, a station agent blew his whistle and yelled.

"Leave the lady alone!"

I barely got a glimpse of him before he ran down the platform and out of the station, a tall, skinny figure in a baggy gray overcoat who propelled himself along with a distinctive off-center gait. It was Kaufman's friend, the one with the wooden leg.

Sheriff Heath and his deputies materialized from their posts inside the station, around the corner, and on the platform opposite. All of them ran after Ewing, leaving the station in utter silence. I was left to play the part of the astonished lady victim.

The girl running the sandwich stand rushed over with a cup of tea and a hot bun, which I saw no reason to refuse. An older gentleman came to sit with me and offered to call a doctor if I needed one. I declined, explaining that I was just taking the train to Ridgewood and would have family waiting for me there.

I finished my tea and rode the train back, then hired a cab to take me home. By the time I stood in my own drive again, it was eight o'clock. A single light burned in the kitchen. There would be a plate set aside for me, and Norma and Fleurette would be standing around anxiously. I wished I could tell them with certainty that Ewing was under arrest. I already knew what Norma would say: If Sheriff Heath couldn't catch up with a one-legged man, we were in worse trouble than we'd imagined.

❧ 44 ❧

THE NEXT MORNING I was helping Norma dust the chickens for mites and keeping a wary eye on the road when the sheriff's wagon pulled into our drive. It was Deputy Morris.

"I'm sorry we ran out on you last night, Miss Kopp," he said.

"Don't worry about me. Did you catch him?"

A wide smile emerged under his beard. "Of course we did. Although he goes awfully fast on that club of his. Anyway, the sheriff wants me to bring you in to view the evidence."

When we arrived, Sheriff Heath was standing over a table looking at some papers. There was the letter I had written to George Ewing to request a meeting, along with other letters addressed to him I didn't recognize. There was also a notebook with a page of scribbles, a handkerchief, and a bottle that looked like it came from a druggist.

"What's this?" I said, pointing to the bottle.

"Chloroform."

Everything went still for a minute. I took a half-step back

from the bottle as if it could reach out and poison me. Sheriff Heath pulled a chair out for me and then sat down next to me. He spoke quietly and carefully. "We believe he intended to take you to a hotel and drug you."

"A hotel? By what means would he have persuaded me to visit a hotel with him?"

He smiled. "I don't think Mr. Ewing considered who he was dealing with. But this is the way these men work. It takes nothing more than a little chloroform on a handkerchief to overpower a lady. We've seen it before."

I shook my head. "Well, he's not very bright if he thought that would work on me."

"Have a look at this." Sheriff Heath pushed the notebook toward me with the end of a pencil. I could barely make out the writing.

"What is it?"

"It appears to be his plan to kidnap Fleurette and sell her to white slavers."

"This is his plan? All written down on notepaper for anyone to read?"

"He makes it easy for us. I'm about to go interview him. That's another thing. He's claiming responsibility for all of the threats against the three of you."

"All the letters from last year? Everything Henry Kaufman did?"

He nodded. "I'm afraid so. He says he acted alone. Says he never heard of a Henry Kaufman."

"But that was him!" I protested. "With the wooden leg! I told you I've seen him with Mr. Kaufman!"

"And you're certain of that? It was the same man?"

"Of course. I told you about his front teeth, didn't I? And

the leg. How many men with wooden legs do we have running around this town?"

"I just want to be sure," he said. "Mr. Ewing was arrested in Somerset County for stripping the lighting wires from their poles with a gang of thieves, all of whom got away. I don't know if they were Kaufman's friends or not. But Mr. Ewing served his sentence in the state prison and was released right before your collision with Henry Kaufman last summer."

Just then the guard opened the door and said that the prisoner was ready to be interviewed. Sheriff Heath stood to leave. "Just be careful," he said. "Stay home and keep quiet for a while. You have your guns. We'll drive by when we can."

I didn't tell him I'd found Lucy. If she was right—if Henry Kaufman really would come after her if she ever went to the police—I didn't want to be the one who brought that down on her. She'd gotten away, even though she hadn't gone far. She could stay hidden a while longer.

SAYS HE WAS KOPP BLACK HAND "GANG"
Confession by Convict Clears
Jersey Blackmail Mystery Case

HACKENSACK, N.J. JAN. 23—"I am alone responsible for the writing of Black Hand letters to Miss Constance Kopp, of Wyckoff, threatening to abduct her pretty sister, Florette. I had learned that the Kopp family were wealthy and I thought this was an easy way to make a bunch of coin."

This was the confession made to-day by George Ewing, an ex-convict, who was captured in the Neshanic Mountains a few days ago by Sheriff Heath, of Hackensack. A bottle of chloroform found in his pocket has led to the discovery, it is believed, of an additional plot to kidnap Florette Kopp and turn her over to "white slavers" in Chicago.

The confession ends a reign of terror that had prevailed in the Kopp home since last July, when Miss Constance Kopp started suit against Henry Kaufman, owner of a silk dyeing establishment in Paterson, to recover damages for being run down by Kaufman's auto. Black Hand letters began to reach the Kopp home, and prowling men appeared after dark, shooting at the house.

"He's claiming responsibility for all of it?" said Fleurette, grabbing the newspaper out of my hand before I could finish. "Why would he do that?"

"To keep Henry Kaufman out of trouble, I suppose," I said. "Can I have my paper back?"

But Fleurette held on to it, reading bits of it aloud but mostly mumbling to herself. "It says here that Ewing planned to entice you to a hotel and use chloroform on you," she said. "I thought I was the one being kidnapped. What does he want with you?"

"Don't talk like that," Norma said. "The fact that you've received the most threats does not make you the most popular."

"What does it make me?"

"The smallest. They are threatening you because you are the smallest and the youngest, and somehow they have the idea that we, therefore, value you the most and would pay more to get you back."

"Well, of course you would."

"Don't be so sure."

"And why would anyone write out the plan for the crime

they intend to commit and carry it around in their pocket like that?"

"You heard what Constance said. This is not the smartest criminal we've ever met."

"We haven't met many criminals. Although if this keeps up, we'll soon know every con man and Black Hander in New Jersey."

"That's enough from both of you," I said, having recovered my newspaper and finished reading the story. "All that matters now is that we caught him."

"Does this mean Henry Kaufman gets away with everything?" Norma asked.

"I don't know."

"Then it's a good thing we went to the papers so all the criminals could learn our particulars," Norma declared. "I don't know why you ever took that man's advice."

"Sheriff Heath? You didn't mind so much when he was issuing you a revolver. You didn't turn down his help then."

"I don't know what choice I had. Now what is he going to do about Mr. Ewing?"

"He'll be sent to jail for the kidnapping attempt," I said. "I have to give a statement to the prosecutor tomorrow, and then I'm going to go take care of a few other things in town." I was going to see Lucy, but I didn't want to say it.

"I'm coming with you!" Fleurette said, scrambling to her feet. "I'll wear my black crepe. I have a very serious sort of hat that would give the impression—"

I stood and took her face in my hands, forcing her to look up at me. Her cheeks were pink with excitement and her eyes were flashing. She had the face of a small, sleek animal, a mink or a fox.

"Listen to me. Under no circumstances will you ever be in the same room with George Ewing or any of his gang. Ever."

She squirmed and got away from me. "It doesn't seem like I'll ever be in the same room with anyone except the two of you," she said, pouting as only a girl of her age could do.

"I'd like that just fine."

⧉ 45 ⧉

THE HOUSE WAS BETTER CARED FOR than most on the block. It had recently been given a fresh coat of white paint, and it sat behind a tidy front garden fringed in a cast-iron fence. Although the garden was covered in gray slush, there were twigs and stalks standing up through the snow, suggesting the possibility of hydrangeas under the windows later on in the year, and a border of daylilies along the walk.

I gave the bell a hard twist. The smoke from some nearby chimney drifted past. The smell of wood burning made me hungry and I realized it had been a long time since breakfast.

After a while I heard a cough and the shuffling of feet. The door opened and the tiniest woman I'd ever seen stood before me. She was as frail as a bird, her small head fringed in white cottony wisps. She wore a gray dress with a collar that buttoned right under her chin, and from under her skirts appeared petite patent leather shoes that could have belonged to a schoolgirl.

She looked me up and down through china-blue eyes. "How do you do?" she said at last.

"I'm here to see Lucy Blake," I said. "I'm a friend of hers. I saw her in the market recently and she invited me to stop in."

She swept her eyes over me again, weighing the likelihood of that. "Lucy's working right now. She's helping my sister."

"I'm so sorry to bother you, Mrs. —"

"Miss Eldridge," she said. "I am the younger Miss Eldridge, by ten minutes."

I smiled. "I won't be but a minute, Miss Eldridge. I simply must ask her about an important matter. May I come inside and wait?"

The sound of footsteps coming down the stairs made Miss Eldridge turn around. Soon Lucy appeared behind her. Her eyes widened when she saw me.

"Excuse me, ma'am," Lucy said. "Just a friend of mine here to see me on a personal matter."

Before her employer could object, Lucy was out on the porch, pulling me by the wrist down the stairs to the entrance to a basement apartment.

"We can talk here," she said quietly, opening the door to a small room that appeared to have been furnished with the Eldridge sisters' cast-offs. There was a tufted red velvet settee so worn that the bare weave of the fabric showed through, and four mahogany dining chairs with embroidered cushions that looked like they could have been completed when the sisters were first learning to sew. A battered wardrobe and trunk must have contained her clothing, and a shelf above a small sink held washing powders and toiletries. A doorway at the back of the room revealed an alcove just large enough for a daybed.

There was a wood stove in one corner, but Lucy made no move to light it. She was probably given only a small quantity of fuel for the winter. With both of us crowded inside, it would soon be warm enough.

Once she closed the door, she grabbed my hands. "I've been waiting for you. Did you bring them?"

"Yes, and I want you to look at them very carefully," I said, pulling the envelope out of my pocketbook. "I hope you might recognize someone."

She turned the envelope over, holding it by the edge as if it might burn her. "What does this say?" she said, squinting at the faint writing on the outside. "Ward?"

"That must be the man who hired them to take the pictures. He never came back to pay for them, so Mr. La-Motte—that's the photographer—he offered them to me."

She slid the photographs out and looked through them, studying each face before going on to the next one. There were businessmen in suits, delivery boys, and little girls playing on the stoop. She paused for an especially long time over a picture of a woman with a bundle over her shoulder. Even if it was a baby, there was no way to know if it was hers.

After she looked at each one of them twice, she passed them back to me. "I'm sorry," she said. "I don't recognize anyone."

"Are you sure? I thought you might have seen one of them come into the factory. Some associate of Henry Kaufman's, maybe." I realized I had no idea what to do next. If the pictures were useless, then I had nothing else to offer her.

She picked at a thread coming loose from the settee. "No. But thank you for bringing them, Miss Kopp."

"I do wish you would come and talk to Sheriff Heath. I wanted to bring him here today, but now that I see your situation, I wouldn't want to raise suspicion among your employers."

She pushed her chin up defiantly. "They already know. The Misses Eldridge have lived very long lives and have seen quite a bit in their time. A girl with a baby hardly comes as a shock to them."

A little silver bell rang above Lucy's door and she stood up.

"Wait," I said, as I followed her out. "Won't you please think about going to see the sheriff? Surely he could help. Now he's arrested one of Mr. Kaufman's friends, and he's working on—"

She turned around and said, "If he puts Henry Kaufman in jail, I'll go talk to him. Not before."

"But—"

There was a hard, defeated look about her. "He set fire to his own boarding house. What would he do to this place?"

At the second ring of the bell, Lucy turned and ran up the stairs, leaving me to latch the door. The diminutive Miss Eldridge stood on the porch and watched me go.

❧ 46 ❧

"CAN'T YOU FIND SOMETHING TO DO?" Norma said crossly after I'd fumbled the third leg band and annoyed yet another pigeon. "I don't need your help. You're just making them nervous."

I was attempting to crowd inside the pigeon loft with her. I had to bend down to avoid tangling my hair in the chicken wire above. All twenty pigeons had retreated to a row of nesting boxes situated as far away from me as they could get. They were climbing over themselves and pecking at one another and making an agitated ruckus. Norma was giving the younger ones their first leg bands and tying on messages. "Wild Geese Never Divorce" was soon to arrive back at the loft, as was "Citizens Asked Not to Tempt Soldiers by Offering Strong Drink."

Norma reached around me and opened the door to the loft. "Go. Go and see what Fleurette's doing. Maybe she needs some help."

"She's practicing her ballet," I said, backing out of the loft as ordered.

"Then polish the doorknobs. Or go start dinner. You can do that, can't you?"

Yes. I could do that.

I pulled some carrots out of a box of sand we kept in the root cellar and took them inside. I was standing at the kitchen sink, scrubbing them and looking out the window at the barn and the barren vegetable patch we'd soon have to replant, when the crunch of wheels on gravel announced that someone was in our drive. I leaned around and saw Francis's wagon pulling up to the door, a load of baskets under an oilcloth in the back.

He jumped down and went to talk to Norma. I scrubbed my carrots a little longer than I needed to. When they were skinned bare and bright orange, I dropped them in the sink and looked around the kitchen. There was the battered old table that had survived decades of dough being pounded on it, noodles being rolled out and sliced, coffee spills, dribbles of jam and preserves, and the arguments of three girls who rarely agreed on anything but sat down together nonetheless. The black iron wood-burning stove had no place in a modern kitchen, but when we moved in, there was no source of gas or electricity, and we learned to live without it. Mother's old scalloped dishes with their pattern of moss roses sat in the cupboard, as familiar as the backs of our hands. There was nothing new in this kitchen but Fleurette's pale blue curtains, stitched all the way around in yellow piping.

I had very little love for kitchens, but I couldn't see us giving this one up.

Francis waved at me through the window as he came up to the door. He had a newspaper in his hand. He'd grown a beard over the winter and there were little flecks of gray in it. Our father used to wear a beard like that. I realized with a start that Francis was almost the same age our father was the last time I saw him.

He pounded his feet on the threshold as he came through the door. "Kopp Black Hand Gang?" he said, tossing the newspaper on the table. "What happened?"

He set his hat on the table and dropped into a chair in front of it. "I thought this was all taken care of. What's been going on out here?"

I dried my hands and sat down across from him. "I told you they were getting ready to arrest Henry Kaufman, and they did."

"Oh, I know. I read about that one in the papers, too. It's how I keep up with my sisters these days. Why didn't you tell me another man was threatening you?"

I leaned back in my chair to get a look out the window. Norma was staying very busy with her pigeons. I wasn't going to get any help from her. Fleurette had put on a recording of a Parisian ballet and I could hear her heel hit the ground each time she made a pirouette.

"What would you have done? I really do think it's over now. This man George Ewing, he was working for Mr. Kaufman. He's back in prison and—"

"But think about it, Constance," Francis said. "Whether they convict him or not doesn't matter. There will be another one after this, and another one. Don't you see? You're easy marks out here. Three girls, living all alone, wealthy as far as anyone can tell."

Rich, lonely women in the countryside. Is that how we looked to those men? I got a little queasy when I tried to see us through their eyes. "And I suppose you think we'd be safer with you."

"Of course! That's what I've been telling you all along. Move in with us and you're living in a neighborhood, not out on some dark road. We have a police officer living down the street from us, and a firefighter. Besides, I'll be there."

"Oh, you're going to protect us? I don't think Henry Kaufman and his gang would be afraid of you," I said.

"They only go after people who provoke them. And I won't."

Through the window I could see Norma strapping a basket of pigeons to Dolley's backside. She was going to ride away and leave me to handle this on my own. Fleurette's record skipped and she started it again.

He pushed his chair back and stood to leave. "You can't afford to keep this place without an income. You know I'm right about that."

He was. We'd spent hardly anything all winter, but our savings were dwindling.

"At least send Fleurette to us," Francis said. "She's the one they're after."

"Fleurette stays with me."

He bent over and said in a whisper, "Shouldn't mothers be more concerned with keeping their children safe?"

I leaned back and stared at him. "What do you think I've been doing?"

He went to the door, and I looked at the seam along the back of his coat, freshly restitched in Bessie's hand. He already had the slight stoop of a man who bore too many burdens. "Do you remember how Mother used to be when something happened on the street?" I said.

He paused and turned back to me, still aggravated.

"One time you and I were out with her," I said, "and a boy

was running past. He tripped and spilled a bag of onions all over the sidewalk. Do you remember that?"

He shook his head.

"I stopped to pick one up, but Mother yanked my arm and told me not to touch it, like it could be some kind of trick."

"She was like that," Francis said, leaning against the door. "She didn't trust anybody."

"That's right," I said. "And for years it never occurred to me that other people would stop if you dropped something, and hand it back to you. Some people—like the men who pulled our wrecked buggy off Fleurette—would run straight toward a disaster, not because they were heedless of the danger, but because they were prepared to do something about it."

Francis shrugged. "Mother had her reasons. It was a different time."

"That's exactly right," I said. "It was a different time. We don't have to hide anymore, and we don't have to run away."

Francis raised his hands in surrender. "Then don't. But you know you can always—"

"I know we can turn up on your doorstep," I said. "I thank you and Bessie for offering. But we've done just fine standing up for ourselves, and I'm glad we did."

He nodded and left. I sat in the kitchen with my eyes closed and listened to the churning of that distant French orchestra on the Victrola, and the sweep of Fleurette's slippers across our uneven parlor floor.

What I didn't say to Francis was that when Lucy grabbed me on the street in Paterson that day, I couldn't understand how anyone would take hold of a stranger and pour out their troubles. But now I realized that people did it all the time. They called for help. And some people would answer, out of a sense of duty and a sense of belonging to the world around them. That's what Sheriff Heath and his men did, lying in wait in our freezing barn, their guns drawn, to get the man who was trying to get us.

If I could give something to Fleurette—if I could give her one silent gift from a mother she didn't know she had—it would be this: the realization that we have to be a part of the world in which we live. We don't scurry away when we're in trouble, or when someone else is. We don't run and hide.

She watched Mother and learned her ways just like I did. But I hoped she would watch me too, and learn something different.

⚜ 47 ⚜

A WEEK LATER, just after dinner, a knock came at the door. I opened it to find Sheriff Heath and Deputy Morris, dripping wet on my front porch. They'd removed their overcoats and stood shivering in their vests and shirtsleeves, the fabric stuck to them like a coat of paint.

They both spoke at once. "We're so sorry to bother you, Miss Kopp," Deputy Morris said.

"Please forgive us, but could we—" Sheriff Heath began, as I opened the door wide and ushered them in.

"We realize we're barging in late," Deputy Morris began again.

"It's all right," I said. "What happened?"

Norma and Fleurette came in from the kitchen, and Norma went off to find towels and blankets for them without waiting for an explanation. Fleurette fussed over both of them, insisting that they kick off their wet shoes and stand by the fire. They crowded around the hearth. The smell of moss and river mud rose off them as their clothes warmed.

Norma returned with a stack of towels and disappeared again to heat the coffee. Fleurette added a log to the fire and settled down in front of them as if anticipating a dramatic recitation. "Do tell us everything," she said. "Were you chasing our Mr. Kaufman out of the creek? Shall we get our guns?"

Deputy Morris shook his head. "No, miss. We were after another crook tonight. A house thief. He stole some jewelry and money and gave the lady of the house a terrible fright. We rounded up some men in the neighborhood, and we've been out chasing him all afternoon, but we lost him when it got dark."

"And then you went for a swim?" Fleurette said.

"Not much of a night for a swim. The fellow we were chasing shot at the sheriff here, and we both fell backward into a creek. We were going to go straight home, but the road—"

"You've been shot?" I said around the hard thing that had leapt into my throat and lodged there.

Sheriff Heath had been looking at the fire while Deputy Morris spoke. He turned to me and said, "No. It just put a hole in my overcoat. He surprised us, that's all."

Fleurette looked up at me and frowned. "There's a tear in his vest."

"Let me see that." I moved toward him but he pulled away. I grabbed him roughly by the arms and turned him to face me. He blinked at me in surprise. "Miss Kopp, I—"

"Stop that," I said. "I think you're in shock." I picked at the tear in his vest and came away with a hand covered in blood.

"You've been shot," I said quietly, pulling him closer to get a look at the wound. "It's too dark in here. Fleurette, get some bandages and soap and things. See if we have anything that will fit a man. The sheriff's going to need another shirt."

He tried to protest. "No, we only stopped because the road—"

"Never mind about that. We're going to get a look at your shoulder right now."

Norma was coming out with coffee as I led the two men to the kitchen. She saw the blood seeping through his vest as we moved into the circle of light cast by the lamp.

"Let them have their drink," I said, "and put on some more water. Light the other side of the stove so Deputy Morris can get warm."

She did as I asked, and I pushed a protesting Sheriff Heath into a chair. Fleurette returned with the bandages and a bundle of Francis's old clothes. She helped me ease the vest off his shoulder. He groaned when we raised his arm to remove it.

"Bend over the table so we can see it in the light," I said. "We're not going to touch it. We're just going to look."

His shirt was soaked in blood across the shoulder and down the back. I lifted it carefully off his skin and Fleurette cut it away with scissors. Underneath was a wide and shallow wound obscured by half-congealed blood.

"I think you're all right," I said under my breath. "It looks like the bullet just grazed you. We'll clean it so we can see better."

He nodded but didn't look up at us. He was gripping the edge of the table with his hands, his knuckles pale.

Norma brought a towel and a bowl of hot water, and Fleurette supplied the soap. I washed the edges of the wound as carefully as I could without actually touching it. The bullet went deep enough to strip away the skin but didn't seem to expose any bone. As I cleaned it, the natural color of his skin returned, pink and white from the hot water. On his shoulder were a string of brown freckles, five of them in all.

He was breathing long, noisy breaths like a captive animal.

"Now we need to wash the wound itself," I said. "Lean back so we don't make a mess."

Without loosening his grip on the table, he eased back toward Fleurette and me. I looked down at him but he didn't meet my eyes. The hair on the top of his head had just begun to dry. Two locks lifted away from the rest.

I squeezed a trickle of water over his shoulder and Fleurette pressed a towel against him to catch it. The water ran bright red, but the wound looked clean. I peered at it closely, breathing in the metallic smell of fresh blood.

"This will have to be sewn up. It won't close on its own."

He pulled away from us and tried to cover himself with the torn remnants of his shirt. "I don't need a doctor," he said.

"Sir, I think the ladies are right," Deputy Morris said. "Shouldn't someone take a look at you tonight?"

He shook his head and tried to stand up. "I'm not going to get a doctor out of bed for this."

"Then sit down," I said, with a tone of authority in my voice that surprised him. "You're not leaving without a bandage and a clean shirt." He sat down wearily and Fleurette and I set about wrapping his shoulder. It was a difficult spot to cover properly and impossible to pin in place. Fleurette sewed a few stitches through the bandage to hold it. Then she produced our brother's old nightshirt. Sheriff Heath removed himself to the washing room to exchange his ruined shirt for Francis's. When he returned, he nodded at me.

"I need to speak to Miss Kopp for a minute."

I opened the kitchen door and he followed me down the

hall to the parlor. The fire we had fed a few minutes earlier was now blazing brightly. I encouraged Sheriff Heath to sit but instead he stood in front of it.

"I'm not quite dry," he said, leaning over the hearth. I took my seat and waited for him to speak. The room was dark except for the fire, but I didn't want to go to the bother of lighting any lamps.

"I can't get Ewing to budge," he said. "He's still claiming responsibility for all the letters and the shots fired and everything."

"All of it?"

The sheriff attempted a nod and then grimaced and laid a hand on his bandage. Behind him the flames hissed and threw sparks on the hearth. He stepped aside and the orange glow illuminated him from below. He looked like an apparition in the flickering light.

"I'm afraid so. If we can't get him to change his story, the prosecutor's going to drop all the charges against Henry Kaufman."

"But why would Mr. Ewing claim responsibility for crimes he didn't commit? He might have been in Mr. Kaufman's gang, but he didn't do it all himself. He couldn't have."

Sheriff Heath shrugged, and then winced from the pain of moving his shoulder. "Money. I think Kaufman has offered him a sum of money in exchange for confessing to crimes he did not commit. It's worth at least a thousand dollars to Kaufman, not to mention the exposure."

"Or he's threatened him."

"Maybe a little of both. I have to assume Kaufman knew that Ewing would get caught. He's the weakest animal in the pack. Easy to sacrifice."

I leaned back and closed my eyes. I couldn't believe that, after all that had happened, Henry Kaufman might get off without so much as a rebuke from the courts, simply by bribing someone else to take the blame.

"But I have one bit of good news," he said. "We're calling in a handwriting expert from New York. William Kinsley. He's an authority on the scientific study of penmanship. He's going to look at the letters and try to connect them to Kaufman."

"I don't see how that could help us," I said. "They were all printed in block lettering."

"Oh, he's got a method, even when someone tries to disguise the handwriting. He's winning cases. There's just one thing. He wants us to gather writing samples not just from Ewing and Kaufman, but from other parties involved in the case. I'd like all three of you to come down and give a sample."

"But why would we write the letters?"

"He just wants to rule out anyone who might be accused of writing the letters themselves to create a sensation."

"And would we be accused of throwing bricks through our own windows? Running down our own buggy?"

"It's only a formality."

The kitchen door opened, and Norma, Fleurette, and Deputy Morris shuffled down the hall. They looked half asleep.

"I'm sorry we kept you," I said, rising to my feet. "You must be wanting to get home."

"I thought there was some trouble with the road," Fleurette said. "Shouldn't they stay the night?"

Both men stiffened in surprise at the suggestion, as did Norma.

"Thank you, Miss Fleurette," Deputy Morris said, "but that won't be necessary. The road is very slow going because of all the ruts in it and the new moon. But now that we are warm and dry, the drive will be more tolerable."

As they went out the door, Sheriff Heath thanked Fleurette for her services as a nurse and Norma for the coffee. To me he said, "Tomorrow, Miss Kopp."

❧ 48 ❧

WE WERE WAITING ON THE FRONT PORCH when Sheriff Heath arrived the next morning. The sun had come out, and the air, while still cold, smelled damp and green.

"I don't approve of us riding around in automobiles," Norma said.

"I should like to learn how to drive one, and I wonder if the sheriff would teach me," Fleurette said. "I was just looking at a charming motoring cap in one of my magazines that I think would suit me."

"Don't bother the sheriff," I said. "He's doing us a favor by bringing us to the station himself. I'm sure he's very busy."

Sheriff Heath brought the car to a stop in our drive and jumped out, grinning, to open the door for me. Norma and Fleurette settled in behind us.

"You're in high spirits for a man who was shot last night," I said.

"We got him. And now he faces an assault charge for shooting at an officer of the law."

"You caught the thief after you left our house last night? In your condition?"

"Oh, not Morris and me. No, we went right home to bed. But one of the men in the posse tracked him all night and brought him in just before dawn. I deputized that fellow on the spot. We could use more like him."

"I'm sure you could."

The men from the dairy were taking advantage of the sunshine and finishing the work on the road, spreading a new layer of crushed stone and pressing it down with a roller. They stepped aside to let us through, although I know that the tires of the automobile only made the road more rutted and pitted. "We should get the county to come out and oil this road," Sheriff Heath said, half to himself. "This macadam is only good for buggies and bicycles."

"If you know a way to get the Board of Freeholders to pay for it, I'd like to hear about it."

"I wish I did. I'm fighting them for every penny right now. They put up that jail at a cost of six hundred thousand dollars but didn't finish it. I had to petition them for sanitary drains and windows that can't be picked open with common tools. There's no laundry facility and no money for me to issue uniforms to the prisoners. You can't imagine what a mess it is."

"Haven't the Freeholders seen it? Aren't any of them on your side?"

"I haven't offered them a tour," he said, smiling.

"Well, perhaps you should. Or show them some pictures. Doesn't anyone have a camera?"

"I suppose I do."

We drove along in silence for a minute. When we bounced over a large pit in the road, his face wound up in pain.

"What did the doctor have to say about your shoulder?"

He didn't look away from the road. He probably wanted to forget being subjected to the amateur nursing efforts of the Kopp household last night. Finally he said, "Mrs. Heath has examined the wound carefully and given it a fresh bandage."

"And she approves of you going right back to work today?"

"She does not."

I wondered what it must have been like for Mrs. Heath to awaken in the night and find her husband shot in the shoulder.

"I think I agree with your wife. You should have stayed home today."

He shrugged and grinned. "The criminals don't stay home, Miss Kopp. You know that. Mrs. Heath knows it too." Nothing could ruin his good mood. It was amazing to see what catching a fugitive could do for his disposition. I was cheered myself by the news.

The sheriff turned around to speak to Norma and Fleurette. "This is merely an exercise to satisfy Mr. Kinsley's rigorous method. No one suspects the Kopps of writing the letters," he said.

"I would think not," Norma said.

"His method is very scientific, the way he looks at each letter and how it's made. He can tell how hard a man presses a pen against the paper, and he knows the difference between how you write a letter at the beginning of the word or in the middle of it. He's winning all kinds of cases in New York. This is all we need to get our Mr. Kaufman convicted."

"He's not our Mr. Kaufman," Norma said.

"I think he is ours after all this time," Fleurette said. "He is our very own personal Black Hander. Most girls don't have one."

Sheriff Heath gave her a grave look. "You mustn't make a joke of this."

"We've been telling her that all along," I said. I turned to scold Fleurette yet again. "Sheriff Heath and his men sacrificed their own safety to guard our house. Don't let me hear you make light of it again, especially at the courthouse."

She shrugged and looked out the window. I wondered if we had worked too hard to protect her. She felt so utterly secure that she seemed to believe no harm could ever come to her.

As we drove into Hackensack, it seemed that the sun had brightened the spirits of the entire town. Schoolchildren were skipping rope in the playground, mothers were out walking with their babies, and shopkeepers were lingering outside their storefronts with cigarettes. I thought I could see buds breaking on the cherry trees, but that might have been my hopeful imagination.

AT THE COURTHOUSE Deputy Morris took charge of us and led us to an empty room where we were to wait our turn. "I'm afraid they're running behind," he said. "But now that the sheriff's back, I'm sure things will move along."

Still we waited for the better part of an hour. I'd brought a book, Norma had her newspaper, and Fleurette just fidgeted and complained that no one told her to bring something to keep herself occupied.

"I'm telling you now," Norma snapped at last. "When you go places, bring things to keep yourself occupied. There."

After an interminable wait, Deputy Morris returned and brought us down the long paneled corridor to the entrance to a courtroom. The door was closed and a few of Sheriff Heath's men stood guard. They looked at us nervously.

"The girls aren't to see him," one of the guards said to Deputy Morris.

"I thought he was finished."

The guard shook his head. "He's still in there yelling and pounding the table and kicking up a fuss. Never seen a man so obstinate. He's not coming to stay with us, is he?"

Deputy Morris frowned. "I don't want him under our roof any more than you do, but if a prison term is what he deserves, that's what he'll get."

"Are you talking about Henry Kaufman?" I said. "Is he in there?"

The men looked at us in surprise as if they'd forgotten all about us. From inside the room came the sound of chairs scuffing around on the floor and men arguing in low voices. One of the guards leaned against the door.

Deputy Morris gestured down the corridor. "Ladies, why don't we just go back and wait."

Just then the door burst open and the guard was knocked off his feet. Henry Kaufman pushed past him, red-faced and wild-eyed, strands of hair plastered against his forehead with sweat. I was standing in front of Fleurette. Before anyone could react, he lunged at me.

"You! You're behind this!" he roared. He rushed at me but I pushed back, shoving him against the wall just as I had the previous summer. The only reason his head didn't hit the wall with the same satisfying crack is that two officers were already on me, tugging at my shoulders and slowing my momentum.

"Take your hands off her," Morris shouted, which elicited a round of smothered laughter from the spectators. Henry Kaufman may have been the aggressor, but I had him pinned and the officers couldn't pull me away from him.

For just a second, Henry Kaufman and I stared each other down. I'd been running from this man for the better part of a year, but now I wanted him to see me. I wanted him to look into the face of the person he'd been tormenting. But although his eyes were forced in my direction, there was a black emptiness to them. They could have been two cold stones for all the humanity they revealed. He may have once been a petulant and spoiled child, but he had become a drunk and deranged man, and I saw in his face little possibility of redemption. That only made me want to shake him harder. Maybe I could knock loose whatever horrible thing was wedged inside of him.

He looked around wildly when he realized that the officers had let go of my arms. They were going to let me have him. I had gathered up his collar in one hand and used the other hand to press his shoulder against the wall.

"Not a word," I said in a low voice meant only for him. It thrilled me to have him in my grasp. I felt like a hawk about to devour a fish.

I heard a rustle behind me and looked around to see Sheriff Heath standing in the doorway, wearing an expression I could not read. No one had ever stared at me as intently as he was at that moment. He seemed to be mesmerized.

In the calmest voice I could muster, I said, "Sheriff Heath, has he given you your writing sample?"

He blinked in surprise and then smiled slowly. "He has not, Miss Kopp. He's been uncooperative."

I looked down at Mr. Kaufman, who was squirming under my grip. "Go and do what the sheriff says," I said. "I'll be waiting right here."

I gave him another hard push against the wall and shoved him toward the doorway. The sheriff clasped him on the shoulder and guided him back into the courtroom, then shot one last strange, still look at me before closing the door.

Once inside, we could hear Mr. Kaufman yell, "What's going to be done about that? I want charges brought up against that lady."

The deputies gathered around the door to hear.

Mr. Kaufman growled something unintelligible, and Sheriff Heath replied, "Now, who would ever believe that you'd have any trouble fighting off a lady, Mr. Kaufman?"

HENRY KAUFMAN did make a handwriting sample that day. When the door opened and Sheriff Heath indicated that all was well, I let Deputy Morris lead us away so we wouldn't run into him again. At last it was our turn to sit in the courtroom with the sheriff and write out our copies of the letters. I hadn't seen the letters since I had turned them over to him. It was unsettling to read them again, and even more unsettling to write out the very words that had been used to threaten us.

If you don't pay we will fire your house. We know your horse and wagon.

We will trap you or burn you.

Have you ever been to Chicago? We believe a girl of your talents would find a nice place for herself with no trouble at all.

Fleurette's hand shook a little as she wrote that line. I watched her face as she bent over the paper and I thought about all the hours Norma and I spent teaching her to write her letters. She copied out poems and stories, wrote notes to her uncles in Brooklyn, and composed messages for Norma's pigeons to carry. Mother taught her to write in French. Francis showed her what little he remembered of musical notation. As I watched her, I couldn't help but see the little girl she used to be, concentrating on her studies, not a nearly grown woman cooperating in a criminal investigation.

AS WE WALKED DOWN the courthouse steps with Deputy Morris, we met a guard holding a prisoner by the arm. It was George Ewing in shabby brown overalls. His limp was worse as he hobbled up the stairs.

I moved to put myself between him and Fleurette, and spun her around to face away from him. He'd threatened to kidnap her. I didn't even want him to see her.

Deputy Morris hurried us past him, but it was too late. Mr. Ewing shouted after us, "Is that you? Constance Kopp? And your sister?"

I froze and gripped Fleurette so she wouldn't move.

The guard shoved him through the courthouse door, but he fought to keep it open and kept shouting at me. "Miss Kopp! Don't let them send me to Trenton! Don't make me go back!"

I stood at the bottom of the stairs and looked at Deputy Morris with astonishment.

"I'm sorry about that, Miss Kopp. They shouldn't have brought him through this way. He's not supposed to see any of you."

In as calm a voice as I could muster, I said, "What was that about going to Trenton?"

Deputy Morris shrugged. "I don't know. He went in for a hearing yesterday about his sentencing. He doesn't want to go back to state prison. I guess he thought he was going to serve his time here."

"What's the difference?" I said.

"Oh, the state prison's terrible. Foul, dark, cold, overrun with rats and lice. Nobody wants to go to state prison."

"There's an easy way to stay out of prison," Norma said. "Don't break the law."

⇥ 49 ⇤

"PLEASE DON'T TELL ME that yet another man is writing threatening letters," Sheriff Heath said when I was admitted to his office the next day. "I haven't the manpower to keep the criminal element away from the Kopp sisters."

"I had an idea about George Ewing," I said.

He leaned back in his chair and laced his fingers behind his head. "Why not? No less than five of the finest legal minds in Bergen County have already reviewed the case, and several of our lesser minds have considered it as well. What's your idea?"

I said nothing but waited for him to remember his manners.

"Pardon me, Miss Kopp. Please. Go ahead."

I sat down across from him. "When he shouted at us on the courthouse steps yesterday—"

"Yes, I'm very sorry about that. We have a passageway for bringing prisoners from the jail to the courthouse, but they were doing some work there. They shouldn't have brought him around without checking to make sure you'd gone home."

"It's all right," I said. "But he said he didn't want to go back to prison in Trenton."

Sheriff Heath shrugged. "Of course he doesn't want to go to Trenton. It's the worst prison in the state."

"He likes it better here?"

"Well, it's clean, the food is edible, and we wash their clothes once in a while. We don't treat them like pigs in filth. And you know, he got beat up in Trenton. That wooden leg makes him a target."

"Then why don't you make a deal with him?" I said.

He didn't say a word, but I could see him considering the idea.

"Offer to let him serve his term here in Hackensack as long as he agrees to tell the truth," I said. "Make him promise not to claim responsibility for crimes he didn't commit."

The sheriff looked up at the ceiling. "It's not a bad thought," he said. "We haven't been able to come up with anything to offer him. It didn't even occur to us that he expected to serve his time here. Now that he knows he's going back to Trenton, maybe he would be more willing to negotiate."

"Is that something you can do? Can you fix it so he stays in Hackensack?"

He jumped to his feet. "I think so. We're still waiting for the sentencing, but we have a good judge on the case. The question is whether we can get Ewing to go along with it. Perhaps you could convince him, Miss Kopp."

I gripped the sides of my chair. "Me? Why should I talk to him?"

"He's been asking about you. He seems to be genuinely sorry for what he's done. Don't worry—there will be steel bars between you. You'll be completely safe. This time I actually can promise you that."

"Right now? But I . . ."

"Unless you haven't the nerve," he said, flashing one of his rare smiles.

"Of course I have the nerve," I muttered.

I followed him out of his office and down a corridor I hadn't seen before, into a narrow room furnished only with a row of white chairs. Along one wall was a series of small metal doors, each the size of a cupboard.

"My guard is bringing Mr. Ewing down now," the sheriff said. "I'll do most of the talking. Don't answer any personal questions."

I nodded and took a seat. He continued, "Just try to win him over and encourage him to tell the truth. Remind him that he'll be out soon and there's no need to claim responsibility for someone else's crimes."

Just then the cupboard door slid open, and I was faced with a row of metal bars and, behind them, a sleepy and surprised George Ewing.

He broke into a smile when he saw me, exposing those crooked front teeth. "Miss Kopp! I didn't think it'd be you!"

Sheriff Heath leaned around so Mr. Ewing could see him and said, "George, Miss Kopp asked especially about coming to visit with you."

The prisoner nodded vigorously, his eyes wide. He had an innocent and earnest air about him. He seemed like the kind of man who could easily be talked into wrongdoing. He was pale and gaunt, with newly shorn hair and a clean shave. His eyes were ever so slightly too far apart, and his lips trembled when he spoke, giving him a kind of stutter.

He turned back to me, leaning into the bars of the window and speaking to me in a near-whisper. "Miss Kopp. Miss

Kopp. Don't let them send me back there. Can't you say a word to the judge? Nothing too terrible happened to you and your sisters, did it? Just a bunch of threats, but you girls are all right, aren't you?"

Sheriff Heath raised his hand to stop him. "George, Miss Kopp came to me this morning with a fine idea. I wonder if you'd be willing to consider it."

He looked back and forth at us with suspicion. "I don't usually like it when the sheriff has an idea."

"I think you'll like this one," Sheriff Heath said. "What would you say if I went to the judge and asked him to let you serve your sentence here in Hackensack?"

He leaned forward and grabbed the bars. "You would do that? Sheriff, you would do that for me?"

"I think I—"

But Mr. Ewing wouldn't let him continue. "You know, I've been in a dozen jails in New Jersey, and there is not a one as fine as yours, Sheriff. I've been telling the other men. Some of them have never been to jail before, so they don't know how good they have it in here, Sheriff. It's a fine place, sir, it really is, and it would be an honor to serve my sentence here. I thank you, sir, for the invitation. I accept. I do. I accept."

"Well, that's not all there is to it, George," he said.

Mr. Ewing let go of the bars and sat back. "What else is there, Sheriff? Do I gotta pay rent? What's the catch?"

Sheriff Heath suppressed a smile. "If I could get rent from each of you, I'd have a much easier time with the Freeholders. No, George, what I need you to do is to stop taking credit for Henry Kaufman's crimes. Just tell the truth about what you did, but don't go around taking responsibility for the rest of it. Henry Kaufman's got to be punished. You need to help us with that."

Ewing filled his cheeks with air and blew them out, then raised his hands in a sign of bewilderment. "I don't know what you mean, Sheriff. Why would any man claim responsibility for a crime he didn't commit?"

"Because he was being paid to do so," I suggested.

"Paid?" George Ewing said, leaning forward in surprise. "You can get paid for that?"

"Or threatened. Did Henry Kaufman threaten to come after you if you didn't confess to the whole thing?"

He looked down at his hands and mumbled, "Something like that."

I leaned over and whispered in the sheriff's ear. "Can't we put him on a train as soon as he's served his time?" Sheriff Heath glanced at me and nodded.

"Listen, George. You just do your part. Tell the truth about this every time you're asked. You might be called to testify at Henry Kaufman's trial. Just tell them what really happened, and I'll keep you right here in Hackensack and make sure no harm comes to you. I'll even put you on a train when we set you free."

"You will?" he said.

Sheriff Heath nodded. "I'll drive you to the train station myself. I'll see that you get on safely. Where would you like to go, George?"

He sat back in his chair and let out a long breath. "Oh, boy, sheriff. I'm going to have to think about that. Can I let you know later?"

Sheriff Heath grinned. "You can let me know in six months, George."

AFTER GEORGE EWING WAS LED AWAY, the sheriff stood and called for the guard to let us out. "I have to say, Miss

Kopp. That was the best break we've had in a long time. I might even go talk to John Ward. With this kind of leverage, maybe we can get a confession out of Kaufman."

"Who's John Ward?" I said, following him down the corridor.

"Kaufman's lawyer. You've seen them together."

I stopped. "Ward? Are you sure that's his name?"

Sheriff Heath turned around and frowned at me. "Of course that's his name. I've known John for years. I serve divorce papers and eviction notices for him. Although why he got mixed up with a man like Kaufman—"

"Then we've got him," I blurted out.

"Who?"

"Just—that's it. We've got him."

❧ 50 ❧

SHERIFF HEATH DROVE ME HOME and waited while I
ran inside for the envelope. I'd hidden it in a bureau that
we'd moved from my room to Mother's to barricade the windows. I stood looking at that bureau, a curiously dark, hand-
painted piece of Viennese artistry, and thought how strange
it was that its latest purpose had been to shield us from bullets.

I rushed down the stairs, saying not a word to Fleurette,
who was at her sewing machine, or to Norma, who was completing some kind of small carpentry project in the washing
room. The sheriff pulled away as soon as I was back in the
car. "Wait," he said. "Let me see it."

He stopped in the middle of the road and took the envelope from me. There, in Henri LaMotte's faint handwriting,
was the lawyer's name: Ward.

"I can't believe I missed this," he said. "These are the same
photographs you showed me before?"

I nodded. "I didn't know who Ward was until you told me."

Without a word, he handed the envelope back to me and lifted his foot from the brake.

THE LAW FIRM OF WARD & McGINNIS kept a suite of rooms in the Second National Bank on Colt Street, one of those monstrous brick and limestone affairs with every sort of column, dormer, tower, and Corinthian flourish known to the stone-carvers of the previous century. It had survived a fire that burned most of the city when Fleurette was a little girl, and traces of black soot were still lodged in the crevices of its scrollwork, giving it the appearance of a building that had been drawn in artist's charcoal.

I didn't know exactly what kind of law Mr. Ward practiced, but as soon as we walked into his office, I could see that he practiced it with sophistication. The walls were lined in mahogany panels that glowed and smelled faintly of furniture polish. A red carpet woven with a diamond pattern muffled the sounds of the street, and the room was lit with new electric brass chandeliers. A pair of fan palms flanked a window, rising from identical Chinese black-and-gold lacquer pots perched on tiny cast-iron claw feet.

Presiding over this stylish lobby was a girl of about twenty in a polka-dotted dress. She sat behind a dainty secretary's desk furnished with a typewriter and a telephone. She looked up at us from under a halo of honey-colored hair, and I could see at once that she was not the usual harried clerk one met in an office in Paterson. She looked more like the kind of girl who posed for the cover of *Vogue*, with enormous blue eyes, three perfect freckles alongside her nose, and lips drawn like a bow tied in red ribbon. They must have held auditions to find a girl like this one. I could not imagine that she walked into their office by chance.

"Good afternoon," she said, offering us a warm and dimpled smile.

"We've come to see Mr. Ward," Sheriff Heath said. "It's an urgent matter. Is he in?"

She lifted her elegantly drawn eyebrows. "If I could keep track of where those two are at any hour of the day, I might be able to run this place like a respectable law office."

I glanced around. "It seems respectable to me."

"Oh, it looks nice enough, but those two—"

The sound of footsteps and laughter in the hallway made the young woman jump up. The door opened and two men burst in, grinning.

"Gertie, you won't believe it," said a tall, thin man with curly hair and a pipe dangling out of his mouth. He stopped when he saw us. The man he was with—shorter, rounder, red-haired, and freckle-faced, with pale green eyes and an eager smile—came to a stop just behind him.

The girl attempted to introduce us, although I hadn't yet given our names. "Mr. Ward, I—"

He pulled his pipe from his mouth and looked me over. "Never mind, Gertie," he said, and then, correcting himself, "Miss Nolan. Bob and I are old friends. Good to see you, Sheriff," he said, taking the sheriff's hand and pumping it vigorously. "What kind of trouble am I in today?"

He grinned at me and I resisted the urge to return his smile. John Ward was not handsome, exactly, but there was something both intelligent and impish about his expression, as if he were about to tell a joke or perform a skit. From the little I'd seen of him in the courtroom, I could only imagine the kind of theatrics he was capable of putting on in front of a judge.

Once his appraisal of me was complete, he remembered his manners and introduced himself. "John Ward, miss. Attorney at law. My partner, Peter McGinnis. And you have met Miss Nolan."

"How do you do," I said. "I am Constance Kopp. I have come—"

"I thought I knew you!" Mr. Ward said, elbowing his partner in the gut. "It's the girl from that Kaufman case. All right, Petey, you go on without me."

"Hey! You're not sticking me with Mrs. Cumberland again!" Mr. McGinnis protested.

John Ward put his pipe between his teeth. "I am. Got to have a few words with Miss Kopp. This way, my dear. You can come too, Bob."

He led us across the lobby to a door bearing matching nameplates. Sheriff Heath followed silently behind me. "Petey and I share an office," he said by way of explanation as he pushed the door open. "We always have. We shared a boarding room in law school and a clerkship in Trenton, and now we even share a desk. We're like an old married couple, except Petey won't iron my shirts."

Before he closed the door, he pushed his head into the reception room and said, "Isn't that right, Petey?"

Mr. McGinnis was whispering something to Miss Nolan. He stood quickly and said, "What's that?"

"I was just telling Miss Kopp here that you won't iron my shirts, even after all I've done for you."

"I did your ironing that once, but it was an exceptional circumstance."

John Ward cackled and closed the door. "He did iron my shirt one time," he said with a note of wonder in his voice. Then, pulling out a chair for me, he added, "I'll tell you that story someday, Miss Kopp. I'd almost forgotten it myself."

I sat down gingerly, my pocketbook in my lap, and the sheriff took the seat next to me. Mr. Ward settled into a leather armchair at one end of an enormous partner's desk, then gestured to an identical chair at the other end of the desk. "That's where Petey takes his afternoon nap," he said, removing his pipe from his teeth and tapping it into a tray. "But you didn't come here for a tour of the office, did you? You're here to see if I'm going to let you beat Henry Kaufman in court again."

Sheriff Heath cleared his throat. He hadn't gotten a word in since we'd arrived, and now I wasn't sure what either of us should say. I had been prepared for a much more serious meeting.

"Well, you don't have to worry about a thing," he said before either of us could compose an answer. "I'm off the case!"

"I'm sorry?" I said. "You're off the case?"

"Your sweetheart Kaufman fired me. He's a maniac, did you know that?"

Now I couldn't help but laugh. "He's not my sweetheart!"

"I knew I could make you smile. Now, Miss Kopp." And here he leaned forward and tried without much success to arrange his features into a more serious expression. "That man put me through hell—excuse me, but he did—and I can't imagine what your year has been like. How do you suppose that sister of his puts up with him?"

"I don't think she does," I said.

He put his pipe back in his mouth and leaned back, looking up at the ceiling and propping his feet on the desk. "No, I don't suppose so. You know, they used to be such nice, quiet clients. Out-of-town family, very routine business, nothing to see. Then the old man decided that the only way to straighten out his miscreant son was to give him a factory to run. I tried to talk him out of it, Miss Kopp. I did. But he signed over the bank account, gave him the keys to the factory, everything. Said he wanted Henry to know he was serious. But the truth is, the old man's always been a little soft when it came to Henry. I've no idea why. Now Mrs. Garfinkel's come to town to try to put it all back the way it was before their father got involved. It's a real mess."

"I'm sorry," I said. "Did you say Mr. Kaufman fired you?"

"Well, you might call it a mutual agreement to part ways. You know those friends of his—they're not the most law-abiding group. Henry kept bringing them in here and asking me to defend them on some petty criminal matter. Pretty soon they were all turning up with their brothers and cousins and neighbors. Harassing Miss Nolan, stinking up the place—I finally told Henry I wasn't taking on any more criminal cases, including his. He stormed out of here and I haven't seen him since."

I shifted in my chair. "If you're not going to defend him at trial, who will?"

He laughed and swung his feet back to the floor. "Some other fool. It won't be the law firm of Ward & McGinnis, that's all I know. But I wouldn't worry, Miss Kopp. Kaufman doesn't have time to find a good attorney, and a bad one will only help your case. Mrs. Garfinkel has finally persuaded her father to give her control of the bank accounts, and I don't think Henry even turns up at the factory anymore. I don't know where he'll get the money to pay another lawyer."

Sheriff Heath cleared his throat. "If I can get a word in, John."

"Sorry, Bob. Of course. I forget myself sometimes."

The sheriff slid the envelope across the desk. "Did you, by any chance, hire a photographer to take some pictures of a building in New York?"

Mr. Ward's mouth fell open. "This is one of LaMotte's jobs!"

"You know him?" I said.

"Course I do! I use him all the time. Did I forget to pay him for these? Oh, I'll be in trouble. Why didn't Gertie take care of this?" He opened the envelope and riffled through the pictures. "Means nothing to me," he muttered, mostly to himself. "I don't know what Kaufman was after."

"So it was him!" I said.

"Oh, sure it was. This was another of his crazy schemes. I should've fired him then."

"What did he hire you to do?" the sheriff asked.

The telephone rang in the lobby and he cocked his head to listen. A knock came at the door, and Miss Nolan looked in. "It's Mrs. Ward."

He dropped his pipe back into the tray. "Not for long she isn't."

Miss Nolan and I both gave a little gasp.

"Pardon me, girls. Don't ever marry, either one of you. Can't you tell her I left with Petey?"

"She just saw him going into the Hamilton Club."

In unison they said, "And that's why she's calling."

Mr. Ward raised his hands in mock surrender. "All right. Tell her to hold the line."

Miss Nolan retreated and closed the door behind her. Mr. Ward flipped through the photographs again and looked back up at Sheriff Heath. "Where were we?"

"John," the sheriff said. "This is serious. Isn't there anything you can tell us about these?"

He pushed the envelope back across the desk. "I don't know, Bob. Like I say, he just asked me to have the building watched. I think Kaufman liked to get me caught up in his lunatic schemes, just to see what I would do. He also wanted to know what was involved with adopting a baby. Can you imagine that? Henry Kaufman with a baby?"

I jumped to my feet. "Adoption?"

Mr. Ward rose as well. "Oh, well, nothing ever came of it. I shouldn't have mentioned it at all. He just came in here asking about orphanages and paperwork. I think he was tight. He usually was."

From the other room, Miss Nolan called for him. "Mr. Ward, she's still holding the line!"

Sheriff Heath started to say something but I grabbed his arm.

"Let's go," I said.

I pulled him into the lobby. Mr. Ward followed us and took up the telephone. As we walked away, we heard him shout into the receiver.

"Peaches? Is that you?"

⊰ 51 ⊱

AS SHERIFF HEATH'S AUTOMOBILE rolled down Colt Street, I said, "Don't you see? He left him in an orphanage. That's where anyone would leave a baby he didn't want to take care of."

"How do you know so much about it?"

I paused. I wasn't about to tell him how I knew.

"People do it all the time," I said. "They drop a child off because they can't feed it, or because the father's gone to jail, or because the mother has to go away and work. They say they'll come back, but they never do. Mr. Ward said he had questions about orphanages. I bet he was just trying to figure out what he would do with a baby once he had one. Lucy was right. He didn't want to pay support, he was tired of being bothered about it, and he thought she was blackmailing him for a share of the family's money. So he took the child and left it at an orphanage for adoption. He might have even believed it was his right to do, as the boy's father."

We stopped for a train crossing. We were fifth in a line of black automobiles. Behind us, two draft horses hauling a wagon of empty wooden barrels huffed and tossed their heads at the scream the train engine made as it went by.

Once the train passed, he said, "I don't see Kaufman grabbing a baby. And what do you suggest we do? Write to every orphanage in New Jersey and New York?"

"We're not writing letters," I said quickly. "I don't think Mr. Kaufman would have gone driving around New York looking for an orphanage. He would have wanted to get out of the city. Why wouldn't he bring it right back to Paterson?"

The sheriff turned to me, puzzled. "Do you expect me to go knocking on the doors of orphanages and ask if they've got an extra boy around the place?"

"No. I'm going, too."

He didn't say anything for a few minutes as we followed the line of cars across the tracks. Then he stopped at an intersection, pushed his hat off his forehead to rub his temples, and said, "All right. We're just down the street from one of them, so we might as well go now. There's another out on McBride, and of course the orphan asylum is down on Market Street. I can't think of any others."

The days of hiding a home for girls in the countryside were over. Mrs. Florence's home in Wyckoff had been closed for years. Any sort of orphanage or home for mothers and children would be found in the city today, near the hospital and the train station.

"Well, then, we have three to visit. We could see them all this afternoon and be home for supper."

He didn't answer, but he turned down Union, and soon we were driving along Albion, a tree-lined street of older homes set back from the road. At the end of the block, we came to a wide and plainly built farmhouse with green shutters and an enormous elm in front. It looked to be a comfortable and clean place for girls in confinement and their babies, but as we reached the door, I could smell rot and mildew inside. Sitting atop that was the odor of cabbage and beans.

A handwritten sign tacked next to the door read "MRS. LIVINGSTON'S HOME FOR THE UNWED AND FRIENDLESS. FORMERLY RESPECTABLE GIRLS ONLY. NO ADOPTIONS OFFERED."

Sheriff Heath rang the bell and a baby wailed in response. Another child joined in, and soon there were three of them. Footsteps echoed back and forth through the front rooms of the house, but no one came to the door.

A skinny cat jumped on the porch and tumbled backward in surprise when it saw us. It hissed at us from its hiding place.

The sheriff rang the bell again and this time the footsteps came closer. A girl in a housedress answered the door. She was only a teenager, and shapeless in a way that suggested that she had recently borne a child herself. Her hair was tied carelessly at the top of her head. I fought to push back memories of my own confinement, and the way I'd hide whenever a knock came at the door. This girl seemed so brazen in comparison.

She had a rag in her hand, which she dropped when she saw the sheriff.

"How do you do, miss," he said. "I am Sheriff Robert Heath, and this is Miss Kopp. We are here to see about a child. May we speak to Mrs. Livingston?"

Without a word she closed the door and left us standing there, the cat nosing at our ankles. Sheriff Heath pushed it off the porch with his boot. He looked over at me, embarrassed. "I don't like cats."

"Neither do I."

We heard footsteps again and the door opened, this time revealing a short, squat woman with hair the color of a cast-iron pan and a disposition to match. She wore a high-necked dress the likes of which I hadn't seen since my grandmother was alive, and spectacles as thick and dusty as the windows in her old home.

"We have no business with you," she said before Sheriff Heath could get in a word. "Our girls come from good homes and the children are carefully placed with families."

She started to close the door, but the sheriff reached out and held it. "We need a word with you," he said. "It concerns a criminal matter. We wish to clear your home of any wrongdoing, but if we're unable to do that today, we'll send detectives around tomorrow. We'd like to keep it out of the papers."

Her face settled into its frown lines, but she stepped aside so we could enter. She closed the door behind us and we stood in a dark foyer next to a stack of old newspapers and a row of empty milk bottles. There were blankets and wooden toys on the stairs, cups and tiny plates on the floor, and the smell of sour milk rising from the carpet. Mrs. Florence never would have tolerated such a mess.

She looked expectantly at us. I cleared my throat and said, "We believe a man deposited a baby boy at a church home or an orphanage last year."

She shook her head. "We would have turned him away. We don't let people do that anymore. Too much trouble for us, and we have enough trouble as it is."

As if to illustrate her point, two girls of a tender age lumbered down the stairs, their bellies so swollen that no dress could hide their condition. Sheriff Heath looked quickly away. When they saw him, they turned without a word and disappeared.

"We're sorry to have disturbed you, Mrs. Livingston," I said. "Can you tell me where such a child would be taken?"

"Not to a home like mine," she said. "And not the Catholic home either. The Orphan Asylum Hospital would take him, but he'd be sent right out for adoption if no one claimed him."

THE ASYLUM WAS HOUSED in a fearsome brick building on Market Street, where it stood as a solemn reminder of the misfortunes that could be inflicted upon small children. More than one parent or vicious older sibling threatened to send little boys and girls there if they misbehaved. Such jokes were strictly banned in our household, but Fleurette knew about the place somehow, and when she was only five, she visited it in her nightmares. I remember lying awake on those nights and fighting the urge to go to her as my mother rose instead to quiet the child.

But compared to Mrs. Livingston's home, the orphan asylum was surprisingly clean and uncluttered. We entered through grand brass doors and were greeted by the smell of floor soap and the sound of a typewriter. A plump older woman sat behind the desk and stopped typing when she saw us.

"Sheriff Heath," she said, pushing her glasses up on her nose. "What a nice surprise. How are dear Cordelia and those sweet children?"

"They're just fine," he said. "May I introduce you to my associate, Miss Kopp. She's helping me with a case." Turning to me, he said, "Mrs. Griggs lived next door to us before we moved to our present living quarters."

"I'm sure Cordelia misses her kitchen," Mrs. Griggs said.

"I think she misses her neighbors even more," he said. "The inmates and guards are no company for a woman. I hope you'll come and pay her a visit."

"Oh!" she said, flustered. "At the prison? I don't think—"

"It's the safest home in Bergen County," I said. Sheriff Heath gave me a grateful look. "I've been there myself, and I can assure you that Mrs. Heath has made it quite comfortable."

"Well, perhaps I will," she said, without enthusiasm.

Sheriff Heath cleared his throat and nodded at me. I explained our purpose.

She squinted up at the two of us. "I don't remember him, but I'm not the only one who greets visitors. What does the boy look like?"

"I'm afraid we don't know," I said. "When the child was last seen, he was just a baby, and we have only the most general description."

She looked up and down the long empty hallway. There were doors on either side, the kind with glass windows and someone's name in gold lettering. "If he was here, we would have a file." After looking around again, she said, "It's almost five o'clock. I don't think anyone else will be in today. Stay here and let me go have a peek in the office."

She disappeared through a door down the corridor. Several nurses and orderlies left for the day, their coats and lunch pails over their arms. They looked at us but said nothing as they walked by.

At last Mrs. Griggs returned with a stack of folders under her arm. "Here are all the children who came in around that time. What are the names again?" she asked.

We gave her every name we could think of connected to

the case. There were a few dozen files to look through, but she paged through them quickly and shook her head.

"I'm sorry," she said. "I don't see any of those names."

"Have these children all been adopted?" I asked.

"Oh, I would think so by now, wouldn't you? Let me see." She paged through them again, placing the files in one of three stacks on her desk.

"These were returned to their families," she said, pointing to the first stack. "These were put up for adoption and placed with someone. And these are still here, or their files are incomplete. I'd have to make some inquiries to find out what happened to them."

I pointed to the second and third stacks. "May I see just the boys?"

I reached into my pocketbook for some notepaper and wrote down the names in the remaining files. There was very little information to record. In some cases it was simply a date, the age and sex of the child, and a line for whatever name people were willing to supply. I saw no Bobby or Robert or Robbie among them, nor any boy of the right age who would have been dropped off around that time.

"Are you sure these are all of them?" I said.

"All but the private placements," she answered. "Some of our records are sealed at the mother's request."

I shook my head. "The mother is the one looking for the child in this case."

Sheriff Heath rose to thank his friend and soon we were outside in the fading afternoon light. The mills had just discharged their workers, and a stream of weavers and dyers and machinists flooded Market Street, each shivering in their work clothes and trudging toward whatever kind of home they knew. Sheriff Heath drove me back to Wyckoff while I sat next to him in silence, my fingers working the edges of the page on which I had written the names of lost and orphaned children and the adults who had deposited them there for safekeeping, or whatever manner of keeping a child might expect in an asylum hospital.

"I don't like it," he said, before I got out of the car. "I don't picture Kaufman and that gang of his stealing a baby and leaving it at an orphanage. How would they even know what to do with a baby?"

I agreed. I couldn't see Henry Kaufman doing a thing like that, either. But I also couldn't believe he wasn't involved somehow.

❧ 52 ❧

THAT NIGHT ANOTHER SNOWFALL made Sicomac Road almost impassable again. Two of the enormous plane trees that lined the road split in half under the force of wind and ice, blocking the way until the weather cleared enough for some of the men to come out and chop them to pieces. Low spots in the road had turned into rivers when it rained and were now frozen. When the ice thawed, the ground heaved and cracked.

In the early morning, a sharp sound propelled me out of bed. Thinking it was a gunshot, I flattened myself against the wall next to the window, which was glazed with ice and impossible to see through. I was trying to force it open when Norma appeared in the doorway, already dressed and wrapped in her winter coat.

"It was a tree," she said. "It hit the barn. Get dressed."

I did as she said and met her in the kitchen, which was dark and so cold that it, too, could have been covered in ice. She handed me a pair of work gloves and a set of earmuffs.

"Watch your step," she said, and pushed the door open. "It's frozen solid out here."

I choked at the first blast of frigid air. Norma tucked her chin into her coat and trudged ahead, making little snorting sounds as she struggled to breathe. Across the drive were the severed branches of an old elm tree that lost the battle with the storm. Only its roots, just lifted out of the ground, were not covered in ice.

The barn door was entirely blocked by fallen limbs, making it impossible to get in to tend the animals. Even worse, a low corner of the roof had crumbled when the tree hit it. I could hear the chickens complaining from their roost.

"Ach. We should have done the roof last summer," I said into my coat collar.

Norma grunted. "We'll do it today."

All morning we chopped away at the tree limbs and hauled them to the woodpile. Norma took a hatchet to the smaller branches while I went after the trunk with an old and unreliable saw. It was slippery and dangerous work, with the ice shifting and melting underneath our feet and the limbs sliding out of our grasp. Once Norma slipped on the ice and fell backward, her hatchet flying out of her hand. "Get away," she yelled, but by the time I saw what I was getting away from, the hatchet had hit its mark, landing atop a fence post in the vegetable garden. I couldn't have moved anyway. The saw was embedded in the tree at that moment, and my gloves were stuck to the saw.

Fleurette took her time getting out of bed, although she must have heard us working below her window. When she finally appeared in the doorway and offered to help, we both yelled, "Coffee!" She retreated indoors and put herself to good use boiling coffee, heating rolls, and frying bacon. We refused to go inside on the grounds that once we got warm, we would not want to go out again. Instead Fleurette carried our breakfast to us and kept up a steady brigade of rolls and hot drinks while we worked.

It must have been after noon by the time we cleared the branches and pushed open the barn door. A chorus of complaints rose from the animals. Dolley stamped and snuffled in her stall and the chickens answered with low cackles. Norma took her hatchet to the frozen water trough while I handed out oats and tossed cracked corn to the chickens. I sat down for just a minute to catch my breath, but as soon as I did my eyes closed and darkness crowded in.

"Get up!" Norma said. "We've got to do something about that roof, and there's more snow on the way."

More snow? I pushed myself to my feet and went to the door. Sure enough, the wind had picked up and brought a few flakes with it. I leaned against the doorway, but Norma butted me with the end of a ladder, pushing me outside.

I didn't think I could stay upright for another minute. "Norma," I said, while she set the ladder up against the side of the barn, "don't you ever wish it were easier?"

"What?"

"This," I said, gesturing at the snow and the ice and the broken limbs. "Living out here on our own like this."

She kicked at the ladder to dig it into the ground. "I've always believed that people who strive for an easy life become dull and lazy. And I don't see the point in living somewhere else, when this place already suits us so well."

"But we might have to. Francis is right. Our money's running out."

"In that case," Norma said, in a voice that suggested that the matter was closed, "it's your turn to figure things out."

"What does that mean?"

"It means that I found this place. I found you, and I found Fleurette." She looked out at the road—at the very spot where she'd stood when she first declared that we would live here, seventeen years ago. Then she turned to look at me, a kind of hard satisfaction in her eyes. "Didn't I?"

For a minute I couldn't say anything. There was just the hollow, distant sound of the wind and the gathering snowfall.

"You did," I said.

"Yes, I did. Now it's your turn. Mother's gone, so who's stopping you? Go and find yourself a little job that pays just enough to keep us. Doesn't that sound like something you'd enjoy?"

"I don't know what I'd enjoy," I said.

"I do," Norma declared. "You've had such a high time running around playing detective. Why don't you become one of those?"

She started to climb the ladder. I tried to pull her down but she shook me off. "What are you talking about?"

"There was an advertisement in the paper last week for female detectives at Wanamaker's," she said, looking down at me. "Didn't you see it? Write a letter and tell them all about yourself, and I'm sure they'll put you right in."

I stood staring up at her. She turned around and kept climbing. The hem of her split skirt, dirty from the mud and snow, brushed against me.

"Just don't let us be reduced to living with Francis."

"Wanamaker's?" I said. "In New York?"

"Take the train," she called down. "You know how to ride the train."

I looked straight ahead at the bottom rungs of the ladder and the weathered old boards of the barn behind them. Had I really just heard my sister tell me to leave the house—not once, but every day—for a job specifically designed to put me in the path of criminals? What had become of us?

"And I've got a job for you right now, if you can stop day-dreaming," she said. "Hold that ladder and pass me the tools."

I handed the saw to her, then stood and watched as she chopped away at the jagged edges of the hole, letting the severed shingles drop into the chicken pen below. Once she had a clean edge to work with, I passed some odd-size chunks of wood to her, and she found a way to nail them in place. I could hear her huffing and panting above me as she worked. I was growing stiff and frozen on the ground, my boots buried once again in snow and my fingers so numb I worried they'd lose their grip on the ladder. A vision of that clean and quiet hotel on Fifth Avenue floated before me, with its white sheets and brass lamps polished by a hand I'd never see. In a place like that, I could have an egg brought to me every day, without ever once having to patch a roof on a chicken coop in the middle of winter.

All afternoon the road was empty and the surrounding pastures silent and still. Smoke drifted over from some distant neighbor's chimney, but then the wind receded and the snow fell down like a blanket, until even the smoke was snuffed out. When Norma stepped off the ladder, she wore a collar of fresh snowfall.

That night Fleurette lit the water heater and boiled some

extra water on the stove so we could both have baths, but Norma didn't want to bother with it and I wanted supper first. We sat silently in the kitchen and ate corned beef and potatoes along with the last of the morning's rolls. I never did get warm enough to do without my coat, so I sat under a mountain of wool and let the snow drip onto the floor below my chair. Norma's fingers were red and chapped from working on the roof. Fleurette offered to rub some cold cream into them, but she refused, wanting only to take tea and a bed warmer upstairs and go right to sleep. I took an extra kettle of hot water to the bathroom and left Fleurette to do the washing up.

The bath was steaming when I sank into it, drawing the blood back to my numb feet. I wiggled my toes until pinpricks of pain ran through them and the sensation returned. The tub was too small for me and I couldn't submerge myself all at once. The only way to get my knees in was to curl in a ball and turn on my side. I awoke just as the water started to cool and put myself to bed.

⊰ 53 ⊱

BY MIDNIGHT I WAS SITTING UP IN THE DARK, listening to a screech owl call to its mate, and thinking quite suddenly of Lucy. I wasn't ready to give up on the idea that the child made it back to Paterson. I saw no other way to go about it than to look into every orphan on the list, and then go to the orphanage in the next county, and the one after that. But I wasn't sure I'd ever get anywhere at that rate.

When the clock downstairs struck one, I still hadn't settled on a course of action. I might have dropped off to sleep, but when the clock chimed three I awoke again, thinking about what Sheriff Heath had said. Henry Kaufman did not seem like the kind of person who would know what to do with a baby, even for an hour, even long enough to grab him and then turn him loose again.

But Marion Garfinkel was that kind of person. She'd know what to do. She'd place him anonymously, claiming that the child was her own. If she needed to, she'd offer enough money to make sure that no one asked any questions.

What was it she told me when I asked about Lucy's child? *It's better off wherever it is now.*

And she probably believed that.

At last sleep caught up with me again and I didn't move until the chickens started cackling at daybreak. The truth was with me, as if I had known it all along.

THE SKY HAD CLEARED and the snow had hardened overnight. Dolley didn't want to be out in it any more than I did, but I nudged her along Sicomac Road anyway. A number of motor cars passed me, each of them honking and swerving and nearly running us off the road. Dolley had never been a high-strung horse, but these black and noisy machines were making a nervous animal out of her. I tried to cluck at her the way Norma did, but she didn't find it soothing.

I stabled her for a few hours in Paterson and walked over to the orphan asylum in the gray sludge that had been pushed aside by the plows. In no time at all I was at the front door, relieved to find Mrs. Griggs at her station.

She was considerably less friendly to me than she had been to Sheriff Heath. When I made my request, she frowned and said, "Shouldn't Sheriff Heath be the one asking the questions?"

I stood a little straighter and spoke in the most commanding voice I could muster.

"He requested my help on a sensitive matter. A girl got into some trouble, and the sheriff thought it best to have a lady make the more delicate inquiries. That's why he brought me here. If you feel his introduction was not satisfactory, I'll go now to Hackensack and return with him for a second one. But I know he won't be happy to be called away from the prison and his important work protecting the citizens of Bergen County simply to do again what he has already done."

She pressed her lips together in a disapproving frown. "You know I can't tell you anything about our private placements. If the mother surrenders a child, the records are sealed forever."

I knew that well enough. The same promise had been made to me. "What if a woman brought a child in and claimed to be its mother, but wasn't?"

"We'd have a look at the birth certificate. We'd ask for identification or a witness."

"But some children are born at home. They don't all have birth certificates."

"What are you looking for, exactly?" Mrs. Griggs asked.

I could tell that I wasn't going to get into those files unless I told her what I suspected. I gave her Marion Garfinkel's name, described her, and told her again the boy's age and when we thought he would have been brought in.

She wrote it all down and then scrutinized the paper in front of her. "You're suggesting the boy was kidnapped."

"It wouldn't be that unusual. Isn't it possible that someone would try a thing like that to cover up a scandal in the family?"

She searched my face thoughtfully for a minute, then rose from her desk and disappeared into the office. After a long wait she returned, clutching a folder to her bosom as if she wasn't sure she was ready to let me see it.

"We had only one private placement of a boy that age during the strikes," she said, easing gingerly back into her chair. "If this is the child you're looking for, then I believe we still have him."

I took a deep breath and dropped into the chair across from her. The realization that I might have done this—that I might have helped Lucy find her son—this sent all the blood to my cheeks and set my heart pounding.

I wasn't sure I trusted myself to speak. She set the file on her desk and ran her hands across it.

At last I said, "Is he here now? Could I see him?"

"Certainly not," she said. "If this is a matter for the sheriff, then the sheriff should come and see the child."

By then I had my breath back. "Of course he will," I said evenly. "I only wish to be sure of the situation before I ask him to take an afternoon away from his duties. Do you know anything more about the circumstances under which the boy was brought here?"

With a long and shaky sigh, Mrs. Griggs opened the file and lifted it toward her so I could not see the papers it held. After flipping through them for a few minutes, she said, "I don't remember this one, but from what I can see, it was an unusual case. A woman brought the baby to us, but had none of the papers we require—no birth certificate, no letter from a doctor, and no list of family members. She wouldn't even provide the boy's name or his last known address. She said that she'd had the baby abroad to avoid suspicion and had only just recently returned. We called him Teddy for lack of another name."

"But the mother—the woman claiming to be the mother—that was Marion Garfinkel?"

She closed the folder. "She gave a very common name and I suppose it could have been false. Our director will have to speak to the sheriff before we can say anything more about it. This may require a hearing before a judge. It's very unusual."

"But the boy is here?"

For the first time, a smile worked around the corners of her lips. "If this is the boy—and I'm not saying it is—we definitely do still have him. There are so many infants that come to us, and those are adopted first. Even a child of one or two years is hard to place."

"Mrs. Griggs, you've done a little boy and his mother a great deal of good today," I said, jumping out of my chair. "The sheriff must be told immediately. Could you place a telephone call to his office?"

She looked down at the brass phone on her desk and drummed her fingers. "I shouldn't make the call," she said. "But our director can."

She ran upstairs and, after another interminable wait, returned with an expression I couldn't read. "As I suspected, you'll have to go to a judge before a claim can be made. But first the child must be identified by its mother. Sheriff Heath said he would fetch the girl and be right over. He said you would know where to find her."

I gave her Lucy Blake's address, and she disappeared again up the wide staircase, her fingers trailing along a banister into which a row of laurel leaves had been carved. I waited the better part of an hour, with Mrs. Griggs running downstairs to tell me that Sheriff Heath was on his way, and then rushing back up to tell the nurses to get the boy ready. From her excited air I gathered that they felt quite sure that one of their charges was going home with its mother. I hope they hadn't given the boy that impression. I couldn't stand to see Lucy shake her head and tell the boy that he did not belong to her.

I paced the lobby and tried to picture Marion Garfinkel carrying a baby in. I couldn't see her without also seeing the chain of errors and misfortune that brought her here. There was Henry Kaufman's father, putting him in charge of a factory he had no ability to run. There was Henry Kaufman himself, forcing his way into Lucy's room with his own disgraceful intentions. And then Lucy, hoping—naively, perhaps stupidly—that he would face up to his obligations.

Finally, there was Marion, the expedient one, the efficient one. She saw a problem and, just as quickly, she saw its solution. It was not difficult to understand how Marion got the idea. If I were to stop a hundred women on the sidewalk in Paterson and ask them what an unmarried factory girl should do if she got herself into trouble, they would all give the same answer.

It was the answer I'd come to myself, seventeen years ago. It was the only sensible solution, and Marion Garfinkel was, I had to admit, eminently sensible.

I stopped pacing and had just sat down across from Mrs. Griggs's desk again when Sheriff Heath pushed the door open and led a trembling and tearful Lucy Blake into the halls of the Paterson Orphan Asylum Hospital.

She hadn't even taken off her apron. When she saw me, she ran across the lobby to me. "I don't know what I'll do if it isn't him," she said.

"It's all right," I said, although I wasn't sure if it was. "Be a brave girl and try not to upset the child."

Mrs. Griggs called a nurse who led us up the stairs, through a locked door, and into a short, windowless corridor. At the end of it was a door with a brass plate marked "BOYS."

She unlocked the door and pushed it open. We stepped into an enormous room with high windows and rows of iron beds on either side. Shoes and jackets and children's blocks were scattered about the room.

And in the middle of it stood one little boy.

Lucy ran for him before any of us had a moment to think. He was in her arms and smothered against her shoulder so fast that I didn't get a good look at his face. As she spun around, all I could see was black hair like his father's, wetted and combed along a neat part, and the back of the smallest blue suit I'd ever seen.

The nurse smiled and stepped back into the doorway to motion for her colleagues, who must have gathered just outside when they heard us come upstairs. Sheriff Heath bowed his head and stepped away to make room for them.

Lucy didn't stop spinning and I began to wonder if she was ever going to let the boy come up for air. They formed their own planet in the middle of the room, rotating around a sun that only they could see.

❧ 54 ❧

LUCY LOOSENED HER GRIP ON THE BOY. She sat down on the edge of a bed and held him in her lap. He had Mr. Kaufman's hair and round forehead, but he'd inherited Lucy's eyes and her fine Irish profile.

Sheriff Heath knelt down in front of them and held out his hand to the boy, who didn't know to shake it but gripped his fingers. He was a fine, plump boy, old enough to walk on his own, but too young to understand what was happening.

"It's nice to meet you, son," was all that Sheriff Heath could say.

I stood in the doorway and talked in a low voice with the nurses. They were willing to fix up a room so that Lucy could stay the night.

"It's better that way," one of them whispered to me. "If we make her go home without him, she could make such a fuss that the other children would hear it. We'd never get them to bed after a scene like that."

Lucy overheard us and rose from the edge of the bed, carrying the boy on her hip as if she'd been doing it every day since he was born. "The sheriff already told me he'd have to stay here tonight," she said. "It's all right. I work for two shut-ins who are expecting their supper. They've been very gracious, but I should go back to them."

"I'll get a judge to see us tomorrow, and I'll take statements from the nurses tonight so we'll be ready for his questions," Sheriff Heath said, and he and I walked downstairs and left Lucy to say her goodbyes. The news had already reached Mrs. Griggs, who was waiting for us at the bottom of the stairs.

She smiled broadly. "This doesn't happen often enough around here. The nurses are terribly pleased."

"In my years as a sheriff, I've never returned a lost child to its parents. And I didn't do it this time, either. We have Miss Kopp to thank for this one."

She nodded at me, still smiling. Then she turned back to the sheriff and said, "I suppose the story will come out before the judge tomorrow and may be in the papers."

"We hope to keep it out of the papers," he said quickly.

"Yes. I gather that the boy's father is not . . ."

"No. The father won't have anything to do with the child. But the girl is in a comfortable situation as a domestic servant for two spinsters who are willing to take in the boy. I spoke to them this afternoon, and they have agreed to sign a letter for the judge. My stenographer will get it written tonight."

"Well," she said. "If the judge is satisfied, we will be, too."

At last Lucy appeared at the top of the stairs, along with a nurse who had no doubt been sent along in case of hysterics. But Lucy's head was high and she seemed to have a firm grip on herself. She walked slowly but deliberately, and smiled bravely when she said, "I told him I had to go and make a bed for him. He's grown too much for the one I had."

The next morning, Sheriff Heath and I were waiting in front of the factory when Marion Garfinkel arrived. "If it's about the trial, you'll have to speak to Henry," she said when she saw us. "I want nothing to do with it. I told him I would pay Mr. Ward's bills, but I'm not paying another attorney. He's on his own now."

She opened the side entrance just enough to let herself in and tried to close it behind her. Sheriff Heath caught the door before she did. "We can speak here, or I can bring you to the courthouse," he said quietly.

Marion shrugged without looking back at him. "We can talk all day if you want. I'm not responsible for my brother anymore. I haven't even seen him in weeks."

We followed her across the empty factory floor. "I've taken over Henry's desk," she said, leading us into his office, which had been thoroughly cleaned and transformed from a clubhouse back into a room where business could take place.

Sheriff Heath closed the door behind him. "This concerns Lucy Blake."

She dropped into her chair and gave an elaborate shrug. "I haven't seen her either. Maybe the two of them ran off together." She picked up a letter opener and slid an envelope open.

That indifferent gesture—the flick of a knife through paper—enraged me. How could this woman sit so casually after what she had done? The sheriff had warned me to stay quiet, but I couldn't.

"We found him," I said. "Right here in Paterson, where you left him."

The letter opener dropped to her desk. She kept her eyes down. The sheriff cleared his throat and leaned forward. "A boy was left at the Paterson Orphan Asylum last year. Lucy Blake has identified the child as hers. One of the nurses at the asylum remembers when you brought in the baby. She described you perfectly last night. And your handwriting is in the file. It isn't your name, but it happens that we brought in an expert on the study of handwriting. He's helping us with the case against your brother."

She lifted her eyebrows and her lips moved, but no words came out.

"Your attorney remembers Henry asking about adopting a baby," I said. "Was it Henry's idea?"

Still Marion said nothing.

"You can make your statement here, or we will take it at the courthouse," the sheriff said.

"I have no statement to make."

"A forthright confession will help you avoid the scandal of a trial. Ask your attorney if you don't believe me. Although he tells me he isn't taking any more criminal cases."

She took in a long, trembling breath and smoothed the papers on her desk. "It might have been Henry's idea, but he wasn't involved. I couldn't trust him to keep it quiet."

I caught myself nodding in agreement. Marion was shrewd. Of the two, she made the better criminal.

"I thought it was best for the child," she continued, so quietly that I had to lean in to hear. "That girl couldn't have raised him on her own. She would have kept coming back for money. She would have dragged us through the courts eventually."

She looked up at us defiantly. "I'm expected to clean up after my brother, so I did. And surely you agree that I did that baby a favor."

I wasn't surprised to hear her say that. But I couldn't picture her sneaking into a building and grabbing the child.

"You had help," I said. "Someone created a commotion inside that building and scared off the unionists. They ran off in the middle of the night, and they never reported the baby missing. You couldn't have frightened them like that yourself."

She tilted her head to one side, and then the other, as if she was weighing her options. Finally she said, "My brother has some rather unsavory friends. But useful."

Mrs. Garfinkel walked out of the office slowly, shakily, with me on one side and Sheriff Heath on the other. She murmured a few words to one of the secretaries who was just walking in. There were two automobiles waiting outside: one to take her to jail, and another to take us to pick up Lucy Blake.

THE ARREST OF MRS. GARFINKEL mattered little to Lucy, who urged us not to press charges at all but to just return her child to her and let her get as far away from the Kaufman family as she could.

"Kidnapping is not a crime we can overlook, Miss Blake," the sheriff said. "But we expect Mrs. Garfinkel to make a full confession and avoid a trial. We should be able to keep it out of the papers. I can't guarantee that Kaufman will leave you alone, but he doesn't know where you live and we'll make sure he doesn't find out."

The hearing was conducted later that morning exactly as

Sheriff Heath said it would be. A judge greeted us in closed chambers and heard testimony from Lucy and Sheriff Heath. (I was introduced only as a friend of Lucy's and had no objection to that.) The letter from Lucy's employer was read aloud and found suitable. Prosecutor Wright stepped in long enough to say that charges had been read against Marion Garfinkel and that she would be detained until arrangements could be made about her bail. The judge heard it all and signed the order before him authorizing the orphanage to release the child to his mother.

Lucy chatted happily as we drove back to the orphanage, describing the sitting room the sisters had agreed to turn into a nursery where little Bobby could spend his days while she worked. She said that they had made substantial donations to their church's building fund years ago and had already written to the minister's wife to ask for help in securing clothing and shoes for the child. Sheriff Heath said he thought his wife might have a few things she could send over, and I offered to have Fleurette sew anything else the boy might need.

We were in high spirits when we arrived. Sheriff Heath and I stood in the lobby while Lucy ran upstairs to collect her boy.

The sheriff held his hat and ran his fingers around the brim. "I owe you an apology, Miss Kopp," he said.

"I don't think you do," I said.

"No, you did this all on your own. You went to New York and found that photographer. I missed John Ward's name on the pictures, but you remembered. And whatever made you think of going around to the orphanages—well, you put it all together very quickly. You make a good detective."

I laughed. "It appears that you and Norma agree on something. If there are any positions for lady detectives, please be sure to tell me," I said.

"What's that?" he said.

"The Kopp sisters need to find jobs or husbands, and soon," I said.

"Who says so?"

"Our bank balance says so." Lucy's feet appeared at the top of the stairs and I ran toward her. "Just don't send any suitors my way," I called back to the sheriff. "I'm trying the other route first." Lucy descended to the landing with her little boy in her arms, and they both fell against me at once, all light and laughter.

❧ 55 ❧

"YOU'RE NOT TAKING A JOB IN NEW YORK!" Fleurette said, dropping the roll she'd been buttering.

"Not yet," I said. "I just wrote to them and asked about the position."

"And what did they say?"

"They sent an immediate reply and said they were quite desperate for extra help this spring and wondered if I'd like to come for an interview right away. I'm going tomorrow."

Fleurette stared at Norma in horror. We had decided not to tell Fleurette of our financial difficulties or of Francis's pressure to sell the farm. We didn't want her to be angry with him.

"What are you going to do?" she asked. "Wrap presents behind the counter?"

"Oh, not at all," I said. "They're hiring store detectives."

WHEN MR. WANAMAKER first opened his store in New York, he made much of the fact that shoppers could wander freely through the sales floor and handle the goods themselves, an idea that was still quite novel back in 1896. His was a glittering bazaar of velvet gloves and leather shoes and miles of ribbon and lace and tailored suits for men and every other convenience a city-dweller might want, straddling two blocks on Broadway and employing a few thousand clerks and stock boys.

He believed that prices should be written on paper tags and affixed directly to the merchandise so that his customers could see for themselves what each item cost. "If everyone is equal before God," he liked to tell his managers, "then everyone should be equal before price."

Unfortunately for Mr. Wanamaker and his Christian principles, the openness of his store invited thievery. To combat this problem, some of his clerks had become detectives, strolling around the sales floor in ordinary dress, posing as shoppers but keeping their eyes on the slim fingers and gaping pocketbooks of a new breed of genteel downtown thief. Even women stole from Wanamaker's, which meant that women had to be employed as detectives to monitor the gloves and lace and undergarments. The job was simply to walk the sales floor, as unobtrusively as possible, wearing one's own clothes, looking like an ordinary shopper. I saw no reason why I couldn't get hired to do a simple thing like that.

I WAS FIFTEEN MINUTES EARLY for my interview with Mrs. Langdon, the ladies' sales manager at Wanamaker's. I wore a wool dress of dark green that Fleurette had just finished for me. It seemed like a smart dress for a store detective—nicely tailored but comfortable, of an ordinary fabric and color that would not call attention to itself. Fleurette had declared it to be a dress for a woman who had important things to do.

I approached a girl selling scarves at a counter near the entrance and asked her where I might find Mrs. Langdon.

"Oh!" she said. "Is Annie all right?"

"Annie?"

"One of the girls. She's been missing and Mrs. Langdon said that her mother was coming in to talk to her. I thought you might have been Annie's mother."

I looked down at my suit and my high leather shoes. I did look matronly.

"I'm here to interview for a position," I said.

"You are?" The girl looked up at me, puzzled. She wore smooth ringlets of brown hair around a perfectly round face that seemed to wear a perpetual expression of surprise. She couldn't have been more than eighteen.

"Won't your husband mind?" she said.

I hadn't time to explain myself. "Perhaps I'll ask at the perfume counter."

"I'm sorry, ma'am," the girl said quickly. "Her office is upstairs and straight to the back. Through the white door without a sign on it."

I made my way past the scarves and the perfume, past the last of the winter gloves and a collection of lace for spring, past a table of sewing notions stocked with pearl buttons and a shelf of leather-bound books sold by the set. At last I reached the white door upstairs, and behind that door was Mrs. Langdon, seated at her desk.

Here, at last, was someone who wasn't eighteen. She wore a neat bun of perfectly white hair, and a crisply starched white cotton blouse to match. Everything in her office, in fact, was white: the walls, the rug, and even her furniture, all painted the color of flawless new snow.

She raised a tiny hand as I walked in to indicate that I should not interrupt her writing. I waited while she scratched her paper and blotted it, and then she turned to face me.

"I'm sorry, my dear," she said. "I'm conducting an interview at two o'clock, and I was just going out to look for the girl. Can someone else help you?"

"I . . . I am the girl," I said, realizing at once how foolish I sounded. "I mean, I am Constance Kopp. You wrote to me. About the detective position."

She made a little gasp that caught in her throat. She rose from her chair, not taking her eyes off me, and walked right up to me. Mrs. Langdon was a petite woman of hardly more than five feet in height, so when she stood in front of me, she looked directly at the button fastened across my breastbone. I took a step back so that she could look me in the eye, but she stepped forward again. I wondered if she was nearsighted. Then she walked around me, slowly, the way one takes in a statue at a museum.

I held my breath. Was this the interview?

She circled back to her desk. There was no other chair in the room, so I remained standing. "I'm sorry, my dear," she said briskly, giving me one last appraisal over the tops of her spectacles. "You won't do at all. We're looking for someone—unobtrusive."

"Unobtrusive?" I said. "I've worn the most ordinary dress, just as you asked."

She shook her head slowly. "It isn't your dress, my dear. It's—well, we can't have a store detective who stands head and shoulders above all the other shoppers. You'll be noticed. The thieves will have no trouble describing you to each other. They do talk, you know."

I didn't know. "But my size could be an advantage," I said, trying to sound cheerful and not at all desperate. "I can see above the other ladies. And if you're trying to catch a pickpocket, surely it would be a help to have a detective with some strength. If someone tried to run away I'd have no trouble keeping hold of them."

Mrs. Langdon gave a small, polite laugh. "My dear. We aren't hiring a police officer. I'm not looking for someone to make a scene on the sales floor. We want more of a"—and here she paused to consider her words—"a gentle presence. Watchful, but polite. Discreet."

It hadn't occurred to me that I'd be turned down after I'd come all this way. Wasn't I polite and discreet?

I let my silence hang in the air for just a second too long. Mrs. Langdon rose and opened the door.

"I don't think we're what you're looking for, my dear," she said, looking up at me with pale blue eyes. "You're better suited for something more rough and tumble."

Rough and tumble?

She patted my arm and gestured through the open door. "You'll find it."

❧ 56 ❧

"A GENTLE PRESENCE?" Norma said, outraged. "Are you sure that's what she said?"

"She thought I would stand out," I said. "She thought I would be too conspicuous."

"Isn't that what a store detective should be?" Fleurette asked. "How else will the thieves know to stay away?"

"It doesn't work that way." I was tired of talking about it already, and embarrassed that I'd lost a job that should have been handed to me easily.

In an effort to change the subject, Norma tossed the newspaper at me. "It appears that Sheriff Heath has won over another criminal with his kindness and hospitality."

SAVED OF PRISON TERM BY SHERIFF

GEORGE EWING OF HACKENSACK, a former convict who was indicted for using the mails to defraud victims throughout the county, was saved from being returned to state prison by Sheriff Heath of Bergen County, who said he thought the convict could be reformed.

Ewing was released from state prison after having served his part of a sentence for theft. He returned to Bergen County and led a good life, said the sheriff. Then he relapsed into his old ways and was arrested.

The sheriff took such a kind interest in him that when the case came up yesterday he appealed to the court, saying that if the prisoner were sentenced to prison he would probably never be reformed. Judge Haight then sentenced Ewing to five months in the Bergen County Jail.

"But that's good news for us!" I said. "It means that he's agreed that he won't claim responsibility for Mr. Kaufman's crimes. We can go forward with the case."

"What makes you think he won't change his mind?" Norma said.

"He agreed to tell the truth if we kept him here in Hackensack, and we've done that."

Norma raised an eyebrow at me. "A criminal has made a promise to tell the truth, and now our case against a violent and unpredictable madman depends upon him. Are you suggesting that we take this to be good news?"

"It was my idea," I said. "I told the sheriff that if Mr. Ewing really wanted to stay in the Hackensack jail, he should use that as leverage."

"Well, I knew it all along," Norma said. "You are good at something."

"What's that?"

"Telling Sheriff Heath what to do."

OVER THE NEXT FEW WEEKS, our case proceeded to trial. Prosecutor Wright called me into his office several times to go over it. The questions struck me as repetitive and unnecessary, but Mr. Wright insisted that we review every detail. Mr. Kinsley, the handwriting expert from New York, was prepared to testify that Mr. Kaufman had written the letters. He also secured a full confession from Marion Garfinkel on the basis of her false signature at the orphanage. Once she saw the way he was planning to put the evidence before a jury, she knew better than to fight the charges. She paid her own bond and was awaiting a sentence from the judge. Because the child had been returned to its mother, it was possible that she, like her brother, would face a fine rather than jail.

When the weather was finally warm enough, Francis and Bessie brought the children out to Wyckoff for what they liked to call "A Day at the Farm." Francis had instituted this tradition to teach the children the value of hard work, and Bessie went along with it to have an excuse to sit in the shade, kick off her shoes, and let the children run wild. So every year in the spring, when the hens were raising their chicks and there were baby rabbits in the field, we'd spend the day outdoors watching the children chase the animals and ruin their play clothes.

We looked forward to A Day at the Farm more than the children did because we never had to cook. Bessie always insisted that a picnic would be more fun in the countryside anyway, but we all knew the real reason: she didn't want to eat our cooking any more than we did. The chief object of the day was to make it through Bessie's wicker hampers: first the stuffed eggs and cucumber sandwiches, then the potato salad, the baked chicken, and aspic, and finally the glorious fruit tarts and peach preserves. This year they'd brought ice cream, and Fleurette made a ginger ale punch that the children drank from Mother's gilded Sèvres teacups.

We pulled every rug out of the house and spread them on the lawn, then piled on all the pillows and cushions we could find, and from that perch we dedicated ourselves to depleting Bessie's hampers. Francis was in better spirits than we'd seen him in some time. He'd shaved his beard for the summer and it gave him an air of youthfulness and lightheartedness that was not entirely in keeping with his character.

"You look better without it," Fleurette said. "You look much younger, and it's easier to know what you're thinking."

"What am I thinking right now?" Francis asked.

Fleurette pulled off the red scarf she'd wrapped around her hair and lay back on a pillow. "You're thinking of buying an automobile and teaching me to drive it," she said.

Norma groaned and said, "We've been riding around in the sheriff's wagon, and it has given Fleurette too many ideas, as I feared it would."

Little Frankie discovered something behind the barn that made him shriek, and Francis jumped up and ran to check on him.

"I hope Henry Kaufman isn't lurking back there again," Fleurette mumbled, half asleep.

I couldn't help but laugh, but Norma took offense. "We must never make a joke out of that man," she said, and, turning back to Bessie, "Please don't listen to her. Henry Kaufman is very nearly out of our lives forever."

Bessie pushed her plate away and rolled over on a pillow too, arranging her purple flowered dress around her knees. "I'm not worried about Henry Kaufman. I only ever worried about the three of you because I was sure one of you would shoot him, and then we'd have to visit you in jail."

"Sheriff Heath would never put Constance in jail," Fleurette said. "He likes her too much."

"He likes all of us," I said briskly, "and we owe him a great deal for all he's done. Although I'm sure he'll be glad when the trial is over and he can forget all about us."

Francis came jogging back carrying little Frankie under his arm like a football. Frankie was shrieking and giggling. Lorraine skipped along behind them, holding out her hands. "We found a little blind possum and now we must wash our hands," she said, seeming to leave out the most interesting part of that story. Lorraine had grown nearly a foot in the last year and was beginning to show a little of Fleurette's dramatic beauty. But today she was covered in dust and straw from the barn, and around her lips were traces of sticky jam.

"Go and wash yourselves off at the pump," Bessie said. "Ask your aunt Fleurette to help you."

Fleurette opened one eye in Lorraine's direction and let out a gasp of mock horror. She jumped to her feet and took each child by the hand, and soon they were shrieking again at the pump and splashing around in a muddy puddle, having forgotten all about getting clean.

"We were just talking about the trial," Bessie said to Francis, in a deliberate manner that suggested that she'd been instructed to find out what was going on.

Francis reached in the basket for a lemon tart and said, "What about it?" before pushing half of it into his mouth.

"It'll all be over next month," I said. "We expect a short trial and a quick conviction, and then we can all go on with our lives."

"And then what?" Francis said without looking at me.

I didn't want to have to give him an accounting of my attempts to find a position for myself. I'd ridden into New York a few times, hoping that Mr. LaMotte would have another photography assignment for me and would be willing to pay me this time. He was never there when I stopped in. I saw him on the sidewalk once, but he appeared to be arguing with a client and he waved me away.

I had even returned to Wanamaker's and wandered the sales floor, trying to pick out the girl they'd hired to be their store detective. I saw any number of pretty, petite girls in fine spring dresses circling the tables and fingering the goods, but not one of them looked capable of handling pickpockets and thieves.

There were very few positions announced in the paper either. Advertisements for bookkeepers and office clerks appeared every few weeks, but always in the men's help wanted section, never the women's. I saw vacancies for housecleaners and cooks, and the mills were always hiring, but none of that would have suited me. I could have taken a stenography course, but there were already three girls running notices each week that they were trained in stenography and looking for positions.

All of this seemed impossible to explain. "I'm looking for something suitable," I said. "A job to help make ends meet. I've been on a few interviews already."

Francis seemed poised to deliver another lecture, but Bessie put a hand on his arm and he smiled at her and settled back down in the contented manner of a well-fed husband who has submitted to his wife's charms. She patted him and said, "You girls are going to have such an adventure, I just know it. Constance will find a good place for herself, and then maybe she'll hear of something that would suit Norma. And who knows what the world has to offer Fleurette? Or what she has to offer the world?"

We all turned at once and looked toward the water pump, where Fleurette had joined the children in a contest to see who could splash the most mud on the other. Both girls had hitched their skirts up around their knees and turned on little Frankie, who had never been more delighted. He dropped into the puddle and grinned at them like the most contented pig in New Jersey.

"Let's do the world a favor," Norma said, "and not unleash Fleurette upon it quite yet."

BY MAY, there was little to do but wait for the trial. I was finally able to get a man out to put new locks on the doors and glaze the broken windows we'd boarded up. Norma expanded the size of her pigeon flock by half again, which gave her an excuse to spend most of her days in the barn fussing with the incubator and keeping the wood stove going. Fleurette took seriously the job of sewing clothes for little Bobby and soon had him outfitted with play clothes, a sailor suit, and a new suit for church. Even Norma took an interest in the boy. On the weekends she brought a basket of pigeons over to Lucy's and let him watch as she tied bright blue ribbons to their legs and released them. He laughed and clapped as they circled overhead and flew away.

I had plenty of work to do. There were tomatoes and pole beans to plant, fences to repair, and blankets and rugs to be brought outside and beaten until the dust had been driven from them. But the chores were only a distraction from our real problems. Any woman in our position would attach herself to a relation with a spare room and make herself useful. If I couldn't come up with a better idea, we would have to do the same, and soon.

And then what? Where the years ahead had once seemed vague and unknowable, amorphous in shape and indeterminate in size, after my mother died I began to see a set of decades stacked neatly in front of me like bricks. First came my thirties, already half gone, and beyond that my forties and my fifties, solid and certain. But after that, the bricks started to crumble. My grandmother died at the age of sixty-two, and my grandfather at seventy-one. Then my mother was gone, having succumbed to pneumonia after only just turning sixty herself.

When I allowed myself to think about the brevity of the time ahead of me, and the futility of spending any more of it on cooking and mending and gardening, it frightened me so much that I almost couldn't breathe.

⊰ 57 ⊱

THE TRIAL WAS SET AT LAST FOR EARLY JUNE. We were
expected in court on a Tuesday morning and hoped to be finished by Friday. Fearing that the long ride back and forth to
Newark would leave us overtired, Sheriff Heath made arrangements for us to stay at the Continental Hotel for the week. On
Monday night we rode the train to Newark with an enormous
trunk of clothes and a stack of hatboxes taller than the girl
who intended to wear them. Fleurette was delirious over the
notion of staying at a hotel and had made herself a new dress
to honor the occasion, an apricot affair that sagged strangely
at the knees in what she called a "bowling pin silhouette."

"I think you went wrong just south of the waist," Norma
said.

"It's Parisian," Fleurette said.

"That didn't come from Paris."

"It came from McCall's, by way of Paris."

Fleurette did look exquisite in the dress, and she knew
it. A porter came running the minute she appeared on the
platform and loaded a cart with our luggage. He escorted us

across the street to the hotel, where Fleurette swept into the lobby ahead of us, her head cocked slightly to show off her wide straw hat (festooned with what Norma called an "audacious" arrangement of silk roses and dyed feathers). It is no exaggeration to say that every head turned in her direction. Norma and I struggled along behind her, hot and dusty from the trip, looking every bit the part of two spinster aunts unable to keep up with their young charge.

The man at the registration desk made a little bow when he saw her. "Evening, miss. You one of Sparks's girls?"

"Sparks?"

"She's *our* girl," I said, rushing up behind her. "Miss Constance Kopp and her sisters, under arrangements made by Mr. Robert Heath."

Norma nudged me, worried, I knew, that I was about to mention the criminal trial. Norma didn't want anyone at the hotel to know that we were there in connection with the sheriff or the courthouse, believing that we would attract the attention of reporters looking for a sensational story.

"What's a Sparks girl?" Fleurette asked.

The desk clerk looked at us nervously. "My mistake, miss. Some—ah—entertainers are lodging with us for the week, and I mistook . . ." He looked down, embarrassed, and shuffled his registration cards. "Here we are! The Misses Kopp."

Just then the tallest and thinnest man I'd ever seen leaned over the desk next to us and said, in a loud and lively voice, one word: "Sparks." Fleurette had to lift the brim of her hat to stare up at him, which she did, open-mouthed. He wore a pinstriped suit made of enough yardage to clothe two ordinary men, and when he leaned over the desk to sign his name to the register, the pen looked like it might snap between his long, bony fingers.

He glanced down at the three of us and tipped his hat. "You ladies in town for the show?"

"What show?" Fleurette said, before I could stop her.

"Sparks Circus, miss. A vision of beauty and splendor, just like yourself." He winked at her and flashed a gold tooth when he grinned.

I took hold of Fleurette's shoulder, but she was effervescent by now and there was no way of stopping her.

"Are you with the circus?"

He turned to her and made a deep bow. "World's tallest man," he said, winking at her as he rose. "Haven't you heard of me?"

Fleurette was quivering. I'd never seen the girl so excited. Norma shot a worried look at me, but I just shrugged. I couldn't see how we'd get her away from him unless we picked her up and carried her off.

"Is—is everyone in the circus staying here?" she asked.

He raised an eyebrow to the desk clerk, who looked alarmed at the possibility, and said, "Only a few old friends of Mr. Cooke's. You know Mr. Cooke, don't you? Used to be a circus agent. One day he was one of us, and now he's a hotel proprietor."

Fleurette turned back to the man handling our registration. "Did you think I was with the circus?" she asked, incredulous.

The world's tallest man stepped in before the clerk could compose an answer. "A little thing like you?" he said. "We'd put you on the trapeze. How do you like heights?"

Norma couldn't stand it any longer. She took Fleurette's arm and dragged her across the lobby, leaving me to sign the register and take the key from the clerk. The circus man apologized to me but then said, "You're not quite the world's tallest girl, but we could find something for you."

Fleurette, still straining to hear us, shouted, "My other sister's got a bird act!"

Norma nearly yanked her off her feet, and they disappeared behind a wide stone column, one of Fleurette's blue feathers sailing along behind them.

WE WERE GIVEN A SUITE of two small rooms and a private bath on the fifth floor. I was reminded immediately of the Mandarin. Although our rooms in Newark looked out not over Fifth Avenue but over Broad Street, giving us a view all the way to the courthouse where our trial would commence in the morning, they had the same cosmopolitan air about them. Both the Continental and the Mandarin furnished their hotels with the busy city-dweller in mind, offering small and well-appointed writing desks and leather armchairs for reading under the electric chandeliers.

Fleurette set about exploring our rooms as if she were snooping around someone's bedroom, opening drawers, peeking into the closet, lifting the sheets, and looking under the mattress. "I'd like a room just like this," she said once she'd examined every corner of it.

Norma didn't voice any opinion of the room, but dropped into a chair and pulled her shoes off with a great sigh of relief. "I wonder if we can have supper on a tray," she said wearily.

"On a tray!" Fleurette said. "In here? Aren't we going to dine downstairs with the circus?" She was already tearing through her trunk in search of a dress that would make precisely the right impression on a room of circus performers. I very much hoped she didn't own such a thing.

Norma gave me a desperate look—she hated to eat in a room full of strangers and had always detested restaurants and lunchrooms—and for once I agreed with her. We needed to rest and settle our minds before the start of the trial.

"I'm sure they can send something up," I said. "Norma's right. We don't need any more excitement tonight. We have a very important job to do tomorrow."

Fleurette flopped across the bed and rolled her eyes up at the ceiling. "I think we deserve one nice evening out before we have to sit in a stuffy courtroom all day."

I sat down next to her and pulled her chin toward me. "We're not just sitting," I said. "Remember what the sheriff has told you. Our testimony will make all the difference. We have to do the best we possibly can. Don't you want to see Mr. Kaufman punished for everything he's done?"

"I suppose," Fleurette said carelessly. "Only—did you really mind so much?"

"Mind what?"

"Henry Kaufman. I mean, wasn't it the most interesting year of our lives? We learned to fire a gun and, and rode in an automobile, and you got to run around with the sheriff, and we never would have met Lucy Blake, and what about—"

"Don't talk like that," I said.

Norma groaned. "We can't let her testify. Can't we say she's too young?"

"No, really," Fleurette said, sitting up and cocking her head at me. "Can you honestly say that you wish Henry Kaufman had never run us down on Market Street? If you could do it again, would you have kept us home from Paterson that day?"

Norma shifted in her chair and she, too, was staring at me. We all knew the answer, but I wasn't about to say it.

⇥ 58 ⇤

CELEBRATED KOPP CASE ON
TRIAL TODAY AT NEWARK

NEWARK, June 3, 1915—Harry Kaufman, a well-known silk dyer, of Paterson, came up today for trial in the United States District Court, Newark, on an indictment charging him with sending threatening letters to Miss Constance Kopp, of Wyckoff.

Sheriff Robert N. Heath, who developed the case against Kaufman, was an important witness for the prosecution.

This case has been pending since last July and sensational testimony is expected as an outcome of the trial.

The published story of the Black Hand letters sent to Miss Kopp caused a discharged inmate of the State prison, whose home was Somerville, to add to the terror of this kind of correspondence by himself writing letters to her promising an exposure of the plot. His capture was cleverly made by Sheriff Heath. He is now serving a sentence in the Bergen County Jail.

• • •

FLEURETTE TOOK THE NEWSPAPER FROM ME, looked it over again to make sure she wasn't mentioned, and then fanned herself with it. The courtroom was hot and crowded. Not a single window could be opened for fear of the proceedings being overheard in the street.

"I intend to deliver the most sensational testimony," Fleurette said.

Sheriff Heath, who was seated just in front of us with his deputies, turned and frowned at me. This was my cue to correct Fleurette.

"You know they only say that to sell papers," I said quietly, but loud enough for the sheriff to hear. "You must give them only the plain and truthful testimony they require. Only answer questions that are asked to you directly. And if anyone—"

"I know! You don't have to keep reminding me," she hissed.

"You don't have to keep treating this like a party game," I said, prompting a kick from Norma.

"Stop it," she whispered. "Both of you." She cast a dramatic glance behind her, and I turned to see the row of reporters waiting to write down anything we said. They had already described Fleurette as "sixteen and so attractive that she had been threatened with kidnapping" in yesterday evening's paper, a line that I knew we would hear repeated for weeks. I didn't want to give them any more salacious details.

The bailiff rose and announced the arrival of the jury. Twelve somber men filed in and took their seats behind the heavy oak partition that separated them from the rest of the courtroom. I looked them over and tried to guess at their dispositions, but their expressions revealed very little. They seemed to be ordinary men, shopkeepers or clerks. They kept their eyes on the empty chair soon to be occupied by the judge.

Once they were seated, the bailiff announced the arrival of Judge Haight, a tall and broad-shouldered man who seemed too young for his steely gray hair. Then the attorneys for each side were introduced. We were represented by United States Attorney Lynch, and Henry Kaufman by a Mr. Joelson. The judge asked Mr. Kaufman to rise and hear the charges against him.

Until then, we had not had a good look at him. He was seated a few rows ahead of us on the other side of the aisle. When he stood, I realized that he was wearing much the same sort of suit he'd had on almost a year ago when his automobile collided with our buggy. It was a finely made suit meant to flatter a vain man, with delicate pinstripes and a series of careful darts that would make even a portly man like Mr. Kaufman look trim and strong. He wore a silk vest of a somber dark blue and a pocket square to match.

He looked so small in the enormous, crowded courtroom, and strangely insignificant. He was an unimportant man who had nonetheless been the most important person in our lives for the last year.

"Mr. Kaufman," said the judge. "You are charged with sending threatening letters through the United States mail to the Misses Constance, Norma, and Fleurette Kopp. How do you respond?"

"I am not guilty, Your Honor." This brought out a murmur from the reporters. The judge cast them a sharp look.

"Please be seated, Mr. Kaufman. Attorney Lynch may call his first witness."

Sheriff Heath slid to the end of the bench and walked to the witness box to take his oath. He wore a better suit then he ordinarily did, a black serge meant for church, and a collar so stiff and high that he could hardly turn his head. He'd been to the barber just that morning for a cut and a shave that I could tell were a bit too close for his liking. His mustache was trimmed a little shorter than he usually wore it, and he looked exposed because of it.

He took his seat and began his testimony, recounting the events of the last year, beginning with our meeting that day in the prosecutor's office. His answers were as brief and colorless as they could possibly be, and the attorney's questions were carefully phrased to keep them that way.

I sat in the courtroom and watched this man, who had been a complete stranger to me a year ago, tell the story of my life. The parts he left out came back to me anyway: the nights I spent sleeping alongside Fleurette with a revolver on my nightstand, listening to her breathe and watching the unmoving but wakeful form of Norma on the floor under the window. Norma and I out in the snow, our revolvers drawn, patrolling on our own after the deputies left. And Lucy Blake, with her arms wrapped around her boy, and those of us who had a hand in his recovery standing by, delighted and a little stunned by the outcome.

The jury heard none of that, but I could hear it all in the silences between Sheriff Heath's answers.

After the sheriff had answered all of the questions put to him, Attorney Lynch dismissed him and called me to the witness stand.

I took my oath. Attorney Lynch asked me to describe the events of July 14, 1914. I didn't look at Mr. Kaufman. I looked at Fleurette, who had shown remarkable restraint in her choice of courtroom attire and made herself a fashionable but dignified skirt and shirtwaist of deep cranberry. The attorney had wanted her in pink, with bows and lace, but she'd refused, saying she was too old for such a thing. She did indeed look older, but as I spoke, I saw her as she had been that day, in her dress of rose-colored taffeta, trapped under our broken buggy with Dolley kicking and groaning alongside her.

At the attorney's prompting, I described my efforts to collect payment for the damages to the buggy and the subsequent threats and insults hurled our way.

"And what did you do in response to the threats?" Attorney Lynch said.

"I got a revolver to protect us." There was a sound from the jury—something like a gasp quickly suppressed. I turned and looked directly at them, which I had been instructed not to do. I didn't care. I wanted their full attention.

"And soon I had use for it," I told them. "A few nights later I looked from my bedroom window on the second floor and saw a man behind the house. When he raised his gun to my window, I shot at him. He returned the fire. The bullets struck the house close to the window where I was."

The jurymen stared at me. Attorney Lynch cleared his throat to draw my attention back to him.

"Please read for the jury the letter you received on November 19, 1914," he said, handing me Mr. Kaufman's letter demanding that I deliver a thousand dollars to a girl in black. I read the letter and handed it back.

"And how was this letter delivered?"

"By the United States Postal Service. You can see the postmark for yourself."

He then asked me to recount the night I spent waiting for

the girl in black and the other particulars of the case. It was exhausting to tell it all at once. Just as I thought I could not bear to answer another question, the attorney thanked me for my testimony and invited Mr. Joelson to take his turn.

"Miss Kopp," Mr. Joelson said. "My client regrets the inconvenience caused by the collision of your buggy and his automobile."

Inconvenience? He paused as if he wanted a response from me, but I'd been instructed to only answer questions. I remained silent. Did he consider everything that happened in the last year an inconvenience?

Getting no response from me, he continued, "And he considers his payment of the fine imposed by the court to be the end of the matter."

Attorney Lynch stood. "Your Honor, does Mr. Joelson have a question for Miss Kopp?"

Before the judge could speak, Mr. Joelson said, "Miss Kopp, did you ever receive a threatening letter signed with the name Henry Kaufman?"

"No, I did not."

"Did you ever receive a letter with Mr. Kaufman's return address on the envelope, or the insignia of his business on the stationery, or any other mark that would indicate that the letter had been sent by him?"

"Just the initials H. K."

"And did you ever see Mr. Kaufman fire a gun at you or your sisters?"

"I saw a dark figure matching his general description."

"What about his automobile? Did these men who threatened you ever arrive in an automobile that you could be certain belonged to Mr. Kaufman?"

"Only the first time," I said. "After that they waited until after dark."

"The first time? Which time are you referring to?" he asked with a false sense of confusion.

"The first time he drove past my house," I said evenly, looking right at Mr. Kaufman now, who quickly looked down at the table when he found my gaze on him. "He and a few other men drove past and shouted insults at Fleurette."

"Ah, yes," Mr. Joelson said with obvious and exaggerated relief. "The time he yelled out of a passing car. I thought you were referring to illegal behavior."

I opened my mouth to speak, and Attorney Lynch knocked a book off the table, making a loud bang on the bare wooden floor. This was my signal to stay quiet.

"Was that incident included in your complaint against my client, Miss Kopp?"

"I don't believe it was."

"Then you have not seen, with your own eyes, this man or his automobile involved in any of the incidents included in your complaint, is that correct?" He pointed dramatically to Henry Kaufman, who had his hands folded quietly on the table in front of him.

"Not precisely," I said.

"And you have no way of knowing if someone else was behind these alleged threats? George Ewing, for example, who I believe was the next man in line to threaten the ever-popular Kopp sisters?"

"I have no reason to believe anyone else was behind it."

"Then you are dismissed, Miss Kopp." I began to rise when he said, "Wait. There is another matter. Please take your seat again, and I do apologize for the inconvenience."

I settled back into my seat and kept my eyes on him. Attorney Lynch had warned me not to look at him if I got confused, as it would make the jury think I was looking for a signal.

"You've paid a visit to Mr. Kaufman's place of business, haven't you?" he asked.

I did my best to keep my face composed and said, "I have never paid a social call on Mr. Kaufman."

There was the sound of stifled laughter from the reporters, which the judge quickly suppressed with his gavel.

Mr. Joelson tried again. In a booming, staccato voice, he said, "What was the purpose of your visit to Mr. Kaufman's factory?"

In an equally loud voice I replied, "To collect the money owed to me for the damages to my buggy."

"And was that all?"

"To make a polite request that he refrain from harassing my family."

"And what was the result?"

"This trial is the result."

The courtroom erupted in laughter. Even the men on the jury wiped their eyes and shook their heads. The judge pounded his gavel and ordered a break for lunch.

I left with great relief for Attorney Lynch's office, where coffee and sandwiches had been brought in so we could discuss the case in private. A pretty young secretary passed the basket of sandwiches around while Attorney Lynch said, "That went as well as we could've expected. Joelson has decided he needs to offer no defense on his client's behalf as long as he can continue to get you girls on the witness stand saying that you never saw Kaufman do a thing. He wants to convince the jury that the evidence is entirely circumstantial. It's exactly what I would do if I were him."

"But it won't work, will it?" I asked.

Attorney Lynch pushed a corner of his ham sandwich into his mouth and shrugged, chewing thoughtfully. "I don't predict the future, Miss Kopp. I just make the case."

NORMA TOOK THE STAND IN THE AFTERNOON and answered the same questions that had been put to me, giving answers even briefer and more terse than my own.

"Did you see the man who threw the bricks through your window?"

"No."

"Did anyone get a look at him?"

"No."

"Not one of you could provide even the most general description?"

"No."

"Isn't that odd, for three such observant girls?"

"We were asleep."

That was the longest answer she gave. Attorney Lynch had asked her to try to soften her expression on the witness stand, but Norma frowned at Mr. Joelson and did not cast a particularly kind look upon me or Sheriff Heath when she left the stand, as if to suggest that we were equally responsible for taking her away from the farm for a week and getting her involved in a federal trial at Newark.

Fleurette took the stand late in the afternoon, looking remarkably cool and unruffled despite the long day in a hot and crowded courtroom. She'd been preparing for her role as if it were a stage debut, and I worried that she might get it in her head to improvise. But she answered Attorney Lynch's questions with a calm composure I don't think she possessed a year ago. Her hair had been carefully rolled into neatly sculpted curls, and she'd powdered her nose and arranged herself in her chair so that she sat perfectly straight, making herself as tall as she could.

"When did you first become aware that you were the target of a kidnapping plot?" Attorney Lynch asked.

"In August," she said. "We received a letter delivered by brick mail."

A few people in the courtroom tittered at her choice of words.

"Do you mean that the letter was tied to a brick and thrown through the window of your family home in Wyckoff?" he asked.

"Yes."

"Thank you. Were there other threats?"

"Yes, a few more, some sent by post."

"And what was done to protect you against those threats?"

Fleurette paused and found me in the crowd. She gave me a long and searching look.

"My sisters learned to shoot a gun," she said, with a note of wonder in her voice, as if she hadn't entirely considered it before. "And on two occasions Constance went to meet the men who were threatening me, to try to stop them."

I shivered. She was looking at me as if she were seeing me for the first time.

"That must have been very dangerous."

She thought for a minute and then, in a quiet voice, she said, "I think it was."

❧ 59 ❧

AFTER THE JURY WAS DISMISSED for the evening and we turned to leave the courtroom, I saw Marion Garfinkel sitting in the back row next to a white-haired man. He had one gnarled hand locked around the brass handle of a cane. As we passed by, she rose and introduced her father.

"Mr. Kaufman," I said. "How do you do?"

He didn't reach for my hand and I didn't offer it. Sheriff Heath had been standing right behind me, and with a nod to his deputy, Norma and Fleurette were escorted out of the room. Henry Kaufman and his attorneys had already left by a side door. We waited until the rest of the spectators had filed out and the four of us were alone.

"Mrs. Garfinkel," Sheriff Heath said. "We weren't expecting you. I'm sure better seats could be arranged for you and your father tomorrow."

"That's fine, Sheriff," she said. "I don't think we'll stay for the rest of the trial. I just wanted my father to hear for himself what Henry did to these girls."

She turned pointedly to her father, who gave a tremulous

nod and spoke in a raspy, uneven voice. "I'm afraid I've mis-judged my son's character, miss," he said. "I thought I knew the boy. It's a terrible thing to see your own child grown into someone you don't recognize."

"I suppose it would be," I said, not wanting to imagine it.

"We could add a witness to tomorrow's docket if you'd like to testify," Sheriff Heath said quietly to Mrs. Garfinkel, but she just shook her head.

"I couldn't. He's still my brother. But we won't hire an at-torney to appeal the charges, and we won't pay his fine. If he's convicted, he should see the inside of a prison cell. Isn't that what we've agreed to?" She put a hand on her father's shoulder and he nodded, his head down. He wore a fine linen suit—I could see where Henry Kaufman got his taste for good tailor-ing—but something about him seemed shabby and defeated. I couldn't look him in the face but stared at his ears, which were red and overgrown and laced with tiny blue capillaries.

"Then we have some hope of seeing justice done this week," Sheriff Heath said. "I'm glad to see you've come around to our way of thinking."

"Yes, I realize . . ." Marion looked at her father and her voice trailed off.

We stood awkwardly for a minute, none of us knowing what to say to the other. Finally the sheriff nodded and took my arm to leave. We'd gone down the hall to join Norma and Fleurette when I heard footsteps and turned to see Marion rushing after us, having left her father in a chair outside the courtroom. When she reached us she put a hand on my arm and said, "The girl. Lucy. Are she and her boy—will they be—"

"They're fine," I said. "They have a comfortable home. Lu-cy's a good mother."

Marion's hand tightened around me. "Of course she is," she said, with an uncharacteristic quiver to her voice. "Could you tell her—"

"I don't think I should," I said quickly. "Lucy wishes to leave things be."

She let me go and turned to look at her father, who was already nodding off in his chair. "Then I'll tell you," she said, without bringing her eyes back to mine. "If that boy ever needs a family . . ."

"He doesn't," I said. "He has one."

THAT NIGHT, we gave in to Fleurette's pleas and took our supper in the enormous dining hall that ran the length of the building. The waiters had rolled a wide green awning out over the sidewalk and set out tables for anyone who preferred the dust and noise of the street to the hushed wicker fans cooling the restaurant. We settled indoors, although Fleurette suspected that the circus performers would prefer to dine in the fresh air. She kept her eyes on the sidewalk all evening, hoping for a glimpse of them. We did see five petite but sturdy women sweep through in identical scarlet gowns, their hair arranged in a theatrical style of braids and curls held together with sparkling glass combs. Fleurette suspected them of being trick riders or magician's assistants. "Or they could be acrobats," she said. "Did you see the way they walked? Just the way they would on a tightrope." Norma and I ate our roast chicken in silence as Fleurette chattered on about her plans to run a tightrope across the meadow and begin practicing as soon as we got home. I think we were both grateful for the distraction. It was exhausting to relive the events of the last year in the courtroom, and even the notion of Fleurette dancing on a wire high above the ground seemed soothing by comparison.

There was a ladies' parlor on the second floor and a sketch room hung with paintings of sailboats and pastoral scenes of horses on mountaintops. A few young women had brought their sketchbooks and were working at copying the paintings, but we had no interest in it and instead settled in the parlor, where Fleurette had insisted that we take a cup of tea before retiring.

"We never get to sit in the ladies' parlor at home," she said as we settled into dainty armchairs arranged around a little beaded lamp on a table. There were three other groups of women seated in their own tight circles around the room, none of whom appeared to be circus performers, to Fleurette's disappointment.

"We sit in the ladies' parlor every evening at home," Norma said. "What else would you call it?"

"But there aren't other ladies there," Fleurette said. "At home it's only us."

Norma looked around at the others, all speaking in a genteel hush to their own friends. "I don't see what difference it makes," she said. "We don't wish to talk to any of them, and they don't seem to take an interest in us."

Of the three of us, Norma was the only one who was impervious to the charms of a hotel. Fleurette liked the opportunity to dress up and be seen, and I just liked living in a clean, modern building, with twice the comforts and none of the chores we faced at home.

Fleurette took as long as possible to finish her tea, but after several conspicuous yawns, Norma convinced her that it was time for bed. We had just begun to climb the stairs when

I heard Sheriff Heath's voice from a room down the hall. I told the two of them to go on and I went back to look for him.

He was just coming out of a smoking lounge at the opposite end of the hall from the ladies' parlor. He had his hat in his hand and carried the same brown coat he wore everywhere. There was a long red carpet between us and a series of tiny tables and settees.

"I didn't know you were staying here," I said as he walked toward me.

"I'm not," he said. "I was due home hours ago. Mr. Lynch kept me out too late."

"Are you all in there planning tomorrow's strategy?"

He shook his head. "We're playing cards. Don't tell Mrs. Heath."

"I didn't know the sheriff was allowed in card rooms."

"Well," he said, considering that. "It's a respectable enough card room. There are only lawyers and judges at the moment."

"Is our judge there?"

"Oh, no," he said. "But don't worry. We have a good judge. The trial's going just fine, everyone says so. And now we know that Mrs. Garfinkel won't be paying his fine, so it looks like he'll spend a little time at the state prison after all."

"The state prison? The same one George Ewing hated so much?"

A waiter came rushing by with a cart covered in a white cloth, and the sheriff and I backed into an alcove off the hall to get out of his way. He gestured to one of the little velvet settees. I sat down and he settled in across from me.

"That's the one," he said. "And by the way, I'm bringing Ewing in with me tomorrow. We still expect him to testify against Kaufman. If I tell him that Kaufman's going to serve his sentence in Trenton, that will be all the more reason for Mr. Ewing to do everything he can to stay with me in Hackensack."

I leaned back and regarded Sheriff Heath in the dim light. We'd been talking about catching and convicting Henry Kaufman for so long that it hardly seemed possible that it was all about to end.

"I hate to admit it," I said, more to fill the silence than anything else, "but I do feel sorry for the elder Mr. Kaufman. It must be a terrible thing to watch one's son on trial."

"And one's daughter," he said. "Although I couldn't tell how much Mrs. Garfinkel had told her father about the kidnapping charge."

"Nor could I. Will she go to jail, too?"

"I won't know for a few more weeks. We're still working on charging the men who helped her. I'd rather put them in jail than Mrs. Garfinkel."

"So would I," I said.

We sat in silence for another minute or two, but as there was nothing to look at in the alcove besides one another, I began to fidget and then realized that Norma and Fleurette would wonder why I'd taken so long. I rose suddenly, knocking my head on the low ceiling above us, and backed out into the hall. Sheriff Heath followed. He walked with me to the wide central staircase, where I would go up to our room and he would go down. The situation must have struck us both as odd, because we laughed at the same time and then the sheriff said, "Tomorrow, Miss Kopp," and jogged down the stairs, two at a time, waving over his shoulder as he crossed the carpeted lobby with its blazing chandeliers and went out into the warm blue night.

❧ 60 ❧

OVER THE NEXT TWO DAYS, the trial proceeded just as we'd hoped it would. Mr. Kinsley's handwriting analysis was accepted by the judge as thoroughly scientific. Mr. Kaufman's only hope—that he could persuade George Ewing to confess to the threatening letters and gunshots in exchange for some sort of bribe—fell apart when Mr. Ewing took the stand and gave a simple and truthful account of his role in the attacks against us. He acknowledged that he'd been in the car on the day of our buggy accident and that he'd been with Mr. Kaufman and some other men on a few other occasions, but said that he hadn't written any letters except the last ones, which contained his signature, and had never taken a shot at our house or thrown a brick through our window. He said that Mr. Kaufman had coerced him into writing those final letters with the idea that they would shift the blame for the entire mess. He added that when he was caught, Mr. Kaufman threatened him harm if he didn't take responsibility for everything.

Henry Kaufman took the stand in his defense but had little to say beyond his denial of the charges.

"Do you admit to having caused your motor car to collide with a buggy driven by the Misses Kopp on July 14 of last year?" Attorney Lynch asked.

"I do," he said, "and I have paid my fine." He spoke woodenly, as if he had memorized the answers. He was paler than when I'd last seen him and a bit thinner. He was no longer a man who looked like he was about to explode. I wondered if his attorney had persuaded him to reduce his drinking before the trial.

"Do you admit to driving to the Kopp home in Wyckoff to harass them and shoot at them after the collision?"

"I do not."

"Are you the writer of the threatening letters sent to the Misses Kopp from August to November of last year?"

"I am not."

"Mr. Kaufman," Attorney Lynch said, approaching the witness stand with a sheaf of papers, "did you not provide these handwriting samples to the sheriff's office, which were used to positively match your handwriting to that of the writer of the letters?"

Mr. Kaufman leaned forward and squinted at the paper. "I admit to writing the name 'Constance Kopp' at the suggestion of the sheriff, but the rest of it was coerced."

"Coerced?" said Attorney Lynch with a smile. "By what means were you coerced?"

Mr. Kaufman looked around until he found me. "She was there!" he said, rising and pointing at me. "She trapped me and forced me to write out handwriting samples against my will."

The men in the jury box smiled.

"Forced you?" Attorney Lynch said, taking a step back in amazement. "By what means does a lady like Miss Kopp force a grown man to do anything he doesn't want to do?"

Mr. Kaufman looked down and mumbled something.

"Could you repeat that for the jury?" Attorney Lynch asked.

He looked up and said, in a loud, plain voice, "She's not a regular lady."

AFTER HIS TESTIMONY CONCLUDED, the jury took only two and a half hours to convict Henry Kaufman. He was fined one thousand dollars and, having no means of paying the fine, was taken into custody. Mrs. Garfinkel and her father hadn't returned for the conclusion of the trial, and none of Mr. Kaufman's associates had made an appearance, either. When he was led away, there was no one to say goodbye to him.

The verdict was read at two-thirty in the afternoon. By three o'clock we were standing in front of the courthouse saying our goodbyes to the sheriff, his deputies, and the attorneys. The reporters were trying to get Fleurette's attention, but Sheriff Heath put Deputy Morris by her side to keep them away.

It was a perfect summer afternoon, with a jewel-blue sky above us and clouds that looked like they had been painted on. A breeze had risen to push the heat out of Newark's fetid streets, and a willow tree planted alongside the courthouse waved its drooping branches, whispering like the rush of water. Everything looked cleaner and brighter than it had when the trial began. The granite courthouse behind us, the rows of brick offices and shops across the street, and the trolleys running along their tracks, all seemed to speak of a crisp and orderly world in which people could walk the streets in peace. The attorneys and deputies laughed and joked with one another, and they, too, seemed younger and brighter in the light of a favorable verdict and a clear June day.

We said all the thanks we could think to say and a silence fell over the group. Norma and Fleurette turned to walk to the train station. Sheriff Heath took me by the arm and led me away from them. We walked down the stairs, and then he stopped and turned to me.

"You had more of a role in this than anyone in that courtroom knew," he said.

"Oh—" I looked at him in surprise. "Well. We all did our part."

The sun glared on the white steps and he squinted at me with that half-smile, half-frown I still hadn't learned to read.

"What you did will serve you well in your new occupation," he said.

I laughed. "Occupation? I have no occupation. That's just the trouble. If we—"

He didn't let me finish. "Miss Kopp. I think you'd make a fine deputy."

"Deputy?"

"Deputy sheriff."

My throat went dry. I had to swallow before I spoke. "I don't understand."

He smiled and looked down at his feet, then raised his eyes to mine.

"I'm offering you a job, Miss Kopp."

Miss CONSTANCE KOPP

Girl Waits with Gun is a fictional account of the real-life adventures of Constance Kopp, shown here in a 1916 newspaper photograph.
Evening World, NOVEMBER 14, 1916

Historical and Source Notes, Acknowledgments

THIS IS A WORK OF HISTORICAL FICTION based on real events and real people. My task as a writer was to take the public record—pieced together from newspaper articles, genealogical records, court documents, and other sources—and invent the rest of the story. All of the major events described in the novel actually happened, with a few notable exceptions: There was no Lucy Blake, which means that every part of the story connected with her—the missing child, Constance's trips to New York, and the scenes at the orphanage—are all fiction. (It is true, however, that children were sent away to live with "strike mothers" during the silk strikes, and that some of those children did not return.) Although Henry Kaufman did have a secretary named M. Garfinkel, the character of Marion Garfinkel is fictional. Another significant difference is that Mrs. Kopp, Norma and Constance's mother, died a few years later than she does in my version of events. Also, to my knowledge, Norma Kopp had no interest in pigeons.

Everything else happened more or less as I described it. I

invented dialogue, personalities, backstories, and scenes that helped piece together the stories behind the events described in the public record. Most of the people who appear here as secondary characters—people such as Bessie Kopp, John Courter, John Ward, Peter McGinnis, and Cordelia Heath—are also real people who led lives that I know little about. The personality traits, ambitions, and actions I ascribed to them are my own embellishments to the few facts I do know about them.

The circumstances surrounding Fleurette's birth are not entirely known, but the basic facts—the identity of her mother and father, the relevant dates, and the fact that Fleurette grew up not knowing the truth—have been verified through court documents and interviews with Fleurette's son.

I used real letters and newspaper articles in the book to help anchor the story in reality. I'd like to acknowledge the following sources for text that I reproduced word for word, or with very slight modifications:

The incidents described on pages 45–46 are all sourced from *New York Times* articles in the 1890s.

The filming of the trolley car accident (page 60) actually happened in Paterson around the time of the Kopp sisters' accident with Henry Kaufman.

The text of the letters from Henry Kaufman on pages 84, 154, 227, 234, and 238 come from court records of the original indictment and multiple newspaper accounts, with slight modifications.

The other crimes Sheriff Heath dealt with, as described on pages 219–20, all actually occurred and were sourced from Hackensack newspapers of the day.

The story that Fleurette read on page 244 came from

Stories of Pioneer Life: For Young Readers by
Florence Bass, published in 1900.

The headline "Girl Waits with Gun" (page 258) came
from the *Philadelphia Sun* article that ran on
November 23, 1914, but most of the text comes from
two similar stories that each ran in the Philadelphia
Evening-Ledger, one titled "Oh, for a Chance to
Shoot at the Nasty Prowlers!" (November 21, 1914)
and the other titled "Girl, Armed, Waits for Black
Handers on Street Corner" (November 23, 1914).

"Arrest in Black Hand Letters Case" (page 271) ran in
the *Bergen Evening-Record* on December 3, 1914,
although I added a line about the fictional Marion
Garfinkel posting bail.

The text of the letter from George Ewing dated
December 21, 1914 (pages 278–79) was printed in
several newspaper accounts, including one in the
Bergen Evening-News on January 23, 1915.

The story of the night watchman beaten to death (page
283) ran in the *New York Times* on December 27,
1914, under the headline "Held in Murder Inquiry."

"Says He Was Kopp Black Hand 'Gang'" (pages 295–96)
ran in the *New York Tribune* on January 23, 1915.

"Saved of Prison Term by Sheriff" (pages 372–73)
appeared in the *Trenton Evening Times* on March 8,
1915.

"Celebrated Kopp Case on Trial Today at Newark" (page
385) appeared in the *Bergen Evening-Record* on June
3, 1915.

"Kopp Sisters Tell of Death Threats," from the *New York
Times,* June 3, 1915, is the source of Constance's

quote in the epigraph and some of her dialogue
during the trial (page 389).

The headlines Norma cut out of the paper and sent by
pigeon post were all actual headlines from Paterson-
area newspapers of the day.

Passaic and Bergen County history buffs will notice that I
took a few liberties with geography, train schedules, streetcar
routes, and other such details. What can I say? This is a work
of fiction, and sometimes the story takes over. If my characters started riding over a bridge, I let them, even if no bridge
existed at that place.

I'd like to thank the following people for their help with
the research: Maria Hopper, genealogist extraordinaire; Jona-
than Rapoport; and the staff and volunteers at the Ridgewood
Public Library, Paterson Public Library, Hackensack Public Library, Hawthorne Historical Society, Bergen County Historical
Society, and the Passaic County Historical Society at Lambert
Castle. Extra heaps of thanks go to Inspector Mickey Bradley
at the Bergen County Sheriff's Office for an impromptu tour
of the old jail and Sheriff Heath's living quarters, as well as his
willingness to preserve and share Heath's photographs.

Most of all, heartfelt thanks go to Dennis and Deanne
O'Dell, John Birgel (father and son), and members of the Heath
and Ward families for their willingness to talk about their ancestors with a complete stranger and to share their stories.

My retelling of the Kopp sisters' story owes its life to four
people who believed in it as much as I did: my husband, Scott
Brown; my first reader, Masie Cochran; my agent, Michelle
Tessler; and my editor, Andrea Schulz. Thanks to everyone at
HMH for giving Constance, Norma, and Fleurette a home.

**Keep reading for a sample from the next
Kopp sisters novel**

LADY COP MAKES TROUBLE

Out in September 2016

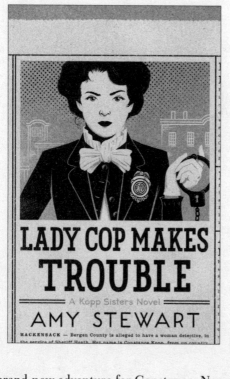

A brand-new adventure for Constance, Norma,
Fleurette, and the gang, from *New York Times*
best-selling author Amy Stewart

YOUNG GIRL WANTED — GOOD WAGE. Well-to-do man seeking a housekeeper who is matrimonially minded. Room and
board offered. Reply to box-holder 4827.

I handed the newspaper back to Mrs. Headison. "I suppose
you replied to the box-holder?"

She nodded briskly. "I did, posing as a girl who had just
come to town from Buffalo, with experience not in housekeeping, but in dancing, and with aspirations for the stage.
We can all imagine what he must have made of that."

I didn't like to imagine it, owing to the fact that a youthful
aspirant to the stage lived under my own roof, but I had to admit that the trick worked. Sheriff Heath and I read the man's
reply, which invited her to visit at her earliest convenience,
and promised an offer of marriage if she proved worthy of it.

"Any number of girls have auditioned for the job and are
still awaiting that offer of marriage," she sniffed. "I've seen
them going in and out of his house. As my position is only

advisory in nature, I'm under instructions to report any suspicious findings to the police chief, who sends an officer
to make the arrest. But this man lives out here in Bergen
County, so we're handing the matter over to you."

Belle Headison was Paterson's first policewoman. She was
a slight figure with narrow shoulders and hair the color of
weak tea. Her eyes were framed by brass-rimmed spectacles
that recalled the inner workings of a standing clock. Everything about her seemed upright and tightly wound.

I was New Jersey's first lady deputy sheriff. I'd never met
another woman in law enforcement. The summer of 1915 felt
like a brave and bright new age.

Mrs. Headison had arranged to meet us at the train station in Ridgewood, not far from the man's house. We stood
on the platform, under the only awning that cast any shade.
In spite of the late August heat, it gave me a bracing thrill to
think about going after anyone who would so casually advertise for a girl in the newspaper.

The sheriff took another look at the letter. "Mr. Meeker,"
he said. "Harold Meeker. Well, ladies, let's go pay him a visit."

Mrs. Headison took a step back. "Oh, I'm not sure what
use I'd be."

But Sheriff Heath wouldn't hear it. "It's your case," he
said cheerfully. "You should get the satisfaction of seeing it
through to the end." Nothing made him happier than catching a criminal, and he couldn't imagine why anyone else
wouldn't feel the same.

"But I don't usually go along with the officers," she said.
"Why don't you go, and Miss Kopp and I will wait here?"

"I brought Miss Kopp along for a reason," the sheriff said,

ushering us both off the platform and into his motor car. Mrs. Headison stepped in with some reluctance and we drove through town.

On the way, Mrs. Headison told us about her work at the Travelers' Aid Society, where she helped girls who came to Paterson with no family or job prospects. "They get off the train and find no difficulty in making their way to the most disreputable boarding houses and the tawdriest dance halls," she said. "And if she's a pretty girl, the saloons will give her supper and drink, free of charge. Of course, nothing comes free, but the girls aren't so easily convinced of that. It's their first time away from home and they've forgotten everything their mothers taught them, if they were taught anything at all."

Mrs. Headison, it developed, had been widowed in 1914. On the first anniversary of the death of her husband, a retired constable, she read about New Jersey's new law allowing women to serve as police officers. "It was as if John were speaking to me from the hereafter and telling me that I had a new calling. I went right to the Paterson police chief and made my application."

Sheriff Heath and I attempted to offer our congratulations but she continued without taking a breath. "Do you know that he hadn't even considered adding a woman to his force? I had to argue my case, and you can be sure I did. Do you know why he was so reluctant? The chief told me himself that if women start going about in uniforms, armed with guns and clubs, we would turn into little men."

I cast the sheriff a look of horror but he kept his eyes straight ahead.

"I assured him that my position in the police department

would be exactly the same as that of a mother in the home. Just as a mother tends to her children and issues a kind word of warning or encouragement, I would carry out my duty as a woman and bring a mother's ideals into the police department. Wouldn't you agree, Miss Kopp? Haven't you become quite the mother hen at the sheriff's department?"

I hadn't thought of myself as a mother hen, but then again, I'd seen a hen peck an errant chick so sharply that she drew blood, so perhaps Mrs. Headison was right. For the last two months, I'd been riding along anytime a woman or a girl was caught up in some criminal matter. I'd served divorce papers to an estranged wife, investigated a charge of illegal cohabitation, chased down a girl attempting to run away on a train, put clothes on a prostitute who was found naked and half-dead from opium in a card room above a tailor's shop, and sat with a mother of three while the sheriff and his men ran through the woods looking for her husband, over whose head she had broken a bottle of brandy. The husband was returned to her, although she wouldn't let him inside until he promised, in front of the sheriff, to bring no more drink into her house.

It would be no exaggeration to say that the moments I have just described were among the finest of my life. The prostitute had soiled herself and had to be washed in the card room's dingy basin, and the girl running for the train bit my arm when I caught her, and still I assert that I had never been more content. Improbable as it may sound, I had, at last, found work that suited me.

I didn't know how to explain any of that to Mrs. Headison. To my relief, we arrived at Mr. Meeker's before I had to.

The sheriff drove just past his house and parked a few doors down.

He lived in a modest shingled home with painted shutters and a small front porch that looked to have been added on recently. There was a window open in his living room and the sound of piano music drifted into the front yard.

"Someone's at home," Sheriff Heath said. "Miss Kopp, you'll knock at the door and we'll stay down here. If there's a girl in there now, I don't want to scare her off. Try to get her to come to you. We're not going to arrest her for waywardness, but she doesn't know that."

"That's fine," I said.

Mrs. Headison stared at the two of us as if we'd just proposed a safari to Africa.

"You aren't going to send her to the door unguarded, are you? What if—"

She stopped when she saw me take my revolver from my handbag and tuck it into my pocket. It was the same one the sheriff issued to me the previous year when my family was being harassed: a Colt police revolver, dark blue, just small enough to conceal in the pockets Fleurette stitched into all my jackets and dresses for that purpose.

"Do they have you carrying a gun? Why, the police chief—"

"I don't work for the police chief." I felt the sheriff's eyes on me when I said it. The fact that we were doing something the police chief wouldn't have dared gave me a great deal of satisfaction.

With my revolver in place, I marched up to the man's door. The two of them stayed just out of sight as the piano music stopped and the door opened.

Harold Meeker was a doughy man of about forty years of age. He came to the door in shirtsleeves and a tie, carrying a pipe in one hand and his shoes in the other. He had a flat forehead that rearranged itself into wrinkles when he saw me.

"Excuse me, ma'am," he said, looking down at his bare feet. "The maid is in today doing some cleaning, and I was trying to stay out of her way."

He offered an abashed grin. I didn't want to waste any time lest the girl run out the back door.

"It's no trouble, Mr. Meeker," I said, loudly enough for the sheriff to hear. "In fact, I've come to see about that maid of yours. I believe I may have something that belongs to her."

I pushed my way in before he could stop me. Inside, I saw the worn carpets and shabby furniture that suggested a man who had never moved out of his mother's house. Every lampshade was painted in pink roses. The upright piano was draped in doilies. There was even a needlepoint sampler on the wall, faded to brown and covered in dust.

Mr. Meeker jumped around in front of me. He was almost my height but of a slighter build. He might have hoped to intimidate me, but he couldn't.

"Lettie was just finishing," he said, looking back toward what I took to be the kitchen. "If you wouldn't mind waiting outside, she'll be out in a minute. Are you a relation, Mrs. . . . ."

I ignored him and went straight for the kitchen. "Lettie, is that you?" I called, pushing the door open.

There, at a little wooden painted table, sat a girl of fifteen with kid curlers in her hair and a cigarette between her fingers. She wore only a thin cambric gown and damask slippers of the kind Fleurette favored. It was an old kitchen with an iron stove and a washtub for a sink. It needed a good cleaning, but Lettie wasn't the one to do it.

She jumped up when she saw me.

"You don't look like a housekeeper," I said, and went alongside her to take her elbow.

"No, I'm just—I'm here visiting until . . ."

Harold Meeker hadn't followed us into the kitchen. I could only assume he'd realized that he was in trouble and tried to run. Sheriff Heath would grab him.

I kept a firm hold of her arm and said, "I'm from the sheriff's department, dear. You're not in any trouble, but we worry that you might have been misled by an advertisement Mr. Meeker placed for a housekeeper."

Lettie was defiant. She jutted out her lower lip and put her free hand on her hip. "I'm allowed to apply for work. There's no law against it."

I heard voices from the other room and knew that Sheriff Heath had caught his man and returned with him.

"We believe he's taking advantage of young girls, and there is a law against that. How long have you been here?"

She twisted around and looked toward the back door, but I pulled her firmly toward me. "When did you get to town, Lettie?"

She sniffed and dropped down to her chair. I eased down next to her. "Just last week." She fingered the sardine tin she used for an ashtray. "I came out on the train from Ohio. I was going to New York, but something got mixed up with my tickets and here I am, with no money and no one to take me in but Mr. Meeker."

Already I hated Mr. Meeker. What kind of man thinks he

can just advertise for girls in the newspaper? "And what happened when he made it plain that he wasn't just looking for a housekeeper?"

She put her face in her hands and didn't answer.

I looked around for something for Lettie to wear and saw an old duster on a hook. "It's all right. I've brought a lady with me who can find a better place for you." I pulled the duster over her head and helped her up. She had a child's bony shoulders. "Have you any things upstairs you'd like to take with you?"

She wiped her eyes. "I lost everything on the platform. My bag went one way and I went the other."

"We'll see what we can do about that." I took her into the living room, where Harold Meeker stood in handcuffs alongside Sheriff Heath and a dazed Mrs. Headison. When Mr. Meeker saw us, he lunged for Lettie but could only rattle his chains at her.

"Did you call the sheriff?" he shouted. "You worthless little tramp, after all I've done—"

Sheriff Heath yanked him back, but they both lost their footing. Mr. Meeker kicked and fought and twisted out of the sheriff's grip. He was free for only a second, and tried to run between us and out the door. I threw myself at him and forced him into a corner. I had my fist around his collar but still he flailed around and tried to push past me. Mrs. Headison gasped and ran across the room to take hold of Lettie.

The sheriff came up behind me and grabbed Harold Meeker's arm. I pulled a little harder on his collar, forcing him to his tiptoes.

There was the tiniest flicker of a glance between me and

the sheriff. Neither one of us wanted to let Mr. Meeker go. We were both enjoying ourselves. The man panted and seemed to wilt between us.

"I'll add avoiding arrest and assaulting an officer to your charges," Sheriff Heath said. "That'll keep you in jail a while longer."

I still had hold of his shirt. His neck had gone red where it pinched him.

"Get her hands off me!" Mr. Meeker gasped. "Who is she, your nurse?"

"She appears to be the deputy putting you under arrest," the sheriff said. "Speak to her if you have a complaint."

A little laugh escaped Lettie's mouth, but I heard nothing from Mrs. Headison.

It was an awkward ride back to Paterson, with me, Lettie, and Mrs. Headison in the back and the men together in the front. I didn't like to put a girl and her tormentor in the same auto, but we saw no other way to do it, as Mrs. Headison was too rattled to take Lettie back on the train alone and Sheriff Heath wanted me with him in case Mr. Meeker tried to escape.

The sheriff waited with his prisoner while I saw Lettie and Mrs. Headison back to the Travelers' Aid office.

"I know you'll take good care of the girl," I said. "It was right of you to call us."

Paterson's first policewoman still seemed agitated. "I'll tell Mr. Headison all about you tonight in my prayers, but I don't think he'll believe me. The things they have you doing—well, I couldn't do it, even if they did pay me."

I stared down at her. Lettie was watching the two of us, open-mouthed.

"Don't they pay you?" My salary was a thousand dollars a year, the same as the other deputies.

"Ah—well, of course not," she said, slowly, still puzzling it out. "The chief expects me to serve out of a sense of duty and honor, and not to take a salary away from a policeman."

I couldn't think of a polite thing to say about that. I wanted only to get back into the wagon with my prisoner and to see him locked in jail where he belonged.

"Do call on us again if you need us, Mrs. Headison," I said, and ran back to Sheriff Heath.

At the jail, he handed Mr. Meeker off to Deputy Morris, a dignified older man who had become a family friend when he guarded our house against Henry Kaufman last year. Morris nodded stiffly and congratulated me on my work as he took the man away.

But when I went to follow him inside, the sheriff called me back.

"Miss Kopp."

There was something uneasy about the way he said it. He nodded toward the garage, a little free-standing stone building that had once been a carriage house and still had two stalls, matted with old hay, for keeping horses. He preferred it for private conversations because it had only one entrance, and there was no worry about someone slipping in a back door.

In the dim shadows under the eaves Sheriff Heath gave me a long and measured look and then said, "There's some trouble about your badge."

Something froze inside of me but I tried to make a joke out

of it. "Have they run out of gold and rubies?" Sheriff Heath's badge held a single ruby, and he was always at pains to say that it had been purchased by his bondsmen, not the taxpayers.

He kept a large mustache that stretched when he smiled. It stayed perfectly still. When he spoke again it was in the manner of a speech he'd been rehearsing. "It has been brought to my attention by an attorney—who is a friend to the office of the sheriff and very much on our side—that I may stand on uncertain legal principle in the appointment of a female deputy sheriff."

My hands went nervously to my shirtfront. I patted myself down, smoothing my skirt and checking a button. "Haven't I been appointed already? Haven't I been doing the job since the middle of June?"

He took a step back and walked in a little circle, nodding. "You have. But it isn't official until the county clerk draws up the papers, and of course we don't yet have the badge itself. The trouble is that Mr.—our attorney friend . . ."

"Didn't the state pass a law allowing for the appointment of women police officers? Isn't that why you offered me the job?" There was a vibrato in my voice that I couldn't control. Even as I said it, I was beginning to understand what had happened.

"Yes. But that's the difficulty. The statute addresses police officers only. The sheriff is elected and governed under a different chapter of the law entirely. No mention was made of women deputies. In fact, the sheriff in New York City tried just such a scheme a few years ago, and had to abandon it because the law there requires that deputies be eligible voters in the county in which they serve, which means that women—"

I cut him off irritably. "Couldn't possibly qualify."

He was standing right in front of me again but I wouldn't look at him. Then he said, "We've no such troubles about voting in New Jersey. It isn't written into our laws that way. But if the lawmakers in Trenton had wanted women to serve as deputies, we can be sure they would have said so, and they didn't."

He had a higher opinion of lawmakers in Trenton than I did. "Couldn't it have been an oversight?" I was practically yelling.

"Yes. And I've been advised to write to all the other sheriffs in New Jersey and ask if any of them have appointed a lady deputy under the new law. It would give us precedence."

"And?"

"So far, no one has."

"And you don't want to be the first."

He lifted his hat, pushed his hair back, and set it down again. "Miss Kopp. I can fight the Freeholders over my budget and how I discharge my duties, but I cannot willfully break the law."

I turned away from him and tried to compose myself. I thought about the day, when I was about ten years of age, when I copied down a list printed in the newspaper under the title "What a Woman Can Do." I wrote down each item in a neat and careful hand, and then crossed most of them out, having considered each. The Profession of Music was thus eliminated, as was Coloring Photographs and Women as Wood Engravers. Housekeeper was blotted out so thoroughly that the paper tore. Dressmaking met the same fate, as did Gardening. In fact, the paper was nearly in tatters under the force of my emphatic little hand.

Only The Profession of Law remained, along with A Lady Government Official, Women of Journalism, and Nursing. Each of those wore faint checks beside them.

I hid that list inside a white glove that needed mending and never showed it to anyone. On it were all the possibilities in the world.

No one, back in 1887, had dared to suggest Woman Deputy.

Now my profession was being taken away from me as quickly as it had been given. Already I'd grown accustomed to thinking of myself as one of the first to prove that a woman could do the job. I wasn't like Mrs. Headison. I wasn't just a chaperone for wayward girls. I carried a gun and handcuffs. I could make an arrest, just like any deputy. I earned a man's salary. People did find it shocking and I didn't mind that one bit.

A blue rectangle of sky lay beyond the garage's wide door. As soon as I walked out, I'd be ordinary again. I hadn't realized, until that moment, how much I hated being ordinary.

I still had my back to Sheriff Heath. I thought it best to leave without letting him see my face again. "Well. I suppose I'll go home."

"There's no need for that," the sheriff said quickly. "I've something else for you, if you'll take it."

That was enough to make me turn around.

"I won't be your stenographer." I wasn't about to sit in a room and take notes about what the other deputies had done.

Now he did smile a little. "It's not as bad as that. And it won't last long. Give me a month and I'll find a way."

I looked him in the eyes at last. They were sunken and soulful, and often carried dark circles around them. The man had a trustworthy face.

"A month?"

"That's all. One month."

The Kopp sisters return in

MISS KOPP'S MIDNIGHT CONFESSIONS

Out in September 2017

MISS KOPP'S
MIDNIGHT
CONFESSIONS

A Kopp Sisters Novel

AMY STEWART

NEW YORK, SEPT. 27.—Constance A. Kopp, the Lady Sheriff of Bergen
county, N. J., hustled into police headquarters last night and said she had a warrant

THE ROUGH GUIDE TO

Thailand

This ninth edition updated by

Ron Emmons, Paul Gray and Phillip Tang

ROUGH GUIDES

roughguides.com

Contents

Introduction to
Thailand

With twenty-five million foreigners flying into the country each year, Thailand is Asia's primary holiday destination. Yet despite this vast influx of visitors, Thailand's cultural integrity remains largely undamaged – a country that adroitly avoided colonization has been able to absorb Western influences while maintaining its own rich heritage. Though the high-rises and neon lights occupy the foreground of the tourist picture, the typical Thai community is still the farming village, and you need not venture far to encounter a more traditional scene of fishing communities, rubber plantations and Buddhist temples. Around forty percent of Thais earn their living from the land, based around the staple rice, which forms the foundation of the country's unique and famously sophisticated cuisine.

Tourism has been just one factor in the country's development which, since the deep-seated uncertainties surrounding the Vietnam War faded, has been free, for the most part, to proceed at death-defying pace – for a time in the 1980s and early 1990s, Thailand boasted the fastest-expanding economy in the world. Politics in Thailand, however, has not been able to keep pace. Since World War II, coups d'état have been as common a method of changing government as general elections; the malnourished democratic system – when the armed forces allow it to operate – is characterized by corruption and cronyism.

Through all the changes of the last sixty years, the much-revered constitutional monarch, King Bhumibol, who sits at the pinnacle of an elaborate hierarchical system of deference covering the whole of Thai society, has lent a measure of stability. Furthermore, some 85 percent of the population are still practising Theravada Buddhists, a unifying faith that colours all aspects of daily life – from the tiered temple rooftops that dominate every skyline, to the omnipresent saffron-robed monks and the packed calendar of festivals.

ABOVE AKHA WOMAN; WAT BENJAMABOPHIT, BANGKOK

Where to go

The clash of tradition and modernity is most intense in **Bangkok**, the first stop on almost any itinerary. Within its historic core you'll find resplendent temples, canalside markets and the opulent indulgence of the eighteenth-century **Grand Palace**, while downtown's forest of skyscrapers shelters cutting-edge fashion and decor boutiques, as well as cool bars and clubs. After touchdown in Bangkok, much of the package-holiday traffic flows east to **Pattaya**, the country's seediest resort, but for prettier beaches you're better off venturing just a little further, to the islands of **Ko Samet** and the **Ko Chang archipelago**, with their squeaky white sand and shorefront bungalows.

Few tourists visit **Isaan**, the poorest and in some ways the most traditionally Thai region. Here, a trip through the gently modulating landscapes of the **Mekong River** valley, which defines Thailand's northeastern extremities, takes in archetypal agricultural villages and a fascinating array of religious sites, while the southern reaches of Isaan hold some of Thailand's best-kept secrets – the magnificent stone temple complexes of **Phimai, Phanom Rung** and **Khao Phra Viharn**, all built by the Khmers of Cambodia almost ten centuries ago. Closer to the capital, **Khao Yai National Park** encapsulates the phenomenal diversity of Thailand's flora and fauna, which here range from wild orchids to strangling figs, elephants to hornbills.

At the heart of the northern uplands, **Chiang Mai** is both an attractive historic city and a vibrant cultural centre, with a strong tradition of arts, crafts and festivals. It does a burgeoning line in self-improvement courses – from ascetic meditation to the more earthly pleasures of Thai cookery classes – while the overriding enticement of the surrounding region is the prospect of **trekking** through villages inhabited by a richly mixed population of tribal peoples. Plenty of outdoor activities and courses, as well as hot springs and massages, can be enjoyed at **Pai**, a surprisingly cosmopolitan hill station for travellers, three hours northwest of Chiang Mai.

FACT FILE

- Divided into 76 provinces or *changwat* and one special administrative area (Bangkok), Thailand was known as **Siam** until 1939 (and again from 1945 to 1949); some academics suggest changing the name back again, to better reflect the country's Thai and non-Thai diversity.

- The **population** of 67 million is made up of ethnic Thais (75 percent) and Chinese (14 percent), with the rest comprising mainly immigrants from neighbouring countries as well as hill-tribespeople.

- Buddhism is the national **religion**, Islam the largest minority religion, but nearly all Thais also practise some form of animism (spirit worship).

- Since 1932 the country has been a **constitutional** monarchy. King Bhumibol, also known as Rama IX (being the ninth ruler of the Chakri dynasty), is the world's longest-ruling head of state, having been on the throne since 1946; Prince Vajiralongkorn is the heir to the throne, while his younger sister, the popular Princess Sirindhorn, is also often seen in public.

- The world record for **nonstop kissing** was set by two Thai men in Pattaya on Valentine's Day, 2012, at a gobsmacking 50 hours, 25 minutes and 1 second.

THAI BOXING

Such is the national obsession with **muay thai**, or Thai boxing, that when Wijan Ponlid returned home from the Sydney 2000 Olympics with the country's only gold medal (for international flyweight boxing), he was paraded through town at the head of a procession of 49 elephants, given a new house and over 20 million baht, and offered a promotion in the police force. Belatedly perhaps, *muay thai* has recently entered the canon of martial-arts cinema: *Ong Bak* (2003), *Tom Yum Goong* (2005) and their various sequels were global box-office hits, and their all-punching, all-kicking star, Tony Jaa, who performed all his own stunts, has been appointed Cultural Ambassador for Thailand.

Though there are boxing venues all around the country, the very best fights are staged at Bangkok's two biggest stadiums, Rajdamnoen and Lumphini, and are well worth attending as a cultural experience even if you have no interest in the sport itself (see p.49 & p.164).

With Chiang Mai and the north so firmly planted on the independent tourist trail, the intervening **central plains** tend to get short shrift. Yet there is rewarding trekking around **Umphang**, near the Burmese border, and the elegant ruins of former capitals **Ayutthaya** and **Sukhothai** embody a glorious artistic heritage, displaying Thailand's distinctive ability to absorb influences from quite different cultures. **Kanchanaburi**, stunningly located on the **River Kwai**, tells of a much darker episode in Thailand's past, for it was along the course of this river that the Japanese army built the Thailand–Burma Railway during World War II, at the cost of thousands of lives.

Author picks

Having finally settled down in Thailand after twenty years of toing and froing, our author, Paul, has plenty to write home about. Here are some of his personal favourites.

Kneads must A good pummelling at the massage pavilions amid the historic, kaleidoscopic architecture of Wat Pho (p.91) is one of Bangkok's unbeatable experiences.

Road trips You'll get to know the mighty Mekong River up close and personal along the Chiang Khan–Nong Khai road in Isaan (p.489), while the three thousand bends of the Mae Hong Son loop reveal the pick of Thailand's upland scenery (p.329).

Islands ahoy Messing about in boats is a big part of island life, and it's hard to beat a short, richly diverse circuit of Ko Tao and the causeway beaches of Ko Nang Yuan (p.570).

Aaaaaah-roy "Delicious" food is never far away in Thailand, be it fluffy deep-fried catfish with a tangy mango salad, toothsome beef green curry, or mango with sticky rice and coconut milk (p.38).

Let yourself go Mad, bad and bawdy carousing at Yasothon's Rocket Festival (p.470) and Phi Ta Kon in Dan Sai (p.483).

Simply celadon Among dozens of highly skilled, good-value handicrafts in Thailand, one that's especially appealing is celadon, elegant stoneware subtly glazed in green (p.300).

Khon It's hard to catch these days, but if you come across a performance, sit down and soak up the haunting music, beautiful costumes and exquisite gestures of Thailand's highest dramatic art (p.48).

Best view? You decide: a godlike panorama of the concrete jungle from Bangkok's *Sky Bar* (p.162), wave after wave of forested mountains from Doi Chang Moob (p.366), or the implausible limestone turrets in Phang Nga bay (p.647)?

> Our author recommendations don't end here. We've flagged up our favourite places – a perfectly sited hotel, an atmospheric café, a special restaurant – throughout the guide, highlighted with the ★ symbol.

OPPOSITE TRAVELLERS ARRIVING ON KO SAMUI **FROM TOP** PHI TA KON PERFORMER; PHANG NGA BAY

Sand and sea are what most Thai holidays are about, though, and the pick of the coasts are in southern Thailand, where the Samui archipelago off the **Gulf coast** is one of the highlights. **Ko Samui** itself has the most sweeping white-sand beaches, and the greatest variety of accommodation and facilities to go with them. **Ko Pha Ngan** next door is still largely backpacker territory, where you have a stark choice between desolate coves and **Hat Rin**, Thailand's party capital. The remotest island, rocky **Ko Tao**, is acquiring increasing sophistication as Southeast Asia's largest dive-training centre.

Across on the other side of the peninsula, the **Andaman coast** boasts even more exhilarating scenery and the finest coral reefs in the country, in particular around the **Ko Similan** island chain, which ranks among the best dive sites in the world. The largest Andaman coast island, **Phuket**, is one of Thailand's top tourist destinations and graced with a dozen fine beaches, though several have been overdeveloped with a glut of high-rises and tacky nightlife. Beautiful little **Ko Phi Phi** is a major party hub, surrounded by the turquoise seas and dramatic limestone cliffs that characterize the coastline throughout **Krabi province**. Large, forested **Ko Lanta** is, for the moment at least, a calmer alternative for families, but for genuine jungle you'll need to head inland, to the rainforests of **Khao Sok National Park**.

Further down the Thai peninsula, in the provinces of the **deep south**, the teeming sea life and unfrequented sands of the **Trang islands** and **Ko Tarutao National Marine Park** are the main draws. There's now the intriguing possibility of **island-hopping** your way down through them – in fact, all the way from Phuket to Penang in Malaysia – without setting foot on the mainland.

When to go

The **climate** of most of Thailand is governed by three seasons: rainy (roughly May–Oct), caused by the southwest monsoon dumping moisture gathered from the Andaman Sea and the Gulf of Thailand; cool (Nov–Feb); and hot (March–May). The **rainy season** is the least predictable of the three, varying in length and intensity from year to year, but it's never a case of the heavens opening in May and not closing again till October: there'll be rain most days, but often only for a few hours in the afternoon or at night. The rains usually gather force

---

SPIRIT HOUSES

Although the vast majority of Thais are Buddhist, nearly everyone also believes that the physical world is inhabited by **spirits**. These spirits can cause trouble if not given enough care and attention, and are apt to wreak havoc when made homeless. Therefore, whenever a new building is constructed – be it a traditional village house or a multistorey office block – the owners will also construct a home for the spirits who previously occupied that land. Crucially, these spirit houses must be given the best spot on the site – which in Bangkok often means on the roof – and must also reflect the status of the building in question, so their architecture can range from the simplest wooden structure to an elaborate scale model of a particularly ornate temple or even a sleek little icon of modernism. Daily **offerings** of flowers, incense and candles are set inside the spirit house, sometimes with morsels of food.

RAT OR RAJA?

There's no standard system of **transliterating** Thai script into Roman, so you're sure to find that the Thai words in this book don't always match the versions you'll see elsewhere. Maps and street signs are the biggest sources of confusion, so we've generally gone for the transliteration that's most common on the spot; where it's a toss-up between two equally popular versions, we've used the one that helps best with pronunciation. However, sometimes you'll need to do a bit of lateral thinking, bearing in mind that a classic variant for the town of Ayutthaya is Ayudhia, while among street names, Thanon Rajavithi could come out as Thanon Ratwithi – and it's not unheard of to find one spelling posted at one end of a road, with another at the opposite end.

---

between June and August, coming to a peak in September and October, when unpaved roads are reduced to mud troughs. The **cool season** is the pleasantest time to visit, although temperatures can still reach a broiling 30°C in the middle of the day. In the **hot season**, when temperatures often rise to 35°C in Bangkok, the best thing to do is to hit the beach.

Within this scheme, slight variations are found from region to region (see p.59). The upland, less humid **north** experiences the greatest range of temperatures: at night in the cool season the thermometer dips markedly, occasionally approaching zero on the higher slopes, and this region is often hotter than the central plains between March and May. It's the **northeast** that gets the very worst of the hot season, with clouds of dust gathering above the parched fields, and humid air too. In **southern Thailand**, temperatures are more consistent throughout the year, with less variation the closer you get to the equator. The rainy season hits the **Andaman coast** of the southern peninsula harder than anywhere else in the country: rainfall can start in April and usually persists until November.

One area of the country, the **Gulf coast** of the southern peninsula, lies outside this general pattern. With the sea immediately to the east, this coast and its offshore islands feel the effects of the northeast monsoon, which brings rain between October and January, especially in November, but suffers less than the Andaman coast from the southwest monsoon.

Overall, the cool season is the **best time** to come to Thailand: as well as having more manageable temperatures and less rain, it offers waterfalls in full spate and the best of the upland flowers in bloom. Bear in mind, however, that it's also the busiest season, so forward planning is essential.

RIGHT BANGKOK AT DUSK

30

things not to miss

It's not possible to see everything that Thailand has to offer in one trip – and we don't suggest you try. What follows, in no particular order, is a selective taste of the country's highlights: beautiful beaches, outstanding national parks, magnificent temples and thrilling activities. All entries have a page reference to take you straight into the Guide, where you can find out more. Coloured numbers refer to chapters in the Guide section.

1 KO KOOD
Page 425
An untamed beauty, fringed by very pretty beaches.

2 AYUTTHAYA
Page 213
River boats and bicycles are the perfect way to explore the scattered temple ruins of this former capital.

3 VEGETARIAN FESTIVAL, PHUKET
Page 623
During Taoist Lent, fasting Chinese devotees test their spiritual resolve with acts of gruesome self-mortification.

14

4 KHMER RUINS
Pages 447, 450 & 460

The Khmers of neighbouring Angkor left a chain of magnificent temple complexes across the northeast, including this one at Phimai.

5 KHAO SOK NATIONAL PARK
Page 604

Mist-clad outcrops, jungle trails serenaded by whooping gibbons, and the vast Cheow Lan Lake all make Khao Sok a rewarding place to explore.

6 CHATUCHAK WEEKEND MARKET
Page 129

Thailand's top shopping experience features over eight thousand stalls selling everything from cooking pots to designer lamps.

7 JIM THOMPSON'S HOUSE
Page 119

The house of the legendary American adventurer, entrepreneur and art collector is a small, personal museum of Thai crafts and architecture.

8 LOY KRATHONG
Page 47

At this festival in honour of the water spirits, Thais float baskets of flowers and lighted candles on rivers, ponds and seashores.

9 WAT PHO
Page 90

A lively and lavish temple, encompassing the awesome Reclining Buddha.

10 NAKHON SI THAMMARAT
Page 575

Home to superb food and the chief religious and cultural riches of the south.

11 SONGKHRAN
Page 46

Thai New Year is the excuse for a national waterfight.

12 KHAO YAI NATIONAL PARK
Page 437

Easy trails and tours, night safaris and a healthy cast of hornbills and gibbons.

13 WAT PHRA THAT DOI SUTHEP, CHIANG MAI
Page 302

One of the most harmonious ensembles of temple architecture in the country.

14 FOLKLORE MUSEUM, PHITSANULOK
Page 234

One of Thailand's best ethnology museums, complete with a reconstructed village home.

15 THE MAE HONG SON LOOP
Page 329

A spectacular 600km trip, winding over steep forested mountains.

16 NIGHT MARKETS
Page 38

Evening gatherings of pushcart kitchens, which are usually the best-value places to eat.

21

22

17 THE GRAND PALACE
Page 84

No visitor should miss this huge complex, which encompasses the country's holiest and most beautiful temple, Wat Phra Kaeo.

18 THAI COOKERY CLASSES IN CHIANG MAI
Page 281

Of the many courses on offer in the town, cookery classes are the most instantly gratifying and popular.

19 NAN
Page 322

Set in rich mountain scenery, with a strong handicraft tradition and some intriguing temples.

20 TRADITIONAL MASSAGE
Page 50

Combining elements of acupressure and yoga, a pleasantly brutal way to end the day.

21 AO PHANG NGA
Page 647

Boat or kayak your way through the bizarre and beautiful rock formations rising out of the Andaman Sea.

22 FULL MOON PARTY AT HAT RIN, KO PHA NGAN
Page 560

Apocalypse Now without the war.

23 KO LANTA
Page 680

A popular choice for families, with its many long beaches and plentiful but low-key resort facilities.

Itineraries

The following itineraries cover Thailand in all its diversity, from running the rapids in the northern mountains to beach-bumming your way through the Andaman archipelagos. Whether you want to feel the buzz of adventure in the great outdoors, feast on the never-ending variety of Thai cuisine, or find the nearest thing to a desert island paradise, these will point the way.

THE GREAT OUTDOORS

Thailand now offers an astonishing range of good-value active pursuits, both on land and in the teeming tropical seas.

❶ **Khao Yai National Park** One of the very few national parks to maintain a network of hiking trails that visitors can explore by themselves, passing dramatic waterfalls, orchids and an abundance of wildlife. **See p.437**

❷ **Chiang Mai** The best single base for outdoor activities, offering cycling day-trips and multi-day tours, mountain biking, trekking, rafting, rock-climbing and many others. **See p.277**

❸ **Pai rafting** A good place for trekking, but the real highlight here is the two-day whitewater rafting trip down the Pai River, taking in waterfalls, hot springs and a night in a jungle camp. **See p.347**

❹ **Umphang trekking** The best way to reach the 200m-high Thi Law Su Falls is by rafting and hiking your way through the jungle on a three-day trip. **See p.265**

❺ **Diving and snorkelling off Ko Similan** The underwater scenery at this remote chain of national park islands is world-class and can be explored on appealing, small-scale live-aboards. **See p.614**

❻ **Sea-canoeing in Ao Phang Nga** Low-impact paddling on day, night or multi-day

trips is the best way to explore the secret caves and mangrove swamps of this extraordinary bay. **See p.618**

❼ **Ko Yao Noi** This relaxing island on the edge of Phang Nga bay is a low-key hub for active visitors, who kayak, snorkel, dive and climb rocks. **See p.643**

❽ **Rock-climbing on the Railay peninsula** Offering courses for beginners, as well as equipment rental and guides, this is Thailand's premier site for climbers, with over seven hundred bolted routes amid awesome scenery. **See p.663**

THE FOODIE TRAIL

We're not daring to claim that the restaurants mentioned below are the very best in Thailand, but they're all locally famous places serving regional specialities where you can eat extremely well.

❶ **Chiang Rai** Not a town renowned for its gastronomy, but *Salungkham* always stops the traffic and delivers the goods – and you might well want to take away some of its home-smoked pork. **See p.354**

❷ **Chiang Mai** The nearest thing to nirvana for foodies: loads of Thai cooking classes, culinary walking tours and a choice between central Thai and Burmese-influenced northern Thai food at restaurants such as *Huen Phen*. **See p.281, p.294 & p.296**

ABOVE SNORKELLERS, KO SIMILAN; DELICIOUS THAI FOOD; HAEW SUWAT FALLS, KHAO YAI NATIONAL PARK

❸ Bangkok Among fifty thousand places to eat in the capital, a couple of restaurants can be singled out for special mention: *Taling Pling*, with a long list of dishes from the four corners of the country praised by Thai food critics; and *Bolan*, for its meticulous commitment to traditional recipes and the "Slow Food" philosophy. **See p.156 & p.158**

❹ Hua Hin Long the favourite seaside retreat of Bangkok's food-loving middle classes, Hua Hin has built up a thriving culinary scene – *Baan Itsara's* creative seafood dishes stand out. **See p.515**

❺ Phuket Among Phuket's swanky, big-name restaurants, *The Seacret* may seem an unlikely choice, but it delivers fantastic local dishes such as dried and smoked shrimp relish (*nam prik kung siap*) and stewed pork belly with cinnamon. **See p.638**

❻ Krabi You may have to queue for a table at *Ko Tung*, but it's worth the wait for the fresh, southern-style seafood such as delicious sweet mussels and baked crab. **See p.651**

❼ Nakhon Si Thammarat *Krua Thale* is almost reason in itself to go to Nakhon – don't miss the chunky mussels in herb soup. **See p.575**

ISLAND-HOPPING ON THE QUIET

Ferries now join up the karst islands of the southern Andaman coast, so it's possible to get from Phuket to Penang in Malaysia without setting foot on the mainland. You can avoid the crowds, and save yourself money and hassle, by bypassing the kiss-me-quick honeypots of Phuket, Ko Phi Phi and Ko Lipe in favour of these island beauties.

❶ Phuket Town Base yourself among the Sino-Portuguese architecture of the island capital, which has better-value and more interesting places to stay and eat than the big-name beaches, and much better transport links. **See p.621**

❷ With around 20km of west-facing sands and a laidback, family-friendly atmosphere, **Ko Lanta** offers a wide range of affordable accommodation and an almost endless choice of beach bars for sundowners. **See p.680**

A short detour from Lanta brings you to **Ko Jum**'s half a dozen wild and lonely beaches facing the sunset, with boat trips to enjoy and a small mountain to climb. **See p.676**

❸ There's a variety of good resorts for all budgets on **Ko Hai** and a gorgeous panorama of jagged limestone islands. **See p.702**

A quick hop from Ko Hai, **Ko Mook**'s main draw is the stunning Emerald Cave, with its inland beach of fine sand at the base of a spectacular natural chimney. **See p.704**

Just southwest of Ko Mook, **Ko Kradan** is a remote island that's uninhabited apart from its half-dozen resorts, with a long, powdery, east-facing strand, crystal-clear waters and a reef for snorkellers to explore. **See p.705**

❹ Ko Tarutao Huge national park island with mangroves and jungle tracks to explore, and the most unspoilt beaches in the area. **See p.708**

TUK-TUK

Basics

Getting there

Thailand currently has seven main international airports: in Bangkok (Suvarnabhumi and Don Muang), Chiang Mai, Hat Yai (see p.697), Krabi, Phuket and Ko Samui. The vast majority of travellers fly into Suvarnabhumi Airport (see p.133).

Air fares to Thailand generally depend on the **season**, with the highest being approximately mid-November to mid-February, when the weather is best (with premium rates charged for flights between mid-Dec and New Year), and in July and August to coincide with school holidays. You will need to book several months in advance to get reasonably priced tickets during these peak periods.

The cheapest way of getting to most **regional Thai airports** is usually to buy a flight to Bangkok and then a separate domestic ticket. However, there are dozens of potentially useful, mostly seasonal, international routes into **Phuket**, including direct flights with several airlines from Australia. Most international flights into Chiang Mai, Krabi, Ko Samui and Don Muang are from Malaysia, Singapore and China (including Hong Kong and Macau). Krabi also handles seasonal, mostly charter flights from Scandinavia, while Korean Airlines from Seoul is a popular route for North American visitors into Chiang Mai Airport, which has links with Myanmar and Laos too.

Flights from the UK and Ireland

The fastest and most comfortable way of reaching Thailand **from the UK** is to fly nonstop from London to Bangkok with Thai Airways (W thaiairways.com), British Airways (W ba.com) or Eva Airways (W evaair .com), a journey of about eleven and a half hours. These airlines sometimes have special promotions, but a typical fare in high season might come in at around £800–900. Fares on indirect scheduled flights to Bangkok are always cheaper than nonstop flights – starting at about £450 in high season if booked well in advance with Qatar Airways (W qatar airways.com), for example – though these journeys can take anything from two to twelve hours longer.

There are no nonstop flights from any **regional airports** in Britain or from any **Irish airports**, but rather than routing via London, you may find it convenient to fly to another hub such as Frankfurt (with Lufthansa; W lufthansa.com), Zurich (with Swiss; W swiss.com), Abu Dhabi (with Etihad; W etihad airways.com) or Istanbul (with Turkish Airlines; W turkishairlines.com), and take a connecting flight

from there. Return flights from Newcastle upon Tyne with Emirates (W emirates.com), for example, currently start at around £500 in high season if booked far in advance, from Dublin via Copenhagen with Emirates, at around €650.

Flights from the US and Canada

Thai Airways (W thaiairways.com) offers convenient flights from LA to Bangkok, with a ninety-minute stop in Seoul, charging from US$1100 in high season if booked well in advance. Plenty of other airlines run to Bangkok from East and West Coast cities with one stop en route; it's generally easier to find a reasonable fare on flights via Asia than via Europe, even if you're departing from the East Coast – if you book far in advance, you can get a flight from New York for as little as US$850 return in high season, including taxes. Air Canada (W aircanada .com) has the most convenient service to Bangkok from the largest number of Canadian cities; from Vancouver, expect to pay from around Can$1200 in high season; from Toronto, Can$1350. Cheaper rates are often available if you're prepared to make two or three stops and take more time.

Minimum **flying times** are twenty hours from New York or Toronto (westbound or eastbound), including stopovers, seventeen hours (nonstop) or nineteen and a half hours (with one stop) from LA, and eighteen hours from Vancouver.

Flights from Australia and New Zealand

There's no shortage of **scheduled flights** to Bangkok and Phuket **from Australia**, with direct services from major cities operated by Thai Airways (W thaiairways.com), Qantas (W qantas.com.au) and

---

A BETTER KIND OF TRAVEL

At Rough Guides we are passionately committed to travel. We believe it helps us understand the world we live in and the people we share it with – and of course tourism is vital to many developing economies. But the scale of modern tourism has also damaged some places irreparably, and climate change is accelerated by most forms of transport, especially flying. All Rough Guides' flights are carbon-offset, and every year we donate money to a variety of environmental charities.

half a dozen others (around 9hr from Sydney and Perth), and plenty of indirect flights via Asian hubs, which take at least eleven and a half hours. There's often not much difference between the fares on nonstop and indirect flights with the major carriers, nor between the fares from the major eastern cities. From Sydney, if you book far in advance, you can get a ticket to Bangkok in high season for around Aus$800, on a low-cost carrier such as Jetstar or through a special promotion with one of the major airlines; nonstop flights with the major airlines more typically cost around Aus$1200. Fares from Perth and Darwin are up to Aus$200 cheaper.

From **New Zealand**, Thai Airways runs nonstop twelve-hour flights between Auckland and Bangkok, costing from around NZ$1250 (including taxes) in high season with advanced booking. British Airways/Qantas flights from Auckland make brief stops in Sydney, adding about three hours to the trip, and other major Asian airlines offer indirect flights via their hubs (from 13hr, but more typically 17hr); fares for indirect flights can start as low as NZ$1100 in high season.

Flights from South Africa

Thai Airways' nonstop code-sharing flights with South African Airways (**W** flysaa.com) from Johannesburg to Bangkok have been discontinued, so you'll be making a stop in East Africa, the Middle East, Singapore or Hong Kong, with fares starting at around ZAR8000 for an advance booking in high season, and a journey time of fourteen hours or more.

AGENTS AND OPERATORS

All Points East UK **T** 023 9225 8859, Thailand **T** 081 885 9490; **W** allpointseast.com. Southeast Asia specialist operating small-group adventure holidays with off-the-beaten-track itineraries.

Andaman Discoveries Thailand **W** andamandiscoveries.com. Village-based homestay community tourism programmes around Khuraburi on the north Andaman coast, which allow visitors to experience daily activities such as cooking and batik-making, cultural activities and the local flora and fauna. Other tours include trips to Ko Surin National Park to learn about Moken life and to Khao Sok.

Asian Trails Thailand **W** asiantrails.travel. Well-regarded company that offers cycling adventures, inland cruises on the River Kwai in Kanchanaburi, plus more typical package tours.

Backpackers Thailand Thailand **W** backpackersthailand.com. Good general resource that offers some interesting tours, including homestays and volunteer programmes in Singburi in the Central Plains and cultural and food tours in Chiang Mai.

Creative Events Asia Thailand **W** creativeeventsasia.com. Wedding specialists for everything from paperwork to the ceremony and guest accommodation.

Eastern & Oriental Express UK **T** 0845 217 0799, US **T** 800 524 2420; **W** belmond.com/eastern-and-oriental-express. Tours by luxury train between Bangkok and Singapore, as well as to northern Thailand.

ETC (Educational Travel Centre) Thailand **W** etc.co.th. Unusual tour programmes including rice-barge cruises up the Chao Phraya River to Ayutthaya, and community-based programmes and homestays that might include trekking and teaching.

Flight Centre Australia **T** 13 31 33, Canada **T** 877 967 5302, New Zealand **T** 0800 243 544, South Africa **T** 0877 405000, UK **T** 0800 678 1134, US **T** 877 409 7018; **W** flightcentre.com. Australian company offering cheap international air fares.

Grasshopper Adventures Australia **T** 03 9016 3172, Thailand **T** 02 280 0832, UK **T** 020 8123 8144, US **T** 818 921 7101; **W** grasshopperadventures.com. Cycling day-tours and two-day trips around Bangkok, longer rides to Kanchanaburi, Chiang Mai, Ko Samui and Krabi, and around Chiang Rai.

Intrepid Travel Australia **T** 1300 797010, Canada **T** 855 299 1211, Ireland **T** 1800 939124, New Zealand **T** 09 520 0972, South Africa **T** 011 471 7400, UK **T** 0808 274 5111, US **T** 800 970 7299; **W** intrepidtravel.com. Well-regarded, small-group, off-the-beaten-track tour operator that offers over forty trips to Thailand.

North South Travel UK **T** 01245 608 291, **W** northsouthtravel .co.uk. Friendly, competitive travel agency, offering discounted fares worldwide. Profits are used to support projects in the developing world, especially the promotion of sustainable tourism.

Origin Asia Thailand **W** alex-kerr.com. Cultural programmes that teach and explain living Thai arts such as dance, music, martial arts, textiles, flower offerings and cooking. Courses last from half a day to a week and are held in Bangkok and Chiang Mai.

Responsible Travel UK **T** 01273 600030, **W** responsibletravel .com. One-stop shop for scores of fair-trade, ethically inclined holidays in Thailand, including trips that focus on wildlife, cuisine, family activities and village life.

Spice Roads Thailand **W** spiceroads.com. Escorted day- and multi-day bike tours – including mountain biking – through all regions of Thailand.

STA Travel UK **T** 0333 321 0099, US **T** 800 781 4040, Australia **T** 134 782, New Zealand **T** 0800 474 400, South Africa **T** 0861 781 781, Thailand **T** 02 236 0262; **W** statravel.co.uk. Worldwide specialists in independent travel; also student IDs, travel insurance, car rental and more. Good discounts for students and under-26s.

Symbiosis Custom Travel UK **T** 0845 123 2844, **W** symbiosis -travel.com. Upmarket, off-the-beaten-track tours with an environmentally sensitive, fair-trade focus, including visiting hill tribes by mountain bike, and kayaking at Khao Sok and Ko Tarutao.

Telltale Travel UK **T** 0800 011 2571, US **T** 866 211 5972, **W** telltaletravel.co.uk. Tailor-made, upscale company that offers off-the-beaten-track wildlife, cultural, family and cooking tours, as well as group trips for solo travellers.

Thailand Birdwatching Thailand **W** thailandbirdwatching.com. Specialist birdwatching tours in national parks and nature reserves.

Trailfinders UK **T** 0207 368 1200, Ireland **T** 021 464 8800, **W** trailfinders.com. One of the best-informed and most efficient agents for independent travellers.

Travel CUTS Canada ☎ 800 667 2887, US ☎ 800 592 2887, ⓦ travelcuts.com. Canadian youth and student travel firm.
USIT Ireland ☎ 01 602 1906, Australia ☎ 1800 092 499, ⓦ usit.ie. Ireland's main student and youth travel specialists, with a branch in Sydney.

Travel via neighbouring countries

Sharing land borders with Myanmar, Laos, Cambodia and Malaysia, Thailand works well as part of many overland itineraries, both across Asia and between Europe and Australia. Bangkok is also one of the major regional flight hubs for Southeast Asia. As part of plans for the ASEAN (Association of South East Asian Nations) Economic Community, which is hoped to be launched by the end of 2015, cross-border links in Southeast Asia have improved considerably recently and are likely to continue to do so in the next few years.

The main restrictions on overland routes in and out of Thailand are determined by where the permitted land crossings lie and by **visas**. All **Asian embassies** are located in Bangkok (see p.170), but waiting times can be shorter at visa-issuing consulates outside the capital: China and India run consulates in Chiang Mai (see p.302), and Laos and Vietnam have consulates in Khon Kaen (see p.477). In Bangkok, many Khao San tour agents offer to get your visa for you, but beware: some are reportedly **faking the stamps**, which could get you into pretty serious trouble, so it's safer to go to the embassy yourself.

The right paperwork is also crucial if you're planning to **drive your own car or motorbike** into Thailand; see the Golden Triangle Rider website (ⓦ gt-rider.com) for advice.

Looking beyond the country's immediate borders, it's possible to get **from Vietnam** into Thailand, via Savannakhet on the Lao–Thai border, in a matter of hours; you'll need to use Vietnam's Lao Bao border crossing, west of Dong Ha, where you can catch a bus to Savannakhet and then another bus across the Mekong bridge to Mukdahan. Coming **from China**, the much-improved Route 3 and the Fourth Thai–Lao Friendship Bridge over the Mekong at Chiang Khong now form a popular link between Yunnan and northern Thailand; travellers can also take cargo boats or sporadic passenger boats down the Mekong from Yunnan to Chiang Saen (see p.371).

Myanmar (Burma)

There are now four overland access points between **Myanmar (Burma)** and Thailand that are open to non-Thais: at Thachileik opposite Mae Sai; at Myawaddy near Mae Sot; at remote Htee Khee opposite Phu Nam Ron in Kanchanaburi province, a crossing that's being developed to facilitate transport between the major new port at Dawei on the Bay of Bengal and Bangkok; and at Kaw Thaung (Victoria Point) near Ranong. At these borders Western tourists can enter Myanmar either forearmed with a Burmese tourist visa, or on a temporary US$10 (or B500) **border pass**, which will allow you to make limited-distance trips into Myanmar, usually just for the day; see relevant accounts for details. The crossing at Three Pagodas Pass near Kanchanaburi is currently open only to Thai tourists, and there are plans – which have been gestating for a long time – to upgrade Dan Singkhon near Prachuap Khiri Khan into a permanent border crossing.

Cambodia

At the time of writing, six overland crossings on the **Thai–Cambodia border** are open to non-Thais; see the relevant town accounts for specific details on all the border crossings.

Most travellers use the crossing at Poipet, which has transport connections with Sisophon, Siem Reap and Phnom Penh and lies just across the border from the Thai town of Aranyaprathet (see p.381), with its transport to Bangkok and, with a change in Sa Kaew, to Chanthaburi; there are now also direct public buses that run all the way between Bangkok and Siem Reap and between Bangkok and Phnom Penh, which should help you dodge the scams and touts at this frontier post. The second most popular route is from Sihanoukville in Cambodia via Koh Kong (Cham Yeam) and Hat Lek to Trat, which is near Ko Chang on Thailand's east coast.

The crossings in northeast Thailand include the Chong Chom–O'Smach border pass, near Kap Choeng in Thailand's Surin province, and the Chong Sa Ngam–Choam border in Thailand's Si Saket province; from both these borders there's transport to Anlong Veng and on to Siem Reap. There are also two little-used crossings in Chanthaburi province, with transport to and from Pailin in Cambodia.

Tourist **visas** for Cambodia are issued to travellers on arrival at all the above-listed overland border crossings. If you want to buy an advance thirty-day visa, you can do so online at Ⓦevisa.gov.kh. Of the land borders discussed here, these "e-visas" can be used only at Poipet and Koh Kong, but they should help you to avoid the more excessive scams at these two frontier posts.

Laos

There are six main points along the **Lao border** where tourists can cross into Thailand: Houayxai (for Chiang Khong); on the Nam Heuang River at the Thai settlement of Tha Li (Loei province); Vientiane (for Nong Khai); Khammouan (aka Thakhek, for Nakhon Phanom); Savannakhet (for Mukdahan); and Pakse (for Chong Mek). Increasing numbers of direct, long-distance public buses, such as those between Loei and Luang Prabang via Tha Li, use these crossings to link major towns in the two countries. There are remoter frontier posts, where transport is a little more difficult, at Huai Kon in Thailand's Nan province and between Paksan and Bueng Kan. All these borders can also be used as exits into Laos; tourist **visas** are available **on arrival** at all of the above-listed land borders except Paksan, or you can buy one in advance from either the Lao Embassy in Bangkok or the Lao Consulate in Khon Kaen.

Malaysia

Travelling between Thailand and **Malaysia** has in the past been a straightforward and very commonly used overland route, with plentiful connections by bus, minibus, share-taxi and train, most of them routed through the southern Thai city and transport hub of Hat Yai. However, because of the ongoing **violence in Thailand's deep south** (see p.697), all major Western governments are currently advising people not to travel to or through Songkhla, Pattani, Yala and Narathiwat provinces, unless essential (and consequently most insurance companies are not covering travel there). This encompasses Hat Yai and the following border crossings to and from Malaysia: at Padang Besar, on the main rail line connecting Butterworth in Malaysia (and, ultimately, Kuala Lumpur and Singapore) with Hat Yai and Bangkok; at Sungai Kolok, terminus of a railway line from Hat Yai and Bangkok, and at adjacent Ban Taba, both of which are connected by road to nearby Kota Bharu in Malaysia; and at the road crossings at Sadao, south

of Hat Yai, and at Betong, south of Yala. (The routes towards Kota Bharu and Betong pass through particularly volatile territory, with martial law declared in Pattani, Yala and Narathiwat provinces; however, martial law is not in effect in Hat Yai itself.)

Nevertheless, the provinces of Trang and Satun on the west coast are not affected, and it's still perfectly possible to travel **overland via Satun**: by ferry between Satun's Thammalang pier and the island of Langkawi, or overland between Satun and Kangar (see p.715); or by boat between Ko Lipe and Langkawi (see p.712). For up-to-the-minute advice, consult your government travel advisory (see p.62).

Most Western tourists can spend thirty days in Malaysia without having bought a visa beforehand, and there are Thai embassies or consulates in Kuala Lumpur, Kota Bharu and Penang (see p.64).

Getting around

Travel in Thailand is inexpensive and efficient, if not always speedy. Unless you travel by plane, long-distance journeys in Thailand can be arduous, especially if a shoestring budget restricts you to hard seats and no air conditioning.

Nonetheless, the wide range of transport options makes travelling around Thailand easier than elsewhere in Southeast Asia. **Buses** are fast, cheap and frequent, and can be quite luxurious; **trains** are slower but safer and offer more chance of sleeping during overnight trips; moreover, if travelling by day you're likely to follow a more scenic route by rail than by road. Inter-town **songthaews**, **air-conditioned minibuses** and **share-taxis** are handy, and **ferries** provide easy access to all major islands. Local transport comes in all sorts of permutations, both public and chartered.

Inter-town buses

Buses, overall the most convenient way of getting around the country, come in four main categories. In ascending order of comfort, speed and cost, they are **ordinary** buses (*rot thammadaa*; not air-conditioned, usually orange-coloured) and three types of **air-conditioned** bus (*rot ae* – "*air*" – or *rot thua*; often blue): second-class, first-class and VIP. Ordinary and many air-conditioned buses are run by the government-controlled Baw Khaw Saw (*borisat khon song*), known in English as the Transport Company, while privately owned, licensed air-conditioned buses (*rot ruam*, usually translated as "join buses"), some of which operate from Baw Khaw Saw terminals, also ply the most popular long-distance routes; on some short-distance routes, air-conditioned minibuses (see p.30) are replacing buses. Be warned that long-distance overnight buses, on which some drivers are rumoured to take amphetamines to stay awake, seem to be involved in more than their fair share of accidents; because of this, some travellers prefer to do the overnight journeys by train and then make a shorter bus connection to their destination.

Ordinary and second-class

On most routes, including nearly all services out of Bangkok, **second-class** (baw sawng; look for the "2" on the side of the vehicle) air-conditioned buses have now replaced **ordinary buses** as the main workhorses of the Thai bus system, though you'll still see plenty of the latter on shorter routes in more remote parts of the country, especially in the north and northeast. Whether air-conditioned or not, these basic buses are incredibly inexpensive, generally run frequently during daylight hours, pack as many people in as possible and stop often, which slows them down considerably.

It's best to ask locally where to catch your bus. Failing that, designated **bus stops** are often marked by **sala**, small, open-sided wooden structures with bench seats, located at intervals along the main long-distance bus route through town or on the fringes of any decent-sized settlement, for example on the main highway that skirts the edge of town. Where there is only a bus shelter on the "wrong" side of the road, you can be sure that buses travelling in both directions will stop there for any waiting passengers; simply leave your bag on the right side of the road to alert the bus driver and wait in the shade. But if you're in the middle of nowhere with no sala in sight, any ordinary or second-class bus should stop for you if you flag it down.

First-class and VIP

Express services, with fewer stops, are mostly operated by **first-class** (baw neung; look for the "1" on the side of the vehicle) and **VIP** (usually written in English on the side) buses. These are your best option for long-distance journeys: you'll generally be allotted specific seats, there'll be a toilet, and on the longest journeys you may get blankets, snacks and nonstop DVDs, though you might want a sweater to cope with excessive air conditioning. The first-class services have fewer seats than second-class and more leg room for reclining,

VIP services fewer seats again. Other nomenclature for the top-of-the-range services is also used, especially by the **private "join" companies**: "999", "super VIP" (with even fewer seats), "Gold Class" and, confusingly, sometimes even "First Class" (in imitation of airlines, with just eighteen huge, well-equipped seats).

On a lot of long-distance routes private "join" buses are indistinguishable from government ones and operate out of the same Baw Khaw Saw bus terminals. The major private companies, such as Nakhon Chai Air (☎1624, ⓦnca.co.th – English-language section "coming soon"), Sombat Tour (☎02 792 1444) and, operating out of Chiang Mai, Green Bus (☎053 266480, ⓦgreenbusthailand.com, with English-language timetables), have roughly similar fares, though naturally with more scope for price variation, and offer comparable facilities and standards of service. The opposite is unfortunately true of a number of the smaller, private, unlicensed companies, which have a poor reputation for service and comfort, but gear themselves towards foreign travellers with bargain fares and convenient timetables. The long-distance tour buses that run **from Thanon Khao San** in Banglamphu to Chiang Mai and Surat Thani are a case in point; though promised VIP buses, travellers on these routes frequently complain about shabby furnishings, ineffective air conditioning, unhelpful (even aggressive) drivers, lateness and a frightening lack of safety awareness – and there are frequent reports of theft from luggage on these routes, too, and even the spraying of "sleeping gas" so that hand luggage can be rifled without interruption. Generally it's best to travel with the government or licensed private bus companies from the main bus terminals (who have a reputation with their regular Thai customers to maintain and now operate a handy ticket office near Bangkok's Thanon Khao San – see p.135) or to go by train instead – the extra comfort and peace of mind are well worth the extra baht.

Tickets and timetables

Tickets for all buses can be bought from the departure terminals, but for ordinary and second-class air-conditioned buses it's normal to buy them on board. First-class and VIP buses may operate from a separate station or office, and tickets for the more popular routes should be booked a day in advance. As a rough indication of **fares**, a trip from Bangkok to Chiang Mai, a distance of 700km, costs around B850 for VIP, around B550 for first-class air-conditioned and around B450 for second-class air-conditioned.

Long-distance buses often depart in clusters around the same time (early morning or late at night, for example), leaving a gap of five or more hours during the day with no services at all. Local TAT offices occasionally keep up-to-date bus **timetables**, and there are useful downtown information and booking offices in Banglamphu in Bangkok (see p.135) and in Chiang Mai (Green Bus – see p.288). Thai Ticket Major's website (W thaiticket major.com) carries timetables in English for many routes as well as useful information on how to buy tickets in advance. Options include buying them online through the site; by phone on ☎ 02 262 3456 (making your payment within 5hr at, for example, any branch of Bangkok Bank); and buying them at 83 affiliated major post offices (as listed on the site), including the Ratchadamnoen post office in Banglamphu and the Thanon Na Phra Lan post office opposite the entrance to the Grand Palace in Ratanakosin.

Songthaews, share-taxis and air-conditioned minibuses

In rural areas, the bus network is often supplemented by **songthaews** (literally "two rows"), which are open-ended vans (or occasionally cattle-trucks) onto which the drivers squash as many passengers as possible on two facing benches, leaving latecomers to swing off the running board at the back. As well as their essential role within towns (see p.32), songthaews ply set routes from larger towns out to their surrounding suburbs and villages, and occasionally, where there's no call for a regular bus service, between small towns: some have destinations written on in Thai, but few are numbered. In most towns you'll find the songthaew "terminal" near the market; to pick one up between destinations just flag it down. To indicate to the driver that you want to get out, the normal practice is to rap hard with a coin on the metal railings as you approach the spot (or press the bell if there is one).

In the deep south (see p.694) they do things with a little more style – share-taxis connect many of the major towns, though they are inexorably being replaced by more comfortable **air-conditioned minibuses** (*rot tuu*, meaning "cupboard cars"). Scores of similar private air-conditioned minibus services are now cropping up all over the country, either operating out of small offices or pavement desks in town centres or from the bus terminals – or from the roads around Bangkok's Victory Monument. Some of these services have a timetable, but many just aim to leave when they have a full complement of passengers; then again, some companies publish a timetable but depart when they're full – whether before or after the published time. They cover the distance faster than buses, but often at breakneck speed, and they can be uncomfortably cramped when full – they're not ideal for travellers with huge rucksacks, who may be required to pay extra. These services are usually licensed and need to keep up their reputation with their regular Thai passengers but, as with full-sized buses (see p.29), you should be wary of unlicensed private companies that offer minibuses solely for farangs from Bangkok's Thanon Khao San.

In many cases, long-distance songthaews and air-conditioned minibuses will drop you at an exact address (for example, a particular guesthouse) if you warn them far enough in advance. As a rule, the **cost** of inter-town songthaews is comparable to that of air-conditioned buses, that of air-conditioned minibuses perhaps a shade more.

Trains

Managed by the State Railway of Thailand (SRT), the **rail** network consists of four main lines and a few branch lines. The **Northern Line** connects Bangkok with Chiang Mai via Ayutthaya, Lopburi, Phitsanulok and Lampang. The **Northeastern Line** splits into two just beyond Ayutthaya, the lower branch running eastwards to Ubon Ratchathani via Khorat and Surin, the more northerly branch linking the capital with Nong Khai (with a very short extension over the Mekong into Laos; see p.494) via Khon Kaen and Udon Thani; a high-speed line on this branch, financed by the Chinese government, is in the pipeline. The **Eastern Line** (slow, third-class only) also has two branches, one of which runs from Bangkok to Aranyaprathet on the Cambodian border, the other of which connects Bangkok with Si Racha and Pattaya. The **Southern Line** extends via Hua Hin, Chumphon and Surat Thani, with spurs off to Trang and Nakhon Si Thammarat, to Hat Yai (see p.697), where it branches: one line continues down the west coast of Malaysia, via Butterworth, where you usually change trains for Kuala Lumpur and Singapore; the other heads down the eastern side of the peninsula to Sungai Kolok on the Thailand–Malaysia border (20km from Pasir Mas on Malaysia's interior railway). At Nakhon Pathom a branch of this line veers off to Nam Tok via Kanchanaburi – this is all that's left of the Death Railway, of *Bridge on the River Kwai* notoriety (see p.188).

TRAIN INFORMATION

The State Railway of Thailand (SRT) offers 24hr **train information** on its free hotline ❶ 1690 and publishes free **timetables** in English, detailing types of trains available on each route (the best place to get hold of them is over the counter at Bangkok's Hualamphong Station). Its main website (ⓦ railway.co.th) carries English-language timetables, while the affiliated ⓦ thairailticket.com gives prices. For more comprehensive information and advice, go to ⓦ seat61.com/thailand.htm.

Fares depend on the class of seat, whether or not you want air conditioning, and on the speed of the train; those quoted here include the supplements for the various "speed" types of train (see below). Hard, wooden or thinly padded third-class seats are much cheaper than buses (Bangkok–Chiang Mai B231 on the Rapid train), and are fine for about three hours, after which numbness sets in; a few trains have air-conditioned third-class carriages. For longer journeys you'd be wise to opt for the padded and usually reclining seats in second class (Bangkok–Chiang Mai B391 on the Rapid train, or B671 on the Special Express with a/c for example). On long-distance trains, you also usually have the option of second-class berths (Bangkok–Chiang Mai B531–581, or B751–821 with a/c, on the Express service, for example), with pairs of day seats facing each other that convert into comfortable curtained-off bunks in the evening; lower bunks, which are more expensive than upper, have a few cubic centimetres more of space, a little more shade from the lights in the carriage, and a window. Travelling first class (Bangkok–Chiang Mai B1253–1453 per person on the Special Express) generally means a two-person sleeping compartment (occasionally a one-person compartment), complete with washbasin and fierce air conditioning.

There are several different types of train, most of which incur various "**speed**" supplements: slowest of all is the third-class-only Ordinary service, which is generally (but not always) available only on short and medium-length journeys and has no speed supplement. Next comes the misleadingly named Rapid train, a trip on which from Bangkok to Chiang Mai, for example, takes fifteen hours; the equally euphemistic Express, which does the Chiang Mai route in about the same time; and the Special Express which covers the ground in around twelve to fourteen hours. The fastest services are usually the daytime Special Express trains, which can usually be relied on to run roughly on time (most other services pay only lip service to their timetables and are sometimes several hours late). Nearly all long-distance trains have **dining cars**, and rail staff will also bring meals to your seat.

Booking at least one day in advance – longer if possible, especially in high season and over national holidays – is strongly recommended for second- and first-class seats on all lengthy journeys, while sleepers should be booked as far in advance as you can (reservations open sixty days before departure). You can make bookings for any journey in Thailand in person (bring your passport) at Hualamphong Station in Bangkok (see p.134) or at the train station in any major town. You can arrange advance bookings from abroad over the internet with reputable Thai travel agencies such as 12Go (ⓦ 12go.asia) or Thailand Train Ticket (ⓦ thailandtrainticket.com).

Ferries

Regular **ferries** connect all major islands with the mainland, and for the vast majority of crossings you simply buy your ticket on board. Safety standards are generally just about adequate but there have been a small number of sinkings in recent years – avoid travelling on boats that are clearly overloaded or in poor condition. In tourist areas competition ensures that prices are kept low, and fares tend to vary with the speed of the crossing: thus Chumphon–Ko Tao costs between B300 (6hr) and B600 (1hr 30min).

On the east coast and the Andaman coast boats generally operate a reduced service during the monsoon season (May–Oct), when the more remote spots become inaccessible. Ferries in the Samui archipelago are fairly constant year-round. Details on island connections are given in the relevant chapters.

Flights

Thai Airways (ⓦ thaiairways.com) now concentrates more on international routes, leaving Bangkok Airways (ⓦ bangkokair.com) as the major full-service airline on the internal **flight** network, which extends to all parts of the country, using some two-dozen airports. Air Asia (ⓦ airasia.com), Nok Air (ⓦ nokair.com), which is part-owned by Thai Airways, Thai Smile (ⓦ thaismileair.com), a subsidiary of Thai Airways, Thai Lion Air (ⓦ lionairthai.com) and the rapidly shrinking Orient Thai (ⓦ flyorient thai.com) provide the main "low-cost" competition; Kan Airlines (ⓦ kanairlines.com) mostly operates small planes out of Chiang Mai Airport and is planning to open an airport on Ko Pha Ngan. In a recently deregulated but ever-expanding market, other smaller airlines come and go with surprising frequency – and while they are operating, schedules tend to be erratic and flights are sometimes cancelled.

In some instances a flight can save you days of travelling: a flight from Chiang Mai to Phuket with Thai Airways or Air Asia, for example, takes two hours, as against a couple of days by meandering train and/or bus. Book early if possible – you can reserve online with all companies – as fares fluctuate wildly. For a fully flexible economy ticket, Bangkok to Chiang Mai costs around B3000 with Thai Airways, but you'll find flights on the same route with the "low-cost" carriers for under B1000 (with restrictions on changes), if you book online far enough in advance.

Local transport

Most sizeable towns have some kind of **local transport system**, comprising a network of buses, songthaews or even longtail boats, with set fares and routes but not rigid timetabling – in many cases vehicles wait until they're full before they leave.

Buses and songthaews

A few larger cities such as Bangkok, Khorat, Ubon Ratchathani and Phitsanulok have a **local bus** network that usually extends to the suburbs and operates from dawn till dusk (through the night in Bangkok). Most vehicles display route numbers in Western numerals – see the relevant accounts for further details.

Within medium-sized and large towns, the main transport role is often played by **songthaews**. The size and shape of vehicle used varies from town to town – and in some places they're known as "tuk-tuks" from the noise they make, not to be confused with the smaller tuk-tuks, described below, that operate as private taxis – but all have the tell-tale two benches (*sawng thaew*) facing each other in the back. In some towns, especially in the northeast, songthaews follow fixed routes; in others, such as Chiang Mai, they act as communal taxis, picking up a number of people who are going in roughly the same direction and taking each of them right to their destination. To hail a songthaew just flag it down, and to indicate that you want to get out, either rap hard with a coin on the metal railings, or ring the bell if there is one. Fares within towns are around B10–20, depending on distance, usually payable when you disembark.

Longtail boats

Wherever there's a decent public waterway, there'll be a **longtail boat** ready to ferry you along it. Another great Thai trademark, these elegant, stream-lined boats are powered by deafening diesel engines – sometimes custom-built, more often adapted from cars or trucks – which drive a propeller mounted on a long shaft that is swivelled for steering. Longtails carry between eight and twenty passengers: generally you'll have to charter the whole boat, but on popular fixed routes, for example between small, inshore islands and the mainland, it's cheaper to wait until the boatman gets his quorum.

Taxi services

Taxis also come in many guises, and in bigger towns you can often choose between taking a tuk-tuk, a samlor and a motorbike taxi. The one thing common to all modes of chartered transport, bar metered taxis in Bangkok and one or two cities in the northeast and the north, is that you must establish the **fare** beforehand: although drivers nearly always pitch their first offers too high, they do calculate with traffic and time of day in mind, as well as according to distance – if successive drivers scoff at your price, you know you've got it wrong.

Tuk-tuks

Named after the noise of its excruciatingly unsilenced engine, the three-wheeled, open-sided **tuk-tuk** is the classic Thai vehicle. Painted in primary colours, tuk-tuks blast their way round towns and cities on two-stroke engines, zipping around faster than any car and taking corners on two wheels. They aren't as dangerous as they look though, and can be an exhilarating way to get around, as long as you're not too fussy about exhaust fumes. Fares come in at around B60 for a short city journey (over B100 in Bangkok) regardless of the number of passengers – three is the safe maximum, though six is not uncommon. It's worth paying attention to advice on how to avoid getting ripped off by Bangkok tuk-tuk drivers (see p.141).

Samlors

Tuk-tuks are also sometimes known as samlors (literally "three wheels"), but the original **samlors** are tricycle rickshaws propelled by pedal power alone. Slower and a great deal more stately than tuk-tuks, samlors still operate in one or two towns around the country.

A further permutation is the motorized samlors (often called "skylabs" in northeastern Thailand), where the driver relies on a motorbike rather than a bicycle to propel passengers to their destination. They look much the same as cycle samlors, but often sound as noisy as tuk-tuks.

Motorbike taxis

Even faster and more precarious than tuk-tuks, **motorbike taxis** feature both in towns and in out-of-the-way places. In towns – where the drivers are identified by coloured, numbered vests – they have the advantage of being able to dodge traffic jams, but are obviously only really suitable for the single traveller, and motorbike taxis aren't the easiest mode of transport if you're carrying luggage. In remote spots, on the other hand, they're often the only alternative to hitching or walking, and are especially useful for getting between bus stops on main roads, around car-free islands and to national parks or ancient ruins.

Within towns motorbike-taxi fares can start at B10 for very short journeys, but for trips to the outskirts the cost rises steeply – reckon on at least B200 for a 20km round trip.

Vehicle rental

Despite first impressions, a high accident rate, especially involving motorcycles, and the obvious mayhem that characterizes Bangkok's roads, **driving** yourself around Thailand can be fairly straightforward. Many roads, particularly in the northeast and the south, are remarkably uncongested. Major routes are clearly signed in English, though this only applies to some minor roads; unfortunately there is no perfect English-language map to compensate (see p.70).

Outside the capital, the eastern seaboard and the major tourist resorts of Ko Samui and Phuket, local drivers are generally considerate and unaggressive; they very rarely use their horns for example, and will often indicate and even swerve away when it's safe for you to overtake. The most inconsiderate and dangerous road-users in Thailand are bus drivers and lorry drivers, many of whom drive ludicrously fast, hog the road, race round bends on the wrong side of the road and use their horns remorselessly; worse still, many of them are tanked up on amphetamines, which makes them quite literally fearless.

Bus and lorry drivers are at their worst after dark (many of them only drive then), so it's best **not to drive at night** – a further hazard being the inevitable stream of unlit bicycles and mopeds in and around built-up areas (often driving on the wrong side of the road), as well as poorly signed roadworks, which are often not made safe or blocked off from unsuspecting traffic. Orange signs, or sometimes just a couple of tree branches or a pile of stones on the road, warn of hazards ahead.

As for local **rules of the road**, Thais drive on the left, and the speed limit is 60km/h within built-up areas and 90km/h outside them. Beyond that, there are few rules that are generally followed – you'll need to keep your concentration up and expect the unexpected from fellow road-users. Watch out especially for vehicles pulling straight out of minor roads, when you might expect them to give way. An oncoming vehicle flashing its lights means it's coming through no matter what; a right indicator signal from the car in front usually means it's not safe for you to overtake, while a left indicator signal usually means that it is safe to do so.

Theoretically, foreigners need an international **driver's licence** to rent any kind of vehicle, but most car-rental companies accept national licences, and the smaller operations have been known not to ask for any kind of proof whatsoever; motorbike renters very rarely bother. A popular rip-off on islands such as Ko Pha Ngan is for small agents to charge renters exorbitant amounts for any minor damage to a jeep or motorbike, even paint chips, that they find on return – they'll claim that it's very expensive to get a new part shipped over from the mainland. Be sure to check out any vehicle carefully before renting.

For **petrol** (*nam man*, which can also mean oil), most Thais use gasohol, which can generally be used in rental cars (though it's worth checking) and currently costs around B28 a litre. The big fuel stations (*pam nam man*) are the least costly places to fill up (*hai tem*), and many of these also have toilets, minimarts and restaurants, though some of the more decrepit-looking fuel stations on the main highways only sell diesel. Most small villages have easy-to-spot roadside huts where the fuel is pumped out of a large barrel or sold in litre bottles.

Renting a car

If you decide to **rent a car**, go to a reputable dealer, such as Avis, Budget or National, or a rental company recommended by TAT, and make sure you get insurance from them. There are international car-rental places at many airports, including Bangkok's Suvarnabhumi, which is not a bad place to kick off, as you're on the edge of the city and within fairly easy, signposted reach of the major regional highways.

Car-rental places in provincial capitals and resorts are listed in the relevant accounts in this book. The price of a small car at a reputable company can start as low as B900 per day if booked online. In some parts of the country, including Chiang Mai, you'll still be able to rent a car or air-conditioned minibus with driver, which will cost from around B1000 for a local day-trip, more for a longer day-trip, up to about B3000 per day for a multi-day trip, including the driver's keep and petrol.

Jeeps or basic 4WDs are a lot more popular with farangs, especially on beach resorts and islands like Pattaya, Phuket and Ko Samui, but they're notoriously dangerous; a huge number of tourists manage to roll their jeeps on steep hillsides and sharp bends. Jeep rental usually works out somewhere around B1000–1200 per day.

International companies will accept your credit-card details as surety, but smaller agents will usually want to hold on to your passport.

CAR RENTAL AGENCIES

Avis Ⓦ avisthailand.com
Budget Ⓦ budget.co.th
Master Ⓦ mastercarrental.com
National Ⓦ nationalcarthailand.com
Thai Rentacar Ⓦ thairentacar.com

Renting a motorbike

One of the best ways of exploring the countryside is to **rent a motorbike**, an especially popular option in the north of the country. You'll almost never be asked for a driving licence, but take it easy out there – Thailand's roads are not really the place to learn to ride a motorbike from scratch. Bikes of around 100cc, either fully automatic or with step-through gears, are best for inexperienced riders, but aren't really suited for long slogs. If you're going to hit the dirt roads you'll certainly need something more powerful, like a 125–250cc trail bike. These have the edge in gear choice and are the best bikes for steep slopes, though an inexperienced rider may find these machines a handful; the less widely available 125–250cc road bikes are easier to control and much cheaper on fuel.

Rental **prices** for the day usually work out at somewhere around B150–200 for a small bike and B500 for a good trail bike, though you can bargain for a discount on a long rental. Renters will usually ask to hold on to your passport as surety but will generally accept a deposit instead; vehicle insurance is not often available (and some travel insurance policies won't cover you for motorcycle mishaps).

Before signing anything, **check the bike** thoroughly – test the brakes, look for oil leaks, check the treads and the odometer, and make sure the chain isn't stretched too tight (a tight chain is more likely to break) – and preferably take it for a test run. As you will have to pay an inflated price for any

damage when you get back, make a note on the contract of any defects such as broken mirrors, indicators and so on. Make sure you know what kind of fuel the bike takes as well.

As far as **equipment** goes, a helmet is essential – most rental places provide poorly made ones, but they're better than nothing. Helmets are obligatory on all motorbike journeys, and the law is often rigidly enforced with on-the-spot fines in major tourist resorts. You'll need sunglasses if your helmet doesn't have a visor. Long trousers, a long-sleeved top and decent shoes will provide a second skin if you go over, which most people do at some stage. Pillions should wear long trousers to avoid getting nasty burns from the exhaust. For the sake of stability, leave most of your luggage in baggage storage and pack as small a bag as possible, strapping it tightly to the bike with bungy cords – these can usually be provided. Once on the road, oil the chain at least every other day, keep the radiator topped up and fill up with oil every 300km or so.

For expert **advice** on motorbike travel in Thailand, check out David Unkovich's website (Ⓦ gt-rider.com).

Cycling

The options for **cycling** in Thailand are numerous, whether you choose to ride the length of the country from the Malaysian border to Chiang Rai, or opt for a dirt-road adventure in the mountains around Chiang Mai. Most Thai roads are in good condition and clearly signposted; although the western and northern borders are mountainous, most of the rest of the country is surprisingly flat. The secondary **roads** (distinguished by their three-digit numbers) are paved but carry far less traffic than the main arteries and are the preferred cycling option. Traffic is reasonably well behaved but the largest vehicles unofficially have – or take – the right of way and there are a fair number of accidents involving cyclists, so you'll need to "ride to survive"; dogs can also be a nuisance on minor roads so it's probably worth having rabies shots before your trip. There are bike shops in nearly every town, and basic equipment and repairs are cheap. Unless you head into the remotest regions around the Burmese border you are rarely more than 25km from food, water and accommodation. Overall, the best time to cycle is during the cool, dry season from November to February.

The traffic into and out of Bangkok is dense so it's worth hopping on a bus or train for the first 50–100km to your starting point. Intercity buses (though sometimes there's a small charge), taxis and some Thai domestic planes will **carry your bike** free of charge. Intercity trains will only transport your bike (for a cargo fare – about the price of a person) if there is a luggage carriage attached, unless you dismantle it and carry it as luggage in the compartment with you. Songthaews will carry your bike on the roof for a fare (about the price of a person).

Local one-day cycle tours and **bike-rental outlets** (from around B50/day for a sit-up-and-beg) are listed throughout this book. There are also a number of longer organized **cycle tours**, both nationwide (see p.26) and from Bangkok (see p.137) and Chiang Mai (see p.278). A very helpful English-language resource, dealing with all aspects of cycling in Thailand, is the **website** Ⓦ bicyclethailand.com, while Ⓦ chiangmaicycling.org is very useful for the Chiang Mai area.

Cycling practicalities

Strong, light, quality **mountain bikes** are the most versatile choice; 26-inch wheels are standard throughout Thailand and are strongly recommended, with dual-use (combined road and off-road) tyres best for touring. As regards panniers and **equipment**, the most important thing is to travel light. Carry a few spare spokes, but don't overdo it with too many tools and spares; parts are cheap in Thailand and most problems can be fixed quickly at any bike shop.

Bringing your bike from home is the best option as you are riding a known quantity. **Importing** it by plane should be straightforward, but check with the airlines for details. Most Asian airlines do not charge extra.

Buying in Thailand is also a possibility: Ⓦ bicycle thailand.com and Ⓦ chiangmaicycling.org give plenty of advice and listings.

Hitching

Public transport being so inexpensive, you should only have to resort to **hitching** in the most remote areas, in which case you'll probably get a lift to the nearest bus or songthaew stop quite quickly. On routes served by buses and trains, hitching is not standard practice, but in other places locals do rely on regular passers-by (such as national park officials), and you can make use of this "service" too. As with hitching anywhere in the world, think twice about hitching solo or at night, especially if you're female. Like bus drivers, truck drivers are notorious users of amphetamines, so you may want to wait for a safer offer.

Accommodation

For the very simplest double room, prices start at a bargain B150 in the outlying regions, around B200 in Bangkok, and B400 in the pricier resorts. Tourist centres invariably offer a tempting range of more upmarket choices but in these areas rates fluctuate according to demand, plummeting during the off-season, peaking over the Christmas and New Year fortnight and, in some places, rising at weekends throughout the year.

Guesthouses, bungalows and hostels

Most of Thailand's **budget accommodation** is in **guesthouses** and **bungalows**. These are small, traveller-friendly hotels whose services nearly always include an inexpensive restaurant, wi-fi and safe storage for valuables and left luggage, and often a tour desk. The difference between guesthouses and bungalows is mostly in their design, with "bungalows" – which are generally found on the beach and in rural areas – mostly comprising

---

ACCOMMODATION PRICES

Throughout this guide, the prices given for guesthouses, bungalows and hotels represent the **minimum** you can expect to pay in each establishment in the **high season** (roughly July, Aug and Nov–Feb) for a typical **double room**, booked via the hotel website where available; there may however be an extra "peak" supplement for the Christmas–New Year period. If travelling on your own, expect to pay between sixty and one hundred percent of the rates quoted for a double room. Where a hostel or guesthouse also offers **dormitory beds**, the minimum price per bed is also given; where a place has both fan-cooled and air-conditioned rooms, we've given the minimum price for a double in each category. Top-end hotels will add **seven percent tax** (though this is due to increase to ten percent) and **ten percent service charge** to your bill; the prices given in the Guide are net rates after these taxes (usually referred to as "plus plus") have been added.

BATHROOM ETIQUETTE

Although modern, Western-style bathrooms are commonplace throughout Thailand, it's as well to be forewarned about local bathroom etiquette.

Sit-down **toilets** are the norm but public amenities, especially at bus and train stations, and in some homes and old-style guesthouses and hotels, tend to be squat toilets. Thais traditionally don't use **paper** but wash rather than wipe themselves after going to the toilet. Modern bathrooms are fitted with a special hose for this purpose, while more primitive bathrooms just provide a **bucket of water and a dipper**. Thais always use their left hand for washing – and their right hand for eating (see p.40). As Thai plumbing is notoriously sluggish, where toilet paper is provided, you're often asked to throw it in the wastebasket and not down the U-bend. If a toilet is not plumbed in, you flush it yourself with water from the bucket. In really basic hotel bathrooms with no **shower** facilities, you also use the bucket and dipper for scoop-and-slosh bathing.

detached or semi-detached rooms in huts, villas, chalets or indeed bungalows, and "guesthouses" being either a purpose-built mini-hotel or a converted home. Showers and flush toilets, whether en-suite or shared, are common in both, but at the cheapest up-country places you might be bathing with a bowl dipped into a large water jar, and using squat toilets.

Many guesthouses and bungalows offer a spread of options to cater for all budgets: their **cheapest rooms** will often be furnished with nothing more than a double bed, a blanket and a fan (window optional, private bathroom extra) and might cost anything from B150–300 for two people, depending on the location and the competition. A similar room with **en-suite** bathroom, and possibly more stylish furnishings, generally comes in at B200–600, while for a room with **air conditioning**, and perhaps a TV and fridge as well, you're looking at B350–1500. In the north of Thailand in the cool season, air conditioning is more or less redundant, but you might want to check that your room has a hot shower.

In the most popular tourist centres at the busiest times of year, the best-known guesthouses are often full night after night. Some will take **bookings** and advance payment via their websites, but for those that don't it's usually a question of turning up and waiting for a vacancy. At most guesthouses **checkout time** is either 11am or noon.

Generally you should be wary of taking accommodation advice from a **tout** or tuk-tuk driver, as they demand commission from guesthouse owners, which, if not passed directly on to you via a higher room price, can have a crippling effect on the smaller guesthouses. If a tout claims your intended accommodation is "full" or "no good" or has "burnt down", it's always worth phoning to

check yourself. Touts can come into their own, however, on islands such as Ko Lanta where it can be a long and expensive ride to your chosen beach, and frustrating if you then discover your bungalow is full; island touts usually sweet-talk you on the boat and then transport you for free to view their accommodation, ideally with no obligation to stay.

With only a dozen or so registered **youth hostels** in the country, bookable via ⓦtyha.org, it's not worth becoming a Hostelling International member just for your trip to Thailand, especially as card-holders get only a small discount and room rates work out the same as or more expensive than guest-house equivalents. In addition, there are a small but growing number of smart, modern, non-affiliated **hostels**, especially in Bangkok. They usually work out more expensive than budget guesthouses but are good places to meet other travellers.

Budget hotels

Thai sales reps and other people travelling for business rather than pleasure rarely use guesthouses, opting instead for **budget hotels**, which offer rooms for around B150–600. Usually run by Chinese-Thais, these functional three- or four-storey places are found in every sizeable town, often near the bus station or central market. Beds are large enough for a couple, so it's quite acceptable for two people to ask and pay for a "single" room (*hawng thiang diaw*, literally a "one-bedded room"). Though the rooms are generally clean, en suite and furnished with either a fan or air conditioning, there's rarely an on-site restaurant and the atmosphere is generally less convivial than at guesthouses. A number of budget hotels also double as brothels, though as a farang you're unlikely to be offered this sideline, and you might not even notice the goings-on.

Advance reservations are accepted over the phone, but this is rarely necessary, as such hotels rarely fill up. The only time you may have difficulty finding a budget hotel room is during Chinese New Year (a moveable three-day period in late Jan or Feb), when many Chinese-run hotels close and others get booked up fast.

Tourist hotels

The rest of the accommodation picture is all about **tourist hotels**, which, like anywhere in the world, come in all sizes and qualities and are often best booked via online discount accommodation booking services such as local outfit Ⓦsawadee .com. One way or another, it's a good idea to **reserve ahead** in popular tourist areas during peak season.

Rates for **middle-ranking hotels** fall between B600 and B2000. For this you can expect many of the trimmings of a top-end hotel – air conditioning, TV and mini-bar in the room, plus an on-site pool, restaurant and possibly faded nightclub – but with dated and possibly faded furnishings and little of the style of the famous big names; they're often the kind of places that once stood at the top of the range, but were outclassed when the multinational luxury hotels muscled in. At these places, breakfast – often referred to as "**ABF**", short for "American Breakfast" – is usually included, as noted in our listings.

Many of Thailand's **expensive hotels** belong to the big international chains: Hilton, Marriott and Sofitel (and the rest of the Accor group) all have a strong presence in the country, alongside upmarket home-grown groups such as Amari, Anantara, Dusit and Centara. Between them they maintain premium standards in Bangkok and major resorts at prices of B3000 and upward for a double – far less than you'd pay for equivalent accommodation in the West.

Thailand also boasts an increasing number of deliciously stylish **luxury hotels**, many of them designed as intimate, small-scale **boutique** hotels, with chic, minimalist decor, exceptional service and excellent facilities that often include private plunge pools and a spa. A night in one of these places will rarely cost you less than B6000, and may set you back more than twice as much, though they're still often outstanding value for the honeymoon-style indulgence that they offer. (As in the West, however, the term "boutique" is overused, and a "boutique" guesthouse or hotel may in practice be little more than "small".)

Homestays

As guesthouses have become increasingly hotel-like and commercial in their facilities and approach, many tourists looking for old-style local hospitality are choosing **homestay accommodation** instead. Homestay facilities are often simple, and cheap at around B200 per person per night, with guests staying in a spare room and eating with the family. Homestays give an unparalleled insight into typical Thai (usually rural) life and can often be incorporated into a programme that includes experiencing village activities such as rice farming, squid fishing, rubber tapping or silk weaving. They are also a positive way of supporting small communities, as all your money will feed right back into the village. As well as listed homestays in Mae Sariang (see p.334), Mae Hong Son (see p.340 & p.345), Chiang Rai (see p.354), Ban Prasat (see p.447), Mukdahan (see p.498), Ban Khiriwong (see p.580), Khuraburi (see p.599) and Krabi (see p.653), there are many others bookable through tour operators (see p.26) or via, for example, Ⓦhomestaybooking.com /homestay-thailand.

National parks and camping

Nearly all the **national parks** have accommodation facilities, usually comprising a series of simple concrete bungalows that cost at least B600 for two or more beds plus a basic bathroom. Because most of their custom comes from Thai families and student groups, park officials are sometimes loath to discount them for lone travellers, though a few parks do offer dorm-style accommodation from around B100 a bed. In most parks, advance booking is unnecessary except at weekends and national holidays.

If you do want to pre-book, you can do so up to sixty days ahead of your stay at Ⓦdnp.go.th/park reserve. As credit-card payment is not possible on this website, you need to pay in cash or via bank draft within two days of booking, for example at any branch of Krung Thai bank or at designated international banks; see the website given above for comprehensive details. Affiliated with the National Parks department, a new private website, Ⓦthai forestbooking.com, allows booking with a credit card (up to 65 days in advance; service charge payable), though it's quite cumbersome to use. If you turn up without booking, check in at the park headquarters, which is usually adjacent to the visitor centre.

In a few parks, private operators have set up low-cost guesthouses on the outskirts, and these generally make more attractive and economical places to stay.

Camping

You can usually **camp** in a national park for a nominal fee of B60 per two-person tent, and some national parks also rent out fully equipped tents from B150 (bookable through a separate section on ⓦdnp.go.th/parkreserve), though the condition of the equipment is sometimes poor. Unless you're planning an extensive tour of national parks, though, there's little point in lugging a tent around Thailand: accommodation everywhere else is very inexpensive, and there are no campsites inside town perimeters, though camping is allowed on nearly all islands and beaches, many of which are national parks in their own right.

Food and drink

Bangkok and Chiang Mai are the country's big culinary centres, boasting the cream of gourmet Thai restaurants and the best international cuisines. The rest of the country is by no means a gastronomic wasteland, however, and you can eat well and cheaply in even the smallest provincial towns, many of which offer the additional attraction of regional specialities. In fact you could eat more than adequately without ever entering a restaurant, as itinerant food vendors hawking hot and cold snacks materialize in even the most remote spots, as well as on trains and buses – and night markets often serve customers from dusk until dawn.

Hygiene is a consideration when eating anywhere in Thailand, but being too cautious means you'll end up spending a lot of money and missing out on some real local treats. Wean your stomach gently by avoiding excessive amounts of chillies and too much fresh fruit in the first few days.

You can be pretty sure that any noodle stall or curry shop that's permanently packed with customers is a safe bet. Furthermore, because most Thai dishes can be cooked in under five minutes, you'll rarely have to contend with stuff that's been left to smoulder and stew. Foods that are generally considered high risk include salads, ice cream, shellfish and raw or undercooked meat, fish or eggs.

Most restaurants in Thailand are open every day for lunch and dinner; we've given full opening hours throughout the Guide. In a few of the country's most expensive restaurants, mostly in Bangkok, a ten percent service charge and possibly even seven percent VAT (due to be increased to ten percent at the end of 2015) may be added to your bill.

For those interested in **learning to cook Thai food**, short courses designed for visitors are held in Bangkok (see p.153), Chiang Mai (see p.281) and dozens of other tourist centres around the country, while Chiang Mai offers fascinating **food walking tours** (see box, p.294).

Where to eat

A lot of tourists eschew the huge range of Thai **places to eat**, despite their obvious attractions, and opt instead for the much "safer" restaurants in guesthouses and hotels. Almost all tourist accommodation has a kitchen, and while some are excellent, the vast majority serve up bland imitations of Western fare alongside equally pale versions of common Thai dishes. Having said that, it can be a relief to get your teeth into a processed-cheese sandwich after five days' trekking in the jungle, and guesthouses do serve comfortingly familiar Western breakfasts.

Throughout the country most **inexpensive Thai restaurants** and cafés specialize in one general food type or preparation method, charging around B40–50 a dish – a "noodle shop", for example, will do fried noodles and/or noodle soups, plus maybe a basic fried rice, but they won't have curries or meat or fish dishes. Similarly, a restaurant displaying whole roast chickens and ducks in its window will offer these sliced, usually with chillies and sauces and served over rice, but their menu probably won't extend to noodles or fish, while in "curry shops" your options are limited to the vats of curries stewing away in the hot cabinet.

To get a wider array of low-cost food, it's better to head for the local **night market** (*talaat yen*), a term for the gatherings of open-air night-time kitchens found in every town. Sometimes operating from 6pm to 6am, they are typically to be found on permanent patches close to the fruit and vegetable market or the bus station, and as often as not they're the best and most entertaining places to eat, not to mention the least expensive – after a lip-smacking feast of savoury dishes, a fruit drink and a dessert you'll come away no more than B150 poorer.

FRUITS OF THAILAND

You'll find **fruit** (*phonlamai*) offered everywhere in Thailand – neatly sliced in glass boxes on hawker carts, blended into delicious shakes and served as a dessert in restaurants. The fruits described here can be found in all parts of Thailand; with enhanced agricultural techniques – and imports – many of them can now be found year-round, but we've given the traditional seasons where applicable below, which is when they should be at their best and cheapest. The country's more familiar fruits include forty varieties of **banana** (*kluay*), dozens of different **mangoes** (*mamuang*), several types of **pineapple** (*sapparot*), **coconuts** (*maprao*), **oranges** (*som*), **limes** (*manao*) and **watermelons** (*taeng moh*). Thailand's most prized and expensive fruit is the **durian** (*thurian*; see p.131).

To avoid stomach trouble, **peel all fruit** before eating it, and use common sense if you're tempted to buy it pre-peeled on the street, avoiding anything that looks fly-blown or seems to have been sitting in the sun for hours.

Custard apple (*noina*; July–Sept). Inside the knobbly, muddy green skin is a creamy, almond-coloured blancmange-like flesh, with a strong flavour of strawberries and pears, and a hint of cinnamon, and many seeds.

Guava (*farang*; year-round). The apple of the tropics has green textured skin and sweet, crisp pink or white flesh, studded with tiny edible seeds. Has five times the vitamin C content of an orange and is sometimes eaten cut into strips and sprinkled with sugar and chilli.

Jackfruit (*khanun*; year-round). This large, pear-shaped fruit can weigh up to 20kg and has a thick, bobbly, greeny-yellow shell protecting sweet yellow flesh. Green, unripe jackfruit is sometimes cooked as a vegetable in curries, especially in the north.

Longan (*lamyai*; July–Oct). A close relative of the lychee, with succulent white flesh covered in thin, brittle skin.

Lychee (*linjii*; April–May). Under rough, reddish-brown skin, the lychee has sweet, richly flavoured white flesh, rose scented and with plenty of vitamin C.

Mangosteen (*mangkut*; April–Sept). The size of a small apple, with smooth, purple skin and a fleshy inside that divides into succulent white segments that are sweet though slightly acidic.

Papaya (paw-paw; *malakaw*; year-round). Looks like an elongated watermelon, with smooth green skin and yellowy-orange flesh that's a rich source of vitamins A and C. It's a favourite in fruit salads and shakes, and sometimes appears in its green, unripe form in salads, notably *som tam*.

Pomelo (*som oh*; Oct–Dec). The largest of all the citrus fruits, it looks rather like a grapefruit, though it is sweeter; sometimes used in delicious salads.

Rambutan (*ngaw*; May–Sept). The bright red rambutan's soft, spiny exterior has given it its name – *rambut* means "hair" in Malay. Usually about the size of a golf ball, it has a white, opaque flesh of delicate flavour, similar to a lychee.

Rose apple (*chomphuu*; year-round). Linked in myth with the golden fruit of immortality; small and pear-shaped, with white, rose-scented flesh.

Sapodilla (sapota; *lamut*; Sept–Dec). These small, brown, rough-skinned ovals look a bit like kiwi fruit and conceal a grainy, yellowish pulp that tastes almost honey-sweet.

Tamarind (*makhaam*; Dec–Jan). A Thai favourite and a pricey delicacy – carrying the seeds is said to make you safe from wounding by knives or bullets. Comes in rough, brown pods containing up to ten seeds, each surrounded by a sticky, dry pulp which has a lemony taste; generally sour, but some parts of the country, notably Phetchabun, produce sweet tamarinds.

A typical night market has maybe thirty-odd "specialist" pushcart kitchens (*rot khen*) jumbled together, each fronted by several sets of tables and stools. Noodle and fried-rice vendors always feature prominently, as do sweets stalls, heaped high with sticky rice cakes wrapped in banana leaves or thick with bags of tiny sweetcorn pancakes hot from the griddle – and no night market is complete without its fruit-drink stall, offering banana shakes and freshly squeezed orange, lemon and tomato juices. In the best setups you'll find a lot more besides: curries, barbecued sweetcorn, satay sticks of pork and chicken, deep-fried insects, fresh pineapple, watermelon and mango and – if the town's by a river or near the sea – heaps of fresh fish. Having decided what you want, you order from the cook (or the cook's dogsbody) and sit down at the nearest table; there is no territorialism about night markets, so it's normal to eat several dishes from separate stalls and rely on the nearest cook to sort out the bill.

Some large markets, particularly in Bangkok, have separate **food court** areas where you buy coupons first and select food and drink to their value at the stalls of your choice. This is also usually the modus operandi in the food courts found in department stores and shopping centres across the country, though some of the more modern ones issue each diner with a plastic card, on which is recorded their expenditure, for payment at the end.

For a more relaxing ambience, Bangkok and the larger towns have a range of more upmarket **restaurants**, many of which serve regional specialities. Some specialize in **"royal" Thai cuisine**, which is differentiated mainly by the quality of the ingredients, the complexity of preparation and the way the food is presented. Great care is taken over how individual dishes look: they are served in small portions and decorated with carved fruit and vegetables in a way that used to be the prerogative of royal cooks, but has now filtered down to the common folk. The cost of such delights is not prohibitive, either – a meal in one of these places is unlikely to cost more than B500 per person.

How to eat

Thai food is eaten with a **fork** (left hand) and a **spoon** (right hand); there is no need for a knife as food is served in bite-sized chunks, which are forked onto the spoon and fed into the mouth. Cutlery is often delivered to the table wrapped in a perplexingly tiny pink napkin: Thais use this, not for their lap, but to give their fork, spoon and plate an extra wipe-down before they eat. Steamed **rice** (*khao*) is served with most meals, and indeed the most commonly heard phrase for "to eat" is *kin khao* (literally, "eat rice"). **Chopsticks** are provided only for noodle dishes, and northeastern and northern sticky-rice dishes are usually eaten with the **fingers of your right hand**. Never eat with the fingers of your left hand, which is used for washing after going to the toilet.

So that complementary taste combinations can be enjoyed, the dishes in a Thai meal are served all at once, even the soup, and shared communally. The more people, the more taste and texture sensations; if there are only two of you, it's normal to order three dishes, plus your own individual plates of steamed rice, while three diners would order four dishes, and so on. Only put a serving of one dish on your rice plate each time, and then only one or two spoonfuls.

Bland food is anathema to Thais, and restaurant tables everywhere come decked out with **condiment sets** featuring the four basic flavours (salty, sour, sweet and spicy): usually fish sauce with chopped chillies; vinegar with chopped chillies; sugar; and dried chillies – and often extra bowls of ground peanuts and a bottle of chilli ketchup as well. Similarly, many individual Thai dishes are

---

VEGETARIANS AND VEGANS

Very few Thais are **vegetarian** (*mangsawirat*) but, if you can make yourself understood, you can often get a non-meat or fish alternative to what's on the menu; simply ask the cook to exclude meat and fish: *mai sai neua, mai sai plaa*. You may end up eating a lot of unexciting vegetable fried rice and *phat thai* minus the shrimps, but in better restaurants you should be able to get veggie versions of most curries; the mushroom version of chicken and coconut soup is also a good standby: ask for *tom kha hed*. Browsing food stalls also expands your options, with barbecued sweetcorn, nuts, fruit and other non-meaty goodies all common. The two ingredients that you will have to consider compromising on are the fermented **fish sauce** and **shrimp paste** that are fundamental to most Thai dishes; only in the vegan Thai restaurants described below, and in tourist spots serving specially concocted Thai and Western veggie dishes, can you be sure of avoiding them.

If you're **vegan** (*jay*, sometimes spelt "*jeh*") you'll need to stress when you order that you don't want egg, as they get used a lot; cheese and other dairy produce, however, don't feature at all in Thai cuisine. Many towns will have one or more **vegan restaurants** (*raan ahaan jay*), which are usually run by members of a temple or Buddhist sect and operate from unadorned premises off the main streets; because strict Buddhists prefer not to eat late in the day, most of the restaurants open early, at around 6 or 7am, and close by 2pm. Most of these places have a yellow and red sign, though few display an English-language name. Nor is there ever a menu: customers simply choose from the trays of veggie stir-fries and curries, nearly all of them made with soya products, that are laid out canteen-style. Most places charge around B40 for a couple of helpings served over a plate of brown rice.

served with their own specific, usually spicy, condiment dip (*nam jim*). If you do bite into a **chilli**, the way to combat the searing heat is to take a mouthful of plain rice and/or beer: swigging water just exacerbates the sensation.

What to eat

Five fundamental tastes are identified in Thai cuisine – spiciness, sourness, bitterness, saltiness and sweetness – and diners aim to share a variety of dishes that impart a balance of these flavours, along with complementary textures. Lemon grass, basil, coriander, galangal, chilli, garlic, lime juice, coconut milk and fermented fish sauce are just some of the distinctive components that bring these tastes to life. A detailed food and drink glossary can be found at the end of "Contexts" (see p.785).

Curries and soups

Thai **curries** (*kaeng*) have a variety of curry pastes as their foundation: elaborate blends of herbs, spices, garlic, shallots and chilli peppers ground together with pestle and mortar. The use of some of these spices, as well as coconut cream, was imported from India long ago; curries that don't use coconut cream are naturally less sweet, spicier and thinner, with the consistency of soups. While some curries, such as *kaeng karii* (mild and yellow) and *kaeng matsaman* ("Muslim curry", with potatoes, peanuts and usually beef), still show their roots, others have been adapted into quintessentially Thai dishes, notably *kaeng khiaw wan* (sweet and green), *kaeng phet* (red and hot) and *kaeng phanaeng* (thick and savoury, with peanuts). *Kaeng som* generally contains fish and takes its distinctive sourness from the addition of tamarind or, in the northeast, okra leaves. Traditionally eaten during the cool season, *kaeng liang* uses up bland vegetables, but is made aromatic with hot peppercorns.

Eaten simultaneously with other dishes, not as a starter, Thai **soups** often have the tang of lemon grass, kaffir lime leaves and galangal, and are sometimes made extremely spicy with chillies. Two favourites are *tom kha kai*, a creamy coconut chicken soup; and *tom yam kung*, a hot and sour prawn soup without coconut milk. *Khao tom*, a starchy rice soup that's generally eaten for breakfast, meets the approval of few Westerners, except as a traditional hangover cure.

Salads

One of the lesser-known delights of Thai cuisine is the *yam* or **salad**, which imparts most of the fundamental flavours in an unusual and refreshing harmony. *Yam* come in many permutations – with noodles, meat, seafood or vegetables – but at the heart of every variety is a liberal squirt of lime juice and a fiery sprinkling of chillies. Salads to look out for include *yam som oh* (pomelo), *yam hua plee* (banana flowers) and *yam plaa duk foo* (fluffy deep-fried catfish).

Noodle and rice dishes

Sold on street stalls everywhere, **noodles** come in assorted varieties – including *kway tiaw* (made with rice flour) and *ba mii* (egg noodles) – and get boiled up as soups (*nam*), doused in gravy (*rat na*) or stir-fried (*haeng*, "dry", or *phat*, "fried"). Most famous of all is *phat thai* ("Thai fry-up"), a delicious combination of noodles (usually *kway tiaw*), egg, tofu and spring onions, sprinkled with ground peanuts and lime, and often spiked with tiny dried shrimps. Other faithful standbys include fried rice (*khao phat*) and cheap, one-dish meals served on a bed of steamed rice, notably *khao kaeng* (with curry).

Regional dishes

Many of the specialities of **northern Thailand** originated in Myanmar, including *khao soi*, featuring both boiled and crispy egg noodles plus beef, chicken or pork in a curried coconut soup; and *kaeng hang lay*, a pork curry with ginger, turmeric and tamarind. Also look out for spicy dipping sauces such as *nam phrik ong*, made with minced pork, roast tomatoes and lemon grass, and served with *khep muu* (deep-fried pork rind), crisp cucumber slices and other raw or blanched vegetables.

The crop most suited to the infertile lands of **Isaan** is sticky rice (*khao niaw*), which replaces the standard grain as the staple for northeasterners. Served in a rattan basket, it's usually eaten with the fingers, rolled up into small balls and dipped into chilli sauces. It's perfect with such spicy local delicacies as *som tam*, a green-papaya salad with raw chillies, green beans, tomatoes, peanuts and dried shrimps (or fresh crab). Although you'll find basted barbecued chicken on a stick (*kai yaang*) all over Thailand, it originated in Isaan and is especially tasty in its home region. Raw minced pork, beef or chicken is the basis of another popular Isaan and northern dish, *laap*, a salad that's subtly flavoured with mint and lime. A similar northeastern salad is *nam tok*, featuring grilled beef or pork and roasted rice powder, which takes its name, "waterfall", from its refreshing blend of complex tastes.

Aside from putting a greater emphasis on seafood, **southern Thai** cuisine displays a marked Malaysian and Muslim aspect as you near the border, notably in *khao mok kai*, the local version of a biryani: chicken and rice cooked with turmeric and other Indian spices, and served with chicken soup. Southern markets often serve *khao yam* for breakfast or lunch, a delicious salad of dried cooked rice, dried shrimp and grated coconut served with a sweet sauce. You'll also find many types of *roti*, a flatbread sold from pushcart griddles and, in its plain form, rolled with condensed milk. Other versions include savoury *mataba*, with minced chicken or beef, and *roti kaeng*, served with curry sauce for breakfast. A huge variety of very spicy curries are also dished up in the south, many substituting shrimp paste for fish sauce. Two of the most distinctive are *kaeng luang*, "yellow curry", featuring fish, turmeric, pineapple, squash, beans and green papaya; and *kaeng tai plaa*, a powerful combination of fish stomach with potatoes, beans, pickled bamboo shoots and turmeric.

Desserts

Desserts (*khanom*) don't really figure on most restaurant menus, but a few places offer bowls of *luk taan cheum*, a jellied concoction of lotus or palm seeds floating in a syrup scented with jasmine or other aromatic flowers. Coconut milk is a feature of most other desserts, notably delicious coconut ice cream, *khao niaw mamuang* (sticky rice with mango), and a royal Thai cuisine special of coconut custard (*sangkhayaa*) cooked inside a small pumpkin, whose flesh you can also eat.

Drinks

Thais don't drink water straight from the tap, and nor should you; plastic bottles of drinking **water** (*nam plao*) are sold countrywide, in even the smallest villages, for around B10 and should be used even when brushing your teeth. Cheap restaurants and hotels generally serve free jugs of boiled water, which should be fine to drink, though they are not as foolproof as the bottles. In some large towns, notably Chiang Mai, you'll come across blue-and-white roadside machines that dispense purified water for B1 for 1–2 litres (bring your own bottle).

Night markets, guesthouses and restaurants do a good line in freshly squeezed **fruit juices** such as lime (*nam manao*) and orange (*nam som*), which often come with salt and sugar already added, particularly upcountry. The same places will usually do **fruit shakes** as well, blending bananas (*nam kluay*), papayas (*nam malakaw*), pineapples (*nam sapparot*) and others with liquid sugar or condensed milk (or yoghurt, to make lassi). Fresh **coconut water** (*nam maprao*) is another great thirst-quencher – you buy the whole fruit dehusked, decapitated and chilled – as is **pandanus-leaf juice** (*bai toey*); Thais are also very partial to freshly squeezed **sugar-cane juice** (*nam awy*), which is sickeningly sweet.

Bottled and canned brand-name **soft drinks** are sold all over the place, with a particularly wide range in the ubiquitous 7-Eleven chain stores. Glass soft-drink bottles are returnable, so some shops and drink stalls have a system of pouring the contents into a small plastic bag (fastened with an elastic band and with a straw inserted) rather than charging you the extra for taking away the bottle. The larger restaurants keep their soft drinks refrigerated, but smaller cafés and shops add **ice** (*nam khaeng*) to glasses and bags. Most ice is produced commercially under hygienic conditions, but it might become less pure in transit so be wary (ice cubes are generally a better bet than shaved ice) – and don't take ice if you have diarrhoea. For those travelling with children, or just partial themselves to **dairy products**, UHT-preserved milk and chilled yoghurt drinks are widely available (especially at 7-Eleven stores), as are a variety of soya drinks.

Weak Chinese **tea** (*nam chaa*) makes a refreshing alternative to water and often gets served in Chinese restaurants and roadside cafés, while posher restaurants keep stronger Chinese and Western-style teas. Instant Nescafé is the most widespread form of **coffee** (*kaafae*), even though fresh Thai-grown coffee – notably several excellent kinds of coffee from the mountains of the north – is now easily available. If you would like to try traditional Thai coffee, most commonly found at Chinese-style cafés in the south of the country or at outdoor markets, and prepared through filtering the grounds through a cloth, ask for *kaafae thung* (literally, "bag coffee"; sometimes known as *kaafae boran* – "traditional coffee" – or *kopii*), normally served very bitter with sugar as well as sweetened condensed milk alongside a glass of black or Chinese tea to wash it down with. Fresh Western-style coffee (*kaafae sot*) in the form of Italian espresso, cappuccino and other derivatives has recently become popular among Thais, so you'll now come across espresso machines in large towns all over the country (though some of these new coffee bars, frustratingly, don't open for breakfast, as locals tend to get their fix later in the day).

Alcoholic drinks

The two most famous local **beers** (*bia*) are Singha (ask for "*bia sing*") and Chang, though many travellers find Singha's weaker brew, Leo, more palatable than either. In shops you can expect to pay around B35–40 for a 330ml bottle of these beers, B70 for a 660ml bottle. All manner of slightly pricier foreign beers are now brewed in Thailand, including Heineken and Asahi, and in the most touristy areas you'll find expensive imported bottles from all over the world.

Wine is now found on plenty of upmarket and tourist-oriented restaurant menus, but expect to be disappointed by both quality and price, which is jacked up by heavy taxation. Thai wine is now produced at several vineyards, including at Château de Loei near Phu Reua National Park in the northeast, which produces quite tasty reds, whites including a dessert wine, a rosé and brandy (see p.486).

At about B100 for a hip-flask-sized 375ml bottle, the local **whisky** is a lot better value, and Thais think nothing of consuming a bottle a night, heavily diluted with ice and soda or Coke. The most palatable and widely available of these is Mekong, which is very pleasant once you've stopped expecting it to taste like Scotch; distilled from rice, Mekong is 35 percent proof, deep gold in colour and tastes slightly sweet. If that's not to your taste, a pricier Thai **rum** is also available, Sang Som, made from sugar cane, and even stronger than the whisky at forty percent proof. Check the menu carefully when ordering a bottle of Mekong from a bar in a tourist area, as they sometimes ask up to five times more than you'd pay in a guesthouse or shop. A hugely popular way to enjoy whisky or rum at beach resorts is to pick up a bucket, containing a quarter-bottle of spirit, a mixer, Red Bull, ice and several straws, for around B200–300: that way you get to share with your friends and build a sandcastle afterwards.

You can **buy** beer and whisky in food stores, guesthouses and most restaurants (by a law that's spottily enforced, it's not meant to be for sale between 2pm and 5pm, when schools are finishing for the day); **bars** aren't strictly an indigenous feature as Thais traditionally don't drink out without eating, but you'll find plenty of Western-style drinking holes in Bangkok and larger centres elsewhere in the country, ranging from ultra-hip haunts in the capital to basic, open-to-the-elements "**bar-beers**".

Culture and etiquette

Tourist literature has marketed Thailand as the "Land of Smiles" so successfully that a lot of farangs arrive in the country expecting to be forgiven any outrageous behaviour. This is just not the case: there are some things so universally sacred in Thailand that even a hint of disrespect will cause deep offence.

The monarchy

It is both socially unacceptable to many Thais and a criminal offence to make critical or defamatory remarks about the **royal family**. Thailand's monarchy might be a constitutional one, but most households display a picture of King Bhumibol and Queen Sirikit in a prominent position, and respectful crowds mass whenever the royals make a public appearance. The second of their four children, Prince Vajiralongkorn, is the heir to the throne; his younger sister, Princess Sirindhorn, is often on TV and in the English-language newspapers as she is involved in many charitable projects. When addressing or speaking about royalty, Thais use a special language full of deference, called *rajasap* (literally "royal language").

Thailand's **lese-majesty laws** are among the most strictly applied in the world, increasingly invoked as the Thai establishment becomes ever more uneasy over the erosion of traditional monarchist sentiments and the rise of critical voices, particularly on the internet (though these are generally quickly censored). Accusations of lese-majesty can be levelled by and against anyone, Thai national or farang, and must be investigated by the police. As a few high-profile cases involving foreigners have demonstrated, they can be raised for seemingly minor infractions, such as defacing a poster or being less than respectful in a work of fiction. Transgressions are met with jail sentences of up to fifteen years for each offence.

Aside from keeping any anti-monarchy sentiments to yourself, you should be prepared to stand when the **king's anthem** is played at the beginning of every cinema programme, and to stop in your tracks if the town you're in plays the **national anthem** over its public address system – many small towns do this twice a day at 8am and again at 6pm, as do some train stations and airports. A less obvious point: as the king's head features on all Thai currency, you should never step on a coin or banknote, which is tantamount to kicking the king in the face.

Religion

Almost equally insensitive would be to disregard certain **religious** precepts. **Buddhism** plays a fundamental role in Thai culture, and Buddhist monuments should be treated with respect – which basically means wearing long trousers or knee-length skirts, covering your arms and removing your shoes whenever you visit one.

All **Buddha images** are sacred, however small, tacky or ruined, and should never be used as a backdrop for a portrait photo, clambered over, placed in a position of inferiority or treated in any manner that could be construed as disrespectful. In an attempt to prevent foreigners from committing any kind of transgression the government requires a special licence for all Buddha statues exported from the country (see p.63).

Monks come only just beneath the monarchy in the social hierarchy, and they too are addressed and discussed in a special language. If there's a monk around, he'll always get a seat on the bus, usually right at the back. Theoretically, monks are forbidden to have any close contact with women, which means that, as a female, you mustn't sit or stand next to a monk, or even brush against his robes; if it's essential to pass him something, put the object down so that he can then pick it up – never hand it over directly. Nuns, however, get treated like ordinary women.

See "Contexts" for more on religious practices in Thailand (see p.738).

The body

The Western liberalism embraced by the Thai sex industry is very unrepresentative of the majority Thai attitude to the body. **Clothing** – or the lack of it – is what bothers Thais most about tourist behaviour. You need to dress modestly when entering temples (see p.85), but the same also applies to other important buildings and all public places. Stuffy and sweaty as it sounds, you should keep short shorts and vests for the real tourist resorts, and be especially diligent about covering up and, for women, wearing bras in rural areas. Baring your flesh on beaches is very much a Western practice: when Thais go swimming they often do so fully clothed, and they find topless and nude bathing offensive.

According to ancient Hindu belief, the **head** is the most sacred part of the body and the **feet** are the most unclean. This belief, imported into Thailand, means that it's very rude to touch another person's head or to point your feet either at a human being or at a sacred image – when sitting on a temple floor, for example, you should **tuck your legs beneath you** rather than stretch them out towards the Buddha. These hierarchies also forbid people from wearing **shoes** (which are even more unclean than feet) inside temples and most private homes, and – by extension – Thais take offence when they see someone sitting on the "head", or prow, of a boat. **Putting your feet up** on a table, a chair or a pillow is also considered very uncouth, and Thais will always take their shoes off if they need to stand on a train or bus seat to get to the luggage rack, for example. On a more practical note, the **left hand** is used for washing after going to the toilet (see p.36), so Thais never use it to put food in their mouth, pass things or shake hands – as a farang, though, you'll be assumed to have different customs, so left-handers shouldn't worry unduly.

Social conventions

Thais rarely shake hands, instead using the **wai** to greet and say goodbye and to acknowledge respect, gratitude or apology. A prayer-like gesture made with raised hands, the *wai* changes according to the relative status of the two people involved: Thais can instantaneously assess which *wai* to use, but as a farang your safest bet is to raise your hands close to your chest, bow your head and place your fingertips just below your nose. If someone makes a *wai* at you, you should generally *wai* back, but it's safer not to initiate.

Public displays of **physical affection** in Thailand are more common between friends of the same sex than between lovers, whether hetero- or homosexual. Holding hands and hugging is as common among male friends as with females, so if you're caressed by a Thai acquaintance of the same sex, don't assume you're being propositioned.

Finally, there are three specifically Thai **concepts** you're bound to come across, which may help you comprehend a sometimes laissez-faire attitude to delayed buses and other inconveniences. The first, **jai yen**, translates literally as "cool heart" and is something everyone tries to maintain: most Thais hate raised voices, visible irritation and confrontations of any kind, so losing one's cool can have a much more inflammatory effect than in more combative cultures. Related to this is the oft-quoted response to a difficulty, **mai pen rai** – "never mind", "no problem" or "it can't be helped" – the verbal equivalent of an open-handed shoulder shrug, which has its basis in the Buddhist notion of karma (see p.739). And then there's **sanuk**, the wide-reaching philosophy of "fun", which, crass as it sounds, Thais do their best to inject into any situation, even work. Hence the crowds of inebriated Thais who congregate at waterfalls and other beauty spots on public holidays (travelling solo is definitely not *sanuk*), the reluctance to do almost anything without high-volume musical accompaniment, and the national waterfight which takes place during Songkhran every April on streets right across Thailand.

Thai names

Although all Thais have a first **name** and a family name, everyone is addressed by their first name – even when meeting strangers – prefixed by the title "**Khun**" (Mr/Ms); no one is ever addressed as Khun Surname, and even the phone book lists people by their given name. In Thailand you will often be addressed in an anglicized version of this convention, as "Mr Paul" or "Miss Lucy" for example. Bear in mind, though, that when a man is introduced to you as Khun Pirom, his wife will definitely not be Khun Pirom as well (that would be like calling them, for instance, "Mr and Mrs Paul"). Among friends and relatives, **Phii** ('older brother/sister') is often used instead of Khun when addressing older familiars (though as a tourist you're on surer ground with Khun), and **Nong** ('younger brother/sister") is used for younger ones.

Many Thai **first names** come from ancient Sanskrit and have an auspicious meaning; for example, Boon means good deeds, Porn means blessings, Siri means glory and Thawee means to increase. However, Thais of all ages are commonly known by the **nickname** given them soon after birth rather than by their official first name. This tradition arises out of a deep-rooted superstition that once a child has been officially named the spirits will begin to take an unhealthy interest in them, so a nickname is used instead to confuse the spirits. Common nicknames – which often bear no resemblance to the adult's personality or physique – include Yai (Big), Uan (Fat) and Muu (Pig); Lek or Noi (Little), Nok (Bird), Nuu (Mouse) and Kung (Shrimp); and English nicknames like Apple, Joy or even Pepsi.

Family names were only introduced in 1913 (by Rama VI, who invented many of the aristocracy's surnames himself), and are used only in very formal situations, always in conjunction with the first name. It's quite usual for good friends never to know each other's surname. Ethnic Thais generally have short surnames like Somboon or Srisai, while the long, convoluted family names – such as

Sonthanasumpun – usually indicate Chinese origin, not because they are phonetically Chinese but because many Chinese immigrants have chosen to adopt new Thai surnames and Thai law states that every newly created surname must be unique. Thus anyone who wants to change their surname must submit a shortlist of five unique Thai names – each to a maximum length of ten Thai characters – to be checked against a database of existing names. As more and more names are taken, Chinese family names get increasingly unwieldy, and more easily distinguishable from the pithy old Thai names.

The media

To keep you abreast of world affairs, there are several English-language newspapers in Thailand, though relatively mild forms of censorship (and self-censorship) affect all newspapers and the predominantly state-controlled media.

Newspapers and magazines

Of the hundreds of **Thai-language newspapers and magazines** published every week, the sensationalist daily tabloid *Thai Rath* attracts the widest readership, with circulation of around a million, while the moderately progressive *Matichon* is the leading quality daily, with an estimated circulation of 600,000.

Alongside these, two daily **English-language papers** – the *Bangkok Post* (🔲 bangkokpost.com) and the *Nation* (🔲 nationmultimedia.com) – are capable of adopting a fairly critical attitude to political goings-on and cover major domestic and international stories as well as tourist-related issues. The *Post's Spectrum* supplement, which comes inside the Sunday edition, carries investigative journalism. Both the *Post* and *Nation* are sold at many newsstands in the capital as well as in major provincial towns and tourist resorts; the more isolated places receive their few copies one day late. Details of local English-language publications are given in the relevant Guide accounts.

You can also pick up **foreign** magazines such as *Newsweek* and *Time* in Bangkok, Chiang Mai and the major resorts. English-language bookshops such as Bookazine and some expensive hotels carry air-freighted, or sometimes locally printed and stapled, copies of foreign national newspapers for at least B50 a copy; the latter are also sold in tourist-oriented minimarkets in the big resorts.

Television

There are six government-controlled, terrestrial **TV channels** in Thailand: channels 3, 5 (owned and operated by the army), 7 and 9 transmit a blend of news, documentaries, soaps, sports, talk and quiz shows, while the more serious-minded PBS and NBT are public-service channels, owned and operated by the government's public relations department. **Cable** networks – available in many guesthouse and hotel rooms – carry channels from all around the world, including CNN or Fox News from the US, BBC World News from the UK and sometimes ABC from Australia, as well as English-language movie channels and various sports, music and documentary channels. Both the *Bangkok Post* and the *Nation* print the daily TV and cable **schedule**.

Radio

Thailand boasts over five hundred **radio stations**, mostly music-oriented, ranging from Eazy (105.5 FM), which serves up Western pop, through *luk thung* (see p.764) on 95FM, to Fat Radio, which plays Thai indie sounds (104.5 FM). Chulalongkorn University Radio (101.5 FM) plays classical music from 9.35pm to midnight every night. Net 107 on 107 FM is one of several stations that include English-language news bulletins.

With a **shortwave radio** or by going **online**, you can listen to the BBC World Service (W bbc.co.uk /worldserviceradio), Radio Australia (W radioaustralia .net.au), Voice of America (W voanews.com), Radio Canada (W rcinet.ca) and other international stations right across Thailand. Times and wavelengths change regularly, so consult the websites for frequency and programme guides.

Festivals

Nearly all Thai festivals have a religious aspect. The most theatrical are generally Brahmin (Hindu) or animistic in origin, honouring elemental spirits and deities with ancient rites and ceremonial costumed parades. Buddhist celebrations usually revolve round the local temple, and while merit-making is a significant feature, a light-hearted atmosphere prevails, as the wat grounds are swamped with food and trinket vendors and makeshift stages are set up to show *likay* folk theatre, singing stars and beauty contests.

Many of the **secular festivals** (like the elephant roundups and the Bridge over the River Kwai spectacle) are outdoor local culture shows, geared specifically towards Thai and farang tourists. Others are thinly veiled but lively trade fairs held in provincial capitals to show off the local speciality, be it exquisite silk weaving or especially tasty rambutans.

Few of the **dates** for religious festivals are fixed, so check with TAT for specifics (W tourismthailand.org). The names of the most touristy celebrations are given here in English; the more low-key festivals are more usually known by their Thai name (*ngan* – usually religious – and *tetsagaan* – usually organized by the municipality – are the words for "festival"). See the relevant town accounts for fuller details of the festivals below; some of them are designated as national holidays (see p.71).

A festival calendar

JANUARY–MARCH

Chinese New Year Nakhon Sawan (Truut Jiin; three days between mid-Jan and late Feb). In Nakhon Sawan, the new Chinese year is welcomed in with particularly exuberant parades of dragons and lion dancers, Chinese opera performances, an international lion-dance competition and a fireworks display. Also celebrated in Chinatowns across the country, especially in Bangkok and Phuket.

Flower Festival Chiang Mai (usually first weekend in Feb). Enormous floral sculptures are paraded through the streets.

Makha Puja Nationwide (particularly Wat Benjamabophit in Bangkok, Wat Phra That Doi Suthep in Chiang Mai and Wat Mahathat in Nakhon Si Thammarat; full-moon day usually in Feb). A day of merit-making marks the occasion when 1250 disciples gathered spontaneously to hear the Buddha preach, and culminates with a candlelit procession round the local temple's bot.

Ngan Phrabat Phra Phutthabat, near Lopburi (early Feb and early March). Pilgrimages to the Holy Footprint attract food and handicraft vendors and travelling players.

King Narai Reign Fair Lopburi (Feb). Costumed processions and a *son et lumière* show at Narai's palace.

Ngan Phra That Phanom That Phanom (Feb). Thousands come to pay homage at the holiest shrine in Isaan, which houses relics of the Buddha.

Kite fights and flying contests Nationwide (particularly Sanam Luang, Bangkok; late Feb to mid-April).

APRIL AND MAY

Poy Sang Long Mae Hong Son and Chiang Mai (early April). Young Thai Yai boys precede their ordination into monkhood by parading the streets in floral headdresses and festive garb.

Songkhran Nationwide (particularly Chiang Mai, and Bangkok's Thanon Khao San; usually April 13–15). The most exuberant of the national festivals welcomes the Thai New Year with massive waterfights, sandcastle building in temple compounds and the inevitable parades and "Miss Songkhran" beauty contests.

Ngan Phanom Rung Prasat Hin Khao Phanom Rung (usually April). The three-day period when the sunrise is perfectly aligned through fifteen doorways at these magnificent eleventh-century Khmer ruins is celebrated with daytime processions and nightly *son et lumière*.

Visakha Puja Nationwide (particularly Bangkok's Wat Benjamabophit, Wat Phra That Doi Suthep in Chiang Mai and Nakhon Si Thammarat's Wat Mahathat; full-moon day usually in May). The holiest day of the Buddhist year, commemorating the birth, enlightenment and death of the Buddha all in one go; the most public and photogenic part is the candlelit evening procession around the wat.

Raek Na Sanam Luang, Bangkok (early May). The royal ploughing ceremony to mark the beginning of the rice-planting season; ceremonially clad Brahmin leaders parade sacred oxen and the royal plough, and interpret omens to forecast the year's rice yield.

Rocket Festival Yasothon (Bun Bang Fai; weekend in mid-May). Beautifully crafted, painted wooden rockets are paraded and fired to ensure plentiful rains; celebrated all over Isaan, but especially raucous and raunchy in Yasothon.

JUNE–SEPTEMBER

Phi Ta Khon Dan Sai, near Loei (end June or beginning July). A re-enactment of the Buddha's penultimate incarnation provides the excuse for bawdy, masked merry-making.

Candle Festival Ubon Ratchathani (Asanha Puja; usually July, three days around the full moon). This nationwide festival marking the Buddha's first sermon and the subsequent beginning of the annual Buddhist retreat period (Khao Pansa) is celebrated across the northeast with parades of enormous wax sculptures, most spectacularly in Ubon Ratchathani.

Tamboon Deuan Sip Nakhon Si Thammarat (Sept or Oct). Merit-making ceremonies to honour dead relatives accompanied by a ten-day fair.

OCTOBER–DECEMBER

Vegetarian Festival Phuket and Trang (Tessagan Kin Jeh; Oct or Nov). Chinese devotees become vegetarian for a nine-day period and then parade through town performing acts of self-mortification such as pushing skewers through their cheeks. Celebrated in Bangkok's Chinatown by most food vendors and restaurants turning vegetarian for about a fortnight.

Bang Fai Phaya Nak Nong Khai and around (usually Oct). The strange appearance of pink balls of fire above the Mekong River draws sightseers from all over Thailand.

Tak Bat Devo and Awk Pansa Nationwide (especially Ubon Ratchathani and Nakhon Phanom; full-moon day usually in Oct). Offerings to monks and general merrymaking to celebrate the Buddha's descent to earth from Tavatimsa heaven and the end of the Khao Pansa retreat. Celebrated in Ubon with a procession of illuminated boats along the rivers, and in Nakhon Phanom with another illuminated boat procession and Thailand–Laos dragon-boat races along the Mekong.

Chak Phra Surat Thani (mid-Oct). The town's chief Buddha images are paraded on floats down the streets and on barges along the river.

Boat Races Nan, Nong Khai, Phimai and elsewhere (Oct to mid-Nov). Longboat races and barge parades along town rivers.

Thawt Kathin Nationwide (the month between Awk Pansa and Loy Krathong, generally Oct–Nov). During the month following the end of the monks' rainy-season retreat, it's traditional for the laity to donate new robes to the monkhood and this is celebrated in most towns with parades and a festival, and occasionally, when it coincides with a kingly anniversary, with a spectacular Royal Barge Procession down the Chao Phraya River in Bangkok.

Loy Krathong Nationwide (particularly Sukhothai and Chiang Mai; full moon in Nov). Baskets (*krathong*) of flowers and lighted candles are floated on any available body of water (such as ponds, rivers, lakes, canals and seashores) to honour water spirits and celebrate the end of the rainy season, and paper hot-air balloons are released into the night sky. Nearly every town puts on a big show, with bazaars, public entertainments and fireworks; in Sukhothai it is the climax of a *son et lumière* festival that's held over several nights.

Ngan Wat Saket Wat Saket, Bangkok (first week of Nov). Probably Thailand's biggest temple fair, held around the Golden Mount, with all the usual festival trappings.

Elephant Roundup Surin (third weekend of Nov). Two hundred elephants play team games, perform complex tasks and parade in battle dress.

River Kwai Bridge Festival Kanchanaburi (ten nights from the last week of Nov into the first week of Dec). Spectacular *son et lumière* at the infamous bridge.

Silk and Phuk Siao Festival Khon Kaen (Nov 29–Dec 10). Weavers from around the province come to town to sell their lengths of silk.

World Heritage Site Festival Ayutthaya (mid-Dec). Week-long celebration, including a nightly historical *son et lumière* romp, to commemorate the town's UNESCO designation.

New Year's Eve Countdown Nationwide (Dec 31). Most cities and tourist destinations welcome in the new year with fireworks, often backed up by food festivals, beauty contests and outdoor performances.

Entertainment and sport

Bangkok is the best place to catch authentic performances of classical Thai dance, though more easily digestible tourist-oriented shows are staged in some of the big tourist centres as well as in Bangkok. The country's two main Thai boxing stadia are also in the capital, but you'll come across local matches in the provinces too.

Drama and dance

Drama pretty much equals **dance** in classical Thai theatre, and many of the traditional dance-dramas are based on the *Ramakien*, the Thai version of the Hindu epic the *Ramayana*, an adventure tale of good versus evil that is taught in all schools. Not understanding the plots can be a major disadvantage, so try reading an abridged version beforehand (see p.780 & p.88) and check out the wonderfully imaginative murals at Wat Phra Kaeo in Bangkok. There are three broad categories of traditional Thai dance-drama – *khon*, *lakhon* and *likay* – described below in descending order of refinement.

Khon

The most spectacular form of traditional Thai theatre is **khon**, a stylized drama performed in masks and elaborate costumes by a troupe of highly trained classical dancers. There's little room for individual interpretation in these dances, as all the movements follow a strict choreography that's been passed down through generations: each graceful, angular gesture depicts a precise event, action or emotion which will be familiar to educated *khon* audiences. The dancers don't speak, and the story is chanted and sung by a chorus who stand at the side of the stage, accompanied by a classical *phipat* orchestra.

A typical *khon* performance features several of the best-known **Ramakien** episodes, in which the main characters are recognized by their masks, headdresses and heavily brocaded costumes. Gods and humans don't wear masks, but the hero Rama and heroine Sita always wear tall gilded headdresses and often appear as a trio with Rama's brother Lakshaman. Monkey **masks** are wide-mouthed: monkey army chief Hanuman always wears white, and his two right-hand men – Nilanol, the god of fire, and Nilapat, the god of death – wear red and black respectively. In contrast, the demons have grim mouths, clamped shut or snarling; Totsagan, king of the demons, wears a green face in battle and a gold one during peace, but always sports a two-tier headdress carved with two rows of faces.

Khon is performed with English subtitles at Bangkok's Sala Chalermkrung (see p.164) and is also featured within the various cultural **shows** staged by tourist restaurants in Bangkok, Phuket and Pattaya. Even if you don't see a show, you're bound to come across finely crafted real and replica *khon* masks both in museums and in souvenir shops all over the country.

Lakhon

Serious and refined, **lakhon** is derived from *khon* but is used to dramatize a greater range of stories, including Buddhist *Jataka* tales, local folk dramas and of course the *Ramakien*.

The form you're most likely to come across is *lakhon chatri*, which is performed at shrines like Bangkok's Erawan and at a city's *lak muang* as entertainment for the spirits and a token of gratitude from worshippers. Usually female, the *lakhon chatri* dancers perform as an ensemble, executing sequences that, like *khon* movements, all have minute and particular symbolism. They also wear ornate costumes, but no masks, and dance to the music of a *phipat* orchestra. Unfortunately, as resident shrine troupes tend to repeat the same dances a dozen times a day, it's rarely the sublime display it's cracked up to be. Bangkok's National Theatre stages the more elegantly executed *lakhon nai*, a dance form that used to be performed at the Thai court and often re-tells the *Ramakien*.

Likay

Likay is a much more popular and dynamic derivative of *khon* – more light-hearted, with lots of comic interludes, bawdy jokes and panto-style over-the-top acting and singing. Some *likay* troupes perform *Ramakien* excerpts, but a lot of them adapt pot-boiler romances or write their own, and most will ham things up with improvisations and up-to-the-minute topical satire. Costumes might be traditional as in *khon* and *lakhon*, modern and Western as in films, or a mixture of both.

Likay troupes travel around the country doing shows on makeshift outdoor stages wherever they think they'll get an audience, most commonly at temple fairs. Performances are often free and generally last for about five hours, with the audience strolling in and out of the show, cheering and joking with the cast throughout. Televised *likay* dramas get huge audiences and always follow romantic soap-opera-style plot-lines. Short *likay* dramas are also a staple of Bangkok's National Theatre, but for more radical and internationally minded *likay*, look out for performances by **Makhampom** (Ⓦmakhampom.net), a famous, long-established troupe with bases in Bangkok and Chiang Dao that pushes *likay* in new directions to promote social causes and involve minority communities.

Nang

Nang, or shadow plays (see p.578), are said to have been the earliest dramas performed in Thailand, but now are rarely seen except in the far south, where the Malaysian influence ensures an appreciative audience for *nang thalung*. Crafted from buffalo hide, the two-dimensional *nang thalung* puppets play out scenes from popular dramas against a backlit screen, while the storyline is told through songs, chants and musical interludes. An even rarer *nang* form is the *nang yai*, which uses enormous cut-outs of whole scenes rather than just individual characters, so the play becomes something like an animated film.

Film

All sizeable towns have a **cinema** or two – Bangkok has over fifty – and tickets generally start at around B100. Several websites give showtimes of movies around the country, including Ⓦmoveedoo.com. In some rural areas, villagers still have to make do with the travelling cinema, or *nang klarng plaeng*, which sets up a mobile screen in wat compounds or other public spaces, and often entertains the whole village in one sitting (in larger towns, you might catch a travelling cinema at a temple festival). However makeshift the cinema, the **king's anthem** is always played before every screening, during which the audience is expected to stand up.

Fast-paced Chinese blockbusters have long dominated the programmes at Thai cinemas, serving up a low-grade cocktail of sex, spooks, violence and comedy. Not understanding the dialogue is rarely a drawback, as the storylines tend to be simple and the visuals more entertaining than the words. In the cities, **Western films** are also popular, and new releases often get subtitled rather than dubbed. They are also quickly available as pirated DVDs sold at street stalls in the main cities and resorts.

In recent years Thailand's own film industry (see p.774) has been enjoying a boom, and in the larger cities and resorts you may be lucky enough to come across one of the bigger Thai hits showing with English subtitles.

Thai boxing

Thai boxing (*muay thai*) enjoys a following similar to football or baseball in the West: every province has a stadium and whenever the sport is shown on TV you can be sure that large, noisy crowds will gather round the sets in streetside restaurants. The best place to see Thai boxing is at one of Bangkok's two main stadia, which between them hold bouts every night of the week (see p.164), but many tourist resorts also stage regular matches.

There's a strong spiritual and **ritualistic** dimension to *muay thai*, adding grace to an otherwise brutal sport. Each boxer enters the ring to the wailing music of a three-piece *phipat* orchestra,

wearing the statutory red or blue shorts and, on his head, a sacred rope headband or *mongkhon*. Tied around his biceps are *phra jiat*, pieces of cloth that are often decorated with cabalistic symbols and may contain Buddhist tablets. The fighter then bows, first in the direction of his birthplace and then to the north, south, east and west, honouring both his teachers and the spirit of the ring. Next he performs a slow dance, claiming the audience's attention and demonstrating his prowess as a performer.

Any part of the body except the head may be used as an **offensive weapon** in *muay thai*, and all parts except the groin are fair targets. Kicks to the head are the blows that cause most knockouts. As the action hots up, so the orchestra speeds up its tempo and the betting in the audience becomes more frenetic. It can be a gruesome business, but it was far bloodier before modern boxing gloves were introduced in the 1930s, when the Queensbury Rules were adapted for *muay* – combatants used to wrap their fists with hemp impregnated with a face-lacerating dosage of ground glass.

A number of *muay thai* gyms and camps offer training **courses** for foreigners, including several in Bangkok, as well as Chiang Mai, Hua Hin, Ko Pha Ngan and Ko Yao Noi – see the relevant accounts for details.

Takraw

Whether in Bangkok or upcountry, you're quite likely to come across some form of **takraw** game being played in a public park, a school, a wat compound or just in a backstreet alley. Played with a very light rattan ball (or one made of plastic to look like rattan), the basic aim of the game is to keep the ball off the ground. To do this you can use any part of your body except your hands, so a well-played *takraw* game looks extremely balletic, with players leaping and arching to get a good strike.

There are at least five versions of **competitive takraw**, based on the same principles. Sepak takraw, the version featured in the Southeast Asian Games and most frequently in school tournaments, is played over a volleyball net and involves two teams of three; the other most popular competitive version has a team ranged round a basketball-type hoop trying to score as many goals as possible within a limited time period before the next team replaces them and tries to outscore them.

Other *takraw* games introduce more complex rules (like kicking the ball backwards with your heels through a ring made with your arms behind your back) and many assign points according to the skill displayed by individual players rather than per goal or dropped ball.

Spas and traditional massage

With their focus on indulgent self-pampering, spas are usually associated with high-spending tourists, but the treatments on offer at Thailand's five-star hotels are often little different from those used by traditional medical practitioners, who have long held that massage and herbs are the best way to restore physical and mental well-being.

Thai massage (*nuad boran*) is based on the principle that many physical and emotional problems are caused by the blocking of vital energy channels within the body. The masseur uses his or her feet, heels, knees and elbows, as well as hands, to exert pressure on these channels, supplementing this acupressure-style technique by pulling and pushing the limbs into yogic stretches. This distinguishes Thai massage from most other massage styles, which are more concerned with tissue manipulation. One is supposed to emerge from a Thai massage feeling both relaxed and energized, and it is said that regular massages produce long-term benefits in muscles as well as stimulating the circulation and aiding natural detoxification.

Thais will visit a masseur for many conditions, including fevers, colds and muscle strain, but bodies that are not sick are also considered to benefit from the restorative powers of a massage, and nearly every hotel and guesthouse will be able to put you in touch with a **masseur**. On the more popular beaches, it can be hard to walk a few hundred metres without being offered a massage – something Thai tourists are just as enthusiastic about as foreigners. Thai masseurs do not traditionally use oils or lotions and the client is treated on a mat or mattress; you'll often be given a pair of loose-fitting trousers and perhaps a loose top to change into. English-speaking masseurs will often ask if there are any areas of your body that you would like them to concentrate on, or if you have any problem areas that you want them to avoid; if your masseur doesn't speak English, the simplest way to signal the latter is to point at the offending

area while saying *mai sabai* ("not well"). If you're in pain during a massage, wincing usually does the trick, perhaps adding *jep* ("it hurts"); if your masseur is pressing too hard for your liking, say *bao bao na khrap/kha* ("gently please").

The best places for a basic massage are usually the government-accredited clinics and hospitals that are found in large towns all over the country. A session should ideally last at least one and a half hours and will cost from around B250. If you're a bit wary of submitting to the full works, try a **foot massage** first, which will apply the same techniques of acupressure and stretching to just your feet and lower legs. Most places also offer **herbal massages**, in which the masseur will knead you with a ball of herbs (*phrakop*) wrapped in a cloth and steam-heated; they're said to be particularly good for stiffness of the neck, shoulders and back.

The **science** behind Thai massage has its roots in Indian Ayurvedic medicine, which classifies each component of the body according to one of the four elements (earth, water, fire and air), and holds that balancing these elements within the body is crucial to good health. Many of the stretches and manipulations fundamental to Thai massage are thought to have derived from yogic practices introduced to Thailand from India by Buddhist missionaries in about the second century BC; Chinese acupuncture and reflexology have also had a strong influence. In the nineteenth century, King Rama III ordered a series of murals illustrating the principles of Thai massage to be painted around the courtyard of Bangkok's Wat Pho, and they are still in place today, along with statues of ascetics depicted in typical massage poses.

Wat Pho has been the leading school of Thai massage for hundreds of years, and it is possible to take courses there as well as to receive a massage (see p.91); it also runs a residential massage school and clinic in Nakhon Pathom province (W watpomassage.com). Masseurs who trained at Wat Pho are considered to be the best in the country and masseurs all across Thailand advertise this as a credential, whether or not it is true. Many Thais consider blind masseurs to be especially sensitive practitioners.

While Wat Pho is the most famous place to take a **course** in Thai massage, many foreigners interested in learning this ancient science head for Chiang Mai, which offers the biggest concentration of massage schools (including another satellite branch of the Wat Pho school), though you will find others all over Thailand, including in Bangkok and at southern beach resorts.

All **spas** in Thailand feature traditional Thai massage and herbal therapies in their programmes, but most also offer dozens of other international treatments, including facials, aromatherapy, Swedish massage and various body wraps. Spa centres in upmarket hotels and resorts are usually open to non-guests but generally need to be booked in advance. Day-spas that are not attached to hotels are generally cheaper and are found in some of the bigger cities and resorts – some of these may not require reservations.

Meditation centres and retreats

Of the hundreds of meditation temples in Thailand, a few cater specifically for foreigners by holding meditation sessions and retreats in English. Novices as well as practised meditators are generally welcome at these wats, but absolute beginners might like to consider the regular retreats at Wat Suan Dork in Chiang Mai or Wat Suan Mokkh on Ko Samui and in Chaiya, which are conducted by supportive and experienced Thai and Western teachers and include talks and interviews on Buddhist teachings and practice. The meditation taught is mostly Vipassana, or "insight", which emphasizes the minute observation of internal sensations; the other main technique you'll come across is Samatha, which aims to calm the mind and develop concentration (these two techniques are not entirely separate, since you cannot have insight without some degree of concentration).

Longer **retreats** are for the serious-minded only. All the temples listed below welcome both male and female English-speakers, but strict segregation of the sexes is enforced and many places observe a vow of silence. Reading and writing are also discouraged, and you'll not be allowed to leave the retreat complex unless absolutely necessary, so try to bring whatever you'll need in with you. All retreats expect you to wear modest clothing, and some require you to wear white – check ahead whether there is a shop at the retreat complex or whether you are expected to bring this with you.

An average day at any one of these monasteries starts with a **wake-up call** at around 4am and includes several hours of **group meditation** and chanting, as well as time put aside for chores and personal reflection. However long their stay, visitors are expected to keep the eight main Buddhist precepts, the most restrictive of these being the abstention from food after midday and from alcohol, tobacco, drugs and sex at all times. Most wats ask for a minimal daily **donation** (around B200) to cover the costs of the simple accommodation and food.

Further details about many of the temples listed below – including how to get there – are given in the relevant sections in the Guide chapters. A useful **resource** is Ⓦwanderingdhamma.org, a very interesting blog written by an American, with some fascinating articles, information on English-speaking retreats in Thailand and lots of good links. Meanwhile, Little Bangkok Sangha (Ⓦlittlebang.org) is a handy blog maintained by a British-born monk, Phra Pandit, which gives details of talks in Bangkok and retreats. Also in Bangkok, keep an eye out for events for English-speakers at the Buddhadasa Indapanno Archives in Chatuchak Park in the north of the city (Ⓦfacebook.com/suanmokkhbangkok/events), a recently built centre in honour of the founder of Wat Suan Mokkh (see p.532).

MEDITATION CENTRES AND RETREAT TEMPLES

In addition to those listed below, additional meditation centres and retreat temples are listed in the Guide chapters, including **Wat Khao Tham** on Ko Pha Ngan (see p.555), **Wat Mahathat** in Bangkok (see p.95), several retreats and sessions in **Chiang Mai** (see p.286), and **Wat Suan Mokkh** on Ko Samui (see p.537) and in Chaiya (see p.532).

House of Dhamma Insight Meditation Centre 26/9 Soi Lardprao 15, Chatuchak, Bangkok ☎ 02 511 0439, Ⓦ houseofdhamma.com. Regular two-day courses in Vipassana, as well as day workshops in Metta (Loving Kindness) meditation. Courses in reiki and other subjects available.

Thailand Vipassana Centres Ⓦ dhamma.org. Frequent courses in a Burmese Vipassana tradition (ten days), in Phitsanulok and eight other centres around Thailand.

Wat Pah Nanachat Ban Bung Wai, Amphoe Warinchamrab, Ubon Ratchathani 34310 Ⓦ watpahnanachat.org. The famous monk, Ajahn Chah, established this forest monastery, 17km west of Ubon Ratchathani, in 1975 specifically to provide monastic training for non-Thais, with English the primary language. Visitors who want to practise with the resident community are welcome, but the atmosphere is serious and intense and not for beginners or curious sightseers, and accommodation for students is limited, so you should write to the monastery before visiting, allowing several weeks to receive a written response.

Wat Phra Si Chom Thong Insight Meditation Centre ☎ 053 826869, ✉ watchomtong@sirimangalo.org. Located in Chom Thong (see p.330), 58km south of Chiang Mai, this is the centre of the Northern Insight Meditation School developed by the well-known Phra Ajarn Tong Sirimangalo (the meditation teachers at Chiang Mai's Wat Ram Poeng and Wat Doi Suthep are all students of Phra Tong). Offers four- to 21-day Vipassana meditation courses taught in English and Thai and some European languages as well. By donation.

World Fellowship of Buddhists (WFB) 616 Benjasiri Park, Soi Medhinivet off Soi 24, Thanon Sukhumvit, Bangkok ☎ 02 661 1284–7, 🌐 wfbhq.org. Headquarters of an influential worldwide organization of (mostly Theravada) Buddhists, founded in Sri Lanka in 1950; its website carries information about meditation retreats in Thailand, especially in the northeast, though it's not updated very often.

Outdoor activities

Many travellers' itineraries take in a few days' trekking in the hills and a stint snorkelling or diving off the beaches of the south. Trekking is concentrated in the north, but there are smaller, less touristy trekking operations in Kanchanaburi, Sangkhlaburi and Umphang. There are also plenty of national parks to explore and opportunities for rock climbing and kayaking.

Diving and snorkelling

Clear, warm waters (averaging 28°C), prolific marine life and affordable prices make Thailand a very rewarding place for **diving** and **snorkelling**. Most islands and beach resorts have at least one dive centre that organizes trips to outlying islands, teaches novice divers and rents out equipment, and in the bigger resorts there are dozens to choose from.

Thailand's three coasts are subject to different monsoon **seasons**, so you can dive all year round; the seasons run from November to April along the Andaman coast (though there is sometimes good diving here up until late Aug), and all year round on the Gulf and east coasts. Though every diver has their favourite reef, Thailand's **premier diving destinations** are generally considered to be Ko Similan, Ko Surin, Richelieu Rock and Hin Muang and Hin Daeng – all of them off the Andaman coast (see p.637). As an accessible base for diving, Ko Tao off the Gulf coast is hard to beat, with deep, clear inshore water and a wide variety of dive sites in very close proximity.

Whether you're snorkelling or diving, try to minimize your impact on the fragile reef structures by **not touching the reefs** and by asking your boatman not to anchor in the middle of one; **don't buy coral souvenirs**, as tourist demand only encourages local entrepreneurs to dynamite reefs.

Should you scrape your skin on coral, wash the wound thoroughly with boiled water, apply antiseptic and keep protected until healed. Wearing a T-shirt is a good idea when snorkelling to stop your back from getting sunburnt.

Diving

It's usually worth having a look at several **dive centres** before committing yourself to a trip or a course. Always verify the dive instructors' and dive shops' PADI (Professional Association of Diving Instructors) or equivalent accreditations as this guarantees a certain level of professionalism. You can view a list of PADI dive shops and resorts in Thailand at 🌐 padi.com.

We've highlighted dive shops that are accredited Five-Star centres, as these are considered by PADI to offer very high standards, but you should always consult other divers first if possible. Some dive operators do fake their PADI credentials. Avoid booking ahead over the internet without knowing anything else about the dive centre, and be wary of any operation offering extremely cheap courses: maintaining diving equipment is an expensive business in Thailand so any place offering unusually good rates will probably be cutting corners and compromising your safety. Ask to **meet your**

THAILAND'S MAIN DIVE RESORTS

THE EAST COAST
Ko Chang (see p.409)
Pattaya (see p.385)

THE GULF COAST
Ko Pha Ngan (see p.553)
Ko Samui (see p.535)
Ko Tao (see p.566)

THE ANDAMAN COAST
Ao Nang (see p.657)
Khao Lak (see p.608)
Ko Lanta (see p.680)
Ko Phi Phi (see p.667)
Phuket (see p.616)

THE DEEP SOUTH
Ko Lipe (see p.711)

instructor or dive leader, find out how many people there'll be in your group, check out the kind of instruction given (some courses are over-reliant on videos) and look over the equipment, checking the quality of the air in the tanks yourself and also ensuring there's an oxygen cylinder on board. Most divers prefer to travel to the dive site in a decent-sized **boat** equipped with a radio and emergency medical equipment rather than in a longtail. If this concerns you, ask the dive company about their boat before you sign up; firms that use longtails generally charge less.

Insurance should be included in the price of courses and introductory dives; for qualified divers, you're better off checking that your general travel insurance covers diving, though some diving shops can organize cover for you. There are **recompression chambers** in Pattaya, on Ko Samui and on Phuket and it's a good idea to check whether your dive centre is a member of one of these outfits, as recompression services are extremely expensive for anyone who's not.

There are a number of useful books available on diving in Thailand (see p.778).

Trips and courses

All dive centres run programmes of one-day **dive trips** (featuring two dives) and **night dives** for B1500–4500 (with reductions if you bring your own gear), and many of the Andaman-coast dive centres also do three- to seven-day **live-aboards** to the exceptional reefs off the remote Similan and Surin islands (from B12,000). Most dive centres can rent **underwater cameras** for about B1500 per day.

All dive centres offer a range of **courses** from beginner to advanced level, with equipment rental usually included in the cost; Ko Tao is now the largest, and most competitive, dive-training centre in Southeast Asia, with around fifty dive companies including plenty of PADI Five-Star centres. The most popular courses are the one-day **introductory** or resort dive (a pep talk and escorted shallow dive, open to anyone aged 10 or over), which costs anything from B2000 for a very local dive to B7000 for an all-inclusive day-trip to the Similan Islands; and the four-day **open-water course**, which entitles you to dive without an instructor (from B9800 on Ko Tao in high season). Kids' Bubblemaker courses, for children aged 8 and up, cost around B2000.

Snorkelling

Boatmen and tour agents on most beaches offer **snorkelling** trips to nearby reefs and many dive operators welcome snorkellers to tag along for discounts of thirty percent or more; not all diving destinations are rewarding for snorkellers, though, so check carefully with the dive shop first. As far as snorkelling **equipment** goes, the most important thing is that you buy or rent a mask that fits. To check the fit, hold the mask against your face, then breathe in and remove your hands – if it falls off, it'll leak water. If you're buying equipment, you should be able to kit yourself out with a mask, snorkel and fins for about B1000, available from most dive centres. Few places rent fins, but a mask and snorkel set usually costs about B150 a day to rent, and if you're going on a snorkelling day-trip they are often included in the price.

National parks and wildlife observation

Thailand's hundred-plus **national parks**, which are administered by the National Park, Wildlife and Plant Conservation Department (W dnp.go.th /parkreserve), are generally the best places to **observe wildlife**. Though you're highly unlikely to encounter tigers or sun bears, you have a good chance of spotting gibbons, civets, mouse deer and hornbills and may even get to see a wild elephant. A number of wetlands also host a rewarding variety of birdlife. Most parks charge an **entrance fee**, which for foreigners is usually B200 (B100 for children), though some charge B100 and a few charge B300, B400 or B500.

Waymarked hiking **trails** in most parks are generally limited and rarely very challenging, and decent park maps are hard to come by, so for serious national park treks you'll need to hire a guide and venture beyond the public routes. Nearly all parks provide **accommodation** and/or campsites (see p.37). Some national parks **close** for several weeks or months every year for conservation, safety or environmental reasons; dates are listed on the National Parks' website.

A detailed guide to Thailand's wildlife and their habitats, a look at the environmental issues, and a list of Thai wildlife charities and volunteer projects are provided in "Contexts" (see p.759).

Rock climbing

The limestone karsts that pepper southern Thailand's Andaman coast make ideal playgrounds for **rock-climbers**, and the sport has really taken off here in the past fifteen years. Most climbing is centred round **East Railay** and **Ton Sai** beaches on Laem Phra Nang in Krabi province (see p.664),

TOP NATIONAL PARKS

Ang Thong (p.552). Spectacular archipelago in the Gulf of Thailand, generally visited on a day-trip from Ko Samui or Ko Pha Ngan.

Doi Inthanon (p.329). Waterfalls, hill tribes, orchids, around four hundred bird species and the country's highest peak.

Erawan (p.197). An exceptionally pretty, seven-tiered waterfall that extends deep into the forest. Hugely popular as a day-trip from Kanchanaburi.

Khao Sam Roi Yot (p.523). Coastal flats on the Gulf coast known for their rich birdlife plus an extensive stalactite-filled cave system.

Khao Sok (p.604). Southern Thailand's most visited park has rainforest trails and caves plus a flooded river system with eerie outcrops and raft-house accommodation.

Khao Yai (p.437). Thailand's most popular national park, three hours from Bangkok, features half a dozen upland trails plus organized treks and night safaris.

Ko Similan (p.614). Remote group of Andaman Sea islands with famously fabulous reefs and fine above-water scenery. Mostly visited by dive boat but limited national park accommodation is provided.

Ko Surin (p.601). National marine park archipelago of beautiful coastal waters in the Andaman Sea, though much of its coral became severely bleached in 2010. Good snorkelling and national park campsites.

Ko Tarutao (p.708). Beautiful and wildly varied land- and seascapes on the main 26km-long island and fifty other smaller islands on its western side.

Phu Kradung (p.483). Dramatic and strange 1300m-high plateau, probably best avoided at weekends.

where there are dozens of routes within easy walking distance of tourist bungalows, restaurants and beaches. **Offshore Deep Water Soloing** – climbing a rock face out at sea, with no ropes, partner or bolts and just the water to break your fall – is also huge round here. Several **climbing schools** at East Railay and Ton Sai provide instruction (from B1000/half-day), as well as guides and equipment rental (about B1300/day for two people). Ko Phi Phi (see p.667) also offers a few routes and a couple of climbing schools, as does the quieter and potentially more interesting Ko Yao Noi (see p.643) and Ko Lao Liang (see p.708). Climbing is also popular near Chiang Mai (see p.278), and there are less developed climbing areas on Ko Tao (see p.566) and in Lopburi province (see p.224). For an introduction to climbing on Railay and elsewhere in south Thailand, see ⓦrailay.com, while *Rock Climbing in Thailand* and *King Climbers: Thailand Route Guide Book* are regularly updated guidebooks that concentrate on Railay, Ton Sai and the islands.

Sea kayaking and whitewater rafting

Sea kayaking is also centred around Thailand's Andaman coast, where the limestone outcrops, sea caves, *hongs* (hidden lagoons), mangrove swamps and picturesque shorelines of Ao Phang Nga in particular (see p.647) make for rewarding paddling. Kayaking day-trips around Ao Phang Nga can be arranged from any resort in Phuket, at Khao Lak, at all Krabi beaches and islands, and on Ko Yao Noi; multi-day kayaking expeditions are also possible. Over on Ko Samui, Blue Stars (see p.553) organize kayaking trips around the picturesque islands of the Ang Thong National Marine Park, while Kayak Chang (see p.412) offers half- to seven-day trips around Ko Chang. Many bungalows at other beach resorts have free kayaks or rent them out (from B100/hr) for casual, independent coastal exploration.

You can go **river kayaking** and **whitewater rafting** on several rivers in north, west and south Thailand. Some stretches of these rivers can run quite fast, particularly during the rainy season from July to November, but there are plenty of options for novices too. The best time is from October through February; during the hot season (March–June), many rivers run too low. The most popular whitewater-rafting rivers include the Umphang and Mae Khlong rivers near Umphang (see p.263) and the Pai River near Pai (see p.347). Gentler rafting excursions take place as part of organized treks in the north, as well as on the River Kwai and its tributaries near Kanchanaburi (see p.186), on the Kok River from Tha Ton (see p.353), and at Mae Hong Son (see p.337) and Pai (see p.345). Southwest of Chiang Mai, raft trips can be arranged at the adjacent national park headquarters for trips in Ob Luang Gorge (see p.332).

Trekking

Trekking in the mountains of north Thailand differs from trekking in most other parts of the world in that the emphasis is not primarily on the scenery but on the region's inhabitants. Northern Thailand's **hill tribes**, now numbering over 800,000 people living in around 3500 villages, have preserved their subsistence-oriented way of life with comparatively little change over thousands of years (see p.769). In recent years, the term **mountain people** (a translation of the Thai *chao khao*) is increasingly used as a less condescending way to describe them; since these groups have no chief, they are technically not tribes. While some of the villages are near enough to a main road to be reached on a day-trip from a major town, to get to the other, more traditional, villages usually entails joining a guided party for a few days, roughing it in a different place each night.

For most visitors, however, these hardships are far outweighed by the experience of encountering peoples of so different a culture, travelling through beautiful tropical countryside and tasting the excitement of elephant riding and river rafting.

On any trek you are necessarily confronted by the **ethics** of your role. About a hundred thousand travellers now go trekking in Thailand each year, the majority heading to certain well-trodden areas such as the Mae Taeng valley, 40km northwest of Chiang Mai, and the hills around the Kok River west of Chiang Rai. Beyond the basic level of disturbance caused by any tourism, this steady flow of trekkers creates pressures for the traditionally insular hill tribes. Foreigners unfamiliar with hill-tribe customs can easily cause grave offence, especially those who go looking for drugs. Though tourism acts as a distraction from their traditional way of life, most tribespeople are genuinely welcoming and hospitable to foreigners, appreciating the contact with Westerners and the minimal material benefits which trekking brings them. Nonetheless, to minimize

---

HILL-TRIBE TREKKING ETIQUETTE

As the guests, it's up to farangs to adapt to the customs of the hill tribes and not to make a nuisance of themselves. Apart from keeping an open mind and not demanding too much of your hosts, a few **simple rules** should be observed.

- Dress modestly, in long trousers or skirt (or at least knee-length shorts if you must) and a T-shirt or shirt. Getting dressed or changing your clothes in front of villagers is also offensive.
- Loud voices and **boisterous behaviour** are out of place. Smiling and nodding establishes good intent. A few hill-tribe phrasebooks and dictionaries are available from local bookshops and you'll be a big hit if you learn some words of the relevant language.
- If travelling with a loved one, avoid **displays of public affection** such as kissing, which are extremely distasteful, and disrespectful, to local people.
- Look out for **taboo signs** (*ta-laew*), woven bamboo strips, on the ground outside the entrance to a village, on the roof above a house entrance or on a fresh tree branch; these mean a special ceremony is taking place and that you should not enter. Be careful about what you touch; in Akha villages, keep your hands off cult structures like the entrance gates and the giant swing. Ask first before entering a house, and do not step or sit on the doorsill, which is often considered the domain of the house spirits. If the house has a raised floor on stilts, take off your shoes. Most hill-tribe houses contain a religious shrine: do not touch or photograph this shrine, or sit underneath it. If you are permitted to watch a ceremony, this is not an invitation to participate unless asked. Like the villagers themselves, you'll be expected to pay a fine for any violation of local customs.
- Some villagers like to be photographed, most do not. Point at your **camera** and nod if you want to take a photograph. Never insist if the answer is an obvious "no". Be particularly careful with the sick and the old, and with pregnant women and babies – most tribes believe cameras affect the soul of the foetus or newborn.
- Taking **gifts** can be dubious practice. If you want to take something, writing materials for children and clothing are welcome, as well as sewing tools (such as needles) for women – ask your guide to pass any gifts to the village headman for fair distribution. However, money, sweets and cigarettes may encourage begging and create unhealthy tastes.
- Do not ask for **opium**, as this will offend your hosts.

disruption, it's important to take a responsible attitude when trekking. While it's possible to trek independently from one or two spots such as *Cave Lodge* near Soppong (see p.344), the lone trekker will learn very little without a guide as intermediary, and is far more likely to commit an unwitting offence against the local customs; it's best to go with a sensitive and knowledgeable **guide** who has the welfare of the local people in mind, and follow the basic guidelines on etiquette outlined below. If you don't fancy an organized trek in a group, it's possible to hire a personal guide from an agent, at a cost of about B1000–1500 per day.

The hill tribes are big business in northern Thailand: in **Chiang Mai** there are hundreds of agencies, which between them cover just about all the trekkable areas in the north. **Chiang Rai** is the second-biggest trekking centre, and agencies can also be found in Nan, Mae Sariang, Mae Hong Son, Pai, Chiang Dao, Tha Ton and Mae Salong, which usually arrange treks only to the villages in their immediate area. Guided trekking on a smaller scale than in the north is available in Umphang, Kanchanaburi and Sangkhlaburi.

The basics

The cool, dry season from November to February is the best time for treks, which can be as short as one day or as long as ten, but are typically of three or four days' duration. The standard size of a group is between five and twelve people; being part of a small group is preferable, enabling you to strike a more informative relationship with your guides and with the villagers. Everybody in the group usually sleeps on a mattress in the village's guest hut, with a guide cooking communal meals, for which some ingredients are brought from outside and others are found locally.

Each trek usually follows a regular **itinerary** established by the agency, although they can sometimes be customized, especially for smaller groups and with agencies in the smaller towns. Some itineraries are geared towards serious hikers while others go at a much gentler pace, but on all treks much of the walking will be up and down steep forested hills, often under a burning sun, so a reasonable level of fitness is required. Many treks now include a ride on an elephant and a trip on a bamboo raft – exciting to the point of being dangerous if the river is running fast. The typical three-day, two-night trek **costs** about B1600–3000 in Chiang Mai (including transport, accommodation, food and guide), sometimes less in other towns, much less without rafting and elephant riding.

Choosing a trek

There are several features to look out for when **choosing a trek**. If you want to trek with a small group, get an assurance from your agency that you won't be tagged onto a larger group. Make sure the trek has at least two guides – a leader and a back-marker; some trekkers have been known to get lost for days after becoming separated from the rest of the group. Check exactly when the trek starts and ends and ask about transport to and from base; most treks begin with a pick-up ride out of town, but on rare occasions the trip can entail a long public bus ride. If at all possible, meet and chat with the other trekkers in advance, as well as the guides, who should speak reasonable English and know about hill-tribe culture, especially the details of etiquette in each village. Finally, ask what meals will be included, check how much walking is involved per day and get a copy of the route map to gauge the terrain.

While everybody and their grandmother act as **agents**, only a few know their guides personally, so choose a reputable agent or guesthouse. When picking an agent, you should check whether they and their guides have licences and certificates from the Tourist Authority of Thailand, which they should be able to show you: this ensures at least a minimum level of training, and provides some comeback in case of problems. Word of mouth is often the best recommendation, so if you hear of a good outfit, try it. Each trek should be **registered** with the tourist police, stating the itinerary, the duration and the participants, in case the party encounters any trouble – it's worth checking with the agency that the trek has been registered with the tourist police before departure.

What to take

The right **clothing** is the first essential on any trek. Strong boots with ankle protection are the best footwear, although in the dry season training shoes are adequate. Wear thin, loose clothes – long trousers should be worn to protect against thorns and, in the wet season, leeches – and a hat, and cover your arms if you're prone to sunburn. Antiseptic, antihistamine cream, anti-diarrhoea **medicine** and insect repellent are essential, as is a mosquito net – check if one will be provided where you're staying. At least two changes of clothing are needed, plus a sarong or towel (women in particular should bring a sarong to wash or change underneath).

If you're going on an organized trek, **water** is usually provided by the guide, as well as a small backpack. **Blankets** or, preferably, a **sleeping bag** are also supplied, but might not be warm enough in the cool season, when night-time temperatures can dip to freezing; you should bring at least a sweater, and perhaps buy a cheap, locally made balaclava to be sure of keeping the chill off.

It's wise not to take anything valuable with you; most guesthouses in trekking-oriented places like Chiang Mai have safes and left-luggage rooms.

Travelling with children

Despite the relative lack of child-centred attractions in Thailand, there's plenty to appeal to families, both on the beach and inland, and Thais are famously welcoming to young visitors.

Of all the **beach resorts** in the country, two of the most family friendly are the islands of Ko Samui and Ko Lanta. Both have plenty of on-the-beach accommodation for mid- and upper-range budgets, and lots of easy-going open-air shorefront restaurants so that adults can eat in relative peace while kids play within view. Both islands also offer many day-tripping activities, from elephant riding to snorkelling. Phuket is another family favourite, though shorefront accommodation here is at a premium; there are also scores of less mainstream alternatives. In many beach resorts older kids will be able to go kayaking or learn rock climbing, and many dive centres will teach the PADI children's scuba courses on request: the Bubblemaker programme is designed for kids of 8 and over, and the Discover Scuba Diving day is open to anyone 10 and over.

Inland, the many **national parks** and their waterfalls and caves are good for days out, and there are lots of opportunities to go **rafting** and **elephant riding**. Kanchanaburi is a rewarding centre for all these, with the added plus that many of the town's guesthouses are set round decent-sized lawns. Chiang Mai is another great hub for all the above and also offers boat trips, an attractive, modern zoo and aquarium, the chance to watch umbrella-makers and other craftspeople at work, and, in the Mae Sa valley, many family-oriented attractions, such as the botanical gardens and **butterfly farms**. Bangkok has several child-friendly **theme parks** and activity centres.

Should you be in Thailand in January, your kids will be able to join in the free entertainments and activities staged all over the country on **National Children's Day** (Wan Dek), which is held on the second Saturday of January. They also get free entry to zoos that day, and free rides on public buses.

Hotels and transport

Many of the expensive **hotels** listed in this guide allow one or two under-12s to share their parents' room for free, as long as no extra bedding is required. It's often possible to cram two adults and two children into the double rooms in budget and mid-range hotels (as opposed to guesthouses), as beds in these places are usually big enough for two. An increasing number of guesthouses now offer three-person rooms, and may even provide special family accommodation. Decent cots are available free in the bigger hotels, and in some smaller ones (though cots in these places can be a bit grotty), and top- and mid-range rooms often come with a small fridge. Many hotels can also provide a **babysitting** service.

Few museums or transport companies offer student reductions, but in some cases children get **discounts**. One of the more bizarre provisos is the State Railway's regulation that a child aged 3 to 12 qualifies for half-fare only if under 150cm tall; some stations have a measuring scale painted onto the ticket-hall wall. Most domestic airlines charge ten percent of the full fare, or are free, for under-2s, and some charge fifty percent for under-12s.

Other practicalities

Although most Thai babies don't wear them, **disposable nappies** (diapers) are sold at convenience stores, pharmacies and supermarkets in big resorts and sizeable towns – Mamy Poko is a reliable Japanese brand, available in supermarkets; for stays on lonely islands, consider bringing some washable ones as back-up. A **changing mat** is another necessity as there are few public toilets in Thailand, let alone ones with baby facilities (though posh hotels are always a useful option). International brands of powdered milk are available throughout the country, and brand-name baby food is sold in big towns and resorts, though some parents find restaurant-cooked rice and bananas go down just as well. Thai women do not **breastfeed** in public.

For touring, child-carrier backpacks are ideal (though make sure that the child's head extends no higher than yours, as there are countless low-hanging obstacles on Thai streets). Opinions are divided on whether or not it's worth bringing a **buggy** or three-wheeled **stroller**. Where they exist, Thailand's pavements are bumpy at best, and there's an almost total absence of ramps; sand is especially difficult for buggies, though less so for three-wheelers. Buggies and strollers do, however, come in handy for feeding small children (and even for daytime naps), as highchairs are provided only in some restaurants (and then often without restraints for smaller toddlers). You can buy buggies fairly cheaply in most towns, but if you bring your own and then wish you hadn't, most hotels and guesthouses will keep it for you until you leave. Bring an appropriately sized **mosquito net** if necessary or buy one locally in any department store; a mini **sun tent** for the beach is also useful. Taxis almost never provide baby **car seats**, and even if you bring your own you'll often find there are no seatbelts to strap them in with; branches of international car-rental companies should be able to provide car seats. Most department stores have dedicated kids' sections selling everything from bottles to dummies. There are even several Mother-care outlets in Bangkok.

Hazards

Even more than their parents, children need protecting from the sun, unsafe drinking water, heat and unfamiliar **food**. Consider packing a jar of a favourite spread so that you can always rely on toast if all else fails to please. As with adults, you should be careful about unwashed fruit and salads and about dishes that have been left uncovered for a long time. As diarrhoea could be dangerous for a child, rehydration solutions (see p.68) are vital if your child goes down with it. Other significant **hazards** include thundering traffic; huge waves, strong currents and jellyfish; and the **sun** – not least because many beaches offer only limited shade, if at all. Sunhats, sunblock and waterproof suntan

lotions are essential, and can be bought in the major resorts. Avoiding mosquitoes is difficult, but low-strength DEET lotions should do the trick. You should also make sure, if possible, that your child is aware of the dangers of **rabies**; keep children away from **animals**, especially dogs and monkeys, and ask your medical advisor about rabies jabs.

INFORMATION AND ADVICE

Bangkok Mothers and Babies International Ⓦ bambiweb.org. For expat mothers and kids, but some of the information and advice on the website should be useful.

Bkk Kids Ⓦ bkkkids.com. Especially good on activities for kids in Bangkok, but also covers health matters and other services thoroughly.

Thailand 4 Kids Ⓦ thailand4kids.com. Lots of advice on the practicalities of family holidays in Thailand.

Travel essentials

Charities and volunteer projects

Reassured by the plethora of well-stocked shopping plazas, efficient services and apparent abundance in the rice fields, it is easy to forget that life is extremely hard for many people in Thailand. Countless **charities** work with Thailand's many poor and disadvantaged communities: listed below are a few that would welcome help in some way from visitors. Longer-term placements, volunteer jobs on charitable wildlife projects and organized holidays that feature community-based programmes are also available (see p.69, p.759 & p.26 respectively).

Andaman Discoveries Khuraburi Ⓦ andamandiscoveries.com. As well as community-based tourism programmes, this organization offers the chance to volunteer in an orphanage, a Burmese learning centre and a special education centre.

ADDRESSES IN THAILAND

Thai **addresses** can be immensely confusing, mainly because property is often numbered twice, first to show which real-estate lot it stands in, and then to distinguish where it is on that lot. Thus 154/7–10 Thanon Rajdamnoen means the building is on lot 154 and occupies numbers 7–10. However, neither of these numbers will necessarily help you to find a particular building on a long street; when asking for directions or talking to taxi drivers, it's best to be able to quote a nearby temple, big hotel or other landmark. There's an additional idiosyncrasy in the way Thai roads are sometimes named: in large cities a minor road running off a major road is often numbered as a soi ("lane" or "alley", though it may be a sizeable thoroughfare), rather than given its own street name. Thanon Sukhumvit for example – Bangkok's longest – has minor roads numbered Soi 1 to Soi 103, with odd numbers on one side of the road and even on the other; so a Thanon Sukhumvit address could read something like 27/9–11 Soi 15, Thanon Sukhumvit, which would mean the property occupies numbers 9–11 on lot 27 on minor road number 15 running off Thanon Sukhumvit.

AVERAGE MAXIMUM DAILY TEMPERATURES AND MONTHLY RAINFALL

	Jan	Feb	Mar	Apr	May	Jun	Jul	Aug	Sep	Oct	Nov	Dec
BANGKOK												
Max temp (°C)	26	28	29	30	30	29	29	28	28	28	27	26
Rainfall (mm)	11	28	31	72	190	152	158	187	320	231	57	9
CHIANG MAI												
Max temp (°C)	21	23	26	29	29	28	27	27	27	26	24	22
Rainfall (mm)	8	6	15	45	153	136	167	227	251	132	44	15
PATTAYA												
Max temp (°C)	26	28	29	30	30	29	29	28	28	28	27	26
Rainfall (mm)	12	23	41	79	165	120	166	166	302	229	66	10
KO SAMUI												
Max temp (°C)	26	26	28	29	29	28	28	28	28	27	26	25
Rainfall (mm)	38	8	12	63	186	113	143	123	209	260	302	98
PHUKET												
Max temp (°C)	27	28	28	29	28	28	28	28	27	27	27	27
Rainfall (mm)	35	31	39	163	348	213	263	263	419	305	207	52

Baan Unrak, Home of Joy Sangkhlaburi Ⓦ baanunrak.org. Works with ethnic-minority refugee women and children from Myanmar. Volunteers and donations welcome. See p.208.

Foundation to Encourage the Potential of Disabled Persons Chiang Mai Ⓦ assistdisabled.org. This foundation provides, among other things, free wheelchairs and home visits for disabled people. Donations of money and equipment and sponsorships for wheelchairs are sought.

Children's World Academy Kapong, near Khao Lak Ⓦ yaowawit .com. Set in quiet countryside on the Takua Pa–Phang Nga road, Yaowawit School was set up for tsunami orphans and socially disadvantaged children. It accepts donations, sponsorships, volunteer teachers and guests who wish to stay at its lodge, a hospitality training centre.

Hill Area and Community Development Foundation Chiang Rai Ⓦ naturalfocus-cbt.com. Aiming to help hill tribes in dealing with problems such as environmental management, HIV/AIDS, child and drug abuse, the foundation has set up a community-based tourism company, Natural Focus (see p.356), to offer mountain-life tours and volunteer opportunities.

Human Development Foundation Klong Toey, Bangkok Ⓦ mercycentre.org. Founded in 1973, Father Joe Maier's organization provides education and support for Bangkok's street kids and slum-dwellers. It now runs two dozen kindergartens in the slums, among many other projects. Contact the centre for information about donations, sponsoring and volunteering. Father Joe's books, *The Slaughterhouse: Stories from Bangkok's Klong Toey Slum* and *The Open Gate of Mercy*, give eye-opening insights into this often invisible side of Thai life.

Koh Yao Children's Community Center Ko Yao Noi Ⓦ koyao-ccc .com. Aims to improve the English-language and lifelong learning skills of islanders on Ko Yao Noi. Visitors, volunteers and donations welcome. See p.645.

Mae Tao Clinic Mae Sot Ⓦ maetaoclinic.org. Award-winning health centre providing free care to Burmese refugees. Donations and volunteers welcome. See p.260.

The Mirror Foundation Chiang Rai and Bangkok Ⓦ themirrorfoundation.org. NGO working with the hill tribes in Chiang Rai province to help combat such issues as drug abuse, lack of citizenship and trafficking of women and children, with a branch in Bangkok dealing with urban problems. It offers trekking and homestays in Chiang Rai (see p.356); volunteers, interns and donations sought.

The Students' Education Trust (SET) Ⓦ thaistudentcharity.org. High-school and further education in Thailand is a luxury that the poorest kids cannot afford so many are sent to live in temples instead. The SET helps such kids pursue their education and escape from the poverty trap. Some of their stories are told in *Little Angels: The Real-Life Stories of Twelve Thai Novice Monks*. SET welcomes donations.

Thai Child Development Foundation Pha To Ⓦ thaichilddevelopment.org. This small Thai-Dutch-run village project near Ranong helps educate and look after needy local children. The foundation welcomes donations, takes on volunteers, and has an ecotourism arm (see p.591).

Climate

There are three main **seasons** in most of Thailand: rainy, caused by the southwest monsoon (the least predictable, but roughly May–Oct); cool (Nov–Feb; felt most distinctly in the far north, but hardly at all in the south); and hot (March–May). The Gulf coast's climate is slightly different: it suffers less from the southwest monsoon, but is then hit by the northeast monsoon, making November its rainiest month.

Costs

Thailand can be a very cheap place to travel. At the bottom of the scale, you can manage on a **budget** of about B650 (£13/US$20) per day if you're willing to opt for basic accommodation, eat, drink and travel as the locals do, and stay away from the more expensive resorts like Phuket, Ko Samui and Ko Phi Phi – and you'd have to work hard to stick to this daily allowance in Bangkok. On this budget, you'll be spending around B200 for a dorm or shared room (more for a single room), around B200 on three meals (eating mainly at night markets and simple noodle shops, and eschewing beer), and the rest on travel (sticking to the cheaper buses and third-class trains where possible) and incidentals. With extras like air conditioning in rooms, taking the various forms of taxi rather than buses or shared songthaews for cross-town journeys, and a meal and beer in a more touristy restaurant, a day's outlay would be at least B1000 (£20/US$30). Staying in well-equipped, mid-range hotels and eating in more upmarket restaurants, you should be able to live comfortably for around B2000 a day (£40/US$60).

Travellers soon get so used to the low cost of living in Thailand that they start **bargaining** at every available opportunity, much as Thai people do. Although it's expected practice for a lot of commercial transactions, particularly at markets and when hiring tuk-tuks and unmetered taxis (though not in supermarkets or department stores), bargaining is a delicate art that requires humour, tact and patience. If your price is way out of line, the vendor's vehement refusal should be enough to make you increase your offer: never forget that the few pennies or cents you're making such a fuss over will go a lot further in a Thai person's hands than in your own.

It's rare that foreigners can bargain a price down as low as a Thai could, anyway, while **two-tier pricing** has been made official at government-run sights, as a kind of informal tourist tax: at national parks, for example, foreigners pay up to B500 entry while Thais pay just B20–40. A number of privately owned tourist attractions follow a similar two-tier system, posting an inflated price in English for foreigners and a lower price in Thai for locals.

Shoppers who are departing via an international airport can save some money by claiming a **Value Added Tax refund** (ⓦrd.go.th/vrt), though it's a bit of a palaver for seven percent (the current rate of VAT, though this is due to increase to ten percent at the end of 2015). The total amount of your purchases (gems are excluded) from participating shops needs to be at least B2000 per person. You'll need to show your passport and fill in an application form (to which original tax invoices need to be attached) at the shop. At the relevant airport, you'll need to show your form and purchases to customs officers before checking in, then make your claim from VAT refund officers – from which fees of at least B100 are deducted.

Crime and personal safety

As long as you keep your wits about you, you shouldn't encounter much trouble in Thailand. **Pickpocketing** and **bag-snatching** are two of the main problems – not surprising considering that a huge percentage of the local population scrape by on under US$10 per day – but the most common cause for concern is the number of con-artists who dupe gullible tourists into parting with their cash. There are various Thai laws that tourists need to be aware of, particularly regarding passports, the age of consent and smoking in public.

Theft

To **prevent theft**, most travellers prefer to carry their valuables with them at all times, but it's often possible to use a safe in a hotel or a locker in a guesthouse – the safest are those that require your own padlock, as there are occasional reports of valuables being stolen by guesthouse staff. **Padlock your luggage** when leaving it in storage or taking it on public transport. Padlocks also come in handy as extra security on your room, particularly on the doors of beachfront bamboo huts.

Theft from some long-distance **buses** is also a problem, with the majority of reported incidents taking place on the temptingly cheap overnight buses run by private companies direct from Bangkok's Thanon Khao San (as opposed to those that depart from the government bus stations) to destinations such as Chiang Mai and southern beach resorts. The best solution is to go direct from the bus stations.

Personal safety

On any bus, private or government, and on any train journey, never keep anything of value in luggage that is stored out of your sight and be wary of accepting food and drink from fellow passengers as it may be drugged. This might sound paranoid, but there have been enough **drug-muggings** for TAT to publish a specific warning about the problem. Drinks can also be spiked in bars and clubs; at full

REPORTING A CRIME OR EMERGENCY

In emergencies, contact the English-speaking **tourist police**, who maintain a 24-hour toll-free nationwide line (☎1155) and have offices in the main tourist centres; getting in touch with the tourist police first is invariably more efficient than directly contacting the local police, ambulance or fire service. The tourist police's job is to offer advice and tell you what to do next, but they do not file crime reports, which must be done at the nearest police station.

The British Embassy in Bangkok provides **advice** for British victims of crime in Thailand and also posts practical tips and a list of useful contacts on its website (☎02 305 8333, ⓦukinthailand.fco.gov.uk/en/help-for-british-nationals).

moon parties on Ko Pha Ngan this has led to sexual assaults against farang women, while prostitutes sometimes spike drinks so they can steal from their victim's room.

Violent crime against tourists is not common, but it does occur, and there have been several serious attacks on travellers in recent years, notably on Ko Pha Ngan and Ko Tao. However, bearing in mind that 25 million foreigners visit Thailand every year, the statistical likelihood of becoming a victim is extremely small. **Obvious precautions** for travellers of either sex include locking accessible windows and doors – preferably with your own padlock (doors in many of the simpler guesthouses and beach bungalows are designed for this) – and taking care at night, especially around bars. You should not risk jumping into an unlicensed taxi at the airport in Bangkok at any time of day: there have been some very violent robberies in these, so take the well-marked licensed, metered taxis instead.

Among hazards to watch out for in the natural world, **riptides** claim a number of tourist lives every year, particularly off Phuket, Ko Chang (Trat), Hua Hin, Cha-am, Rayong, Pattaya and the Ko Samui archipelago during stormy periods of the monsoon season, so always pay attention to warning signs and red flags, and always ask locally if unsure. **Jellyfish** can be a problem on any coast, especially just after a storm (see p.67).

Unfortunately, it is also necessary for female tourists to think twice about spending time alone with a **monk**, as not all men of the cloth uphold the Buddhist precepts and there have been rapes and murders committed by men wearing the saffron robes of the monkhood.

Though unpalatable and distressing, Thailand's high-profile **sex industry** is relatively unthreatening for Western women, with its energy focused exclusively on farang men; it's also quite easily avoided, being contained within certain pockets of the cities and beach resorts.

As for **harassment** from men, it's hard to generalize, but most Western women find it less of a problem in Thailand than they do back home. Outside the main tourist spots, you're more likely to be of interest as a foreigner rather than a woman and, if travelling alone, as an object of concern rather than of sexual aggression.

Regional issues

It's advisable to travel with a guide if you're going off the roads in a few **border areas** or, at the very least, to take advice before setting off. As these regions are generally covered in dense unmapped jungle, you shouldn't find yourself alone in the area anyway. In the immediate vicinity of the Burmese border, fighting on the other side of the frontier very occasionally spills over and there are rare clashes between Thai security forces and illegal traffickers. Certain areas of the border between Cambodia and southern Isaan are littered with unexploded mines, and there have been recent clashes between the Thai and Cambodian armies over the disputed line of the border, especially at Khao Phra Viharn (Preah Vihear).

Because of the **violence in the deep south**, all Western governments are currently advising against travel to or through the border provinces of Songkhla, Yala, Pattani and Narathiwat, unless essential (see p.697). For up-to-the-minute advice on current political trouble-spots, consult your government's travel advisory (see box, p.62).

Scams

Despite the best efforts of guidebook writers, TAT and the Thai tourist police, countless travellers to Thailand get scammed every year. Nearly all **scams** are easily avoided if you're on your guard against anyone who makes an unnatural effort to befriend you. We have outlined the main scams in the relevant sections of this guide, but con-artists are nothing if not creative, so if in doubt walk away at the earliest opportunity. The worst areas for scammers are the busy tourist centres, including many parts of Bangkok and the main beach resorts.

GOVERNMENTAL TRAVEL ADVISORIES

Australian Department of Foreign Affairs ⓦ dfat.gov.au.
British Foreign & Commonwealth Office ⓦ gov.uk/government/organisations/foreign
-commonwealth-office.
Canadian Department of Foreign Affairs ⓦ international.gc.ca.
Irish Department of Foreign Affairs ⓦ dfa.ie.
New Zealand Ministry of Foreign Affairs ⓦ mfat.govt.nz.
South African Department of Foreign Affairs ⓦ www.dfa.gov.za.
US State Department ⓦ state.gov.

Many **tuk-tuk drivers** earn most of their living through securing **commissions** from tourist-oriented shops; this is especially true in Bangkok, where they will do their damnedest to get you to go to a gem shop (see p.170). The most common tactic is for drivers to pretend that the Grand Palace or other major sight you intended to visit is closed for the day (see p.86), and to then offer to take you on a round-city tour instead, perhaps even for free. The tour will invariably include a visit to a gem shop. The easiest way to avoid all this is to take a **metered taxi**; if you're fixed on taking a tuk-tuk, ignore any tuk-tuk that is parked up or loitering and be firm about where you want to go.

Self-styled **tourist guides**, **touts** and anyone else who might introduce themselves as **students** or **business people** and offer to take you somewhere of interest, or invite you to meet their family, are often the first piece of bait in a well-honed chain of con-artists. If you bite, chances are you'll end up either at a gem shop or in a gambling den, or, at best, at a tour operator or hotel that you had not planned to patronize. This is not to say that you should never accept an invitation from a local person, but be extremely wary of doing so following a street encounter in Bangkok or the resorts. Tourist guides' ID cards are easily faked.

For many of these characters, the goal is to get you inside a dodgy **gem shop**, nearly all of which are located in Bangkok (see box, p.170), but the bottom line is that if you are not experienced at buying and trading in valuable gems you will definitely be ripped off, possibly even to the tune of several thousand dollars.

A less common but potentially more frightening scam involves a similar cast of warm-up artists leading tourists into a **gambling** game. The scammers invite their victim home on an innocent-sounding pretext, get out a pack of cards, and then set about fleecing the incomer in any number of subtle or unsubtle ways. Often this can be especially scary as the venue is likely to be far from hotels or recognizable landmarks, and there have

been stories of visitors being forced to withdraw large amounts of money from ATMs. You're unlikely to get any sympathy from police, as gambling is **illegal** in Thailand.

An increasing number of travel agents in tourist centres all over the country are trying to pass themselves off as official government tourist information offices, displaying nothing but "**Tourist Information**" on their shop signs or calling themselves names like "TAD" (note that the actual TAT, the Tourism Authority of Thailand, does not book hotels or sell any kind of travel ticket). Fakers like this are more likely to sell you tickets for services that turn out to be sub-standard or even not to exist. A word of warning also about **jet skis**: operators, who usually ask for a passport as guarantee, will often try to charge renters exorbitant amounts of money for any minor damage they claim to find on return.

Age restrictions and other laws

Thai law requires that tourists **carry their original passports** at all times, though sometimes it's more practical to carry a photocopy and keep the original locked in a safety deposit. The **age of consent** is 15, but the law allows anyone under the age of 18, or their parents, to file charges in retrospect even if they consented to sex at the time. It is against the law to have sex with a prostitute who is under 18. It is illegal for **under-18s** to buy cigarettes or to drive and you must be 20 or over to **buy alcohol** or be allowed into a **bar or club** (ID checks are sometimes enforced in Bangkok). It is illegal for anyone to **gamble** in Thailand (though many do).

Smoking in public is widely prohibited. The ban covers all public buildings (including restaurants, bars and clubs) and trains, buses and planes and can even be extended to parks and the street; violators may be subject to a B2000–5000 fine. Dropping cigarette butts, **littering** and spitting in public places can also earn you a B2000–5000 fine. There are fines for **overstaying your visa** (see p.64), **working without a permit**, **not wearing a motorcycle helmet** and violating other **traffic laws**.

Drugs

Drug-smuggling carries a maximum penalty in Thailand of death, and **dealing drugs** will get you anything from four years to life in a Thai prison; penalties depend on the drug and the amount involved. Travellers caught with even the smallest amount of drugs at airports and international borders are prosecuted for trafficking, and no one charged with trafficking offences gets bail. Heroin, amphetamines, LSD and ecstasy are classed as Category 1 drugs and carry the most severe penalties: even **possession** of Category 1 drugs for personal use can result in a **life sentence**. Away from international borders, most foreigners arrested in possession of small amounts of cannabis are released on bail, then fined and deported, but the law is complex and prison sentences are possible.

Despite occasional royal pardons, don't expect special treatment as a farang: you only need to read one of the first-hand accounts by foreign former prisoners (see p.778) or read the blogs at ⓦthai prisonlife.com to get the picture. The **police** actively look for tourists doing drugs, reportedly searching people regularly and randomly on Thanon Khao San, for example. They have the power to order a urine test if they have reasonable grounds for suspicion, and even a positive result for marijuana consumption could lead to a year's imprisonment. Be wary also of **being shopped** by a farang or local dealer keen to earn a financial reward for a successful bust (there are setups at the Ko Pha Ngan full moon parties, for example), or having substances slipped into your luggage (simple enough to perpetrate unless all fastenings are secured with padlocks).

If you are arrested, ask for your embassy to be contacted immediately (see p.170), which is your right under Thai law, and embassy staff will talk you through procedures; the website of the British Embassy in Thailand also posts useful information, including a list of English-speaking lawyers, at ⓦukinthailand.fco.gov .uk/en/help-for-british-nationals. The British charity Prisoners Abroad (ⓦprisonersabroad.org.uk) carries a detailed survival guide on its website, which outlines what to expect if arrested in Thailand, from the point of apprehension through trial and conviction to life in a Thai jail; if contacted, the charity may also be able to offer direct support to a British citizen facing imprisonment in a Thai jail.

Customs regulations

The **duty-free** allowance on entry to Thailand is 200 cigarettes (or 250g of tobacco or cigars) and a litre of spirits or wine (see ⓦcustoms.go.th for more information).

To **export antiques** or newly cast **Buddha images** from Thailand, you need to have a licence granted by the Fine Arts Department (the export of religious antiques, especially Buddha images, is forbidden). Licences can be obtained for example through the Office of Archeology and National Museums, 81/1 Thanon Si Ayutthaya (near the National Library), Bangkok (☎02 628 5032), or through the national museum in Chiang Mai. Applications take at least three working days in Bangkok, generally more in the provinces, and need to be accompanied by the object itself, some evidence of its rightful possession, two postcard-sized colour photos of it, taken face-on and against a white background, and photocopies of the applicant's passport; furthermore, if the object is a Buddha image, the passport photocopies need to be certified by your embassy in Bangkok. Some antiques shops can organize all this for you.

Electricity

Mains **electricity** is supplied at 220 volts AC and is available at all but the most remote villages and basic beach huts. Where electricity is supplied by generators and/or solar power, for example on the smaller, less populated islands, it is often rationed to evenings only. If you're packing phone and camera chargers, a hair dryer, laptop or other appliance, you'll need to take a set of travel-plug adapters with you as several plug types are commonly in use, most usually with two round pins, but also with two flat-blade pins or three round pins.

Entry requirements

There are three main entry categories for visitors to Thailand; for all of them, under International Air Travel Association rules, your passport should be valid for at least six months. As visa requirements are subject to frequent change, you should always consult before departure a Thai embassy or consulate, a reliable travel agent, or the Thai Ministry of Foreign Affairs' website at ⓦmfa.go.th. For further, unofficial but usually reliable, details on all visa matters – especially as the rules are not consistently enforced across all Thai border checkpoints and immigration offices – go to the moderated forums on ⓦthaivisa.com.

Most Western passport holders (that includes citizens of the UK, Ireland, the US, Canada, Australia, New Zealand and South Africa) are allowed to enter the country for short **stays** without having to apply for a visa – officially termed the **tourist visa exemption** (not to be confused with "visas on arrival", another category of entry that's not available to citizens of the countries listed above). You'll be granted a thirty-day stay at an international airport, while at an overland border, most visitors are given fifteen days, but citizens of G7 countries, including the UK, US and Canada, are allowed thirty days; the period of stay will be stamped into your passport by immigration officials upon entry. You're somehow supposed to be able to show proof of means of living while in the country (B10,000 per person, B20,000 per family), and in theory you may be put back on the next plane without it or sent back to get a sixty-day tourist visa from the nearest Thai embassy, but this is unheard of. You are also required to show proof of tickets to leave Thailand again within the allotted time, though the Thai immigration authorities do not appear to be consistent about checking this (it seems to be more likely at land borders). However, if you have a one-way air ticket to Thailand and no evidence of onward travel arrangements, it's best to buy a tourist visa in advance: many airlines will stop you boarding the plane without one, as they would be liable for flying you back to your point of origin if you did happen to be stopped.

If you're fairly certain you may want to stay longer than fifteen/thirty days, then from the outset you should apply for a **sixty-day tourist visa** from a Thai embassy or consulate, accompanying your application – which generally takes several days to process – with your passport and one or two photos. The sixty-day visa currently costs B1000 or rough equivalent; multiple-entry versions are available, costing B1000 per entry, which may be handy if you're going to be leaving and re-entering Thailand. Ordinary tourist visas are valid for three months; ie you must enter Thailand within three months of the visa being issued by the Thai embassy or consulate, while multiple-entry versions are valid for six months. Visa application forms can be downloaded from, for example, the Thai Ministry of Foreign Affairs' website.

Thai embassies also consider applications for **ninety-day non-immigrant visas** (B2000 or rough equivalent for single entry, B5000 for multiple-entry) as long as you can offer a reason for your visit, such as study, business or visiting family (there are different categories of non-immigrant visa for which different levels of proof are needed). As it can be a hassle to organize a ninety-day visa, it's generally easier to apply for a thirty-day extension to your sixty-day visa once inside Thai borders.

It's not a good idea to **overstay** your visa limits. Once you're at the airport or the border, you'll have to pay a fine of B500 per day before you can leave Thailand (and there is talk, at the time of writing, of stiffening the sanctions). More importantly, however, if you're in the country with an expired visa and you get involved with police or immigration officials for any reason, however trivial, they are obliged to take you to court, possibly imprison you, and deport you.

Extensions, border runs and re-entry permits

Tourist visa exemptions, as well as sixty-day tourist visas, can be **extended** within Thailand for a further thirty days, at the discretion of immigration officials; extensions cost B1900 and are issued over the counter at immigration offices (*kaan khao muang* or *taw maw*; ☎ 1111 for 24hr information in English, �🌐 immigration.go.th) in nearly every provincial capital. You'll need to bring one or two photos, one or two photocopies of the main pages of your passport including your Thai departure card, arrival stamp and visa; you may be asked for proof of tickets to leave Thailand again within the proposed time and evidence of where you're staying, and it's possible though unlikely that you'll be asked for proof of means of living while in Thailand. Many Khao San tour agents offer to get your visa extension for you, but beware: some are reportedly faking the stamps, which could get you into serious trouble. In 2014, the Thai immigration authorities started clamping down again on foreigners who stay in Thailand long-term by doing back-to-back **border runs** for tourist visa exemptions; however, it's still possible for ordinary travellers to get one new fifteen/thirty-day tourist visa exemption by hopping **across the border** into a neighbouring country and back. Immigration offices also issue **re-entry permits** (B1000 single re-entry, B3800 multiple) if you want to leave the country and come back again while maintaining the validity of your existing visa.

THAI EMBASSIES AND CONSULATES ABROAD

For a full listing of Thai diplomatic missions abroad, consult the Thai Ministry of Foreign Affairs' website at ⓦ mfa.go.th/web/2712.php; its other site, ⓦ thaiembassy.org, has links to the websites of most of the offices below.

Australia 111 Empire Circuit, Yarralumla, Canberra ACT 2600 ☎ 02 6206 0100; plus consulate at 131 Macquarrie St, Sydney, NSW 2000 ☎ 02 9241 2542–3.

Cambodia 196 Preah Norodom Blvd, Sangkat Tonle Bassac, Khan Chamcar Mon, Phnom Penh ☎ 023 726306–8.

Canada 180 Island Park Drive, Ottawa, ON, K1Y 0A2 ☎ 613 722 4444; plus consulate at 1040 Burrard St, Vancouver, BC, V6Z 2R9 ☎ 604 687 1143.

Laos Vientiane: embassy at Avenue Kaysone Phomvihane, Saysettha District ☎ 021 214581–2, consular section at Unit 15 Bourichane Rd, Ban Phone Si Nuan, Muang Si Sattanak ☎ 021 453916; plus consulate at Khanthabouly District, Savannakhet Province, PO Box 513 ☎ 041 212373.

Malaysia 206 Jalan Ampang, 50450 Kuala Lumpur ☎ 03 2148 8222; plus consulates at 4426 Jalan Pengkalan Chepa, 15400 Kota Bharu ☎ 09 748 2545; and 1 Jalan Tunku Abdul Rahman, 10350 Penang ☎ 04 226 9484.

Myanmar 94 Pyay Rd, Dagon Township, Rangoon ☎ 01 226721.

New Zealand 110 Molesworth St, Thorndon, Wellington ☎ 04 476 8616.

Singapore 370 Orchard Rd, Singapore 238870 ☎ 6737 2158.

South Africa 428 Pretorius/Hill St, Arcadia, Pretoria 0083 ☎ 012 342 5470.

UK and Ireland 29–30 Queens Gate, London SW7 5JB ☎ 020 7589 2944. In Ireland, visa applications by post can be sent to the consulate in Dublin (ⓦ thaiconsulateireland.com).

US 1024 Wisconsin Ave NW, Suite 401, Washington, DC 20007 ☎ 202 944 3600; plus consulates at 700 North Rush St, Chicago, IL 60611 ☎ 312 664 3129; 611 North Larchmont Blvd, 2nd Floor, Los Angeles, CA 90004 ☎ 323 962 9574; and 351 E 52nd St, New York, NY 10022 ☎ 212 754 1770.

Vietnam 63–65 Hoang Dieu St, Hanoi ☎ 04 3823-5092–4; plus consulate at 77 Tran Quoc Thao St, District 3, Ho Chi Minh City ☎ 08 3932-7637–8.

Gay and lesbian Thailand

Buddhist tolerance and a national abhorrence of confrontation and victimization combine to make Thai society relatively tolerant of **homosexuality**, if not exactly positive about same-sex relationships. Most Thais are extremely private and discreet about being gay, generally pursuing a "don't ask, don't tell" understanding with their family. The majority of people are horrified by the idea of gay-bashing and generally regard it as unthinkable to spurn a child or relative for being gay.

Hardly any Thai celebrities are out, yet the predilections of several respected social, political and entertainment figures are widely known and accepted. There is no mention of homosexuality at all in Thai law, which means that the **age of consent** for gay sex is fifteen, the same as for heterosexuals. However, this also means that gay rights are not protected under Thai law.

Although excessively physical displays of affection are frowned upon for both heterosexuals and homosexuals, Western gay couples should get no hassle about being seen together in public – it's much more acceptable, and common, in fact, for friends of the same sex (gay or not) to walk hand-in-hand, than for heterosexual couples to do so.

Katoey (which can refer both to transgender women and to effeminate gay men, so often translated as "ladyboys") are also a lot more visible in Thailand than in the West. You'll find transgender women doing ordinary jobs, even in small upcountry towns, and there are a number of *katoey* in the public eye too – including national volleyball stars and champion *muay thai* boxers. The government tourist office vigorously promotes the transgender cabarets in Pattaya, Phuket and Bangkok, all of which are advertised as family entertainment. *Katoey* also regularly appear as characters in soap operas, TV comedies and films, where they are depicted as stereotyped but harmless figures of fun. Richard Totman's *The Third Sex* offers an interesting insight into Thai *katoey*, their experiences in society and public attitudes towards them.

The scene

Thailand's gay scene is mainly focused on **mainstream venues** like karaoke bars, restaurants, massage parlours, gyms, saunas and escort agencies. For the sake of discretion, gay venues are often intermingled with straight ones. Bangkok, Phuket and Pattaya have the biggest concentrations of farang-friendly gay bars and clubs, and Chiang Mai has an established bar scene. For a detailed though slightly outdated guide to the gay and lesbian scene throughout the country, see the *Utopia Guide to Thailand* by John Goss.

Thai **lesbians** generally eschew the word lesbian, which in Thailand is associated with male fantasies, instead referring to themselves as either *tom* (for tomboy) or *dee* (for lady). There are hardly any dedicated *tom-dee* venues in Thailand, but we've listed established ones where possible; unless otherwise specified, gay means male throughout this Guide.

The farang-oriented gay **sex industry** is a tiny but highly visible part of Thailand's gay scene. With its tawdry floor shows and host services, it bears a dispiriting resemblance to the straight sex trade, and is similarly most active in Bangkok, Pattaya, Patong (on Phuket) and Chiang Mai. Like their female counterparts in the heterosexual fleshpots, many of the boys working in the gay sex bars that dominate these districts are underage; note that anyone caught having sex with a prostitute below the age of 18 faces imprisonment. A significant number of gay prostitutes are gay by economic necessity rather than by inclination. As with the straight sex scene, we do not list commercial gay sex bars in the Guide.

INFORMATION AND CONTACTS FOR GAY TRAVELLERS

Bangkok Lesbian Ⓦ bangkoklesbian.com. Organized by foreign lesbians living in Thailand, Bangkok Lesbian posts general info and listings of the capital's lesbian-friendly hangouts on its website.

Dreaded Ned's Ⓦ dreadedned.com. Guide to the scene in Thailand with extensive listings.

Gay People in Thailand Ⓦ thaivisa.com/forum/forum/27-gay -people-in-thailand. Popular forum for gay expats.

Travel Gay Asia Ⓦ travelgayasia.com/destination/gay-thailand. Active, frequently updated site that covers listings and events all over the country.

Utopia Ⓦ utopia-asia.com and Ⓦ utopia-asia.com/womthai.htm. Lists clubs, bars, accommodation, tour operators, organizations and resources for gays and lesbians.

Health

Although Thailand's climate, wildlife and cuisine present Western travellers with fewer health worries than in many Asian destinations, it's as well to know in advance what the risks might be, and what preventive or curative measures you should take.

For a start, there's no need to bring huge supplies of non-prescription medicines with you, as Thai **pharmacies** (*raan khai yaa*; typically open daily 8.30am–8pm) are well stocked with local and inter-national branded medicaments, and of course they are generally much less expensive than at home. Nearly all pharmacies are run by trained English-speaking pharmacists, who are usually the best people to talk to if your symptoms aren't acute enough to warrant seeing a doctor. The British pharmacy chain, Boots, now has branches in many big cities (see Ⓦ th.boots.com for locations). These are the best place to stock up on some Western products such as **tampons** (which Thai women do not use).

Hospital (*rong phayabaan*) cleanliness and efficiency vary, but generally hygiene and health-care standards are good and the ratio of medical staff to patients is considerably higher than in most parts of the West. As with head pharmacists, doctors speak English. Several Bangkok hospitals are highly regarded (see p.171), and all provincial capitals have at least one hospital: if you need to get to one, ask at your accommodation for advice on, and possibly transport to, the nearest or most suitable. In the event of a major health crisis, get someone to contact your embassy (see p.170) and insurance company – it may be best to get yourself transported to Bangkok or even home.

Inoculations

There are no compulsory **inoculation** requirements for people travelling to Thailand from the West, but you should consult a doctor or other health profes-sional, preferably at least four weeks in advance of your trip, for the latest information on recom-mended immunizations. In addition to making sure that your recommended immunizations for life in your home country are up to date, most doctors strongly advise vaccinations or boosters against tetanus, diphtheria, hepatitis A and, in many cases, typhoid, and in some cases they might also recommend protecting yourself against Japanese encephalitis, rabies and hepatitis B. There is currently no vaccine against malaria. If you forget to have all your inoculations before leaving home, or don't leave yourself sufficient time, you can get them in Bangkok at, for example, the Thai Red Cross Society's Queen Saovabha Institute or Global Doctor (see p.171).

Mosquito-borne diseases

Mosquitoes in Thailand can spread not only malaria, but also diseases such as dengue fever and the very similar chikungunya fever, especially during the rainy season. The main message, therefore, is to **avoid being bitten** by mosquitoes. You should smother yourself and your clothes in **mosquito repellent** containing the chemical compound DEET, reapplying regularly (shops, guesthouses and department stores all over Thailand stock it, but if you want the highest-strength repellent, or convenient roll-ons or sprays, do your shopping before you leave home, or at a branch of Boots in Thailand). DEET is strong stuff, and if you have sensitive skin, a natural alternative is citronella (available in the UK as Mosi-guard), made from a blend of eucalyptus oils; the Thai version is made with lemon grass.

At night you should sleep either under a **mosquito net** sprayed with DEET or in a bedroom with **mosquito screens** across the windows (or in an enclosed a/c room). Accommodation in tourist spots nearly always provides screens or a net (check both for holes), but if you're planning to go way off the beaten track or want the security of having your own mosquito net just in case, wait until you get to Bangkok to buy one, where department stores sell them for much less than you'd pay in the West. Plug-in insecticide vaporizers, insect room sprays and mosquito coils – also widely available in Thailand – help keep the insects at bay; electronic "buzzers" are useless. If you are bitten, applying locally made yellow oil (see p.406) is effective at reducing the itch.

Malaria

Thailand is **malarial**, with the disease being carried by mosquitoes that bite from dusk to dawn, but the risks involved vary across the country.

There is a significant risk of malaria, mainly in rural and forested areas, in a narrow strip along the **borders with Cambodia** (excluding Ko Chang), **Laos** and **Myanmar** (the highest-risk area, including the countryside around Mae Hong Son, but excluding, for example, Chiang Mai, Chiang Rai and Kanchanaburi towns, and resorts and road and rail routes along the Gulf coast). Discuss with your travel health adviser which anti-malarial drugs are currently likely to be effective in these areas, as prophylaxis advice can change from year to year.

Elsewhere in Thailand the risk of malaria is considered to be so low that anti-malarial tablets are not advised.

The **signs of malaria** are often similar to flu, but are very variable. The incubation period for malignant malaria, which can be fatal, is usually 7–28 days, but it can take up to a year for symptoms of the benign form to occur. The most important symptom is a raised temperature of at least 38°C beginning a week or more after the first potential exposure to malaria: if you suspect anything, go to a hospital or clinic immediately.

Dengue fever

Dengue fever, a debilitating and occasionally fatal viral disease that is particularly prevalent during and just after the rainy season, is on the increase throughout tropical Asia, and is endemic to many areas of Thailand, with over 150,000 reported cases in 2013. Unlike malaria, dengue fever is spread by mosquitoes that can bite during daylight hours, so you should also use mosquito repellent during the day. Symptoms may include fever, headaches, fierce joint and muscle pain ("breakbone fever" is another name for dengue), and possibly a rash, and usually develop between five and eight days after being bitten.

There is no vaccine against dengue fever; the only treatment is lots of rest, liquids and paracetamol (or any other acetaminophen painkiller, not aspirin), though more serious cases may require hospitalization.

Rabies

Rabies is widespread in Thailand, mainly carried by dogs (between four and seven percent of stray dogs in Bangkok are reported to be rabid), but also cats and monkeys. It is transmitted by bites, scratches or even occasionally licks. Dogs are everywhere in Thailand, and even if kept as pets they're often not very well cared for; hopefully their mangy appearance will discourage the urge to pat them, as you should steer well clear of them. Rabies is invariably fatal if the patient waits until symptoms begin, though modern vaccines and treatments are very effective and deaths are rare. The important thing is, if you are bitten, licked or scratched by an animal, to vigorously clean the wound with soap and disinfect it, preferably with something containing iodine, and to seek medical advice regarding treatment right away.

Other bites and stings

Thailand's seas are home to a few dangerous creatures that you should look out for, notably **jellyfish**, which tend to be washed towards the beach by rough seas during the monsoon season but can appear at any time of year. All manner of stinging and non-stinging jellyfish can be found in Thailand – as a general rule, those with the longest tentacles tend to have the worst stings – but reports of serious incidents are rare; ask around at your resort or at a local dive shop to see if there have been any sightings of venomous varieties. You also need to be wary of venomous **sea snakes**, **sea urchins** and a couple of less conspicuous species – **stingrays**, which often lie buried in the sand, and **stonefish**, whose potentially lethal venomous spikes are easily stepped on because the fish look like stones and lie motionless on the sea bed.

If **stung or bitten**, you should always seek medical advice as soon as possible, but there are a few ways of alleviating the pain or administering your own first aid in the meantime. If you're stung by a jellyfish, wash the affected area with salt water (not fresh water) and, if possible, with vinegar (failing that, ammonia, citrus fruit juice or even urine may do the trick), and try to remove the fragments of tentacles from the skin with a gloved hand, forceps, thick cloth or credit card. The best way to minimize the risk of stepping on the toxic spines of sea urchins, stingrays and stonefish is to wear thick-soled shoes, though these cannot provide total protection; sea urchin spikes should be removed after softening the skin with ointment, though some people recommend applying urine to help dissolve the spines; for stingray and stonefish stings, alleviate the pain by immersing the wound in hot water while awaiting help.

In the case of a **venomous snake bite**, don't try sucking out the venom or applying a tourniquet: wrap up and immobilize the bitten limb and try to stay still and calm until medical help arrives; all provincial hospitals in Thailand carry supplies of antivenins.

Some of Thailand's wilder, less developed beaches are plagued by **sandflies**, tiny, barely visible midges whose bites can trigger an allergic response, leaving big red weals and an unbearable itch, and possible infection if scratched too vigorously. Many islanders say that slathering yourself in (widely available) coconut oil is the best deterrent as sandflies apparently don't like the smell. Applying locally made camphor-based yellow oil (see p.406) quells the itch, but you may need to resort to antihistamines for the inflammation. **Leeches** aren't dangerous but can be a bother when walking in forested areas, especially during and just after the rainy season. The most effective way to get leeches off your skin is to burn them with a lighted cigarette, or douse them in salt; oily suntan lotion or insect repellent sometimes makes them lose their grip and fall off.

Worms and flukes

Worms can be picked up through the soles of your feet, so avoid going barefoot. They can also be ingested by eating undercooked meat, and liver **flukes** by eating raw or undercooked freshwater fish. Worms which cause schistosomiasis (bilharziasis) by attaching themselves to your bladder or intestines can be found in freshwater rivers and lakes. The risk of contracting this disease is low, but you should avoid swimming in the southern reaches of the Mekong River and in most freshwater lakes.

Digestive problems

By far the most common travellers' complaint in Thailand, **digestive troubles** are often caused by contaminated food and water, or sometimes just by an overdose of unfamiliar foodstuffs (see p.38 & p.42).

Stomach trouble usually manifests itself as simple **diarrhoea**, which should clear up without medical treatment within three to seven days and is best combated by drinking lots of fluids. If this doesn't work, you're in danger of getting **dehydrated** and should take some kind of rehydration solution, either a commercial sachet of ORS (oral rehydration solution), sold in all Thai pharmacies, or a do-it-yourself version, which can be made by adding a handful of sugar and a pinch of salt to every litre of boiled or bottled water (soft drinks are not a viable alternative). If you can eat, avoid fatty foods.

Anti-diarrhoeal agents such as Imodium are useful for blocking you up on long bus journeys, but only attack the symptoms and may prolong infections; an antibiotic such as ciprofloxacin,

however, can often reduce a typical attack of traveller's diarrhoea to one day. If the diarrhoea persists for a week or more, or if you have blood or mucus in your stools, or an accompanying fever, go to a doctor or hospital.

HIV and AIDS

HIV infection is widespread in Thailand, primarily because of the sex trade (see p.127). **Condoms** (*meechai*) are sold in pharmacies, convenience stores, department stores, hairdressers and even street markets. Due to rigorous screening methods, Thailand's medical blood supply is now considered safe from HIV/AIDS infection.

MEDICAL RESOURCES

Canadian Society for International Health ☎ 613 241 5785, ⓦ csih.org. Extensive list of travel health centres.

CDC ☎ 800 232 4636, ⓦ cdc.gov/travel. Official US government travel health site.

Hospital for Tropical Diseases Travel Clinic UK ⓦ thehtd.org.

International Society for Travel Medicine US ☎ 404 373 8282, ⓦ istm.org. Has a full list of travel health clinics.

MASTA (Medical Advisory Service for Travellers Abroad) UK ⓦ masta-travel-health.com.

NHS Travel Health Website UK ⓦ fitfortravel.scot.nhs.uk.

The Travel Doctor – TMVC ☎ 1300 658 844, ⓦ tmvc.com.au. Lists travel clinics in Australia, New Zealand and South Africa.

Tropical Medical Bureau Ireland ☎ 1850 487 674, ⓦ tmb.ie.

Insurance

Most visitors to Thailand will need to take out **specialist travel insurance**, though you should check exactly what's covered. Insurers will generally not cover travel in Songkhla, Yala, Pattani and Narathiwat provinces in the deep south, as Western governments are currently advising against going to these areas unless it's essential (see p.697). Policies generally also exclude so-called **dangerous sports** unless an extra premium is paid: in Thailand this can mean such things as scuba diving, whitewater rafting and trekking, sometimes even riding a motorbike.

Internet

Internet access is now almost ubiquitous in Thailand. The country is covered by 3G networks and wi-fi is available in nearly all guesthouses, bungalow resorts and hotels; in cheaper places, the signal may not stretch to all bedrooms; a rapidly dwindling number of backward-looking luxury hotels are still charging for the privilege of receiving

ROUGH GUIDES TRAVEL INSURANCE

Rough Guides has teamed up with WorldNomads.com to offer great travel insurance deals. Policies are available to residents of over 150 countries, with cover for a wide range of adventure sports, 24hr emergency assistance, high levels of medical and evacuation cover and a stream of travel safety information. Roughguides.com users can take advantage of their policies online 24/7, from anywhere in the world – even if you're already travelling. And since plans often change when you're on the road, you can extend your policy and even claim online. Roughguides.com users who buy travel insurance with WorldNomads.com can also leave a positive footprint and donate to a community development project. For more information, go to ⓦ roughguides.com/travel-insurance.

wi-fi in your room. Loads of cafés, restaurants, bars and other locations across the country, especially in big towns and tourist resorts, also provide wi-fi free of charge. Given all this, internet cafés are inexorably disappearing. If you're travelling without a mobile device, ask at your accommodation for advice or keep an eye out for online games centres, favourite after-school haunts that are easily spotted from the piles of orange schoolboy pumps outside the door.

Laundry

Guesthouses and cheap hotels all over the country run low-cost, same- or next-day **laundry** services, though in luxury hotels it'll cost an arm and a leg. In some places you pay per item, in others you're charged by the kilo (generally around B30–50/kg); ironing is often included in the price.

Left luggage

Most major train stations have **left-luggage** facilities (around B30–80 per item per day); at bus stations you can usually persuade someone official to look after your stuff for a few hours. Many guesthouses and basic hotels also offer an inexpensive and usually reliable service, while upmarket hotels should be able to look after your luggage for free. There's also left luggage at Bangkok, Chiang Mai and Phuket international airports (B75–200/day).

Living in Thailand

The most common source of **employment** in Thailand is **teaching English**, and Bangkok and Chiang Mai are the most fruitful places to look for jobs. You can search for openings at schools all over Thailand on ⓦajarn.com (*ajarn* means "teacher"), which also features extensive general advice on teaching and living in Thailand. Another useful resource is the excellent ⓦthaivisa.com, whose scores of well-used forums focus on specific topics that range from employment in Thailand to legal issues and cultural and practical topics.

If you're a qualified **dive instructor**, you might be able to get seasonal work at one of the major resorts – in Phuket, Khao Lak and Ao Nang and on Ko Chang, Ko Phi Phi, Ko Lanta, Ko Samui and Ko Tao, for example. Guesthouse noticeboards occasionally carry adverts for more unusual jobs, such as playing extras in Thai movies. A tourist visa does not entitle you to work in Thailand, so, legally, you'll need to apply for a **work permit**.

STUDY, WORK AND VOLUNTEER PROGRAMMES

In addition to the programmes listed below, voluntary opportunities with smaller grassroots projects (see p.58) and wildlife charity projects (see p.759) are available.

AFS Intercultural Programs Australia ☎ 1300131736, Canada ☎ 800 361 7248, NZ ☎ 0800 600 300, South Africa ☎ 11 4310113, US ☎ AFS INFO; ⓦ afs.org. Intercultural exchange organization with programmes in over fifty countries.

Council on International Educational Exchange (CIEE) US ☎ 207 553 4000, ⓦ ciee.org. Leading NGO that organizes paid placements for five months or more as English teachers in schools in Thailand, for US citizens.

Phuket English teachers ⓦ www.phukethasbeengoodtous.org. Welcomes short- and longer-term volunteers to teach and assist on its English-language programmes at schools on Phuket, as well as donations and sponsors. The aim of this non-profit foundation is to improve kids' standards of English so that they can get the better-paid jobs in Phuket's tourist industry.

Volunteer Teaching in Thailand ⓦ volunteerteacherthailand.org. Continuing the good work begun by the thousands of volunteers who came to Khao Lak to help rebuild lives and homes following the 2004 tsunami, this non-profit organization teaches English to Khao Lak kids and adults to enhance their future prospects in the local tourist industry. Teaching experience is appreciated but not essential.

Volunthai ⓦ volunthai.com. Invites volunteers to teach English in rural schools mostly in northeast Thailand. The minimal fees cover homestay accommodation.

Thai language classes

The most popular places to **study Thai** are Chiang Mai and Bangkok, where there's plenty of choice, including private and group lessons for both tourists and expats; note, however, that some schools' main reason for existence is to provide educational visas for long-staying foreigners. The longest-running and best-regarded courses and private lessons are provided by AUA (American University Alumni; ⓦauathailand.org), which has outlets in Bangkok, Pattaya, Rayong and Chiang Mai (see p.302).

Mail

Overseas airmail usually takes around seven days from Bangkok, a little longer from the more isolated areas (it's worth asking at the post office about its express EMS services, which can cut this down to three days and aren't prohibitively expensive). **Post offices** in Thailand (ⓦthailandpost.com) have recently been quite successfully privatized, and many now offer money-wiring facilities (in association with Western Union), parcel boxes, long-distance bus tickets, amulets, whitening cream, you name it. They're generally open Monday to Friday 8.30am to 4.30pm, Saturday 9am to noon; some close Monday to Friday noon to 1pm and may stay open until 6pm, and a few open 9am to noon on Sundays and public holidays. Almost all main post offices across the country operate a **poste restante** service and will hold letters for one to three months. Mail should be addressed: *Name* (family name underlined or capitalized), Poste Restante, GPO, *Town or City*, Thailand. It will be filed by surname, though it's always wise to check under your first and middle names as well. The smaller post offices pay scant attention to who takes what, but in the busier GPOs you need to show your passport. Post offices are the best places to buy **stamps**, though hotels and guesthouses often sell them too.

Maps

For most major destinations, the **maps** in this book should be all you need, though you may want to supplement them with larger-scale maps of Bangkok and the whole country. Bangkok bookshops are the best source of these; where appropriate, detailed local maps and their stockists are recommended throughout the Guide. Decent maps of the whole country include the 1:1,500,000 versions produced by Nelles and Bartholomew.

For **drivers**, the best atlas is *Thailand Deluxe Atlas* published by thinknet (ⓦthinknet.co.th): at a scale of 1:550,000, it's bilingual and fairly regularly updated, but costs B550. It's available at most bookshops in Thailand where English-language material is sold. They also have a *Thailand Handy Atlas* and a *Bangkok Handy Atlas*, both costing B299, and their mapping is available online at ⓦmap guidethailand.com.

Trekking maps are hard to come by, except in the most popular national parks where you can usually pick up a free handout showing the main trails.

Money and banks

Thailand's unit of currency is the **baht** (abbreviated in this guide to "B"), divided into 100 satang – which are rarely seen these days. Coins come in B1 (silver), B2 (golden), B5 (silver) and B10 (mostly golden, encircled by a silver ring) denominations, notes in B20, B50, B100, B500 and B1000 denominations, inscribed with Western as well as Thai numerals, and generally increasing in size according to value.

At the time of writing, **exchange rates** were around B30 to US$1, B35 to €1 and B50 to £1. A good site for current exchange rates is ⓦxe.com. Note that Thailand has no black market in foreign currency.

Banking hours are generally Monday to Friday from 8.30am to 3.30 or 4.30pm, though branches in out-of-town shopping centres and supermarkets are often open longer hours and at weekends. Streetside exchange kiosks run by the banks in the main tourist centres are always open till at least 5pm, sometimes 10pm, and upmarket hotels change money (at poor rates) 24 hours a day. The Suvarnabhumi Airport exchange counters also operate 24 hours, while exchange kiosks at overseas airports with flights to Thailand usually keep Thai currency.

Travellers' cheques are accepted by banks and exchange booths in every sizeable Thai town; everyone offers better rates for cheques than for straight cash. Generally, a total of B153 in commission and duty is charged per cheque, so you'll save money if you deal in larger cheque denominations. Note that Scottish and Northern Irish sterling notes may not be accepted in some places.

Visa and MasterCard **credit and debit cards** are accepted at upmarket guesthouses and hotels as well as in posh restaurants, department stores, tourist shops and travel agents; American Express is less widely accepted. It's common for smaller businesses to add on a surcharge of three percent, which amounts to the fee that Visa and Mastercard charge them for the privilege. Beware theft and forgery – try not to let the card out of your sight, and never leave cards in baggage storage. With a debit or credit card and personal identification number (PIN), you can also withdraw cash from hundreds of 24hr **ATMs** around the country. Almost every town now has at least one bank with an ATM outside that accepts overseas cards (all the banks marked on our maps throughout the Guide have ATMs), and there is a huge number of standalone ATMs, in shopping malls and on the streets, often outside supermarkets and post offices. However, Thai banks now make a charge of B150–180 per ATM withdrawal (on top of whatever your bank at home will be charging you); to get around this, go into a bank with your card and passport instead and ask for a cash advance, or check with your bank before you come to Thailand – some overseas banks will not pass on to customers the B150–180 levied at Thai ATMs.

Opening hours and public holidays

Most shops **open** long hours, usually Monday to Saturday or Sunday from about 8am to 8pm, while department stores and shopping malls operate daily from around 10am to 9pm. Private office hours are generally Monday to Friday 8am to 5pm and Saturday 8am to noon, though in tourist areas these hours are longer, with weekends worked like any other day. Government offices work Monday to Friday 8.30am to 4.30pm (often closing for lunch between noon and 1pm), and national museums tend to stick to these hours too, but some close on Mondays and Tuesdays rather than at weekends. Temples generally open their gates every day from dawn to dusk.

Many tourists only register **national holidays** because trains and buses suddenly get extraordinarily crowded, especially if the holiday is moved from a Saturday or a Sunday to a Monday or a Friday as a substitution day, thus creating a long weekend: although government offices shut on these days, most shops and tourist-oriented businesses carry on regardless, and TAT branches continue to hand out free maps. (Bank holidays vary slightly from the government office holidays given below: banks close on May 1 and July 1, but not for the Royal Ploughing Ceremony nor for Khao Pansa.) Some national holidays are celebrated with theatrical festivals (see p.46). The only time an inconvenient number of shops, restaurants and

hotels do close is during **Chinese New Year**, which, though not marked as an official national holiday, brings many businesses to a standstill for several days in late January or February. You'll notice it particularly in the south, where many service industries are Chinese-managed.

Thais use both the Western Gregorian **calendar** and a Buddhist calendar – the Buddha is said to have died (or entered Nirvana) in the year 543 BC, so Thai dates start from that point: thus 2016 AD becomes 2559 BE (Buddhist Era).

NATIONAL HOLIDAYS

Jan 1 Western New Year's Day.

Feb (day of full moon) Makha Puja. Commemorates the Buddha preaching to a spontaneously assembled crowd of 1250.

April 6 Chakri Day. The founding of the Chakri dynasty, the current royal family.

April (usually 13–15) Songkhran. Thai New Year.

May 5 Coronation Day.

May (early in the month) Royal Ploughing Ceremony. Marks the traditional start of the rice-planting season.

May (day of full moon) Visakha Puja. The holiest of all Buddhist holidays, which celebrates the birth, enlightenment and death of the Buddha.

July (day of full moon) Asanha Puja. The anniversary of the Buddha's first sermon.

July (day after Asanha Puja) Khao Pansa. The start of the annual three-month Buddhist rains retreat, when new monks are ordained.

Aug 12 Queen's birthday and Mothers' Day.

Oct 23 Chulalongkorn Day. The anniversary of Rama V's death.

Dec 5 King's birthday and Fathers' Day. Also now celebrated as National Day (instead of Constitution Day).

Dec 10 Constitution Day.

Dec 31 Western New Year's Eve.

Phones

Most foreign **mobile-phone** networks have links with Thai networks but you need to check on roaming rates, which are often exorbitant, before you leave home. To get round this, most travellers purchase a Thai pre-paid SIM card (providers include AIS, DTAC and True Move) either for their mobile phone (*moe thoe*), for an old phone brought from home or for a new set cheaply purchased in Thailand (which can most easily be done in a shopping centre, especially Mah Boon Krong opposite Siam Square in Bangkok – see p.166). Available for as little as B50 (sometimes free at airports) and refillable at 7-Elevens around the country, Thai SIM cards offer very cheap calls, both domestically and internationally (especially if you use low-cost international prefixes such as 008, 009

INTERNATIONAL DIALLING CODES

Calling from abroad, the international **country code** for Thailand is **66**, after which you leave off the initial zero of the Thai number.

Calling from Thailand, you'll need the relevant country code (see p.71 for information on prefixes):

Australia 61	**South Africa** 27
Canada 1	
Ireland 353	**UK** 44
New Zealand 64	**US** 1

For **international directory enquiries** and operator services, call ☎ 100.

---

or 1-2-Call's 005 or 00500, rather than the standard 001 or 007 prefixes). They also offer data packages (3G is now nationwide, while 4G is available in Bangkok and Chiang Mai, and spreading), very cheap texting and are, of course, free of charge for all incoming calls. A data package or wi-fi on your own mobile device will also allow you to make free or very cheap video or voice calls via Skype or a similar service.

When **dialling** any number in Thailand, you must now always preface it with what used to be the area code, even when dialling from the same area. Where we've given several line numbers – eg ☎ 02 431 1802–9 – you can substitute the last digit, 2, with any digit between 3 and 9. For **directory enquiries** within Thailand, call ☎ 1133.

Mobile-phone numbers in Thailand have ten digits, beginning "08" or "09". Note, however, that Thais tend to change mobile-phone providers – and therefore numbers – comparatively frequently, in search of a better deal.

One final local idiosyncrasy: Thai phone books list people by their first name, not their family name.

Photography

Most towns and all resorts have at least one **camera shop** where you will be able to get your digital pictures downloaded from your memory card for around B100–150; new cards can be bought in electronic shops in shopping centres or in dedicated IT malls such as Panthip Plaza in Bangkok.

Time

Thailand is in the same time zone year-round, with no daylight savings period. It's five hours ahead of South Africa, seven hours ahead of GMT, twelve hours ahead of US Eastern Standard Time, three hours behind Australian Eastern Standard Time and five hours behind New Zealand Standard Time.

Tipping

It is usual to **tip** hotel bellboys and porters B20–40, and to round up taxi fares to the nearest B10. Most guides, drivers, masseurs, waiters and maids also depend on tips. Some upmarket hotels and restaurants will add an automatic ten percent service charge to your bill, though this is not always shared out.

Tourist information

The **Tourism Authority of Thailand**, or **TAT** (🌐 tourismthailand.org), maintains offices in several cities abroad and has dozens of branches within Thailand (all open daily 8.30am–4.30pm, though a few close noon–1pm). Regional offices should have up-to-date information on local festival dates and perhaps transport schedules, but service varies widely; none of them offers accommodation, tour or transport booking. You can contact the helpful TAT tourist assistance phoneline from anywhere in the country for free on ☎ 1672 (daily 8am–8pm). In Bangkok, the Bangkok Tourism Division is a better source of information on the capital (see p.142). In some smaller towns that don't qualify for a local TAT office, the information gap is filled by a **municipal tourist assistance office**; some of these are very helpful, but at others you may find it hard to locate a fluent English-speaker.

TAT OFFICES ABROAD

Australia and New Zealand Suite 2002, Level 20, 56 Pitt St, Sydney, NSW 2000 ☎ 02 9247 7549, 🌐 thailand.net.au.
South Africa Contact the UK office.
UK and Ireland 1st Floor, 17–19 Cockspur St, London SW1Y 5BL ☎ 020 7925 2511, ✉ info@tourismthailand.co.uk.
US and Canada 61 Broadway, Suite 2810, New York, NY 10006 ☎ 212 432 0433, ✉ info@tatny.com; 611 North Larchmont Blvd, 1st Floor, Los Angeles, CA 90004 ☎ 323 461 9814, ✉ tatla@tat.or.th.

Travellers with disabilities

Thailand makes few provisions for its disabled citizens and this obviously affects **travellers with disabilities**, but taxis, comfortable hotels and personal tour guides are all more affordable than in the West and most travellers with disabilities find Thais only too happy to offer assistance where they can. Hiring a local tour guide to accompany you on a day's sightseeing is particularly recommended: government-licensed tour guides can be arranged through any TAT office.

Most **wheelchair-users** end up driving on the roads because it's too hard to negotiate the uneven pavements, which are high to allow for flooding and invariably lack dropped kerbs. Crossing the road can be a trial, particularly in Bangkok and other big cities, where it's usually a question of climbing steps up to a bridge rather than taking a ramped underpass. Few buildings, buses and trains have ramps, but in Bangkok some Skytrain stations and all subway stations have lifts.

Several **tour companies** in Thailand specialize in organizing trips featuring adapted facilities, accessible transport and escorts. The Bangkok-based Help and Care Travel Company (☎ 081 375 0792, ⓦ wheelchair tours.com) designs **accessible holidays** in Thailand for slow walkers and wheelchair-users, as well as offering airport transfers, personal assistants and many other services. In Chiang Mai, Thai Focus (☎ 053 818754, ⓦ thaifocus.com) is used to designing trips for disabled travellers and can provide wheelchair rental. Mermaid's Dive Centre in Pattaya runs Disabled Divers International programmes for **disabled divers** and instructors (see p.388).

Bangkok

WAT PHRA KAEO

1

Bangkok

The headlong pace and flawed modernity of Bangkok match few people's visions of the capital of exotic Siam. Spiked with scores of high-rise buildings of concrete and glass, it's a vast flatness that holds an estimated population of nearly fifteen million, and feels even bigger. Yet under the shadow of the skyscrapers you'll find a heady mix of chaos and refinement, of frenetic markets, snail's-pace traffic jams and hushed golden temples, of dispiriting, zombie-like sex shows and early-morning alms-giving ceremonies. Plenty of visitors enjoy the challenge of taking on the "Big Mango", but one way or another, the place is sure to get under your skin.

Most budget travellers head for the **Banglamphu** district, where if you're not careful you could end up watching DVDs all day long and selling your shoes when you run out of money. The district is far from having a monopoly on Bangkok accommodation, but it does have the advantage of being just a short walk from the major sights in the **Ratanakosin** area: the dazzling ostentation of the **Grand Palace** and **Wat Phra Kaeo**, lively and grandiose **Wat Pho** and the **National Museum**'s hoard of exquisite works of art. Once those cultural essentials have been seen, you can choose from a whole bevy of lesser sights, including **Wat Benjamabophit** (the "Marble Temple"), especially at festival time, and **Jim Thompson's House**, a small, personal museum of Thai design.

For livelier scenes, explore the dark alleys of **Chinatown**'s bazaars or head for the water: the great **Chao Phraya River**, which breaks up and adds zest to the city's landscape, is the backbone of a network of **canals** that remains fundamentally intact in the west-bank Thonburi district. Inevitably the waterways have earned Bangkok the title of "Venice of the East", a tag that seems all too apt when you're wading through flooded streets in the rainy season. Back on dry land, **shopping** varies from touristic outlets pushing silks, handicrafts and counterfeit watches, through home-grown boutiques selling street-wise fashions and stunning contemporary decor, to thronging local markets where half the fun is watching the crowds. Thailand's long calendar of festivals (see p.46) is one of the few things that has been largely decentralized away from the capital, but Bangkok does offer the country's most varied **entertainment**,

THE SKY BAR

Highlights

❶ The Grand Palace The country's most unmissable sight, incorporating its holiest and most dazzling temple, Wat Phra Kaeo. **See p.84**

❷ Wat Pho Admire the Reclining Buddha and the lavish architecture, and leave time for a relaxing massage. **See p.90**

❸ The National Museum The central repository of the country's artistic riches. **See p.95**

❹ Thanon Khao San Legendary hangout for Southeast Asia backpackers; the place for cheap sleeps, baggy trousers and tall tales. **See p.98**

❺ The canals of Thonburi See the Bangkok of yesteryear on a touristy but memorable longtail-boat ride. **See p.111**

❻ Jim Thompson's House An elegant Thai design classic. **See p.119**

❼ Chatuchak Weekend Market Eight thousand open-air stalls selling everything from triangular pillows to secondhand Levis. **See p.129**

❽ 63rd-floor sundowner Fine cocktails and jaw-dropping views, especially at sunset, at The Sky Bar and Distil. **See p.162**

❾ Thai boxing Nightly bouts at the national stadiums, complete with live musical accompaniment and frenetic betting. **See p.164**

HIGHLIGHTS ARE MARKED ON THE MAP ON P.79

1

ORIENTATION

Bangkok ("Krung Thep" in Thai) can be a tricky place to get your bearings as it's huge and ridiculously congested, with largely featureless modern buildings and no obvious centre. The boldest line on the map is the **Chao Phraya River**, which divides the city into Bangkok proper on the east bank, and **Thonburi**, part of Greater Bangkok, on the west.

The historical core of Bangkok proper, site of the original royal palace, is **Ratanakosin**, cradled in a bend in the river. Three concentric canals radiate eastwards around Ratanakosin: the southern part of the area between the canals is the old-style trading enclave of **Chinatown** and Indian **Pahurat**, connected to the old palace by Thanon Charoen Krung (aka New Road); the northern part is characterized by old temples and the **Democracy Monument**, west of which is the backpackers' ghetto of **Banglamphu**. Beyond the canals to the north, **Dusit** is the site of many government buildings and the nineteenth-century Vimanmek Palace, and is linked to Ratanakosin by the three stately avenues, Thanon Rajdamnoen Nok, Thanon Rajdamnoen Klang and Thanon Rajdamnoen Nai.

"New" Bangkok begins to the east of the canals and beyond the main rail line and Hualamphong Station, and stretches as far as the eye can see to the east and north. The main business district is south of **Thanon Rama IV**, with the port of Khlong Toey at its eastern edge. The diverse area north of Thanon Rama IV includes the sprawling campus of Chulalongkorn University, huge shopping centres around **Siam Square** and a variety of other businesses. A couple of blocks northeast of Siam Square stands the tallest building in Bangkok, the 84-storey **Baiyoke II Tower**, whose golden spire makes a good point of reference. To the east lies the swish residential quarter of **Thanon Sukhumvit**.

ranging from traditional dancing and the orchestrated bedlam of Thai boxing, to cool bars, clubs, cafés and microbreweries, and beyond to the farang-only sex bars of the notorious Patpong district, a tinseltown Babylon that's the tip of a dangerous iceberg. Even if the above doesn't appeal, you'll almost certainly pass through Bangkok once, if not several times – not only is it Thailand's main port of entry, it's also the obvious place to sort out onward travel, with a convenient menu of embassies for visas to neighbouring countries.

Brief history

Bangkok is a relatively young capital, established in 1782 after the Burmese sacked Ayutthaya, the former capital. A temporary base was set up on the western bank of the Chao Phraya River, in what is now **Thonburi**, before work started on the more defensible east bank, where the French had built a grand, but short-lived, fort in the 1660s. The first king of the new dynasty, Rama I (1782–1809), built his palace at **Ratanakosin**, within a defensive ring of two (later expanded to three) canals, and this remains the city's spiritual heart.

Initially, the city was largely **amphibious**: only the temples and royal palaces were built on dry land, while ordinary residences floated on thick bamboo rafts on the river and canals; even shops and warehouses were moored to the river bank. A major shift in emphasis came in the second half of the nineteenth century, first under Rama IV (1851–68), who as part of his effort to restyle the capital along European lines built Bangkok's first roads, and then under Rama V (1868–1910), who constructed a new residential palace in **Dusit**, north of Ratanakosin, and laid out that area's grand boulevards.

The modern metropolis

Since World War II, and especially from the mid-1960s onwards, Bangkok has seen an explosion of **modernization**, which has blown away earlier attempts at orderly planning and left the city without an obvious centre. Most of the canals have been filled in, replaced by endless rows of cheap, functional concrete shophouses, high-rises and housing estates, sprawling across a built-up area of over 300 square kilometres. The benefits of Thailand's **economic boom** since the 1980s have been concentrated in

Bangkok, attracting migration from all over the country and making the capital ever more dominant: the population, over half of which is under 30 years of age, is now nearly forty times that of the second city, Chiang Mai.

Every aspect of national life is centralized in the city, but the mayor of Bangkok is not granted enough power to deal with the ensuing problems, notably that of **traffic** – which in Bangkok now comprises four-fifths of the nation's automobiles. The Skytrain and the subway have undoubtedly helped, but the competing systems don't intersect properly or ticket jointly, and it's left to ingenious, local solutions such as the Khlong Saen Saeb canal boats and side-street motorbike taxis to keep the city moving. And there's precious little chance to escape from the pollution in green space: the city has only 0.4 square metres of public parkland per inhabitant, the lowest figure in the world, compared, for example, to London's 30.4 square metres per person.

GREATER BANGKOK

■ ACCOMMODATION

Anantara Riverside	3
Mariya Boutique Residence	1
Novotel Suvarnabhumi	2

HIGHLIGHTS

1. The Grand Palace
2. Wat Pho
3. National Museum
4. Thanon Khao San
5. The canals of Thonburi
6. Jim Thompson's House
7. Chatuchak Weekend Market
8. 63rd-floor sundowner
9. Thai boxing

■ BAR

Viva 8	1

- (S) — BTS Skytrain and terminus
- (M) — Subway and terminus
- (A) — Suvarnabhumi Airport Rail Link and station

CENTRAL BANGKOK

- ─S─ BTS Skytrain and station
- ─M─ Subway and station
- ─A─ Suvarnabhumi Airport Rail Link and station
- ☆ Khlong Saen Saeb boat stop

N

Nonthaburi

DUSIT

Vimanmek Palace Parliament

National Library

Support Museum

Elephant Museum Dusit Zoo

Suan Amporn

Rama V Statue

Chitrlada Palace

Wat Benjamabophit

BANGLAMPHU

Royal Barge Museum

Royal Turf Club

Government House

Siriraj Hospital & Museums

Rajdamnoen Stadium

TAT

National Museum

Bangkok Mission

LAN LUANG

Sanam Luang

Democracy Monument

Wat Rajnadda

Tha Phan Fah

Golden Mount

Khlong Saen Saeb

Wat Rakhang

Wat Phra Kaeo

Grand Palace

RATANAKOSIN

Wat Suthat

Wat Pho

Wat Arun

Chalermkrung Theatre

Wat Mangkon Kamalawat

Pak Khlong Talat

Wat Kanlayanamit

Wat Chakrawat

CHINATOWN

Wat Traimit

Santa Cruz

Wat Prayoon

Hualamphong Station

Khao Mor Cemetery

M Hua Lamphong

THONBURI

River City

Wongwian Yai Train Station

Taksin Monument

Wongwian Yai

Krung Thonburi

Saphan Taksin

Surasak

■ ACCOMMODATION

Anantara Sathorn	4
ETZ Hostel	1
Malaysia	2
Sala Thai Daily Mansion	3

■ BARS

Raintree	2
Saxophone	1

Northern Bus Terminal (Mo Chit), Chatuchak Weekend Market & Don Muang Airport

CENTRAL CHAO PHRAYA EXPRESS-BOAT PIERS

N15	◁ ▲ ▷	Thewet (all boats)
N14		Rama VIII Bridge (no flag)
N13	▷	Phra Arthit (no flag and orange flag)
N12	◁ ▲ ▷	Phra Pinklao Bridge (all boats)
N11	▷	Thonburi Railway Station (no flag and orange flag)
N10	◁ ▲ ▷	Wang Lang (all boats)
N9	▲ ▷	Chang (no flag, green flag and orange flag)
N8	▷	Thien (no flag and orange flag)
N7		Ratchini (no flag)
N6	▷	Saphan Phut (no flag and orange flag)
N5	◁ ▲ ▷	Rachawongse (all boats)
N4	▷	Marine (Harbour) Department (no flag and orange flag)
N3	◁ ▲ ▷	Si Phraya (all boats)
N2		Wat Muang Kae (no flag)
N1	▷	Oriental (no flag and orange flag)
Central	◁ ▲ ▷	Sathorn (all boats)

| ▷ All-day | ◁ ▲ Rush hour only (Mon–Fri) |
| Rush-hour no-flag boats stop at all piers (Mon–Fri) | |

Samsen Station

Phya Thai Palace

Victory Monument

Victory Monument

Jim Thompson's House

Tha Saphan Hua Chang

National Stadium

Phaya Thai

Phaya Thai

Suan Pakkad Palace Museum

Ratchaprarop

Baiyoke II Tower

Pratunam Market

Ratchathevi

Central Station (Siam)

SIAM SQUARE

Chit Lom

Tha Pratunam

Tha Witthayu

Bumrungrad

Tha Nana Nua

TAT HQ

Tha Asoke

Makkasan

Phetchaburi

Rama IX (Phra Ram 9)

THANON PHETCHABURI MAI

British Embassy

Erawan Shrine

Ratcha-damri

Phloen Chit

Chulalongkorn University

Royal Bangkok Sports Club

American Embassy

Nana

Asok

Sukhumvit

Ban Kamthieng

Queen Saovabha Institute

Sam Yan

Lumphini Park

Benjakiti Park

Emporium

Phrom Pong

Bangkok Christian

Si Lom

Sala Daeng

Alliance Française

Chong Nonsi

BNH

Lumphini

Goethe Institut

Khlong Toei

Queen Sirikit National Convention Centre (QSNCC)

M. R. Kukrit's Heritage Home

THANON RAJWITHI

THANON PHAHOLYOTHIN

Ari

Sanam Pao

THANON RANGNAM

THANON RAJAPRAROP

THANON WIPHAWADI RANGSIT (TOLLWAY)

THANON ASOKE DINDAENG

THANON PHETCHABURI

THANON PHRAYATHAI

THANON PLOENCHIT

THANON WITTHAYU (WIRELESS)

THANON SUKHUMVIT

THANON RAMA IV

EXPRESSWAY

Suvarnabhumi Airport

Eastern Bus Terminal (Ekamai)

0 — 500
metres

Ratanakosin

The only place to start your exploration of Bangkok is **Ratanakosin**, the royal island on the east bank of the Chao Phraya, where the city's most important and extravagant sights are located. When Rama I developed Ratanakosin for his new capital in 1782, after the sacking of Ayutthaya and a temporary stay across the river in Thonburi, he paid tribute to its precursor by imitating Ayutthaya's layout and architecture – he even shipped the building materials downstream from the ruins of the old city. Like Ayutthaya, the new capital was sited for protection beside a river and turned into an artificial island by the construction of defensive canals, with a central **Grand Palace** and adjoining royal temple, **Wat Phra Kaeo**, fronted by an open field, **Sanam Luang**; the Wang Na (Palace of the Second King), now the **National Museum**, was also built at this time. **Wat Pho**, which predates the capital's founding, was further embellished by Rama I's successors, who have consolidated Ratanakosin's pre-eminence by building several grand European-style palaces (now housing government institutions): **Wat Mahathat**, the most important centre of Buddhist learning in Southeast Asia; the National Theatre; the National Gallery; and Thammasat and Silpakorn universities.

Bangkok has expanded eastwards away from the river, leaving the Grand Palace a good 5km from the city's commercial heart, and the royal family has long since moved its residence to Dusit, but Ratanakosin remains the ceremonial centre of the whole kingdom – so much so that it feels as if it might sink into the boggy ground under the weight of its own mighty edifices. The heavy, stately feel is lightened by traditional shophouses selling herbal medicines, pavement amulet-sellers and studenty canteens along the riverside road, **Thanon Maharat**; and by Sanam Luang, still used for cremations and royal ceremonies, but also functioning as a popular open park and the hub of the modern city's bus system. Despite containing several of the country's main sights, the area is busy enough in its own right not to have become a swarming tourist zone, and strikes a neat balance between liveliness and grandeur.

RATANAKOSIN

RESTAURANTS
Navy Club
(Krua Khun Kung) **1**
Vivi: The Coffee Place **2**

SHOP
Queen Sirikit Museum
of Textiles Shop **1**

BAR
Po **1**

Bangkok Tourism ⓘ

N11 Tha Bangkok Noi

Bus stop 5 ★

PHRA PINKLAO BRIDGE

THANON PHRA ARTHIT

CHAO FA

RAJINEE

National Gallery

THANON CHAKRABONGSE

THONBURI

Tha Prachan

National Theatre

National Museum

RAJDAMNOEN KLANG

N10 Tha Wang Lang (Siriraj)

THANON PHRA CHAN

Thammasat University

THANON NA PHRA THAT

Royal Ratanakosin Hotel

Minibuses to Kanchanaburi ★

Tha Maharat

Wat Mahathat

Sanam Luang

THANON RAJDAMNOEN NAI

Mae Toranee statue ⊙

Night Market

THANON RACHINI

THANON ATSADANG

Chao Phraya River

Tha Chang N9

THANON MAHARAT

Art Centre

THANON NA PHRA LAN ⓘ

Lak Muang

THANON LAKMUANG

N

①

Wat Phra Kaeo

THANON BAMRUNG MUANG

Grand Palace

THANON SANAM CHAI

THANON SARANROM

Wat Rajapradit

THANON RACHINI

THANON ATSADANG

Wat Rajabophit

Inner Palace

Khlong Lod

THANON FUANG NAKHON

THANON THAI WANG

Tha Thien N8

THANON CHAROEN KRUNG (NEW ROAD)

Wat Arun

Wat Pho

SOI CHETUPHON

Wat Pho Massage School

SOI SATTHAKAN

Museum of Siam

0   250
metres

ACCOMMODATION
Arun Residence **4**
The Asadang **2**
Aurum The River Place **5**
Chakrabongse Villas **6**
Ibrik Resort by the River **1**
Sala Arun **3**

N1 Express-boat pier

N7 Tha Ratchini

Banglamphu

Democracy Monument

Wat Suthat

Pahurat & Chinatown

ARRIVAL AND DEPARTURE

Ratanakosin is within easy walking distance of Banglamphu, but is best approached from the river, via the **express-boat piers** (see p.139) of Tha Chang (the former bathing place of the royal elephants, which gives access to the Grand Palace) or Tha Thien (for Wat Pho). An extension of the **subway** line from Hualamphong is being built (its opening currently proposed for 2017), with a new station at the Museum of Siam, 5min walk from Wat Pho, 10min from Tha Thien express boat pier and 15min from the entrance to the Grand Palace.

Wat Phra Kaeo and the Grand Palace

Thanon Na Phra Lan • Daily 8.30am–4pm, last admission 3.30pm (weapons museum, Phra Thinang Amarin Winichai and Dusit Maha Prasat interiors closed Sat & Sun) • B500, including a map and admission, within 7 days, to Dusit Park (see p.114) or Sanam Chandra Palace in Nakhon Pathom (see p.178); 2hr personal audioguide B200, with passport or credit card as deposit • ⓦ palaces.thai.net

Hanging together in a precarious harmony of strangely beautiful colours and shapes, **Wat Phra Kaeo** is the apogee of Thai religious art and the holiest Buddhist site in the country, housing the most important image, the **Emerald Buddha**. Built as the private royal temple, Wat Phra Kaeo occupies the northeast corner of the huge **Grand Palace**, whose official opening in 1785 marked the founding of the new capital and the rebirth of the Thai nation after the Burmese invasion. Successive kings have all left their mark here, and the palace complex now covers 2 acres, though very little apart from the wat is open to tourists.

The only **entrance** to the complex in 2km of crenellated walls is the Gate of Glorious Victory in the middle of the north side, on Thanon Na Phra Lan. This brings you onto a driveway with a tantalizing view of the temple's glittering spires on the left and the dowdy buildings of the Offices of the Royal Household on the right: this is the powerhouse of the kingdom's ceremonial life, providing everything down to chairs and catering, even lending an urn when someone of rank dies. Among these buildings, the

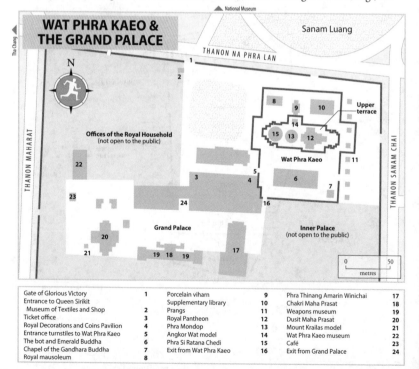

Gate of Glorious Victory	1	Porcelain viharn	9	Phra Thinang Amarin Winichai	17
Entrance to Queen Sirikit		Supplementary library	10	Chakri Maha Prasat	18
Museum of Textiles and Shop	2	Prangs	11	Weapons museum	19
Ticket office	3	Royal Pantheon	12	Dusit Maha Prasat	20
Royal Decorations and Coins Pavilion	4	Phra Mondop	13	Mount Krailas model	21
Entrance turnstiles to Wat Phra Kaeo	5	Angkor Wat model	14	Wat Phra Kaeo museum	22
The bot and Emerald Buddha	6	Phra Si Ratana Chedi	15	Café	23
Chapel of the Gandhara Buddha	7	Exit from Wat Phra Kaeo	16	Exit from Grand Palace	24
Royal mausoleum	8				

CITY OF ANGELS

When **Rama I** was crowned in 1782, he gave his new capital a grand 43-syllable name to match his ambitious plans for the building of the city. Since then, 21 more syllables have been added. Krungthepmahanakhornbowornrattanakosinmahintarayutthayamahadilokpopnopparatrat chathaniburiromudomratchaniwetmahasathanamornpimanavatarnsathitsakkathattiyavi snu-kamprasit is certified by the *Guinness Book of Records* as the longest place-name in the world, roughly translating as "Great city of angels, the supreme repository of divine jewels, the great land unconquerable, the grand and prominent realm, the royal and delightful capital city full of nine noble gems, the highest royal dwelling and grand palace, the divine shelter and living place of the reincarnated spirits". Fortunately, all Thais refer to the city simply as **Krung Thep**, "City of Angels", though plenty can recite the full name at the drop of a hat. **Bangkok** – "Village of the Plum Olive" – was the name of the original village on the Thonburi side; with remarkable persistence, it has remained in use by foreigners since the time of the French garrison.

hagiographic Queen Sirikit Museum of Textiles, which claims to show how she invented the Thai national dress in the 1960s, is included in the admission ticket but well worth missing, though you might want to check out the museum shop (see p.166). Turn left at the end of the driveway for the ticket office and entrance turnstiles.

As this is Thailand's most sacred site, you have to **dress in smart clothes**: no vests or see-through clothes; men must wear full-length trousers, women trousers or over-the-knee skirts. Suitable garments can be borrowed from the office to the right just inside the Gate of Glorious Victory (free, deposit of B200 per item).

Wat Phra Kaeo

It makes you laugh with delight to think that anything so fantastic could exist on this sombre earth.
W. Somerset Maugham, *The Gentlemen in the Parlour*

Entering the temple is like stepping onto a lavishly detailed stage set, from the immaculate flagstones right up to the gaudy roofs. Reinforcing the sense of unreality, the whole compound is surrounded by arcaded walls, decorated with extraordinary murals of scenes from the *Ramayana*. Although it receives hundreds of foreign sightseers and at least as many Thai pilgrims every day, the temple, which has no monks in residence, maintains an unnervingly sanitized look, as if it were built only yesterday.

The approach to the bot

Inside the entrance turnstiles, you're confronted by 6m-tall **yaksha**, gaudy demons from the *Ramayana*, who watch over the Emerald Buddha from every gate of the temple and ward off evil spirits; the king of the demons, green, ten-faced Totsagan (labelled "Tosakanth"), stands to the left of the entrance by the southwest corner of the golden Phra Si Ratana Chedi. Less threatening is the toothless old codger, cast in bronze and sitting on a plinth immediately inside the turnstiles by the back wall of the bot, who represents a Hindu **hermit** credited with inventing yoga and herbal medicine. In front of him is a large grinding stone where previously herbal practitioners could come to grind their ingredients – with enhanced powers, of course. Skirting around the bot, you'll reach its **main entrance** on the eastern side, in front of which stands a cluster of grey **statues**, which have a strong Chinese feel: next to Kuan Im, the Chinese *bodhisattva* of mercy shown holding a bottle of *amritsa* (sacred elixir), are a sturdy pillar topped by a lotus flower, which Bangkok's Chinese community presented to Rama IV during his 27 years as a monk, and two handsome cows which commemorate Rama I's birth in the Year of the Cow. Worshippers make their offerings to the Emerald Buddha at two small, stand-in Buddhas here, where they can look at the main image through the open doors of the bot without messing up its pristine interior with gold leaf, candle wax and joss-stick ash.

1

A WORD OF WARNING

When you're heading for the Grand Palace or Wat Pho, you may well be approached by someone, possibly pretending to be a student or an official, who will tell you that the sight is closed when it's not, or some other lies to try to lead you away from the entrance, because they want to take you on a shopping trip for souvenirs, tailored clothes or, if you seem really gullible, gems (see p.170). The opening hours of the Grand Palace – but not Wat Pho – are indeed sometimes erratic because of state occasions, but you can check the details out on its website, ⓦ palaces.thai.net – and even if it's closed on the day you want to visit, that's no reason to throw yourself at the mercy of these shysters.

The bot and the Emerald Buddha

The **bot**, the largest building of the temple, is one of the few original structures left at Wat Phra Kaeo, though it has been augmented so often it looks like the work of a wildly inspired child. Eight *sema* stones mark the boundary of the consecrated area around the bot, each sheltering in a psychedelic fairy castle, joined by a low wall decorated with Chinese porcelain tiles, which depict delicate landscapes. The walls of the bot itself, sparkling with gilt and coloured glass, are supported by 112 golden garudas (birdmen) holding nagas (serpents), representing the god Indra saving the world by slaying the serpent-cloud that had swallowed up all the water. The symbolism reflects the king's traditional role as a rainmaker.

Of the bot's three doorways, the largest, in the middle, is reserved for the king himself. Inside, a 9m-high pedestal supports the tiny **Emerald Buddha**, a figure whose mystique draws pilgrims from all over Thailand – as well as politicians accused of corruption, who traditionally come here to publicly swear their innocence. Here especially you must act with respect, sitting with your feet pointing away from the Buddha. The spiritual power of the 60cm jadeite image derives from its legendary past. Reputed to have been created by the gods in India, it was discovered when lightning cracked open an ancient chedi in Chiang Rai in the early fifteenth century. The image was then moved around the north, dispensing miracles wherever it went, before being taken to Laos for two hundred years. As it was believed to bring great fortune to its possessor, the future Rama I snatched it back when he captured Vientiane in 1779, installing it at the heart of his new capital as a talisman for king and country.

Seated in the *Dhyana Mudra* (meditation), the Emerald Buddha has three **costumes**, one for each season: the crown and ornaments of an Ayutthayan king for the hot season; a gilt monastic robe for the rainy season, when the monks retreat into the temples; this is augmented with a full-length gold shawl in the cool season. To this day it's the job of the king himself to ceremonially change the Buddha's costumes – though in recent years, due to the present king's age, the Crown Prince has conducted proceedings. The Buddha was granted a new set of these three costumes in 1997: the old set is now in the Wat Phra Kaeo Museum (see p.90) while the two costumes of the new set that are not in use are on display among the blinding glitter of crowns and jewels in the Royal Decorations and Coins Pavilion, which lies between the ticket office and the entrance to Wat Phra Kaeo.

Among the paraphernalia in front of the pedestal sits the tiny, silver **Phra Chai Lang Chang** (Victory Buddha), which Rama I always carried into battle on the back of his elephant for luck and which still plays an important part in coronation ceremonies. Recently covered in gold, it occupies a prestigious spot dead centre, but is obscured by the umbrella of a larger gold Buddha in front. The tallest pair of a dozen standing Buddha images, all made of bronze but encased in gold and raising both hands to dispel fear, are at the front: Rama III dedicated the one on the Emerald Buddha's left to Rama I, the one on his right to Rama II, and Rama IV enshrined relics of the Buddha in their crowns.

The Chapel of the Gandhara Buddha

Near the entrance to the bot, in the southeastern corner of the temple precinct, look out for the exquisite scenes of rice sheaves, fish and turtles painted in gold on blue glass on the doors and windows of the **Chapel of the Gandhara Buddha** (labelled "Hor Phra Kanthara Rat"). The decorations allude to the fertility of the rice fields, as this building was crucial to the old royal rainmaking ritual and is still used during the Royal Ploughing Ceremony (see p.94). Adorning the roof are thousands of nagas, symbolizing water; inside the locked chapel, among the paraphernalia used in the ritual, is kept the Gandhara Buddha, a bronze image in the gesture of calling down the rain with its right hand, while cupping the left to catch it. In times of drought the king would order a week-long rainmaking ceremony to be conducted, during which he was bathed regularly and kept away from the opposite sex while Buddhist monks and Hindu Brahmins chanted continuously.

The Royal Pantheon and minor buildings

On the north side of the bot, the eastern end of the **upper terrace** is taken up with the **Prasat Phra Thep Bidorn**, known as the **Royal Pantheon**, a splendid hash of styles. The pantheon has its roots in the Khmer concept of *devaraja*, or the divinity of kings: inside are bronze and gold statues, precisely life-size, of all the kings since Bangkok became the Thai capital. Constructed by Rama IV, the building is open only on special occasions, such as Chakri Day (April 6), when the dynasty is commemorated, and Coronation Day (May 5).

From here you get the best view of the **royal mausoleum**, the **porcelain viharn** and the **supplementary library** to the north (all of which are closed to tourists, though you can sometimes glimpse Thai Buddhists worshipping in the library), and, running along the east side of the temple, a row of eight bullet-like **prangs**, each of which has a different nasty ceramic colour. Described as "monstrous vegetables" by Somerset Maugham, they represent, from north to south, the Buddha, Buddhist scripture, the monkhood, the nunhood, the Buddhas who attained enlightenment but did not preach, previous emperors, the Buddha in his previous lives and the future Buddha.

The Phra Mondop and Phra Si Ratana Chedi

In the middle of the terrace, dressed in deep-green glass mosaics, the **Phra Mondop** was built by Rama I to house the *Tripitaka*, or Buddhist scripture, which the king had rewritten at Wat Mahathat in 1788, the previous versions having all been lost in the sacking of Ayutthaya. It's famous for the mother-of-pearl cabinet and solid-silver mats inside, but is never open. Four tiny **memorials** at each corner of the mondop show the symbols of each of the nine Chakri kings, from the ancient crown representing Rama I to the present king's discus, while the bronze statues surrounding the memorials portray each king's lucky white elephants, labelled by name and pedigree. A contribution of Rama IV, on the north side of the mondop, is a **scale model of Angkor Wat**, the prodigious Cambodian temple, which during his reign (1851–68) was under Thai rule (apparently, the king had wanted to shift a whole Khmer temple to Bangkok but, fortunately, was dissuaded by his officials). At the western end of the terrace, you can't miss the golden dazzle of the **Phra Si Ratana Chedi**, which Rama IV erected, in imitation of the famous bell-shaped chedis at Ayutthaya's Wat Phra Si Sanphet (see p.217), to enshrine a piece of the Buddha's breastbone.

The murals

Extending for about a kilometre in the arcades that run inside the wat walls, the **murals of the Ramayana** depict every blow of this ancient story of the triumph of good over evil, using the vibrant buildings of the temple itself as backdrops, and setting them off against the subdued colours of richly detailed landscapes. Because of the damaging humidity, none of the original work of Rama I's time survives: maintenance is a never-ending process, so you'll always find an artist working on one of the scenes. The story is told in 178 panels, labelled and numbered in Thai only, starting in the middle

1

THE RAMAYANA/RAMAKIEN

The **Ramayana** is generally thought to have originated as an oral epic in India, where it appears in numerous dialects. The most famous version is that of the sage Valmiki, who is said to have drawn together the collection of stories as a tribute to his king over two thousand years ago. From India, the *Ramayana* spread to all the Hindu-influenced countries of Southeast Asia and was passed down through the Khmers to Thailand, where as the **Ramakien** it has become the national epic, acting as an affirmation of the Thai monarchy and its divine Hindu links. As a source of inspiration for literature, painting, sculpture and dance-drama, it has acquired the authority of holy writ, providing Thais with moral and practical lessons, while its appearance in the form of films and comic strips shows its huge popular appeal. The version current in Thailand was composed by a committee of poets sponsored by Rama I (all previous Thai texts were lost in the sacking of Ayutthaya in 1767), and runs to three thousand pages – available in an abridged English translation by M.L. Manich Jumsai (see p.780).

The central story of the *Ramayana* concerns **Rama** (in Thai, Phra Ram), son of the king of Ayodhya, and his beautiful wife **Sita**, whose hand he wins by lifting, stringing – and breaking – a magic bow. The couple's adventures begin when they are exiled to the forest, along with Rama's good brother, **Lakshaman** (Phra Lak), by the hero's father under the influence of his evil stepmother. Meanwhile, in the city of Lanka (Longka), the demon king **Ravana** (Totsagan) has conceived a passionate desire for Sita and, disguised as a hermit, sets out to kidnap her. By transforming one of his demon subjects into a beautiful deer, which Rama and Lakshaman go off to hunt, Ravana catches Sita alone and takes her back to Lanka. Rama then wages a long war against the demons of Lanka, into which are woven many battles, spy scenes and diversionary episodes, and eventually kills Ravana and rescues Sita.

The Thai version shows some characteristic differences from the Indian, emphasizing the typically Buddhist virtues of filial obedience and willing renunciation. In addition, Hanuman, the loyal monkey general, is given a much more playful role in the *Ramakien*, with the addition of many episodes which display his cunning and talent for mischief, not to mention his promiscuity. However, the major alteration comes at the end of the story, when Phra Ram doubts Sita's faithfulness after rescuing her from Totsagan. In the Indian story, this ends with Sita being swallowed up by the earth so that she doesn't have to suffer Rama's doubts any more; in the *Ramakien* the ending is a happy one, with Phra Ram and Sita living together happily ever after.

of the northern side opposite the porcelain viharn: in the first episode, a hermit, while out ploughing, finds the baby Sita, the heroine, floating in a gold urn on a lotus leaf and brings her to the city. Panel 109 near the gate leading to the palace buildings shows the climax of the story, when Rama, the hero, kills the ten-headed demon Totsagan (Ravana), and the ladies of the enemy city weep at the demon's death. Panel 110 depicts his elaborate funeral procession, and in 113 you can see the funeral fair, with acrobats, sword-jugglers and tightrope-walkers. In between, Sita – Rama's wife – has to walk on fire to prove that she has been faithful during her fourteen years of imprisonment by Totsagan. If you haven't the stamina for the long walk round, you could sneak a look at the end of the story, to the left of the first panel, where Rama holds a victory parade and distributes thank-you gifts.

The palace buildings

The exit in the southwest corner of Wat Phra Kaeo brings you to the palace proper, a vast area of buildings and gardens, of which only the northern edge is on show to the public. Though the king now lives in the Chitrlada Palace in Dusit, the **Grand Palace** is still used for state receptions and official ceremonies, during which there is no public access to any part of the palace.

Phra Maha Monthien

Coming out of the temple compound, you'll first of all see to your right a beautiful Chinese gate covered in innumerable tiny porcelain tiles. Extending in a straight line behind the gate is the **Phra Maha Monthien**, which was the grand residential complex of earlier kings.

Only the **Phra Thinang Amarin Winichai**, the main audience hall at the front of the complex, is open to the public. The supreme court in the era of the absolute monarchy, it nowadays serves as the venue for ceremonies such as the king's birthday speech. Dominating the hall are two gleaming, intricately carved thrones that date from the reign of Rama I: a white umbrella with the full nine tiers owing to a king shelters the front seat, while the unusual *busbok* behind is topped with a spired roof and floats on a boat-shaped base. The rear buildings are still used for the most important part of the elaborate coronation ceremony, and each new king is supposed to spend a night there to show solidarity with his forefathers.

Chakri Maha Prasat

Next door you can admire the facade of the "farang with a Thai crown", as the **Chakri Maha Prasat** is nicknamed. Rama V, whose portrait you can see over its entrance, employed an English architect to design a purely Neoclassical residence, but other members of the royal family prevailed on the king to add the three Thai spires. This used to be the site of the elephant stables: the large red tethering posts are still there and the bronze elephants were installed as a reminder. The building displays the emblem of the Chakri dynasty on its gable, which has a trident (*ri*) coming out of a *chak* (a discus with a sharpened rim). The only part of the Chakri Maha Prasat open to the public is the ground-floor **weapons museum**, which houses a forgettable display of hooks, pikes and guns.

The Inner Palace

The **Inner Palace** (closed to the public), which used to be the king's harem, lies behind the gate on the left-hand side of the Chakri Maha Prasat. Vividly described in M.R. Kukrit Pramoj's *Si Phaendin* (see p.780), the harem was a town in itself, with shops, law courts and an all-female police force for the huge population: as well as the current queens, the minor wives and their children (including pre-pubescent boys) and servants, this was home to the daughters and consorts of former kings, and the daughters of the aristocracy who attended the harem's finishing school. Today, the Inner Palace houses a school of cooking, fruit-carving and other domestic sciences for well-bred young Thais.

Dusit Maha Prasat

On the western side of the courtyard, the delicately proportioned **Dusit Maha Prasat**, an audience hall built by Rama I, epitomizes traditional Thai architecture. Outside, the soaring tiers of its red, gold and green roof culminate in a gilded *mongkut*, a spire shaped like the king's crown, which symbolizes the 33 Buddhist levels of perfection. Each tier of the roof bears a typical *chofa*, a slender, stylized bird's-head finial, and

---

THE ROYAL TONSURE CEREMONY

To the right and behind the Dusit Maha Prasat rises a strange model mountain, decorated with fabulous animals and topped by a castle and prang. It represents **Mount Krailas**, the Himalayan home of the Hindu god Shiva (Phra Isuan in Thai), and was built by Rama IV as the site of the **royal tonsure ceremony**, last held here in 1932, just three months before the end of the absolute monarchy. In former times, Thai children generally had shaved heads, except for a tuft or topknot on the crown, which, between the age of eleven and thirteen, was cut in a Hindu initiation rite to welcome adolescence. For the royal children, the rite was an elaborate ceremony that sometimes lasted seven days, culminating with the king's cutting of the hair knot, which was then floated away on the Chao Phraya River. The child was then bathed at the model Krailas, in water representing the original river of the universe flowing down the central mountain.

1

several *hang hong* (swans' tails), which represent three-headed nagas. Inside, you can still see the original throne, the **Phra Ratcha Banlang Pradap Muk**, a masterpiece of mother-of-pearl inlaid work. When a senior member of the royal family dies, the hall is used for the lying-in-state: the body, embalmed and seated in a huge sealed urn, is placed in the west transept, waiting up to two years for an auspicious day to be cremated.

The Wat Phra Kaeo Museum

In the nineteenth-century Royal Mint in front of the Dusit Maha Prasat – next to a small, basic **café** – the **Wat Phra Kaeo Museum** houses a mildly interesting collection of artefacts donated to the Emerald Buddha, along with architectural elements rescued from the Grand Palace grounds during restoration in the 1980s. Highlights include the bones of various kings' white elephants, and upstairs, the Emerald Buddha's original costumes and two useful scale models of the Grand Palace, one as it is now, the other as it was when first built. Also on the first floor stands the grey stone slab of the Manangasila Seat, where Ramkhamhaeng, the great thirteenth-century king of Sukhothai, is said to have sat and taught his subjects. It was discovered in 1833 by Rama IV during his monkhood and brought to Bangkok, where Rama VI used it as the throne for his coronation.

Wat Pho (Wat Phra Chetuphon)

Soi Chetuphon, to the south of the Grand Palace · Daily 8am–6.30pm · B200 · Ⓦ watpho.com

Where Wat Phra Kaeo may seem too perfect and shrink-wrapped for some, **Wat Pho** is lively and shambolic, a complex arrangement of lavish structures which jostle with classrooms, basketball courts and a turtle pond. Busloads of tourists shuffle in and out of the **north entrance**, stopping only to gawp at the colossal Reclining Buddha, but you can avoid the worst of the crowds by using the **main entrance** on Soi Chetuphon to explore the huge compound.

Wat Pho is the oldest temple in Bangkok and is older than the city itself, having been founded in the seventeenth century under the name Wat Photaram. Foreigners have stuck to the contraction of this old name, even though Rama I, after enlarging the temple, changed the name in 1801 to **Wat Phra Chetuphon**, which is how it is generally known to Thais. The temple had another major overhaul in 1832, when Rama III built the chapel of the Reclining Buddha, and turned the temple into a public centre of learning by

WAT PHO

THANON THAI WANG

0   50
metres

Visitors' entrances	1
Entrances to the bot	2
The bot	3
Massage Pavilions	4
Traditional Medicine Pavilions	5
Rama II Chedi	6
Phra Si Sanphet Chedi	7
Rama III Chedi	8
Rama IV Chedi	9
Chapel of the Reclining Buddha	10
Chinese Pavilion	11
Library	12
European Pavilion	13
Café	14
Monks' Quarters	15
Grand Palace	16

THANON MAHARAT

SOI CHETUPHON

THANON SANAM CHAI

Tha Thien

N

TRADITIONAL MASSAGE AND SPAS IN BANGKOK

Thai massage sessions and courses are held most famously at Wat Pho, while luxurious and indulgent spa and massage treatments are available at many posh hotels across the city, as well as at the following stand-alone places.

Divana Massage and Spa 7 Soi 25, Thanon Sukhumvit ☎02 661 6784–5, ⓦdivanaspa.com; map p.123. Delightful spa serving up Thai massages (B1100/70min), foot, aromatherapy and herbal massages, as well as facials and Ayurvedic treatments. Tues–Fri 11am–11pm, Sat, Sun & Mon 10am–11pm.

Health Land 55/5 Soi 1, Thanon Asok Montri (Sukhumvit Soi 21) ☎02 261 1110, ⓦhealthlandspa .com; map p.123. Excellent Thai (B500/2hr) and other massages, reflexology, facials and body polishes, in swish surroundings, with several other locations around Bangkok. Daily 9am–11pm.

Nicolie Sun Square, a small shopping arcade on the south side of Thanon Silom between sois 21 and 23 ☎02 233 6957, ⓦnicolie-th.com; map p.125. Superb Thai (B1900/90min) and other massages, as well as facials and scrubs, in a soothing environment decorated with Asian objets d'art. Daily 11am–10pm.

Pian's Soi Susie Pub, which runs between the east end of Thanon Khao San and Thanon Ram Bhuttri ☎02 629 0924; map p.100. Uninvitingly clinical-looking but highly rated a/c massage centre, offering Thai massages (B220/hr) as well as foot, oil and herbal massages; you can also study Thai massage here. Daily 8am–midnight.

Pimmalai Thanon Sukhumvit, 50m east of BTS On Nut, exit 1, between sois 81 and 83 ☎02 742 6452, ⓦpimmalai.com. In a nice old wooden house, Thai massages (B250/1hr), plus foot, herbal and oil massages, herbal steam treatments, body scrubs, masks and facials. Mon–Fri 9.30am–10pm, Sat & Sun 9.30am–10.30pm.

Ruen Nuad 42 Thanon Convent, near Thanon Sathon Nua ☎02 632 2662–3; map p.125. Excellent Thai massages (B350/1hr, B600/2hr), as well as aromatherapy and foot massages and a juice bar, in an a/c, characterful wooden house, down an alley opposite the BNH Hospital and behind *Naj* restaurant. Daily 10am–9.30pm.

Wat Pho (see opposite). Excellent massages are available in two a/c buildings on the east side of Wat Pho's main compound; allow 2hr for the full works (B420/hr; foot reflexology massage B420/hr). There are often long queues here, however, so you might be better off heading over to the massage centre's other premises just outside the temple, at 392/33–4 Soi Pen Phat 1, Thanon Maharat (the soi is unmarked but look for the *Coconut Palm* restaurant on the corner; daily 8am–6pm; ☎02 622 3533 or ☎02 622 3551, ⓦwatpomassage .com). Here you can also enrol on a 30hr massage training course in English, over five days (B9500), and foot-massage courses for B7500. Daily 8am–5pm.

decorating the walls and pillars with inscriptions and diagrams on subjects such as history, literature, animal husbandry and astrology. Dubbed Thailand's first university, the wat is still an important centre for traditional medicine, notably **Thai massage** (see box above), which is used against all kinds of illnesses, from backaches to viruses.

The eastern courtyard

The main entrance on Soi Chetuphon is one of a series of sixteen monumental gates around the main compound, each guarded by stone **giants**, many of them comic Westerners in wide-brimmed hats – ships that exported rice to China would bring these statues back as ballast.

The entrance brings you into the eastern half of the main complex, where a courtyard of structures radiates from the bot in a disorientating symmetry. To get to the bot, the principal congregation and ordination hall, turn right and cut through the two surrounding cloisters, which are lined with hundreds of Buddha images. The elegant **bot** has beautiful teak doors decorated with mother-of-pearl, showing stories from the *Ramayana* (see p.88) in minute detail. Look out also for the stone bas-reliefs around the base of the bot, which narrate the story of the capture and rescue of Sita from the *Ramayana* in 152 action-packed panels. The plush interior has a well-proportioned altar on which ten statues of disciples frame a graceful, Ayutthayan Buddha image containing the remains of Rama I, the founder of Bangkok (Rama IV placed them there so that the public could worship him at the same time as the Buddha).

1

Back outside the entrance to the double cloister, keep your eyes open for a miniature mountain covered in statues of naked men in tall hats who appear to be gesturing rudely: they are *rishis* (hermits), demonstrating various positions of healing massage. Skirting the southwestern corner of the cloisters, you'll come to two pavilions between the eastern and western courtyards, which display plaques inscribed with the precepts of traditional medicine, as well as anatomical pictures showing the different pressure points and the illnesses that can be cured by massaging them.

The western courtyard

Among the 99 chedis strewn about the grounds, the four **great chedis** in the western courtyard stand out as much for their covering of garish tiles as for their size. The central chedi is the oldest, erected by Rama I to hold the remains of the most sacred Buddha image of Ayutthaya, the Phra Si Sanphet. Later, Rama III built the chedi to the north for the ashes of Rama II and the chedi to the south to hold his own remains; Rama IV built the fourth, with bright blue tiles, though its purpose is uncertain.

In the northwest corner of the courtyard stands the chapel of the **Reclining Buddha**, a 45m-long gilded statue of plaster-covered brick which depicts the Buddha entering Nirvana, a common motif in Buddhist iconography. The chapel is only slightly bigger than the statue – you can't get far enough away to take in anything but a surreal close-up view of the beaming 5m smile. As for the feet, the vast black soles are beautifully inlaid with delicate mother-of-pearl showing the 108 *lakshanas*, or auspicious signs, which distinguish the true Buddha. Along one side of the statue are 108 bowls: putting a coin in each will bring you good luck and a long life.

Museum of Siam (National Discovery Museum)

Thanon Sanam Chai • Tues–Sun 10am–6pm • B300, free after 4pm • ☏ 02 225 2777, ⓦ museumsiam.com

The excellent **Museum of Siam** is a high-tech, mostly bilingual attraction that occupies the century-old, European-style, former Ministry of Commerce. It looks at what it is to be Thai, with lots of humorous short films and imaginative touches such as shadow-puppet cartoons and war video games. In addition, the museum stages playful temporary exhibitions, which in the past have let visitors have a go at rice-growing, and examine Thailand's enduring love affair with foreign commodities. Generally, it's great fun for adults and kids, and there's a nice little indoor-outdoor **café-restaurant** in the grounds run by the Black Canyon chain. The museum hosts **Noise Market** over three weekends a year (ⓦfacebook.com/noisemarketfest), a great little festival-cum-market of indie music, handicrafts and food.

The museum exhibition kicks off with the prehistory of Southeast Asia, or Suvarnabhumi (Land of Gold) as ancient Indian documents refer to it, and the legendary arrival of Buddhism via missionaries sent by the great Indian emperor, Ashoka (Asoke). Much space is devoted to Ayutthaya, where we learn that during that kingdom's four-hundred-year history, there were no fewer than twenty outbreaks of war with the Burmese states, before the final annihilation in 1767. Beyond this, look out for a fascinating map of Thonburi, King Taksin's new capital between 1768 and 1782, as drawn by a Burmese spy. In the Bangkok period, there's coverage of the Chinese in Thailand and of early twentieth-century racialism, but next to nothing on the country's Muslims. Towards the end, under the banner of westernization, visitors can wind up cartoon peep-shows and dress up in colonial-style uniform shirts.

Sanam Luang

Sprawling across 30 acres north of the Grand Palace, **Sanam Luang** is one of the last open spaces left in Bangkok, a bare field where residents of the capital gather in the

1

KITE FLYING

Flying intricate and colourful **kites** is now done mostly for fun in Thailand, but it has its roots in more serious activities. Filled with gunpowder and fitted with long fuses, kites were deployed in the first Thai kingdom at Sukhothai (1240–1438) as machines of war. In the same era, special *ngao* kites, with heads in the shape of bamboo bows, were used in Brahmin rituals: the string of the bow would vibrate in the wind and make a noise to frighten away evil spirits (nowadays noisy kites are still used, though only by farmers, to scare the birds). By the height of the Ayutthayan period (1351–1767) kites had become largely decorative: royal ceremonies were enhanced by fantastically shaped kites, adorned with jingling bells and ornamental lamps.

In the nineteenth century, Rama V, by his enthusiastic lead, popularized kite flying as a wholesome and fashionable recreation. **Contests** are now held all over the country between February and April, when winds are strong enough and farmers traditionally have free time after harvesting the rice. These contests fall into two broad categories: those involving manoeuvrable flat kites, often in the shapes of animals; and those in which the beauty of static display kites is judged. The most popular contest of all, which comes under the first category, matches two teams, one flying star-shaped *chulas*, 2m-high "male" kites, the other flying the smaller, more agile *pakpaos*, diamond-shaped "females". Each team uses its skill and teamwork to ensnare the other's kites and drag them back across a dividing line.

early evening to meet, eat and play. On its western side and spreading around Thammasat University and Wat Mahathat, especially on Sundays, scores of small-time hawkers sell amulets (see p.104), taking advantage of the spiritually auspicious location. In the early part of the year, especially in March, the sky is filled with **kite-fighting** contests (see box above).

The field is also the venue for national ceremonies, such as **royal cremations**, when huge, intricate, wooden *meru* or *phra mane* (funeral pyres) are constructed, representing Mount Meru, the Himalayan centre of the Hindu-Buddhist universe; and the **Ploughing Ceremony**, held in May at a time selected by astrologers to bring good fortune and rain to the coming rice harvest. Revived in 1960 to boost the status of the monarchy during the Cold War, the elaborate Brahmin ceremony is led by an official from the Ministry of Agriculture, who stands in for the king in case the royal power were to be reduced by any failure in the ritual. At the designated time, the official cuts a series of circular furrows with a plough drawn by two white oxen, and scatters rice from the king's experimental crop station at Chitrlada Palace, which has been sprinkled with lustral water by the Brahmin priests of the court. When the ritual is over, spectators rush in to grab handfuls of the rice, which they then plant in their own paddies for good luck.

The lak muang

Thanon Rajdamnoen Nai, southeast corner of Sanam Luang

At 6.54am on April 21, 1782 – the astrologically determined time for the auspicious founding of Bangkok – a pillar containing the city's horoscope was ceremonially driven into the ground opposite the northeast corner of the Grand Palace. This phallic pillar, the **lak muang** – all Thai cities have one, to provide a home for their guardian spirits – was made from a 4m tree trunk carved with a lotus-shaped crown. In the nineteenth century, Rama IV had a new, shorter *lak muang* made, and the two pillars now amicably cohabit in an elegant shrine surrounded by immaculate gardens.

Hundreds of worshippers come every day to pray and offer flowers, particularly childless couples seeking the gift of fertility. In one corner of the gardens you can often see short performances of **classical dancing**, paid for by well-off families when they have a piece of good fortune to celebrate.

Silpakorn University Art Centre

Thanon Na Phra Lan, directly across the road from the entrance to the Grand Palace • Mon–Fri 9am–7pm, Sat 9am–4pm • Free • ☎ 02 623 6115 ext 11418 or 11419, ⓦ www.art-centre.su.ac.th

Housed partly in the throne hall of a palace built during the reign of Rama I, the **Silpakorn University Art Centre** stages regular exhibitions by students, teachers, artists-in-residence and national artists. The country's first art school, Silpakorn was founded in 1935 by Professor Silpa Bhirasri, the much-revered, naturalized Italian sculptor; a charming, shady garden along the east wall of the art centre is dotted with his sculptures.

Wat Mahathat

Main entrance on Thanon Maharat, plus a back entrance on Thanon Na Phra That on Sanam Luang

Eighteenth-century **Wat Mahathat** provides a welcome respite from the surrounding tourist hype, and a chance to engage with the eager monks studying at **Mahachulalongkorn Buddhist University** here. As the nation's centre for the Mahanikai monastic sect (where Rama IV spent many years as a monk before becoming king in 1851), and housing one of the two Buddhist universities in Bangkok, the wat buzzes with purpose. It's this activity, and the chance of interaction and participation, rather than any special architectural features, that make a visit so rewarding. The many university-attending monks at the wat are friendly and keen to practise their English, and are more than likely to approach you: diverting topics might range from the poetry of Dylan Thomas to English football results.

Vipassana Meditation Centre

Section Five, Wat Mahathat • Practice daily 7–11am, 1–4pm & 6–8/9pm • Donations welcome • ☎ 02 222 6011 or ☎ 02 222 4981

At the wat's **Vipassana Meditation Centre**, where the monk teachers speak some English, sitting and walking meditation practice, with chanting and dhamma talks, is available (there's now a competing "Meditation Study and Retreat Center", nearby in Section One of the wat, but this is less geared towards foreign meditators). Participants generally stay in the simple surroundings of the meditation building itself, and must wear white clothes (available to rent at the centre) and observe the eight main Buddhist precepts (see p.740).

The National Museum

Thanon Na Phra That, northwest corner of Sanam Luang • Wed–Sun 9am–4pm, some rooms may close at lunchtime; free English guided tours Wed & Thurs 9.30am; usually some rooms are closed for restoration, as advertised at the ticket office • B200 • ☎ 02 224 1333

The **National Museum** houses a colossal hoard of Thailand's chief artistic riches, ranging from sculptural treasures in the north and south wings, through bizarre decorative objects in the older buildings, to outlandish funeral chariots and the exquisite Buddhaisawan chapel, as well as sometimes staging worthwhile temporary exhibitions. It's worth making time for the free guided tours in English run by the National Museum Volunteers (who also organize interesting lectures and excursions; ⓦwww .museumvolunteersbkk.net): they're generally entertaining and their explication of the choicest exhibits provides a good introduction to Thai religion and culture. There's also a restaurant inside the museum grounds, by the funeral chariots building, which dishes up decent, inexpensive Thai food.

History building

The first building you'll come to near the ticket office houses an overview of the authorized history of Thailand, including a small archeological gem: a black stone **inscription** (see also p.241), credited to King Ramkhamhaeng of Sukhothai, which became the first capital of the Thai nation (c.1278–99) under his rule. Discovered in 1833 by the future Rama IV, Mongkut, it's the oldest extant inscription using the Thai alphabet. This, combined with the description it records of prosperity and piety in

1

Sukhothai's Golden Age, has made the stone a symbol of Thai nationhood. There's recently been much controversy over the stone's origins, arising from the suggestion that it was a fake made by Mongkut, but it seems most likely that it is indeed genuine, and was written partly as a kind of prospectus for Sukhothai, to attract traders and settlers to the underpopulated kingdom.

The main collection: southern building

At the back of the compound, two large modern buildings, flanking an old converted palace, house the museum's **main collection**, kicking off on the ground floor of the **southern building**. Look out here for some historic sculptures from the rest of Asia (S1), including one of the earliest representations of the Buddha, from Gandhara in modern-day Pakistan. Alexander the Great left a garrison at Gandhara, which explains why the image is in the style of Classical Greek sculpture: for example, the *ushnisha*, the supernatural bump on the top of the head, which symbolizes the Buddha's intellectual and spiritual power, is rationalized into a bun of thick, wavy hair.

Upstairs, the **prehistory** room (S6) displays axe heads and spear points from Ban Chiang in the northeast of Thailand (see p.480), one of the earliest Bronze Age cultures ever discovered. Alongside are many roughly contemporaneous metal artefacts from Kanchanaburi province, as well as some excellent examples of the developments of Ban Chiang's famous pottery. In the adjacent **Dvaravati** room (S7; sixth to eleventh centuries), the pick of the stone and terracotta Buddhas is a small head in smooth, pink clay from Wat Phra Ngam, Nakhon Pathom, whose downcast eyes and faintly smiling full lips typify the serene look of this era. At the far end of the first floor, you can't miss a voluptuous Javanese statue of elephant-headed Ganesh, Hindu god of wisdom and the arts, which, being the symbol of the Fine Arts Department, is always freshly garlanded. As Ganesh is known as the clearer of obstacles, Hindus always worship him before other gods, so by tradition he has grown fat through getting first choice of the offerings – witness his trunk jammed into a bowl of food in this sculpture.

Room S9 next door contains the most famous piece of **Srivijaya** art (seventh to thirteenth centuries), a bronze Bodhisattva Padmapani found at Chaiya (according to Mahayana Buddhism, a *bodhisattva* is a saint who has postponed his passage into Nirvana to help ordinary believers gain enlightenment). With its pouting face and lithe torso, this image has become the ubiquitous emblem of southern Thailand. The rough chronological order of the collection continues back downstairs with an exhibition of **Khmer** and **Lopburi** sculpture (seventh to fourteenth centuries), most notably some dynamic bronze statuettes and stone lintels. Look out for an elaborate lintel from Ku Suan Tang, Buriram (S3), which depicts Vishnu reclining on the dragon Ananta in the sea of eternity, dreaming up a new universe after the old one has been annihilated in the Hindu cycle of creation and destruction. Out of his navel comes a lotus, and out of this emerges four-headed Brahma, who will put the dream into practice.

The main collection: northern building

The second half of the survey, in the northern building, begins upstairs with the **Sukhothai** collection (thirteenth to fifteenth centuries; N7–8), which features some typically elegant and sinuous Buddha images, as well as chunky bronzes of Hindu gods and a wide range of ceramics. The **Lanna** rooms (roughly thirteenth to sixteenth centuries; N5–6) include a miniature set of golden regalia, among them tiny umbrellas and a cute pair of filigree flip-flops, which would have been enshrined in a chedi. An ungainly but serene Buddha head, carved from grainy, pink sandstone, represents the **Ayutthaya** style of sculpture (fourteenth to eighteenth centuries; N9–10): the faintest incision of a moustache above the lips betrays the Khmer influences that came to Ayutthaya after its conquest of Angkor. A sumptuous scripture cabinet, showing a cityscape of old Ayutthaya, is a more unusual piece, one of a surviving handful of such carved and painted items of furniture.

Downstairs in the section on **Bangkok** or **Ratanakosin** art (eighteenth century onwards; N1), a stiffly realistic standing bronze brings you full circle. In his zeal for Western naturalism, Rama V had the statue made in the Gandhara style of the earliest Buddha image displayed in the first room of the museum.

The funeral chariots
To the east of the northern building, beyond the café on the left, stands a large garage where the fantastically elaborate **funeral chariots** of the royal family are stored. Pre-eminent among these is the Royal Chariot of Great Victory, built by Rama I in about 1789 for carrying the urn at his father's funeral. The 11m-high structure symbolizes heaven on Mount Meru, while the dragons and divinities around the sides – piled in five golden tiers to suggest the flames of the cremation – represent the mythological inhabitants of the mountain's forests. Each weighing around forty tonnes and requiring the pulling power of three hundred men, the teak chariots last had an outing in 2012, for the funeral of the only child of Rama VI, Princess Bejaratana.

Wang Na (Palace of the Second King)
The sprawling central building of the compound was originally part of the **Wang Na**, a huge palace stretching across Sanam Luang to Khlong Lod, which housed the "second king", appointed by the reigning monarch as his heir and deputy. When Rama V did away with the office in 1887, he turned the palace into a museum, which now contains a fascinating array of Thai objets d'art. As you enter (room 5), the display of sumptuous rare gold pieces behind heavy iron bars includes a well-preserved armlet taken from the ruined prang of fifteenth-century Wat Ratburana in Ayutthaya. In adjacent room 6, an intricately carved ivory seat turns out, with gruesome irony, to be a *howdah*, for use on an elephant's back. Among the masks worn by *khon* actors next door (room 7), look out especially for a fierce Hanuman, the white monkey-warrior in the *Ramayana* epic, gleaming with mother-of-pearl.

The huge and varied ceramic collection in room 8 includes some sophisticated pieces from Sukhothai, while the room behind (9) holds a riot of mother-of-pearl items, whose flaming rainbow of colours comes from the shell of the turbo snail from the Gulf of Thailand. It's also worth seeking out the display of richly decorated musical instruments in room 15.

The Buddhaisawan chapel
The second-holiest image in Thailand, after the Emerald Buddha, is housed in the **Buddhaisawan chapel**, the vast hall in front of the eastern entrance to the Wang Na. Inside, the fine proportions of the hall, with its ornate coffered ceiling and lacquered window shutters, are enhanced by painted rows of divinities and converted demons, all turned to face the chubby, glowing **Phra Sihing Buddha**, which according to legend was magically created in Sri Lanka in the second century and sent to Sukhothai in the thirteenth century. Like the Emerald Buddha, the image was believed to bring good luck to its owner and was frequently snatched from one northern town to another, until Rama I brought it down from Chiang Mai in 1795 and installed it here in the second king's private chapel. Two other images (in Nakhon Si Thammarat and Chiang Mai) now claim to be the authentic Phra Sihing Buddha, but all three are in fact derived from a lost original – this one is in a fifteenth-century Sukhothai style. It's still much loved by ordinary people and at Thai New Year in April is carried out to the nearby City Hall, where it sits for three days while worshippers sprinkle it with water as a merit-making gesture.

The careful detail and rich, soothing colours of the surrounding two-hundred-year-old **murals** are surprisingly well preserved; the bottom row between the windows narrates the life of the Buddha, beginning in the far right-hand corner with his parents' wedding.

1

Tamnak Daeng

On the south side of the Buddhaisawan chapel, the gaudily restored **Tamnak Daeng** (Red House) stands out, a large, airy Ayutthaya-style house made of rare golden teak, surmounted by a multi-tiered roof decorated with swan's-tail finials. Originally part of the private quarters of Princess Sri Sudarak, elder sister of Rama I, it was moved from the Grand Palace to the old palace in Thonburi for Queen Sri Suriyen, wife of Rama II; when her son became second king to Rama IV, he dismantled the edifice again and shipped it here to the Wang Na compound. Inside, it's furnished in the style of the early Bangkok period, with some of the beautiful objects that once belonged to Sri Suriyen, a huge, ornately carved box-bed, and the uncommon luxury of an indoor bathroom.

The National Gallery

4 Thanon Chao Fa, across from the National Theatre on the north side of Sanam Luang • Wed–Sun 9am–4pm • B200 • ☎ 02 281 2224, Ⓦ ngbangkok.wordpress.com

If wandering around Bangkok's National Museum doesn't finish you off, the **National Gallery** nearby probably will. In its upstairs gallery, it displays some rather beautiful early twentieth-century temple banners depicting Buddhist subjects, but the permanent collection of twentieth-century Thai art downstairs is largely uninspiring and derivative. Its temporary exhibitions can be pretty good, however. The fine old building that houses the gallery is also worth more than a cursory glance – it was constructed in typical early twentieth-century, Neoclassical style, by Carlo Allegri, Rama V's court architect, as the Royal Mint.

Banglamphu and the Democracy Monument area

Immediately north of Ratanakosin, **Banglamphu**'s most notorious attraction is **Thanon Khao San**, a tiny sliver of a road built over a canal in 1892, whose multiple guesthouses and buzzing, budget-minded nightlife have made it an unmissable way-station for travellers through Southeast Asia. There is plenty of cultural interest too, in a medley of idiosyncratic temples within a few blocks of nearby landmark **Democracy Monument**, and in the typical Bangkok neighbourhoods that connect them, many of which still feel charmingly old-fashioned.

ARRIVAL AND DEPARTURE   BANGLAMPHU AND THE DEMOCRACY MONUMENT AREA

By boat Chao Phraya express-boat stops N13 (Phra Arthit), N14 (Rama VIII bridge) and N15 (Thewet) are nearby (see p.139). Banglamphu is also served by public boats along Khlong Saen Saeb to and from their Phan Fah terminus, which are useful for Siam Square and the Skytrain.

By Skytrain In addition to connecting to the Skytrain via Khlong Saen Saeb boat, the other fast way to get on to the BTS system is to take a taxi from Banglamphu to BTS National Stadium.

By bus Dozens of useful buses serve Banglamphu (see boxes opposite & p.138).

Thanon Khao San

At the heart of Banglamphu is the legendary **Thanon Khao San**, almost a caricature of a travellers' centre, its pavements lined with cheap backpackers' fashions, racks of bootleg DVDs, tattooists and hair-braiders. It's a lively, high-energy base: great for shopping and making travel arrangements – though beware the innumerable Khao San scams (see p.61) – and a good place to meet other travellers. It's especially fun at night when young Thais from all over the city gather here to browse the clothes stalls, mingle with the crowds of foreigners and squash into the bars and clubs that have made Khao San a great place to party. Even if you're staying elsewhere, the Khao San area is a cultural curiosity in its own right, a unique and continually evolving expression of global youth culture fuelled by Thai entrepreneurship.

Thanon Phra Arthit and the riverside walkway

Students from nearby Thammasat University inject an arty Thai vibe into the Banglamphu mix, particularly along **Thanon Phra Arthit**, which borders the Chao Phraya River. There's an attractive **riverside walkway** here too, which begins at Phra Pinklao Bridge and takes you past a couple of beautifully restored century-old mansions, currently occupied by Unicef and the UN's FAO; they show their most elegant faces to the river since in their heyday most visitors would have arrived by boat. The walkway ends at the whitewashed, renovated octagonal tower of **Phra Sumen Fortress** (Phra Sumeru), one of fourteen built by Rama I in 1783 to protect the royal island of Ratanakosin – the only other surviving tower, also renovated, is Phra Mahakhan Fortress, next to the Golden Mount. Nowadays there's nothing to see inside the fort, but the area around it has been remodelled as grassy riverside **Santichaiprakarn Park**.

Wat Indraviharn

Thanon Wisut Kasat, about 20min walk north of Khao San • 10min walk from Chao Phraya express-boat stops N14 and N15

Though it can't match the graceful serenity of Ratanakosin's enormous Reclining Buddha at Wat Pho, Banglamphu has its own super-sized Standing Buddha at **Wat Indraviharn** (also spelt Wat Intharawihan or Wat In), a glittering 32m-high mirror-plated statue of the Buddha bearing an alms bowl. Commissioned by Rama IV in the mid-nineteenth century to enshrine a Buddha relic from Sri Lanka (in the topknot), it's hardly the most elegant of images, but the 30cm-long toenails peep out beneath offertory garlands of fragrant jasmine, and you can get reasonable views of the neighbourhood by climbing the stairways of the supporting tower; when unlocked, the doorways in the upper tower give access to the statue's hollow interior, affording vistas from shoulder level. The rest of the temple compound features the usual amalgam of architectural and spiritual styles, including a Chinese shrine and statues of Ramas IV and V.

Unfortunately, Wat In is an established hangout for **con-artists** (see p.61) offering tourists a tuk-tuk tour of Bangkok for a bargain B20, which invariably features a

BANGLAMPHU'S BUS STOPS AND ROUTES

The main bus stops serving Banglamphu are on Thanon Rajdamnoen Klang: with nearly thirty westbound and eastbound routes, you can get just about anywhere in the city from here. But there are some other useful pick-up points in Banglamphu for routes running out of the area. To make things simpler, we've assigned numbers to these **bus stops**, though they are not numbered on the ground. Where there are two stops served by the same buses they share a number. Bus stops are marked on the Banglamphu map (see p.100).

Bus stop 1: Thanon Krung Kasem, north side
#53 (clockwise) to Hualamphong train station
Bus stop 2: Thanon Phra Sumen, south side; and Thanon Phra Arthit, east side
#53 (anticlockwise) to the Grand Palace and Chinatown
Bus stop 3: Thanon Phra Arthit, west side; and Thanon Phra Sumen, north side
#3 to Chatuchak Weekend Market and Northern Bus Terminal
#53 (clockwise) to Hualamphong train station (change at Bus Stop 1, but same ticket)
Bus stop 4: Thanon Chakrabongse
#3 to Wat Pho, the Museum of Siam, Pak Khlong Talat and Wongwian Yai train station
#15 to Jim Thompson's House, Siam Square and Thanon Silom
Bus Stop 5: Thanon Rajinee (Rachini)
#124 to Southern Bus Terminal

■ ACCOMMODATION	
Baan Dinso	26
Baan Manusarn	4
Bella Bella House	16
The Bhuthorn	29
Boonsiri Place	27
Buddy Lodge	23
Charoendee	
Boutique Hostel	22
Donna Guesthouse	24
KC Guest House	11
Khao San Palace Inn	21
Lamphu House	14
Lamphu Treehouse	19
Lek House	20
Merry V	12
Nakorn Ping	8
Nap Park	18
Navalai River Resort	10
New Siam 2	17
New Siam Riverside	13
Old Bangkok Inn	25
Peachy Guest House	15
Phra Nakorn Norn Len	6
Praya Palazzo	7
Rajata	9
Sawatdee	3
Sri Ayutthaya	5
Ssip	1
Tavee	2
The Warehouse	28

● RESTAURANTS & CAFÉS	
Aquatini	7
Chabad House	14
Chomp	5
Chote Chitr	20
Hemlock	12
Jok Phochana	23
Kai Yang Boran	17
Kaloang Home Kitchen	2
Kinlom Chom Saphan	1
Kor Panit	4
Krua Apsorn	19
Kway Jap Yuan Khun Daeng	11
May Kaidee	15
May Kaidee 2	8
Nattaporn	21
Nittaya	13
Padthai Thipsamai	18
Popiang	10
Roti Mataba	6
Steve Café and Cuisine	3

■ BARS & CLUBS	
Ad here the 13th (Blues Bar)	2
Bangkok Bar	5
Brick Bar	8
Brown Sugar	9
The Club	7
Dickinson's Culture Café	3
Hippie de Bar	6
Jazz Happens	4
Phra Nakorn	10
Sheepshank	1

■ SHOPS	
Lofty Bamboo	4
Shaman Books	3
Taekee Taekon	1
Ton's Booksellers	2

BANGLAMPHU AND THE DEMOCRACY MONUMENT AREA

Dusit

0   200
metres

N

Rajdamnoen Stadium

TAT

RAJDAMNOEN NOK

THANON PRACHA THIPATAI

Wat Bowoniwes

THANON PHRA SUMEN

THANON PHRA SUMEN

Queen's Gallery

THANON BORIPHAT

LAN LUANG

King Prajadhipok (Rama VIII Museum)

Tha Phan Fah

Khlong Saen Saeb

DAMRONG RAK

Golden Mount & Wat Saket

Phra Mahakhan Fortress Community

Khlong Ong Ang

THANON MAHACHAI

Loha Prasat

Wat Rajnadda

RAJDAMNOEN KLANG

Democracy Monument

THANON DINSO

THANON DINSO

City Hall

Sao Ching Cha

THANON BAMRUNG MUANG

Wat Suthat

THANON MAHANNOP

Ratchadamnoen P.O.

DAMNOEN KLANG NEUA

Bus stop 7

THANON TANAO

Lomprayah

THANON RAM BHUTTRI

THANON TANI

Banglamphubon P.O.

SOI SIPSAM HANG

THANON KROMBOMPHRAPHONG

TROK KRAISI

Night Market

THANON RAM BHUTTRI

SOI RAM BHUTTRI

Bus stop 4

Wat Chana Songkhram

Pian's

Plan's

ETC

THANON KHAO SAN

DAMNOEN KLANG NEUA

RAJDAMNOEN KLANG

THANON SOI DAMNOEN KLANG TAI

SOI DAMNOEN KLANG TAI

THANON SOI DAMNOEN KLANG TAI

TROK SIN

TROK NAWA

Temple Supplies

Wat Rajbophit

TROK MAYOM

Police Station

THANON CHAKRABONGSE

True

Bus stop 6

ATS

Olavi Travel

Royal Ratanakosin Hotel

Minibuses to Kanchanaburi

TROK SA-KE

Night Market

THANON BURANASIT

THANON TANAO

BUNSRI

San Chao Poh Seua

THANON PHRAENG PHUTON

THANON KANUKYANA MAITRI

THANON ATSADANG

Sor Vorapin's Gym

National Gallery

SOI RAM BHUTTRI

TROK RONG MAI

CHAO FA

Mae Toranee statue

THANON RAJDAMNOEN NAI

Sanam Luang

THANON NA PHRA LAN

Lak Muang

THANON LAK MUANG

Khlong Saen Saeb boat stop

Express-boat pier

PHRA PINKLAO BRIDGE

RAJINEE

National Theatre

National Museum

Thammasat University

Wat Mahathat

THANON NA PHRA THAT

Bus stop 5

1

THE OCTOBER 14 MEMORIAL

One of the biggest and most notorious demonstrations around the Democracy Monument was the fateful student-led protest of October 14, 1973, when half a million people gathered on Rajdamnoen Klang to demand an end to the autocratic regime of the so-called "Three Tyrants". It was savagely quashed and turned into a bloody riot that culminated in the death of several hundred protesters at the hands of the police and the military; the Three Tyrants were forced into exile and a new coalition government was soon formed. After three decades of procrastination, the events of this catastrophic day were finally commemorated with the erection of the **October 14 Memorial**, a small granite amphitheatre encircling an elegant modern chedi bearing the names of some of the dead; photographs and a bilingual account of the ten-day protest fill the back wall. The memorial stands in front of the former headquarters of Colonel Narong Kittikachorn, one of the Three Tyrants, 200m west of Democracy Monument, at the corner of Rajdamnoen Klang and Thanon Tanao.

hard-sell visit to a jewellery shop (see p.170). Avoid all these hassles by hailing a passing metered taxi instead, or by catching one of the dozens of buses that run along Thanon Samsen.

Democracy Monument

The megalithic yellow-tinged wings of **Democracy Monument** (*Anu Sawari Pracha Tippatai*) loom provocatively over Thanon Rajdamnoen Klang, the avenue that connects the Grand Palace and the new royal district of Dusit, and have since their erection in 1939 acted as a focus for pro-democracy rallies. Conceived as a testimony to the ideals that fuelled the 1932 revolution and the changeover to a constitutional monarchy, the monument's positioning between the royal residences is significant, as are its dimensions, which allude to June 24, 2475 BE (1932 AD), the date the system was changed. In the decades since, Thailand's leaders have promulgated numerous interim charters and constitutions, the more repressive and regressive of which have been vigorously challenged in demonstrations on these very streets.

Thanon Tanao

A stroll down **Thanon Tanao** brings you into some engagingly old-fashioned neighbourhoods of nineteenth-century wooden shophouses, which are especially famous for their specialist **traditional Thai foods**. Many of these places have been making their specialities for generations, and there are all sorts of fun things to browse here, even if you're not inclined to taste, from beef noodles to pigs' brain soup, home-made ice cream to sticky rice with mango. If you are after some recommendations on what to eat the *Good Eats Ratanakosin* map (published by Pan Siam Publishing and available in major bookshops) is an exhaustive survey, which is especially handy given that few of these places have English-language signs or shop numbers.

The area around the south end of Thanon Tanao is also sometimes referred to as **Sao Ching Cha** (see opposite), after the **Giant Swing**, which is easily reached either by following any of the east-bound lanes off Tanao to Thanon Dinso, or by browsing the Buddhist paraphernalia stalls that take you there via Thanon Bamrung Muang. Alternatively, if you continue one block south along Tanao you'll reach the lovely little temple of Wat Rajabophit.

San Chao Poh Seua

Thanon Tanao • Daily 6am–5pm, till 9pm during the Vegetarian Festival (see p.154) • Free

Not far south of Thanon Rajdamnoen Klang sits **San Chao Poh Seua**, the **Tiger God Shrine**, an atmospheric, incense-filled Taoist shrine honouring the Chinese tiger guardian spirit and the God of the North Stars, whose image graces the centre of the main altar. It's a favourite with Chinese-Thais who come here to pray for power, prestige and successful pregnancy and offer in return pork rashers, fresh eggs, sticky rice, bottles of oil and sugar tigers.

Wat Rajabophit

Thanon Rajabophit, one block south of the Tanao/Bamrung Muang intersection, just to the east of Khlong Lod (see map, p.83)

One of Bangkok's prettiest temples, **Wat Rajabophit** is another example of the Chinese influence in this neighbourhood. It was built by Rama V in 1869–70 and, typical of him, is unusual in its design, particularly the circular cloister that encloses a chedi and links the rectangular bot and viharn. Every external wall in the compound is covered in the pastel shades of Chinese *bencharong* ceramic tiles, creating a stunning overall effect, while the bot interior looks like a tiny banqueting hall, with gilded Gothic vaults and intricate mother-of-pearl doors.

Thanon Bamrung Muang

Thanon Bamrung Muang, which runs east from Thanon Tanao to Sao Ching Cha and Wat Suthat, was an old elephant trail that, a hundred years ago, became one of the first paved streets in Bangkok. It's famous as the best place in Thailand to buy **Buddhist paraphernalia**, or *sanghapan*, and is well worth a browse. The road is lined with shops selling everything a good Buddhist might need, from household offertory tables to temple umbrellas and cellophane-wrapped Buddha images up to 2m high. They also sell special alms packs for donating to monks, which typically come in saffron-coloured plastic buckets (used by monks for washing their robes, or themselves), and include such necessities as soap, toothpaste, soap powder, toilet roll, candles and incense.

Sao Ching Cha

Midway along Thanon Bamrung Muang, just in front of Wat Suthat

You can't miss the towering, red-painted teak posts of **Sao Ching Cha**, otherwise known as the **Giant Swing**. This strange contraption was once the focal point of a Brahmin ceremony to honour the Hindu god Shiva's annual visit to earth, in which teams of young men competed to swing up to a height of 25m and grab a suspended bag of gold with their teeth. The act of swinging probably symbolized the rising and setting of the sun, though legend also has it that Shiva and his consort Uma were banned from swinging in heaven because doing so caused cataclysmic floods on earth – prompting Shiva to demand that the practice be continued on earth to ensure moderate rains and bountiful harvests. Accidents were so common with the terrestrial version that it was outlawed in the 1930s.

Wat Suthat

Thanon Bamrung Muang • Daily 8.30am–4pm • B20

Wat Suthat is one of Thailand's six most important temples, built in the early nineteenth century to house the 8m-high statue of the meditating **Phra Sri Sakyamuni Buddha**, which is said to date from 1361 and was brought all the way down from Sukhothai by river. It now sits on a glittering mosaic dais, which contains some of the ashes of Rama VIII, the elder brother of the current king, surrounded with surreal murals that depict the last 24 lives of the Buddha rather than the more usual ten. The encircling galleries contain 156 serenely posed Buddha images, making a nice contrast to the **Chinese statues** dotted around the temple courtyards, most of which were brought over from China during Rama I's reign, as ballast in rice boats; there are some fun character studies among them, including gormless Western sailors and pompous Chinese scholars.

AMULETS

To invite good fortune, ward off malevolent spirits and gain protection from physical harm, many Thais wear or carry at least one **amulet** at all times. The most popular images are copies of sacred statues from famous wats, while others show revered monks, kings (Rama V is a favourite) or healers. On the reverse side, a yantra is often inscribed, a combination of letters and figures also designed to deflect evil, sometimes of a very specific nature: protecting your durian orchards from gales, for example, or your tuk-tuk from oncoming traffic. Individually hand-crafted or mass-produced, amulets can be made from bronze, clay, plaster or gold, and some even have sacred ingredients added, such as special herbs, or the ashes of burnt holy texts. But what really determines an amulet's efficacy is its history: where and by whom it was made, who or what it represents and who consecrated it. Stories of miracle cures and lucky escapes also prompt a rush on whatever amulet the survivor was wearing. Monks are often involved in the making of the images and are always called upon to consecrate them – the more charismatic the monk, the more powerful the amulet. Religious authorities take a relaxed view of the amulet industry, despite its anomalous and commercial functions, and proceeds contribute to wat funds and good causes.

The **belief in amulets** is thought to have originated in India, where tiny images were sold to pilgrims who visited the four holy sites associated with the Buddha's life. But not all amulets are Buddhist-related; there's a whole range of other enchanted objects to wear for protection, including tigers' teeth, rose quartz, tamarind seeds, coloured threads and miniature phalluses. Worn around the waist rather than the neck, the phallus amulets provide protection for the genitals as well as being associated with fertility, and are of Hindu origin.

For some people, amulets are not only a vital form of spiritual protection, but valuable **collectors' items** as well. Amulet-collecting mania is something akin to stamp collecting and there are at least half a dozen Thai magazines for collectors, which give histories of certain types, tips on distinguishing between genuine items and fakes, and personal accounts of particularly powerful amulet experiences. The most rewarding places to watch the collectors and browse the wares yourself are at Wat Rajnadda Buddha Centre (see below), the biggest amulet market and probably the best place in Bangkok; along "Amulet Alley" on Trok Mahathat, between Wat Mahathat (see p.95) and the river, where streetside vendors will have cheaper examples; and at Chatuchak Weekend Market (see p.129). Prices start as low as B50 and rise into the thousands.

Wat Rajnadda

5min walk east of Democracy Monument, at the point where Rajdamnoen Klang meets Thanon Mahachai • **Loha Prasat** Daily 9am–5pm • Free

Among the assortment of religious buildings known collectively as **Wat Rajnadda**, the most striking is the multi-tiered, castle-like, early nineteenth-century **Loha Prasat**, or "Iron Monastery", whose 37 forbidding metal spires represent the 37 virtues necessary for attaining enlightenment. Modelled on a Sri Lankan monastery, its tiers are pierced by passageways running north–south and east–west (fifteen in each direction at ground level) with small meditation cells at each point of intersection.

Wat Rajnadda Buddha Centre

In the southeast (Thanon Mahachai) corner of the temple compound, Bangkok's biggest **amulet market**, the **Wat Rajnadda Buddha Centre**, comprises at least a hundred stalls selling tiny Buddha images of all designs. Alongside these miniature charms are statues of Hindu deities, dolls and carved wooden phalluses, also bought to placate or ward off disgruntled spirits, as well as love potions and CDs of sacred music.

Phra Mahakhan Fortress community

Thanon Mahachai

The **Phra Mahakhan Fortress community**, across the road from Wat Rajnadda, occupies the land between the whitewashed crenellations of the renovated eighteenth-century city walls and Khlong Ong Ang. It's a historic, working-class neighbourhood where some of the houses date from the early nineteenth century and has been the object of a recent urban renovation programme. It now welcomes visitors with informative signboards describing some of its traditions, including massage therapy, fish bladder soup and *likay* popular theatre. In the block of shops on Thanon Mahachai, immediately south of the crenellations, are a famous traditional Thai perfume shop and several places specializing in Thai and Chinese antiques.

Wat Saket

Easiest access is along Thanon Boriphat (the specialist street for custom-carved wooden doors), 5min walk south from the khlong bridge and Phan Fah canal-boat stop at the eastern end of Rajdamnoen Klang

Beautifully illuminated at night, when it seems to float unsupported above the neighbourhood, the gleaming gold chedi of late eighteenth-century **Wat Saket** actually sits atop a structure known as the Golden Mount. Being outside the capital's city walls, the wat initially served as a crematorium and then a dumping ground for sixty thousand plague victims left to the vultures because they couldn't afford funeral pyres. There's no sign of this grim episode at modern-day Wat Saket of course, which these days is a smart, buzzing hive of religious activity at the base of the golden hilltop chedi. Wat Saket hosts an enormous annual **temple fair** in the first week of November, when the mount is illuminated with lanterns and the compound seethes with funfair rides and travelling theatre shows.

The Golden Mount

Daily 8am–5pm • B20

The **Golden Mount**, or **Phu Khao Tong**, dates back to the early nineteenth century, when Rama III commissioned a huge chedi to be constructed here, using building materials from the ruined fortresses and walls of the former capital, Ayutthaya. However, the ground proved too soft to support the chedi. The whole thing collapsed into a hill of rubble, but as Buddhist law states that a religious building can never be destroyed, however tumbledown, fifty years later Rama V simply crowned it with the more sensibly sized chedi we see today, in which he placed some relics of the Buddha's teeth from India, donated by the British government. These days the old rubbly base is picturesquely planted with shrubs and shady trees and dotted with gravestones and memorials. Winding stairways take you up to the chedi terrace and a fine view over Banglamphu and Ratanakosin landmarks, including the golden spires of the Grand Palace, the finely proportioned prangs of Wat Arun across the river beyond and, further upriver, the striking superstructure of the Rama VIII bridge.

The Queen's Gallery

North across Rajdamnoen Klang from Wat Rajnadda, on the corner of Thanon Phra Sumen • Mon, Tues & Thurs–Sun 10am–7pm • B30 • ☎ 02 281 5361, ⓦ queengallery.org

The privately funded, five-storey **Queen's Gallery** hosts temporary shows of contemporary Thai art, plus the occasional exhibition by foreign artists, and makes a more stimulating alternative to the rather staid National Gallery down the other end of Rajdamnoen Klang. Its bookshop sells hard-to-find Thai art books.

Chinatown and Pahurat

When the newly crowned Rama I decided to move his capital across to the east bank of the river in 1782, the Chinese community living on the proposed site of his palace was obliged to relocate downriver, to the **Sampeng** area. Two centuries on, **Chinatown** has grown into the country's largest Chinese district, a sprawl of narrow alleyways, temples and shophouses packed between Charoen Krung (New Road) and the river, separated

1

HUALAMPHONG, CHINATOWN AND PAHURAT

N

THONBURI

Chao Phraya River

Khlong Krung Kasem

Hualamphong Train Station

Wat Traimit

Chinese Arch

Wat Mangkon Kamalawat

Wat Ga Buang Kim

Wat Chakrawat

Tha Rajavongse

Chalermkrung Theatre

Merry King

Old Siam Plaza

Pahurat Market

Rama 1 Statue

Memorial Bridge Night Bazaar

Pak Khlong Talat

Tha Saphan Phut

THANON RONG MUANG

THANON LUANG

THANON MANGKON

THANON MAITRI CHIT

THANON MAITRI CHIT

JULY 22 CIRCLE

THANON MITRPHAN

THANON SANTI PHAP

THANON PLAPLACHAI

PLABPLACHAIT

THANON PLAENGNAM

SOI 21

SOI 16

SOI 6

THANON YAOWARAT

THANON SONGWAT

THANON SONGWAT

THANON CHAROEN KRUNG (NEW ROAD)

THANON CHAKRAWAT

THANON CHAKKRAPHET

THANON CHAKKRAWAT

THANON BORIPHAT

THANON PAHURAT

THANON BANMO

THANON TRIPHET

SAMPENG LANE (SOI WANIT 1)

BAMRUNG RAT

THANON KWANG HIM TAENG

THANON SAN CHAO MAI

SOI ISSARANUPHAP (SOI 16)

ANA WONG

THANON RATCHAWONG

THANON MAHACHAI

THANON YAMMARAI SUKHUM

THANON CHAKKHAMROP

(NEW ROAD)

THANON RAMA IV

THANON CHAROEN KRUNG

THANON KHAO LAM

THANON MAHA PHRUTHARAM

SOI SUKON 1

THANON MITTRAPHAP THAI-CHINA

THANON MAHA NAKHON

EXPRESSWAY

TROK LA-O

SOI CHADONG KRUNG

TROK LA-O

Hualamphong (M)

THANON TRAI MIT

SOI CHAROEN PHANIT

SOI PHANU RANGSI

SOI THANADIKAN (TEAS)

Wat Traimit

Chao Phraya River

THANON KHWAE HIM TAENG

Tha Rajavongse N5

Tha Saphan Phut N6

MEMORIAL BRIDGE (SAPHAN PHUT)

PHRA PORKLAO BRIDGE (RAMA VII)

Khlong Ong Ang

▲ Banglamphu
▲ Wat Prayoon
▼ Rattanakosin
▼ Wat Prayoon

-●(M)-●- Subway and station

0 250

metres

■ ACCOMMODATION

@ Hualamphong 3
Baan Hualamphong 6
Grand China 5
Shanghai Mansion 1
.... 4
.... 2

● RESTAURANTS

Hua Seng Hong 3
Jong Kee 6
Raan Khun Yah 5
Royal India 1
Shangarila 2
T&K (Toi & Kid's Seafood) 4

from Ratanakosin by the Indian area of **Pahurat** – famous for its cloth and dressmakers' trimmings – and bordered to the east by **Hualamphong** train station.

The **Chinese influence** on Thai culture and commerce has been significant ever since the first Chinese merchants gained a toehold in Ayutthaya in the fourteenth century. Following centuries of immigration and intermarriage, there is now some Chinese blood in almost every Thai citizen, including the king, and Chinese-Thai business interests play an enormous role in the Thai economy. This is played out at its most frantic in Chinatown, whose real estate is said to be among the most valuable in the country; there are over a hundred gold and jewellery shops along Thanon Yaowarat alone.

For the tourist, Chinatown is chiefly interesting for its **markets**, shophouses, open-fronted warehouses and remnants of colonial-style architecture, though it also harbours a few noteworthy **temples**. A meander through its most interesting neighbourhoods could easily fill up a whole day, allowing for frequent breaks from the thundering traffic and choking fumes. For the most authentic Chinatown experience, it's best to come during the week, as some shops and stalls shut at weekends; on weekdays they begin closing around 5pm, after which time the neighbourhood's other big draw – its **food** – takes centre stage.

ARRIVAL AND GETTING AROUND CHINATOWN AND PAHURAT

Arrival The easiest way to reach Chinatown is either by subway to Hualamphong Station, or by Chao Phraya express boat to Tha Rachawongse (Rajawong; N5) at the southern end of Thanon Rajawong. A westward extension of the subway is being built (with a proposed opening in 2017), with new stations at Wat Mangkon Kamalawat and Pahurat. This part of the city is also well served by buses, with Hualamphong a useful and easily recognized place to disembark. Be warned that buses and taxis may take an unexpectedly circuitous route due to the many and complex one-way systems in Chinatown.

Getting around Orientation in Chinatown can be tricky: the alleys (often known as trok rather than the more usual soi) are extremely narrow, their turn-offs and other road signs often obscured by mounds of merchandise and thronging crowds, and the longer ones can change their names several times. For a detailed tour of the alleys and markets, use *Nancy Chandler's Map of Bangkok* (see p.142); alternatively, ask for help at the BMA tourist information booth (Mon–Sat 9am–5pm) just northwest of the Chinese Arch at the beginning of Thanon Yaowarat, beside Soi 5.

Wat Traimit

Thanon Mittaphap Thai-China, just west of Hualamphong train and subway stations (exit 1) • Daily 8am–5pm; exhibitions closed Mon • Golden Buddha only B40; Golden Buddha and exhibitions B100 • ⓦ wattraimitr-withayaram.com

The obvious place to start a Chinatown tour is on its eastern perimeter, with **Wat Traimit** and its famous Golden Buddha. You can see the temple mondop's golden spire from quite a distance, a fitting beacon for the gleaming treasure housed on its third floor, the world's largest solid-gold Buddha. It's an apt attraction for a community so closely linked with the gold trade, even if the image has nothing to do with China's spiritual heritage. A recent attempt has been made to bridge this gap, with the installation of exhibitions of varying interest on the mondop's first and second floors, covering the history of Chinatown and of the iconic Buddha image.

The Golden Buddha

Over 3m tall and weighing five tonnes, the **Golden Buddha** gleams as if coated in liquid metal, seated on a white marble lotus-pad pedestal and surrounded with offerings of lotus flowers. It's a fine example of the curvaceous grace of Sukhothai art, slim-waisted and beautifully proportioned. Cast in the thirteenth century, the image was brought to Bangkok by Rama III, completely encased in stucco – a common ruse to conceal valuable statues from would-be thieves. The disguise was so good that no one guessed what was underneath until 1955 when the image was accidentally knocked in the process of being moved to Wat Traimit, and the stucco cracked to reveal a patch of gold. Just in time for Buddhism's 2500th anniversary, the discovery launched a

1

country-wide craze for tapping away at plaster Buddhas in search of hidden precious metals, but Wat Traimit's is still the most valuable – it is valued, by weight alone, at over US$10 million.

The exhibitions

The exhibition on the making and history of the Golden Buddha, on the second floor of the mondop, is fairly missable, but the **Yaowarat Chinatown Heritage Centre** on the floor below is rather more compelling. Interesting though sanitized, its display boards trace the rapid expansion of the Chinese presence in Bangkok from the late eighteenth century, first as junk traders, later as labourers and tax farmers. Enhancing the story are a diorama of life on board a junk, lots of interesting photos from the late nineteenth century onwards and a fascinating scale model of Thanon Yaowarat in its 1950s heyday, when it was Bangkok's business and entertainment hub.

Sampeng Lane

From Wat Traimit, walk northwest from the big China Gate roundabout along Thanon Yaowarat, and make a left turn onto Thanon Songsawat to reach Sampeng Lane

One of Chinatown's most enjoyable shopping alleys, **Sampeng Lane** (also signposted as Soi Wanit 1) is where the Chinese community first settled in the area, when they were moved from Ratanakosin in the late eighteenth century to make way for the Grand Palace. Stretching southeast–northwest for about 1km, it's a great place to browse, unfurling itself like a serpentine department store and selling everything from Chinese silk pyjama trousers to computer games at bargain rates. Similar goods are more or less gathered in sections, so at the eastern end you'll find mostly cheap jewellery and hair accessories, for example, before passing through stalls specializing in ceramics, Chinese lanterns, then shoes, clothes (west of Thanon Rajawong) and, as you near Pahurat, fabrics, haberdashery and irresistibly girlie accessories.

Soi Issaranuphap

Taking a right turn about halfway down Sampeng Lane will bring you into **Soi Issaranuphap** (also signed along its course as Yaowarat Soi 11, then Soi 6, and later Charoen Krung sois 16 and 21). Packed with people from dawn till dusk, this long, dark alleyway, which also traverses Charoen Krung, is where locals come in search of ginseng roots (essential for good health), quivering fish heads, cubes of cockroach-killer chalk and a gastronome's choice of dried mushrooms and brine-pickled vegetables. Alleys branch off to florid Chinese temples and tiny squares before Soi Issaranuphap finally ends at the Thanon Plaplachai intersection amid a flurry of shops specializing in paper **funeral art**. Believing that the deceased should be well provided for in their afterlife, Chinese people buy miniature paper replicas of necessities to be burned with the body: especially popular are houses, cars, suits of clothing and, of course, money.

Wat Mangkon Kamalawat

Best approached via its dramatic multi-tiered gateway 10m up Thanon Charoen Krung from the Soi Issaranuphap junction

If Soi Issaranuphap epitomizes age-old Chinatown commerce, then **Wat Mangkon Kamalawat** (also known as **Wat Leng Noei Yee** or, in English, "Dragon Flower Temple") stands as a fine example of the community's spiritual practices. Built in 1871, it receives a constant stream of devotees, who come to leave offerings at the altars inside this important Mahayana Buddhist temple. As with the Theravada Buddhism espoused by the Thais, Mahayana Buddhism fuses with other ancient religious beliefs, notably Confucianism and Taoism, and the statues and shrines within Wat Mangkon cover the spectrum. As you pass through the secondary gateway, under the glazed ceramic gables topped with undulating Chinese dragons, you're greeted by a set of four outsize statues of bearded and rather forbidding sages, each symbolically clasping either a parasol, a pagoda, a snake's head or a mandolin. Beyond them, a series of Buddha images swathed in saffron netting occupies the next chamber, a lovely open-sided room of gold paintwork, red-lacquered wood, lattice lanterns and pictorial wall panels inlaid with mother-of-pearl. Elsewhere in the compound are booths selling devotional paraphernalia, a Chinese medicine stall and a fortune-teller.

Wat Ga Buang Kim

From Thanon Rajawong, take a right turn into Thanon Anawong and a further right turn into the narrow, two-pronged Soi Krai

The typical neighbourhood temple of **Wat Ga Buang Kim** is set around a tiny, enclosed courtyard. This particular wat is remarkable for its exquisitely ornamented "vegetarian hall", a one-room shrine with altar centrepiece framed by intricately carved wooden tableaux of gold-painted miniatures arranged as if in sequence, with recognizable characters reappearing in new positions and in different moods. The hall's outer wall is adorned with small tableaux, too, the area around the doorway at the top of the stairs peopled with finely crafted ceramic figurines drawn from Chinese opera stories. The other building in the wat compound is a stage used for Chinese opera performances.

Pahurat

West of Khlong Ong Ang, in the small square south of the intersection of Chakraphet and Pahurat roads, is the area known as **Pahurat**, where Bangkok's sizeable Indian community congregates. Unless you're looking for *bidi* cigarettes, Punjabi sweets or Bollywood VCDs, curiosity-shopping is not as rewarding here as in Chinatown, but it's good for all sorts of **fabrics**, from shirting to curtain materials and saree lengths.

Also here, at the Charoen Krung/Thanon Triphet intersection, is **Old Siam Plaza**, a colonial-look shopping centre whose nostalgia theme continues in part inside, with its ground-floor concourse given over to stalls selling traditional, handmade Thai snacks, sweets and sticky desserts. The adjacent Sala Chalermkrung Theatre sometimes stages classical Thai drama for non-Thai speakers (see p.164).

Pak Khlong Talat and Memorial Bridge night bazaar

Pak Khlong Talat West of the north side of Memorial Bridge · Daily 24hr · **Memorial Bridge night bazaar** Tues–Sun roughly 6pm–midnight · Chao Phraya express boat to Tha Saphan Phut (N6)

A browse through the 24-hour flower and vegetable market, **Pak Khlong Talat**, is a fitting way to round off a day in Chinatown, though it's also a great place to come before dawn, when market gardeners from Thonburi and beyond boat and drive their freshly picked produce across the Chao Phraya ready for sale to shopkeepers, restaurateurs and hoteliers. The market has been operating from covered halls between the southern ends of Khlong Lod, Thanon Banmo, Thanon Chakraphet and the river bank since the nineteenth century and is the biggest wholesale market in the capital. The flower stalls, selling twenty different varieties of cut orchids and countless other tropical blooms, spill onto the streets along the riverfront, and though prices are lowest in the early morning, you can still get some good bargains in the afternoon. Most evenings, the riverside end of nearby Thanon Triphet and the area around the base of **Memorial Bridge** (Saphan Phut) hosts a huge **night bazaar** that's dominated by cheap and idiosyncratic fashions – and by throngs of teenage fashion victims.

For the most interesting **approach** to the flower market from the Old Siam Plaza, turn west across Thanon Triphet to reach Thanon Banmo, and then follow this road south down towards the Chao Phraya. As you near the river, notice the facing rows of traditional Chinese shophouses, still in use today, which retain their characteristic (peeling)

1

pastel-painted facades, shutters and stucco curlicues. There's an entrance into the market on your right and just after sundown this southernmost stretch of Thanon Banmo fills with handcarts and vans unloading the most amazing mountains of fresh blooms.

Thonburi

For fifteen years between the fall of Ayutthaya in 1767 and the founding of Bangkok in 1782, the west-bank town of **Thonburi**, across the Chao Phraya from modern-day Bangkok, stood in as the Thai capital, under the rule of General Phraya Taksin. Its time in the spotlight was too brief for the building of the fine monuments and temples that graced earlier capitals at Sukhothai and Ayutthaya, but some of its centuries-old **canals**, which once transported everyone and everything, have endured; it is these and the ways of life that depend on them that constitute Thonburi's main attractions. In some quarters, life on this side of the river still revolves around these khlongs: vendors of food and household goods paddle their boats along the canals that crisscross the residential areas, and canalside factories use them to ferry their wares to the Chao Phraya River artery. Venture onto the backroads just three or four kilometres west of the river and you find yourself surrounded by market gardens and rural homes, with no hint of the throbbing metropolis across on the other bank. The most popular way to explore these old neighbourhoods is by **boat**, but joining a bicycle tour of the older neighbourhoods is also very rewarding (see p.137). Most boat trips also encompass Thonburi's imposing riverside Temple of the Dawn, **Wat Arun**, and often the **Royal Barge Museum** as well, though both are easily visited independently, as are the small but historic temple of **Wat Rakhang** and the surprisingly intriguing and child-friendly cemetery at **Wat Prayoon**.

ARRIVAL AND GETTING AROUND

Arrival Getting to Thonburi is generally just a matter of crossing the river. Either use Phra Pinklao or Memorial/Phra Pokklao bridge, take a cross-river ferry, or hop on one of the express boats, which make several stops on the Thonburi bank. The planned subway extension from Hualamphong, currently scheduled to open in 2017, will include a station near Wat Arun.

Getting around If you're not exploring Thonburi on a boat tour (see box opposite), getting around the district can be complicated as the lack of footbridges over canals means that walking between sights often involves using the heavily trafficked Thanon Arun Amarin. A more convoluted alternative would be to leapfrog your way up or down the river by boat, using the various cross-river ferries that connect the Thonburi bank with the Chao Phraya express-boat stops on the other side.

Royal Barge Museum

Soi Wat Dusitaram, north bank of Khlong Bangkok Noi • Daily 9am–5pm • B100, plus B100 for a camera permit • Take the Chao Phraya express boat to Tha Phra Pinklao (N12), or cross-river ferry from under Pinklao Bridge in Banglamphu to Tha Phra Pinklao, then walk up the road 100m and take the first left down Soi Wat Dusitaram; if coming by bus from the Bangkok side (#507, #509 and #511 all cross the river here), get off at the first stop on the Thonburi side, which is at the mouth of Soi Wat Dusitaram – signs from Soi Wat Dusitaram lead you through a jumble of walkways and stilt-houses to the museum (10min)

Since the Ayutthaya era, kings of Thailand have been conveyed along their country's waterways in royal barges. For centuries, these slender, exquisitely elegant, black-and-gold wooden vessels were used on all important royal outings, and even up until 1967 the current king would process down the Chao Phraya to Wat Arun in a flotilla of royal barges at least once a year, on the occasion of Kathin, the annual donation of robes by the laity to the temple at the end of the rainy season. But the boats, some of which are a hundred years old, are becoming quite frail, so **royal barge processions** are now held only every few years to mark special anniversaries. However, if your trip happens to coincide with one of these magnificent events, you shouldn't miss it (see ⓦtourismthailand.org). Fifty or more barges fill the width of the river and stretch for

EXPLORING THONBURI BY BOAT

The most popular way to explore the sights of Thonburi is by **boat**, taking in Wat Arun and the Royal Barge Museum, then continuing along Thonburi's network of small canals. We've detailed some interesting, fixed-price tours below, but generally it's just a question of turning up at a pier on the Bangkok side of the Chao Phraya and chartering a longtail. At Tha Phra Arthit express-boat pier or at the pier about 100m south of it in front of *Venice Vanich Restaurant*, a kiss-me-quick hour-long ride will cost B1000, while a two-hour trip, taking in an orchid farm deep among the Thonburi canals, costs B1800. You can also charter your own longtail from Tha Thien near Wat Pho, River City shopping centre, Tha Sathorn and other piers.

Many tours include visits to one of Thonburi's two main **floating markets**, both of which are heavily touristed and rather contrived. **Wat Sai** floating market is very small, very commercialized and worth avoiding. **Taling Chan** floating market is also fairly manufactured but more fun, though it only operates on Saturdays and Sundays (roughly 9am–4pm). Taling Chan market is held on Khlong Chak Phra, in front of Taling Chan District Office, a couple of kilometres west of Thonburi train station, and can also be reached by catching a/c bus #79 from Thanon Rajdamnoen Klang in Banglamphu. For a more authentic floating-market experience, consider heading out of Bangkok to Amphawa, in Samut Songkhram province (see p.184).

Arguably more photogenic, and certainly a lot more genuine than the floating markets, are the individual **floating vendors** who continue to paddle from house to house in Thonburi, touting anything from hot food to plastic buckets. You've a good chance of seeing some of them in action on almost any longtail boat tour on any day of the week, particularly in the morning.

Mitchaopaya Travel Service Tha Chang – on the left at the start of the pier, as you walk in from Thanon Na Phra Lan ☎ 02 623 6169. Licensed by TAT, offering fixed-price trips along the Thonburi canals of varying durations: in 1hr (B1000/boat, maximum 6 people, or B450/person if you can join in with other people), you'll pass Wat Arun and the Royal Barge Museum without stopping; in 90min (B1300), you'd have time to stop at either; while in 2hr (B1500) you'll have time to go right down the back canals on the Thonburi side and visit an orchid farm. On Saturday and Sunday, the 2hr trip takes in Taling Chan floating market, or you could head to the more authentic Lat

Mayom floating market in 3hr (B2500; best in the morning), far to the west in a leafy, more traditional part of Thonburi.
Pandan Tour 780/488 Thanon Charoen Krung ☎ 087 109 8873, ⓦ thaicanaltour.com. A selection of full-day tours of the Thonburi canals, the floating markets and beyond on an eco-friendly, natural-gas-powered teak boat, in small groups with a good English-speaking guide, starting from B2300/person, including lunch.
Real Asia 10/5–7 Soi Aree, Soi 26, Thanon Sukhumvit ☎ 02 665 6364, ⓦ realasia.net. Runs guided full-day walking and boat tours of the Thonburi canals for B2400/person, including lunch.

almost 1km, drifting slowly to the measured beat of a drum and the hypnotic strains of ancient boating hymns, chanted by over two thousand oarsmen dressed in luscious brocades.

The eight beautifully crafted vessels at the heart of the ceremony are housed in the **Royal Barge Museum**. Up to 50m long and intricately lacquered and gilded all over, they taper at the prow into imposing mythical figures after a design first used by the kings of Ayutthaya. Rama I had the boats copied and, when those fell into disrepair, Rama VI commissioned exact reconstructions, some of which are still in use today. The most important is *Sri Suphanahongse*, which bears the king and queen and is graced by a glittering 5m-high prow representing the golden swan Hamsa, mount of the Hindu god Brahma; constructed from a single piece of timber, it's said to be the largest dugout boat in the world. In front of it floats *Anantanagaraj*, fronted by a magnificent seven-headed naga and bearing a Buddha image. The newest addition to the fleet is *Narai Song Suban*, which was commissioned by the current king for his golden jubilee in 1996; it is a copy of the mid-nineteenth-century original and is crowned with a black Vishnu (Narai) astride a garuda figurehead. A display of miniaturized royal barges at the back of the museum re-creates the exact formation of a traditional procession.

Wat Rakhang

Take a cross-river ferry from Tha Chang express-boat pier (near the Grand Palace) to Wat Rakhang's pier, or walk 5min from the Tha Wang Lang express-boat pier, south (left) through the Phrannok pierside market

The charming riverside temple of **Wat Rakhang** (Temple of the Bells) gets its name from the five large bells donated by King Rama I and is notable for the hundreds of smaller chimes that tinkle away under the eaves of the main bot and, more accessibly, in the temple courtyard, where devotees come to strike them and hope for a run of good luck. To be extra certain of having their wishes granted, visitors also buy loaves of bread from the temple stalls and feed the frenzy of fat fish in the Chao Phraya River below. Behind the bot stands an attractive eighteenth-century wooden *ho trai* (scripture library) that still boasts some original murals on the wooden panels inside, as well as exquisitely renovated gold-leaf paintwork on the window shutters and pillars.

Walking to Wat Rakhang from the Tha Wang Lang express-boat pier, you'll pass through the enjoyable **Phrannok pierside market**, which is good for cheap clothes and tempting home-made snacks, especially sweet ones.

Wat Arun

Daily 8.30am–6pm · B50 · ⊚ watarun.org · Take the cross-river ferry from the pier adjacent to the Chao Phraya express-boat pier at Tha Thien

Almost directly across the river from Wat Pho rises the enormous, five-spired prang of **Wat Arun**, the Temple of Dawn, probably Bangkok's most memorable landmark and familiar as the silhouette used in the TAT logo. It looks particularly impressive from the river as you head downstream from the Grand Palace towards the *Oriental Hotel*, but is ornate enough to be well worth stopping off for a closer look. However, the temple is currently in the middle of a B150 million restoration project, swathing the main prang in scaffolding: it's still possible to get into the temple, but not to climb the prang.

A wat has occupied this site since the Ayutthaya period, but only in 1768 did it become known as the Temple of Dawn – when General Phraya Taksin reputedly reached his new capital at the break of day. The temple served as his royal chapel and housed the recaptured Emerald Buddha for several years until the image was moved to Wat Phra Kaeo in 1785. Despite losing its special status after the relocation, Wat Arun continued to be revered, and its corncob prang was reconstructed and enlarged to its present height of 81m by Rama II and Rama III.

The prang that you see today is classic Ayutthayan style, built as a representation of Mount Meru, the home of the gods in Khmer cosmology. Both the **central prang** and the four minor ones that encircle it are studded all over with bits of broken porcelain, ceramic shards and tiny bowls that have been fashioned into an amazing array of polychromatic flowers. The statues of mythical *yaksha* demons and half-bird, half-human *kinnari* that support the different levels are similarly decorated. The crockery probably came from China, possibly from commercial shipments that were damaged at sea, and the overall effect is highly decorative and far more subtle than the dazzling glass mosaics that clad most wat buildings. On the first terrace, the mondops at each cardinal point contain statues of the Buddha at birth (north), in meditation (east), preaching his first sermon (south) and entering Nirvana (west). The second platform surrounds the base of the prang proper, whose closed entranceways are guarded by four statues of the Hindu god Indra on his three-headed elephant Erawan. In the niches of the smaller prangs stand statues of Phra Pai, the god of the wind, on horseback.

Wat Prayoon

Off Thanon Pracha Thipok, 3min walk from Memorial Bridge; though on the Thonburi bank, it's easiest to reach from the Bangkok side, by walking over Memorial Bridge from the express ferry stop at Tha Saphan Phut (N6)

Just west of the Thonburi approach to Memorial Bridge, the unusual **Khao Mor cemetery** makes an unexpectedly enjoyable place to take the kids, with its miniaturized shrines and resident turtles. Its dollshouse-sized chedis and shrines are set on an artificial hillock, which was constructed by Rama III to replicate the pleasing shapes made by dripping candle wax; it's the most famous *khao mor* (miniature mountain) in Bangkok, an art form that's been practised in Thailand since the early eighteenth century. Wedged in among the grottoes, caverns and ledges of this uneven mass are numerous memorials to the departed, forming a not-at-all sombre gallery of different styles, from traditional Thai chedis, bots and prangs to more foreign designs like the tiny Wild West house complete with cacti at the front door. Turtles fill the pond surrounding the mound and you can feed them with the bags of banana and papaya sold nearby. The cemetery is part of **Wat Prayoon** (officially Wat Prayurawongsawat) but located in a separate compound to the southeast side of the wat.

Memorial Bridge

It wasn't until 1932 that Thonburi was linked to Bangkok proper by the **Memorial Bridge**, or **Saphan Phut**, constructed by Dorman Long who also built the Sydney Harbour Bridge. It commemorates the hundred and fiftieth anniversary of the foundation of the Chakri dynasty and of Bangkok, and is dedicated to Rama I (or Phra Buddha Yodfa, to give him his official title), whose bronze statue sits at the Bangkok approach. It proved to be such a crucial river-crossing that the bridge has since been supplemented by the adjacent twin-track **Saphan Phra Pokklao**.

Dusit

Connected to Ratanakosin via the boulevards of Rajdamnoen Klang and Rajdamnoen Nok, the spacious, leafy area known as **Dusit** has been a royal district since the reign of Rama V, King Chulalongkorn (1860–1910). The first Thai monarch to visit Europe, Rama V returned with radical plans for the modernization of his capital, the fruits of which are most visible in Dusit, notably at **Vimanmek Palace** and **Wat Benjamabophit**, the so-called "Marble Temple". Even now, **Rama V** still commands a loyal following and the statue of him, helmeted and on horseback, which stands in Royal Plaza at the Thanon U-Thong Nai/Thanon Sri Ayutthaya crossroads, is presented with offerings every week and is also the focus of celebrations on Chulalongkorn Day (Oct 23). On December 2, Dusit is also the venue for the spectacular annual **Trooping the Colour**, when hundreds of magnificently uniformed Royal Guards demonstrate their allegiance to the king by parading around Royal Plaza. Across from Chitrlada Palace, **Dusit Zoo** makes a pleasant enough place to take the kids.

Today, the Dusit area retains its European feel, and much of the country's decision-making goes on behind the high fences and impressive facades along its tree-lined avenues: the building that houses the National Parliament is here, as is Government House, and the king's official residence, Chitrlada Palace, occupies the eastern edge of the area. Normally a calm, stately district, in both 2008 and 2013 Dusit became the focus of **mass anti-government protests** by royalist yellow-shirts, who occupied Thanon Rajdamnoen Nok for several months on both occasions, creating a heavily defended temporary village in this most refined of neighbourhoods.

ARRIVAL AND DEPARTURE   **DUSIT**

By bus From Banglamphu, you can get to Dusit by taking the #70 (non-expressway) bus from Rajdamnoen Klang and getting off near the Rama V statue for Wat Benjamabophit, or outside the zoo and Elephant Museum on Thanon U-Thong Nai; or the #56 from Thanon Phra Sumen and alighting at the corner of Thanon Ratchasima and Thanon Rajwithi (known as the Kan Reuan inter-section), near the main entrance to Dusit Park. From

1

downtown Bangkok, easiest access is by bus from the Skytrain stop at Victory Monument; there are many services from here, including #28 and #108.

By boat Take the express boat to Tha Thewet and then it's about a 30min walk to Dusit Park, the zoo or Wat Benjamabophit.

Dusit Park

Main entrance on Thanon Rajwithi, with another ticket gate opposite Dusit Zoo on Thanon U-Thong Nai • Tues–Sun 9.30am–4.30pm, last admission 3.15pm • B100, or free with a Grand Palace ticket, which remains valid for one week • ⓦ vimanmek.com

The outstanding feature of what's known as **Dusit Park** is the breezy, elegant **Vimanmek Palace**, which was originally built by Rama V as a summer retreat on Ko Si Chang; however, he realized that the palace was strategically too vulnerable, after the French briefly invaded the island in the 1890s, and had it transported here bit by bit in 1901. The ticket price also covers entry to a dozen other specialist collections in Dusit Park, which these days resembles a theme park, with piped muzak, cafés, souvenir shops, heavy security and lots of coach tours. Among these collections, which include antique textiles, photographs taken by the king, royal ceremonial paraphernalia and antique clocks, housed in handsome, pastel-painted, former royal residences, the most interesting are the Support Museum and Elephant Museum. Note that the same **dress rules** apply here as to the Grand Palace (see p.85), though T-shirts and sarongs are for sale for those who do not pass muster.

Vimanmek Palace

Dusit Park • Free guided tours in English at 11am & 2pm

Built almost entirely of golden teak without a single nail, the coffee-coloured, L-shaped **Vimanmek Palace** is encircled by delicate latticework verandas that look out onto well-kept lawns, flower gardens and lotus ponds. Not surprisingly, this "Celestial Residence" soon became Rama V's favourite palace, and he and his enormous retinue of officials, concubines and children stayed here for lengthy periods between 1902 and 1906. All of Vimanmek's 81 rooms were out of bounds to male visitors, except for the king's own apartments in the octagonal tower, which were entered by a separate staircase.

On display inside is Rama V's collection of **artefacts** from all over the world, including *bencharong* ceramics, European furniture and bejewelled Thai betel-nut sets. Considered progressive in his day, Rama V introduced many newfangled ideas to Thailand: the country's first indoor bathroom is here, as is the earliest typewriter with Thai characters, and some of the first portrait paintings – portraiture had until then been seen as a way of stealing part of the sitter's soul.

The Support Museum

Immediately behind (to the east of) Vimanmek Palace, Dusit Park

The **Support Museum** is housed in a very pretty hundred-year-old building, the Abhisek Dusit Throne Hall, which was formerly used for meetings and banquets. It showcases the exquisite handicrafts produced under Queen Sirikit's charity project, Support, which works to revitalize traditional Thai arts and crafts. Outstanding exhibits include a collection of handbags, baskets and pots woven from the *lipao* fern that grows wild in southern Thailand; jewellery and figurines inlaid with the iridescent wings of beetles; gold and silver nielloware; and lengths of intricately woven silk from the northeast.

Chang Ton Royal Elephant National Museum

Just behind (to the east of) the Support Museum, inside the Thanon U-Thong Nai entrance to Dusit Park

These two whitewashed buildings once served as the stables for the king's white elephants. Now that the sacred pachyderms have been relocated, the stables have been turned into the **Royal Elephant National Museum**. Inside you'll find some interesting pieces of elephant paraphernalia, including sacred ropes, mahouts' amulets and magic

THE ROYAL WHITE ELEPHANTS

In Thailand, the most revered of all elephants are the so-called **white elephants** – actually tawny brown albinos – which are considered so sacred that they all, whether wild or captive, belong to the king by law. Their special status originates from Buddhist mythology, which tells how the previously barren Queen Maya became pregnant with the future Buddha after dreaming one night that a white elephant had entered her womb. The thirteenth-century King Ramkhamhaeng of Sukhothai adopted the beast as a symbol of the great and the divine, decreeing that a Thai king's greatness should be measured by the number of white elephants he owns. A white elephant appeared on the Thai national flag until 1917, and the present king, Rama IX, has ten white elephants, the largest royal collection to date.

Before an elephant can be granted official "white elephant" status, it has to pass a stringent assessment of its physical and behavioural **characteristics**. Key qualities include a paleness of seven crucial areas – eyes, nails, palate, hair, outer edges of the ears, tail and testicles – and an all-round genteel demeanour, manifested, for instance, in the way in which it cleans its food before eating, or in a tendency to sleep in a kneeling position. Tradition holds that an elaborate ceremony should take place every time a new white elephant is presented to the king: the animal is paraded with great pomp from its place of capture to Dusit, where it's anointed with holy water in front of an audience of priests and dignitaries, before being housed in the royal stables. Recently, though, the king has called time on this exorbitantly expensive ritual, and the royal white elephants now live in less luxurious, rural accommodation under the care of the Thai Elephant Conservation Centre (see p.315).

The expression "white elephant" probably derives from the legend that the kings used to present certain troublesome noblemen with one of these exotic creatures. The animal required expensive attention but, being royal, could not be put to work in order to pay for its upkeep.

formulae, as well as photos of the all-important ceremony in which a white elephant is granted royal status (see p.316).

Dusit Zoo (Khao Din)

Entrances on Thanon Rajwithi, on Thanon U-Thong Nai across from the Elephant Museum in Dusit Park, and on Thanon Rama V, within walking distance of Wat Benjamabophit • Daily 8am–6pm • B150 • ⓦ dusitzoo.org

Dusit Zoo, also known as **Khao Din**, was once part of the Chitrlada Palace gardens, but is now a public park. All the usual suspects are here in the zoo, including big cats, elephants, orang-utans, chimpanzees and a reptile house, but the enclosures are pretty basic. However, it's a reasonable place for kids to let off steam, with plenty of shade, a full complement of English-language signs, a lake with pedalos, tram rides and lots of food stalls and cafés.

Wat Benjamabophit

Corner of Thanon Sri Ayutthaya and Thanon Rama V: 200m south of the zoo's east entrance, or about 600m from Vimanmek's U-Thong Nai gate • Daily 7am–6pm • B20 • ⓦ facebook.com/watbencha

Wat Benjamabophit (aka Wat Ben) is a fascinating fusion of classical Thai and nineteenth-century European design, with the Carrara-marble walls of its bot – hence the tourist tag "**The Marble Temple**" – pierced by unusual stained-glass windows, neo-Gothic in style but depicting figures from Thai mythology. Rama V commissioned the temple in 1899, at a time when he was keen to show the major regional powers, Britain and France, that Thailand was *siwilai* (civilized), in order to baulk their usual excuse for colonizing. The temple's sema stones are a telling example of the compromises involved: they're usually prominent markers of the bot's sacred area, but here they're hard to spot, decorative and almost apologetic – look for the two small, stone lotus buds at the front of the bot on top of the white, Italianate balustrade. Inside the unusually cruciform bot, a fine replica of the highly revered Phra Buddha Chinnarat image of Phitsanulok presides over the small room containing some of Rama V's ashes. The

1

courtyard behind the bot houses a gallery of Buddha images from all over Asia, set up by Rama V as an overview of different representations of the Buddha.

Wat Benjamabophit is one of the best temples in Bangkok to see religious **festivals** and rituals. Whereas monks elsewhere tend to go out on the streets every morning in search of alms, at the Marble Temple the ritual is reversed, and merit-makers come to them. Between about 5.30 and 7 or 7.30am, the monks line up on Thanon Nakhon Pathom, their bowls ready to receive donations of curry and rice, lotus buds, incense, even toilet paper and Coca-Cola; the demure row of saffron-robed monks is a sight that's well worth getting up early for. The evening candlelight processions around the bot during the Buddhist festivals of Maha Puja (in Feb) and Visakha Puja (in May) are among the most entrancing in the country.

Museum of Floral Culture

315 Yaek Soi Ongkarak 13 (continuation northwards of Thanon Nakhon Ratchasima), Soi 28, Thanon Samsen • Tues–Sun 10am–6pm • B150 includes guide • ☏ 02 669 3633–4, ⓦ floralmuseum.com • 20min walk (northeast), or a motorcycle-taxi ride, from Tha Payap (N18) express-boat pier, served by orange-flag boats

Said to be the only one of its kind in the world, the **Museum of Floral Culture** has been recently opened by the renowned floral artist, Sakul Intakul. The terms are deliberately generalized here, as this is about not only flower arranging, but so much more: floral designs and uses in Thailand and other Asian cultures. Guides will lead you around the beautiful garden and the century-old, colonial-style, teak mansion, where the diverse exhibits cover temple offerings of flowers, sketches of some of Khun Sakul's most famous designs and floral artefacts from his travels around Asia. There's a lovely tea shop on one of the verandas, and the museum holds occasional floral workshops for adults and children.

Downtown Bangkok

Extending east from the main rail line and south to Thanon Sathorn and beyond, **downtown Bangkok** is central to the colossal expanse of Bangkok as a whole, but rather peripheral in a sightseer's perception of the city. In this modern high-rise area, you'll find the main shopping centres around **Siam Square**, though don't come looking for an elegant commercial piazza here: the "square" is in fact a grid of small streets, sheltering trendy fashion shops, cinemas and inexpensive restaurants. It lies to the southeast of **Pathumwan intersection**, the junction of Thanon Rama I (in Thai, "Thanon Phra Ram Neung") and Thanon Phrayathai, and the name is applied freely to the surrounding area. Further east, you'll find yet more shopping malls around the noisy and glittering **Erawan Shrine**, where Rama I becomes Thanon Ploenchit, an intersection known as **Ratchaprasong**. It was here that the opposition redshirts set up a fortified camp for several months in early 2010, before the Democrat Party government sent in the troops, leading to the deaths of 91 people. It's possible to stroll in peace above the cracked pavements, noise and fumes of Thanon Rama I, by using the elevated **walkway** that runs beneath the Skytrain lines all the way from the Siam Paragon shopping centre to the Erawan Shrine (further progress is blocked by Central and Chitlom Skytrain stations). East of Ratchaprasong, you pass under the expressway flyover and enter the farang hotel, shopping and entertainment quarter of **Thanon Sukhumvit**.

The area south of Thanon Rama I is dominated by Thailand's most prestigious centre of higher learning, Chulalongkorn University, and the green expanse of **Lumphini Park**. Thanon Rama IV (in Thai "Thanon Phra Ram Sii") then marks another change of character: downtown proper, centring around the high-rise, American-style boulevard of **Thanon Silom**, the heart of the financial district, extends from here to the river. Alongside the smoked-glass banks and offices, and opposite Convent Road, site of Bangkok's Carmelite nunnery, lies the dark heart of Bangkok nightlife, **Patpong**.

▲ Thanon Sukhumvit

■ ACCOMMODATION	
A-One Inn	6
Anantara Siam	12
Centara Grand	4
at Central World	
Centara Watergate Pavillion	1
Courtyard by Marriott	11
Golden House	8
Jim's Lodge	13
Lub d	9
Luxx XL	15
Pathumwan Princess Hotel	10
Siam Kempinski	3
Swissôtel Nai Lert Park	2
Ten Face	14
Wendy House	5
White Lodge	7

■ BARS	
Coco Walk	1
Hyde and Seek	2

● SHOPS	
Alexander Lamont	13/17
Asia Books	8
B2S	16
Books Kinokuniya	1/4
Central Embassy	19
Central World	9
Chabatik	6
Doi Tung Lifestyle	10
Exotique Thai	5
Jim Thompson	3
Lofty Bamboo	22
Mah Boon Krong (MBK)	21
Narai Phand	15
OTOP	18
Propaganda	11
Siam Center	12
Siam Square	20
Thann	14
Viera by Ragazze	2/7

● RESTAURANTS & CAFES			
Aoi	4	Mah Boon Krong	17
Din Tai Fung	14	Food Courts	
Eathai	15	Polo Fried Chicken	23
Food Loft	12	(Kai Thawt Jay Kee Soi Polo)	
Gianni	20	Red Sky	9
Hinata	16	Royal India	5
Home Kitchen	19	Sanguansri	13
(Khrua Nai Baan)		Somboon Seafood	11/18
Honmono Sushi	22	Som Tam (Nua)	8
Inter	21	Sra Bua	2
Jim Thompson's Restaurant	3	Taling Pling	6/10
Kai Ton Pratunam	1	Vanilla Brasserie	7

DOWNTOWN: AROUND SIAM SQUARE AND THANON PLOENCHIT

─(S)─ BTS Skytrain and station
☆ Khlong Saen Saeb boat stop

0 ⎯⎯⎯ 250 metres

1

Surprisingly, among downtown's vast expanse of skyscraping concrete, the main attractions for visitors are four attractive museums housed in historic teak houses: **Jim Thompson's House**, the **Ban Kamthieng**, the **Suan Pakkad Palace Museum** and **M.R. Kukrit's Heritage Home**. The area's other tourist highlight is **Siam Ocean World**, a high-tech aquarium that both kids and adults can enjoy. The accounts of the sights below are arranged roughly north–south.

ARRIVAL AND DEPARTURE   **DOWNTOWN BANGKOK**

By Skytrain and subway All of the sights reviewed here are within walking range of a Skytrain station; some are also served by the subway.

By boat The fastest way to head downtown from Banglamphu is by public boat along Khlong Saen Saeb,

beginning near Democracy Monument. A slower but much more scenic route (and during rush hours, possibly quicker than a bus from Banglamphu downtown) is to take an express boat downriver, then change onto the Skytrain at BTS Saphan Taksin.

Victory Monument

Northern downtown is cut through by several major thoroughfares, including the original road to the north, Thanon Phaholyothin, which runs past the weekend market and doesn't stop until it gets to the border with Myanmar at Mae Sai, 900km away – though it's now more commonly known as Highway 1, at least in between towns. The start of Phaholyothin is marked by the stone obelisk of **Victory Monument** (*Anu Sawari Chaisamoraphum*, or just *Anu Sawari*), which can be seen most spectacularly from Skytrains as they snake their way round it. It was erected after the Indo-Chinese War of 1940–41, when Thailand pinched back some territory in Laos and Cambodia while the French government was otherwise occupied in World War II, but nowadays it commemorates all of Thailand's past military glories.

Suan Pakkad Palace Museum

352–4 Thanon Sri Ayutthaya · Daily 9am–4pm · B100 · ☎ 02 246 1775–6 ext 229, ⊛ suanpakkad.com · 5min walk from BTS Phaya Thai

The **Suan Pakkad Palace Museum** stands on what was once a cabbage patch (*suan pakkad*) but is now one of the finest gardens in Bangkok. Most of this private collection of beautiful Thai objects from all periods is displayed in four groups of traditional wooden houses, which were transported to Bangkok from various parts of the country.

In House no. 8, as well as in the Ban Chiang Gallery in the modern Chumbhot-Pantip Center of Arts in the palace grounds, you'll find a very good collection of elegant, whorled pottery and bronze jewellery, which the former owner of Suan Pakkad Palace, Princess Chumbhot, excavated from tombs at Ban Chiang, the major Bronze Age settlement in the northeast (see p.480). Scattered around the rest of the museum are some fine ceramics and attractive Thai and Khmer religious sculptures; an extensive collection of colourful papier-mâché *khon* masks; beautiful betel-nut sets (see box, p.283); monks' elegant ceremonial fans; and some rich teak carvings, including a two-hundred-year-old temple door showing episodes from *Sang Thong*, a folk tale about a childless king and queen who discover a handsome son in a conch shell.

The Lacquer Pavilion

The highlight of Suan Pakkad is the renovated **Lacquer Pavilion**, across the reedy pond at the back of the grounds. Set on stilts, the pavilion is actually an amalgam of two eighteenth- or late seventeenth-century temple buildings, a *ho trai* (library) and a *ho khien* (writing room), one inside the other, which were found between Ayutthaya and Bang Pa-In. The interior walls are beautifully decorated with gilt on black lacquer: the upper panels depict the life of the Buddha while the lower ones show scenes from the *Ramayana*. Look out especially for the grisly details in the tableau on the back wall, showing the earth goddess drowning the evil forces of Mara. Underneath are depicted some European dandies on horseback, probably merchants, whose presence suggests that the work was executed before the fall of Ayutthaya in 1767. The carefully observed details of daily life and nature are skilful and lively, especially considering the restraints that the lacquering technique places on the artist, who has no opportunity for corrections or touching up.

Jim Thompson's House

Just off Siam Square at the north end of Soi Kasemsan 2, Thanon Rama I · Daily from 9am, viewing on frequent 30–40min guided tours, last tour 5pm; shop 9am–8pm · B100 · ☎ 02 216 7368, ⌨ jimthompsonhouse.com · BTS National Stadium, or via a canalside path from the Khlong Saen Saeb pier at Saphan Hua Chang

Jim Thompson's House is a kind of Ideal Home in elegant Thai style, and a peaceful refuge from downtown chaos. The house was the residence of the legendary American adventurer, entrepreneur, art collector and all-round character whose mysterious

THE LEGEND OF JIM THOMPSON

Thai silk-weavers, art dealers and conspiracy theorists all owe a debt to **Jim Thompson**, who even now, nearly fifty years after his disappearance, remains Thailand's most famous farang. An architect by trade, Thompson left his New York practice in 1940 to join the Office of Strategic Services (later to become the CIA), a tour of duty that was to see him involved in clandestine operations in North Africa, Europe and, in 1945, the Far East, where he was detailed to a unit preparing for the invasion of Thailand. When the mission was pre-empted by the Japanese surrender, he served for a year as OSS station chief in Bangkok, forming links that were later to provide grist for endless speculation.

After an unhappy and short-lived stint as part-owner of the *Oriental Hotel*, Thompson found his calling with the struggling **silk-weavers** of the area near the present Jim Thompson House, whose traditional product was unknown in the West and had been all but abandoned by Thais in favour of less costly imported textiles. Encouragement from society friends and an enthusiastic write-up in *Vogue* convinced him there was a foreign market for Thai silk, and by 1948 he had founded the Thai Silk Company Ltd. Success was assured when, two years later, the company was commissioned to make the costumes for the Broadway run of *The King and I*. Thompson's celebrated eye for colour combinations and his tireless promotion – in the early days, he could often be seen in the lobby of the *Oriental* with bolts of silk slung over his shoulder, waiting to pounce on any remotely curious tourist – quickly made his name synonymous with Thai silk.

Like a character in a Somerset Maugham novel, Thompson played the role of Western exile to the hilt. Though he spoke no Thai, he made it his personal mission to preserve traditional arts and architecture (at a time when most Thais were more keen to emulate the West), assembling his famous Thai house and stuffing it with all manner of Oriental objets d'art. At the same time he held firmly to his farang roots and society connections: no foreign gathering in Bangkok was complete without Jim Thompson, and virtually every Western luminary passing through Bangkok – from Truman Capote to Ethel Merman – dined at his table (even though the food was notoriously bad).

If Thompson's life was the stuff of legend, his disappearance and presumed death only added to the mystique. On Easter Sunday, 1967, Thompson, while staying with friends in a cottage in Malaysia's Cameron Highlands, went out for a stroll and never came back. A massive search of the area, employing local guides, tracker dogs and even shamans, turned up no clues, provoking a rash of fascinating but entirely unsubstantiated theories. The grandfather of them all, advanced by a Dutch psychic, held that Thompson had been lured into an ambush by the disgraced former prime minister of Thailand, Pridi Panomyong, and spirited off to Cambodia for indeterminate purposes; later versions, supposing that Thompson had remained a covert CIA operative all his life, proposed that he was abducted by Vietnamese Communists and brainwashed to be displayed as a high-profile defector to Communism. More recently, an amateur sleuth claims to have found evidence that Thompson met a more mundane fate, having been killed by a careless truck driver and hastily buried.

1

disappearance in the jungles of Malaysia in 1967 has made him even more of a legend among Thailand's farang community.

Apart from putting together this beautiful home, completed in 1959, Thompson's most concrete contribution was to turn traditional silk-weaving in Thailand from a dying art into the highly successful international industry it is today. The complex now includes a **shop**, part of the Jim Thompson Thai Silk Company chain (see p.167), and an excellent **bar-restaurant** (see p.155).

Above the shop, the **Jim Thompson Center for the Arts** is a fascinating gallery that hosts both traditional and modern temporary exhibitions on textiles and the arts, such as royal maps of Siam in the nineteenth century or *mor lam*, the folk music of the northeast (see p.765). Ignore any con-men at the entrance to the soi looking for gullible tourists to escort on rip-off shopping trips, who'll tell you that the house is closed when it isn't.

The house

The grand, rambling **house** is in fact a combination of six teak houses, some from as far afield as Ayutthaya and most more than two hundred years old. Like all traditional houses, they were built in wall sections hung together without nails on a frame of wooden pillars, which made it easy to dismantle them, pile them onto a barge and float them to their new location. Although he had trained as an architect, Thompson had more difficulty in putting them back together again; in the end, he had to go back to Ayutthaya to hunt down a group of carpenters who still practised the old house-building methods. Thompson added a few unconventional touches of his own, incorporating the elaborately carved front wall of a Chinese pawnshop between the drawing room and the bedroom, and reversing the other walls in the drawing room so that their carvings faced into the room.

The impeccably tasteful **interior** has been left as it was during Jim Thompson's life, even down to the place settings on the dining table – Thompson entertained guests most nights and to that end designed the house like a stage set. Complementing the fine artefacts from throughout Southeast Asia is a stunning array of Thai arts and crafts, including one of the best collections of traditional Thai paintings in the world. Thompson picked up plenty of bargains from the Thieves' Quarter (Nakhon Kasem) in Chinatown, before collecting Thai art became fashionable and expensive. Other pieces were liberated from decay and destruction in upcountry temples, while many of the Buddha images were turned over by ploughs, especially around Ayutthaya. Some of the exhibits are very rare, such as a headless but elegant seventh-century Dvaravati Buddha and a seventeenth-century Ayutthayan teak Buddha.

After the guided tour, you're free to look again, at your leisure, at the former rice barn and gardener's and maid's houses in the small, jungly **garden**, which display some gorgeous traditional Thai paintings and drawings, as well as small-scale statues and Chinese ceramics.

Bangkok Art and Cultural Centre

Junction of Rama I and Phrayathai roads • Tues–Sun 10am–9pm • Free • ☏ 02 214 6630–1, ⓦ bacc.or.th • BTS National Stadium

A striking, white hunk of modernity, the prestigious **Bangkok Art and Cultural Centre** houses several galleries on its upper floors, connected by spiralling ramps like New York's Guggenheim, as well as several performance spaces. It hosts temporary shows by contemporary artists from Thailand and abroad across all media, from the visual arts to music and design, and there's usually something interesting on here – coming in from BTS National Stadium, there's a blackboard inside the entrance where the day's events and shows are chalked up in English.

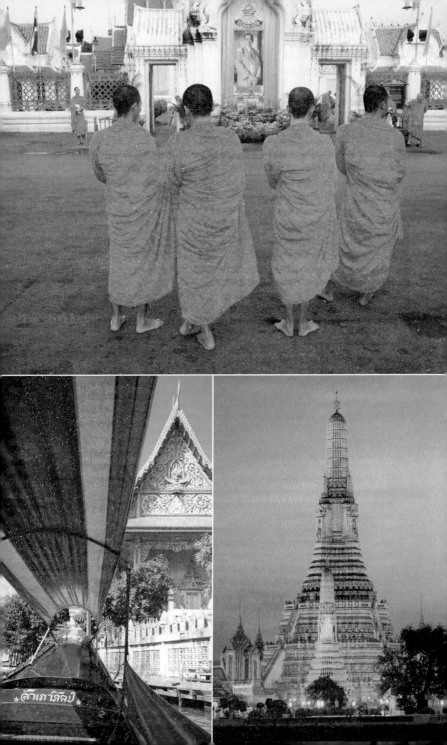

1

BANGKOK FOR KIDS

The following activities centres, theme parks and amusement centres are all designed for kids, the main drawbacks being that many are located a long way from the city centre. Other attractions kids should enjoy include the Museum of Siam (see p.92), feeding the turtles at Wat Prayoon (see p.112), Dusit Zoo (see p.115), Sea Life Bangkok Ocean World aquarium (see p.122), the Snake Farm (see p.124), cycling around Muang Boran Ancient City (see p.132), taking a canal boat through Thonburi (see p.111) and pedal-boating in Lumphini Park (see p.126). A useful resource for tips on travelling with kids (see p.57) in Bangkok is ⓦ bkkkids.com.

Bangkok Butterfly Garden and Insectarium Suan Rotfai (Railway Park), just north of Chatuchak Weekend Market; Tues–Sun 8.30am–4.30pm; free; ☎ 02 272 4359. Over five hundred butterflies flutter within an enormous landscaped dome. There's also a study centre, plus family-oriented cycle routes and bikes (with infant seats) for rent in the adjacent park, which also has a kids' playground. The park is walkable from BTS Mo Chit or Chatuchak Park subway.

Dream World Ten minutes' drive north of Don Muang Airport at kilometre-stone 7 Thanon Rangsit–Ongkarak; Mon–Fri 10am–5pm, Sat & Sun 10am–7pm; B1000/person including transfers; ⓦ dreamworld.co.th. Theme park with different areas such as Snow Town and Fairytale Land, including water rides, a hanging roller coaster and other amusements.

Funarium Soi 26, Thanon Sukhumvit, down towards Thanon Rama IV; Mon–Thurs 9am–6pm, Fri–Sun 9am–7pm; B110–320, depending on height of visitor; ⓦ funarium.co.th. Huge indoor playground, with an arts and crafts room, cooking classes and a restaurant.

KidZania Floor 5, Siam Paragon shopping centre, Thanon Rama I; Mon–Fri 10am–5pm, Sat & Sun 10.30am–8.30pm; B350–850, depending on age; ⓦ bangkok.kidzania.com. Imaginative and varied new activities centre, where kids can play at being doctors and nurses, Japanese chefs, and even fortune tellers.

Safari World On the northeastern outskirts at 99 Thanon Ramindra, Minburi; daily 9am–5pm; joint ticket to both parks B1200, children B650; ⓦ www .safariworld.com. Bus tours through a huge safari park, with monkeys, lions, giraffes and zebras, plus a separate marine park with dolphins and sea lions, as well as various animal shows (phone ☎ 02 914 4100– 19 for times).

Siam Park City On the far eastern edge of town at 101 Thanon Sukhapiban 2; daily 10am–6pm; B500, children 100–130cm B120, under 100cm free, with extra charges for some rides, or B900 for an unlimited day pass; ⓦ siamparkcity.com. Water-slides, whirlpools and artificial surf, plus roller coasters and other rides.

Sea Life Bangkok Ocean World

Basement of Siam Paragon shopping centre (east end), Thanon Rama I • Daily 10am–9pm, last admission 8pm; shark feeds 1pm & 4pm, as well as many other timed feedings (detailed on the website) • B990 (online, weekday early-bird and family discounts available); B2000 including "Ocean Walker"; behind-the-scenes tour B200; shark dive from B5300; 5D films B250 • ☎ 02 687 2000, ⓦ sealifebangkok.com • BTS Siam

Spread over two spacious floors, **Bangkok Ocean World** is an impressive, Australian-built aquarium. Despite the high admission price, it gets crowded at weekends and during holidays, and can be busy with school groups on weekday afternoons. Among outstanding features of this US$30-million development are an 8m-deep glass-walled tank, which displays the multicoloured variety of a coral reef drop-off to great effect, and a long, under-ocean tunnel where you can watch sharks and rays swimming over your head. In this global piscatorial display of around four hundred species, locals such as the Mekong giant catfish are not forgotten, while regularly spaced touch-screen terminals provide information in English about the creatures on view. It's even possible to walk in an underwater tunnel wearing a diving helmet (the "Ocean Walker"), or dive with the sharks, whether you're a licensed diver or not. You can also take a behind-the-scenes tour and watch – through 3D glasses – underwater cartoons in "5D Cinema Xtreme", where the chairs move and there are occasional sprays of water.

The Erawan Shrine

Corner of Thanon Ploenchit and Thanon Rajdamri • Daily 24hr • Free • BTS Chit Lom

For a glimpse of the variety and ubiquity of Thai religion, drop in on the **Erawan Shrine** (*Saan Phra Prom* in Thai). Remarkable as much for its setting as anything else, this shrine to Brahma, the ancient Hindu creation god, and Erawan, the many-headed elephant he created, squeezes in on one of the busiest and noisiest intersections in modern Bangkok. And it's not the only one: half a dozen other Hindu shrines are dotted around Ratchaphrasong intersection, most notably **Trimurti**, who combines the three main gods, Brahma, Vishnu and Shiva, on Thanon Rajdamri outside Central World near the intersection's opposite corner. Modern Bangkokians see Trimurti as a sort of Cupid figure, and those looking for love bring red offerings.

The *Grand Hyatt Erawan Hotel*, towering over the Erawan Shrine, is the reason for its existence and its name. When a string of calamities held up the building of the original hotel in the 1950s, spirit doctors were called in, who instructed the owners to build a new home for the offended local spirits: the hotel was then finished without further mishap. Ill fortune struck the shrine itself, however, in early 2006, when a young Muslim man, who was suffering from mental illness, smashed the Brahma statue to

BARS & CLUBS

Apoteka	3
Cheap Charlie's	4
Clouds	9
Finnegan's	6
Glow	5
The Iron Fairies	10
Long Table	7
Mikkeller	11
Nest	2
Q Bar (Q Up)	1
Studio Lam	12
WTF	8

ACCOMMODATION

Amari Boulevard	1
The Atlanta	3
Hilton Sukhumvit	8
Imm Fusion	7
Napa Place	6
Park Plaza	5
Seven	4
Suk 11	2

SHOPS

Books Kinokuniya	5
Dasa Book Café	6
Emporium	3
Krishna's	1
The Shop @ TCDC	4
Sop Moei Arts	7
Thai Craft Fairs	2

RESTAURANTS & CAFÉS

Aoi	11	Le Dalat	1
Baan Khanitha	2	The Myth of MahaNaga	9
Barcelona Gaudí	6	Ramentei	10
Beirut	3	Royal India	12
Bolan	16	Soul Food Mahanakorn	14
Cabbages and		Suk 11	4
Condoms	7	Supanniga Eating Room	17
Dosa King	5	Vientiane Kitchen	
Himali Cha-Cha	8	(Khrua Vientiane)	15
Imoya	13		

THANON SUKHUMVIT

1

pieces with a hammer – and was then brutally beaten to death by an angry mob. An exact replica of the statue was quickly installed, incorporating the remains of the old statue to preserve the spirit of the deity.

Be prepared for sensory overload here: the main structure shines with lurid glass of all colours and the overcrowded precinct around it is almost buried under scented garlands and incense candles. You might also catch a group of traditional dancers performing here to the strains of a small classical orchestra – worshippers hire them to give thanks for a stroke of good fortune. To increase their future chances of such good fortune, visitors buy a bird or two from the flocks incarcerated in cages here; the bird-seller transfers the requested number of captives to a tiny hand-held cage, from which the customer duly liberates the animals, thereby accruing merit. People set on less abstract rewards will invest in a lottery ticket from one of the physically disabled sellers: they're thought to be the luckiest you can buy.

Ban Kamthieng (Kamthieng House)

131 Thanon Asok Montri (Soi 21 off Thanon Sukhumvit) • Tues–Sat 9am–5pm • B100 • Ⓦ siam-society.org • BTS Asok or Sukhumvit subway

A traditional northern Thai residence, **Ban Kamthieng** was moved in the 1960s from Chiang Mai to just off Thanon Sukhumvit and set up as an ethnological museum by the Siam Society. The delightful complex of polished teak buildings makes a pleasing oasis beneath the towering glass skyscrapers that dominate the rest of Sukhumvit. It differs from Suan Pakkad, Jim Thompson's House and M.R. Kukrit's Heritage Home in being the home of a rural family, and the objects on display give a fair insight into country life for the well-heeled in northern Thailand.

The house was built on the banks of the Ping River in the mid-nineteenth century, and the ground-level display of farming tools and fish traps evokes the upcountry practice of fishing in flooded rice paddies to supplement the supply from the rivers. Upstairs, the main display focuses on the ritual life of a typical Lanna household, explaining the role of the spirits, the practice of making offerings, and the belief in talismans, magic shirts and male tattoos. The rectangular lintel above the door is a *hum yon*, carved in floral patterns that represent testicles and are designed to ward off evil spirits. Walk along the open veranda to the authentically equipped kitchen to see a video lesson in making spicy frog soup, and to the granary to find an interesting exhibition on the ritual practices associated with rice farming.

Thailand Creative and Design Centre (TCDC)

6th floor of the Emporium Shopping Centre, Thanon Sukhumvit between sois 22 and 24 • Tues–Sun 10.30am–9pm • Free • Ⓦ tcdc.or.th • BTS Phrom Pong

Appropriately located in Emporium, one of Bangkok's most fashion-conscious shopping plazas, the **Thailand Creative and Design Centre** seeks to celebrate, promote and inspire innovative design through exhibitions, talks, a resource centre and shop (see p.167). Alongside often fascinating temporary exhibitions, the concise but thought-provoking permanent bilingual display focuses on the cultural contexts of design classics from around the world, beginning with the Louis Vuitton trunk of 1854 and including Thai fabrics and playful household items.

The Queen Saovabha Memorial Institute (Snake Farm)

Corner of Thanon Rama IV and Thanon Henri Dunant • Live shows Mon–Fri 2.30pm, Sat, Sun & hols 11am • B200 • Ⓦ saovabha.com • 10min walk from BTS Sala Daeng, or from Sam Yan or Si Lom subway stations

The **Queen Saovabha Memorial Institute** (*Sathan Saovabha*) is a bit of a circus act, but an entertaining, informative and worthy one at that. It's often simply known as the **Snake Farm**, but takes its formal name from one of Rama V's wives, who was a notable

DOWNTOWN: SOUTH OF THANON RAMA IV

● SHOPS
A Song Tailor	4
Ah Song Tailor	3
Asian Institute of Gemological Sciences	10
Golden Wool	7
Jim Thompson	2
Khomapastr	1
Lambert	11
The Legend	5
Silom Village	8
Tamnan Mingmuang	6

■ ACCOMMODATION
Baan Saladaeng	10
La Residence	4
Lub d	7
Luxx	8
New Road Guest House	2
Peninsula Bangkok	5
Rose	11
Sukhothai	1
Swan	9
Swiss Lodge	6
Tarntawan Place	3

● RESTAURANTS & CAFÉS
Aoi	11	Indian Hut	5
Baan Khanitha	4	Krua Aroy Aroy	14
Beirut	10	Le Bouchon	8
Celadon	2	Mei Jiang	9
Eat Me	15	Ramentei	7
Harmonique	1	Ruen Urai	2
Himali Cha-Cha	3/12	Sara Jane's	18
Home Cuisine	11	Somboon Seafood	6
Islamic Restaurant	4	Taling Pling	13

■ BARS
Flann O'Brien's	11
The Sky Bar & Distil	12
Tapas Room Club	7
Tawandang	13
German Brewery	1
Viva Aviv: The River	1

■ GAY BARS & CLUBS
The Balcony	8
Dick's Café	2
Disco Disco	10
DJ Station	6
GOD (Guys on Display)	5
JJ Park	4
Sphinx	9
Telephone Pub	3

S — BTS Skytrain and station
M — Subway and station
N1 — Express-boat pier

1

campaigner. Run by the Thai Red Cross, the institute has a double function: to produce snake-bite serums, and to educate the public on the dangers of Thai snakes. The latter mission involves putting on live demonstrations of snake handling and feeding. Well presented and safe, these displays gain a perverse fascination from the knowledge that the strongest venoms of the snakes on show can kill in only three minutes. If you're still not herpetologically sated, you can look round the attached exhibition space, where dozens of Thai snakes live in cages.

Lumphini Park

Thanon Rama IV • Daily roughly 5am–9pm • Free • BTS Saladaeng or Si Lom or Lumphini subway stations

If you're sick of cars and concrete, head for **Lumphini Park** (*Suan Lum*), where the air is almost fresh and the traffic noise dies down to a low murmur. Named after the town in Nepal where the Buddha was born, it was the country's first public park, donated by Rama VI, whose statue by Silpa Bhirasri (see p.751) stands at the main, southwest entrance. The park is arrayed around two lakes, where you can join the locals in feeding the turtles and fish with bread or take out a pedalo or rowing boat, and is landscaped with a wide variety of local trees and numerous pagodas and pavilions, usually occupied by chess-players. In the early morning and at dusk, people hit the outdoor gym on the southwest side of the park, or en masse do aerobics, balletic t'ai chi or jogging along the yellow-marked circuit, stopping for the twice-daily broadcast of the national anthem. On late Sunday afternoons in the cool season (usually Dec to mid-Feb), free classical concerts by the Bangkok Symphony Orchestra (⊕bangkoksymphony.org) draw in scores of urban picnickers.

Patpong

Concentrated into two lanes running between the eastern ends of Thanon Silom and Thanon Suriwong, the neon-lit go-go bars of the **Patpong** district loom like rides in a tawdry sexual Disneyland. In front of each bar, girls cajole passers-by with a lifeless sensuality while insistent touts proffer printed menus and photographs detailing the degradations on show. Inside, bikini-clad women gyrate to Western music and play hostess to the (almost exclusively male) spectators; upstairs, live shows feature women who, to use Spalding Gray's phrase in *Swimming to Cambodia*, "do everything with their vaginas except have babies".

Patpong was no more than a sea of mud when the capital was founded on the marshy river bank to the west, but by the 1960s it had grown into a flash district of dance halls for rich Thais, owned by a Chinese millionaire godfather, educated at the London School of Economics and by the OSS (forerunner of the CIA), who gave his name to the area. In 1969, an American entrepreneur turned an existing teahouse into a luxurious nightclub to satisfy the tastes of soldiers on R&R trips from Vietnam, and so Patpong's transformation into a Western sex reservation began. At first, the area was rough and violent, but over the years it has wised up to the desires of the affluent farang, and now markets itself as a packaged concept of Oriental decadence.

The centre of the skin trade lies along the interconnected sois of **Patpong 1 and 2**, where lines of go-go bars share their patch with respectable restaurants, a 24-hour supermarket and an overabundance of pharmacies. Even the most demure tourists – of both sexes – turn out to do some shopping at the night market down the middle of Patpong 1, where hawkers sell fake watches, bags and designer T-shirts. By day, a relaxed hangover descends on the place. Farang men slump at the open-air bars on Patpong 2, drinking and watching videos, unable to find anything else to do in the whole of Bangkok. Running parallel to the east, **Soi Thaniya** is Patpong's Japanese counterpart, lined with hostess bars and some good restaurants, while the focus of Bangkok's gay scene, **Silom 2** (ie Soi 2, Thanon Silom) and the more mixed **Silom 4**, flank Thaniya.

THAILAND'S SEX INDUSTRY

Bangkok owes its reputation as the carnal capital of the world to a **sex industry** adept at peddling fantasies of cheap thrills on tap. More than a thousand sex-related businesses operate in the city, but the gaudy neon fleshpots of Patpong and Sukhumvit's Soi Nana and Soi Cowboy give a misleading impression of an activity that is deeply rooted in Thai culture: the overwhelming majority of Thailand's prostitutes of both sexes (estimated at anywhere between 200,000 and 700,000) work with Thai men, not farangs.

Prostitution and polygamy have long been intrinsic to the Thai way of life. Until Rama VI broke with the custom in 1910, Thai kings had always kept concubines, only a few of whom would be elevated to royal mothers. The practice was aped by the nobility and, from the early nineteenth century, by newly rich merchants keen to have lots of sons. Though the monarch is now monogamous, many men of all classes still keep **mistresses**, known as *mia noi* (minor wives), or have casual girlfriends (*gig*); the common view is that an official wife (*mia luang*) should be treated like the temple's main Buddha image – respected and elevated upon the altar – whereas the minor wife is like an amulet, to be taken along wherever you go. For less wealthy men, prostitution is a far cheaper option: at least two-fifths of sexually active Thai men are thought to visit brothels twice a month.

The **farang sex industry** is a relatively new development, having started during the Vietnam War, when the American military set up seven bases around Thailand. The GIs' appetite for "entertainment" attracted women from surrounding rural areas to cash in on the boom, and Bangkok joined the fray in the late 1960s. By the mid-1970s, the GIs had left, but tourists replaced them, lured by advertising that diverted most of the traffic to Bangkok and Pattaya. Sex tourism has since grown to become an established part of the Thai economy and has spread to Phuket, Hat Yai, Ko Samui and Chiang Mai.

The majority of the women who work in the country's go-go bars and "bar-beers" (outdoor hostess bars) come from the poorest areas of north and northeast Thailand. **Economic refugees**, they're easily drawn into an industry in which they can make in a single night what would take a month to earn in the rice fields. Many women opt for a couple of years in the sex bars to help pay off family debts and improve the living conditions of parents stuck in the poverty trap.

Many bar girls, and male prostitutes too, are looking for longer-term **relationships** with their farang customers, bringing a temporary respite from bar work and perhaps even a ticket out. A surprising number of one-night transactions do develop into some sort of holiday romance, with the young woman accompanying her farang "boyfriend" (often twice her age) around the country and maintaining contact after he's returned home. It's a common joke that some bar girls field half a dozen mobile phones so they can juggle all their various "sponsors". An entire sub-genre of novels and confessional memoirs (among them the classic *Hello, My Big Big Honey!: Letters to Bangkok Bar Girls and Their Revealing Interviews*) testifies to the role money plays in all this, and highlights the delusions common to both parties, not to mention the cross-cultural incomprehension.

Despite its ubiquity, prostitution has been **illegal** in Thailand since 1960, but sex-industry bosses easily circumvent the law by registering their establishments as clubs, karaoke bars or massage parlours, and making payoffs to the police and politicians. Sex workers, on the other hand, often endure exploitation and violence from pimps and customers rather than face fines and long rehabilitation sentences. Hardly surprising that many prefer to go freelance, working the clubs and bars in non-red-light zones such as Thanon Khao San. Life is made even more difficult because abortion is illegal in Thailand. The **anti-prostitution law**, however, does attempt to treat sex workers as victims rather than criminals and penalizes parents who sell their children. A high-profile voice in the struggle to improve the **rights of sex workers** is the Empower Foundation (ⓦempowerfoundation.org), which not only organizes campaigns and runs education centres for bar workers but also manages its own bar in Chiang Mai.

Inevitably, **child prostitution** is a significant issue in Thailand, but NGOs such as ECPAT (ⓦecpat.net) say numbers have declined over the last decade, due to zero-tolerance and awareness campaigns. The government has also strengthened legislation against hiring a prostitute under the age of 18, and anyone caught having sex with an under-15 is now charged with rape. The disadvantaged are still targeted by traffickers however, who "buy" children from desperately poor hill tribe and other minority families and keep them as bonded slaves until the debt has been repaid.

1

The west end of Thanon Silom

Further west along **Thanon Silom** from Patpong, in a still-thriving South Indian enclave, lies the colourful landmark of the **Maha Uma Devi Temple**. Also known as **Sri Mahamariamman** or **Wat Khaek**, this vibrant, gaudy Hindu shrine was built in 1895 in honour of Shiva's consort, Uma. Carrying on to the river, the strip west of Charoen Krung (New Road) reveals some of the history of Bangkok's early dealings with foreigners in the fading grandeur of the old trading quarter. Here you'll find the only place in Bangkok where you might be able to eke out an architectural walk, though it's hardly compelling. Incongruous churches and "colonial" buildings – the best being the Authors' Wing of the *Oriental Hotel*, where nostalgic afternoon teas are served – are hemmed in by the spice shops and *halal* canteens of the growing Muslim area around Thanon Charoen Krung.

M.R. Kukrit's Heritage Home

19 Soi Phra Pinit (Soi 7, Thanon Narathiwat Ratchanakharin) • Daily 10am–4pm, though it's often closed for social engagements, so worth phoning ahead to check • B50 • ☎ 02 286 8185, 🌐 kukritshousefund.com • 10min walk south then east from Thanon Sathorn; 20min walk from BTS Chong Nonsi

M.R. Kukrit's Heritage Home (*Baan Mom Kukrit*) is the beautiful traditional house and gardens of one of Thailand's leading figures of the twentieth century. M.R. (*Mom Rajawongse*, a princely title) **Kukrit Pramoj** (1911–95) was a remarkable all-rounder, descended from Rama II on his father's side and, on his mother's side, from the influential ministerial family, the Bunnags. Kukrit graduated in Philosophy, Politics and Economics from Oxford University and went on to become a university lecturer back in Thailand, but his greatest claim to fame is probably as a writer: he founded, owned and penned a daily column for *Siam Rath*, the most influential Thai-language newspaper, and wrote short stories, novels, plays and poetry. He was also a respected performer in classical dance-drama (*khon*), and he starred as an Asian prime minister, opposite Marlon Brando, in the Hollywood film, *The Ugly American*. In 1974, during an especially turbulent period for Thailand, life imitated art, when Kukrit was called on to become Thailand's prime minister at the head of a coalition of seventeen parties. However, just four hundred days into his premiership, the Thai military leadership dismissed him for being too anti-American.

The **residence**, which has been left just as it was when Kukrit was alive, reflects his complex character. In the large, open-sided *sala* (pavilion) for public functions, near the entrance, is an attractive display of *khon* masks, including a gold one that Kukrit wore when he played the demon king, Totsagan (Ravana). In and around the adjoining Khmer-styled garden, keep your eyes peeled for the *mai dut*, sculpted miniature trees similar to bonsai, some of which Kukrit worked on for decades. The living quarters beyond are made up of five teak houses on stilts, assembled from various parts of central Thailand and joined by an open veranda. The bedroom, study and various sitting rooms are decked out with beautiful objets d'art; look out especially for the carved bed that belonged to Rama II and the very delicate, two-hundred-year-old nielloware (gold inlay) from Nakhon Si Thammarat in the formal reception room. In the small family prayer room, Kukrit Pramoj's ashes are enshrined in the base of a reproduction of the Emerald Buddha.

The city outskirts

The amorphous clutter of Greater Bangkok doesn't harbour many attractions, but there are a handful of places that make pleasant half-day escapes, principally **Chatuchak Weekend Market**, the cultural theme-park of **Muang Boran**, the upstream town of **Nonthaburi** and the tranquil artificial island of **Ko Kred** (see map, p.79).

Chatuchak Weekend Market (JJ)

1

Occupies a huge patch of ground extending northwest from the corner of Phaholyothin and Kamphaeng Phet roads • Sat & Sun roughly 9am–6/7pm, though many stalls open earlier and some close later • ⓦ chatuchak.org

With over eight thousand open-air stalls to peruse, and wares as diverse as Lao silk, Siamese kittens and designer lamps, the enormous **Chatuchak Weekend Market**, or **JJ** as it's usually abbreviated (from "Jatu Jak"), is Bangkok's most enjoyable – and exhausting – shopping experience.

The market also contains a controversial **wildlife** section that has long doubled as a clearing house for protected and endangered species such as gibbons, palm cockatoos and Indian pied hornbills, many of them smuggled in from Laos and Cambodia and sold to private animal collectors and foreign zoos. The illegal trade goes on beneath the counter, despite occasional crackdowns, but you're bound to come across fighting cocks around the back, miniature flying squirrels being fed milk through pipettes, and iridescent red-and-blue Siamese fighting fish, kept in individual jars and shielded from each other's aggressive stares by sheets of cardboard.

Where to shop

Chatuchak is divided into 27 numbered **sections**, plus a dozen unnumbered ones, each of them more or less dedicated to a particular genre, for example household items, plants and secondhand books, and if you have several hours to spare, it's fun just to browse at whim. The market's primary customers are Bangkok residents in search of idiosyncratic fashion clothing (try sections 5 and 6) and homewares (sections 2, 3, 4, 7 and 8), but Chatuchak also has plenty of collector- and tourist-oriented **stalls**; best buys include antique lacquerware, unusual sarongs, traditional cotton clothing and crafts from the north, silver jewellery, and ceramics, particularly the five-coloured *bencharong*. For handicrafts (including musical instruments) and traditional textiles, you should start with sections 22, 24, 25 (which features textiles from northern Thailand) and 26, which are all in a cluster at the southwest (Kamphaeng Phet subway) end of the market; sections A, B and C, behind the market's head office and information centre, are also full of interesting artefacts.

Foodies will want to check out **Talat Or Tor Khor** (the Agricultural Market Organization), a covered market that sells a fantastic array of fruit, veg and other produce from around the country, as well as prepared dishes to take away or to eat at the food court; it's on the south side of Thanon Kamphaeng Phet, next to Kamphaeng Phet subway station. The best place to get a drink in the market is *Viva* (see p.163).

ARRIVAL AND GETTING AROUND

CHATUCHAK WEEKEND MARKET

Arrival Kamphaeng Phet subway station exits right into the most interesting, southwestern, corner of the market; on the northeast side of the market are Chatuchak Park subway and Mochit BTS stations. Coming from Banglamphu, either get a bus to BTS National Stadium or BTS Ratchathewi, or take the #503 (non-expressway version) or #509 bus all the way (about 1hr) from Rajdamnoen Klang (see p.99); once the MRT extension has opened, it should be possible to catch an express-boat to Tha Tien, then walk 5min to Sanam Chai station, for subway trains to Chatuchak Park or Kamphaeng Phet stations.

Getting around A few very small electric trams circulate around the market's main inner ring road, transporting weary shoppers for free, though they always seem to be full.

INFORMATION

Maps *Nancy Chandler's Map of Bangkok* has a fabulously detailed and informatively annotated map of all the sections in the market. Maps are also posted at various points around the market, including in the subway stations.

For specific help you can ask at the market office, on the main inner ring road near Gate 1 off Thanon Kamphaeng Phet 2, which also has ATMs and currency exchange booths.

1

The Prasart Museum

9 Soi 4A, Soi Krungthep Kreetha, Thanon Krungthep Kreetha • Tues–Sun 9am–2pm • B1000 for 1 person; for 2 people or more, B500 per person • Call ☎ 02 379 3601 to book the compulsory tour

Located on the far eastern edge of the city, the **Prasart Museum** is an unusual open-air exhibition of traditional Asian buildings, put together by wealthy entrepreneur and art-lover Khun Prasart. The museum is rarely visited – partly because of the intentionally limited opening hours and inflated admission price, and partly because it takes a long time to get there by public transport – but it makes a pleasant day out and is worth the effort.

Set in a gorgeously lush tropical garden, the museum comprises about a dozen beautifully crafted replicas of **traditional buildings**, including a golden teak palace inspired by the Tamnak Daeng at the National Museum, a Chinese temple and water garden, a Khmer shrine and a Sukhothai-era teak library set over a lotus pond. Some have been pieced together from ruined originals, while others were constructed from scratch. Many are filled with antique **artefacts**, including Burmese woodcarvings, prehistoric pottery from Ban Chiang and Lopburi-era statuettes. There's also an exquisite collection of *bencharong* ceramics.

ARRIVAL AND DEPARTURE
THE PRASART MUSEUM

By bus Regular and a/c bus #93 runs almost to the door: pick it up near its starting point on Thanon Si Phraya near River City and the GPO, or anywhere along its route on Phetchaburi and Phetchaburi Mai roads (both the Khlong Saen Saeb canal boats and the subway have potentially useful stops at the Thanon Asok Montri/Sukhumvit Soi 21 junction with Thanon Phetchaburi Mai). The #93 terminates on Thanon Krungthep Kreetha, but you should get off a couple of stops before the terminus, at the first stop on Thanon Krungthep Kreetha, as soon as you see the sign for the Prasart Museum (about 1hr 15min by bus from Si Phraya). Follow the sign down Soi Krungthep Kreetha, go

past the golf course and, after about a 15min walk, turn off down Soi 4A.

By boat To speed things up, instead of a bus ride, you could take the Khlong Saen Saeb canal boat all the way to Tha The Mall Bangkapi (about 40min from Phan Fah, seven stops after the confusingly similar Tha The Mall Ram stop). It is then a very short taxi ride to the museum.

By train Another time saver is to take the Suvarnabhumi Airport Rail Link from Phaya Thai to Hua Mark station, which leaves you within a very short taxi ride of the museum.

Nonthaburi

Chao Phraya Express Boat to Nonthaburi, the last stop upriver for most (N30), under 1hr from Central Pier (Sathorn) on an orange-flag boat

A trip to **NONTHABURI**, the first town and province beyond the northern boundary of Bangkok, is the easiest excursion you can make from the centre of the city and affords a perfect opportunity to recharge your batteries. Nonthaburi is the last stop upriver for most express boats and the ride itself is most of the fun, weaving round huge, crawling sand barges and tiny canoes. The slow pace of the boat gives you plenty of time to take in the sights on the way. On the north side of Banglamphu, beyond the elegant, new **Rama VIII Bridge**, which shelters the Mekong whisky distillery on the west bank, you'll pass in turn, on the east bank: the Bangkhunprom Palace and the adjacent Devaves Palace, two gleamingly restored former princely residences in the Bank of Thailand compound; the royal boathouse at Tha Wasukri in front of the National Library, where you can glimpse the minor ceremonial boats that escort the grand royal barges; the city's first Catholic church, Holy Conception, founded in the seventeenth century during King Narai of Ayutthaya's reign and rebuilt in the early nineteenth; and, beyond Krungthon Bridge, the Singha brewery. Along the route are dazzling Buddhist temples and drably painted mosques, catering for Bangkok's growing Muslim population, as well as a few remaining communities who still live in houses on stilts or houseboats – around Krungthon Bridge, for example, you'll see people living on the huge teak vessels used to carry rice, sand and charcoal.

DURIANS

The naturalist Alfred Russel Wallace, eulogizing the taste of the **durian**, compared it to "rich butter-like custard highly flavoured with almonds, but intermingled with wafts of flavour that call to mind cream cheese, onion sauce, brown sherry and other incongruities". He neglected to discuss the smell of the fruit's skin, which is so bad – somewhere between detergent and dog excrement – that durians are barred from Thai hotels and aeroplanes. The different **varieties** bear strange names that do nothing to make them more appetizing: "frog", "golden pillow", "gibbon" and so on. However, the durian has fervent admirers, perhaps because it's such an acquired taste, and because it's considered a strong aphrodisiac. Aficionados discuss the varieties with as much subtlety as if they were vintage Champagnes, and treat the durian as a social fruit, to be shared around, despite a price tag of up to B3000 each. They also pour scorn on the Thai government scientists who have recently genetically developed an odourless variety, the Chanthaburi 1 durian.

The most famous durian orchards are around Nonthaburi, where the fruits are said to have an incomparably rich and nutty flavour due to the fine clay soil. To see these and other plantations such as mango, pomelo and jackfruit, your best bet is to hire a longtail from Nonthaburi pier to take you west along Khlong Om Non. If you don't smell them first, you can recognize durians by their sci-fi appearance: the shape and size of a rugby ball, but slightly deflated, they're covered in a thick, pale-green shell which is heavily armoured with short, sharp spikes (*duri* means "thorn" in Malay). By cutting along one of the faint seams with a good knife, you'll reveal a white pith in which are set a handful of yellow blobs with the texture of a wrinkled soufflé: this is what you eat. The taste is best when the smell is at its highest, about three days after the fruit has dropped. Be careful when out walking near the trees: because of its great weight and sharp spikes, a falling durian can lead to serious injury, or even an ignominious death.

Disembarking at suburban Nonthaburi, on the east bank of the river, you won't find a great deal to do, in truth. There's a market that's famous for the quality of its fruit, while the attractive, old Provincial Office across the road is covered in wooden latticework. To break up your trip with a slow, scenic drink or lunch, you'll find a floating seafood restaurant, *Rim Fang*, to the right at the end of the prom.

Wat Chalerm Phra Kiat

1km north of Nonthaburi pier on the west bank of the river • From the express-boat pier take the ferry straight across the Chao Phraya and then catch a motorbike taxi or walk

Set in relaxing grounds on the west bank of the river, elegant **Wat Chalerm Phra Kiat** injects a splash of urban refinement among a grove of breadfruit trees. The beautifully proportioned temple, which has been lavishly restored, was built by Rama III in memory of his mother, whose family lived and presided over vast orchards in the area. Inside the walls of the temple compound, you feel as if you've come upon a stately folly in a secret garden, and a strong Chinese influence shows itself in the unusual ribbed roofs and elegantly curved gables, decorated with pastel ceramics. The restorers have done their best work inside: look out especially for the simple, delicate landscapes on the shutters.

Ko Kred

The tiny island of **KO KRED** lies in a particularly sharp bend in the Chao Phraya, about 7km north of Nonthaburi pier, cut off from the east bank by a waterway created in the eighteenth century to make the cargo route from Ayutthaya to the Gulf of Thailand just that little bit faster. Although it's been discovered by day-trippers from Bangkok, this artificial island remains something of a time capsule, a little oasis of village life completely at odds with the metropolitan chaos downriver. Roughly 10 square kilometres in all, Ko Kred has no roads, just a concrete track that follows its circumference, with a few arterial walkways branching off towards the interior.

1

Villagers, the majority of whom are Mon (see box, p.209), descendants of immigrants from Myanmar during the reigns of Taksin and Rama II, use a small fleet of motorbike taxis to cross their island, but as a sightseer you're much better off on a rental bicycle or just on foot: a round-island walk takes about an hour and a half.

There are few sights as such on Ko Kred, but its lushness and comparative emptiness make it a perfect place in which to wander. You'll no doubt come across one of the island's potteries and kilns, which churn out the regionally famous earthenware flowerpots and small water-storage jars and employ a large percentage of the village workforce. The island's clay is very rich in nutrients and therefore excellent for fruit-growing, and banana trees, coconut palms, pomelo, papaya, mango and durian trees all grow in abundance on Ko Kred, fed by an intricate network of irrigation channels that crisscrosses the interior. In among the orchards, the Mons have built their wooden houses, mostly in traditional style and raised high above the marshy ground on stilts.

Wat Paramaiyikawat

Ko Kred boasts a handful of attractive riverside wats, most notably **Wat Paramaiyikawat** (also called **Wat Poramai**), at the main pier at the northeast tip of the island. This engagingly ramshackle eighteenth-century temple was restored by Rama V in honour of his grandmother, with a Buddha relic placed in its leaning, white, riverside chedi, which is a replica of the Mutao Pagoda in Hanthawadi (now Bago), capital of the Mon kingdom in Myanmar. Among an open-air scattering of Burmese-style alabaster Buddha images, the tall bot shelters some fascinating nineteenth-century murals, depicting scenes from temple life at ground level and the life of the Buddha above, all set in delicate imaginary landscapes.

ARRIVAL AND DEPARTURE   **KO KRED**

The easiest but busiest time to visit Ko Kred is at the weekend, when you can take a boat tour from central Bangkok. At other times, getting there by public transport is a bit of a chore.

By boat tour The Mitchaopaya Travel Service (B300; ☎02 623 6169 or ☎02 225 6179) runs boat tours to Ko Kred on Saturdays, Sundays and public holidays, leaving Tha Chang in Ratanakosin at 9am, returning at about 4.30pm. On the way, you'll cruise along Khlong Bangkok Noi and Khlong Om, and call in at the Royal Barge Museum (see p.110), Wat Chalerm Phra Kiat in Nonthaburi (see p.131) and Wat Poramai and Ban Khanom Thai on Ko Kred, where you can buy traditional sweets and watch them being made.

By public transport Your best option is to take a Chao Phraya Express Boat to Nonthaburi, then bus #32 (ordinary and a/c, coming from Wat Pho via Banglamphu) or a taxi

(about B100) to Pakkred or a chartered longtail boat direct to Ko Kred (about B300). There are also fast, ordinary and a/c #166 buses from the northwest side of Victory Monument (accessible by Skytrain) to Pakkred, which are your best option for getting back as the #32 stops a fair way from Nonthaburi pier on its inbound journey. From Pakkred, the easiest way of getting across to the island is to hire a longtail boat, although shuttle boats cross at the river's narrowest point to Wat Poramai from Wat Sanam Neua, about 1km walk or motorbike-taxi ride south of the Pakkred pier (getting off the bus at Tesco Lotus in Pakkred will cut down the walk to Wat Sanam Neua).

Muang Boran Ancient City

33km southeast of central Bangkok in Samut Prakan • Daily 9am–7pm • B700 9am–4pm, B350 4–7pm • ⓦ ancientcitygroup.net • A/c bus #511 from Bearing Skytrain station (or from Thanon Rama I or Banglamphu) to Samut Prakan, then songthaew #36 to Muang Boran; otherwise, Muang Boran operates free pick-ups three times a day from Bearing Skytrain station (see their website for times), via Erawan Museum, an overblown exercise in spiritual psychedelia under the same ownership

A day-trip out to the **Muang Boran Ancient City** open-air museum is a great way to enjoy the best of Thailand's architectural heritage in relative peace and without much effort. Occupying a huge park shaped like Thailand itself, the museum comprises more than a hundred traditional Thai buildings scattered around pleasantly landscaped grounds and is best toured by rented **bicycle** (B50), though doing it on foot is just about possible. Many of the buildings are copies of the country's most famous monuments, and are located in the appropriate "region" of the park, with everything from Bangkok's Grand Palace (central region) to the spectacularly sited, hilltop Khmer Khao Phra Viharn sanctuary (northeast) represented here. There are also some original structures, including a rare scripture library rescued from Samut Songkhram (south), and some painstaking reconstructions from contemporary documents of long-vanished gems, of which the Ayutthaya-period Sanphet Prasat Palace (central) is a particularly fine example, as well as some purely imaginary designs. A sizeable team of restorers and skilled craftspeople maintains the buildings and helps keep some of the traditional techniques alive; if you come here during the week you can watch them at work.

ARRIVAL AND DEPARTURE   BANGKOK

Unless you arrive in Bangkok by train, be prepared for a long trip into the city centre. Suvarnabhumi and Don Muang airports are both 25km out and the three bus stations are not much closer in, though at least the Eastern Terminal is close to a Skytrain stop.

BY PLANE
When departing from Bangkok, leave plenty of time to get to Suvarnabhumi or Don Muang, as getting there by road can be severely hampered by traffic jams.

SUVARNABHUMI
Bangkok's main airport (coded "BKK" and pronounced "soo-wanna-poom"; ⓦ suvarnabhumiairport.com) is situated 25km east of central Bangkok between highways 7 and 34. The large airport is well stocked with 24hr exchange booths, ATMs, places to eat, pharmacies and a post office. The airport authority operates no fewer than ten generally helpful information counters and there's a tourist police booth in the arrivals hall on Floor 2; there are 24hr left-luggage depots (B100/item/day) in arrivals and in the departures hall on Floor 4. There are a number of accommodation options near Suvarnabhumi (see p.150).
Public Transportation Centre Situated on the other side of the huge airport complex from the terminal building, the Public Transportation Centre is reached by a free 10min ride on an "Express" shuttle bus (every 15min) from Gate 5 outside arrivals or Gate 5 outside departures – be sure not to confuse these with the much slower "Ordinary" shuttle buses, which ferry airport staff around the complex.
Suvarnabhumi Airport Rail Link The high-speed rail link (SARL; ⓦ srtet.co.th; daily 6am–midnight) from the basement of Suvarnabhumi is generally the quickest means of getting downtown, though it also serves as an important link for commuters and can get very crowded (the pricier express trains have recently been discontinued). There's only one set of elevated tracks, ending at Phaya Thai station, with trains running roughly every 12–15min (26min; B45), stopping at Makkasan, Ratchaprarop and four other stations. Phaya Thai is an interchange with the Skytrain system, and is served by a/c and non-a/c #59 buses (heading south on Thanon Phrayathai) to Thanon Rajadamnoen Klang, for Banglamphu.
Taxis Taxis to the centre are comfortable, a/c and reasonably priced, although the driving can be hairy. Walk past the pricey taxis and limousines on offer within the baggage hall and arrivals hall, and ignore any tout who may offer a cheap ride in an unlicensed and unmetered vehicle, as newly arrived travellers are seen as easy prey for robbery and the cabs are untraceable. Licensed and metered public taxis are operated from clearly signposted and well-regulated counters, outside Floor 1's Gates 4 and 7. Including the B50 airport pick-up fee and around B70 tolls for the overhead expressways, a journey to Thanon Silom downtown, for example, should set you back around B300–400, depending on the traffic. Heading back to the airport, drivers will nearly always try to leave their meters off and agree an inflated price with you – say "*poet meter, dai mai khrap/kha?*" to get them to switch the meter on. If you leave the downtown areas before 7am or after 9pm you can get to the airport in half an hour, but at other times you should set off about an hour and a half before you have to check in.
City buses and minibuses The most economical way of getting into the city is by public a/c bus or a/c minibus operated by the Bangkok Mass Transit Authority, but they're designed for airport staff and only a couple of minibus routes are likely to be useful to visitors: #551 to Victory Monument (every 20min; B40); and #552 to On Nut Skytrain station (every 20min; B20). These public minibuses start at the Public Transportation Centre and pick up outside the terminal's Floor 1 (Gates 1 and 8, with an information counter inside near Gate 8); however, if they fill up at the Public Transportation Centre, there'll be no pick-up at the terminal. On departure, many travellers opt for one of the private minibus services to Suvarnabhumi (B130–150) organized through guesthouses and travel agents in Banglamphu and elsewhere around the city.
Long-distance buses From the Public Transportation Centre, there are public (Baw Khaw Saw) long-distance buses to Pattaya, Chanthaburi, Trat, Khorat, Khon Kaen, Udon Thani and Nong Khai. Because of the inconvenience involved, most of these services also stop at Gate 8, Floor 1 of the terminal building (with an information counter

inside near Gate 7); in the opposite direction, some of these buses continue to Bangkok's Eastern or Northern (Mo Chit) Bus Terminals.

Car rental companies The car-rental companies in the arrivals hall (Floor 2) near Gate 8 include Avis and Budget (see p.141). You will have to pick your car up from the Public Transportation Centre.

DON MUANG

The old Don Muang Airport (coded "DMK"; ⓦdonmueang airportthai.com), 25km north of the city, is now Bangkok's main base for low-cost airlines (though some still use Suvarnabhumi – check your booking carefully). It shelters currency exchange booths, ATMs and a limited choice of places to eat.

By taxi The easiest way to get into the city centre is by licensed, metered taxi from the desk outside Arrivals, costing about B300–400, including B50 airport fee and expressway fees (B110 to Banglamphu, for instance).

By shuttle bus Roughly every 15min, shuttle buses from outside Arrivals (B30) run to Mo Chit Skytrain and Chatuchak Park subway stations and the nearby Northern Bus Terminal (Mo Chit).

By bus to/from Suvarnabhumi Airport Operating between every 30min and every hour (see ⓦsuvarnabhumi airport.com for times), an a/c transfer bus that's free to passengers runs between the airports; at Suvarnabhumi, it picks up outside Gate 3, Floor 2, and drops off outside Gate 5, Floor 4.

By bus to/from Banglamphu The #59 bus, stopping on the main highway that runs north–south in front of the airport buildings, will drop you off on Thanon Rajdamnoen Klang.

By minibus from the centre On departure, many travellers opt for one of the private minibus services to Don Muang (B130–150) organized through guesthouses and travel agents in Banglamphu and elsewhere around the city.

By train You can spare yourself the trip into Bangkok if you're planning to head north or northeast by train, as all services to these parts stop at Don Muang station. To reach the station, which is beside the *Amari Airport Hotel* across the main highway, follow the signs from Arrivals.

Destinations Chiang Mai (25 daily; 1hr); Chiang Rai (14 daily; 1hr 15min); Chumphon (3 daily; 1hr); Khon Kaen (10 daily; 55min); Ko Samui (20 daily; 1hr–1hr 30min); Krabi (up to 15 daily; 1hr 20min); Lampang (5 daily; 1hr 15min); Loei (2 daily; 1hr); Mae Sot (3–4 daily; 1hr 15min); Nakhon Phanom (3 daily; 1hr 15min); Nakhon Si Thammarat (14 daily; 1hr 10min); Nan (6 daily; 1hr 10min–1hr 40min); Phitsanulok (5 daily; 50min); Phrae (1 daily; 1hr); Phuket (30 daily; 1hr 20min); Ranong (2 daily; 1hr 30min); Sukhothai (2 daily; 1hr 20min); Surat Thani (14 daily; 1hr 15min); Trang (5 daily; 1hr 30min); Trat (3 daily; 1hr); Ubon Ratchathani (11 daily; 1hr 5min); Udon Thani (26 daily; 1hr).

BY TRAIN

Travelling to Bangkok by train from Malaysia and most parts of Thailand, you arrive at the main Hualamphong Station. Trains from Kanchanaburi, however, plus a handful from Nakhon Pathom, Hua Hin and other slow, local trains on the Southern line, pull in at Thonburi Station, while Samut Sakhon trains use Wongwian Yai Station (see p.182), also in Thonburi.

HUALAMPHONG STATION

Centrally located at the edge of Chinatown, Hualamphong Station is on the subway line and is connected to Banglamphu by bus #53. Station facilities include an exchange booth, several ATMs and a left-luggage office at the front of the main concourse (daily 4am–11pm; B20–80/day). The 24-hour State Railways (SRT) information booth in the main concourse, on the right, keeps English-language timetables, while tickets can be bought at any ticket counter. Train tickets can also be bought through almost any travel agent and through some hotels and guesthouses for a booking fee of about B50. See "Basics" for more information on tickets and timetables (see p.30). Beware, the station area is fertile ground for con-artists who are looking to prey on new arrivals. Anyone who comes up to you in or around the station concourse and offers help/information/transport or ticket-booking services is probably a scammer, however many official-looking ID tags are hanging round their neck. Hualamphong also nurtures plenty of dishonest tuk-tuk drivers – take a metered taxi or public transport instead.

Destinations Aranyaprathet (2 daily; 6hr); Ayutthaya (35 daily; 1hr 30min–2hr); Butterworth (Malaysia; 1 daily; 21hr); Cha-am (2–3 daily; 3hr 10min–3hr 50min); Chiang Mai (5 daily; 12–14hr); Chumphon (10 daily; 7hr–9hr 30min); Hua Hin (10–11 daily; 3hr 30min–5hr); Khon Kaen (4 daily; 8hr 30min–9hr 45min); Khorat (10 daily; 4hr 30min–6hr 40min); Lampang (5 daily; 10–12hr); Lamphun (5 daily; 12–14hr); Lopburi (15 daily; 2hr 30min–3hr); Nakhon Pathom (12 daily; 1hr 30min); Nakhon Si Thammarat (2 daily; 15–16hr); Nong Khai (3 daily; 10hr 30min–13hr); Pak Chong (for Khao Yai National Park; 10 daily; 3hr 30min–4hr 45min); Pattaya (1 daily; 4hr); Phetchaburi (11 daily; 2hr 45min–3hr 45min); Phitsanulok (11 daily; 5hr 30min–8hr); Prachuap Khiri Khan (11 daily; 5–7hr); Pranburi (1 daily; 5hr–5hr 30min); Si Racha (1 daily; 3hr 30min); Si Saket (8 daily; 8–11hr); Surat Thani (10 daily; 9–12hr); Surin (10 daily; 6hr 30min–9hr 30min); Tha Naleng (near Vientiane, Laos; 1 daily; 13hr 30min); Trang (2 daily; 15–16hr); Ubon Ratchathani (7 daily; 8hr 35min–12hr 15min); Udon Thani (4 daily; 10–12hr).

THONBURI STATION

Thonburi Station (sometimes still referred to by its former name, Bangkok Noi Station) is a short ride in a red public

OVERLAND TO OTHER ASIAN COUNTRIES

Most travellers who choose to make their way **overland from Thailand** to Laos, Cambodia or Malaysia (see p.27) do so slowly, but it is possible to do the border-hop in one swoop from Bangkok, though in most cases you'll need to spend a night somewhere on the way. To get **from Bangkok to Laos**, there are public (Baw Khaw Saw) buses direct from Mo Chit to Vientiane (1 daily; 10hr) and Pakse (2 daily; 11hr 30min), or you can take a bus to the border at Chiang Khong, Nong Khai (which also has a train service from the capital), Nakhon Phanom (which also has an airport), Mukdahan or Chong Mek. For transport **to Cambodia**, there are public buses direct from Mo Chit to Siem Reap (2 daily; 7hr 30min) and Phnom Penh (1 daily; 11hr) or you can take a bus from Bangkok to Trat (for Sihanoukville) or a train or bus from Bangkok to Aranyaprathet (for Siem Reap). Khao San travel agents offer cheap direct buses to Siem Reap, but scams and discomfort on these services are common (see p.381). The easiest way of travelling from Bangkok **to Malaysia** is by train to the west coast of the peninsula. There is one train a day from Bangkok's Hualamphong Station to Butterworth (for Penang; 22hr), which costs about B1100 in a second-class sleeper; it's possible to make onward train connections to Kuala Lumpur and Singapore.

All the **foreign embassies and consulates** in Bangkok are located in the downtown area (see p.170). Phone ahead to check the opening hours (usually very limited) and documentation required. Some travellers prefer to avoid the hassle of trudging out to the relevant embassy by paying one of the Khao San travel agencies to get their visa for them; beware of doing this, however, as some agencies are reportedly **faking the stamps**, which causes serious problems at immigration.

songthaew or an 850m walk west from the N11 express-boat pier, just across the Chao Phraya River from Banglamphu and Ratanakosin.

Destinations Cha-am (3 daily; 3hr 30min–4hr 30min); Hua Hin (4 daily; 4–5hr); Kanchanaburi (2 daily; 3hr); Nakhon Pathom (2 daily; 1hr 10min); Nam Tok (2 daily; 4hr 35min); Phetchaburi (2 daily; 2hr 45min–3hr 45min); Pranburi (2 daily; 5hr–5hr 30min).

BY BUS

Bangkok's three main bus terminals, all of which have left-luggage facilities of some kind, are distributed around the outskirts of town. On departure, leave plenty of time to reach them, especially if setting off from Banglamphu, from where you should allow at least 1hr 30min (outside rush hour) to get to the Eastern Bus Terminal, and a good hour to get to the Northern or Southern terminals. Seats on the most popular long-distance a/c bus services (such as to Chiang Mai, Krabi, Phuket and Surat Thani) should be reserved ahead of time, most easily at the ATS (Advanced Technology Systems; Mon–Fri 9am–5pm) office near the *Royal Ratanakosin Hotel* on Thanon Rajdamnoen Klang in Banglamphu, the official seller of government bus tickets. Otherwise, go to the relevant bus station or use any of the ways described in Basics (see p.30), as guesthouses may book you on to one of the dodgy tourist services (see p.136).

NORTHERN AND NORTHEASTERN BUS TERMINAL (MO CHIT)

All services from the north and northeast terminate at Bangkok's biggest bus station, the Northern and Northeastern Bus Terminal (Mo Chit) on Thanon Kamphaeng Phet 2; some buses from the south and the east coast also use Mo Chit (there are plans to move Mo Chit to another, bigger site in northern Bangkok within the next 2–3 years or so). The quickest way to get into the city centre from Mo Chit is to hop onto the Skytrain at Mo Chit Station on Thanon Phaholyothin, or the subway at the adjacent Chatuchak Park Station or at Kamphaeng Phet Station (at the bottom of Thanon Kamphaeng Phet 2), all of which are about a 15min walk from the bus terminal, and then change onto a city bus if necessary. Otherwise, it's a long bus or taxi ride into town: city buses from the Northern Bus Terminal include ordinary and a/c #3, and a/c #509 to Banglamphu.

Destinations Aranyaprathet (at least hourly; 4hr 30min); Ayutthaya (every 20min; 1hr 30min–2hr); Chanthaburi (13 daily; 3–4hr); Chiang Khan (4 daily; 9–11hr); Chiang Khong (9 daily; 13–14hr); Chiang Mai (30 daily; 10–11hr); Chiang Rai (24 daily; 11–13hr); Chong Mek (5 daily; 10hr); Kamphaeng Phet (hourly; 6hr 30min); Kanchanaburi (8 daily; 3hr); Khon Kaen (every 30min; 6–7hr); Khorat (every 40min; 3–4hr); Khong Chiam (2 daily; 11hr); Lampang (at least hourly; 8–9hr); Loei (hourly; 8–10hr); Lopburi (every 20min; 2hr 30min–3hr); Mae Hong Son (2–3 daily; 16hr); Mae Sai (12 daily; 13hr); Mae Sariang (3 daily; 12hr); Mae Sot (12 daily; 8hr 30min); Mukdahan (20 daily; 11hr); Nakhon Phanom (21 daily; 12hr); Nan (12 daily; 11hr); Nong Khai (8 daily; 11hr); Pak Chong (for Khao Yai National Park; hourly; 2–3hr); Pakse (Laos; 1 daily; 12hr); Pattaya (every 30min; 2hr 30min–3hr 30min); Phitsanulok (70 daily; 5–6hr); Phnom Penh (Cambodia; 1 daily; 11hr); Phrae (13 daily; 8hr); Sangkhlaburi (2 daily; 7hr); Siem Reap (Cambodia; 2 daily; 7hr); Si Racha (every 40min; 2hr); Si Saket (3 daily; 7hr); Sukhothai (every 30min; 6–7hr); Surin (at least hourly; 7hr);

1

That Phanom (4 daily; 12hr); Trat (6 daily; 4hr 30min); Ubon Ratchathani (hourly; 10–12hrs); Udon Thani (every 30min; 9hr); Vientiane (Laos; 1 daily; 11hr).

EASTERN BUS TERMINAL (EKAMAI)

Most buses to and from east-coast destinations such as Pattaya, Ban Phe (for Ko Samet) and Trat (for Ko Chang) use the Eastern Bus Terminal (Ekamai) between sois 40 and 42 on Thanon Sukhumvit. This bus station is right beside the Ekamai Skytrain stop and is also served by lots of city buses, including a/c #511 to and from Banglamphu and the Southern Bus Terminal. Alternatively, you can use the Khlong Saen Saeb canal-boat service, which runs westwards almost as far as Banglamphu (see p.139); there's a pier called Tha Charn Issara, near the northern end of Sukhumvit Soi 63 (Soi Ekamai), which is easiest reached from the bus station by taxi.

Destinations Ban Phe (for Ko Samet; 14 daily; 3hr–3hr 30min); Chanthaburi (at least hourly; 4–5hr); Laem Ngop (for Ko Chang; 3–4 daily; 5hr 15min); Pattaya (every 30min; 2hr 30min–3hr 30min); Si Racha (every 40min; 1hr 30min–2hr 30min); Trat (6 daily; 4hr 30min–6hr).

SOUTHERN BUS TERMINAL (SATHAANII SAI TAI)

The huge, airport-like Southern Bus Terminal, or Sathaanii Sai Tai, handles transport to and from all points south of the capital, including Hua Hin, Chumphon (for Ko Tao), Surat Thani (for Ko Samui), Phuket and Krabi, as well as buses for destinations west of Bangkok, such as Amphawa, Nakhon Pathom and Kanchanaburi. The terminal lies at the junction of Thanon Borom Ratchonni and Thanon Phutthamonthon Sai 1 in Taling Chan, an interminable 11km west of the Chao Phraya River and Banglamphu, so access to and from city accommodation can take an age, even in a taxi. City buses serving the Southern Bus Terminal include #124 for Banglamphu, #511 for Banglamphu, Thanon Sukhumvit and Ekamai, and #516 for Banglamphu and Thewet, but note that when arriving in Bangkok most long-distance bus services make a more convenient stop before reaching the terminus (via a time-consuming U-turn), towards the eastern end of Thanon Borom Ratchonni, much nearer Phra Pinklao Bridge and the river; the majority of passengers get off here and it's highly recommended to do the same rather than continue to the terminal. The above-listed city buses all cross the river from this bus drop, as do many additional services, and this is also a faster and cheaper place to grab a taxi into town.

Destinations Amphawa (roughly every 40min; 2hr); Cha-am (every 1hr 30min; 2hr 45min–3hr 15min); Chumphon (roughly hourly; 7–9hr); Damnoen Saduak (every 40min; 2hr); Hua Hin (every 1hr 30min; 3–4hr); Kanchanaburi (every 2hr; 2hr 30min); Khao Lak (3 daily; 12hr); Ko Pha Ngan (2 daily; 14hr); Ko Samui (9–10 daily; 13hr); Krabi (12 daily; 12–14hr); Nakhon Pathom (every

10min; 40min–1hr 20min); Nakhon Si Thammarat (20 daily; 12hr); Phang Nga (5 daily; 13hr); Phetchaburi (at least every 30min; 2hr 15min); Phuket (21 daily; 12hr); Prachuap Khiri Khan (roughly every 30min; 4–5hr); Pranburi (every 30min; 3hr 30min); Ranong (15 daily; 9hr); Samut Songkhram (every 20min; 1hr 30min); Satun (4 daily; 16hr); Surat Thani (12 daily; 10–12hr); Trang (10 daily; 12hr).

BY AIR-CONDITIONED MINIBUS

For short- and medium-distance journeys, a faster, more convenient alternative to traipsing out to the bus terminals is to make use of *rot tuu*, the licensed, a/c minibus services (see p.30) that depart from central downtown locations. There's a particularly convenient service to Kanchanaburi that leaves from outside the *Royal Ratanakosin Hotel* at the west end of Rajdamnoen Klang in Banglamphu, but most other services depart from the Victory Monument roundabout (*Anu Sawari*), most easily reached via the Victory Monument Skytrain station. See the accounts of the relevant destinations for details.

BY TOURIST BUS

Many Bangkok tour operators sell tickets for unlicensed budget tourist buses and minibuses to popular long-distance destinations such as Chiang Mai, Surat Thani (for Ko Samui) and Krabi (for Ko Phi Phi), and to places closer at hand such as Kanchanaburi, Ko Samet and Ko Chang. Their only advantage is convenience, as they mostly leave from the Khao San area in Banglamphu. Prices, however, can vary considerably but rarely work out cheaper than buses from the public terminals or licensed a/c minibuses. The big drawbacks, however, are the lack of comfort and poor safety, which particularly applies to the long-distance overnight services. It is standard practice for budget tour operators, especially those on Thanon Khao San, to assure you that overnight transport will be in a large, luxury VIP bus despite knowing it's actually a clapped-out old banger. Security on overnight tourist buses is a serious problem, and because they're run by unlicensed private companies there is no insurance against loss or theft of baggage: don't keep anything of value in luggage that's stored out of sight, even if it's padlocked, as luggage sometimes gets slashed and rifled in the roomy baggage compartment. In addition, passengers often find themselves dumped on the outskirts of their destination city, at the mercy of unscrupulous touts. Services to Ko Samet (about B450 including boat transfer) and Ko Chang (about B600 including boat) are usually by a/c minibus; these are usually cramped and can go scarily fast but luggage is generally secure. Bear in mind that Khao San tour operators open up and go bust all the time; never hand over any money until you see the ticket. One tourist company that is licensed and reliable is Lomprayah, who operate catamarans to Ko Tao, Ko Pha Ngan and Ko Samui

TOURS OF THE CITY

Unlikely as it sounds, the most popular organized **tours** in Bangkok for independent travellers are by bicycle, heading to the city's outer neighbourhoods and beyond; these are an excellent way to gain a different perspective on Thai life and offer a unique chance to see traditional communities close up. In addition to those listed below, other tour options include Thonburi canal tours (see p.111), Chao Phraya Express tourist boats (see p.139), boat tours to Ko Kred (see p.131) and dinner cruises along the Chao Phraya River (see p.151).

ABC Amazing Bangkok Cyclist Tours 10/5–7 Soi Aree, Soi 26, Thanon Sukhumvit ☎02 665 6364, ⓦrealasia.net. ABC's are the most popular and longest-running bicycle tours, starting in the Sukhumvit area and taking you across the river to surprisingly rural khlong- and riverside communities (including a floating market at weekends); they also offer cycle-and-dine tours in the evening. Tours operate every day year-round, cover up to 30km depending on the itinerary, and need to be reserved in advance (B1300–2400 including bicycle).

Bangkok Bike Rides (Spice Roads) 45 Soi Pannee, Soi Pridi Banomyong 26, Soi 71, Thanon Sukhumvit ☎02 381 7490, ⓦbangkokbikerides.com or ⓦspiceroads.com. Bangkok Bike Rides runs a programme of different day and half-day tours within Greater Bangkok (B1200–3850/person, minimum two people), including

Ko Kred, as well as to the floating markets and canalside neighbourhoods of Damnoen Saduak and to Ayutthaya. Also offers multi-day trips out of the city.

Real Asia 10/5–7 Soi Aree, Soi 26, Thanon Sukhumvit ☎02 665 6364, ⓦrealasia.net. Part of the same company as ABC, Real Asia does full-day canal and walking tours through Thonburi and a "Backdoors to Bangkok" half-day tour, as well as leading outings by train to the historic fishing port of Samut Sakhon (all B2400, including lunch and boat trips).

Velo Thailand Soi 4, Thanon Samsen ☎02 628 8628, ⓦvelothailand.com. Velo Thailand runs half a dozen different bike tours of the capital (and further afield) out of its cycle shop on the edge of Banglamphu, including an after-dark tour (6–10pm; B1100) that takes in floodlit sights including Wat Pho, Wat Arun and the Pak Khlong Talat flower market.

and connecting buses from Banglamphu to Chumphon. They have an office at 154 Thanon Ram Buttri (☎02 629 2569–70, ⓦlomprayah.com). Recommended travel agents are listed in the Directory (see p.171).

GETTING AROUND

Getting around can undoubtedly be a headache in a city where it's not unusual for residents to spend 3hr getting to work. The main form of transport is **buses**, and once you've mastered the labyrinthine complexity of the route maps you'll be able to get to any part of the city, albeit slowly. Catching the various kinds of **taxi** is more expensive, and you'll still get held up by the daytime traffic jams. **Boats** are obviously more limited in their range, but they're regular and as cheap as buses, and you'll save a lot of time by using them whenever possible – a journey between Banglamphu and Saphan Taksin, for instance, will take around 30min by water, half what it would usually take on land. The **Skytrain** and **subway** each have a similarly limited range but are also worth using whenever suitable for all or part of your journey; their networks roughly coincide with each other at the east end of Thanon Silom, at the corner of Soi Asoke and Thanon Sukhumvit, and on Thanon Phaholyothin by Chatuchak Park (Mo Chit), while the Skytrain joins up with the Chao Phraya River express boats at the vital hub of Sathorn/Saphan Taksin (Taksin Bridge). At each Skytrain and subway station, you'll find a useful map of the immediate neighbourhood. Also under construction in the north of the city are the elevated metro lines known as the SRT Red Lines from Bang Sue (to connect with the subway), one of which will (eventually) stop at Don Muang airport.

BY BUS

Bangkok has reputedly the world's largest bus network, on which operate two main types of bus service. On ordinary (non-a/c) buses, which are mostly red and white or blue and white, fares range from B6.50 to B8.50 (though some are currently free); most routes operate from about 5am to 11pm, but some maintain a 24hr service (see box, p.138). Air-conditioned buses are either blue, orange or yellow (some are articulated) and charge between B10 and B34 according to distance travelled; most stop in the late evening, but a few of the more popular routes run 24hr services. As buses can only go as fast as the car in front, which at the moment is averaging 4km/h, you'll probably be spending a long time on each journey, so you'd be well advised to pay the extra for cool air – and the a/c buses are usually less crowded, too. For a comprehensive roundup of bus routes in the capital, buy a bus map or try logging onto the Bangkok Mass Transit Authority website (ⓦbmta.co.th), which gives hard-to-follow details of all city-bus routes.

1

USEFUL BUS ROUTES

In addition to those listed below, there are also bus routes from Suvarnabhumi Airport (see p.133) and Don Muang (see p.134). In Banglamphu, finding the right bus stop can sometimes be tricky (see p.99).

#3 (ordinary and a/c)
Northern Bus Terminal–Chatuchak Weekend Market–Thanon Phaholyothin–Thanon Samsen–Thanon Chakrabongse/Thanon Phra Arthit (for Banglamphu guesthouses)–Thanon Sanam Chai (for Museum of Siam)–Thanon Triphet–Memorial Bridge (for Pak Khlong Talat)–Taksin Monument (for Wongwian Yai) –Khlong San.

#15 (ordinary)
The Mall Tha Pra–Krung Thep Bridge–Thanon Charoen Krung (for Asiatique and Tha Sathorn)–Thanon Silom–Thanon Rajdamri–Siam Square–Thanon Lan Luang–Democracy Monument–Thanon Phra Arthit/Thanon Chakrabongse (for Banglamphu guesthouses)–Sanam Luang.

#16 (ordinary and a/c)
Northern Bus Terminal–Chatuchak Weekend Market–Thanon Samsen–Thewet (for guesthouses)–Thanon Phitsanulok–Thanon Phrayathai–Siam Square–Thanon Suriwong.

#25 (ordinary)
Pak Nam (for Ancient City buses)–Thanon Sukhumvit–Eastern Bus Terminal–Siam Square–Hualamphong Station–Thanon Yaowarat (for Chinatown)–Pahurat–Wat Pho–Tha Chang (for the Grand Palace).

#53 circular (also anticlockwise; ordinary)
Thewet–Thanon Krung Kasem– Hualamphong Station–Thanon Yaowarat (for Chinatown)–Pahurat–Pak Khlong Talat–Thanon Maharat (for Wat Pho and the Grand Palace)–Sanam Luang (for National Museum)–Thanon Phra Arthit and Thanon Samsen (for Banglamphu guesthouses)–Thewet.

#124 (ordinary)
Sanam Luang–Thanon Rajinee (for Banglamphu guesthouses)–Phra Pinklao Bridge–Southern Bus Terminal–Mahidol University.

#503 (a/c)
Sanam Luang–Democracy Monument (for Banglamphu guesthouses)–Thanon Rajdamnoen Nok (for TAT and boxing stadium)–Wat Benjamabophit–Thanon Sri Ayutthaya–Victory Monument–Chatuchak Weekend Market–Rangsit.

#508 (ordinary and a/c)
Sanam Luang–Grand Palace–Siam Square–Thanon Sukhumvit–Eastern Bus Terminal–Pak Nam (for Ancient City buses).

#509 (a/c)
Northern Bus Terminal–Chatuchak Weekend Market–Victory Monument–Thanon Rajwithi–Thanon Sawankhalok–Thanon Phitsanulok–Thanon Rajdamnoen Nok (for TAT and boxing stadium)–Democracy Monument–Thanon Rajdamnoen Klang (for Banglamphu guesthouses)–Phra Pinklao Bridge–Thonburi.

#511 (a/c)
Southern Bus Terminal–Phra Pinklao Bridge (for Banglamphu guesthouses)–Democracy Monument–Thanon Lan Luang–Thanon Phetchaburi–Thanon Sukhumvit–Eastern Bus Terminal–Pak Nam (for Ancient City buses).

Maps To get around Bangkok on the cheap, you'll need to buy a bus map. Thinknet's regularly updated *Bangkok Bus Guide*, which charts a/c and non-a/c buses, with close-up maps of Banglamphu and Victory Monument, is the most widely available. Bangkok Guide's *Bus Routes & Map* also charts all major a/c and non-a/c bus routes, as well as carrying detailed written itineraries of some two hundred routes, but is more difficult to come across these days.

BY BOAT

Bangkok was built as an amphibious city around a network of canals (khlongs) and the first streets were constructed only in the second half of the nineteenth century. Many canals remain on the Thonburi side of the river, but most of those on the Bangkok side have been turned into roads. The Chao Phraya River itself is still a major transport route for residents and non-residents alike, forming more of a link than a barrier between the two halves of the city.

EXPRESS BOATS

The Chao Phraya Express Boat Company operates the vital express-boat (*reua duan*; ⓦ chaophrayaexpressboat.com) services, using large water buses to plough up and down the river, between clearly signed piers (*tha*), which appear on all Bangkok maps. Tha Sathorn, which gives access to the Skytrain network, has been designated "Central Pier", with piers to the south of here numbered S1, S2, etc, those to the north N1, N2 and so on (see box below and map, p.80). Boats do not necessarily stop at every landing – they only pull in if people want to get on or off, and when they do stop, it's not for long – so when you want to get off, be ready at the back of the boat in good time for your pier. No-flag, local-line boats call at every pier between Nonthaburi and Wat Rajsingkorn, 90min away to the south beyond Sathorn, but only operate during rush hour (Mon–Fri, departing roughly 6.45–7.30am & 4–4.30pm; B10–14). The only boats to run all day, every day, are on the limited-stop orange-flag service (Nonthaburi to Wat Rajsingkorn in 1hr; roughly 6am–7pm, every 5–20min; B15). Other limited-stop services run during rush hour, flying either a yellow flag (between Nonthaburi and Rajburana, far downriver beyond Krung Thep Bridge, via Tha Sathorn, in about 50min; Mon–Fri roughly 6.15–8.20am & 4.45–8pm; B20–29) or a green flag (Pakkred to Tha Sathorn Mon–Fri 6.10–8.10am, Tha Sathorn to Pakkred Mon–Fri 4.05–6.05pm; about 50min; B13–32). Tickets can be bought on board; don't discard your ticket until you're off the boat, as the staff at some piers impose a B1 fine on anyone disembarking without one.

TOURIST BOATS

The Chao Phraya Express Boat Company also runs tourist boats, distinguished by their light-blue flags, between Sathorn (every 30min; 9.30am–4pm) and Phra Arthit piers (every 30min; 10am–5pm). In between (in both directions), these boats call in at Oriental, Si Phraya, Rachawongse, Thien, Maharat (near Wat Mahathat and the Grand Palace) and Wang Lang. On-board guides provide running commentaries, and a one-day ticket for unlimited trips, which also allows you to use other express boats within the same route on the same day, costs B150; one-way tickets are also available, costing B40.

CROSS-RIVER FERRIES

Smaller than express boats are the slow cross-river ferries (*reua kham fak*), which shuttle back and forth between the same two points. Found at or beside every express-boat stop and plenty of other piers in between, they are especially useful for exploring Thonburi. Fares are generally B3–4, payable at the entrance to the pier.

CANAL BOATS

Longtail boats (*reua hang yao*) ply the canals of Thonburi like commuter buses, stopping at designated shelters (fares are in line with those of express boats), and are available for individual rental here and on the river (see box, p.111). On the Bangkok side, Khlong Saen Saeb is well served by passenger boats, which run at least every 20min during daylight hours (eastbound services start and end a little later; ⓦ khlongsaensaep.com). They start from the Phan Fah pier (Panfa Leelard) at the Golden Mount (handy for Banglamphu,

---

CENTRAL STOPS FOR THE CHAO PHRAYA EXPRESS BOATS

N15 Thewet (all express boats) – for Thewet guesthouses.

N14 Rama VIII Bridge (no flag) – for Samsen Soi 5.

N13 Phra Arthit (no flag and orange flag) – for Thanon Phra Arthit, Thanon Khao San and Banglamphu guesthouses.

N12 Phra Pinklao Bridge (all boats) – for Royal Barge Museum.

N11 Thonburi Railway Station (or Bangkok Noi; no flag and orange flag) – for trains to Kanchanaburi.

N10 Wang Lang (aka Siriraj or Prannok; all boats) – for Wat Rakhang.

N9 Chang (no flag, green flag and orange flag) – for the Grand Palace, Sanam Luang and the National Museum.

N8 Thien (no flag and orange flag) – for Wat Pho, and the cross-river ferry to Wat Arun.

N7 Ratchini (aka Rajinee; no flag).

N6 Saphan Phut (Memorial Bridge; no flag and orange flag) – for Pahurat, Pak Khlong Talat and Wat Prayoon.

N5 Rachawongse (aka Rajawong; all boats) – for Chinatown.

N4 Harbour (Marine) Department (no flag and orange flag).

N3 Si Phraya (all boats) – walk north past the *Sheraton Royal Orchid Hotel* for River City shopping complex.

N2 Wat Muang Kae (no flag).

N1 Oriental (no flag and orange flag) – for Thanon Silom.

Central Sathorn (all boats) – for the Skytrain and Thanon Sathorn.

1

Ratanakosin and Chinatown), and head way out east to Wat Sribunruang, with useful stops at Thanon Phrayathai, aka Saphan Hua Chang (for Jim Thompson's House and Ratchathevi Skytrain stop); Pratunam (for the Erawan Shrine); Soi Chitlom; Thanon Witthayu (Wireless Road); and Soi Nana Nua (Soi 3), Thanon Asok Montri (Soi 21, for TAT headquarters and Phetchaburi subway stop), Soi Thonglo (Soi 55) and Charn Issara, near Soi Ekamai (Soi 63), all off Thanon Sukhumvit. This is your quickest and most interesting way of getting between the west and east parts of town, if you can stand the stench of the canal. You may have trouble actually locating the piers as few are signed in English and they all look very unassuming and rickety (see map, p.80); keep your eyes peeled for a plain wooden jetty – most jetties serve boats running in both directions. Once on the boat, state your destination to the conductor when he collects your fare, which will be between B10 and B20. Due to the construction of some low bridges, all

passengers change onto a different boat at Tha Pratunam – just follow the crowd.

BY SKYTRAIN

Although its network is limited, the BTS Skytrain, or *rot fai faa* (ⓦ www.bts.co.th), provides a much faster alternative to the bus, and is clean, efficient and over-vigorously air-conditioned. There are only two Skytrain lines, which interconnect at Siam Square (Central Station). Both run every few minutes from around 6am to midnight, with fares of B15–52/trip depending on distance travelled. You buy tickets from machines that accept only coins, but you can change notes at staffed counters. You'd really have to be motoring to justify buying a day pass at B130, while the various multi-trip cards are designed for long-distance commuters. The Sukhumvit Line runs from Mo Chit (stop N8) in the northern part of the city, via the interchange at

Phayathai (N2) with the airport rail line, to Bearing (Soi 105, Thanon Sukhumvit; E14) in around 40min. The Silom Line runs from the National Stadium (W1) via Saphan Taksin (Taksin, or Sathorn, Bridge; S6), to link up with the full gamut of express boats on the Chao Phraya River (though there are plans to close down Saphan Taksin Station and build a moving walkway between the river and Surasak Station), to Bang Wa (S12) in Thonburi (on Thanon Phetkasem, Highway 4).

BY SUBWAY

Bangkok's underground rail system, the MRT subway (or metro; in Thai, *rot fai tai din*; ⊕ www.bangkokmetro.co.th), has similar advantages to the Skytrain, though its current single line connects few places of interest for visitors. It runs every few minutes between around 6am and midnight from Hualamphong train station, via Silom (near Sala Daeng Skytrain station), Sukhumvit (near Asoke Skytrain) and Chatuchak Park (near Mo Chit Skytrain), to Bang Sue train station in the north of the city. Building work is under way to continue the line westwards from Hualamphong to Wat Mangkon Kamalawat in Chinatown, Pahurat, Thanon Sanam Chai in Ratanakosin, then across to Thonburi (currently due for completion in 2017); the eventual plan is to complete a loop back to Bang Sue. Pay your fare (B16–42) at a staffed counter or machine, where you'll receive a token to put through an entrance gate (the various day-passes and stored-value cards available are unlikely to be worthwhile for visitors).

BY TAXI

Bangkok taxis come in three forms, and are so plentiful that you rarely have to wait more than a couple of minutes before spotting an empty one of any description. Neither tuk-tuks nor motorbike taxis have meters, so you should agree on a price before setting off, and expect to do a fair amount of haggling.

METERED TAXIS

For nearly all journeys, the best and most comfortable option is to flag down one of Bangkok's metered, a/c taxi cabs; look out for the "TAXI METER" sign on the roof, and a red light in the windscreen in front of the passenger seat, which means the cab is available for hire. Starting at B35, fares are displayed on a clearly visible meter that the driver should reset at the start of each trip (say "*poet meter, dai mai khrap/kha?*" to ask him to switch it on), and increase in stages on a combined distance/time formula; as an example, a medium-range journey from Thanon Ploenchit to Thanon Sathorn will cost around B50 at a quiet time of day. Try to have change with you as cabs tend not to carry a lot of money; tipping of up to ten percent is common, though occasionally a cabbie will round down the fare on the meter. If a driver tries to quote a flat fare (often the case

with taxis that park outside tourist hotels waiting for business) rather than using the meter, let him go, and avoid the now-rare unmetered cabs (denoted by a "TAXI" sign on the roof). Getting a metered taxi in the middle of the afternoon when the cars return to base for a change of drivers can sometimes be a problem. If you want to book a metered taxi (B20–50 surcharge), try Siam Taxi Co-operative on ☎ 1661 or Taxi Radio on ☎ 1681.

TUK-TUKS

Somewhat less stable though typically Thai, tuk-tuks in Bangkok have very little to recommend them. These noisy, three-wheeled, open-sided buggies, which can carry three medium-sized passengers comfortably, fully expose you to the worst of Bangkok's pollution and weather. You'll have to bargain very hard to get a fare lower than the taxi-cab flagfall of B35; for a longer trip, for example from Thanon Convent to Siam Square, drivers will ask for as much as B200. Be aware, also, that tuk-tuk drivers tend to speak less English than taxi drivers – and there have been cases of robberies and attacks on women passengers late at night. During the day it's quite common for tuk-tuk drivers to try and con their passengers into visiting a jewellery, tailor's or expensive souvenir shop with them (see p.61).

MOTORBIKE TAXIS

Motorbike taxis generally congregate at the entrances to long sois – pick the riders out by their numbered, coloured vests – and charge from B10 for short trips down into the side streets. If you're short on time and have nerves of steel, it's also possible to charter them for hairy journeys out on the main roads (a short trip from Sanam Luang to Thanon Samsen will cost around B40). Crash helmets are compulsory on all main roads in the capital (traffic police fine non-wearers on the spot), though they're rarely worn on trips down the sois.

CAR RENTAL

You'd be mad to rent a self-drive car for getting around Bangkok, especially as taxis are so cheap, but you may want to start a driving tour around the country here.

Avis Branches are at 40 Thanon Sathorn Nua (delivery and collection anywhere in Bangkok), as well as Suvarnabhumi and Don Muang airports (☎ 02 251 1131–2, ⊕ avis thailand.com).

Budget Branches can be found at the following locations: 19/23 Building A, Royal City Avenue, Thanon Phetchaburi Mai; Suvarnabhumi Airport; and Don Muang Airport (☎ 02 203 9222, ⊕ budget.co.th).

BICYCLE RENTAL

Velo Thailand Soi 4, Thanon Samsen ☎ 02 628 8628, ⊕ velothailand.com. Offers good-quality bikes for B300/day to brave/foolhardy souls.

1

INFORMATION

Bangkok Tourism Division The official source of information on the capital, whose head office is currently next to Phra Pinklao Bridge at 17/1 Thanon Phra Arthit in Banglamphu (Mon–Fri 8am–7pm, Sat & Sun 9am–5pm; ☎02 225 7612–4, ⍟bangkoktourist.com); however, it's slated to move to an inconvenient location on the west side of Rama VIII Bridge over in Thonburi, though an information booth may be left in its place. The head office is supported by about twenty strategically placed satellite booths around the capital; most open Mon–Sat 9am–5pm, though some open Sun too, including in front of the Grand Palace, at Paragon and Mah Boon Krong shopping centres, and in front of Banglamphu's Wat Bowoniwes.

Tourism Authority of Thailand TAT (freephone tourist assistance 8am–8pm ☎1672; ⍟tourismthailand.org) maintains tourist information counters (both ones listed here are open daily 8.30am–4.30pm) at its head office, which is rather inconveniently located at 1600 Thanon Phetchaburi Mai, and, within walking distance of Banglamphu, at the Ministry of Tourism and Sports, 4 Rajdamnoen Nok – it's a 20min stroll from Thanon Khao San, or a short ride in a/c bus #503. Note, however, that the many other travel agents, shops and private offices across the capital displaying "TAT Tourist Information" signs or similar are not official Tourism Authority of Thailand information centres and will not be dispensing impartial advice (they may be licensed by TAT to run their business, but that doesn't make them government information offices). The Tourism Authority of Thailand never uses the acronym TAT on its office-fronts or in its logo, and doesn't book hotels or sell transport tickets.

Listings Listings magazines rise and fall with confusing rapidity in Bangkok; the best of the current publications is the free, weekly *Bk Magazine*, and its online counterpart, ⍟bk.asia-city.com, which gives a decent rundown of the art and drama scenes, live music and club nights for the week ahead. If you're interested in Bangkok's contemporary art scene, pick up a copy of the free, monthly Bangkok Art Map for exhibition listings (⍟facebook.com/bangkok artmap).

City maps For a personal guide to Bangkok's most interesting shops, markets, restaurants and backstreets, look for the famously idiosyncratic hand-drawn *Nancy Chandler's Map of Bangkok* and *Nancy Chandler's Map of Khao San and Old Bangkok*. Both carry a mass of annotated recommendations, are impressively accurate and regularly reissued; they're sold in most tourist areas, and copies and interim updates are also available at ⍟nancychandler .net. Maps are also available for Bangkok's bus routes (see p.138).

ACCOMMODATION

If your time in Bangkok is limited, you should think especially carefully about what you want to do in the city before deciding which part of town to stay in. Traffic jams are so appalling here that easy access to Skytrain, subway or river transport can be crucial. Advance reservations are recommended where possible during high season (Nov–Feb), though some guesthouses will only take cash deposits. For ultra-cheap double rooms under B500, your widest choice lies on and around **Banglamphu's** Thanon Khao San. The most inexpensive rooms here are no-frills crash-pads – small and often windowless, with fans, thin walls and shared bathrooms – but Banglamphu also offers plenty of well-appointed mid-priced options with a/c and swimming pools. Other, far smaller and less interesting travellers' ghettoes that might be worth bearing in mind are the generally dingy **Soi Ngam Duphli**, off the south side of Thanon Rama IV, which nevertheless harbours a couple of decent shoestring options; and **Soi Kasemsan I**, which is very handily placed next to Siam Square and firmly occupies the moderate range, though with a few rooms for around B600. Otherwise, the majority of the city's moderate and expensive rooms are scattered widely across the **downtown areas**, around Siam Square and Thanon Ploenchit, to the south of Thanon Rama IV and along **Thanon Sukhumvit**, and to a lesser extent in **Chinatown**. As well as easy access to transport links and shops, the downtown views from accommodation in these areas are a real plus, especially from the deluxe hotels that are scenically sited along the banks of the Chao Phraya River. In the reviews that follow, accommodation is a/c, unless specified.

RATANAKOSIN AND AROUND

Several small, upmarket hotels have recently opened on the west side of Ratanakosin, which put you in a peerless location, in a quiet, traditional, heavily Chinese neighbourhood of low-rise shophouses, overlooking the river and on the doorsteps of Wat Pho and the Grand Palace. The restaurants and nightlife of Banglamphu are within walking distance if you fancy a bit more of a buzz, while the sights of Thonburi and Chinatown, and Saphan Taksin Skytrain station are just a public boat ride away. It's also well worth considering *Ibrik Resort by the River*, a small, appealing hotel directly opposite Ratanakosin on the Thonburi bank of the Chao Phraya, whose main link with the rest of the city is by cross-river boat.

Arun Residence 36 Soi Pratu Nokyung, Thanon Maharat ☎02 221 9158, ⍟arunresidence.com; map p.83. Stunning views of Wat Arun and charming, wooden-floored rooms and suites that mix traditional and contemporary Thai styles. Occupying an eccentrically converted shophouse (plumbing can sometimes be a problem), the hotel also has an attractive lounge, a rooftop bar and a good European and Thai restaurant, *The Deck*, where breakfast (included in the price) is served. B4000

The Asadang Thanon Atsadang, corner of Thanon Phraya Si ☎085 180 7100, ⓦtheasadang.com; map p.83. In an early-twentieth-century Neoclassical mansion on Ratanakosin's doorstep, this very upscale B&B is perhaps a little truer to Thai roots than its sister, *The Bhuthorn* (see p.146), showcasing antique Thai furniture, carved lintels and attractive local fabrics; it's certainly airier and more spacious, with white wooden walls throughout. If you can manage the narrow, steep spiral staircase (and the higher rate, B4800), plump for the cute roof-top "Ratchabopit" overlooking the eponymous temple, which boasts a rocking chair, full-length windows and a private terrace overlooking Wat Rajabophit. Breakfast included. B3300

Aurum The River Place 394/27–29 Soi Pansook, Thanon Maharat ☎02 622 2248, ⓦaurum-bangkok .com; map p.83. Modelled on a French townhouse, with wooden shutters and wrought-iron balconies, this spruce, four-storey hotel is set back very slightly from the river and four of the rooms are "City View" only, but the other eight offer at least partial views of the water. Splashed with colourful Thai fabrics and sporting heavily varnished wooden floors, the well-equipped rooms are a little on the small side, apart from those on the top floor. There's a daytime riverside café, *Vivi: The Coffee Place* (see p.151), where complimentary breakfast is served. B3500

Chakrabongse Villas 396 Thanon Maharat ☎02 222 1290, ⓦthaivillas.com; map p.83. Upmarket riverside accommodation with a difference: nine tranquil rooms, suites and villas beautifully furnished in a choice of Thai, Chinese and Moroccan styles, set in the luxuriant gardens of hundred-year-old Chakrabongse House overlooking Wat Arun. All have a/c and cable TV, and there's a small, attractive swimming pool and a riverfront pavilion for relaxing or dining (if ordered in advance). There are canoes and bicycles available for guests to use. B5620

★**Ibrik Resort by the River** 256 Soi Wat Rakhang ☎02 848 9220, ⓦibrikresort.com; map p.83. With just three rooms, this is the most bijou of boutique resorts. Each room is beautifully appointed in boho-chic style, with traditional wood floors, modernist white walls and sparkling silk accessories – and two of them have balconies right over the Chao Phraya River. It's just like staying at a trendy friend's home, in a neighbourhood that sees hardly any other tourists. Located next door to *Supatra River House* restaurant and 5min walk from either express-boat stop Tha Wang Lang or the cross-river pier at Wat Rakhang (for Tha Chang and the Grand Palace). Breakfast included. B4000

Sala Arun 47 Soi Tha Thien, Thanon Maharat ☎02 622 2932–3, ⓦsalaarun.com; map p.83. Sister property to *Arun Residence*, also on the river, two blocks up. The six

teak-floored rooms (and one suite) feature objets d'art from the owners' worldwide travels, DVDs, iPod docks and balconies, while complimentary breakfast is served in the boldly coloured ground-floor café, which has a small terrace with armchairs facing Wat Arun (to get a view of the river and temple from your room, you'll have to pay B4200). B3500

BANGLAMPHU AND DEMOCRACY MONUMENT AREA

Nearly all backpackers head straight for Banglamphu, Bangkok's long-established travellers' ghetto just north of the Grand Palace, location of the cheapest accommodation, the best traveller-oriented facilities and some of the most enjoyable bars and restaurants in the city. A growing number of Khao San guesthouses are reinventing themselves as good-value mini-hotels boasting chic decor, swimming pools, and even views from the windows, but the cheap sleeps are still there, particularly immediately west of Khao San, around the neighbourhood temple Wat Chana Songkram, and along riverside Thanon Phra Arthit – where you'll also find some upscale places offering prime views over the Chao Phraya. About a 10min walk north from Thanon Khao San, the handful of guesthouses scattered among the shophouses of the Thanon Samsen sois enjoy a more authentically Thai environment, while the Thewet area, a further 15min walk in the same direction or a 7min walk from the Thewet express-boat stop, is more local still. Heading south from Khao San, across multi-laned Rajdamnoen Klang, to the upscale guesthouses in the area immediately south of Democracy also puts you plumb in the middle of an interesting old neighbourhood, famous for its traditional shophouse restaurants. Theft is a problem in Banglamphu, particularly at the cheaper guesthouses, so don't leave anything valuable in your room and heed the guesthouses' notices about padlocks and safety lockers.

THANON KHAO SAN AND AROUND

Buddy Lodge 265 Thanon Khao San ☎02 629 4477, ⓦbuddylodge.com; map pp.100–101. Stylish hotel right in the thick of the action, whose charming, colonial-style rooms are done out in cream, with louvred shutters, balconies, marble bathrooms, a/c and polished dark-wood floors. There's a beautiful rooftop pool, a spa, a gym and several bars downstairs in the *Buddy Village* complex. Specify an upper-floor location away from Khao San to ensure a quieter night's sleep. B1300

Charoendee Boutique Hostel 189 Thanon Khao San ☎02 629 1980, ⓔcharoendeehotel@gmail.com; map pp.100–101. Pleasantly surprising compound of pretty, colonial-style edifices with wooden shutters and lattice-work around a small, plant-strewn courtyard, hemmed in by a mess of surrounding buildings. Fan rooms share hot-water bathrooms, but it's well worth paying the extra for

1

an a/c, en-suite room in the airy original building; good rates for singles. Free coffee and toast for breakfast. It's located at the bottom of a narrow alley, so is quieter than many nearby places. Fan B450, a/c B650

Donna Guesthouse 75 Thanon Ratchadamnoen Klang ☎ 02 281 9374; map pp.100–101. Down a tiny alley and hemmed in by other buildings, this friendly, bright, and very clean establishment occupies a cute, white, clapboard house opposite the west wall of Ratchadamnoen post office. Downstairs, the tile-floored, a/c rooms with en-suite cold showers are small but manageable, while upstairs, the seven wood-floored, fan rooms share three cold-water bathrooms. Fan B270, a/c B380

Khao San Palace Inn 139 Thanon Khao San ☎ 02 282 0578, ⊛ khaosanpalace.com; map pp.100–101. Clean and well-appointed hotel, hung with appealing black-and-white photos of Bangkok, with a rooftop pool. Even the cheapest rooms have bathrooms, windows, a/c and satellite TV and are nicely tiled, making them good value, while some have panoramic views. B750

Lek House 125 Thanon Khao San ☎ 02 281 8441; map pp.100–101. Classic old-style Khao San guesthouse, in a stand-alone, multi-storey, yellow building, so most of the twenty rooms have windows; go for one on the front with a balcony, if you want the full Khao San blast. Bedrooms are small and basic, with fans and thin partition walls, and bathrooms are shared and cold-water. Less shabby than many others in the same price bracket and friendlier than most. Can get noisy at night as it's right next to popular *The Club* (see p.159). B240

Nap Park 5 Thanon Tani ☎ 02 282 2324, ⊛ nappark .com; map pp.100–101. On a surprisingly untouristed street just north of Thanon Khao San, this lively new hostel shelters smart dorm beds with personal TVs, lockers and hot showers, as well as plenty of space for lounging, either inside in front of the TV or outside in the tamarind-shaded front yard. Women-only dorm and laundry available. B399

AROUND WAT CHANA SONGKHRAM AND PHRA ARTHIT

Bella Bella House Soi Ram Bhuttri ☎ 02 629 3090; map pp.100–101. Above an attractive, plant-strewn café, the pastel-coloured rooms here are no frills but well priced, and a few boast lovely views over Wat Chana Songkhram. The cheapest share cold-water bathrooms, a notch up gets you an en-suite hot shower, while the most expensive have a/c. Fan B350, a/c B530

KC Guest House 64 Trok Kai Chae, corner of Thanon Phra Sumen ☎ 02 282 0618, ⊛ kc64guesthouse.com; map pp.100–101. Friendly, family-run guesthouse offering exceptionally clean, colourful rooms, either en suite (with hot water) or with shared, cold-water bathrooms. There's also a rooftop terrace and a decked eating area on the soi in front of 7-Eleven. Fan B450, a/c B750

Lamphu House 75 Soi Ram Bhuttri ☎ 02 629 5861–2, ⊛ lamphuhouse.com; map pp.100–101. With smart bamboo beds, coconut-wood furniture and elegant rattan lamps in all the rooms, this travellers' hotel set round a quiet courtyard has a calm, modern feel. Cheapest fan rooms share facilities and have no outside view, while the more expensive options have balconies overlooking the courtyard and the triples and four-bed rooms are popular with families. Fan B460, a/c B690

Merry V Soi Ram Bhuttri ☎ 02 282 9267; map pp.100–101. Large, efficiently run guesthouse offering some of the cheapest accommodation in Banglamphu. Bottom-end rooms are basic and small, many share bathrooms and it's pot luck whether you get a window or not. Better en-suites with hot showers and a/c versions are also available. Decent rates for singles. Fan B240, a/c B550

Navalai River Resort 45/1 Thanon Phra Arthit ☎ 02 280 9955, ⊛ navalai.com; map pp.100–101. Style-conscious riverfront hotel, with an elegant rooftop pool, modishly furnished rooms, and river views from the most desirable rooms. There's a/c, DVDs, bathtubs and private balconies, and the excellent riverside *Aquatini* restaurant is at ground level (see p.152). B2900

★**New Siam 2** 50 Trok Rong Mai ☎ 02 282 2795, ⊛ newsiam.net; map pp.100–101. Very pleasant and well-run small hotel whose en-suite rooms with fan and cold shower or a/c and hot shower stand out for their thoughtfully designed extras such as in-room safes, cable TV and drying rails on the balconies. Occupies a quiet but convenient location and has a small streetside pool. Popular with families, and a/c triple rooms are also available. Fan B740, a/c B840

New Siam Riverside 21 Thanon Phra Arthit ☎ 02 629 3535, ⊛ newsiam.net; map pp.100–101. Occupying a prime riverside spot, the latest in the *New Siam* empire offers well-designed, good-value rooms. Even the cheapest have a/c and full amenities, while the best of them boast fabulous river views from windows or private balconies. Also has a large riverside swimming pool and terrace restaurant. Breakfast included. B1490

Peachy Guest House 10 Thanon Phra Arthit ☎ 02 281 6471; map pp.100–101. Popular, good-value, long-running Bangkok institution set round a small, late-night courtyard bar. Offers lots of clean, simple, wooden-floored rooms, most with shared bathrooms but some with a/c. Fan B160, a/c B250

★**Praya Palazzo** 757/1 Soi 2, Thanon Somdet Phra Pinklao ☎ 02 883 2998, ⊛ prayapalazzo.com; map pp.100–101. A peaceful riverside sanctuary right opposite Banglamphu, this large, graceful, Italianate mansion has been lovingly restored by an architecture professor, with great attention to detail – right down to the wallpaper and lampshades – to give the feel of its 1920s origins. Twenty-first-century luxuries have been overlaid, of course, such as DVDs and, in the bathrooms, big-head showers to go alongside the brass taps and swathes of coloured marble. There's a lovely pool in the garden and an excellent restaurant too, serving royal Thai cuisine as well as afternoon tea. Access is by the free hotel boat, which shuttles across to Phra Arthit express-boat pier and up to Wat Rajathiwat (for Dusit) on demand. Breakfast included. B5370

SAMSEN SOIS AND THEWET

Baan Manusarn 8/11 Thanon Krung Kasem, Thewet ☎02 281 2976, ⓦbaanmanusarn.com; map pp.100–101. A genuine B&B, friendly and helpful, in a pleasant white building near the pier, offering large a/c rooms with lovely polished wooden floors, some sharing hot showers, and access to a kitchen and washing machine. Breakfast included. B1400

Lamphu Treehouse 155 Saphan Wanchat, Thanon Phracha Thipatai ☎02 282 0991–2, ⓦlamphutree hotel.com; map pp.100–101. Named after the *lamphu* trees that line the adjacent canal, after which Banglamphu ("the riverside village with mangrove apple trees") is named, this attractively turned-out guesthouse offers a pool and smart, a/c rooms, all with balconies and plenty of polished wood fittings made of recycled golden teak, among other traditional Thai decorative elements. It's in a quiet neighbourhood but just a few minutes' walk from Democracy. Breakfast included. B1650

Nakorn Ping 9/1 Soi 6, Thanon Samsen ☎02 281 6574, ⓦnakornpinghotel.com; map pp.100–101. In a low-rise, orange building dotted with plants on a fairly quiet soi, this place sports some classic elements of a Thai-Chinese hotel: spittoons for waste baskets, gnarly wooden furniture and little natural light. However, it's very clean, efficiently run and good value, offering fridges, cable TV and bathrooms in all rooms, and hot showers in the a/c options. Fan B460, a/c B560

★Old Bangkok Inn 609 Thanon Phra Sumen ☎02 629 1787, ⓦoldbangkokinn.com; map pp.100–101. This chic little boutique guesthouse with an eco-friendly philosophy has just ten a/c rooms, each of them individually styled in dark wood, with antique northern Thai partitions, Burmese doors, beds and ironwork lamps, plus elegant contemporary-accented bathrooms. All rooms have a DVD player, some also have a tiny private garden. The guest-house is located a 10min walk from Khao San. Long-stay discounts available. Breakfast included. B3200

★Phra Nakorn Norn Len 46 Thewet Soi 1, Thewet ☎02 628 8188–9, ⓦphranakorn-nornlen.com; map pp.100–101. What was once a seedy short-time motel has been transformed into a bohemian haven with genuine eco-conscious and socially engaged sensibilities and a tangible fair-trade philosophy. Every one of the comfort-able, though not luxurious, rooms has been hand-painted

to a different retro Thai design, and each has a cute bathroom, balcony and a/c. The rooftop bar enjoys unrivalled views of Wat Indraviharn's huge standing Buddha, and all kinds of free workshops, such as soap-making and cooking, are laid on for guests. Mostly organic vegetarian breakfast included. B2200

★Rajata Soi 6, Thanon Samsen ☎02 281 8977–8, ⓦrajatahotel.com; map pp.100–101. This traditional motel of large bedrooms and bathrooms around a quiet courtyard has been subtly transformed with retro furniture, hundreds of plants and a friendly welcome. All of the shining white, spotlessly clean accommodation has a/c, satellite TV, hot showers, mini-bars and a complimentary breakfast in the courtyard café. B1000

Sawatdee 71 Thanon Sri Ayutthaya (at Soi 16), Thewet ☎02 281 0757; map pp.100–101. Cheap and basic, but friendlier than many in the Thewet area, this long-running old-style guesthouse offers no-frills fan rooms with partition walls, some with en-suite bathrooms. B250

Sri Ayutthaya 23/11 Thanon Sri Ayutthaya (at Soi 14), Thewet ☎02 282 5942, ⓦfacebook.com/sriayuttaya; map pp.100–101. The most attractive guesthouse in Thewet, where most of the good-sized rooms (choose between fan rooms without private bathroom and en suites with a/c) are elegantly done out with wood-panelled walls and beautiful polished wood floors; these have been augmented by a few modern, "Superior" rooms (B1200) done out in bright, fetching colours. Hot showers throughout. Fan B500, a/c B700

Ssip 42 Thanon Phitsanulok, Thewet ☎02 282 1899, ⓦssiphotelthailand.com; map pp.100–101. Genteel and helpful upmarket B&B where guests are served delicious and beautifully presented breakfasts. It's in a new building on busy Thanon Phitsanulok, but fitted with antique furniture and fixtures and polished-wood floors, as well as a/c, hot showers, TVs and fridges. B3500

★Tavee 83 Soi 14, Thanon Sri Ayutthaya, Thewet ☎02 280 1447, ⓦfacebook.com/taveeguesthouse; map pp.100–101. *Tavee* is located down a pedestrian alley behind *Sri Ayutthaya* and is owned by the same family, but is the quieter and friendlier of the two options. Behind the stylish little café, the fan rooms sport attractive wood floors and share chic hot-water bathrooms, while the en-suite a/c options are larger and enjoy a few more decorative touches. Fan B450, a/c B750

SOUTH OF DEMOCRACY

Baan Dinso 113 Trok Sin, Thanon Dinso ☎02 622 0560, ⓦbaandinso.com; map pp.100–101. This tasteful, upmarket little guesthouse occupies an elegant, carefully restored 1920s Thai house all done out in cool buttermilk paintwork and polished teak floors. Prices are a little steep considering that all but the deluxe rooms have to use shared ground-floor, hot-water bathrooms, but they all have a/c,

1

mini-bars and DVD players. Hostelling International members get a ten percent discount. Breakfast is included. Very good single rates. **B2000**

★**The Bhuthorn** 96 Thanon Phraeng Phuthon, just off Thanon Kanlayana Maitri ☏02 622 2270, ⓦthebhuthorn.com; map pp.100–101. The architect-owners have beautifully converted this hundred-year-old shophouse into a B&B. Behind the small lobby lie just three elegant rooms (including a junior suite with a mezzanine for B5200), fitted with Chinese, Thai and Western dark-wood antique furniture, chandeliers, *khon* masks and other objets d'art, as well as modern comforts. Breakfast included. **B4200**

Boonsiri Place 55 Thanon Buranasart ☏02 622 2189–91, ⓦboonsiriplace.com; map pp.100–101. Run by two charming sisters, this mid-sized hotel is notable for its good value, environmentally conscious policies and location in a lively, seedy old neighbourhood, just a 10min walk from the Grand Palace. Each of its 48 large a/c rooms with hot showers (an extra B300 buys you considerably more space in a "Deluxe" room) is painted in vibrant colours and hung with a different artwork commissioned from the late Thai traditional temple artist Chanok Chunchob. Buffet breakfast included. **B1400**

The Warehouse 120 Thanon Bunsri ☏02 622 2935, ⓦthewarehousebangkok.com; map pp.100–101. Just down the road from Boonsiri Place, this new low-rise hotel offers an appealing version of industrial chic, reinforced by its punningly named Forklift Café. Emblazoned with playful health and safety slogans, the a/c, en-suite rooms sport polished concrete floors, exposed wiring, blonde-wood furniture and crisp white linens. **B1480**

HUALAMPHONG, CHINATOWN AND PAHURAT

Set between the Ratanakosin sights and downtown, Chinatown is among the most frantic and fume-choked parts of Bangkok – and there's quite some competition. If you're in the mood, however, it's got plenty of interest, sees barely any Western overnighters, and is also very handy for Hualamphong Station, which is on the subway system.

@ Hualamphong 326/1 Thanon Rama IV ☏02 639 1925, ⓦat-hualamphong.com; map p.106. Directly opposite Hualamphong train station on busy Thanon Rama IV, a modern a/c hostel with bright, appealing private rooms and four- and six-bed mixed dorms, plenty of common areas and a left-luggage service. Dorms **B400**, doubles **B1050**

Baan Hualamphong 336/20 Soi Chalong Krung ☏02 639 8054, ⓦbaanhualampong.com; map p.106. Just 5min from Hualamphong, this stylish wooden guesthouse is the most welcoming of several similar places in the soi, with a traveller-friendly vibe. There are big, bright, twin rooms plus five-person dorms, but most bedrooms share

bathrooms. It also has kitchen and laundry facilities, inviting lounging areas and a left-luggage service, and is open 24hr. Very good single rates. Dorms **B250**, fan doubles **B590**, a/c doubles **B700**

Grand China 215 Thanon Yaowarat ☏02 224 9977, ⓦgrandchina.com; map p.106. The poshest hotel in Chinatown boasts fairly luxurious accommodation in a richly coloured, contemporary style, in its 25-storey tower close to the heart of the bustle, with stunning views over all the city landmarks (the best take in the river) and a revolving panoramic restaurant. **B2600**

★**Shanghai Mansion** 479 Thanon Yaowarat, next to Scala shark's fin restaurant ☏02 221 2121, ⓦshanghaimansion.com; map p.106. The most design-conscious accommodation in Chinatown has embraced the modern Chinoiserie look with gusto. It's not actually an historic mansion, but has been purpose-built on the site of a former Beijing opera house, with most bedrooms (and their windows and private terraces) facing onto an appealing, four-storey atrium, and thus cosily isolated from the Chinatown frenzy. Rooms are prettily done out in silks, lacquer-look furniture and lanterns, featuring a lot of sumptuous reds and purples, as well as a/c, hot showers and complimentary mini-bars. **B3020**

DOWNTOWN: AROUND SIAM SQUARE AND THANON PLOENCHIT

Siam Square and nearby Thanon Ploenchit are as central as Bangkok gets: all the accommodation listed here is within walking distance of a Skytrain or subway station. On hand are the city's best shopping possibilities – notably the phalanx of malls along Thanon Rama I – and a wide choice of Thai and international restaurants and food courts. There's no ultra-cheap accommodation around here, but a few scaled-up guesthouses complement the expensive hotels. Concentrated in their own small "ghetto" on Soi Kasemsan 1, which runs north off Thanon Rama I, between the Bangkok Art and Cultural Centre and Jim Thompson's House, these offer typical travellers' facilities and basic hotel comforts – a/c and en-suite hot-water bathrooms – at moderate prices; the Khlong Saen Saeb canal-boat pier, Tha Saphan Hua Chang (easily accessed via Thanon Phrayathai), is especially handy for heading west to the Golden Mount and beyond, to Ratanakosin.

A-One Inn 25/13 Soi Kasemsan 1, Thanon Rama I ☏02 215 3029 or ☏02 216 4770, ⓦwww.aoneinn.com; map p.117. The original upmarket guesthouse on this soi, and still justifiably popular, with plenty of facilities including a reliable left-luggage room. All bedrooms have fridges and satellite TV and come in a variety of sizes, including triples; breakfast included. **B1400**

Anantara Siam 155 Thanon Rajdamri ☏02 126 8866, ⓦanantara.com; map p.117. The stately home of Bangkok's top hotels, formerly the *Four Seasons*. Afternoon tea is still served in the monumental lobby, which is adorned with magnificent, vibrant eighteenth-century-style murals depicting the Thai cosmology, and flanked by acclaimed Thai, Italian and Japanese restaurants, a steakhouse and an opulent spa. The large and luxurious rooms are decorated in warm Thai colours and dark wood, and there's an excellent concierge service. B7885

Centara Grand at Central World 999/99 Thanon Rama 1 ☎02 100 1234, ⓦcentarahotelsresorts.com; map p.117. Occupying floors 23 to 55 atop the north end of the huge, glossy Central World mall with its fifty restaurants and fifteen cinema screens, this is a luxurious cocoon high above the hot, noisy city. Views from the brightly coloured, contemporary rooms and the restaurants – particularly *Red Sky* (see p.155) – are panoramic, and shared by the invitingly large swimming pool. A spa, gym and floodlit tennis courts flesh out the picture. B4450

Centara Watergate Pavillion 567 Thanon Ratchaprarop ☎02 625 1234, ⓦcentarahotelsresorts .com; map p.117. Bright and vibrant four-star hotel opposite Pratunam Market, 10min walk from the Airport Rail Link at Ratchaprop. There's no pool but there is a jacuzzi-cum-water feature where you can take a dip, and there's a spa and rooftop restaurant and bar; rooms have big-head showers but no bathtubs. B2280

Courtyard by Marriott 155/1 Soi Mahadlekluang 1, Thanon Rajdamri ☎02 690 1888, ⓦmarriott.com; map p.117. On a quiet but very handy soi, this hotel offers most of the facilities of a five-star, but at more manageable prices. The modern design is seductive, gleaming white outside, candy colours and plenty of natural light inside, and there's a long, narrow, infinity pool, a fitness centre and a spa. B3810

Golden House 1025/5–9 Thanon Ploenchit ☎02 252 9535–7, ⓦgoldenhousebangkok.com; map p.117. A very clean and welcoming small hotel in a peerless location, situated down a short soi by Chit Lom BTS. The plain but attractive parquet-floored bedrooms are equipped with a/c, hot water, cable TV and mini-bar – ask for one of the larger front rooms with bay windows, which leave just enough space for an armchair or two. Breakfast is included. B1610

Jim's Lodge 125/7 Soi Ruam Rudee, Thanon Ploenchit ☎02 255 3100, ⓦjimslodge.com; map p.117. In a relatively peaceful residential area, with friendly and helpful staff, offering international-standard facilities, including a/c, hot showers, satellite TV and mini-bars, at bargain prices. B1100

Lub d 925/9 Thanon Rama I ☎02 612 4999, ⓦlubd .com; map p.117. Branch of the hip, well-run Silom hostel (see p.149), with similar style and facilities (including women-only dorms). It's right on Thanon Rama I, under BTS National Stadium, so handy for just about everything but rather noisy. Dorms B430, doubles B1560

Luxx XL 82/8 Soi Lang Suan ☎02 684 1111, ⓦstaywithluxx.com; map p.117. Quietly set back behind *Thang Long* restaurant, this hip boutique hotel is the younger, but bigger, brother of the original Silom *Luxx*. It shelters large, balconied "Studio" rooms in a seductive contemporary style, all red wood and grey stone, with DVD players (and a movie library), as well as a 13m, infinity-edge, slate pool. Discounts for longer stays. B1660

Pathumwan Princess Hotel 444 Thanon Phrayathai ☎02 216 3700, ⓦpprincess.com; map p.117. Central luxury hotel, at the southern end of MBK Shopping Centre, that's been refurbished in a crisp, modern style. Service is of a high standard, and the facilities include a very good Italian restaurant, overlooking a large, saltwater swimming pool on the eighth floor, a spa and a huge, popular fitness club, The Olympic, that encompasses squash and tennis courts and a 400m jogging track. B4200

Siam Kempinski 991/9 Thanon Rama I ☎02 162 9000, ⓦkempinski.com/bangkok; map p.117. Though it's in downtown's throbbing heart, right behind Paragon shopping centre, this top-of-the-range offering from Europe's oldest luxury hotel group styles itself as a resort: all rooms turn in on an artfully landscaped triangular garden with three pools (some ground-floor rooms even have direct access to one of the pools). As the site used to be part of the "lotus-pond palace", Wang Sra Pathum, the interior designers have made subtle but striking use of lotus motifs, complemented by over two hundred specially commissioned paintings and sculptures by Thai artists, amid the Art Deco-inspired architecture. There's also a beautiful spa and an excellent contemporary Thai restaurant, *Sra Bua* (see p.155). B10,240

★**Swissôtel Nai Lert Park** 2 Thanon Witthayu ☎02 253 0123, ⓦswissotel.com; map p.117. This welcoming, low-rise hotel is distinguished by its lushly beautiful gardens, overlooked by many of the chic and spacious, balconied bedrooms; set into the grounds are a landscaped swimming pool, tennis courts, squash court and popular spa and health club. Good deli-café, cool bar and fine Japanese and Chinese restaurants. B4025

Ten Face 81 Soi 2, Soi Ruam Rudee ☎02 695 4242, ⓦtenfacebangkok.com; map p.117. The name comes from Totsagan, the ten-faced demon of the *Ramakien*, and this place ingeniously combines sleek, contemporary design with striking artworks inspired by the national myth, without being gimmicky. All the rooms are spacious suites with espresso machines, free SIM cards and iPods, some with small kitchens; ask for a room at the back if you're worried about noise from the nearby expressway. There's a fusion restaurant, fitness centre, long, narrow "dipping" pool and shuttle service to Ploen Chit Skytrain, plus a special concierge, who DJs in the ultra-hip *Sita Bar* and dispenses the lowdown on Bangkok parties and happenings. B2900

1

Wendy House 36/2 Soi Kasemsan 1, Thanon Rama I ☎ 02 214 1149, ⓦ wendyguesthouse.com; map p.117. Friendly and well-run guesthouse, with smart, clean and comfortable rooms, all with fridge and cable TV, most with queen-size double beds. Breakfast (included in the price) is available in the ground-floor café, and there's reliable luggage storage among a host of useful facilities. Long-stay discounts available. **B1380**

White Lodge 36/8 Soi Kasemsan 1, Thanon Rama I ☎ 02 216 8867 or ☎ 02 215 3041; map p.117. The cheapest guesthouse on the soi, and not always the cleanest, with plain white cubicles and a lively, welcoming atmosphere – the best rooms, bright and quiet, are on the upper floors. **B600**

THANON SUKHUMVIT

Thanon Sukhumvit is Bangkok's longest road – it keeps going east all the way to Cambodia – but for such an important artery it's far too narrow for the volume of traffic that needs to use it, and is further hemmed in by the Skytrain line that runs above it. Packed with high-rise hotels and office blocks, an impressive array of specialist restaurants (from Lebanese to Lao), and stall after stall selling cheap souvenirs and T-shirts, it's a lively place that attracts a high proportion of single male tourists to its enclaves of girlie bars on Soi Nana Tai and Soi Cowboy. But for the most part it's not a seedy area, and is home to many expats and middle-class Thais. The majority of overnighters are business travellers, though Sukhumvit also has several very good mid-priced guesthouses. Even at the west end of Sukhumvit, many of the sois are refreshingly quiet, even leafy; transport down the longer sois is provided by motorbike-taxi (*mohtoesai*) drivers who wait at the soi's mouth, clad in numbered waistcoats. Hotels further east are quite convenient for Suvarnabhumi Airport but far from the main shopping and eating hubs. Odd-numbered sois run off the north side of Thanon Sukhumvit, even-numbered off the south side; some of the sois have become important enough to earn their own names, which are often used in preference to their numbers; many sois are long enough to have sub-sois running off them, which usually have their own numbers (or names).

Amari Boulevard Soi 5 ☎ 02 255 2930, ⓦ amari.com; map p.123. At this long-running but modernized four-star tourist hotel, it's worth paying a little extra for a deluxe room to enjoy fine views of the Bangkok skyline and have a bit more space and a DVD player. The attractive sixth-floor rooftop swimming pool and garden terrace becomes the Thai-food restaurant *Season* in the evenings. **B3700**

The Atlanta At the far southern end of Soi 2 ☎ 02 252 1650, ⓦ theatlantahotelbangkok.com; map p.123. A Bangkok institution, this classic, five-storey budget hotel was built in 1952 around a famously photogenic Art Deco-style lobby and continues to emphasize an old-fashioned

hospitality. It offers some of the cheapest accommodation on Sukhumvit: rooms are plain and simple, though they are all en suite and some have a/c and hot water; many have small balconies. There's a swimming pool and kids' pool in the garden, a good restaurant and a free left-luggage facility. Fan **B940**, a/c **B1050**

Hilton Sukhumvit 11 Soi 24 ☎ 02 259 9017, ⓦ hilton .com; map p.123. This new high-rise luxury hotel cleverly links the skyscraper cities of New York and Bangkok, with an Art Deco-influenced contemporary design that's intended to suggest 1920s Manhattan. The design continues in the excellent Italian restaurant, *Scalini*, and in the capacious bedrooms and their opulent bathrooms; on the rooftop are an infinity pool and a gym. **B4760**

Imm Fusion 1594/50 Thanon Sukhumvit, 30m walk west along Thanon Sukhumvit from BTS On Nut, exit 2, beyond Soi 50 ☎ 02 331 5555, ⓦ immhotel.com; map p.123. Step through the entrance of this attractively themed hotel and you could be in Morocco, with its rich earthy colours, wrought ironwork, pretty tiles and plenty of Moorish arches. The rooms are comfortable and equally tasteful, and come with a/c, hot showers, TV and breakfast. There's a gorgeous indoor pool, and the staff are charming. **B1140**

Napa Place 11/3 Soi Naphasap 2, off Soi 36 ☎ 02 661 5525, ⓦ napaplace.com; map p.123. Down a quiet sub-soi (second right off Soi 36), a 10min walk from BTS Thong Lo, this welcoming, family-friendly guesthouse offers plenty of cosy public spaces and large bedrooms, all with their own sitting areas. Teak floors and furniture are set off by cream furnishings and other natural colours in the very clean rooms, which feature a/c, hot water, mini-bars and cable TV. Breakfast included. **B3040**

Park Plaza 9 Soi 18 ☎ 02 658 7000, ⓦ parkplaza.com; map p.123. The quieter and newer of two nearby Park Plazas, this small hotel is topped by an appealing, open-air 20m pool, gym and bar-restaurant on the eighth floor. Fitted with DVD players, the rooms sport a perky contemporary look, with bright colours set against businessman's black. **B2600**

Seven 3/15 Soi Sawasdee 1, off Soi 31 ☎ 02 662 0951, ⓦ sleepatseven.com; map p.123. A personable welcome and plenty of local advice awaits once you head down the quiet alley to this super-stylish B&B. Bold, cartoon-like murals, as well as DVDs, iPod docks, big-head showers and balconies, enhance the six rooms, which are priced according to size. All include a good continental breakfast, local calls and the loan of a local mobile phone. **B3000**

Suk 11 Behind the 7-Eleven store at 1/33 Soi 11 ☎ 02 253 5927–8, ⓦ suk11.com; map p.123. One of the most unusual little hotels in Bangkok, this is also the most backpacker-orientated guesthouse in the area, well run and thoughtfully appointed. The interior of the apparently ordinary apartment-style building has been transformed to resemble a village of traditional wooden houses, accessed by a dimly lit plankway that winds past a variety of guest rooms, terraces and lounging areas. The rooms themselves are simple but comfortable, all with a/c, and some are en suite; all showers are hot. Good rates for singles; triples and family rooms also available. **B749**

DOWNTOWN: SOUTH OF THANON RAMA IV

South of Thanon Rama IV, the area sometimes known as Bangrak contains a full cross section of accommodation. Tucked away at its eastern edge, there are a few cheap places that are worth recommending in the small travellers' haunt of Soi Ngam Duphli and adjacent Soi Sri Bamphen and Soi Saphan Khu. The neighbourhood is often traffic-clogged and occasionally seedy, but is close to Lumphini Park and subway station and fairly handy for Suvarnabhumi Airport. As well as a fair scattering of medium-range places, the arc between Thanon Rama IV and the river also lays claim to the capital's biggest selection of top hotels, which are among the most opulent in the world. Traversed by the Skytrain, this area is especially good for eating and for gay and straight nightlife, mostly near the east end of Thanon Silom (around which several gay-friendly hotels are scattered). Staying by the river itself in the atmospheric area around Thanon Charoen Krung, also known as New Road, has the added advantage of easy access to express boats.

★**Anantara Riverside** 257 Thanon Charoennakorn ☎02 476 0022, ⓦanantara.com; map p.79. A luxury retreat from the frenetic city centre, well to the south on the Thonburi bank, but connected to Taksin Bridge (for the Skytrain and Chao Phraya express boats), 15min away, and to Asiatique, just across the river, by hotel ferries every 30min. Arrayed around a highly appealing, landscaped swimming pool, the tranquil, riverside gardens are filled with birdsong, while the stylish and spacious bedrooms come with varnished hardwood floors and balconies. There's a fitness centre, tennis courts, kids' club, a spa, and among a wide choice of places to eat, a good Japanese teppanyaki house. **B4700**

Anantara Sathorn 36 Thanon Narathiwat Ratchanakharin ☎02 210 9000, ⓦanantara.com; map pp.80–81. With its enclosed, 32m outdoor pool at the centre of activity, toddlers' pool and wide choice of suites, this high-rise hotel is very popular with families. There's also a gym, a tennis court, a very good spa and a fourtieth-floor roof-top bar-restaurant, while the spacious, balconied rooms show restrained contemporary decor. Hotel mini-buses run to BTS Chong Nonsi hourly during the day, which is otherwise a 15min walk away. **B2880**

Baan Saladaeng 69/2 Soi 3, Thanon Saladaeng ☎02 636 3038, ⓦbaansaladaeng.com; map p.125. On a tiny, central alley, this chic, gay-friendly designer

guesthouse offers eleven individually styled and priced rooms, such as the Pop Art Mania Room and the Mediterranean Suite, some with bathtubs and balconies and one with its bath on the balcony. A/c, rain showers, mini-bars, cable TV and comfy beds throughout. No children. Breakfast included. **B1300**

ETZ Hostel 5/3 Soi Ngam Duphli ☎02 286 9424, ⓦetzhostel.com; map pp.80–81. Owned by the recommended ETC travel agent, and very handy for Lumphini subway and Thanon Rama IV, though consequently a little noisy. Helpful and very clean, the hostel sports playful contemporary decor in primary colours, a popular roof terrace and a large, attractive lounge. The a/c dorms share hot showers and fit four to twelve people (one is women-only), or you could upgrade to a bright white double with large, en-suite, hot-water bathroom. Breakfast and luggage storage are available. Dorms **B200**, doubles **B950**

La Residence 173/8–9 Thanon Suriwong ☎02 266 5400–1, ⓦlaresidencebangkok.com; map p.125. A small, intimate boutique hotel where the tasteful, individually decorated bedrooms – including proper single rooms at proper single rates – stretch to mini-bars, safes and cable TV. Continental breakfast included. **B1930**

Lub d 4 Thanon Decho ☎02 634 7999, ⓦlubd.com; map p.125. Meaning "sleep well" (*lap dii*), this buzzing, upmarket hostel has a/c and hot water throughout and an industrial feel to its stylishly lit decor. This crisp modernity extends to the bedrooms, among which the dorms (some women-only) and the bunk-bedded "Railway" private rooms ("Railway" twin B1150) share large bathroom areas, while the top-of-the-range en-suite doubles boast TVs. The hostel lays on some interesting activities and tours, and there's a popular bar and café, a movie lounge, washing machines and free storage facilities, but no kitchen. Dorms **B350**, doubles **B1720**

Luxx 6/11 Thanon Decho ☎02 635 8800, ⓦstay withluxx.com; map p.125. Welcoming boutique hotel offering a good dose of contemporary style at reasonable prices. Decorated in white, grey and natural teak, the rooms feature DVD players and cute wooden baths surmounted by rain showers. There are discounts for longer stays. **B1170**

Malaysia 54 Soi Ngam Duphli ☎02 679 7127–36, ⓦmalaysiahotelbkk.com; map pp.80–81. Once a travellers' legend famous for its compendious noticeboard, now better known for its seedy 24hr coffee shop and massage parlour. The accommodation itself is reasonable value though: the rooms are large and have a/c, mini-bars and hot-water bathrooms; some have cable TV. There's also a swimming pool. Gay-friendly. **B828**

★**New Road Guest House** 1216/1 Thanon Charoen Krung, between sois 34 and 36 ☎02 630 9371, ⓦnewroadguesthouse.com; map p.125. Thai

1

headquarters of Danish backpacker tour operator, Visit Beyond, offering a wide choice of accommodation around a courtyard off New Road, as well as a helpful service centre and travel agent, and interesting Thailand tours. There are mixed and women-only a/c dorms, as well as "Backpacker" fan rooms with mini-bars and well-equipped, hot-water bathrooms; a/c rooms sport attractive wooden floors, Thai decorative touches and cable TV. Guests can hang out in the restaurant, the sociable bar with pool table or the DVD room; free baggage storage available. Dorms B250, fan doubles B550, a/c doubles B1000

★**Peninsula Bangkok** 333 Thanon Charoennakorn ☎02 861 2888, ⓦ peninsula.com; map p.125. Located on the Thonburi bank, with shuttle boats down to Taksin Bridge and its BTS station, this is a superb top-class hotel: service is flawless, the ultra-luxurious decor stylishly blends traditional Western and Asian design, and every room has a panoramic view of the Chao Phraya. The lovely riverside gardens shelter a three-tiered pool, a beautiful spa, a fitness centre and a tennis court, while restaurants include the classy *Mei Jiang* Cantonese restaurant (see p.158). B11,000

Rose 118 Thanon Suriwong ☎02 266 8268–72, ⓦ rosehotelbkk.com; map p.125. Set back from the main road but very handy for the city's nightlife, this hotel has been recently refurbished: the compact rooms (all with bathtubs) now boast a simple but stylish, modernist look, enhanced by paintings and silk cushions. The ground-floor public rooms are more elegant again, and there's a beautiful swimming pool and a good Thai restaurant, Ruen Urai (see p.158), at the back. B1800

★**Sala Thai Daily Mansion** 15 Soi Saphan Khu ☎02 287 1436, ✉ salathai.guesthouse@hotmail.com; map pp.80–81. The last and best of several budget guesthouses on this quiet, narrow alleyway off Soi Saphan Khu, near Soi Sri Bamphen. A clean and efficiently run place, with bright, cheerful rooms with wall fans, sharing hot-water bathrooms, and a large, leafy roof garden. Decent rates for single rooms. Fan B400, a/c B600

★**Sukhothai** 13/3 Thanon Sathorn Tai ☎02 344 8888, ⓦ sukhothai.com; map p.125. The most elegant of Bangkok's top hotels, its decor inspired by the walled city of Sukhothai, offers low-rise accommodation, as well as a beautiful garden spa, all coolly furnished in silks, teak and granite. Service is of the highest standard and the architecture makes the most of the views of the surrounding six acres of gardens, lotus ponds and pools dotted with statuary. There's also a health club, 25m

infinity pool, squash and tennis courts, and excellent restaurants including *Celadon* (see p.157). B12,800

Swan 31 Soi 36, Thanon Charoen Krung ☎02 235 9271–3, ⓦ swanhotelbkk.com; map p.125. Next to the stately residence of the French ambassador, this good-value, well-run and welcoming Chinese hotel has successfully upgraded, with regular renovations, to keep up with the times. Arrayed around a 15m pool, the rooms are bright, clean and spacious (though bathrooms in the standard rooms are small), with a/c, hot water, cable TV, mini-bars and safes; some have balconies with armchairs. Breakfast included. B1500

Swiss Lodge 3 Thanon Convent ☎02 233 5345, ⓦ swisslodge.com; map p.125. Swish, friendly, good-value and eco-friendly boutique hotel, with high standards of service, just off Thanon Silom and ideally placed for business and nightlife. The tiny terrace swimming pool confirms the national stereotypes of neatness and clever design, while the restaurant offers a range of savoury and sweet fondues. Buffet breakfast included. B1940

Tarntawan Place 119/5–10 Thanon Suriwong ☎02 238 2620, ⓦ tarntawan.com; map p.125. Set back from the main road, a pretty, flower-strewn lobby announces this welcoming and well-run, gay-friendly hotel. The decent-sized, well-equipped rooms are gracefully furnished in natural colours, and all have bathtubs. Guests also receive reduced-price entry to a gym and swimming pool on Soi Thaniya. Discounts for longer stays. B2080

SUVARNABHUMI AIRPORT

Mariya Boutique Residence 1627/2 Thanon Latkrabang ☎02 326 7854–5, ⓦ mariyahotel.com; map p.79. Five minutes' drive from the airport to the northwest (with pick-ups available 24hr), this well-organized hotel offers hot water, a/c, fridge, cable TV, microwave, kettle and DVD players (on request) in all of the bedrooms, which feature some traditional Thai touches in the appealing decor. B1280

Novotel Suvarnabhumi ☎02 131 1111, ⓦ novotel .com; map p.79. The official airport hotel, set within the complex and a 10min walk from arrivals via a walkway in the basement (or catch the shuttle bus from outside arrivals Gate 4). Offering smart, contemporary rooms with marble bathrooms, Thai, Japanese, Cantonese and international restaurants, a swimming pool and fitness centre, the *Novotel* operates on a 24hr basis — you can check in at any time, and check out 24hr later. B6015

EATING

As you'd expect, nowhere in Thailand can compete with Bangkok's diversity when it comes to food: it boasts an astonishing fifty thousand places to eat, almost one for every hundred citizens. Although prices are generally higher here than in the provinces, it's still easy to dine well on a budget. For **Thai** food, the best gourmet restaurants in the country operate from the downtown districts, proffering wonderful royal, traditional and regional cuisines that definitely merit a visit. At the lower end of the price scale, one-dish meals from around the country are rustled up at the **food courts** of shopping centres and department stores, as well as at **night markets** and **street stalls**, which are so numerous in Bangkok that we can only flag the most promising areas. For the non-Thai cuisines, Chinatown naturally rates as the most authentic district for pure **Chinese** food; likewise neighbouring Pahurat, the capital's Indian enclave, is best for unadulterated **Indian** dishes, while there's a sprinkling of Indian and (mostly southern Thai) **Muslim** restaurants around Silom's Maha Uma Devi Temple and nearby Thanon Charoen Krung. Sukhumvit's Soi 3 is a hub for **Middle Eastern** cafés, complete with hookah pipes at the outdoor tables; good, comparatively cheap **Japanese** restaurants are concentrated, for example, on and around Soi Thaniya, at the east end of Thanon Silom; and there's a Korean enclave in Sukhumvit Plaza, at the corner of Soi 12. In the more expensive restaurants listed below you may have to pay a ten percent **service charge** and seven percent VAT.

RATANAKOSIN

The places reviewed below are especially handy for sightseers, but there are also plenty of street stalls around Tha Chang and a load of simple, studenty restaurants off the north end of Thanon Maharat near Thammasat University, as well as a decent restaurant at *Arun Residence* (see p.142).

Navy Club (Krua Khun Kung) Tha Chang ☎02 222 0081; map p.83. Walk on by the prominent but overpriced *Navy Club 77 Café* on the corner of Na Phra Lan and Maharat roads, to find this place immediately on the south side of the express-boat pier, announced by an English sign and a navy guard (don't be put off – anyone can eat here, even farangs). The decor's deeply institutionalized but the view is the shaded terrace built over the river, where you can enjoy excellent dried prawn and lemon-grass salad (B120), *haw mok thalay* (seafood curry soufflé; B150) and other marine delights. Mon–Fri 11am–2pm & 4–10pm, Sat & Sun 11am–10pm.

Vivi: The Coffee Place Opposite Aurum on Soi Pansook, Thanon Maharat ☎02 226 4672; map p.83. Handy for Wat Pho, this cute café with a riverside terrace and an a/c room serves coffee and a wide range of drinks, plus cakes, sandwiches and snack portions of lasagne (B70). Daily 10am–8pm.

BANGLAMPHU AND THE DEMOCRACY MONUMENT AREA

Copycat entrepreneurship means that Khao San is stacked full of backpacker restaurants serving near-identical Western and (mostly) watered-down Thai food; there's even a lane, one block east, parallel to Thanon Tanao (behind *Burger King*), that's dominated by vegetarian cafés, following a trend started by *May Kaidee*. Hot-food stalls selling very cheap night-market snacks operate until the early hours. Things are more varied down on Thanon Phra Arthit, with its arty little café-restaurants favoured by Thammasat University students, while the riverside places, on Phra Arthit and further north off Thanon Samsen and in Thewet, tend to be best for seafood with a view. For the real old-fashioned Thai taste though, browse southern Thanon Tanao, where traditional shophouses have been selling specialist sweets and savouries for generations.

AROUND THANON KHAO SAN

Chabad House 96 Thanon Ram Bhuttri ⓦkosher thailand.com; map pp.100–101. A little piece of Israel, run by the Bangkok branch of the Jewish outreach Chabad-Lubavitch movement. Serves a well-priced, tasty kosher menu of schnitzels (B160), baba ganoush, falafels, hummus, salads and Jewish breads in a/c calm, on the ground floor of a long-established community centre and

DINNER CRUISES

The **Chao Phraya River** looks fabulous at night, when most of the noisy longtails have stopped terrorizing the ferries, and the riverside temples, other fine monuments such as the Grand Palace and an increasing number of historic houses are elegantly illuminated. Joining one of the nightly **dinner cruises** along the river is a great way to appreciate it all, especially on one of the converted, wooden rice-barges listed below, which are far preferable to the big, modern party boats. Call ahead to reserve a table and check departure details – some cruises may not run during the rainy season (May–Oct).

Loy Nava ☎02 437 4932, ⓦloynava.com. The original, 40-year-old converted rice-barge service still departs Si Phraya pier twice nightly, at 6pm (to catch the sunset) and 8.10pm, with pick-ups also at Tha Sathorn. During the cruise you can enjoy a Thai, seafood or vegetarian meal, accompanied by live traditional music and dancing. B1400, including hotel pick-up in central Bangkok.

Manohra ☎02 476 0022, ⓦmanohracruises.com. Beautiful converted rice-barge operated by the *Anantara Riverside Resort*, south of Taksin Bridge in Thonburi, serving Thai set dinners. Departs hotel at 7.30pm, returning 9.30pm, with pick-ups at Tha Sathorn possible. From B1750.

guesthouse; the best deal is five taster plates for B60. Mon–Thurs & Sun 10am–10pm, Fri 10am–3pm.

★May Kaidee East off Thanon Tanao ⓦmaykaidee .com; map pp.100–101. Simple, neighbourhood Thai vegetarian restaurant that still serves some of the best veggie food in Banglamphu despite having spawned several competitors on the same alley. Come for Western breakfasts or try the tasty green curry, the Vietnamese-style veggie spring rolls or the sticky black-rice pudding with mango or banana. Most dishes B70–90. Also runs a variety of cookery courses (see opposite). Daily 9am–10pm.

Nittaya 136 Thanon Chakrabongse; map pp.100–101. This shop is nationally famous for its *nam phrik* (chilli dips) and curry pastes (which are available vacuum-packed), but it serves all kinds of food to take away – perhaps to eat in nearby Santichaiprakarn Park (see p.99) – including snacks and desserts. Mon–Sat 9am–6.30pm.

Popiang 43 Soi Ram Bhuttri; map pp.100–101. Very popular, friendly place for cheap seafood: BBQ mussels cost just B80, squid B140. Eat in the low-rent restaurant area or on the street beneath the temple wall. Claims to open daily 24hr.

PHRA ARTHIT AREA

Aquatini Navalai River Resort, 45/1 Thanon Phra Arthit ☎02 280 9955; map pp.100–101. Occupying a nice wooden deck in a perfect breezy riverfront spot beside the express-boat pier (even better after sunset when the boats stop running), this hotel restaurant does exceptionally good mid-priced Thai food. Seafood's a speciality: the deep-fried ruby fish served with cashew nuts and bell peppers is very good, and their tangy coconut-milk *tom kha kai* soup is especially delicious. Most seafood mains B200–300. Daily 6.30am–11.45pm.

★Hemlock 56 Thanon Phra Arthit ☎02 282 7507; map pp.100–101. Small, stylish, a/c restaurant that's very popular with students and young Thai couples. Offers a long and interesting menu of unusual Thai dishes, including delicious green curry (B100) and several kinds of *laap* (spicy ground meat salad). The traditional *miang* starters (shiny green wild tea leaves filled with chopped vegetables, fish, prawn or meat) are also very tasty, and there's a good vegetarian selection. Worth reserving a table on Fri and Sat nights. Mon–Sat 4–11pm.

Kway Jap Yuan Khun Daeng Thanon Phra Arthit ☎085 246 0111; map pp.100–101. This basic, bustling canteen does a roaring trade with Thammasat University students, who come for the delicious *kway jap yuan*, noodle soup similar to Vietnamese *pho* but a little starchier – go for the version with egg (B57) and you're set up for the day. Find it in an historic shophouse, unmistakably painted white and green – colours which the flamboyant owner often sports himself. Mon–Sat 11am–9.30pm.

Roti Mataba 136 Thanon Phra Arthit ☎02 282 2119; map pp.100–101. Famous 70-year-old outlet for the ever-popular fried Indian breads, or *rotis*, served here in lots of sweet and savoury varieties, including with vegetable and meat curries (from B51), stuffed with meat and veg (*mataba*), and with bananas and condensed milk (B35); biryanis (*khao mok*) are also on offer. Choose between pavement tables and a basic upstairs a/c room. Tues–Thurs 10am–9pm, Fri–Sun 9.30am–9.30pm.

THANON SAMSEN AND THEWET

Chomp Corner of Soi 1, Thanon Samsen, ⓦfacebook .com/chompcafe; map pp.100–101. Cool café and social hub where polished-concrete floors and walls add to the rough-hewn look, offering tasty comfort food such as Western breakfasts and pasta mushroom alfredo (B160) and activities such as yoga and art exhibitions. Very child-friendly with playgroups and babies' and kids' menus. Mon & Wed–Sun 8am–11pm.

Jok Phochana Soi 2, Thanon Samsen; map pp.100–101. This bare-basics, forty-year-old restaurant, which has featured on national TV, is about as real as you're going to get near Thanon Khao San; a green curry costs B70. The day's ingredients are colourfully displayed at the front of the shop, and the quiet pavement tables get more crowded as the night wears on. Daily 5pm–2am.

Kaloang Home Kitchen Beside the river (follow the bend round) at the far western end of Thanon Sri Ayutthaya ☎02 281 9228; map pp.100–101. Flamboyant service and excellent seafood attracts an almost exclusively Thai clientele to this open-air, no-frills, bare-wood restaurant that perches on stilts over the river. Dishes well worth sampling include the fried rolled shrimps served with a sweet dip and any of the host of Thai salads. Most mains are B100–150; expect to pay more for crab, shrimp and some fish dishes. Daily 11am–10pm.

Kinlom Chom Saphan Riverside end of Thanon Samsen Soi 3 ☎02 628 8382–3, ⓦkhinlomchomsaphan .com; map pp.100–101. This sprawling, waterside restaurant boasts close-up views of the lyre-like Rama VIII Bridge and is always busy with a youngish Thai crowd. The predominantly seafood menu (mostly B150–300) features everything from crab to grouper cooked in multiple ways, including with curry, garlic or sweet basil sauces, but never with MSG. Daily 11am–2am.

Krua Apsorn Thanon Samsen, opposite Thanon Uthong Nok on the southwestern edge of Dusit ☎02 668 8788; map pp.100–101; Thanon Dinso ☎02 685 4531; map pp.100–101; ⓦkruaapsorn.com. Very good, spicy and authentic food and a genteel welcome make this unpretentious, a/c restaurant popular with the area's civil servants – as well as the royalty whom they serve. Try the green fish-ball curry (B100) or the yellow curry with river prawns and lotus shoots (B120), both recommended by the leading Thai restaurant guide, MacDang, and then put out the fire in

THAI COOKERY CLASSES IN BANGKOK

Baipai 8/91 Soi 54, Thanon Ngam Wongwan ☏ 02 561 1404, ⌨ baipai.com. Thorough, four-hour classes in a quiet, suburban house in northern Bangkok. The classes cost B2200, including transfers from central hotels. Closed Sun.

Helping Hands Klong Toey ⌨ cookingwithpoo.com. Set up with the help of a Christian charity, a chance to experience the slums of Klong Toey and spend a morning with the ebullient Khun Poo learning to cook. The price of B1500 includes a market tour and free transfers from next to Phrom Pong BTS station. Closed Sun.

May Kaidee East of Thanon Khao San, off Thanon Tanao ☏ 089 137 3173, ⌨ maykaidee.com.

Banglamphu's famous vegetarian restaurant (see opposite) offers a huge variety of courses lasting anything from 2hr (B1000) to 10 days (B15,000), including raw food and fruit-carving classes.

Thai House 22km from central Bangkok in Bangmuang ☏ 02 903 9611 or ☏ 02 997 5161, ⌨ thaihouse.co.th. Set in a rural part of Nonthaburi province, here you can do one- (B3800) to three-day (B16,650) cooking courses, all including transfers from downtown. The three-day course includes vegetable and fruit carving, a market visit, all meals and homestay accommodation in a traditional wooden house.

---

your mouth with home-made coconut sorbet. Thanon Samsen Mon–Sat 10.30am–7.30pm (generally closes early on Sat); Thanon Dinso Mon–Sat 10.30am–8pm.

May Kaidee 2 33 Thanon Samsen, between the khlong and Soi 1 ⌨ maykaidee.com; map pp.100–101. This a/c branch of Banglamphu's best-loved Thai veggie restaurant (see opposite) specializes in salads, raw food and juices. Daily 9am–10pm.

Steve Café and Cuisine Wat Thawarad ☏ 02 281 0915, ⌨ stevecafeandcuisine.com; map pp.100–101. In a lovely riverside setting with views of Rama VIII Bridge, come here for great service and a huge menu that encompasses southern Thai specialities, traditional central Thai and fusion dishes, including a very tasty and spicy salmon *laap* (B200). It's easy to see, right across the mouth of Khlong Krung Kasem from Tha Thewet express-boat pier, though harder to get there, walking round and right through the grounds of the temple. Mon–Fri 11.30am–2.30pm & 4.30–11pm, Sat & Sun 11.30am–11pm.

SOUTH OF DEMOCRACY

Chote Chitr 146 Thanon Phraeng Phuton ☏ 02 221 4082, ⌨ www.chotechitr.ch; map pp.100–101. The word's out about this unreconstructed, 80-year-old, shophouse restaurant of just half a dozen tables – it's been featured in the *New York Times* and the *FT*. However, the wide-ranging menu of Thai dishes (most about B100) in large, homely portions is still excellent. The formidable owner will explain what's good today, perhaps *nam phrik pla thu* (chilli dip with mackerel). Not everyone will be a fan of the pet dogs running around the tables. Mon–Sat noon–9pm.

Kai Yang Boran 474–476 Thanon Tanao, immediately to the south of the Chao Poh Seua Chinese shrine ☏ 02 622 2349; map pp.100–101. Locally famous grilled chicken (B200 for a small bird) and *som tam* (green papaya salad; B60) restaurant (with a/c), wallpapered with photos

of celebrities who have eaten here. *Nam tok* salad with roast pork and several kinds of *laap* round out the northeastern menu. Daily 8.30am–9pm.

Kor Panit 431–433 Thanon Tanao, on the east side, directly opposite Thanon Phraeng Phuton; map pp.100–101. Outstanding takeaway coconut-laced sticky rice (currently B180/kg) has been sold here since 1932. No English sign, but look for the mango vendors outside, where you choose your variety to accompany the delicious *khao niaw* (sticky rice with coconut milk). Daily 7am–6pm.

Nattaporn 94 Thanon Phraeng Phuton, just off Thanon Kanlayana Maitri ☏ 02 221 3954; map pp.100–101. This family has been specializing in its famous home-made fresh coconut ice cream for over sixty years, topping it with classic Thai condiments like sweetcorn, red beans and taro balls. They also do mango, chocolate, coffee and tea flavours. No English sign, but it's a basic shophouse, right next door to *The Bhuthorn* guesthouse. Mon–Sat 8am–4pm.

Padthai Thipsamai 313 Thanon Mahachai (no English sign), near Wat Rajnadda ☏ 02 221 6280; map pp.100–101. The most famous *phat thai* in Bangkok, flash-fried by the same husband-and-wife team since 1966. The "special" option is huge, comes with especially juicy prawns, and is wrapped in a translucent, paper-thin omelette. Best washed down with fresh coconut juice. Daily, except alternate Wed, 5.30pm–1am.

HUALAMPHONG, CHINATOWN AND PAHURAT

Much of the fun of Chinatown dining is in the browsing of the night-time hot-food stalls that open up all along Thanon Yaowarat, around the mouth of Soi Issaranuphap (Yaowarat Soi 11) and along Soi Phadungdao (Soi Texas); wherever there's a crowd you'll be sure of good food. Pan Siam's *Good Eats: Chinatown* map, available from major bookshops, is also a great resource for the weirder local specialities.

1

Hua Seng Hong 371 Thanon Yaowarat ☎ 02 222 7053; ⓦ huasenghong.com; map p.106. Vibrant, ever-popular, few-frills restaurant, with an open kitchen out front alongside a stall that does a brisk, all-day trade in dim sum. Dishes from around B100, less for noodle soup, more for delicacies such as braised geese's feet. Daily 9am–1am.

Jong Kee 84 Soi Sukon 1, near Wat Traimit; map p.106. Famous, basic café serving nothing but delicious pork satay (B70 for 10 sticks) and sweet toast. No English sign, but look for the Shell sign (proof of a "Shell Chuan Chim" recommendation, a respected accolade for restaurants in Thailand). Mon 9.30am–2pm, Tues–Sun 9.30am–6pm.

Raan Khun Yah Wat Traimit; map p.106. Just to the right inside the temple's Thanon Mittaphap entrance, this basic, very traditional restaurant, now in its third generation of operation, is especially famous for its delicious and cheap *kaeng khiaw wan neua* (green beef curry; B35), on a menu that otherwise changes daily – look out for *lon*, a chilli dip with coconut milk, and *khanom jiin nam yaa*, rice noodles topped with spicy fish sauce. Mon–Fri 6.30am–1pm (some things will sell out earlier than that).

Royal India Just off Thanon Chakraphet at 392/1 ☎ 02 221 6565; map p.106; basement, Siam Paragon ☎ 02 610 7667; map p.117; Floor 5, Emporium shopping centre ☎ 086 973 8266; map p.123; ⓦ royalindiathailand .com. Great dhal, perfect parathas and famously good North Indian curries (from around B130), served in a dark, basic little a/c café in the heart of Bangkok's most Punjabi of neighbourhoods to an almost exclusively South Asian clientele. Daily 10am–10pm.

Shangarila 306 Thanon Yaowarat (corner of Thanon Rajawong) ☎ 02 224 5933; map p.106. Cavernous, upmarket banquet hall serving Cantonese classics, including lots of seafood (mostly sold by weight), and lunchtime dim sum. Very popular, especially for family gatherings. Try the huge, very tasty, seared scallops with XO sauce (chillies, dried shrimps and brandy) for B500. Daily 10am–10pm.

T&K (Toi & Kid's Seafood) 49 Soi Phadungdao, corner of Thanon Yaowarat; map p.106. Hectic, rough-hewn street restaurant known for its barbecued seafood, with everything from prawns (from B150 a serving) to whole fish and clams on offer. Eat at crowded pavement tables by the busy road or inside in the basic a/c rooms. Tues–Sun 4.30pm–1am.

DOWNTOWN: AROUND SIAM SQUARE AND THANON PLOENCHIT

In this area, there are also branches of *Taling Pling* (see p.158), *Royal India* (see above), *Aoi* (see p.157) and *Somboon Seafood* (see p.158).

Din Tai Fung Floor 5, Central Embassy ⓦ dintaifung .com.sg; map p.117. This attractive and efficient all-day dim sum place is a branch of a Hong Kong restaurant that has a Michelin star. Its superb speciality is steamed pork dumplings with clear broth inside each one (B160), but other dishes such as spring rolls with duck and spring onion (B170) are also very tasty. Mon–Fri 11am–9.30pm, Sat & Sun 10.30am–9.30pm.

Eathai Basement, Central Embassy ⓦ centralembassy .com/eathai; map p.117. This upmarket food court – including a branch of Chiang Mai's *Khun Churn* (see p.296) – is a great place to learn about the huge variety of Thai food, with kitchens from the various regions rustling up their local dishes, plus seafood, *nam phrik* and vegetarian specialities, traditional drinks and dessert stalls and a section devoted to street food. Daily 10am–9.30pm.

Food Loft Floor 7, Central Chidlom, Thanon Ploenchit ⓦ centralfoodloft.com; map p.117. Bangkok's top department store lays on a suitably upscale food court of all hues – Thai, Vietnamese, Chinese, Japanese, Korean, Indian, and Italian by *Gianni* (see opposite). Choose your own ingredients and watch them cooked in front of you, eat by the huge windows in the stylish, minimalist seating areas and then ponder whether you have room for a Thai or Western dessert. Daily 10am–10pm.

YELLOW-FLAG HEAVEN FOR VEGGIES

Every year, for nine days during the ninth lunar month (between late Sept and Nov), Thailand's Chinese community goes on a **meat-free** diet to mark the onset of the Vegetarian Festival (Ngan Kin Jeh), a sort of Taoist version of Lent. Though the Chinese citizens of Bangkok don't go in for skewering themselves like their compatriots in Phuket (see p.623), they do celebrate the Vegetarian Festival with gusto: some people choose to wear only white for the duration, all the temples throng with activity, and nearly every restaurant and food stall in Chinatown turns vegetarian for the period, flying small yellow flags to show that they are upholding the tradition and participating in what's essentially a nightly veggie food jamboree. For vegetarian tourists this is a great time to be in town – just look for the yellow flag and you can be sure all dishes will be one hundred percent vegetarian. Soya substitutes are a popular feature on the vegetarian Chinese menu, so don't be surprised to find pink prawn-shaped objects floating in your noodle soup or unappetizingly realistic slices of fake duck. Many hotel restaurants also get in on the act during the Vegetarian Festival, running special veggie promotions for a week or two.

1

Gianni 34/1 Soi Tonson, Thanon Ploenchit ☎ 02 252 1619, ⓦ giannibkk.com; map p.117. Probably Bangkok's best independent Italian restaurant, offering a sophisticated blend of traditional and modern in both its decor and food. Twice-weekly shipments of artisan ingredients from the old country are used in dishes such as lobster and artichoke risotto and squid-ink spaghetti with clams, prawns and asparagus. Best to come for lunch Mon–Fri when there's a good-value set menu for B550. Daily 11.30am–2pm & 6–10pm.

★ **Hinata** Central Embassy, Thanon Ploenchit ☎ 02 160 5935, ⓦ shin-hinata.com; map p.117. This branch of a famous Nagoya restaurant offers exquisite sushi and great views over the leafy British Embassy grounds – or you can pay extra to sit at the counter and watch the master at work. Sets from B1200 for six pieces of nigiri sushi and six *maki* rolls (with a few extras thrown in if you come for lunch). Daily 11am–9.30pm.

★ **Home Kitchen (Khrua Nai Baan)** 94 Soi Lang Suan ☎ 02 253 1888, ⓦ khruanaibaan.com; map p.117. This congenial, unpretentious spot in an attractive a/c villa is like an upcountry restaurant in the heart of the city. On the reasonably priced Thai and Chinese picture menu, you're bound to find something delicious, including dozens of soups – try the *kaeng som*, with shrimp and acacia shoot omelette, for B150 – six kinds of *laap* and a huge array of seafood. Daily 8am–midnight.

Honmono Sushi Siam Paragon, Thanon Rama I ☎ 02 610 9240; map p.117. Owned by the Japanese expert on Thailand's version of Iron Chef, this place imports its seafood from Tokyo's Tsukiji Market five times a week and offers a very good-value sushi set for B380, including salad, miso soup, pickles and fruit. Daily 11am–10pm.

Inter 432/1–2 Soi 9, Siam Square ☎ 02 251 4689; map p.117. Honest, efficient Thai restaurant that's popular with students and shoppers, serving good one-dish meals from B68, as well as curries, soups, salads and fish, in a no-frills, fluorescent-lit canteen atmosphere. Daily 11am–10pm.

Jim Thompson's Restaurant Jim Thompson's House, 6 Soi Kasemsan 2, Thanon Rama I ☎ 02 612 3601, ⓦ jimthompson.com; map p.117. A civilized, moderately priced haven in the must-see house museum (see p.119), with delicious Thai dishes (around B200) such as grilled mushroom salad as well as desserts, cakes and other Western food. Daily 11am–5pm & 7–11pm.

Kai Ton Pratunam Thanon Phetchaburi, on the corner of Soi 30; map p.117. Famous anti-hangover refuge that serves just one dish: delicious *khao man kai*, boiled chicken breast with broth, dipping sauces and rice that's been cooked in chicken stock. It'll set you back just B40, more if you ask for liver and other innards (*khreuang nai*, literally "the inner workings"). More choice is offered by the string of other popular food stalls on the same strip near the corner of Phetchaburi and Rajdamri roads. Daily 5.30am–2pm & 5pm–2am.

Mah Boon Krong Food Courts Corner of Rama I and Phrayathai rds ⓦ mbk-center.co.th; map p.117. Two decent food-courts at the north end of MBK: the long-running area on Floor 6 is a good introduction to Thai food, with English names and pictures of a huge variety of tasty, cheap one-dish meals from all over the country displayed at the various stalls (including vegetarian options), as well as fresh juices and a wide range of desserts; the upmarket version on Floor 5 is an international affair, spanning India, Italy, Vietnam, China, Indonesia, Mexico and Japan, plus good moussaka at *Olive*. Floor 6 daily 10am–roughly 8.30pm; Floor 5 daily 10am–10pm.

Polo Fried Chicken (Kai Thawt Jay Kee Soi Polo) Soi Polo, Thanon Witthayu ☎ 02 655 8489; map p.117. On the access road to the snobby polo club, this simple restaurant is Bangkok's most famous purveyor of the ultimate Thai peasant dish, fried chicken. All manner of northeastern dishes, including fish, sausages and loads of salads, fill out the menu, but it would be a bit perverse to come here and not have the classic combo of finger-licking chicken (B100 for a half), *som tam* and sticky rice. Daily 7am–10pm.

Red Sky Centara Grand, 999/99 Thanon Rama 1 ☎ 02 100 1234, ⓦ centarahotelsresorts.com; map p.117. Opulent, blow-out restaurant, named for the great sunset views from its indoor-outdoor, fifty-fifth-floor perch. It purveys "the best of the land, sky and water" – be that Maine lobster, Dutch veal or Kobe beef – beautifully presented in complex, meticulous preparations, with a signature splash of red in each dish (B1000 upwards). Daily 5.30pm–1am.

Sanguansri 59/1 Thanon Witthayu ☎ 02 251 9378; map p.117. The rest of the street may be a multi-storey building site but this low-rise, canteen-like old-timer, run by a friendly bunch of middle-aged women, clings on. And where else around here can you lunch on a sweet, thick and toothsome *kaeng matsaman* for B70? It goes well with *kung pla*, a tasty, fresh prawn and lemon-grass salad that can be spiced to order. Mon–Sat 10am–3pm.

Som Tam (Nua) 392/14 Soi 5, Siam Square ☎ 02 251 4880; map p.117; Floor 4, Siam Centre ☎ 02 658 1000; map p.117. This basic but lively modern restaurant on a pedestrian alley is a great place to get to know the full range of Thai spicy salads. The *som tam* with pork crackling and sausage goes well with the very tasty deep-fried chicken (B115), or there's northeastern *laap* and *nam tok*, and central Thai salads (*yam*) by the dozen. Soi 5, Siam Square daily 10.45am–9.30pm; Siam Centre daily 10.45am–9pm.

Sra Bua Siam Kempinski Hotel (see p.147); map p.117. Molecular gastronomy comes to Bangkok, with great success. Operated by Copenhagen's Thai Michelin one-star, *Kiin Kiin*, this place applies some serious creativity and theatricality to Thai cuisine, in dishes such as frozen red curry with lobster salad, which perfectly distils the taste of the *kaeng daeng*. The grand decor, which encompasses two lotus ponds (*sra bua*), is matched by the prices, with the full works costing B2200–2700 for a multi-course set dinner. Daily noon–2pm (last orders) & 6–10pm.

Vanilla Brasserie Ground floor, Siam Paragon shopping centre ☎02 610 9383, ⓦvanillaindustry .com; map p.117. A sophisticated shrine to Western gourmet delights that combines restaurant, patisserie, crêperie and chocolatier. On offer are delicious parma ham and mascarpone crêpes (B390), salads and other main courses, spot-on desserts, and excellent teas and coffees. Daily 10am–10pm.

THANON SUKHUMVIT

In this area, there are also branches of *Aoi* (see opposite), *Royal India* (see p.154), *Ramentei* (see p.158) and *Himali Cha-Cha* (see opposite). For street food, check out the big, bustling night market at the mouth of Soi 38 (BTS Thong Lo), which includes popular stalls for *phat thai* and *khao man kai* (chicken served with marinated rice and chicken broth) and stays open till the early hours.

Baan Khanitha 36/1 Soi 23 ☎02 258 4128; map p.123; 69 Thanon Sathorn Tai, at the corner of Soi Suan Phlu ☎02 675 4200–1; map p.125; ⓦbaan-khanitha .com. The big attraction at this long-running favourite haunt of Sukhumvit expats is the setting in a traditional Thai house and leafy garden. The food is upmarket Thai and fairly pricey, and includes lots of fiery salads (*yam*), and a good range of *tom yam* soups, green curries and seafood curries. Most mains cost B200–500. Daily 11am–11pm.

Barcelona Gaudí Ground floor, Le Premier 1 Condo, Soi 23 ☎02 661 7410, ⓦfacebook.com/barcelona gaudithailand; map p.123. This appealing Catalan café offers lovely outdoor tables under a broad, shady tree and a short menu of very good Spanish dishes, including salads, paellas and tapas, as well as tasty *crema catalana* (a bit like a crème brûlée) and on-the-money espressos. It's great value at lunchtime, when set menus start at B150, and is also popular at weekends for watching Spanish football games, when the house wine at B60/glass goes down a storm. Daily 11am–11pm; sometimes closed Mon.

★ **Beirut** Basement, Ploenchit Centre, at the mouth of Soi 2 ☎02 656 7377; map p.123; 64 Silom Building, set back off Thanon Silom behind Sabushi, opposite the Silom Complex ☎02 632 7448; map p.125 ⓦbeirut -restaurant.com. It's worth crossing the road from Bangkok's main Middle Eastern ghetto (Soi 3 and Soi 3/1) for the top-notch Lebanese food in this comfortable, a/c restaurant. Among dozens of salads and stuffed breads, the superb *motabel* (baba ganoush; B100) is fluffy and smoky, while the falafels are suitably moist inside and crunchy out. Good baklava, too. Ploenchit Centre daily 10am–10pm; 64 Silom Building daily 11.30am–midnight.

★ **Bolan** 24 Soi 53 (5min walk from BTS Thong Lo) ☎02 260 2961–2, ⓦbolan.co.th; map p.123. Meticulous and hugely successful attempt to produce authentic traditional food in all its complexity, while upholding the "Slow Food" philosophy. It'll give you a lipsmacking education in Thai cuisine, best enjoyed on the "Bolan Balance" set dinner menu (B2280). For lunch you might be offered *khanom jiin* and a dessert for B380. Tues & Wed 6–10.30pm (last orders), Thurs–Sun noon–2.30pm & 6–10.30pm.

Cabbages and Condoms 6–8 Soi 12 ☎02 229 4610, ⓦpda.or.th/restaurant; map p.123. The Population and Community Development Association of Thailand (PDA) runs this relaxing restaurant, decorated with condoms from around the world and the slogan "our food is guaranteed not to cause pregnancy". Try the chicken in pandanus leaves (B220) or the seafood green curry (B250); there's also a varied vegetarian menu. Daily 11am–10pm.

Dosa King Soi 11/1, with a back entrance on Soi 11 ☎02 651 1700, ⓦdosaking.net; map p.123. Usually busy with expat Indian diners, this vegetarian Indian restaurant serves good food from both north and south, including over a dozen different dosa (southern pancake) dishes, tandooris and the like. It's an alcohol-free zone so you'll have to make do with sweet lassi instead. Most dishes B100–200. Daily 11am–11pm.

Imoya Floor 3, Terminal Shop Cabin, 2/17–19 Soi 24 ☎02 663 5185–6; map p.123. The setting, in a block of shops beside Emporium where staircases seem to have been an afterthought, is unpromising, but this retro-style restaurant, decorated with old film posters, battered wood and corrugated iron, serves up consistently good Japanese food of all kinds, including sushi (from B60). Daily 5pm–midnight.

Le Dalat 57 Soi 23 (Soi Prasanmit) ☎02 259 9593, ⓦledalatbkk.com; map p.123. There's Indochinese romance aplenty at this delightful, re-created Vietnamese brick mansion decked out with pot plants, plenty of photos and eclectic curiosities. The extensive, high-class Vietnamese menu features favourites such as a *goi ca* salad of aromatic herbs and raw fish (B250) and *chao tom* shrimp sticks on sugar cane (B360). Good-value lunchtime sets (B360). Daily 11.30am–2.30pm & 5.30–10.30pm.

The Myth of MahaNaga 2 Soi 29 ☎02 662 3060, ⓦthemythbangkok.com; map p.123. The dining experience at this tranquil enclave is best appreciated after dark, when the fountain-courtyard tables are romantically lit. Cuisine is Thai fine dining, updated with contemporary techniques and some Western ingredients, featuring such tasty delights as *kaeng matsaman* with slow-cooked chicken breast and crispy sweet lotus (B300). Daily 5.30–11pm.

Soul Food Mahanakorn 56/10 Soi 55 (Soi Thong Lo; Exit 3 from BTS Thong Lo, then it's 100m up the soi on the right) ☎02 714 7708, ⓦsoulfoodmahanakorn .com; map p.123. If you already have your favourite stall for *som tam* or *laap*, this is not for you, but if not, this trim, welcoming, American–Thai bistro makes a great introduction to street food from around Thailand, using top-quality ingredients. The beef *khao soi* (curried noodle soup; B220) is thick and creamy, and the *som tam* (B150) is served with crispy chicken skin. Daily blackboard specials, and a huge selection of creative cocktails. Daily 5.30pm–midnight.

Suk 11 Soi 11 ☎ 02 253 5468; map p.123. Part of the idiosyncratic *Suk 11* guesthouse (see p.148), with which it shares a traffic-free sub-soi, this restaurant also re-creates an atmosphere of old-fashioned village Thailand, with its wooden building, fairy lights and plentiful foliage. The food is good, authentic Thai (mostly B150–300), with plenty of spicy *yam* salads, delicious mushroom *laap*, tasty *phanaeng* curry plus cocktails and imported wines by the glass. Daily 4–10.45pm.

Supanniga Eating Room About 1km up Soi 55 (Soi Thong Lo) on the right from Thong Lo BTS ☎ 02 714 7508, ⓦ supannigaeatingroom.com; map p.123. This three-storey rustic-chic restaurant, decorated with lots of brass and gnarly wood, is a great place to try the distinctive cuisine of Chanthaburi, famous for its herbs and spices – the delicious *moo cha muang* (B170), a mild red pork curry, is a great place to start. The restaurant's other specialities are crab dishes and food from Isaan, where the family have a boutique hotel in Khon Kaen (see p.476). Daily 11.30am–2.30pm & 5.30–11.30pm.

★**Vientiane Kitchen (Khrua Vientiane)** 8 Soi 36, about 50m south off Thanon Sukhumvit ☎ 02 258 6171, ⓦ facebook.com/vientianekitchen; map p.123. Just a 3min walk west then south from BTS Thong Lo (Exit 2) and you're transported into a little piece of Isaan, where the menu's stocked full of northeastern delicacies, a live band sets the mood with heart-felt, sometimes over-amplified *pong lang* folk songs (see p.762), and there are even performances by a troupe of traditional dancers (daily from 7.30pm). The Isaan-accented menu (mostly B100–300) includes vegetable soup with ants' eggs, spicy-fried frog, jackfruit curry and freshwater fish (from around B400), plus there's a decent range of veggie options such as *som tam* and sweet and sour dishes, and Thai desserts. With its airy, barn-like interior and mixed clientele of Thais and expats, it's a very enjoyable dining experience. Daily noon–midnight (last food orders 10.30pm).

DOWNTOWN: SOUTH OF THANON RAMA IV

Several popular groupings of street stalls are worth noting here: the top end of Thanon Convent, just off Thanon Silom; away to the west opposite the Maha Uma Devi Temple, Silom Soi 20; and the late-night noodle soup stalls on the east end of Thanon Suriwong. In this area, there are also branches of *Baan Khanitha* (see opposite) and *Beirut* (see opposite).

★**Aoi** 132/10–11 Soi 6, Thanon Silom ☎ 02 235 2321–2; map p.125; ground floor, Siam Paragon ☎ 02 129 4348–50; map p.117; Floor 4, Emporium shopping centre; ☎ 02 664 8590–2; map p.123; ⓦ aoi-bkk.com. One of the best places in town for a Japanese blowout, justifiably popular with the expat community. Excellent authentic food and elegant decor, with a superb sushi bar (around B1000 for a set). Thanon Silom daily 11.30am–2.30pm & 5.30/6pm–10.30/11pm; Siam Paragon Mon–Fri 11.30am–2.30pm & 5.30–10.30pm, Sat & Sun 11am–10.30pm; Emporium shopping centre daily 11/11.30am–2.30/3.30pm & 5/5.30–10.30pm.

★**Celadon** Sukhothai Hotel, 13/3 Thanon Sathorn Tai ☎ 02 344 8888; map p.125. Consistently rated as one of the best hotel restaurants in Bangkok and a favourite with locals, serving outstanding traditional and contemporary Thai food from all over the country – try the delicious southern dipping sauce of spicy dried shrimps and the northern-style pork belly curry – in an elegant setting surrounded by lotus ponds. Daily noon–2.30pm (last orders) & 6.30–10.30pm.

Eat Me 1/6 Soi Phiphat 2, Thanon Convent ☎ 02 238 0931, ⓦ eatmerestaurant.com; map p.125. Justly fashionable art gallery and restaurant in a striking, white modernist building, with changing exhibitions on the walls and a temptingly relaxing balcony. The eclectic, far-reaching menu features such mains as Japanese black cod with spicy coconut cream (B575), and the lemon-grass crème brûlée is not to be missed. Daily 3pm–1am.

Harmonique 22 Soi 34, Thanon Charoen Krung, on the lane leading to Wat Muang Kae express-boat pier ☎ 02 237 8175; map p.125. A relaxing, welcoming, moderately priced restaurant (most mains B100–200) that's well worth a trip: tables are scattered throughout several converted shophouses, decorated with antiques and bric-a-brac, and a quiet, leafy courtyard, and the Thai food is varied and excellent, notably the house speciality crab curry. Mon–Sat 11am–10pm.

Himali Cha-Cha 1229/11 Soi 47/1, Thanon Charoen Krung ☎ 02 235 1569; map p.125; down a short alley off the north end of Thanon Convent ☎ 02 238 1478; map p.125; Sukhumvit Soi 31 ☎ 02 259 6677; map p.123; ⓦ himalichacha.com. Fine, moderately priced North Indian restaurant, founded by a character who was chef to numerous Indian ambassadors, and now run by his son. Tasty chicken tikka masala (B195) and a good vegetarian selection, with a homely atmosphere and attentive service. Daily 11am–3.30pm & 6–10.30pm.

Home Cuisine Islamic Restaurant 186 Soi 36, Thanon Charoen Krung ☎ 02 234 7911, ⓦ facebook .com/homecuisineislamic; map p.125. The short, cheap menu of Indian and southern Thai dishes here has proved popular enough to warrant a refurbishment in green and white, with comfy booths, pot plants, a/c inside and

1

a few outdoor tables overlooking the colonial-style French embassy. The *khao mok kai* signature dish (B85), a typical hybrid version of a chicken biryani, served with aubergine curry, is delicious. Mon–Sat 11am–9.30pm, Sun 6–9.30pm.

Indian Hut 418 Thanon Suriwong ☎02 237 8812, ⓦindianhut-bangkok.com; map p.125. Bright, white-tablecloth, North Indian restaurant – look out for the Pizza Hut-style sign – that's reasonably priced (most mains B200–300) and justly popular with local Indians. For carnivores, tandoori's the thing, but there's also a wide selection of mostly vegetarian pakoras and other appetizers, as well as plenty of veggie main courses and breads, and a hard-to-resist house dhal. Daily 11am–11pm.

★**Krua Aroy Aroy** 3/1 Thanon Pan (opposite the Maha Uma Devi Temple) ☎02 635 2365, ⓦfacebook.com /kruaaroyaroy; map p.125. Aptly named "Delicious, Delicious Kitchen", this simple shophouse restaurant stands out for its choice of cheap, tasty, well-prepared dishes from all around the kingdom, notably *khao soi* (a curried soup with egg noodles from northern Thailand), *kaeng matsaman* and *khanom jiin* (rice noodles topped with curry). Daily 7am–about 8pm, or earlier if the food runs out.

Le Bouchon 37/17 Patpong 2, near Thanon Suriwong ☎02 234 9109; map p.125. Cosy Lyonnais bar-bistro that's much frequented by the city's French expats, offering home cooking such as salmon in white wine sauce (B540) and a good-value lunch set menu (B450); booking is strongly recommended. Mon–Sat noon–3pm & 6.30–11pm.

Mei Jiang Peninsula Hotel, 333 Thanon Charoennakorn ☎02 861 2888, ⓦpeninsula.com; map p.125. Probably Bangkok's best Chinese restaurant, with beautiful views of the hotel's riverside gardens, and very attentive and graceful staff. Cantonese specialities include excellent lunchtime dim sum, lobster rolls, cold marinated chicken with Szechuan chilli sauce (B460) and delicious teas. Daily 11.30am–2.30pm & 6–10.30pm.

★**Ramentei** 23/8–9 Soi Thaniya ☎02 234 8082; map p.125; Sukhumvit Soi 33/1 ☎02 662 0050; map p.123. Excellent Japanese noodle café, bright, clean and welcoming, under the same ownership as *Aoi* (see p.157).

The open kitchen turns out especially good, huge bowls of miso ramen, which goes very well with the gyoza dumplings. Most dishes B150–200. Soi Thaniya daily 11am–2am; Soi 33/1 daily 11am–midnight.

Ruen Urai *Rose Hotel*, 118 Thanon Suriwong ☎02 266 8268–72, ⓦruen-urai.com; map p.125. Set back behind the hotel, this peaceful, hundred-year-old, traditional house, with fine balcony tables overlooking the beautiful hotel pool, comes as a welcome surprise in this full-on downtown area. The varied Thai food is of a high quality: try the *tom khlong talay* (B300), a delicious, refined, spicy and sour soup from the northeast, with tamarind juice and herbs. Daily noon–11pm.

Sara Jane's 55/21 Thanon Narathiwat Ratchanakharin, between sois 4 & 6 ☎02 676 3338–9; map p.125. Long-standing, basic, a/c restaurant, popular with Bangkok's Isaan population, serving good, simple northeastern dishes, including a huge array of *nam tok*, *laap* and *som tam*, as well as Italian food – and a very tasty fusion of the two, spaghetti with *sai krok*, spicy Isaan sausage (B240). Daily 11am–2.30pm & 5.30–10pm.

Somboon Seafood Thanon Suriwong, corner of Thanon Narathiwat Ratchanakharin ☎02 233 3104; map p.125; Floor 5, Central Embassy ☎02 160 5965–6; map p.117; ⓦsomboonseafood.com. Highly favoured, bustling seafood restaurant, known especially for its crab curry (from about B300, depending on weight), with functional, modern decor and an array of marine life lined up in tanks awaiting its gastronomic fate. Thanon Suriwong daily 4–11.30pm; Central Embassy daily 11am–10pm.

★**Taling Pling** 653 Building 7, Ban Silom Arcade, Thanon Silom ☎02 236 4829–30; map p.125; Ground floor of Siam Paragon ☎02 129 4353–4; map p.117; Floor 3, Central World ☎02 613 1360–1; map p.117. One of the best Thai restaurants in the city outside of the big hotels, specializing in classic dishes from the four corners of the kingdom. The house deep-fried fish salad (B145) is delicious and refreshing, while the deeply flavoured green beef curry (B145) with roti is recommended by the leading Thai restaurant guides. The atmosphere's convivial and relaxing, too. Ban Silom Arcade and Siam Paragon branches daily 11am–10pm; Central World daily 11am–9.30pm.

DRINKING AND NIGHTLIFE

For many of Bangkok's male visitors, nightfall is the signal to hit the city's sex bars, most notoriously in the area off the east end of Thanon Silom known as Patpong (see p.126). Fortunately, Bangkok's **nightlife** has thoroughly grown up in the past ten years to leave these neon sumps behind, and now offers everything from microbreweries and vertiginous, rooftop cocktail bars to fiercely chic clubs and dance bars, hosting top-class DJs. The high-concept bars of Sukhumvit and the lively, teeming venues of Banglamphu, in particular, pull in the style-conscious cream of Thai youth and are tempting an increasing number of travellers to stuff their party gear into their rucksacks. During the cool season, an evening out at one of the pop-up **beer gardens (usually Dec)** is a pleasant way of soaking up the urban atmosphere (and the traffic fumes); you'll find them in hotel forecourts or sprawled in front of dozens of shopping centres all over the city, most notably

1

Central World. Among the city's **club nights**, look out for the interesting regular events organized by Zudrangma Record Store (ⓦzudrangmarecords.com), especially at their own bar *Studio Lam*, which mix up dance music from all around Thailand and from all over the world. Getting back to your lodgings should be no problem in the small hours: many bus routes run a (reduced) service throughout the night, and tuk-tuks and taxis are always at hand – though it's probably best for unaccompanied women to avoid using tuk-tuks late at night.

RATANAKOSIN

Po 203/1 Tha Thien, Thanon Maharat ☎02 622 3081; map p.83. When the Chao Phraya express boats start to wind down, this bar takes over the rustic wooden pier and the balcony above with their great sunset views across the river to Wat Arun. It's popular with local students and office workers, hence the loud Thai pop music; avoid the food in favour of beer and Thai whisky. Daily 6–11pm.

BANGLAMPHU AND THE DEMOCRACY MONUMENT AREA

The travellers' enclave of Banglamphu takes on a new personality after dark, when its hub, Thanon Khao San, becomes a "walking street", closed to all traffic but open to almost any kind of makeshift stall, selling everything from fried bananas and buckets of "very strong" cocktails to share, to bargain fashions and one-off artworks. Young Thais crowd the area to browse and snack before piling in to Banglamphu's more stylish bars and indie live-music clubs, most of which are free to enter (though some ask you to show ID first).

Ad Here the 13th (Blues Bar) 13 Thanon Samsen, opposite Soi 2, right by the start of the bridge over Khlong Banglamphu ☎089 7694613, ⓦon.fb.me /1FMLhg5; map pp.100–101. Relaxed little neighbourhood live-music joint with sociable seats out on the pavement, where musos congregate nightly to listen to Thai and expat blues and jazz bands (from about 9.30pm onwards). Well-priced beer and plenty of cocktails. Daily 6pm–midnight.

Bangkok Bar 100 Thanon Ram Bhuttri ☎02 281 2899; map pp.100–101. By far the most ambitious and best of several live-music places on this street, whose Thai indie-rock bands and DJs – including occasional big-name appearances – are popular with young locals. In a multi-tiered bar-restaurant around a fountain courtyard, the stage is on the first floor but can also be viewed from the second-floor balconies. Daily 6pm–late.

Brick Bar Buddy Village complex, 265 Thanon Khao San ⓦbrickbarkhaosan.com; map pp.100–101. Massive red-brick vault of a live-music bar whose regular roster of reggae, ska, rock'n'roll and Thai pop bands, and occasional one-off appearances, is hugely popular with Thai twenty-somethings and teens. Big, sociable tables are set right under the stage and there's food too. The biggest nights are Fri and Sat when there's sometimes an entry charge, depending on who's on. Daily 7pm–1.30am.

Brown Sugar 469 Thanon Phra Sumen ⓦbrownsugar bangkok.com; map pp.100–101. Bangkok's best jazz club is settling nicely into its smart, atmospherically lit new premises, which are hung with colourful modernist gig posters and include a leafy canalside terrace. It still has its famous Sun jam session, but is now allowing in a few early-evening acoustic sessions each week. The prices of drinks are pumped up to pay for the talent, though they include imported beers on draught and in bottles. Café Tues–Sun roughly noon–10/11pm; bar-restaurant Tues–Thurs & Sun 5pm–midnight/1am, Fri & Sat 5pm–2am.

The Club 123 Thanon Khao San ☎02 629 1010, ⓦtheclubkhaosan.com; map pp.100–101. Thumping house tunes from an elevated, central DJ station with state-of-the-art lighting draw a sophisticated young Thai and international crowd. Daily 9pm–late.

Dickinson's Culture Café 64 Thanon Phra Arthit ☎089 497 8422, ⓦon.fb.me/1aG0Rzk; map pp.100–101. Grungy shophouse café decorated with a mess of empty

OPENING HOURS, ID CHECKS AND ADMISSION CHARGES

Most bars and clubs in Bangkok are meant to **close** at 1am, while those at the east end of Silom and on Royal City Avenue can stay open until 2am. In previous years, there have been regular "social order" clampdowns by the police, strictly enforcing these closing times, conducting occasional urine tests for drugs on bar customers, and setting up widespread ID checks to curb under-age drinking (you have to be 20 or over to drink in bars and clubs). However, at the time of writing, things were much more chilled, with many bars and clubs staying open into the wee hours on busy nights and ID checks in only a few places. It's hard to predict how the situation might develop, but you'll soon get an idea of how the wind is blowing when you arrive in Bangkok – and there's little harm in taking a copy of your passport out with you, just in case. Nearly all bars and clubs in Bangkok are free, but the most popular of them will sometimes levy an admission charge of a couple of hundred baht on their busiest nights (which will usually include a drink or two), though this can vary from week to week.

1

picture frames and traffic cones, which hosts some great DJs throughout the week – check out their Facebook page for line-ups. Sip on cocktails (including dozens of martinis) or buckets. Ask about the same owners' Café Democ and Club Culture, which are currently looking for new venues. Daily 9am–2pm.

★**Hippie de Bar** 46 Thanon Khao San ☎02 629 3508; map pp.100–101. Inviting courtyard bar set away from the main fray, surrounded by graffitied walls, TV screens and its own-brand fashion boutique. Attracts a mixed studenty/arty/high-society, mostly Thai crowd, to drink cheapish beer at its wrought-iron tables and park benches. Indoors is totally given over to kitsch, with plastic armchairs, Donny Osmond posters and ancient TVs. Daily 4pm–2am.

Jazz Happens Thanon Phra Arthit ☎02 282 9934, ⊚facebook.com/jazzhappens; map pp.100–101. Typical Phra Arthit bar, full of students, with just one small room and a few sociable pavement tables, but what sets this place apart is that some of the students are from Silpakorn University's Faculty of Jazz, playing jazz here every night. Tuck into a decent selection of well-priced cocktails and a narrower choice of food while you're listening. Daily 7pm–1am.

Phra Nakorn 58/2 Soi Damnoen Klang Tai ☎02 622 0282; map pp.100–101. Styles itself as "a hangout place for art lovers", and it successfully pulls in the capital's artists and art students, who can admire the floodlit view of the Golden Mount from the candlelit rooftop terrace, tuck into good food and reasonably priced drinks and browse one of the regular exhibitions on the first floor. Daily 6pm–1am.

Sheepshank Tha Phra Arthit express-boat pier ⊚sheepshankpublichouse.com; map pp.100–101. Banglamphu's coolest new bar, set in a former boat-repair yard overlooking the Chao Phraya and the riverside walkway and sporting an industrial look that features black leather, silver studs, pulleys and girders. There's a wide selection of bottled craft beers from the US and Japan, as well as imaginative bar snacks and a long menu of more substantial gastropub dishes. Tues–Thurs 5.30pm–midnight, Fri–Sun 5.30pm–1am.

DOWNTOWN: AROUND SIAM SQUARE AND THANON PLOENCHIT

Downtown, Siam Square has much less to offer after dark than Thanon Silom, further south. Out to the northeast, running south off Thanon Rama IX, lies RCA (Royal City Avenue). An officially sanctioned "nightlife zone" that's allowed to stay open until 2am, it's lined mostly with warehouse-like clubs that have a reputation as meat markets.

Coco Walk Thanon Phrayathai; map p.117. It would be hard not to enjoy yourself at this covered parade of loosely interchangeable but buzzing good-time bars, right beside Ratchathewi BTS. Popular with local students, they variously offer pool tables, live musicians, DJs and cover bands, but all have reasonably priced beer and food. Daily roughly 6pm–1am.

Hyde and Seek Ground floor, Athenée Residence, 65/1 Soi Ruam Rudee ☎02 168 5152–3, ⊚hydeandseek .com; map p.117. Classy but buzzy gastrobar, with nightly DJs and lots of attractive garden seating. Amid a huge range of drinks, there's a good selection of wines by the glass and imported beers on draught; the food menu features bar bites, pastas, salads and familiar dishes such as bangers and mash. Daily 11am–1am.

Raintree 116/63–4 Soi Ruamjit, Thanon Rangnam ☎02 245 7230, ⊚raintreepub.com; map pp.80–81. Near Victory Monument, two ordinary shophouses have been converted into this friendly, typical "good ol' boys" bar, with lots of rough timber furniture and the biggest water-buffalo skulls you've ever seen. Live, nightly music is mostly Songs for Life (see p.763), mixed in with some *luk thung*, starting out low-key and soothing, and getting more raucous and danceworthy as the night hots up. Daily 5pm–1.30am.

Saxophone 3/8 Victory Monument (southeast corner), just off Thanon Phrayathai ☎02 246 5472, ⊚saxophonepub.com; map pp.80–81. Lively, easy-going, spacious venue with decent Thai and Western food and a diverse roster of bands – mostly jazz and blues, plus acoustic guitar, funk, rock and reggae (details on their website) – which attracts a good mix of Thais and foreigners. Daily 6pm–2am.

THANON SUKHUMVIT

A night out on Thanon Sukhumvit could be subsumed by the girlie bars and hostess-run bar-beers (open-sided drinking halls with huge circular bars) on sois Nana and Cowboy, but there's plenty of style on Sukhumvit too, especially in the rooftop bars and enjoyably trendy clubs. The scene has been gravitating eastwards over the last few years: the fashionable bars and clubs on and around Soi Thong Lo (Soi 55) attract a "hi-so" (high-society) crowd, while those over on Soi Ekamai (Soi 63) are perhaps a little more studenty.

Apoteka Soi 11 ⊚apotekabangkok.com; map p.123. Attractive new bar, with exposed brick walls, a tempting snug off to one side and terrace tables facing Q Bar. Live nightly blues bands add to the appeal, though drinks are pricey. Daily 11am–1pm.

Cheap Charlie's Soi 11; map p.123. Idiosyncratic, long-running, low-tech, open-air bar that's famous for its cheap beer and customers' hall-of-fame gallery. It now offers the luxury of plastic tables and chairs, on a quiet, pedestrianized side-alley. Mon–Sat roughly 4.30pm–12.30am.

1

Clouds Ground floor, Seen Space, Soi 13, Soi Thong Lo (Soi 55) ☎ 02 185 2365, ⓦ facebook.com/cloudsbar; map p.123. On a sub-soi of Thong Lo, a couple of minutes' walk (west) from the co-owned *Iron Fairies*, this stylish open-fronted DJ bar is decorated with bouncing baubles and revolving clocks and plays mostly hip-hop and R&B. It gives onto a raucous shared courtyard, where you can tuck into raw oysters, fish'n'chips and draught and bottled imported beers. Mon–Thurs & Sun 5pm–1.30am, Fri & Sat 5pm–2am.

Finnegan's 23/1 Soi 4 (Nana Tai) ☎ 02 656 8160; map p.123. Probably the most authentically Irish of Bangkok's many "Oirish" bars, friendly *Finnegan's* offers draught Guinness, homely wood and leather decor, popular food and a wide array of TV sports, including rugby and Gaelic games. Daily 9am–1am.

Glow 96/4–5 Soi 23 ⓦ facebook.com/glowbkk; map p.123. This small, three-storey venue is one of the clubs of the moment, attracting an interesting roster of Thai and international DJs, such as Goldie and Fabio, to play house, techno and drum'n'bass. Daily 10pm–roughly 3am.

The Iron Fairies Just over 1km up Soi Thong Lo (Soi 55) from BTS Thong Lo ☎ 099 918 1600, ⓦ theironfairies .com; map p.123. High-concept bar that's designed to evoke a magical fairytale, with low lighting, jars of glitter (fairy dust) lining the walls and windows, gargoyles and lots of wooden structures including higgledy-piggledy staircases. Nightly live jazz including an open-mike night on Monday. Daily 6pm–2am.

Long Table Column Tower, 48 Soi 16 ☎ 02 302 2557–9, ⓦ longtablebangkok.com; map p.123. This achingly fashionable 25th-floor restaurant is named for its 25m-long communal centrepiece table, which seats seventy and serves contemporary Thai cuisine. But the real attraction is the sleek, Shanghai-style open-sided balcony bar whose "long-tail" cocktails give you ample time to lounge glamorously on the leather sofas and soak up the wraparound panoramas across downtown skyscrapers. Daily 5pm–2am.

Mikkeller 26 Yaek 2, Soi 10, Soi Ekamai (Soi 63) ☎ 02 381 9891, ⓦ mikkellerbangkok.com; map p.123. This branch of the famous Danish microbrewery offers thirty craft beers on tap in a handsome suburban house furnished in blonde wood, with bean bags out on the lawn. Located (and signposted) down a sub-soi of a sub-soi of Ekamai and with the beer working out at about B500/pint, it's one for the beer geeks. Daily 5pm–midnight.

Nest 9th Floor, Le Fenix hotel, Soi 11 ☎ 02 255 0638, ⓦ thenestbangkok.com; map p.123. Whether you unfurl on a daybed, curl up in a basket chair or recline under a hooded chaise longue at this aptly named, leafy, rooftop eyrie you'll get an airy view of the condo-spiked skyline (there are covers for wet days) and a good choice of cocktails, Thai, Western and fusion main courses and tapas. There's music every night, be it DJs, singer-songwriters,

Latin nights or occasional parties. Not as slick or spectacular as the more famous downtown sky bars but very pleasant. Daily 6pm–2am.

Q Bar (Q Up) 34 Soi 11 ☎ 082 308 3246, ⓦ qbarbangkok .com; map p.123. Very dark, very trendy, New York-style bar-club occupying two floors and a terrace. Famous for its music from local and international DJs, *Q Bar* appeals to a mixed crowd of fashionable people, particularly on Fri and Sat nights. Its weekly roster currently features a live band on Wed, R&B all night on Fri and "Soulful Sundays". Don't turn up in shorts, singlets or sandals if you're male; ID required. Daily 10pm–2am.

Studio Lam About 100m up Soi 51 on the left, on the corner of the first sub-soi, about 5min walk west of BTS Thong Lo ☎ 02 261 6661, ⓦ facebook.com /studiolambangkok; map p.123. This friendly, cosy neighbourhood bar is the latest project of Zudrangma Records (see p.767), whose record shop is just up the sub-soi to the left. The soundproofing and massive, purpose-built sound system give the game away: the music's the thing here, with DJs and live musicians playing driving *mor lam* and an eclectic choice of world sounds nightly. Tues–Sun 5/6pm–1/2am.

WTF 7 Soi 51 ☎ 02 662 6246, ⓦ wtfbangkok.com; map p.123. Small, hip, Spanish-influenced bar-café and art gallery, which hosts occasional movie nights, left-field DJs and gigs. Adorned with luridly coloured Thai film posters and a great soundtrack, it offers global tapas, pâtés and a tempting variety of cocktails and wines. It's 5min walk west of BTS Thong Lo, 100m up Soi 51, near the mouth of a small sub-soi on the left. Tues–Sun 6pm–1am.

DOWNTOWN: SOUTH OF THANON RAMA IV

Most of the action here happens around the east end of Thanon Silom, though a few bars further west lay on great views of the river or the vast cityscape. If, among all the choice of nightlife around Silom, you do end up at one of Patpong's sex shows, watch out for hyper-inflated bar bills and other cons – plenty of customers get ripped off in some way, and stories of menacing bouncers are legion.

Flann O'Brien's Corner of Silom and Thaniya roads ☎ 02 632 7515; map p.125. Welcoming Irish bar that's especially good for watching TV sport. A wide range of beers on draught including Guinness and Kilkenny bitter, popular food and varied live music Wed & Fri evenings. Daily 8am–1am.

★ The Sky Bar & Distil Floor 63, State Tower, 1055 Thanon Silom, corner of Thanon Charoen Krung ☎ 02 624 9555, ⓦ lebua.com; map p.125. Thrill-seekers and view addicts shouldn't miss forking out for an alfresco drink here, 275m above the city's pavements – come around 6pm to enjoy the stunning panoramas in both the light and the dark. It's standing-only at *The Sky Bar*, a circular

1

restaurant-bar built over the edge of the building with almost 360-degree views, but for the sunset itself, you're better off on the outside terrace of *Distil* on the other side of the building (where bookings are accepted), which has a wider choice of drinks, charming service and huge couches to recline on. The bars have become very popular since featuring in *The Hangover II* movie and have introduced a strict, smart-casual dress code. Daily 5/6pm–1am.

Tapas Room Club Soi 4, Thanon Silom ☎ 02 234 4737, ⓦ facebook.com/tapas.room; map p.125. Vaguely Spanish-oriented, pricey bar (but no tapas) with Moorish-style decor, whose outside tables are probably the best spot for checking out the comings and goings on this pedestrianized, partly gay soi. In the multi-roomed interior, which stretches up to a third-floor roof terrace, the music is mostly house, with added percussionists at the weekend. Daily 6/7pm–2am.

★**Tawandang German Brewery** 462/61 Thanon Rama III ☎ 02 678 1114–6, ⓦ tawandang.com; map p.125. A taxi-ride south of Chong Nonsi BTS down Thanon Narathiwat Ratchanakharin – and best to book a table in

advance – this vast all-rounder is well worth the effort. Under a huge dome, up to 1600 revellers enjoy good food, great micro-brewed German beer and a mercurial, hugely entertaining cabaret, featuring Fong Nam, who blend Thai classical and popular with Western styles of music, as well as magic shows, ballet and hip-hop dancing. Daily 5pm–1am.

Viva Aviv: The River Ground floor, River City shopping centre ☎ 02 639 6305, ⓦ vivaaviv.com; map p.125. With a lovely terrace on the river and a gnarly interior decor of hide-bound chairs and ships' winches, this bar offers cool sounds, some serious cocktails, good coffees and smoothies, as well as comfort food such as gourmet hot dogs, pizzas and salads. Daily 11am–midnight.

CHATUCHAK WEEKEND MARKET

Viva 8 Section 8 ☎ 02 618 7425; map p.125. Classy, relaxing bar that serves great cocktails, juices and coffees, where you can rest your feet while listening to DJs (from about 4pm) or tuck into paella that's theatrically prepared in a huge pan by a Spanish chef. Sat & Sun 7am–10pm.

GAY BANGKOK

The bars, clubs and café-restaurants listed here, located around the east end of Thanon Silom and especially in the narrow alleys of Soi 2 and Soi 4, are the most notable of Bangkok's **gay nightlife** venues. Another strip of mostly gay bars can be found on the west end of Soi Sarasin at the top of Lumphini Park, but there are plans to redevelop the whole block. More general background on gay life in Thailand, plus contacts and sources of information, most of them concentrated in Bangkok, can be found in Basics (see p.65). Advice on opening hours, admission charges and ID is given in Drinking and Nightlife (see p.159) – Soi 2, for example, operates a strict ID policy.

The Balcony Soi 4, Thanon Silom ☎ 02 235 5891, ⓦ balconypub.com; map p.125. Unpretentious, fun place with plenty of outdoor seats for people-watching, welcoming staff, reasonably priced drinks, upstairs karaoke and decent Thai and Western food. Happy hour till 8pm. Daily 5.30pm–late.

Dick's Café Duangthawee Plaza, 894/7–8 Soi Pratuchai, Thanon Suriwong ☎ 02 637 0078, ⓦ dickscafe.com; map p.125. Elegant day-and-night café-bar-restaurant, with a *Casablanca* theme to the decor (styling itself on *Rick's Café Americain*) and occasional art exhibitions. On a traffic-free soi of go-go bars off the north side of Suriwong, it's ideal for drinking, eating decent Thai and Western food or just chilling out. Daily 11am–2am.

Disco Disco Soi 2, Thanon Silom; map p.125. Small, pared-down DJ bar with a minimalist, retro feel, playing good dance music to a fun young crowd. Daily 10pm–2am.

DJ Station Soi 2, Thanon Silom ☎ 02 266 4029, ⓦ dj-station.com; map p.125. Bangkok's most famous club, a highly fashionable but unpretentious three-storey venue, packed at weekends, attracting a mix of Thais and farangs, with a cabaret show nightly at around 11pm. Daily 10pm–2am.

GOD (Guys on Display) 60/18–21 Soi 2/1, Thanon Silom, in a small pedestrianized alley between Soi Thaniya and Soi 2 ☎ 02 632 8033; map p.125. Large, busy, three-level club with go-go dancers, somewhat more Thai-oriented than *DJ Station*. It tends not to fill up until *DJ Station* has closed; however, at the time of writing, since the military coup, GOD has been opening only on weekends, until 2/3am, though this is likely to be a temporary thing. Usually daily roughly 11pm–6am.

JJ Park 8/3 Soi 2, Thanon Silom ☎ 02 235 1227; map p.125. Classy, Thai-oriented bar, for relaxed socializing among an older set rather than raving, with karaoke and live music, and a Moroccan-themed chill-out annexe, *Club Café*, next door. Daily 10pm–2am.

Sphinx 98–104 Soi 4, Thanon Silom ☎ 02 234 7249; map p.125. Plush decor with a vaguely Egyptian theme, terrace seating and very good Thai and Western food attract a sophisticated crowd to this ground-floor bar and restaurant; karaoke upstairs at *Pharaoh's* on Fri & Sat. Daily 5pm–2am.

Telephone Pub 114/11–13 Soi 4, Thanon Silom ☎ 02 234 3279, ⓦ telephonepub.com; map p.125. Bangkok's first Western-style gay bar when it opened in 1987, this cruisy, dimly lit eating and drinking venue has a terrace on the alley, telephones on the tables inside for making new friends and karaoke upstairs. Daily 6pm–late.

1

ENTERTAINMENT

On the cultural front, the most accessible of the capital's performing arts is **Thai dancing**, particularly when served up in bite-size portions in tourist shows. **Thai boxing** is also well worth watching: the raucous live experience at either of Bangkok's two main national stadiums far outshines the TV coverage.

CINEMAS

Central Bangkok has more than forty cinemas, many of them on the top floors of shopping centres. Most show recent American and European releases with their original dialogue and Thai subtitles, screening shows around four times a day. Several websites give showtimes of movies in Bangkok, including ⓦ moveedoo.com; cinema locations are printed on *Nancy Chandler's Map of Bangkok* (see p.142). Whatever cinema you're in, you're expected to stand for the king's anthem, which is played before every performance.

Alliance Française 179 Thanon Witthayu, opposite the east side of Lumpini Park behind the Japanese Embassy ☎02 670 4200, ⓦ afthailande.org. Movies at the French cultural centre (every Wed 7pm; free) are usually subtitled in English.

Apex Lido Thanon Rama I, Siam Square ☎02 252 6498, ⓦ apexsiam-square.com. Among half a dozen cinemas in and around Siam Square, this is your best bet for independent foreign films.

Goethe Institut 18/1 Soi Goethe, between Thanon Sathorn Tai and Soi Ngam Duphli ☎02 108 8231–2, ⓦ goethe.de/thailand. In the cool season (Dec–Feb), the German cultural centre screens an interesting free programme of recent movies from German-speaking countries, always subtitled in English, outdoors in the garden; check their website for a detailed map. Wed 7.30pm.

House Royal City Avenue (RCA) ☎02 641 5177, ⓦ houserama.com. Bangkok's only art-house cinema, well to the northeast of the centre. The nearest subway station, Phetchaburi, is a long walk away, so it's best to come by taxi.

CULTURE SHOWS AND PERFORMING ARTS

Because of the language barrier, most Thai theatre is inaccessible to foreigners and so, with a few exceptions, the best way to experience the traditional performing arts is at shows designed for tourists, most notably at Siam Niramit. You can, however, witness Thai dancing being performed for its original ritual purpose, usually several times a day, at the Lak Muang Shrine behind the Grand Palace (see p.94) and the Erawan Shrine on the corner of Thanon Ploenchit (see p.123). Background information on Thai classical dance and traditional theatre can be found in Basics (see p.47). Meanwhile, more glitzy and occasionally ribald entertainment is the order of the day at the capital's ladyboy cabaret shows.

Calypso Cabaret Asiatique (see opposite), Thanon Charoen Krung, 2km south of Saphan Taksin BTS ☎02 688 1415–7, ⓦ calypsocabaret.com. A bevy of luscious

transvestites don glamorous outfits and perform over-the-top song-and-dance routines twice a night. B1200, or B900 if booked online, including one drink.

Chalermkrung Theatre (Sala Chalermkrung) 66 Thanon Charoen Krung, on the intersection with Thanon Triphet in Pahurat, next to Old Siam Plaza ☎02 222 0434, ⓦ salachalermkrung.com or ⓦ thai ticketmajor.com. This Art Deco former cinema, dating from 1933, hosts mainstream traditional and contemporary theatre, plus regular *khon* performances with English subtitles. Performances cost from B800. Thurs & Fri 7.30pm.

National Theatre Sanam Luang, Ratanakosin ☎02 224 1342. Closed for renovation at the time of writing, but usually hosts roughly weekly shows of traditional performing arts such as *khon*, plus twice-monthly medley shows of music, dancing and *lakhon* (classical dance-drama) for tourists and other beginners (usually the first and last Fri of the month at 5pm). However, it's difficult to get information about what's on in English – try the nearby Bangkok Tourism Division (see p.142).

Siam Niramit 19 Thanon Tiam Ruammit, 5min walk (or a free shuttle ride from Exit 1) from Thailand Cultural Centre subway, following signs for the South Korean embassy ☎02 649 9222, ⓦ siamniramit.com. Unashamedly tourist-oriented but the easiest place to get a glimpse of the variety and spectacle intrinsic to traditional Thai theatre. The 80min show presents a history of regional Thailand's culture and beliefs in a high-tech spectacular of fantastic costumes and huge chorus numbers, enlivened by acrobatics and flashy special effects. The complex also includes crafts outlets and a buffet restaurant (dinner plus show from B1850). Tickets (from B1500) can be bought on the spot, online or through most travel agents. Daily 8pm.

Silom Village Thanon Silom ☎02 234 4581, ⓦ silom village.co.th. This complex of tourist shops stages a nightly 45min show at its Ruen Thep theatre (8.15pm; B700) to accompany a set menu of Thai food (available from 7.30pm).

Thailand Cultural Centre Thanon Ratchadapisek ☎02 247 0028, ⓦ thaiticketmajor.com; Thailand Cultural Centre subway. All-purpose venue, under the control of the Ministry of Culture, that hosts mainstream classical concerts, traditional and contemporary theatre, and visiting international dance and theatre shows.

THAI BOXING

The violence of the average Thai boxing match (see p.49) may be off-putting to some, but spending a couple of hours at one of Bangkok's two main stadiums, Rajdamnoen and Lumphini (which has recently moved out of the centre), can be immensely entertaining, not least for the enthusiasm of the spectators and the ritualistic aspects of the fights. Seats for foreigners cost B1000–2000 (cheaper, standing tickets are reserved for Thais). Sessions usually feature ten bouts, each consisting of five 3min rounds with 2min rests in between each round, so if you're not a big fan it may be worth turning up an hour late, as the better fights tend to happen later in the billing. To engage in a little *muay thai* yourself, visit one of several gyms around Bangkok that offer classes to foreigners.

Chacrit Muay Thai School 15/2 Soi 39, Thanon Sukhumvit ☎089 499 2052, ⓦchacritmuaythaischool .com. Drop-in sessions cost B800/hr; longer courses are available.

Lumphini Stadium Thanon Ram Intra ⓦmuay thailumpinee.net. This sixty-year-old stadium moved way out into the northern suburbs near Don Muang Airport in 2014. The schedule of upcoming fights is posted on its website. Usually Tues & Fri 6/6.30pm, Sat 4pm & 9pm.

Rajdamnoen Stadium Thanon Rajdamnoen Nok ⓦrajadamnern.com. Bangkok's other main stadium is handily located next to the TAT office near Banglamphu (and handily surrounded by restaurants selling north-eastern food), though the view from the B1000 section for foreigners is partially obscured. Usually Mon, Wed & Thurs 6.30pm, Sun 5pm & 8.30pm.

Sor Vorapin's Gym 13 Trok Kasap, off Thanon Chakrabongse in Banglamphu ☎02 282 3551, ⓦthai boxings.com. Holds *muay thai* classes twice daily (B500 per session). Sor Vorapin also offers extended training and a homestay at a second gym in Thonburi (B6500 all-in for 1 week) – see the website for details.

SHOPPING

Bangkok has a good reputation for shopping, particularly for antiques, gems, contemporary interior design and fashion, where the range and quality are streets ahead of other Thai cities. Silk and handicrafts are good buys too, though shopping for these in Chiang Mai has many advantages. As always, watch out for **fakes**: cut glass masquerading as precious stones, old, damaged goods being passed off as antiques, counterfeit designer clothes and accessories, pirated CDs and DVDs, even mocked-up international driver's licences (though Thai travel agents and other organizations aren't that easily fooled). Bangkok also has the best English-language bookshops in the country. Downtown is full of smart, multi-storey **shopping plazas** like Siam Centre, Siam Paragon and Central World on Thanon Rama I, Central Embassy on Thanon Ploenchit and Emporium on Thanon Sukhumvit, which is where you'll find the majority of the city's fashion stores, as well as designer lifestyle goods and bookshops. The plazas tend to be pleasantly air-conditioned and thronging with trendy young Thais, but don't hold much interest for tourists unless you happen to be looking for a new outfit. Shopping centres, department stores and tourist-oriented shops in the city keep late **hours**, opening daily at 10 or 11am and closing at about 9pm; many small, upmarket boutiques, for example along Thanon Charoen Krung and Thanon Silom, close on Sundays, one or two even on Saturdays. Monday is meant to be no-street-vendor day throughout Bangkok, a chance for the pavements to get cleaned and for pedestrians to finally see where they're going, but plenty of stalls manage to flout the rule.

MARKETS

For travellers, spectating, not shopping, is apt to be the main draw of Bangkok's neighbourhood markets – notably the bazaars of Chinatown and the blooms and scents of Pak Khlong Talat, the flower and vegetable market just west of Memorial Bridge (see p.109). The massive Chatuchak Weekend Market is an exception, being both a tourist attraction and a marvellous shopping experience (see p.129). With the notable exception of Chatuchak, most markets operate daily from dawn till early afternoon; early morning is often the best time to go to beat the heat and crowds.

Asiatique About 2km south of Taksin Bridge, between the river and Thanon Charoen Krung ⓦwww.thai asiatique.com. New night-time market for tourists in ten rebuilt 1930s warehouses and sawmills that belonged to the Danish East Asiatic Company. Several of them are given over to souvenirs and to clothes stalls, which tend to morph into bigger, more chic and expensive fashion outlets the closer to the river you get. Warehouse 1, devoted to furniture and home decor is probably the most interesting section, featuring some creative contemporary designs.

There's plenty to eat, of course, with the poshest restaurants, including a branch of *Baan Khanitha*, occupying the pleasant riverside boardwalk. Free ferries shuttle back and forth from Tha Sathorn pier, though the queues are often very long. Currently, the Chao Phraya Express tourist boats leaving Phra Arthit at 4pm, 4.30pm and 5pm are extending their route from Tha Sathorn to Asiatique. You could also catch an orange-flag express boat to Wat Rajsingkorn, leaving a 10min walk through the wat and down Thanon Charoen Krung to Asiatique. Daily 5pm–midnight.

HANDICRAFTS, TEXTILES AND CONTEMPORARY DESIGN

Samples of nearly all regionally produced handicrafts end up in Bangkok, so the selection is phenomenal. Many of the shopping plazas have at least one classy handicraft outlet, and competition keeps prices in the city at upcountry levels, with the main exception of household objects – particularly wickerware and tin bowls and basins – which get palmed off relatively expensively in Bangkok. Several

1

SHOPPING FOR EVERYDAY STUFF

You're most likely to find useful everyday items in one of the city's numerous **department stores**: seven-storey Central Chidlom on Thanon Ploenchit (daily 10am–10pm), which boasts handy services like watch-, garment- and shoe-repair booths as well as a huge product selection (including large sizes), is probably the city's best. For **children's stuff**, Central Chidlom also has a branch of Mothercare, as do the Emporium, Central World and Siam Paragon shopping centres. Meanwhile, the British chain of **pharmacies**, Boots, has scores of branches across the city, including on Thanon Chakrabongse in Banglamphu, in Siam Paragon, in Central World, in Emporium and at the Thanon Suriwong end of Patpong 1.

The best place to buy anything to do with **mobile phones** (see p.71) is the scores of small booths on the third floor of Mah Boon Krong (MBK) Shopping Centre at the Rama I/Phrayathai intersection. For **computer** hardware and genuine and pirated software, as well as digital cameras, Panthip Plaza, at 604/3 Thanon Phetchaburi, is the best place; it's slightly off the main shopping routes, but handy for Khlong Saen Saeb boat stop Tha Pratunam, or a longer walk from BTS Ratchathevi. Mac-heads are catered for here, including authorized resellers, and there are dozens of repair and secondhand booths, especially towards the back of the shopping centre and on the upper floors.

places on and around Thanon Khao San sell reasonably priced triangular "axe" pillows (*mawn khwaan*) in traditional fabrics, which make fantastic souvenirs but are heavy to post home; some places sell unstuffed versions which are simple to mail home, but a pain to fill when you return. The cheapest outlet for traditional northern and northeastern textiles is Chatuchak Weekend Market (see p.129), where you'll also be able to nose out some interesting handicrafts. Most Thai silk, which is noted for its thickness and sheen, comes from the northeast and the north, where shopping for it is probably more fun. However, there is a decent range of outlets in the capital, including many branches of Jim Thompson. Bangkok also has a good reputation for its contemporary interior design, fusing minimalist Western ideals with traditional Thai and other Asian craft elements.

RATANAKOSIN

Queen Sirikit Museum of Textiles Shop Grand Palace (on the right just inside the Gate of Glorious Victory) ⓦ qsmtthailand.org/museum_shop; map p.83. Not-for-profit shop under the auspices of the Queen's Support Foundation, which is especially good for beautiful, top-quality *yan lipao*, traditional basketware made from delicately woven fern stems. Daily 9am–5pm (except when the Grand Palace is closed for royal events).

BANGLAMPHU AND THE DEMOCRACY MONUMENT AREA

Lofty Bamboo Buddy Hotel shopping complex, 265 Thanon Khao San; map pp.100–101; Floor 2, Mah Boon Krong (MBK) Centre, corner of Thanon Phrayathai and Thanon Rama I; map p.117; ⓦ loftybamboo.com. Fair-trade outlet for Thai crafts, accessories, clothes and jewellery, including silver and bags made by Karen people

and textiles and accessories by Lisu people from northern Thailand. Buddy Hotel shopping complex daily 10.30am–7.30pm; Mah Boon Krong (MBK) Centre daily 10.30am–8pm.

Taekee Taekon 118 Thanon Phra Arthit ☎ 02 629 1473, ⓦ on.fb.me/1DzAOFb; map pp.100–101. Tasteful assortment of handicraft gifts, souvenirs and textiles, plus a selection of Thai art cards and black-and-white photocards. Mon–Sat 9am–6pm.

DOWNTOWN: AROUND SIAM SQUARE AND THANON PLOENCHIT

Alexander Lamont Floor 3, Gaysorn Plaza; Central Embassy; ⓦ alexanderlamont.com; map p.117. Beautiful lacquerware bowls, vases and boxes, as well as objects using bronze, glass, crystal, ceramic, parchment, gold leaf and petrified wood, all in imaginative contemporary, Asian-inspired styles. Daily 10am–8pm.

Chabatik Floor 4, Siam Paragon ⓦ chabatik.com; map p.117. Gorgeous scarves, wraps and hangings in a rainbow of colours, made from soft Khon Kaen silk. Daily 10am–8pm.

Doi Tung Lifestyle Floor 2, Siam Discovery Centre ⓦ www.doitung.org; map p.117. Part of the late Princess Mother's development project based at Doi Tung, selling very striking and attractive cotton and linen in warm colours, made up into clothes, cushion covers, rugs and so on, as well as coffee and macadamia nuts from the Chiang Rai mountains. Mon–Thurs 11am–8pm, Fri–Sun 11am–9pm.

Exotique Thai Floor 4, Siam Paragon ⓦ siamparagon .co.th; map p.117. A collection of small outlets from around the city and the country – including silk-makers and designers from Chiang Mai – makes a good, upmarket one-stop shop, that is much more interesting than Narai

Phand (see below). There's everything from jewellery and beauty products to celadons and axe pillows (see p.471) at Mon Thai. Daily 10am–10pm.

Narai Phand Ground floor, President Tower Arcade, just west of Gaysorn Plaza, Thanon Ploenchit ⓦ narai phand.com; map p.117. This souvenir centre was set up to ensure the preservation of traditional crafts and to maintain standards of quality, as a joint venture with the Ministry of Industry in the 1930s, and has a duly institutional feel, though it makes a reasonable one-stop shop for last-minute presents. It offers a huge assortment of reasonably priced, good-quality goods from all over the country, including silk and cotton, *khon* masks, *bencharong*, celadon, woodcarving, lacquerware, silver, brass, bronze, *yan lipao* basketware and axe cushions. Daily 10am–8pm.

OTOP Central Embassy ⓦ centralembassy.com/brands /otop-heritage; map p.117. An attractive selection of the more high-end handicrafts made under the national OTOP (One Tambon, One Product) scheme. Daily 10am–8pm.

Propaganda Floor 4, Siam Discovery Centre ⓦ propagandaonline.com; map p.117. All sorts of poppy and playful stuff, often with a sexual or scatological theme, ranging from bags to dental floss holders. Daily 10am–9pm.

Thann Floor 3, Gaysorn Plaza ⓦ thann.info; map p.117. Striking contemporary rugs, cushion covers, vases and wooden objects, plus famous spa and beauty products (with a high-concept modern spa next door and a café outside). Daily 10am–8pm.

THANON SUKHUMVIT

Krishna's Just west of Soi 11 ⓦ krishnasasianarts.com; map p.123. Large emporium of mostly mass-produced but good-quality household and decorative items in ceramic, brass, fibreglass and sandstone, especially figurines and Buddha statues. Mon–Sat 9am–7pm.

The Shop @ TCDC Thailand Creative and Design Centre, Floor 6, Emporium, Thanon Sukhumvit, between sois 22 and 24 ⓦ tcdc.or.th; map p.123. The retail outlet at Bangkok's design centre sells innovative products dreamt up by local creatives, mostly stocking-fillers, bags and household items, with more than a whiff of kitsch. Tues– Sun 10.30am–9pm.

Sop Moei Arts 8 Soi 49 ⓦ sopmoeiarts.com; map p.123. If you're not going up to Chiang Mai, it's well worth checking out the lovely fabrics and basketware at this small branch shop. Tues–Sat 9.30am–5pm.

Thai Craft Fairs Floor L, Jasmine City Building, corner of Thanon Sukhumvit and Soi 23 ⓦ thaicraft.org; map p.123. Roughly monthly craft sales and demonstrations, involving about seventy groups of artisans from all over the country, run on fair-trade principles by the Thai Craft Association, an independent development organization.

DOWNTOWN: SOUTH OF THANON RAMA IV

Jim Thompson 9 Thanon Suriwong, corner of Thanon Rama IV; map p.125; branches at the Jim Thompson House Museum (see p.119), Don Muang Airport and many department stores, malls and hotels around the city; ⓦ jimthompson.com. A good place to start looking for traditional Thai fabric, or at least to get an idea of what's out there. Stocks silk, linen and cotton by the metre and ready-made items from shirts to cushion covers, which are well designed and of good quality, but pricey. They also have a home-furnishings section (daily 9am–7pm). If you're keen on a bargain, they have a factory outlet way out east of the centre on Soi 93, Thanon Sukhumvit (daily 9am–6pm). Daily 9am–9pm.

Khomapastr 56–58 Thanon Naret, between Suriwong and Si Phraya ⓦ khomapastrfabrics.com; map p.125. Branch of the famous Hua Hin shop (see p.515), selling brightly coloured, hand-printed cotton in traditional Thai patterns. Mon–Sat 9am–5.30pm.

The Legend Floor 3, Thaniya Plaza, corner of Soi Thaniya and Thanon Silom ☏ 02 231 2170; map p.125. Stocks a small selection of well-made Thai handicrafts, from wood and wickerware to pretty fabrics and celadon and other ceramics, at reasonable prices. Daily 10am–7pm.

Silom Village 286/1 Thanon Silom ⓦ silomvillage .co.th; map p.125. An open-air complex of low-rise shops that attempts to create a relaxing, upcountry atmosphere as a backdrop for its diverse, fairly pricey handicrafts. Most shops daily 10am–9/10pm.

Tamnan Mingmuang Floor 3, Thaniya Plaza, corner of Soi Thaniya and Thanon Silom ☏ 02 231 2120; map p.125. Subsidiary of *The Legend* (see above), which sells clay figurines but concentrates on basketry from all over the country: among the unusual items on offer are trays and boxes for tobacco and betel nut made from *yan lipao* (intricately woven fern vines), and bambooware sticky-rice containers, baskets and lampshades. Daily 10am–7pm.

TAILORED CLOTHES

Inexpensive tailoring shops crowd Silom, Sukhumvit and Khao San roads, but the best single area to head for is the short stretch of Thanon Charoen Krung between Thanon Suriwong and Thanon Silom (near the Chao Phraya express-boat stops at Tha Oriental and Tha Wat Muang Kae, or a 10min walk from Saphan Taksin Skytrain station), where the recommended tailors below can be found. It's generally advisable to avoid tailors in tourist areas such as Thanon Khao San, shopping malls and Thanon Sukhumvit, although if you're lucky it's still possible to come up trumps here. For cheap and reasonable shirt and dress material other than silk go for a browse around Pahurat market (see p.109), though the suit materials are mostly poor and best avoided.

1

HAVING CLOTHES TAILOR-MADE

Bangkok can be an excellent place to get tailor-made suits, dresses, shirts and trousers at a fraction of the price you'd pay in the West. Tailors here can copy a sample brought from home and will also work from any photographs you can provide; most also carry a good selection of catalogues. The bad news is that many tourist-oriented tailors aren't terribly good, often attempting to get away with poor work and shoddy materials (and sometimes trying to delay delivery until just before you leave the city, so that you don't have time to complain). However, with a little effort and thought, both men and women can get some fantastic clothes made to measure.

Choosing a tailor can be tricky, and unless you're particularly knowledgeable about material, shopping around won't necessarily tell you much. However, don't make a decision wholly on prices quoted – picking a tailor simply because they're the cheapest usually leads to poor work, and cheap suits don't last. Special deals offering two suits, two shirts, two ties and a kimono for US$99 should be left well alone. Above all, ignore recommendations by anyone with a vested interest in bringing your custom to a particular shop.

Prices vary widely depending on material and the tailor's skill. As a very rough guide, for labour alone expect to pay B5000–6000 for a two-piece suit, though some tailors will charge rather more (check whether or not the price you're quoted includes the lining). For middling **material**, expect to pay about B3000–5000, or anything up to B20,000 for top-class cloth. With the exception of silk, local materials are frequently of poor quality and for suits in particular you're far better off using English or Italian cloth. Most tailors stock both imported and local fabrics, but bringing your own from home can work out significantly cheaper.

Give yourself as much **time** as possible. For suits, insist on two fittings. Most good tailors require around three days for a suit (some require ten days or more), although a few have enough staff to produce good work in a day or two. The more **detail** you can give the tailor the better. As well as deciding on the obvious features such as single- or double-breasted and number of buttons, think about the width of lapels, style of trousers, whether you want the jacket with vents or not, and so forth. Specifying factors like this will make all the difference as to whether you're happy with your suit, so it's worth discussing them with the tailor; a good tailor should be able to give good advice. Finally, don't be afraid to be an awkward customer until you're completely happy with the finished product – after all, the whole point of getting clothes tailor-made is to get exactly what you want.

A Song Tailor 8 Trok Chartered Bank, just round the corner from OP Place shopping centre off Thanon Charoen Krung, near the Oriental Hotel ☎ 02 630 9708; map p.125. Friendly, helpful small shop that's a good first port of call if you're on a budget. Men's and women's suits and shirts; ideally three to four days with two fittings, but can turn work around in two days. Mon–Sat 10am–7pm.

Ah Song Tailor 1203 Thanon Charoen Krung, opposite Soi 36 ☎ 02 233 7574; map p.125. Younger brother of the above (neither of them should be confused with the nearby Ah Sun Tailor), a meticulous tailor who takes pride in his work. Men's and women's suits and shirts in around four days, with two fittings. Mon–Sat 10am–7pm.

Golden Wool 1340–2 Thanon Charoen Krung ☎ 02 233 0149, ⓦ golden-wool.com; map p.125. A larger operation than both of the above, which can turn around decent work for men and women in two days, though prices are slightly on the high side. Mon–Sat 9.30am–8pm.

FASHION

Thanon Khao San is lined with stalls selling low-priced fashion clothing: the baggy cotton fisherman's trousers, elephant pants and embroidered blouses are all aimed at backpackers, but they're supplemented by cheap contemporary fashions that appeal to urban Thais as well. Downtown, the most famous area for low-cost, low-quality casual clothes is the warren-like Pratunam Market and surrounding malls such as Platinum Fashion Mall around the junction of Phetchaburi and Ratchaprarop roads (see map, p.117), but for the best and latest trends from Thai designers, you should check out the shops in Siam Square and across the road in the more upmarket Siam Centre. Prices vary considerably: street gear in Siam Square is undoubtedly inexpensive (and look out for outlet stores such as Jaspal's in Amarin Plaza on Thanon Ploenchit), while genuine Western brand names are generally competitive but not breathtakingly cheaper than at home; larger sizes can be hard to find. Shoes and leather goods are good buys in Bangkok, being generally handmade from high-quality leather and quite a bargain.

Central Embassy Thanon Ploenchit ⓦ centralembassy .com; map p.117. This new mall, built on land sold off by the British Embassy, is bidding to become the most chic of the city's shopping plazas: here you'll find Gucci and Chanel – and gentlemen can get a very civilized haircut or shave at a branch of the London barber, Truefitt and Hill – while a few upmarket Thai names have made it to the party, notably Fly Now, which mounts dramatic displays of women's party and formal gear. Daily 10am–10pm.

Central World Ratchaprasong Intersection, corner of Rama I and Rajdamri Ⓦ centralworld.co.th; map p.117. This shopping centre – refurbished after it was torched during the suppression of the red-shirt street protests in 2010 – is so huge that it defies easy classification, but you'll find plenty of Thai and international fashions on its lower floors and in the attached Zen department store at its southern end. Daily 10am–9/10pm.

Emporium Thanon Sukhumvit, between sois 22 and 24 Ⓦ emporiumthailand.com; map p.123. Large and rather glamorous shopping plaza, with its own department store and a good range of fashion outlets, from exclusive designer wear to trendy high-street gear. Genuine brand-name shops include Prada, Chanel, Louis Vuitton, as well as established local labels such as Soda and Asava. Two adjoining sister malls are being built, Emquartier and Emsphere. Daily 10am–8/10pm.

Mah Boon Krong (MBK) At the Rama I/Phrayathai intersection Ⓦ mbk-center.co.th; map p.117. Vivacious, labyrinthine shopping centre which most closely resembles a traditional Thai market that's been rammed into a huge mall. It houses hundreds of small, mostly fairly inexpensive outlets, including plenty of high-street fashion shops. Daily 10am–9/10pm.

Siam Centre Thanon Rama I Ⓦ siamcenter.co.th; map p.117. Particularly good for hip local labels (especially on Floor 3), many of which have made the step up from the booths of Siam Square across the road – look out for Greyhound, Baking Soda and Theatre – as well as international names like DKNY and Lacoste. Daily 10am–9pm.

Siam Square map p.117. It's worth poking around the alleys here and the "mini-malls" inside the blocks. All manner of inexpensive boutiques, some little more than booths, sell colourful street-gear to the capital's fashionable students and teenagers.

Viera by Ragazze Floor 2, Central World and in the attached Isetan and Zen department stores Ⓦ ragazze .co.th; map p.117. Stylish, Italian-influenced leather goods. Daily 10am–9/9.30pm.

BOOKS

English-language bookshops in Bangkok are always well stocked with everything to do with Thailand, and most carry fiction classics and popular paperbacks as well. The capital's secondhand bookshops are not cheap, but you can usually part-exchange your unwanted titles.

Asia Books Flagship store in Central World on Thanon Rama I, plus dozens of other branches around town Ⓦ asiabooks.com; map p.117. English-language bookshop (and publishing house) that's especially recommended for its

books on Asia – everything from guidebooks to cookery books, novels to art. Also stocks bestselling novels and coffee-table books. Daily 10am–9.30pm.

B2S Floor 7, Central Chidlom, Thanon Ploenchit Ⓦ b2s .co.th; map p.117. This shop sells a decent selection of English-language books, but is most notable for its huge selection of magazines, newspapers and stationery. There are dozens of branches around town. Daily 10am–10pm.

Books Kinokuniya 3rd Floor, Emporium Shopping Centre, Thanon Sukhumvit; map p.123; Floor 6, Isetan, in Central World, Thanon Rama I; map p.117; Floor 3, Siam Paragon, Thanon Rama I; map p.117; Ⓦ thailand .kinokuniya.com. Huge, efficient, Japanese-owned, English-language bookshop with a wide selection of books ranging from bestsellers to travel literature and from classics to sci-fi; not so hot on books about Asia, though. All daily 10am–10pm.

Dasa Book Cafe Between sois 26 and 28, Thanon Sukhumvit Ⓦ dasabookcafe.com; map p.123. Bangkok's best secondhand bookshop, Dasa is appealingly calm and intelligently, and alphabetically, categorized, with sections on everything from Asia to chick lit, health to gay and lesbian interest. Browse its stock online, or enjoy coffee and cakes *in situ*. Daily 10am–8pm.

Shaman Books 71 Thanon Khao San, Banglamphu ☎ 02 629 0419; map pp.100–101. Well-stocked secondhand bookshop, with lots of books on Asia (travel, fiction, politics and history), as well as a decent range of novels and general-interest books. Daily 9am–10pm.

Ton's Booksellers 327/5 Thanon Ram Bhuttri, Banglamphu; map pp.100–101. Small bookshop where you're likely to find a bus map or *Nancy Chandler's map of Bangkok*, as well as books on Southeast Asia and a section of English literary classics. Daily 11am–8pm.

JEWELLERY AND GEMS

Bangkok boasts the country's best gem and jewellery shops, and some of the finest lapidaries in the world, making this *the* place to buy cut and uncut stones such as rubies, blue sapphires and diamonds. However, countless gem-buying tourists get badly ripped off, so remember to be extremely wary.

Asian Institute of Gemological Sciences Jewelry Trade Center, 919 Thanon Silom ☎ 02 267 4325 (laboratory) or ☎ 02 267 4315 (school), Ⓦ aigsthailand .com; map p.125. Independent professional advice and precious stones certification from its laboratory. Also runs reputable courses, such as a five-day introduction to gems and gemology (US$700). Mon–Fri 8am–6pm.

Jewelry Trade Center West end of Thanon Silom Ⓦ jewelrytradecenter.com; map p.125. Dozens of members of the Thai Gem and Jewelry Traders Association have outlets in this shopping mall (and on the surrounding streets). Daily roughly 11am–8pm.

1

GEM SCAMS

Gem scams are so common in Bangkok that TAT has published a brochure about it and there are lots of web pages on the subject, including ⓦen.wikipedia.org/wiki/Gem_scam and the very informative ⓦ2bangkok.com/2bangkok-scams-sapphire.html, which describes typical scams in detail. Never buy anything through a tout or from any shop recommended by a "government official"/"student"/"businessperson"/tuk-tuk driver who just happens to engage you in conversation on the street, and note that there are no government jewellery shops, despite any information you may be given to the contrary, and no special government promotions or sales on gems.

The basic **scam** is to charge a lot more than what the gem is worth based on its carat weight – at the very least, get it **tested** on the spot, ask for a written guarantee and receipt. Don't even consider **buying gems in bulk** to sell at a supposedly vast profit elsewhere: many a gullible traveller has invested thousands of dollars on a handful of worthless multicoloured stones, believing the vendor's reassurance that the goods will fetch at least a hundred percent more when resold at home.

If you're determined to buy precious stones, check that the shop is a member of the **Thai Gem and Jewelry Traders Association** by visiting their website, which has a directory of members (ⓦthaigemjewelry.or.th). To be doubly sure, you may want to seek out shops that also belong to the TGJTA's **Jewel Fest Club** (look for the window stickers), which guarantees quality and will offer refunds.

Lambert Floor 4, Silom Shanghai Building, Soi 17, 807–9 Thanon Silom ☎02 236 4343, ⓦlambertgems .com; map p.125. Thoroughly reputable, thirty-year-old, American-owned outlet, offering a full service: loose stones and pearls, including collectors' stones, ready-made pieces, cutting, design, redesign and repairs. Mon–Fri 9am–5pm, Sat 9am–4pm.

ANTIQUES

Bangkok is the entrepôt for the finest Thai, Burmese and Cambodian antiques, but the market has long been sewn up, so don't expect to happen upon any undiscovered treasure. Even experts admit that they sometimes find it hard to tell real antiques from fakes, so the best policy is just to buy on the grounds of attractiveness. The River City shopping complex (☎02 237 0077, ⓦrivercity.co.th) off

Thanon Charoen Krung, which is near Si Phraya and Harbour Department express-boat piers, devotes its third, fourth and some of its second floors to a bewildering array of pricey treasures, ranging from Buddha images to tribal masks, as well as holding an auction on the first Saturday of every month (viewing during the preceding week). The other main area for antiques is the nearby section of Charoen Krung that runs down to the bottom of Thanon Silom, and the stretch of Silom running east from here up to and including the multistorey Jewelry Trade Center. Here you'll find a good selection of largely reputable individual businesses specializing in woodcarvings, ceramics, bronze statues and stone sculptures culled from all parts of Thailand and neighbouring countries as well. Remember that most antiques require an export permit (see p.63).

DIRECTORY

Banks and Exchange The Suvarnabhumi Airport exchange desks and those in the upmarket hotels are open 24hr, while many other exchange booths stay open till 8pm or later, especially along Khao San, Sukhumvit and Silom roads and in the major shopping malls. You can also withdraw cash from hundreds of ATMs around the city and at the airports.

Couriers DHL Worldwide (☎02 345 5000, ⓦdhl.co.th) has several Bangkok depots.

Embassies and consulates Australia, 37 Thanon Sathorn Tai ☎02 344 6300, ⓦthailand.embassy.gov.au; Myanmar (Burma), 132 Thanon Sathorn Nua ☎02 234 4789; Cambodia, 518/4 Thanon Pracha Uthit (Soi Ramkamhaeng 39) ☎02 957 5851–2; Canada, 15th floor, Abdulrahim Place, 990 Thanon Rama IV ☎02 646 4300,

ⓦthailand.gc.ca; China, 57 Thanon Rajadapisek ☎02 245 7033 or ☎02 245 7036; India, 46 Sukhumvit Soi 23 ☎02 258 0300–6, ⓦindianembassy.in.th; Indonesia, 600–602 Thanon Phetchaburi ☎02 252 3135–9, ⓦkemlu.go.id /bangkok; Ireland, Floor 23, Athenee Tower, 63 Thanon Witthayu ☎02 126 8092; Laos, 502/1–3 Soi Sahakarn-pramoon, Thanon Pracha Uthit ☎02 539 6667–8 ext 106, ⓦlaoembassybkk.gov.la; Malaysia, 35 Thanon Sathorn Tai ☎02 629 6800; New Zealand, 14th Floor, M Thai Tower, All Seasons Place, 87 Thanon Witthayu ☎02 254 2530, ⓦnzembassy.com/thailand; Singapore, 129 Thanon Sathorn Tai ☎02 286 2111; South Africa, Floor 12A, M Thai Tower, All Seasons Place, 87 Thanon Witthayu ☎02 659 2900, ⓦwww.dirco.gov.za/bangkok; UK, 14 Thanon Witthayu ☎02 305 8333; US, 120 Thanon Witthayu ☎02

205 4000; Vietnam, 83/1 Thanon Witthayu ☎02 650 8979. For further details about Bangkok's diplomatic corps, go to ⓦmfa.go.th/main/en/information on the Thai Ministry of Foreign Affairs' website.

Emergencies For English-speaking help in any emergency, call the tourist police on their free 24hr phoneline ☎1155. The tourist police are based on the grounds of Suvarnabhumi Airport (☎02 134 0521, ⓦtourist.police.go.th), or drop in at the more convenient Chana Songkhram Police Station at the west end of Thanon Khao San in Banglamphu (☎02 282 2323).

Hospitals, clinics and dentists Most expats rate the private Bumrungrad International Hospital, 33 Sukhumvit Soi 3 (☎02 667 1000, emergency ☎02 667 2999, ⓦbumrungrad.com), as the best and most comfortable in the city, followed by the BNH (Bangkok Nursing Home) Hospital, 9 Thanon Convent (☎02 686 2700, ⓦbnhhospital.com); and the Bangkok Hospital Medical Centre, 2 Soi Soonvijai 7, Thanon Phetchaburi Mai (☎02 310 3000 or ☎1719, ⓦbangkokhospital.com). You can get travel vaccinations and malaria advice, as well as rabies advice and treatment, at the Thai Red Cross Society's Queen Saovabha Memorial Institute (QSMI) and Snake Farm on the corner of Thanon Rama IV and Thanon Henri Dunant (Mon–Fri 8.30am–4.30pm, Sat 8.30am–noon; ☎02 252 0161–4 ext 125 or 132, ⓦsaovabha.com). Among general clinics, Global Doctor, Ground Floor, *Holiday Inn Hotel*, 981 Thanon Silom (corner of Thanon Surasak; ☎02 236 8442–4, ⓦglobaldoctorclinic.com), is recommended. For dental problems, try the Bumrungrad Hospital's dental department on ☎02 667 2300; the Dental Hospital, 88/88 Sukhumvit Soi 49 (☎02 260 5000–15, ⓦdentalhospitalbangkok.com); or Siam Family Dental Clinic, 209 Thanon Phrayathai, opposite MBK (☎081 987 7700, ⓦsiamfamilydental.com).

Immigration office North of the centre off Thanon Wiphawadi Rangsit at Floor 2, B Building, Government Complex, Soi 7, Thanon Chaengwattana (Mon–Fri 8.30am–noon & 1–4.30pm; ☎02 141 9889, ⓦbangkok.immigration.go.th, which includes a map). When trying to extend your visa (see p.63), be very wary of any Khao San tour agents who offer to organize a visa extension for you: some are reportedly faking the relevant stamps and this has caused problems at immigration.

Internet access As well as 4G (see p.71), there's free wi-fi in nearly all hotels and guesthouses and many restaurants and bars in Bangkok. If you want to use high-speed computers or print, you could head for *True*, housed in an early twentieth-century villa in a courtyard off the western end of Thanon

Khao San, where you also can sip coffee (daily 9.30am–8pm); or *True Urban Park* on Floor 3 of Siam Paragon shopping centre, Thanon Rama I (daily 10am–10pm), which also sells coffee and mobile phone packages.

Laundry Nearly all guesthouses and hotels offer same-day laundry services (about B40/kg at a guesthouse, much more at a hotel), or there are several self-service laundries on and around Thanon Khao San.

Left luggage Luggage can be left at Suvarnabhumi Airport (B100/day); Don Muang Airport (B75/day); Hualamphong train station (B20–80/day); the bus terminals and most hotels and guesthouses.

Post offices If you're staying in Banglamphu, it's probably most convenient to use the local postal, packing and poste restante services at Banglamphubon PO, Soi Sibsam Hang, Bangkok 10203 (daily 8am–5pm). Downtown, Prasanmit PO, 12/3–4 Soi 23 (Soi Prasanmit), Thanon Sukhumvit, Bangkok 10110 (Mon–Fri 8.30am–5.30pm, Sat 9am–noon), is handy for both the BTS and the subway.

Telephones It's best to buy a Thai SIM card for both international and domestic calls (see p.166). Otherwise, you can easily access Skype with your own device through Bangkok's plentiful wi-fi networks or at an internet café.

Travel agents If you are buying onward international air tickets, be warned that there are many dodgy, transient travel agents in Bangkok, particularly on and around Thanon Khao San, which is known for its shady operators who display fake TAT licences, issue false tickets and flee with travellers' money overnight. The best advice is to use one of the tried and tested agents listed here. Never hand over any money until you've been given the ticket and checked it carefully. Asian Trails, 9th Floor, SG Tower, 161/1 Soi Mahadlek Luang 3, Thanon Rajdamri (☎02 626 2000, ⓦasiantrails.travel), sells flights, does interesting Thailand tours and runs airport transfers; Educational Travel Centre (ETC) sells air and bus tickets, Thailand tours and day-trips, including homestays and volunteer work, and has offices at 180 Thanon Khao San, Banglamphu (☎02 629 1885), and inside *ETZ Hostel*, off Thanon Rama IV (see p.149); *New Road Guest House* (see p.149) is a reliable agent for train and bus tickets, as well as their own unusual tours; Olavi Travel sells air, train and bus tickets and is opposite the west end of Thanon Khao San at 53 Thanon Chakrabongse, Banglamphu (☎02 629 4710, ⓦolavi.com); and the Bangkok branches of the worldwide STA Travel (ⓦstatravel.co.th) are reliable outlets for cheap international flights and local tours: *Viengtai Hotel*, Thanon Ram Bhuttri, Banglamphu (☎098 284 6163), and 14th Floor, Wall Street Tower, 33/70 Thanon Suriwong (☎02 236 0262).

The central plains

WAT PHRA SI SANPHET, AYUTTHAYA

The central plains

North and west of the capital, the unwieldy urban mass of Greater Bangkok peters out into the vast, well-watered central plains, a region that for centuries has grown the bulk of the nation's food and been a tantalizing temptation for neighbouring power-mongers. The most densely populated region of Thailand, with sizeable towns sprinkled among patchworks of paddy, orchards and sugar-cane fields, the plains are fundamental to Thailand's agricultural economy. Its rivers are the key to this area's fecundity, especially the Nan and the Ping, whose waters irrigate the northern plains before merging to form the Chao Phraya, which meanders slowly south through Bangkok and out into the Gulf of Thailand. Further west, the Mae Khlong River sustains the many market gardens and fills the canals that dominate the hinterlands of the estuary at Samut Songkhram, a centre for the few remaining floating markets in the country.

Sited at the confluence of the Kwai Yai and Kwai Noi rivers, the town of **Kanchanaburi** has long attracted visitors to the notorious **Bridge over the River Kwai** and is now well established as a tourist hub, with everything from floating raft-house accommodation to waterside boutique hotels. Few tourists venture much further upriver, except as passengers on the remaining stretch of the **Death Railway** – the most tangible wartime reminder of all – but the remote little hilltop town of **Sangkhlaburi** holds enough understated allure to make the extra kilometres worthwhile.

On the plains north of Bangkok, the historic heartland of the country, the major sites are the **ruined ancient cities**, most of which are conserved as historical parks, covering the spectrum of Thailand's art and architecture. Closest to Bangkok, **Ayutthaya** served as the country's capital for the four hundred years prior to the 1782 foundation of Bangkok, and its ruins evoke an era of courtly sophistication. A short hop to the north, the remnants of **Lopburi** hark back to an earlier time, when the predominantly Hindu Khmers held sway over this region.

Highlights

❶ Kanchanaburi and the River Kwai Stay in a raft house, take a scenic train ride along the Death Railway and visit some moving World War II memorials. **See p.186**

❷ Erawan Waterfall Seven breathtakingly beautiful crystal pools in a jungle setting. **See p.197**

❸ Sangkhlaburi Search for the sunken temple of Wat Sam Phrasop at this peaceful lakeside town near the Burmese border. **See p.207**

❹ Ayutthaya Atmospheric ruined temples, three fine museums and laidback guesthouses in the broad, grassy spaces of the former capital. **See p.213**

❺ Wat Phra Phutthabat A vibrant introduction to Thai religion at the Temple of the Buddha's Footprint. **See p.228**

❻ Sergeant Major Thawee Folklore Museum, Phitsanulok Housed in a series of wooden pavilions, this is one of the country's best ethnology museums, offering a fascinating insight into rural life. **See p.234**

❼ Sukhothai The nation's first capital is packed with elegant thirteenth-century ruins and inviting guesthouses. **See p.238**

❽ Umphang Wildlife Sanctuary A remote border region with spectacular waterfalls, river-rafting and Karen villages. **See p.263**

HIGHLIGHTS ARE MARKED ON THE MAP ON PP.176–177

GULF OF THAILAND

MYANMAR

TENASSERIM MOUNTAINS

MAE KHLONG MOUNTAINS

Mae Khlong River

KHAO YAI NATIONAL PARK

SAI YOK NATIONAL PARK

ERAWAN NATIONAL PARK

THAM THAN LOT (CHALOEM RATTANAKOSIN) NATIONAL PARK

Khorat

Aranyaprathet

Prachin Buri

Pak Chong

Lam Takong

Nakhon Nayok

Chachoengsao

Phanat Nikhon

Si Racha

Chonburi

Suvarnabhumi Airport

Ancient City

Don Muang Airport

BANGKOK

Samut Prakan

Samut Sakhon

Samut Songkhram

Don Hoi Lot

Ban Tha Kha

Damnoen Saduak

Ban Phe

Phatharam

Bang Khonthi

Amphawa

Pak Tho

Ratchaburi

Nakhon Pathom

Ban Pong

Ban Phe

Mae Khlong

Phetchaburi

Chai Badan

Lopburi

Saraburi

Phra Phutthabat ⑤

Ang Thong

Ayutthaya ④

Bang Pa-In

Chao Phraya River

Suphanburi

Singburi

Chai Nat

Uthai Thani

Ban Rai

Nongprue

Bo Phloi

U Thong

Kanchanaburi ①

Death Railway

Ban Kao

Muang Singh

Phu Nau Ron

Htee Khee

Nam Tok ②

Tham Wang Badan

Hellfire Pass

Sai Yok

River Kwai Yai

Sri Nakarind

Si Sawat

Thong Pha Phum

River Kwai Noi

Hin Dat Hot Springs

Wat Sunyataram

Kroeng Kravia Falls

Vajiralongkorn (Khao Laem) Reservoir

Sangkhlaburi ③

Three Pagodas Pass

N

0 kilometres 25

205

21

1

2

33

33

304

315

349

331

7

3

34

305

9

1

9

35

4

32

309

311

322

3086

324

323

3199

323

323

3277

322

HIGHLIGHTS

① Kanchanaburi and the River Kwai
② Erawan Waterfall
③ Sangkhlaburi
④ Ayutthaya
⑤ Wat Phra Phutthabat
⑥ Sergeant Major Thawee Folklore Museum, Phitsanulok
⑦ Sukhothai
⑧ Umphang Wildlife Sanctuary

A separate nucleus of sites in the northern neck of the plains centres on **Sukhothai**, birthplace of the Thai kingdom in the thirteenth century. The buildings and sculpture produced during the Sukhothai era are the acme of Thai art, and the restored ruins of the country's first official capital are the best place to appreciate them, though two satellite cities – **Si Satchanalai** and **Kamphaeng Phet** – make good alternatives if you don't like crowds, and the city of **Phitsanulok** also serves as a good base for exploring the area. West of Sukhothai, on the Burmese border, the town of **Mae Sot** makes a refreshing change from ancient history and is the departure point for the rivers and waterfalls of **Umphang**, a remote border region that's becoming increasingly popular for trekking and rafting.

Chiang Mai makes an obvious next stop after exploring the sights north of Bangkok, chiefly because the **Northern Rail Line** makes connections painless. Or you could branch east into Isaan, by train or bus. It's also possible to **fly** out of Sukhothai, Phitsanulok and Mae Sot.

Nakhon Pathom

Even if you're just passing through, you can't miss the star attraction of **NAKHON PATHOM**: the enormous stupa **Phra Pathom Chedi** dominates the skyline of this otherwise unexceptional provincial capital, 56km west of Bangkok. Probably Thailand's oldest town, Nakhon Pathom (derived from the Pali for "First City") is thought to be the point at which **Buddhism** first entered the region now known as Thailand, more than two thousand years ago. Then the capital of a sizeable Mon kingdom, it was important enough to rate a visit from two missionaries dispatched by King Ashoka of India, one of Buddhism's great early evangelists. Even today, the province of Nakhon Pathom retains a high Buddhist profile – aside from housing the country's holiest chedi, it also contains **Phuttamonthon**, Thailand's most important Buddhist sanctuary and home of its supreme patriarch.

The **Phra Pathom Chedi** is easily visited while travelling from Bangkok to Kanchanaburi or vice versa; alternatively, since it's on train lines heading to Hua Hin, Surat Thani and Malaysia, the town works well as a stopover on the way south from Bangkok. Everything described below is within walking distance of the railway station.

Phra Pathom Chedi

400m south of the train station · Daily 7am–5pm · B60

Although the Buddha never actually came to Thailand, legend held that he rested in Nakhon Pathom after wandering the country, and the original **Phra Pathom Chedi** may have been erected to represent this. The first structure resembled Ashoka's great stupa at Sanchi in India, with its inverted bowl shape and spire that topped 39m. Local chronicles, however, tell how the chedi was built in the sixth century as an act of atonement by the foundling Phraya Pan who murdered the tyrant Mon king before realizing that he was his father. Statues of both father and son stand inside the viharns of the present chedi.

Whatever its true origins, the first chedi fell into disrepair and was later rebuilt with a prang during the Khmer period, between the eighth and twelfth centuries. Abandoned to the jungle once more, it was rediscovered by the future Rama IV in 1853 who, mindful that all Buddhist monuments are sacred however dilapidated, set about encasing the old prang in the enormous new 120m-high plunger-shaped chedi, making it one of the tallest stupas in the world. Its distinctive cladding of shimmering golden-brown tiles was completed several decades later.

The present-day chedi is much revered and holds its own week-long Phra Pathom Chedi **fair**, around the time of Loy Krathong in mid-November, which attracts musicians, fortune-tellers and of course plenty of food stalls.

Around the chedi

Approaching the chedi from the main (northern) staircase, you're greeted by the 8m-high Sukhothai-style Buddha image known as **Phra Ruang Rojanarit**, installed in front of the north viharn. There's a viharn at each of the cardinal points and they all have an inner and an outer chamber containing tableaux of the life of the Buddha.

Proceeding clockwise around the chedi, as is the custom at all Buddhist monuments, you can weave between the outer promenade and the inner cloister via ornate doors that punctuate the dividing wall. The outer promenade is ringed by Buddha images employing a wide variety of mudras, or hand gestures, each of which has a specific meaning for Buddhists, and most of them are explained on plaques beside them. Throughout the rest of the country, most Buddha images portray one of just five or six common mudras, making this collection rather unique. The promenade is also dotted with **trees**, many of which have religious significance, such as the bodhi tree (*ficus religiosa*) under one of which the Buddha was meditating when he achieved enlightenment.

The wall of the **east viharn** features a diagrammatic cross section of the chedi showing the encased original at its core, while beside the **south viharn** staircase is a three-dimensional replica of the original chedi with its Khmer prang (east side) and a model of the venerated chedi at Nakhon Si Thammarat (west side). The **west viharn** houses two reclining Buddhas: a sturdy, 9m-long figure in the outer chamber and a more delicate portrayal in the inner one.

Phra Pathom Chedi National Museum

Just east from the bottom of the chedi's south staircase • Wed–Sun 9am–noon & 1–4pm • B100

Within the chedi compound are a couple of similarly named museums. The newer, more formal setup, the **Phra Pathom Chedi National Museum**, displays a good collection of Dvaravati-era (sixth to eleventh centuries) artefacts excavated nearby, including Wheels of Law – an emblem introduced by Theravada Buddhists before naturalistic images were permitted – and Buddha statuary with the U-shaped robe and thick facial features characteristic of Dvaravati sculpture. Together, the exhibits tell the story of how external influences, particularly those from India, shaped local beliefs.

Phra Pathom Chedi Museum

Halfway up the steps near the east viharn • Wed–Sun 9am–noon & 1–4pm • Free

The **Phra Pathom Chedi Museum** is a magpie's nest of a collection, offering a broader, more domestic introduction to Nakhon Pathom's history than the National Museum. More a curiosity shop than a museum, the small room and entranceway are filled with Buddhist amulets, seashells, gold and silver needles, Chinese ceramics, Thai musical instruments and ancient statues – enough for a short but satisfying browse.

Sanam Chandra Palace

A 10min walk west of the chedi along Thanon Rajdamnoen (or a B30 ride on a motorbike taxi) • Daily 9am–4pm (ticket office closes at 3.30pm) • B50 or free with ticket for Bangkok's Grand Palace • Electric cart rental: B400 first hour, B100 for subsequent hours • ⊕ palaces.thai.net

Before ascending to the throne in 1910, Rama VI made several pilgrimages to the Phra Pathom Chedi, eventually choosing this 335-acre plot west of the pagoda as the location for a convenient new country retreat. The resulting complex of elegant wooden buildings, known as **Sanam Chandra Palace**, was designed to blend Western and Eastern styles, and a handful of its main buildings are now open to the public. Its principal structure, the **Jalimangalasana Residence**, evokes a miniature Bavarian castle, complete with turrets and red-tiled roof; the **Marirajrattabalang Residence** is a more oriental-style pavilion, built of teak and painted a deep rose colour inside and out; and the **Thub Kwan Residence** is an unadorned traditional Thai-style house of polished, unpainted golden teak. They each contain royal artefacts and memorabilia and, as such, visitors should take care to dress appropriately. All three buildings are within walking distance of the two main entrances to the palace grounds, so it's only worth hiring an electric cart if you want to explore the outer reaches of the extensive grounds.

Contemporary Thai Art Centre

Just outside Sanam Chandra's southern perimeter, behind the Thub Kwan Residence on Thanon Rajamanka Nai • Tues–Sun 9am–4pm • Free • ⦿ su.ac.th • If coming from the chedi, expect to pay around B30 for a motorbike taxi

If you're interested in modern Thai art it's well worth seeing what's on at the **Contemporary Thai Art Centre**. A purpose-built art centre set among outlying Sanam Chandra villas, it's the exhibition space for Bangkok's premier art school, Silpakorn University, whose satellite campus is just across the road. Their annual student show, held here every September and October, is usually very interesting.

ARRIVAL AND SERVICES   NAKHON PATHOM

By train To get to the chedi compound's northern gate from the train station, walk south for 200m down Thanon Rotfai, across the khlong and past the covered market.
Destinations Bangkok Hualamphong (12 daily; 1hr 35min); Bangkok Thonburi (2 daily; 1hr 10min); Butterworth (Malaysia; 2 daily; 19hr); Chumphon (11 daily; 5hr 40min–8hr 30min); Hat Yai (6 daily; 12hr 15min–16hr); Hua Hin (12 daily; 2hr 15min–3hr 15min); Kanchanaburi (2 daily; 1hr 25min); Nakhon Si Thammarat (2 daily; 14–15hr); Nam Tok (2 daily; 3hr 30min); Phetchaburi (10 daily; 1hr 20min–2hr 20min); Surat Thani (11 daily; 8hr–11hr 30min); Trang (2 daily; 13hr 30min–14hr 30min).

By bus Bus connections to Nakhon Pathom are good, especially from Bangkok's Southern Bus Terminal, Damnoen Saduak and Kanchanaburi. On arrival, buses drop

passengers either in front of the police station across from the chedi's southern entrance, or beside the khlong, 100m from the northern gate. Buses heading for Kanchanaburi, Damnoen Saduak and Phetchaburi collect passengers outside the police station across Thanon Kwaa Phra from the chedi's southern gate. Buses bound for Bangkok pick up from Thanon Phaya Pan on the north bank of the khlong, across from the *Mitpaisal Hotel*.
Destinations Bangkok (every 10min; 40min–1hr 20min); Damnoen Saduak (every 20min; 1hr); Kanchanaburi (every 20min; 1hr 45min–2hr).

Services You can change money at the exchange booth (open banking hours only) on Thanon Rotfai, beside the bridge over the khlong, one block south of the train station; several nearby banks also have ATMs.

ACCOMMODATION AND EATING

Fairy Tale 307 Thanon Rotfai, just south of the train station ☏ 081 913 8033. Almost hidden behind the food stalls that line the street, this cosy a/c café serves yummy crêpes, waffles and even French fries. It's an ideal spot to while away time waiting for a train. Mon–Sat 10.30am–7pm.

Hot-food stalls Just outside the chedi compound's southern wall, near the museum. The obvious place to eat during the day. There are lots of options here, from noodle soup to grilled chicken and rice dishes (mostly B30–60). Daily early morning till dusk.

Market In front of the station. Serves the usual takeaway or sit-down-and-eat goodies, including *khao kha moo*, stewed pork leg on rice served with pickled cabbage and a boiled egg (B30). The market really hits its stride after sunset. Hours vary, but usually at least mid-morning until around 9pm.

Mitpaisal Hotel 120/30 Thanon Phaya Pan ☏ 034 242422. This Chinese-Thai hotel is long overdue a make-over, but it's dimly lit, a/c rooms are just passable, and it enjoys a convenient location, close to the train station and less than 200m from the chedi's north gateway. Wi-fi doesn't reach upper floors. Fan B300, a/c B450

Damnoen Saduak

To get an idea of what shopping in Bangkok used to be like before all the canals were tarmacked over, many people take an early-morning trip to the **floating market** (*talat khlong*) at **DAMNOEN SADUAK**. Sixty kilometres south of Nakhon Pathom and just over a hundred kilometres from Bangkok, it's just about accessible on a day-trip from the capital with a very early start. Vineyards and orchards here back onto a labyrinth of narrow canals, and every morning between 6am and 11am local market gardeners ply

2

VISITING THE FLOATING MARKETS

For many visitors to Thailand, an essential item on their itinerary is a trip to a **floating market**, to witness scenes of vendors selling fruit, flowers, vegetables and noodle dishes from **sampans** on the canals that were once the principal means of travelling around the country. Unfortunately, such bucolic scenes are from a bygone era, and while it's still possible to visit a floating market, many visitors regret the experience, feeling they've been led into a tourist trap, which is often exactly the case.

Most day tours from Bangkok head for **Damnoen Saduak**, where visitors are whisked around in noisy longtail boats, which pause for souvenir hawkers to make their pitch in between staged photos of smiling vendors dressed in traditional outfits with neatly arranged boatloads of produce. Such day-trips also include visits to dubious animal shows or handicraft workshops in an attempt to extract more tourist dollars.

In recent years, Thais have started heading for **Amphawa** (see p.184) at weekends, which has a more authentic atmosphere than Damnoen Saduak, though the least commercialized floating market is at **Tha Ka** (see p.186) on weekends and certain dates in the lunar calendar. While most boat trips in these places focus on the markets, it's also possible to venture out onto the canals after dark to **watch the fireflies** twinkling romantically in their favourite lamphu trees like delicate strings of fairylights.

One problem of visits to this area is that most markets, with the exception of Amphawa, are at their best at the crack of dawn, but since they are around 100km from Bangkok, it takes at least a couple of hours for tour groups to get there. If you're keen to see them in the early hours, it's worth staying overnight in Damnoen Saduak, Amphawa or even Samut Songkhram (see p.182) and making arrangements for an early morning start; Tha Ka market is about 10km from each of these places. While they cover less distance than the longtail boats, rowing boats make for a much more relaxing experience, and generally offer a ninety-minute ride for around B400; they are available for hire from Ton Kem pier in Damnoen Saduak, the main jetty in Amphawa or any of the resorts in Samut Songkhram. Don't forget to take a hat or umbrella and plenty of sunscreen.

these waterways in paddleboats full of fresh fruit, vegetables and tourist-tempting soft drinks and souvenirs. Most dress in the blue denim jacket and high-topped straw hat traditionally favoured by Thai farmers, so it all looks very picturesque; however, the setup is clearly geared to tourists rather than locals, so the place lacks an authentic aura. For a more engaging experience, consider going instead to the floating markets at Amphawa, 10km south of Damnoen Saduak (see p.184), or at Tha Ka, 10km to the east of Damnoen Saduak (see p.186).

The market

Daily 6–11am

The target for most tour groups is **Talat Khlong Ton Kem**, 2km west of Damnoen Saduak's tiny town centre at the intersection of Khlong Damnoen Saduak and Khlong Thong Lang. Many of the wooden houses here have been converted into warehouse-style souvenir shops and tourist restaurants, diverting trade away from the khlong vendors and into the hands of large commercial enterprises. Nonetheless, a semblance of traditional water trade continues, and the two bridges between Ton Kem and **Talat Khlong Hia Kui** (a little further south down Khlong Thong Lang) make decent vantage points.

Touts invariably congregate at the Ton Kem pier to hassle you into taking a **rowing boat trip** around the khlong network; this is worth considering and far preferable to being propelled between markets at top speed in one of the noisy longtail boats, which cost far more to charter. For a less hectic and more sensitive look at the markets, explore via the walkways beside the canals.

BY BUS
From/to Bangkok Damnoen Saduak is 109km from Bangkok, so to reach the market in good time you have to catch one of the earliest a/c buses from the capital's Southern Bus Terminal (#78; every 40min from 6am; 2hr). Alternatively, you can join one of the day-trips from Bangkok, which generally give you two hours at the market, then stop at a handicraft village and/or animal show before dropping you back in the capital.

From Kanchanaburi Take a Ratchaburi-bound bus as far as Bang Phe (#461; every 15min from 5.10am; 1hr 15min), then change to bus #78 for the 30min journey to Damnoen Saduak.

From Phetchaburi and beyond To get to Damnoen Saduak from Phetchaburi or points further south, catch any

Bangkok-bound bus and change at Samut Songkhram.

Getting into town Damnoen Saduak's bus terminal is just north of Thanarat Bridge and Khlong Damnoen Saduak, on the main Nakhon Pathom–Samut Songkhram road, Highway 325. Frequent yellow songthaews cover the 2km to Ton Kem.

ACCOMMODATION
Maikaew Damnoen Resort 333 Moo 9 ☎032 254120–1, ⓦmaikaew.com. Just a few steps east of the floating market, this relaxing resort has a variety of luxurious rooms, some of which look out over the pool. They also offer a range of boat trips in the area (see website for details), so it makes a good springboard for exploration of the nearby canals. **B1500**

Samut Songkhram

Rarely visited by foreign tourists and yet within easy reach of Bangkok, the tiny estuarine province of **Samut Songkhram** is nourished by the Mae Khlong River as it meanders through on the last leg of its route to the Gulf. Fishing is an important industry round here, and big wooden boats are still built in riverside yards near the estuary; further inland, fruit is the main source of income, particularly pomelos, lychees, guavas and coconuts. But for visitors it is the network of three hundred **canals** woven around the river, and the traditional way of life the waterways still support, that makes a stay of a few days or more appealing. As well as some of the most interesting **floating markets** in Thailand – notably at **Amphawa** and **Tha Ka** – there are chances to witness traditional cottage industries such as palm-sugar production and *bencharong* ceramic-painting, plus more than a hundred historic temples to admire, a number of them dating back to the reign of Rama II, who was born in the province. The other famous sons of the region are Eng and Chang, the "original" Siamese twins, who grew up in the province (see box opposite).

Samut Songkhram town

The provincial capital – officially called **SAMUT SONGKHRAM** but often referred to by locals as **Mae Khlong**, after the river that cuts through it – is a useful jumping-off point for trips to the floating markets at Amphawa and Tha Ka. It's a pleasant enough market town, which, despite its proximity to Bangkok, remains relatively unaffected by Western influences. However, there's little reason to linger here as all the local sights are out of town, mainly in **Amphawa** district a few kilometres upriver (see p.184).

To savour a real Thai seaside atmosphere, make the 10km trip to Don Hoi Lot (regular songthaews run there from the bus station), from where you can gaze out across the murky waters of the Gulf of Thailand from the shade of casuarina trees. Thais flock here in droves to gobble up *hoi lot*, or worm shells, which are harvested in their sackloads at low tide. You can order them in any restaurant here, or buy them from street stalls, rent a mat and enjoy a picnic Thai-style.

BY TRAIN
Samut Songkhram's train station is in the middle of town, on the eastern side of the Mae Klong River, with four trains a day making the 1hr trip from and to Ban Laem, where you can connect with trains from/to Bangkok. It's a slow and convoluted journey, but more fun than the bus.

ENG AND CHANG, THE SIAMESE TWINS

Eng (In) and Chang (Chan), the "original" **Siamese twins**, were born in Samut Songkhram in 1811, when Thailand was known as Siam. The boys' bodies were joined from breastbone to navel by a short fleshy ligament, but they shared no vital organs and eventually managed to stretch their connecting tissue so that they could stand almost side by side instead of permanently facing each other.

In 1824 the boys were spotted by entrepreneurial Scottish trader Robert Hunter, who returned five years later with an American sea merchant, Captain Abel Coffin, to convince the twins' mother to let them take her sons on a world tour. Hunter and Coffin anticipated a lucrative career as producer-managers of an exotic **freak show**, and were not disappointed. They launched the twins in Boston, advertising them as "the Monster" and charging the public 50 cents to watch the boys demonstrate how they walked and ran. Though shabbily treated and poorly paid, the twins soon developed a more theatrical show, enthralling their audiences with acrobatics and feats of strength, and earning the soubriquet "the eighth wonder of the world". At the age of 21, having split from their exploitative managers, the twins became self-employed, but continued to tour with other companies across the world. Wherever they went, they would always be given a thorough examination by local **medics**, partly to counter accusations of fakery, but also because this was the first time the world and its doctors had been introduced to conjoined twins. Such was the twins' international celebrity that the term "Siamese twins" has been used ever since. Chang and Eng also sought advice from these doctors on surgical separation – an issue they returned to repeatedly right until their deaths but never acted upon, despite plenty of gruesome suggestions.

By 1840 the twins had become quite wealthy and decided to settle down. They were granted American citizenship, assumed the family name Bunker, and became slave-owning **plantation farmers** in North Carolina. Three years later they married two local sisters, Addie and Sally Yates, and between them went on to father 21 children. The families lived in separate houses and the twins shuttled between the two, keeping to a strict timetable of three days in each household; for an intriguing imagined account of this bizarre state of affairs, read Darin Strauss's novel *Chang and Eng* (see p.781). Chang and Eng had quite different personalities, and relations between the two couples soured, leading to the division of their assets, with Chang's family getting most of the land, and Eng's most of the slaves. To support their dependants, the twins were obliged to take their show back on the road several times, on occasion working with the infamous showman P. T. Barnum. Their final tour was born out of financial desperation following the 1861–65 Civil War, which had wiped out most of the twins' riches and led to the liberation of all their slaves.

In 1874, Chang succumbed to bronchitis and died; Eng, who might have survived on his own if an operation had been performed immediately, died a few hours later, possibly of shock. They were 62. The twins are buried in White Plains in North Carolina, but there's a **statue** of them near their birthplace in Samut Songkhram, on an untended plot of land surrounded by local government buildings just south of Route 3092, aka Thanon Ekachai, about 4km northeast of town.

BY BUS OR MINIBUS

The journey to Samut Songkhram from Bangkok's Southern Bus Terminal (every 20min in both directions; 1hr 30min) is fast, but the views are mostly dominated by urban sprawl. Samut Songkhram's bus station is south of the market, across from the Siam Commercial Bank off Thanon Ratchayadruksa. When returning to Bangkok, there's also a minibus service to Victory Monument (approximately hourly; about 1hr 30min), which departs from Thanon Si Jumpa, about 100m east of the *Maeklong Hotel*.

CONNECTIONS TO AMPHAWA AND DAMNOEN SADUAK

By songthaew or bus Songthaews to Amphawa (approximately every 30min; 15min) and local buses to Amphawa and Damnoen Saduak, via Highway 325, leave from the bus station.

By taxi-boat Taxi-boats operate from the Mae Khlong River pier, 50m west of the train station and market in the town centre. The journey upstream to Amphawa should take 20–30min.

By motorbike taxi At the Mae Khlong River pier, ferries (B2) take passengers across to the other side of the river, where motorbike taxis are available for the short ride to Amphawa (B40).

SERVICES

Banks and ATMs Currency exchange and ATMs are available at the branches of the main banks around the edge of Samut Songkhram market.

ACCOMMODATION AND EATING

Few people choose to stay in the town itself; however, there is a growing number of well-equipped resorts tucked away in the countryside around town. The **food stalls** near the pier, in the centre of town, make a pleasant spot for a cheap seafood lunch – for dessert, head to the **market**, near the train station, where you can buy fresh bananas, rambutans and watermelon slices. In the evening, food stalls along Thanon Si Jumpa just north of the railway station offer a wide variety of options.

Asita Eco Resort Beside a small canal about 1km west of town and just north of Highway 35 (Thanon Rama II) ☎ 034 767333, ⓦ asitaresort.com. Choose between a Thai house and thatched villa at this small resort, which is crafted from eco-friendly materials. There's a good-sized pool, a spa and rowing boats on the adjacent canal for guests' use, plus a variety of tours on offer. Considerable discounts for weekday stays. B5000

The Legend Maeklong 1285 Thanon Pathummalai ☎ 034 701121 ⓦ thelegendmaeklong.com. Located 100m north of the ferry landing on the western edge of the river, this place offers rooms in three beautiful wooden houses, including a shuttered colonial building by the waterfront that dates back to the early 1900s. There are wooden furnishings throughout, plus a riverside restaurant with excellent river views. B2000

Maeklong Hotel 526/10–13 Thanon Si Jumpa ☎ 034 711150. This recently refurbished, small hotel in the town centre (150m north of the train station) is good value, with spacious and clean a/c rooms, though service is a bit hit and miss. Ask for a room out front, as these are much brighter than those out back. It's ideally located for browsing the many food stalls that set up along the street in the evening. B600

Amphawa

The district town of **AMPHAWA** is smaller and more atmospheric than Samut Songkhram, retaining original charm alongside modern development. Its old neighbourhoods hug the banks of the Mae Khlong River and the Khlong Amphawa tributary, the wooden homes and shops facing the water and accessed either by boat or on foot along one of the waterfront walkways. The tradition of holding a **floating market** on the canal near Wat Amphawan has been revived for tourists, with traders setting up at around noon and staying out until after sunset every Friday, Saturday and Sunday.

King Rama II Memorial Park

5min walk west of Amphawa market and khlong • **Park and Museum** daily 8.30am–5pm • Adults B30 • Accessible by both boat and road

King Rama II was born in Amphawa (his mother's home town) in 1767 and is honoured with a memorial park and temple erected on the site of his probable birthplace, beside the Mae Khlong River on the western edge of Amphawa town.

Rama II, or Phra Buddhalertla Naphalai as he is known in Thai, was a famously cultured king and a respected poet and playwright, and the **museum** at the heart of the **King Rama II Memorial Park** displays lots of rather esoteric Rama II memorabilia, including a big collection of nineteenth-century musical instruments and a gallery of *khon* masks used in traditional theatre.

On the edge of the park, **Wat Amphawan** is graced with a statue of the king and decorated with murals that depict scenes from his life, including a behind-the-altar panorama of nineteenth-century Bangkok, with Ratanakosin Island's Grand Palace, Wat Pho and Sanam Luang still recognizable to modern eyes.

Amphawa Chaipattananurak

Beside Khlong Amphawa, a 5min walk west of Amphawa market • ⓦ amphawanurak.com • Mon–Fri 9am–5pm; Sat–Sun 9am–9pm • Free

The **Amphawa Chaipattananurak** centre was established to conserve the cultural heritage of the town, and is divided into five areas, each of which provides interesting information about the traditional lifestyle of the region. The Community Exhibition Room reflects the way of life of local communities, the Agricultural Demonstration Farm features many of the local fruit trees, and the Nakhawarang Cultural Ground is used for performances of traditional music and puppet shows. There are also community shops selling local products and souvenirs, and an atmospheric coffee shop and tea house beside the canal with a retro interior.

Wat Chulamani

Beside Khlong Amphawa, a 20min walk east of Amphawa market, or a 5min boat ride

The canalside **Wat Chulamani** was until the late 1980s the domain of the locally famous abbot Luang Pho Nuang, a man believed by many to possess special powers, and followers still come to the temple to pay respects to his body, which is preserved in a glass-sided coffin in the main viharn. The breathtakingly detailed decor inside the viharn is testament to the devotion he inspired: the intricate black-and-gold lacquered artwork that covers every surface took years and cost millions of baht to complete. Across the temple compound, the bot's modern, pastel-toned murals tell the story of the Buddha's life, beginning inside the door on the right with a scene showing the young Buddha emerging from a tent (his birth) and being able to walk on lilypads straight away. The death of the Buddha and his entry into Nirvana are depicted on the wall behind the altar.

Pinsuwan bencharong showroom and workshop

A few hundred metres down the road from Wat Chulamani, just west of H325 (look for the P Ben sign in front of a compound of traditional houses) • Showroom daily 8am–noon & 1–5pm, workshop Mon–Sat 8am–noon & 1–5pm • Free • Accessible on foot, by bus or by canal

The Pinsuwan **bencharong workshop** specializes in reproductions of famous antique *bencharong* ceramics, the exquisite five-coloured pottery that used to be the tableware of choice for the Thai aristocracy and is now a prized collectors' item. Here you can watch the manufacturing process in action (though the workshop is closed on Sundays), and then buy items off the shelf or even order your own glittering, custom-made bowls, which can then be delivered to your hotel or shipped back home.

ARRIVAL AND DEPARTURE — AMPHAWA

From/to Bangkok Direct buses connect Amphawa with Bangkok's Southern Bus Terminal (every 20min; 2hr). Returning to Bangkok, hourly buses head for the Southern Bus Terminal, while several buses a day make the journey to the Northern Mo Chit terminal. There's no bus station in tiny Amphawa, but buses pull up by the market in the town centre.

From/to Samut Songkhram Frequent songthaews and local buses (both approximately every 30min; 15min) connect Amphawa market, which sets up beside the khlong, just back from its confluence with the river, with the market in Samut Songkhram.

GETTING AROUND

By boat The most appealing way to explore the area is by boat – see box, p.181, for more details.
By bicycle Some resorts, such as Baan Amphawa Resort & Spa, offer free use of bicycles for guests, or you can rent one from *Amphawa Na Non* (see below). Alternatively, you could join a one-day cycling tour of the area from Bangkok with Bangkok Bike Rides (see p.137) for B3200 per person.

ACCOMMODATION AND EATING

Amphawa Na Non 36 Thanon Prachaset ☎ 034 752111 ⓦ amphawananon.com. This stylish new place sits on Amphawa's main street just a minute's walk from the floating market. It caters mostly to Thais but staff speak good English and the big, bright rooms offer every comfort. There's a ten percent discount on weekdays. B2500
Baan Amphawa Resort & Spa 22 Thanon Bangkapom Kaewfah ☎ 034 752222, ⓦ baanamphawa.com. A large, business-friendly resort hotel with attractive rooms in a series of traditional-style wooden buildings. There's a pool, a spa, and a reasonable restaurant, but prices are high. B3800
Baanrak Amphawa Beside Amphawa canal, just 300m from the market ☎ 089 1283838, ⓦ baanrak -amphawa.com. A clean, convenient and cosy homestay where rates on a weekday start from B1000, though weekend rates are considerably higher. Rooms are sparsely decorated but the owners are very helpful. B1600
Saban-Nga Baan Amphawa Resort & Spa, 22 Thanon Bangkapom Kaewfah ☎ 034 752222, ⓦ baanamphawa .com. The fresh fish dishes (try the stewed mackerel in sugar-cane juice and garlic; B150) at this spa hotel's upmarket restaurant are tasty enough, and the riverfront terrace is a great spot for an evening drink. However, the service sometimes struggles to match up to the surroundings. Daily 7am–10pm.

Tha Ka floating market

On Khlong Phanla in Ban Tha Ka • Sat & Sun roughly 7am–noon, plus the second, seventh and twelfth mornings of every fifteen-day lunar cycle (contact any TAT office for exact dates) • By boat, it can be reached in about half an hour from Amphawa or Damnoen Saduak; by car, it's signposted to the east of H325 between Damnoen Saduak and Amphawa

Unlike at the over-touristed market at nearby Damnoen Saduak, the **floating market** in the village of **Tha Ka** is still largely the province of local residents. It's possible to get here by boat from Amphawa or Damnoen Saduak, though most visitors come by road and begin their boat tour here. Market gardeners paddle up here in their small wooden sampans, or motor along in their noisy longtails, the boats piled high either with whatever's in season, be it pomelos or betel nuts, rambutans or okra, or with perennially popular snacks like hot noodle soup and freshly cooked satay. Their main customers are canalside residents and other traders, so the atmosphere is still pleasingly, but not artificially, traditional. As with the other markets in the area, boatmen also offer evening rides to watch the fireflies. The Tha Ka market attracts Thai tourist groups and occasional adventurous foreigners. It's best to pre-arrange a trip the day before through your accommodation in the area; expect to pay around B1000 for a half-day tour.

Kanchanaburi

Set at the confluence of two rivers, the Kwai Noi and the Kwai Yai, the provincial capital of **KANCHANABURI** makes the perfect getaway from Bangkok, a two- to three-hour bus ride away. With its rich wartime history, plentiful supply of traveller-oriented accommodation and countless possibilities for easy forays into the surrounding countryside, there are plenty of reasons to linger here, and many visitors end up staying longer than planned. The big appeal is the river: that it's the famous River Kwai (pronounced "kwae" as in "quaint" rather than "kwai" as in "quite") is a bonus, but the more immediate attractions are the guesthouses and restaurants that overlook the waterway, many of them offering fine views of the jagged limestone peaks beyond.

The heart of Kanchanaburi's ever-expanding travellers' scene dominates the southern end of **Thanon Maenam Kwai** (also spelt Kwae) and is within easy reach of the train station, but the real town centre is some distance away, running north from the bus station up the town's main drag, **Thanon Saeng Chuto**. Between this road and the river you'll find most of the town's **war sights**, with the infamous **Bridge over the River Kwai** marking the northern limit. Every day, tour groups and day-trippers descend on the Bridge, a symbol of Japanese atrocities in the region, though the town's main **war museum** and **cemeteries** are actually much more moving. Many veterans returning to visit the graves of their wartime comrades are understandably resentful that others have in some cases insensitively exploited the POW experience – the commercial buzz around the Bridge is a case in point. On the other hand, the **Thailand–Burma Railway Centre** provides shockingly instructive accounts of a period not publicly documented outside this region.

The **Chungkai war cemetery** and a handful of moderately interesting temples – including cave temples at **Wat Tham Khao Poon** and **Wat Ban Tham**, the hilltop twins of **Wat Tham Sua** and **Wat Tham Khao Noi** – provide the focus for pleasurable trips west of the town centre.

It's worth noting that Kanchanaburi gets packed during its annual *son et lumière* **River Kwai Bridge Festival**, held over ten nights from the end of November to commemorate the first Allied bombing of the Bridge on November 28, 1944, so book accommodation well ahead if you're planning a visit then.

KANCHANABURI

● SHOPS
Good Times Travel	4
KTC Travel	3
River Kwai Bookshop	2
Safarine	1

● EATING
Bell's Pizzeria	6
Blue Rice	3
Good Times	2
Mangosteen Garden	1
On's Thai Issan Vegetarian	5
Prueksa	4
Schluck	7
Sri Rung Rueng	8

■ DRINKING
One More Bar	2
The Resort	1

■ ACCOMMODATION
Apple's Retreat	4
Bluestar Guesthouse	7
Chitanun Guest House	11
Good Time Resort	3
My Home	14
Ploy River Kwai	9
River Kwai Hotel	6
Sabai@Kan	2
Sam's House	8
Tamarind Guest House	12
Tara Bed & Breakfast	10
Tara Raft	5
T & T	13
U Inchantree	1

2

THE DEATH RAILWAY

Shortly after entering World War II in December 1941, Japan, fearing an Allied blockade of the Bay of Bengal, began looking for an alternative supply route to connect its newly acquired territories that stretched from Singapore to the Myanmar–India border. In spite of the almost impenetrable terrain, the River Kwai basin was chosen as the route for a new **Thailand–Burma Railway**, the aim being to join the existing terminals of Nong Pladuk in Thailand (51km southeast of Kanchanaburi) and Thanbuyazat in Myanmar – a total distance of 415km.

About sixty thousand Allied POWs were shipped up from captured Southeast Asian territories to work on the link, their numbers later augmented by as many as two hundred thousand conscripted Asian labourers. Work began at both ends in June 1942. Three million cubic metres of rock were shifted and 14km of bridges built with little else but picks and shovels, dynamite and pulleys. By the time the line was completed, fifteen months later, it had more than earned its nickname, the **Death Railway**: an estimated sixteen thousand POWs and a hundred thousand Asian labourers died while working on it.

The appalling conditions and Japanese brutality were the consequences of the **samurai code**: Japanese soldiers abhorred the disgrace of imprisonment – to them, ritual suicide was the only honourable option open to a prisoner – and therefore considered that Allied POWs had forfeited any rights as human beings. Food rations were meagre for men forced into backbreaking eighteen-hour shifts, often followed by night-long marches to the next camp. Many suffered from beriberi, many more died of dysentery-induced starvation, but the biggest killers were cholera and malaria, particularly during the monsoon. It is said that one man died for every sleeper laid on the track.

The two lines finally met at Konkuita, just south of present-day Sangkhlaburi. But as if to underscore its tragic futility, the Thailand–Myanmar link saw less than two years of active service: after the Japanese surrender on August 15, 1945, the railway came under the jurisdiction of the British who, thinking it would be used to supply Karen separatists in Myanmar, tore up 4km of track at Three Pagodas Pass, thereby cutting the Thailand–Myanmar link forever. When the Thais finally gained control of the rest of the railway, they destroyed the track all the way down to Nam Tok, apparently because it was uneconomic. Recently, however, an Australian–Thai group of volunteers and former POWs has salvaged sections of track near the fearsome stretch of line known as **Hellfire Pass**, creating a memorial walk at the pass and founding an excellent museum at the site (see p.204). There have been a number of books written about the Death Railway, including *The Railway Man* by Eric Lomax, which was made into a successful film (2013). The Thailand–Burma Railway Centre stocks a selection of such books, as do the town's bookshops.

Thailand–Burma Railway Centre

Opposite the train station, next to the Don Rak Kanchanaburi War Cemetery on Thanon Jaokannun • Daily 9am–5pm • B160 • ⓦ tbrconline.com

The modern **Thailand–Burma Railway Centre** is by far the best place to start any tour of Kanchanaburi's World War II memorials. It was founded to provide an informed context and research centre for the thousands who visit the POW graves every week. The result is a comprehensive and sophisticated history of the entire Thailand–Burma Railway line, with plenty of original artefacts, illustrations and scale models, and particularly strong sections on the planning and construction of the railway, and on the subsequent operation, destruction and decommissioning of the line. There is more of a focus on the line itself here than at the more emotive Hellfire Pass Memorial Museum (see p.204), but the human stories are well documented too, notably via some extraordinary original photographs and video footage shot by Japanese engineers, as well as through unique interviews with surviving Asian labourers on the railway.

The shop inside the entrance stocks some interesting books on the railway and also sells products made by the Weaving for Women project in Sangkhlaburi. Admission includes a free tea or coffee in the upstairs café.

CLOCKWISE FROM TOP WAT WANG WIWEKARAM, SANGKHLABURI (P.209); DAMNOEN SADUAK FLOATING MARKET (P.180); DETAIL FROM WAT WANG WIWEKARAM (P.209) >

Kanchanaburi War Cemetery (Don Rak)

Opposite the train station on Thanon Saeng Chuto • Free

One Allied POW died for each railway sleeper laid on the Thailand–Burma Railway (see box, p.188), or so the story goes, and many of them are buried in Kanchanaburi's two war cemeteries, **Don Rak Kanchanaburi War Cemetery** and Chungkai Cemetery (see opposite). Of all the region's war sights, the cemeteries are the only places to have remained untouched by commercial enterprise. Don Rak is the bigger of the two, with 6982 POW graves laid out in straight lines amid immaculate lawns and flowering shrubs, maintained by the Commonwealth War Graves Commission. It was established after the war, on a plot adjacent to the town's Chinese cemetery, as the final resting place for the remains that had been hurriedly interred at dozens of makeshift POW-camp gravesites all the way up the line. Many of the identical stone memorial slabs in Don Rak state simply, "A man who died for his country"; others, inscribed with names, dates and regiments, indicate that the overwhelming majority of the dead were under 25 years old. A commemorative service is held here, and at Hellfire Pass (see p.204), every year on April 25, Anzac Day.

The Bridge over the River Kwai

Just west of the River Kwai Bridge Train Station • A 15–20min walk north of the main Thanon Maenam Kwai guesthouse area; alternatively, cycle or take a tuk-tuk (about B30–40)

For most people, the plain steel arches of the **Bridge over the River Kwai** come as a disappointment: as a war memorial it lacks both the emotive punch of the museums and the perceptible drama of spots further up the line, and as a bridge it looks nothing out of the ordinary – certainly not as awesomely hard to construct as it appears in David Lean's famous 1957 film, *Bridge on the River Kwai* (which was in fact shot in Sri Lanka). But it is the link with the multi-Oscar-winning film, of course, that draws tour buses by the dozen, and makes the Bridge approach seethe with trinket-sellers and touts. For all the commercialization of the place, however, you can't really come to the Kwai and not see it.

The fording of the Kwai Yai at the point just north of Kanchanaburi known as Tha Makkham was one of the first major obstacles in the construction of the Thailand–Burma Railway. Sections of a steel bridge were brought up from Java and reassembled by POWs using only pulleys and derricks. A temporary **wooden bridge** was built alongside it, taking its first train in February 1943; three months later the steel bridge was finished. Both bridges were severely damaged by Allied bombers (rather than commando-saboteurs as in the film) in 1944 and 1945, but the steel bridge was repaired after the war and is still in use today. The best way to see the bridge is by walking gingerly across it, or taking the **train** right over it: the Kanchanaburi–Nam Tok service crosses it three times a day in each direction, stopping briefly at the River Kwai Bridge station on the east bank of the river.

Thanon Pak Phraek

Between Rattanakarn Bridge and City Gate

Running north from Kanchanaburi's only remaining city gate, the historical significance of **Thanon Pak Phraek** has led the TAT to place information boards outside many of the old buildings, explaining their origin and use over the years. Most of these houses were built just outside the city walls in the late nineteenth or early twentieth century by Chinese and Vietnamese immigrants and reflect a variety of architectural styles. While some of the properties along the street are nothing more than run-down shophouses, others have been carefully restored and boast elaborate balconies with balustrades. Sadly, the tangle of electric cables along the street makes them less photogenic than they would otherwise be.

It's worth dropping by the TAT office (see p.193) before coming here to pick up an informative brochure and map of the street, so you can find out more about the buildings as you stroll along the street. The more interesting buildings include the former Sumitrakarn Hotel, the first hotel in Kanchanaburi, which was built in 1937 and finally closed its doors to the public in 1979; it now functions as a shop selling household goods. Others worth a close look are Sitthisang house, built in 1920 and renovated in 2009; and Boonyiam Jiaranai house, which has some elaborate stucco arches on the upstairs balcony.

2

Chungkai Cemetery

On the west bank of the Kwai Noi, 2km from Rattanakarn Bridge, along Route 3228 • 5–10min by tuk-tuk from the main Thanon Maenam Kwai guesthouse area

Scrupulously well-trimmed **Chungkai Cemetery** occupies a fairly tranquil roadside spot on the west bank of the Kwai Noi, at the site of a former POW camp. Some 1750 POWs are buried here; most of the gravestone inscriptions include a name and regimental insignia, and some with epitaphs such as "One corner of the world which is forever England". However, a number of the graves remain unnamed – at the upcountry camps, bodies were thrown onto mass funeral pyres, making identification impossible. The cemetery makes a pleasant cycle ride from Rattanakarn Bridge – much of the land in this area is sugar-cane country, for which Kanchanaburi has earned the title "sugar capital of Thailand".

Wat Tham Khao Poon

On the west bank of the Kwai Noi, 2km west along Route 3228 from Chungkai Cemetery and then Route 3305 (turn left at the railway line), or 4km from Rattanakarn Bridge • Daily dawn–dusk • B30 • Often included in boat trips from the bridge

At the top of Route 3305's only hill sits the cave temple **Wat Tham Khao Poon**. The attraction here is a nine-chambered cave connected by a labyrinth of dank stalactite-filled passages, where almost every ledge and knob of rock is filled with religious icons, the most important being the Reclining Buddha in the main chamber. Once out of the cave system, you can walk through a bamboo "museum" with some blurry pictures from World War II. If you arrived by road, follow the sealed road through the temple compound for 150m to reach a good vantage point over the Kwai Noi, just above the train tracks, presided over by an outsized, pot-bellied golden Buddha statue; if arriving by boat, you enter the wat compound via the cliff-side steps here.

Wat Ban Tham

12km south of town • Cross the Mae Khlong River at Thanon Mae Khlong, then turn left for the 6km ride south; alternatively, it can be reached by boat in around 30min from the centre

Because of the limestone landscape, caves are found right around Kanchanaburi and many of them have been sanctified as shrines. **Wat Ban Tham** is one such place, and is intriguing enough to make the 12km trip from the town centre worthwhile. Travelling south down the Mae Khlong to get to the temple is especially pleasant by longtail or kayak, but can also be done by road.

Wat Ban Tham was founded around six hundred years ago but its fame rests on the seventeenth-century love story that was supposedly played out in a cave on this site. A young woman called Nang Bua Klee was forced to choose between duty to her criminal father and love for the local hero by whom she had fallen pregnant; her father eventually persuaded Bua Klee to poison her sweetheart's food, but the soldier learned of the plot and killed both Bua Klee and their unborn son, whose souls are now said to be trapped in the cave at Wat Ban Tham. The cave is approached via an ostentatious Chinese-style dragon's mouth staircase, whose upper levels relate the legend in a gallery of brightly painted modern murals on the right-hand walls. Inside the cave, a woman-shaped stone has been painted in the image of the dead mother and is a popular object of worship for women trying to conceive: hopeful devotees bring pretty dresses and shoes for the image, which are hung in wardrobes to the side of the shrine, as well as toys for her son.

Wat Tham Sua and Wat Tham Khao Noi

16km south of the town centre • Coming by car, head south out of town along Highway 323 and cross the river via the signed Mae Khlong Dam, then follow signs to the right; otherwise, take any local bus as far as Tha Muang, 12km south along Highway 323, then change to a motorbike taxi to the temples (about B60) • **Cable car** at Wat Tham Khao Noi Mon–Fri 7.30am–4.30pm, Sat & Sun 7.30am–5.30pm • B20

If you're in the mood for more temples, the modern hilltop wats of Tham Sua and Tham Khao Noi both afford expansive views over the Mae Khlong river valley and out to the mountains beyond. Designed by a Thai architect at the end of the twentieth century, **Wat Tham Sua** was conceived in typical grandiose style around a massive chedi covered with tiles similar to but smaller than those used at Nakhon Pathom. Inside, a placid seated Buddha takes centre stage, his huge palms raised to show the Wheels of Law inscribed like stigmata across them; a conveyor belt transports devotees' offerings into the enormous alms bowl set into his lap. The neighbouring Chinese-designed **Wat Tham Khao Noi** was built at the same time and is a fabulously gaudy, seven-tiered Chinese pagoda within which a laughing Buddha competes for attention with a host of gesturing and grimacing statues and painted characters.

ARRIVAL AND DEPARTURE   KANCHANABURI

BY TRAIN

The main Kanchanaburi train station (📞034 511285), not to be confused with the River Kwai Bridge station, is on Thanon Saeng Chuto, about 2km north of the town centre, but within walking distance of some of the Thanon Maenam Kwai accommodation. A samlor or tuk-tuk ride from here to Thanon Maenam Kwai accommodation will cost around B50.

Services to Kanchanaburi Trains are the most scenic way to get to Kanchanaburi, but there are only two daily from Bangkok's Thonburi station via Nakhon Pathom (7.45am and 1.55pm). If coming from Hua Hin, Chumphon and points further south, take the train to Ban Pong and then change to a Kanchanaburi-bound train (or bus – the bus stop is at the clocktower, about 1km from Ban Pong train station).

Moving on To get to northern Thailand, take a minibus to Ayutthaya (see opposite), where you can pick up the Northern Rail Line. For southern Thailand, take a train (or chartered minibus or public bus #81) to Ban Pong and change to a night train headed for Chumphon, Surat Thani or beyond.

Reservations and tickets Reservations for any rail journey can be made at Kanchanaburi train station, or through Good Times tour agency (see p.196) for an extra B50. Tickets for the train ride to Bangkok or along the Death Railway to Nam Tok (see p.202) don't need advance booking.

Destinations Bangkok Thonburi (2 daily; 3hr); Nakhon Pathom (2 daily; 1hr 40min–2hr); Nam Tok (3 daily; 2hr 20min).

BY BUS

Kanchanaburi's bus station (📞034 515907) is at the southern edge of the town centre, a good 2km from most accommodation. Tuk-tuks and samlors wait here and will run you into the main Thanon Maenam Kwai accommodation area for around B60.

Services to Kanchanaburi The buses from Bangkok's Southern Bus Terminal and Northern Mo Chit terminal are faster than the train. From Lopburi, Ayutthaya (connecting with trains from Chiang Mai), or points further north, you'll have to return to Bangkok, use a minibus service or change buses (onto #411) at Suphanburi, about 90km north of Kanchanaburi. Coming from Phetchaburi and Hua Hin, you need to change buses (onto #461) at Ratchaburi.

Moving on Government buses run from the bus station to Bangkok's Northern Mo Chit bus terminal, the Southern Bus Terminal, and to all destinations listed below. The first-class ticket office and departure point is beside the main road on the edge of the bus station, while the office for all other services is in the middle of the depot.

Destinations Bangkok (Northern Mo Chit terminal; 8 daily; 3hr); Bangkok (Southern Bus Terminal; every 20min; 2hr 30min); Chiang Mai (2 daily; 11hr); Erawan (every 50min; 1hr 30min); Hua Hin (hourly; 3hr 30min); Nam Tok (every 30min; 1hr 30min); Nong Khai (2 daily; 11hr); Phu Nam Ron (4 daily; 1hr 30min); Ratchaburi (every 20min; 2hr); Rayong (2 daily; 7hr 30min); Sai Yok (every 30min; 2hr 30min); Sangkhlaburi (4 daily; 3hr); Suphanburi (every 20min; 2hr); Thong Pha Phum (every 30min; 3hr 30min); Three Pagodas Pass (3 daily; 4hr).

CROSSING THE MYANMAR BORDER AT PHU NAM RON

If you have a visa for Myanmar, you can enter the country via the international border crossing at **Phu Nam Ron** (daily 6.30am–6.30pm), 70km west of Kanchanaburi and 200km from Bangkok. Four buses run here daily from Kanchanaburi, departing between 6am and 2.30pm from the bus station. Until recently, the crossing was mostly used for renewing Thai visas; however, it's possible to get from Htee Khee on the Myanmar side of the border to Dawei on the coast. Contact 📧 threedawei@gmail.com to pre-arrange transport there.

2

BY MINIBUS

Minibuses for Bangkok, Ayutthaya, Sangkhlaburi and Suvarnabhumi Airport arrive at and depart from the main bus station. Coming from Bangkok, a/c minibuses leave regularly from Thanon Khao San and Victory Monument; they are faster but more cramped than regular buses. Returning to Bangkok, if you book through your guesthouse they will pick you up at a designated time.

Destinations Ayutthaya (daily; 3hr; timed to connect with the night trains to Chiang Mai); Bangkok, Victory Monument (hourly; 2hr); Sangkhlaburi (every 20min; 3hr; tickets available from a booth at the back of the bus station); Suvarnabhumi Airport (6 daily; 2hr 30min–3hr).

GETTING AROUND

With tuk-tuks plying the main route between the bus station and the Bridge, and boatmen waiting to ferry you along the waterways, it's easy to get to and from Kanchanaburi's main sights.

By tuk-tuk A tuk-tuk from the guesthouses to the Bridge will cost around B30–40.

By songthaew Orange public songthaews run along Thanon Saeng Chuto, originating from outside the Focus Optic optician's, three blocks north of the bus station, and travelling north via the Kanchanaburi War Cemetery (Don Rak), Thai–Burma Railway Centre, train station and access road to the Bridge (#2; every 15min until 6pm; 15min to the Bridge turn-off; B10).

By motorbike Many outlets, such as Mek and Mee (☎081 7571194) on Thanon Maenam Kwai, rent out motorbikes for around B200 per day.

By longtail boat Boats wait beside the Bridge for trips to riverside sights such as Wat Tham Khao Poon. Most of them ask around B900 for a 90min trip that includes about three stops.

By bicycle Guesthouses and tour agencies rent out bicycles for B50 a day – ideal for exploring the main town sights and the quiet rural backroads.

By kayak A green and sedate way of exploring the area is by kayak; you can rent one on the east side of the river just north of the Bridge or from tour agencies on Thanon Maenam Kwai. Alternatively, try specialists Safarine (see p.197), who charge B350 for 1hr 30min.

INFORMATION

Tourist information The helpful TAT office (daily 8.30am–4.30pm; ☎034 511200, 📧tatkan@tat.or.th) is just south of the bus station on Thanon Saeng Chuto and keeps up-to-date bus and train timetables. They can also provide a good map of the town and province, plus a booklet on Pak Phraek Cultural Road (see p.190).

ACCOMMODATION

Many people choose to make the most of the inspiring scenery by staying on or near the river, in either a **raft house** or a **guesthouse**, and the options are constantly increasing as the town's building boom continues. The most popular area is around **Thanon Maenam Kwai**, which stretches 2km from Soi Rongheabaow to the Bridge, and is *the* backpackers' hub, crammed with bars, restaurants and tour agents; most guesthouses are at the riverside end of the small sois running off this thoroughfare, though few rooms actually have river views. For those that have views (which naturally have higher rates), the idyll can be plagued by roaring longtail engines during the day and floating karaoke rafts at night, so you might want to book in for just one night until you've experienced the decibel levels for yourself. Bring mosquito repellent too, as many huts float among lotus swamps.

There is also raft-house accommodation further **upstream** in Tham Lawa (see p.203).

KANCHANABURI

Apple's Retreat On the west side of the river, 600m from Thanon Maenam Kwai ☎034 512017, 🌐applenoi-kanchanaburi.com. *Apple's Retreat* sits in a green and tranquil spot, with a lovely Kwai-side restaurant and terrace on the opposite side of the road by the river. The rather plain rooms with platform beds are in a two-storey building, enjoying views across farmland to the hills

2

beyond, and there's a peaceful garden. Breakfast costs B200 extra. **B790**

Bluestar Guesthouse 241 Thanon Maenam Kwai ☎ 034 512161, ⊛ bluestar-guesthouse.com. Popular, clued-up guesthouse with a wide range of good-value accommodation including very cheap, basic fan rooms and attractive, well-priced a/c bungalows set over a lotus swamp; and cabins raised on elevated piles with downstairs bathrooms and high-level bedrooms or private upper-level terraces. Fan doubles **B200**, a/c doubles **B350**, bungalows **B650**

Chitanun Guest House 47/3 Thanon Maenam Kwai, on the opposite side of the road from the river ☎ 034 624785, ⊛ chitanungroup.com. A range of en-suite rooms – from basic white-walled crash pads with cold-water bathrooms to quite luxurious affairs with a/c and TV – set in a private compound full of tropical plants. It's a friendly place but beginning to look a bit worn. Fan **B250**, a/c **B600**

★ **Good Times Resort** 265/5–7 Thanon Maenam Kwai ☎ 034 514241, ⊛ good-times-resort.com. This is one of the newest and most attractive resorts in town, with a prime location by the river just north of the Sudjai Bridge. Just about all of the 36 spacious rooms have a balcony, some with pool view, but only one with river view. It's a good base for families as some rooms are connecting. The owner/manager Chalee is helpful and knowledgeable, and rates include a filling breakfast. **B1050**

My Home 1/16–18 Thanon Maenam Kwai, signposted down an unnamed soi just north of the Water Authority building ☎ 034 625555, ⊛ myhomekan.com. This clean and smart place, on a quiet soi between Thanon Maenam Kwai and the river, is far enough away from all of the noisy bars to ensure a restful sleep, but still relatively central. The great-value en-suite, a/c rooms occupy a modern single-storey block, which backs onto a courtyard, and have brightly painted walls, while fan rooms are sparsely furnished and share bathrooms. Fan **B350**, a/c **B600**

Ploy River Kwai 79/2 Thanon Maenam Kwai ☎ 082 4753443, ⊛ ploygh.com. Strikingly different in style from other guesthouses on this road, this is a smart little enclave set back off the road but with distant river views only from the restaurant. The chic, sleek, contemporary-look rooms have platform beds and a/c, with extra charged for those with open-air bathrooms or TVs. Good discounts if you book online. **B1000**

River Kwai Hotel 284/15–16 Thanon Saeng Chuto ☎ 034 510111, ⊛ riverkwai.co.th. Despite the name, the town centre's top hotel is nowhere near the river, but it's very good value even if it lacks the atmosphere of its riverside competitors. Rooms are of a high standard, and all have a/c and cable TV. Facilities include a pool, spa and nightclub. **B1800**

★ **Sabai@Kan** 317/4 Thanon Maenam Kwai ☎ 034 625544, ⊛ sabaiatkan.com. This relaxing boutique hotel

is located towards the northern end of Thanon Maenam Kwai, and while there are no river views, all rooms have wall-to-wall windows that overlook a pleasant prospect of a pool and shady garden. Rooms are spacious and well-equipped, with thick mattresses on the beds. A decent buffet breakfast is included in the rate and staff are very efficient and helpful. **B1400**

Sam's House 14/2 Thanon Maenam Kwai ☎ 034 515956, ⊛ samsguesthouse.com. A huge variety of rooms, ranging from stone bungalows to raft houses on the river, some with great views though they're squeezed closely together. Staff are very helpful and can arrange boat pick-ups from the jetty. Fan **B500**, a/c **B600**

Tamarind Guest House 29/1 Thanon Maenam Kwai ☎ 034 518790, ✉ tamarind_guesthouse@yahoo.co.th. Smaller rooms than in some of the other riverside guesthouses, but the place is very clean throughout and managed by considerate, friendly staff. Sleep in the two-storey house, or down by the waterfront in one of the rafthouse rooms, which have river views and share a breezy terrace. Fan **B400**, a/c **B600**

Tara Raft 15/1 Soi Rongheabaow ☎ 086 3967349, ⊛ tararoom.com. In a pretty location on a quiet stretch of the river just south of the Maenam Kwai hub, this place offers stylish raft-house rooms with great views for B900: they're large, en suite, and come with king-size beds and big TVs; the best have lovely outlooks from tiny terraces, and there's a large sundeck on top of the raft. The cheapest rooms have no view, and breakfast is not included. They also run *Tara Bed and Breakfast* (fan B250, a/c B350) at 99–101 Thanon Maenam Kwai. **B600**

T & T 1/14 Thanon Maenam Kwai, just north of My Home, on a soi leading down towards the river ☎ 034 514846, ⊛ tandt-kanchanaburiguesthouse.com. A friendly and relaxing budget choice, with a small but attractive terrace overlooking the Kwai Yai. Sleeping options include small, fan-cooled singles with clean shared bathrooms, doubles in a floating raft house which have mattresses on the floor (also with shared bathrooms), and more luxurious rooms with a/c and private bathrooms. Fan **B250**, a/c **B500**

U Inchantree 443 Thanon Maenam Kwai ☎ 034 521584, ⊛ ukanchanaburi.com. Spectacularly located on a bend in the Kwai Yai River, a 5min walk north of the Bridge (get off at the River Kwai Bridge train station if arriving by train), this luxurious, 26-room retreat has charming staff and what must be Kanchanaburi's most style-conscious rooms. They're not huge, but the powerful rain showers, snuggly white duvets and in-room iPod docks more than compensate. Outside, facilities include a riverside pool, a peaceful glass-fronted library and a restaurant serving superb buffet breakfasts. Best of all, you can keep your room for a full 24 hours, regardless of when you check in. **B2700**

2

OUT OF TOWN

Oriental Kwai 194/5 Moo 1, Ladya (off Route 3199) ☎034 588168, ⓦorientalkwai.com; map p.199. In a quiet spot beside the Kwai Yai, 15km north of town, this Dutch–Thai-run little hotel offers just twelve thoughtfully designed cottages in a lush tropical garden with a pool. Cottages are a/c, have DVD players (with a big library of films to choose from) and are tastefully decorated in modern Asian accents; some are wheelchair accessible. There's nothing to see in the immediate area but the owners will give you plenty of ideas for exploring the area, including boat rides to the Bridge. B2800

Royal River Kwai Resort 88 Moo 2, Thanon Kanchanaburi-Saiyok (about 7km northwest of town to the north of H323) ☎034 653342, ⓦroyalriverkwai resort.com; map p.199. It's worth making the short trip out of town to this riverside resort with beautiful gardens, an excellent pool and well-maintained rooms, if only for its relaxing atmosphere. If you want river views, opt for the mini suite. There's also a very good restaurant and probably the best spa in the area. B1800

★Xanadu 2008 19/5 Moo 1, Tambon Nong Bua ☎080 021 3346, ⓦxanaduresort2008.com; map p.199. With just ten en-suite bungalows in a sloping, tropical garden that leads down towards a peaceful section of the river, this welcoming place is ideal for families or couples in search of peace and quiet. There's a well-maintained pool, and English–Thai owners Dennis and Nee do everything they can to fill guests in on local happenings. Nee is an excellent cook, and the generous portions have to be seen to be believed, while Dennis has extensive local knowledge. It's a 9km drive from the Bridge, on the northern bank of the River Kwai Yai; join Route 3199 as you head north out of town, then turn left towards Nong Bua. B1200

EATING

Most of Kanchanaburi's guesthouses and raft houses have **restaurants**, and there's a cluster of floating restaurants beside the Bridge, serving good if rather pricey seafood to accompany the river views. A cheaper place to enjoy genuine local food is at the ever-reliable **night market**, which sets up alongside Thanon Saeng Chuto on the edge of the bus station. There are also a few food stalls at the **night bazaar**, which operates in front of the train station (Mon, Tues & Thurs–Sun 6–10pm).

Bell's Pizzeria 24/5 Thanon Maenam Kwai ☎081 010 6614, ⓦbellspizzeria.com. This popular Italian place has tables inside and out, and the menu, which runs from carbonara right through to *phanaeng* curries, is extremely diverse. Pizzas from B170. Daily 5–11pm.

Blue Rice 153/4 Moo 4, Tamakam (cross the Sudjai Bridge to the west side then turn north) ☎034 512017, ⓦapplenoi-kanchanaburi.com. Reliably tasty food prepared to traditional Thai recipes by Kanchanaburi's most famous cooking school. The short menu (B90–250) includes coconut- and cashew-laced *matsaman* curries – both meat and vegetarian varieties – as well as outstanding yellow curries. Every dish is prepared to order, so service can be slow. Also offers cookery classes (see p.196). Daily noon–2pm & 6–10pm.

Good Times 265/5–7 Thanon Maenam Kwai ☎034 514241, ⓦgood-times-resort.com. Located on the riverside just north of the Sudjai Bridge (walk through the resort to get there), this open-sided place offers a broad selection of well-prepared Thai and Western dishes. A fillet steak with all the trimmings will set you back B260, while fish and chips and meat pies (both B150) are other options. Most Thai dishes are priced at around B100, and it's a good choice for a filling breakfast if it's not included with your accommodation. Daily 7am–10pm.

★Mangosteen Garden 74/12 Moo 4, Tamakam (about 300m northwest of Sudjai Bridge, beyond Apple's Resort) ☎034 511814, ⓦmangosteencafe.net. This stand-out restaurant recently moved from its tiny shophouse on Thanon Maenam Kwai to a two-storey house and garden on the west side of the river, and now offers dining on a downstairs or upstairs terrace or in an a/c room, plus a play area for kids. The menu features tempting dishes such as red curry with duck (B130) and salmon steak on crushed potatoes with prawns and vegetables (B230), as well as smoothies, cocktails and wines. Daily 11.30am–10pm.

On's Thai Issan Vegetarian 36 Thanon Maenam Kwai ☎087 3642264, ⓦonthaiissan.com. There's a lively buzz around this simple streetside place, which only serves vegetarian dishes such as seaweed soup and *phat thai* (around B50 a dish). The buzz comes from On's students who learn how to make their favourite dishes on the street out front (see p.196). Daily 10am–9pm.

Prueksa 89 Thanon Maenam Kwai ☎094 4069921. This simple thatched hut turns out classic Thai dishes such as green curry (B60) at very reasonable prices, and cheap beers too. Daily 11am–11pm.

Schluck 20/1 Thanon Maenam Kwai ☎081 3559477. Cosy a/c restaurant that entices a regular crowd of expats with its menu of pizzas, salads and steaks (from B150), plus its decent selection of authentically spicy fish and yam dishes (B70–90) and French pastries too. Also has a few tables outside. Daily 4–10pm.

Sri Rung Rueng 10/1 Thanon Maenam Kwai ☎092 7981828. Well-priced restaurant with a huge menu of *tom kha*, *tom yam* and curries (yellow, red, green, *phanaeng* and *matsaman*), lots of which are available in veggie and non-veggie versions (from B70), plus steaks, seafood and cocktails. Daily 10am–10pm.

2

DRINKING

Nightlife in Kanchanaburi is relatively low-key, though there's a string of hostess bars at the southern end of Thanon Maenam Kwai, offering loud music and cheapish beer, with sports on TV as an added attraction. Further north up the strip are several simple bars without hostesses, and some classy venues that attract a mostly Thai crowd.

One More Bar 44/3 Thanon Maenam Kwai ☎084 801 3933. A lively, sociable place to head to after dark, not least because it has a refreshing no-bar-girls policy. Staff are friendly, and there's a range of Thai and Western food complemented by a comprehensive range of beers, spirits and cocktails. Daily 8am–2am.

The Resort 318/2 Thanon Maenam Kwai ☎034

624606. For a taste of Thai nightlife, head up towards the north end of Thanon Maenam Kwai to this slick restaurant and bar, with fairy lights twinkling in the trees outside and various cosy corners in the a/c interior. There's live music every night from 8pm, and a wide range of draught and imported beers. Daily 5.30pm–1am.

DIRECTORY

Airline tickets Domestic and international tickets can be bought from Good Times Travel, 63/1 Thanon Maenam Kwai (☎034 624441, ⓦgood-times-travel.com).

Banks and ATMs There are several banks with money-changing facilities and ATMs on Thanon Saeng Chuto, immediately to the north of the Thanon U Thong junction, and around the Bridge.

Books There are several secondhand bookshops on Thanon Maenam Kwai, but the best stocked is the River Kwai Bookshop, 293 Thanon Maenam Kwai (☎034 511676; Mon, Tues & Thurs–Sun 10am–10pm).

Cookery classes Most famously at *Blue Rice*, run by *Khun Apple*: shop at the morning market and learn how to cook the basic Thai dishes at professional cooking stations (daily 9.30am–3pm; B1550). Vegetarians should sign up for classes with Khun On at On's Thai Issan Vegetarian, 36 Thanon Maenam Kwai (see p.195); she'll teach you how to make three dishes in two hours for B600, any time between 10am and 6pm.

Hospitals The private Thanakan Hospital (☎034

622366–75) is at 20/20 Thanon Saeng Chuto, at the southern end of town, near the junction with Thanon Chukkadon; the government-run Phahon Phonphayulasena Hospital (☎034 511233 or ☎034 622999) is further south at 572/1 Thanon Saeng Chuto, near the junction with Thanon Mae Khlong.

Immigration office At 100/22 Thanon Mae Khlong ☎034 564279.

Spa The Rantee Spa at the Royal River Kwai Resort (☎034 653342, ⓦroyalriverkwairesort.com; daily 10am–8pm), located a few kilometres northwest of town, offers a two-hour traditional Thai massage for B1000, as well as facials and body scrubs.

Post office The GPO is 1km south of the TAT office on Thanon Saeng Chuto.

Tourist police For all emergencies, call the tourist police on the free, 24hr phone line (☎1155), or contact them at their booth on Thanon Saeng Chuto (daily 9am–6pm; ☎034 512795), a short way east of the Bridge.

Around Kanchanaburi

The parallel valleys of the Kwai Noi and the Kwai Yai, northwest of Kanchanaburi, are stacked full of great day-tripping opportunities, from **elephant camps** to the exceptionally beautiful **Erawan Falls**, the drama of a ride on the **Death Railway** and the pathos of the **Hellfire Pass Memorial Museum and Walk**. There are Stone Age artefacts at the **Ban Kao Museum**, twelfth-century Khmer temple ruins at **Prasat Muang Singh**, the (controversial) opportunity to get up close to a tiger at the **Tiger Sanctuary Temple** and several good caves, including at **Tham Than Lot National Park** and the riverside **Tham Lawa**.

Many of these attractions are served by public **transport**, the train being an obvious option along the Kwai Noi valley as far as its **Nam Tok** terminus, with buses useful along both valleys. However, most people find it more convenient to combine several attractions and activities by signing up for one of the many mix-and-match **tours** offered by Kanchanaburi agents (see box opposite), or rent a motorbike for a day. Distances are not large, and there's a handy connecting road between the two valleys just south of Nam Tok.

Elephants' World

99/4 Moo 4, Ban Nong Hoi, Tambon Wang Dong (32km northwest of Kanchanaburi) • ☎ 086 3355332, ⓦ elephantsworld.org

Elephants' World is the most popular of several elephant camps in the vicinity of Kanchanaburi, probably because of their sensitive and non-exploitative way of dealing with these gentle giants. You can sign up on their website for a one-, two- or three-day programme, with prices ranging from B2500 to B9800, for which they will pick you up and drop you off and provide all meals and accommodation. Their motto is "We work for the elephants, and not the elephants for us", and activities include preparing food for them, feeding them and bathing them. Don't forget to take along a change of clothes, as caring for these huge beasts can be a messy business.

Erawan Falls

Daily 8am–4.30pm, tiers 1 and 2 until 5pm • National park fee B300; car B30, motorbike B20 • ☎ 034 574222, ⓦ dnp.go.th/parkreserve

Considered by many to be the most beautiful falls in Thailand, the **Erawan Falls** are the star attraction of **Erawan National Park**. It's a great day out and combines well with a visit to an elephant camp and/or a ride on the Death Railway.

The falls really are astonishingly lovely: the clear glacial-blue waters gush through the forest, dropping in a series of seven tiers along a route of around 2km. At each tier, cascades feed a pool shaded by bamboo, rattan and liana, and the whole course can be walked, along a riverside trail that gets increasingly tricky the further up you go. The distance between tiers, and the ascent to each, is clearly spelled out on signs in the park. It's just 500m from the visitor centre to level one, and then fairly easy going on and up to the dramatically stepped fifth stage (1800m). Food and drink are not permitted beyond level two, apart from bottles of water for which you must pay a deposit of B20, returnable on showing the bottle as you come down.

The route on to the sixth and seventh levels is steep and slippery when wet, and features some dilapidated bridges and ladders: wear appropriate shoes and avoid doing the last bit alone, if you can; it's about a ninety-minute hike from bottom to top. The best pools for swimming are level two (which gets the most crowded) and level seven, which is a hard slog but rarely busy, and also boasts stunning views over the jungle.

DAY-TRIPS, RAFTING AND TREKKING AROUND KANCHANABURI

All the places listed below advertise **day- and overnight trips** around the Kanchanaburi and Sangkhlaburi areas, including infinite permutations of bamboo rafting, elephant-riding, Erawan Falls, Hellfire Pass and the Death Railway, sometimes with a short trek thrown in. Prices listed are per person, usually for a minimum of four. They all also do tailor-made guided tours to the war sights (often by boat or raft) and will provide a cheap transport service – car plus driver but no guide – for the more accessible attractions. If you're given the opportunity to visit Kanchanaburi's "**Monkey School**" as part of your tour, you're strongly advised to turn it down. The monkeys here are said to have been rescued from abusive owners, but they spend their days chained up by the neck or being coerced into performing circus tricks like shooting hoops and riding children's bicycles.

Good Times Travel 63/1 Thanon Maenam Kwai ☎ 034 624441, ⓦ good-times-travel.com. Energetically run, with competitively priced day-trips (around B2000/person for a group of four) and longer treks that get good reviews. Especially popular for its two-day trip to a Karen area near Hin Dat hot springs, which includes four hours' trekking each day (B4700/person, based on four sharing).
KTC Travel 99–101 Thanon Maenam Kwai ☎ 086 396 7349 or ☎ 087 153 4147, ⓦ tourkanchanaburi

.com. Offers a twice-daily trip out to bathe elephants in the river (B690) as well as short canoeing trips (B350). Longer full-day trips are also available (B750–3500), and for your fee you're promised lunch, fruit, drinking water and an English-speaking guide.
Safarine 117 Soi Tha Makham, Moo 2 (to the northwest of town) ☎ 086 049 1662, ⓦ safarine.com. French-run canoeing specialist offering short and half-day canoeing trips in the Kanchanaburi area for B350–450.

2

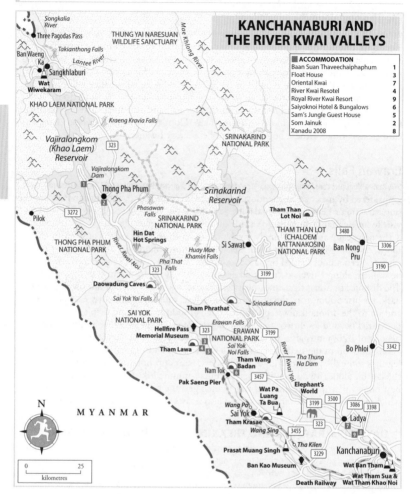

KANCHANABURI AND THE RIVER KWAI VALLEYS

■ ACCOMMODATION	
Baan Suan Thaveechaiphaphum	1
Float House	3
Oriental Kwai	7
River Kwai Resotel	4
Royal River Kwai Resort	9
Saiyoknoi Hotel & Bungalows	6
Sam's Jungle Guest House	5
Som Jainuk	2
Xanadu 2008	8

The seventh tier is topped by a triple cascade and is the one that gave the falls their name: Erawan is the three-headed god of Hindu mythology.

Tham Phrathat

12km from Erawan Waterfall • Daily 8am–4.30pm (last entry 3.30pm)

With your own transport you might also want to visit the park's other significant feature, the 200m-long stalactite-filled cave, **Tham Phrathat**, 12km by road from the falls, then a 500m walk. It's of particular interest to geologists for its clearly visible disjointed strata, evidence of the Sri Sawat fault line that runs under the Kwai Yai.

ARRIVAL AND DEPARTURE   ERAWAN FALLS

Erawan Waterfall is 70km northwest of Kanchanaburi, via Route 3199 along the Kwai Yai valley, or 40km from Nam Tok. Most foreign tourists **charter return transport** to Erawan Falls from Kanchanaburi but you can also get a public **bus**. On day tours, the falls are commonly combined with a ride on the Death Railway.

By bus From Kanchanaburi, take bus #8170 to the national park visitor centre (every 50min; 1hr 30min); the last bus back to Kanchanaburi departs at 4pm.

By chartered transport Guesthouses in Kanchanaburi can arrange private transport to the falls (around B1500/car, depending on fuel prices).

ACCOMMODATION AND EATING

National park accommodation ☎034 574222, ⓦdnp.go.th. The park has a series of basic bungalows, terraced "houses" and tents. Reserve online or through the National Parks office in Bangkok (☎02 562 0760). You can also pitch your own tent in the park. Camping per person B30, bungalows B800, tents B225

Food stalls and restaurants You'll find several food stalls, restaurants, showers and shops near the trailhead and tiers one and two. Daily 8am–8pm.

Huay Mae Khamin Falls

30km northwest of Tham Phrathat • National park fee (Srinakarind National Park, aka Khuean Srinagarindra National Park) B300 • ☎081 0106966, ⓦdnp.go.th/parkreserve

Though the Erewan Falls are certainly beautiful, they're often crowded, which can make it difficult to relax there. Arguably just as attractive but much less crowded (though it can get busy at weekends), the Huay Mae Khamin Falls also consist of seven levels, with the most spectacular cataract at level four right beside the national park headquarters. The peculiar beauty of these falls is that mineral deposits create symmetrical ledges, over which the clear waters flow like a curtain. Informative signboards beside the wooden walkway and stairway (levels one to four) point out intriguing features of the landscape. There is no walkway above level four but there are plenty of pools where you can plunge in and cool off in the therapeutic waters.

Getting to the falls once necessitated a long and expensive boat ride across the **Srinakarind Reservoir**, which is fed by the dammed waters of the Mae Khlong and the Kha Khaeng and gives rise to the Kwai Yai, but there's now a sealed road (Route 6073) leading up the west side of the reservoir from Tham Phrathat in Erewan National Park. It's not on many tour itineraries yet, but that is likely to change given the relatively easy access.

ARRIVAL AND ACCOMMODATION   HUAY MAE KHAMIN FALLS

There's no public transport to the falls, so you'll need a rented vehicle or to join a tour. Follow directions to Erewan Falls and on to Tham Phrathat, then keep going for another 30km along a rollercoaster of a road (R6073) to the national park headquarters.

National park accommodation ☎034 532 027, ⓦdnp.go.th. There are several bungalows sleeping three people and a large campsite that is very popular among Thais at weekends. Reserve online or through the National Parks office in Bangkok (☎02 562 0760). You can also pitch your own tent in the park. Camping per person B30, bungalows B900, tents B225

Food stalls and restaurants There are several food stalls, for which you'll need to buy coupons, beside the Visitors' Centre. They serve simple rice and noodle dishes as well as drinks. Daily dawn–dusk.

Tham Than Lot (Chaloem Rattanakosin) National Park

97km north of Kanchanaburi • B200 • ☎034 547020, ⓦdnp.go.th

Tiny **Tham Than Lot National Park** (also known as **Chaloem Rattanakosin National Park**) covers just 59 square kilometres but boasts two stalactite-strewn **caves** (bring a torch), a decent **waterfall** and an enjoyable hiking trail that links them.

From the visitor centre, follow the signed trail for about ten minutes to reach the first cave, **Tham Than Lot Noi**, which is 400m deep and illuminated if there are enough people (for example at weekends). A very picturesque 2.5km, two-hour **trail** runs on from the other side of Tham Than Lot Noi, along a stream and through a ravine to the first of three **waterfalls**, about an hour and a half's easy walk away and passing towering dipterocarps, fine jungle views and plenty of butterflies en route. The path gets more difficult after the first waterfall, and dangerously slippery in the wet season, running via another couple of waterfalls before coming to the larger of the park's two caves, the impressively deep sink-hole **Tham Than Lot Yai**, site of a small Buddhist shrine. Another ten minutes along the trail brings you to a small forest temple, from where you'll need to retrace your steps to return to the visitor centre.

ARRIVAL AND ACCOMMODATION   **THAM THAN LOT NATIONAL PARK**

If you'd rather not drive, your best bet is to organize a private tour from Kanchanaburi.

By car From the city, follow Route 3199 until you reach Ladya, and then join Route 3086. Turn left at Amphoe Nongprue and then follow the road for 18km until you reach the park.

Accommodation and eating A handful of simple, government-owned bungalows (B1200) sit within the park – bedding and fan are provided. For eating, there's a very basic restaurant at the park's headquarters.

Ban Kao Museum

35km west of Kanchanaburi and 8km from Prasat Muang Singh • Wed–Sun 9am–4pm • B50 • ☎ 081 9949873 • No public transport; follow Highway 323 north out of Kanchanaburi until you get to the junction with minor road 3229, then follow this road southwest for about 16km before joining minor road 3445 for the last 2km

The **Ban Kao Museum** is devoted to relics from an advanced prehistoric civilization (8000 to 1000 BC) that once settled on the banks of the Kwai Noi. Items on display include unique, curiously designed pots dated to around 1770 BC that were found buried at the head and feet of fifty skeletons; polished stone tools from around 8000 BC; and inscribed bronze pots and bangles transferred from a nearby bronze-culture site, which have been placed at around 1000 BC – somewhat later than the bronze artefacts from Ban Chiang in the northeast (see p.480). The hollowed-out tree trunks in the museum once functioned as coffins.

Prasat Muang Singh

8km northwest of Ban Kao Museum, on minor road 3445 • Daily 7.45am–4.30pm • B100, plus B50 per car, B20 per motorbike or B10 per bicycle • ☎ 034 591122

Eight hundred years ago, the Khmer empire extended west as far as Muang Singh (City of Lions), an outpost strategically sited on the banks of the River Kwai Noi, 43km west of present-day Kanchanaburi. Thought to have been built at the end of the twelfth century, the temple complex of **Prasat Muang Singh** follows Khmer religious and architectural precepts, but its origins are obscure – the City of Lions gets no mention in any of the recognized chronicles until the nineteenth century.

Prasat Muang Singh covers one-third of a square kilometre, bordered by moats and ramparts that had cosmological as well as defensive significance, and with an enclosed **shrine complex** at its heart. Restorations now give an idea of the crude grandeur of the original structure, which was constructed entirely from blocks of rough, russet laterite.

As with all Khmer prasats, the pivotal feature of Muang Singh is the main prang, surrounded by a series of walls and a covered gallery, with gateways marking the cardinal points. The prang faces east, towards Angkor, and is guarded by a fine sandstone statue of **Avalokitesvara**, one of the five great *bodhisattvas* of Mahayana Buddhism, would-be Buddhas who have postponed their entrance into Nirvana to help others attain enlightenment. He's depicted here in characteristic style, his eight arms and torso covered with tiny Buddha reliefs and his hair tied in a topknot. In Mahayanist mythology, Avalokitesvara represents mercy, while the other statue found in the prasat, the female figure of **Prajnaparamita**, symbolizes wisdom – when wisdom and mercy join forces, enlightenment ensues. Just visible on the inside of the north wall surrounding the prang is the only intact example of the stucco carving that once ornamented every facade. Other fragments and sculptures found at this and nearby sites are displayed beside the north gate; especially tantalizing is the single segment of what must have been a gigantic face hewn from several massive blocks of stone.

ARRIVAL AND DEPARTURE **PRASAT MUANG SINGH**

By car From Kanchanaburi either follow directions given for Ban Kao Museum (see opposite), or continue along Highway 323 as far as kilometre-stone 90 to take Route 3445 southwest to Muang Singh.

By train You can get to Muang Singh by taking the Death

Railway train: get off at Tha Kilen (1hr 15min from Kanchanaburi; see box, p.202), walk straight out of the station for 500m, turn right at the crossroads and continue for another 1km to reach the ruins.

2

Wat Pa Luang Ta Bua Yannasampanno: the Tiger Temple

37km from Kanchanaburi, signed off Highway 323 at kilometre-stone 94 • Daily noon–4.45pm (last admission 3.15pm); also opens for private visits 7.30–11am • B600, or B5000 for private visits • ☎ 034 531557, ⓦ tigertemple.org • No vests or shorts, and no red clothing (which antagonizes the tigers) • Transport arranged through Kanchanaburi tour operators costs around B130 return per person

At the time of writing, **Wat Pa Luang Ta Bua Yannasampanno** had just been raided by wildlife protection officers after reports that it was trafficking illegal wildlife; many rare birds, including several hornbills, for which the temple had no authorization, were impounded. However, it was allowed to keep its tigers, which have made it the province's top money-spinning attraction.

Temples are traditionally regarded as sanctuaries for unwanted and illegally captured animals, and Wat Pa Luang Ta Bua has been taking in tigers since 1999, when a distressed young tiger cub was brought here. Since then, the temple's tiger population has grown to over 140, attracting swarms of Thai and foreign visitors every day to have their photo taken with a tiger or a cub.

However, a lot of people return discouraged by the experience, not least because the animals are housed in small, bare cages and only let out to be paraded in front of visitors in the afternoons. Moreover, the temple has been accused of exploiting the animals as a money-making tourist attraction (private morning visits cost B5000). Undercover investigators sent by the British animal welfare charity Care for the Wild International (ⓦ careforthewild.org) have alleged a range of **welfare problems** and other malpractices, including unauthorized trading of tigers with a breeding centre in Laos.

Our advice is not to bother with the Tiger Temple. Visitors who pay B600 for the regular afternoon visit enter the park en masse, only to be huddled together by staff, who quickly try to sell you a variety of optional "experiences", such as tiger cub feeding (B1000). Meanwhile, the tired- and bored-looking tigers are brought down to a shady gravel area and chained up with little room to move, as queues of tourists crowd around for their chance to take photos.

Nam Tok

There's not much more to the tiny town of **NAM TOK** than the terminus of the Death Railway line. Tour groups of Thais and foreigners flock to the roadside **Sai Yok Noi Falls**, 2km north, but if you're filling time between trains, you'd be better off stretching your legs on the short trek to the nearby Wang Badan cave or taking a boat trip on the Kwai Noi River. It's also straightforward to get a bus on to Hellfire Pass.

Tham Wang Badan

1.5km north of Nam Tok train station • Daily 8.30am–4.30pm • National park admission B300

Impressive stalactites, fathomless chambers and unnerving heat make **Tham Wang Badan**, part of the Erawan National Park, one of the more interesting underground experiences in the region, though whether it's worth the park fee of B300 is debatable.

It's easily reached by a **trail** that's signposted east off Highway 323, 600m northwest from the station road T-junction, 1.5km from the station itself. About 1km into the trail, you arrive at the park warden's office where you can rent feeble **torches**; it's better to bring your own or to pay the warden a nominal fee to accompany you and turn on the cave lights. From the office it's 2km of easy walking to the cave, and as most tourists bypass Tham Wang Badan in favour of Erawan Falls, in another area of the park (see p.197), it's usually quiet here.

ARRIVAL AND SERVICES NAM TOK

By train The train station is at the top of the town, 900m north of Highway 323, and a further 2km from the Kwai Noi River. To reach the highway from the station, walk up the station approach road, cross the tracks, turn left at the spirit-house roundabout, then first right through the small town, passing a water tower and market on your left.
By bus All Kanchanaburi–Hellfire Pass–Thong Pha Phum

buses pass through Nam Tok, generally making a stop near the T-junction of the highway and the station road (#8203; every 30min; last bus back to Kanchanaburi at 5pm); it's about 1hr 30min from Kanchanaburi to Nam Tok and 30min from Nam Tok to Hellfire Pass.
Services There's an ATM on the station road, near the T-junction.

ACCOMMODATION AND EATING

There are several tourist-oriented **restaurants** at the station (open all day), and cheap **hot-food stalls** in the market (evening only), halfway along the station road. There are also a few restaurants with English menus on Highway 323, about 2km north of town opposite Sai Yok Noi Falls.

RIDING THE DEATH RAILWAY

The two-hour journey along the notorious Thailand–Burma **Death Railway** from Kanchanaburi to Nam Tok is one of Thailand's most scenic and most popular train rides. Though the views are lovely, it's the history that makes the ride so special, so it's worth visiting the Thailand–Burma Railway Centre in Kanchanaburi before making the trip, as this provides a context for the enormous loss of human life and the extraordinary feat of engineering behind the line's construction (see p.188). Alternatively, take a bus from Kanchanaburi to the **Hellfire Pass Memorial Museum and Walk** (see p.204), 18km from the line's current Nam Tok terminus, which provides an equally illuminating introduction to the railway's history, then take a bus back to Nam Tok and return to Kanchanaburi by train. A good tip, to get the best views, is to make sure you sit (or stand) on the right-hand side of the train on the journey back to Kanchanaburi, and on the left-hand side when travelling towards Nam Tok.

Leaving Kanchanaburi via the Bridge over the River Kwai, the train chugs through the Kwai Noi valley, stopping frequently at country stations decked with frangipani and jasmine. The first stop of note is Tha Kilen (1hr 15min), where you can alight for Prasat Muang Singh (see p.200). About twenty minutes later the most hair-raising section of track begins: at **Wang Sing**, also known as Arrow Hill, the train squeezes through 30m-deep solid rock cuttings, dug at the cost of numerous POW lives; 6km further, it slows to a crawl at the approach to the **Wang Po viaduct**, where a 300m-long trestle bridge clings to the cliff face as it curves with the Kwai Noi – almost every man who worked on this part of the railway died. The station at the northern end of the trestle bridge is called **Tham Krasae**, after the cave that's hollowed out of the rock face beside the bridge; you can see the cave's resident Buddha image from the train. North of Tham Krasae, the train pulls in at **Wang Po Station** before continuing alongside a particularly lovely stretch of the Kwai Noi, its banks thick with jungle and not a raft house in sight, the whole vista framed by distant tree-clad peaks. Thirty minutes later, the train reaches **Nam Tok**, a small town that thrives chiefly on its position at the end of the line.

Three trains operate daily along the Death Railway in both directions, but they don't always run on time. Currently they're scheduled to leave Kanchanaburi at 6.07am, 10.35am and 4.26pm and to return from Nam Tok at 5.20am, 12.55pm and 3.30pm; Kanchanaburi TAT keeps up-to-date timetables (see p.193). If you're up at the Bridge, you can join the train five minutes later.

BOAT TRIPS FROM NAM TOK

You can rent a longtail **boat** (plus driver) from the Nam Tok's **Pak Saeng pier** ("Tha Pak Saeng") for the ride upstream to **Tham Lawa** or **Sai Yok Yai Falls**. To reach the pier from the Highway 323 T-junction, cross the road, turn southeast towards Kanchanaburi, then take the first road on your right; it's 2km from here to the river. The return journey to the cave takes roughly two hours, including half an hour there, and costs B1200 for the eight-seater boat; for B2800 you can continue to Sai Yok Yai Falls, a six-hour return trip (see p.205), though this trip is not possible when water levels are low (Feb–May). You can also rent a boat for an hour's sightseeing (around B800) along this pretty stretch of river.

2

Saiyoknoi Hotel & Bungalow 132 Moo 3, Thasao, Sai Yok ☎ 034 634397. Few tourists stay in Nam Tok, but should you get stuck here, head for this spot on the main road (coming from the railway station, turn right on H323 and it's just beyond the petrol station). There are spacious a/c bungalows and cheaper, motel-style, dimly lit rooms with cold-water bathrooms, but no other facilities. Doubles B400, bungalows B600

Upriver on the Kwai Noi

About 10km north of Nam Tok, a side road turns off Highway 323 at kilometre-stone 129 and runs down to the river, giving access to a beautiful stretch of the Kwai Noi, the **Resotel pier** and several pleasant places to stay. There's no development along the banks apart from a few raft houses and shore-bound little hotels.

Tham Lawa

60km northwest of Kanchanaburi, just south of Route 323 • Daily 8am–4.30pm • National park fee B300 • Can be reached via a longtail ride upriver from the Pak Saeng Pier in Nam Tok (see above), by road on the south side of the river from Nam Tok, or by walking from nearby accommodation

The most famous attraction around here is **Tham Lawa**, the largest stalactite cave in the area and home to three species of bat. A steep set of stairs leads to the entrance, beyond which are five large chambers, connected by an illuminated concrete path. There are also light switches that should illuminate the more striking formations, but often don't work; it's best to take your own torch. The walk through the cave and back takes around thirty minutes, but the stalactites and stalagmites are not especially impressive and you'd need to be very keen on caves to find it worthwhile.

The Mon village

You can visit the **Mon village** just below Tham Lawa, where you're encouraged to browse the sarongs and other artefacts made and sold by the villagers, take an elephant ride and visit the local school. The Mon villagers fled here from Myanmar in the late 1950s but have still not been granted Thai ID papers, which means the children can't study at Thai secondary schools and adults have difficulty finding work. This village has close links with resorts operated by Serenata (including the *Resotel* and *Float House*), and many of its residents work at the hotels. For more on the Mon people, see the box later in this chapter (p.209).

ARRIVAL AND GETTING AROUND	UPRIVER ON THE KWAI NOI

By bus Any Kanchanaburi–Thong Pha Phum bus will drop you at the turn-off to the Resotel pier. Heading back to Kanchanaburi, you should be able to flag down buses on the main road.

ACCOMMODATION

Float House Just upstream from the Resotel (see p.204) and Tham Lawa ☎ 02 642 5497, ☻ thefloathouse riverkwai.com; map p.199. This is the newest resort operated by Serenata, a company with something of a monopoly on luxury accommodation in the region. In a gorgeous setting, with lush jungle all round and the river flowing beneath, this floating resort features beautiful thatched but a/c rooms with every comfort, including private terraces looking out over the river. Online rates are cheaper. B7600

River Kwai Resotel On the west bank of the river (take a boat from the Resotel pier) ☎ 02 642 5497, ⓦ riverkwairesotel.net; map p.199. Serenata's flagship resort is a classy, upmarket spot, comprising an open-air restaurant, some charming thatched riverside chalets (some with their own private hot tubs) and a turquoise swimming pool. B3500

Sam's Jungle Guest House About 1km off the highway at kilometre-stone 129 ☎ 081 948 3448, ⓦ samsguesthouse.com; map p.199. Occupying a large swathe of steep and densely grown riverbank, this place offers a range of well-priced fan and a/c accommodation, plus a swimming pool, in a strange and rather unstylish assortment of buildings that nonetheless enjoy an exceptionally tranquil setting; there's kayak rental too. Staff keep the front gate closed while working down by the river, so call ahead if you can. Fan B400, a/c B500

Hellfire Pass

Although the rail line north of Nam Tok was ripped up soon after the end of World War II, it casts its dreadful shadow all the way up the Kwai Noi valley into Myanmar. The remnants of track are most visible at **Hellfire Pass**, and many of the villages in the **area** are former POW sites – locals frequently stumble across burial sites, now reclaimed by the encroaching jungle. To keep the Death Railway level through the uneven course of the Kwai valley, the POWs had to build a series of embankments and trestle bridges and, at dishearteningly frequent intervals, gouge deep cuttings through solid rock. The most concentrated digging was at **Konyu**, 18km beyond Nam Tok, where seven separate cuttings were made over a 3.5km stretch. The longest and most brutal of these was Hellfire Pass, which got its name from the hellish-looking lights and shadows of the fires the POWs used when working at night. The job took three months of round-the-clock labour with the most primitive tools.

Hellfire Pass Memorial Museum

Daily 9am–4pm • Donation requested

The story of the POWs who died on the Hellfire Pass is documented at the beautifully designed **Hellfire Pass Memorial Museum**, the best and most informative of all the World War II museums in the Kanchanaburi region. Inside, wartime relics, POW memorabilia, photos and first-hand accounts tell the sobering history of the construction of this stretch of the Thailand–Burma Railway, along with slide shows and videos. Founded by an Australian–Thai volunteer group, the museum now serves as a sort of pilgrimage site for the families and friends of Australian POWs.

Hellfire Pass Memorial Walk

The same Australian–Thai group responsible for the Hellfire Pass Memorial Museum has also cleared a one-hour circular **memorial walk**, which begins at the museum and follows the old rail route through the 18m-deep cutting and back, and a longer, three-hour walk going on to Hin Tok creek along a course relaid with some of the original narrow-gauge track. The creek was originally forded by a trestle bridge so unstable that it was nicknamed the Pack of Cards Bridge, but this has long since crumbled away. There's an excellent audio tour available at the museum (B200 deposit), which gives a detailed commentary at fourteen points along the route.

ARRIVAL AND DEPARTURE   **HELLFIRE PASS**

Hellfire Pass is 18km north of Nam Tok, on the west side of Highway 323 just after kilometre-stone 139. Most Kanchanaburi tour-operators offer **day-trips** featuring Hellfire Pass. It's also possible to get here on your own by bus, or by a combination of train and bus.

By train Take the Death Railway (see box, p.202) to Nam Tok, then a bus to Hellfire Pass; returning to Kanchanaburi, follow this in reverse.

By bus From Kanchanaburi or Nam Tok, take any bus bound for Thong Pha Phum or Sangkhlaburi and ask to be dropped off at Hellfire Pass; it's about a 1hr 30min journey from Kanchanaburi or 30min from Nam Tok. The last return bus to Kanchanaburi passes Hellfire Pass at 5pm; if you're continuing to Sangkhlaburi, the last onward bus comes past at about 2.15pm.

Sai Yok National Park

B300; car B30, motorbike B20 • ☎ 034 686024, ⓦ dnp.go.th

Expanses of impenetrable mountain wilderness characterize the Kwai Noi valley to the north of Hellfire Pass, a landscape typified by the dense monsoon forests of **Sai Yok National Park**, which stretches all the way to the Burmese border. The park makes a refreshing enough stopover between Nam Tok and Sangkhlaburi, particularly if you have your own transport. Its teak forests are best known for the much-photographed though unexceptional **Sai Yok Yai Falls** and for the eight stalactite-filled chambers of **Daowadung Caves**. Short trails to these attractions start from near the park's visitor centre. It's also home to the smallest-known mammal in the world, the elusive hog-nosed or bumblebee bat, which weighs just 1.75g and has a wingspan of 1.6cm.

ARRIVAL AND DEPARTURE SAI YOK NATIONAL PARK

The park is 97km north of Kanchanaburi, signed off Highway 323 between kilometre-stones 155 and 156.

By bus Any of the Kanchanaburi–Thong Pha Phum buses will stop at the road entrance to Sai Yok, from where it's a 3km walk to the visitor centre, trailheads and river (motorbike taxis sometimes hang around the road entrance). The last bus to Sangkhlaburi passes at around 2.30pm and the last bus to Kanchanaburi at about 4.30pm.

By boat The most scenic approach to Sai Yok is by longtail from Nam Tok, a 6hr return trip (see p.203), though it's not always possible in the dry season (Feb–May).

ACCOMMODATION AND EATING

There are plenty of **hot-food stalls** (daily 6am–8pm) near the visitor centre.

National park accommodation ☎ 034 686024, ⓦ dnp.go.th. You can stay in the national park's simple, fan-cooled bungalows, which sleep between four and seven people, but it's worth booking ahead online. **B800**

Pha Tad Falls and Hin Dat hot springs

Pha Tad Falls (national park fee) B300; cars B30, motorbikes B20 • Hin Dat hot springs B40

North of Sai Yok National Park, signs off Highway 323 direct you to the two long, gently sloping cascades of **Pha Tad Falls**, which are very attractive in the wet season (June–Nov), though there's almost no water in the late dry season (Feb–May). Nearer the main road is **Hin Dat** (Hindad) **hot springs**, where, after paying the entry fee, you can immerse yourself in a big pool of soothingly warm water. Close by is a much cooler stream – perfect for leaping into after a good soak in the springs – and you can make use of the nearby showers and food stalls.

ARRIVAL AND DEPARTURE PHA TAD FALLS AND HIN DAT HOT SPRINGS

Both Pha Tad Falls and Hin Dat hot springs are off Highway 323.

To/from Pha Tad Falls The falls are 9km east from kilometre-stone 178 and can only be reached with your own transport or on a tour.

To/from Hin Dat The hot springs are 1km east from kilometre-stone 180; any Thong Pha Phum bus from Kanchanaburi will drop you at the Hin Dat access track, from where it's an easy walk across to the springs. Returning in the afternoon, flag down a bus from Thong Pha Phum or Sangkhlaburi for the trip back to Kanchanaburi (last bus around 4pm).

Thong Pha Phum and around

The first significant town northwest of Sai Yok is **Thong Pha Phum** (147km from Kanchanaburi), which sits at the southern edge of the massive Vajiralongkorn Reservoir, where you'll find some pleasant waterside accommodation. It's a mid-sized market town with bus connections to Sangkhlaburi and Kanchanaburi and plenty of small food shops.

Vajiralongkorn Reservoir

12km west of Thong Pha Phum market

With your own transport, a much more scenic overnight option than staying in town is to drive 12km west of Thong Pha Phum market to the southeastern fringes of nearby **Vajiralongkorn Reservoir** (formerly Khao Laem Reservoir). This vast body of water stretches all the way to Sangkhlaburi 73km to the north and, when created in the early 1980s, flooded every village in the vicinity. Hotels make the most of the refreshing, almost Scandinavian, landscape of forested hills and clear, still water that's perfect for swimming.

ARRIVAL AND DEPARTURE   THONG PHA PHUM

By bus Take bus #8203 from Kanchanaburi (about 3hr 30min) or from Sangkhlaburi (about 1hr 30min). Occasional yellow songthaews travel to the reservoir from Thong Pha Phum market.

ACCOMMODATION

THONG PHA PHUM TOWN
Som Jainuk 29/9 Moo 1, between the police station and the main market ☏ 034 599001. The A-frame fan rooms out front are a bit dingy, but the a/c rooms set back from the road are a good deal. Look for the wooden "Hotel" sign (no English name) on Thong Pha Phum's main street. Fan B250, a/c B400

VAJIRALONGKORN RESERVOIR
Ban Suan Thaveechaiphaphum 401/8 Moo 1 Thakanun, about 10km from Thong Pha Phum town ☏ 034 598578, ⓦ thaveechaiphaphum.com. The nicest of the English-speaking hotels by the water, *Ban Suan* offers stylishly decorated fan and a/c rooms overlooking the garden or lake. The best rooms have private, stilted chill-out pavilions built over the water. The location is great and they can also arrange boat trips around the lake. To drive here, follow signs for the Vajiralongkorn Dam, then instead of turning right for the dam continue along the left-hand branch of the road for another 6km. Closed July–Sept. B2100

Thong Pha Phum National Park

About 60km from Thong Pha Phum along Route 3272 • B200 • ☏ 081 3820359, ⓦ dnp.go.th/parkreserve

The final 30km of the road to **Thong Pha Phum National Park** twists like a roller coaster and is slow but surfaced. If you have your own wheels the effort is worth it; this is a remote and lovely place to escape to, barely visited by foreign tourists and home to a population of mountain goats, buffalo and barking deer. If you stay overnight, the big pleasure here is waking to see the foggy jungle below. During the day you can follow several **trails** that lead to the park's waterfalls.

ARRIVAL AND ACCOMMODATION   THONG PHA PHUM NATIONAL PARK

By songthaew Occasional songthaews head to Pilok on the Myanmar border from the market in Thong Pha Phum, taking around 1hr 30min.
Eating There's a restaurant on site but options are limited, so it's worth bringing some of your own supplies.
National park accommodation ☏ 083 6144432.

There are a number of rather basic bungalows near park headquarters, including a couple of treehouses with fans and en-suite bathrooms (B600). Call in advance to reserve. It's also possible to camp here – you can bring your own tent, or rent one. Camping B30, tents B225, bungalows B800

Sangkhlaburi and around

Beyond Thong Pha Phum the views get increasingly spectacular as Highway 323 climbs through the remaining swathes of montane rainforest, occasionally hugging the eastern shore of the Vajiralongkorn Reservoir until 73km later it comes to an end at **Sangkhlaburi** (often called **Sangkhla** for short). In the early 1980s, the old town was lost under the rising waters of the newly created Khao Laem (now Vajiralongkorn) Reservoir (see opposite). Its residents were relocated to the northeastern tip of the lake, beside the Songkalia River, where modern-day Sangkhla now enjoys an eerily beautiful view of semi-submerged trees and raft houses. It's a tiny town with no unmissable attractions, but the atmosphere is pleasantly low-key and the best of the accommodation occupies scenic lakeside spots so it's a great place to slow down for a while.

Cultural interest is to be found in the villages, markets and temples of the area's Mon, Karen and Thai populations, including at **Ban Waeng Ka** across the water, and there's natural beauty in various waterfalls, whitewater rivers and the remote Thung Yai Naresuan Wildlife Sanctuary. It sees relatively few farang tourists, but it's a popular destination for weekending Thais (come during the week for better deals on accommodation) and resident NGO volunteers add a positive vibe. Though the Burmese border is just 22km away at **Three Pagodas Pass**, at the time of writing it was closed to foreigners.

SANGKHLABURI AND BAN WAENG KA

■ ACCOMMODATION	
Burmese Inn	2
J Family Bed and Breakfast	1
P Guest House	3

● RESTAURANTS & CAFÉS	
Bakery	4
Birdland	3
Blend	1
Blue Rock	2
P Guest House	5

WEAVING FOR WOMEN

A community project worth supporting in Sangkhlaburi is **Weaving for Women**, set up by a group of Karen refugees in 1989. Their Hilltribe Handicrafts and coffee **shop** (next to the *Bakery*, see p.211; ⓦ weavingforwomen.org) carries a huge selection of hand-woven items, much of it in *mut mee* design and all of it made from good-quality Chiang Mai cotton, including tablecloths, sarongs, shirts and bags. For more on the Karen, see our box later in this chapter (see p.261).

2

Wat Sam Phrasop

Aside from crossing the famous wooden bridge over the lake to the Mon village of Ban Waeng Ka, the main pastime in Sangkhlaburi is **boating** across the reservoir in search of **Wat Sam Phrasop**, the **sunken temple** which was all but submerged when the valley was flooded. However, at the time of research it was no longer "sunken"; water levels had dropped such that in the dry season it now stands on dry land beside the reservoir. *P Guest House* rents out two-person **canoes** for independent exploring (B150/hr, or B300 for half a day), or you can join a longtail boat trip (B400 for five people; 1hr) from either *P Guest House* or *Burmese Inn* (see p.211).

Baan Unrak

99-1 Moo 1 Nonglu · ☎ 034 510778, ⓦ baanunrak.org

Sangkhla's location so close to the Burmese border, along with the upheavals caused by the creation of the reservoir, mean that the town is full of displaced people, many of whom are in dire straits. Several organizations work with refugees in the area, including **Baan Unrak**, a farang-managed programme founded by the Neo Humanist Foundation that has run an orphans' home here since 1991 and has also established a school and a weaving project for destitute women and children. To help support the project you can buy handicrafts at the Si Tung Mai Coffee Shop next to the *Bakery* (see p.211) or make donations of books, clothes and money, and get directions to the orphanage, which welcomes visitors and holds an open day every Wednesday during term-time. Volunteer placements are also possible.

Ban Waeng Ka

The Mon village of **BAN WAENG KA**, across the reservoir from Sangkhlaburi, was founded in the late 1940s after the outbreak of civil war in Myanmar forced many to flee across the Thai border (see box opposite). The **Mon** people's homeland, Mon State, lies just west of the Tenasserim Mountains, so thousands of Mon ended up in Sangkhlaburi, illegal immigrants whose presence was permitted but not officially recognized. Most now have official Sangkhlaburi residency, but still endure limited rights and must apply for expensive seven-day permits if they wish to travel out of the district, a system that lends itself to corruption.

Getting to Ban Waeng Ka is simply a matter of crossing the narrow northern neck of the lake, near the influx of the Songkalia River. Pedestrians can use the spider's web of a **wooden bridge** that is Sangkhla's unofficial town symbol. At almost 400m it is said to be the longest hand-built wooden bridge in the world and it can be reached either by following signs from near the post office to *Samprasop Resort*, which overlooks the structure, or by using the connecting footbridge near the *Burmese Inn*. The concrete road bridge is several hundred metres further north. Once across the wooden bridge, turn left to get into the village – a sprawling collection of traditional wooden houses lining a network of steep tracks, with a small but lively dry-goods market at its heart.

Wat Wang Wiwekaram
About 2km west from the bridgehead

Wat Wang Wiwekaram (also known as **Wat Luang Pho Uttama**) is Ban Waeng Ka's most dramatic sight, its massive, golden **chedi** clearly visible from Sangkhlaburi. Built in a fusion of Thai, Indian and Burmese styles, the imposing square-sided stupa is modelled on the centrepiece of India's Bodh Gaya, the sacred site of the Buddha's enlightenment,

---

THE MON IN THAILAND

2

Dubbed by some "the Palestinians of Asia", the **Mon** people – numbering between two and four million in Myanmar and an estimated one hundred thousand in Thailand (chiefly in the western provinces of Kanchanaburi and Ratchaburi, in the Gulf province of Samut Sakhon and in Nonthaburi and Pathum Thani, just north of Bangkok) – have endured centuries of persecution, displacement and forced assimilation.

Ethnologists speculate that the Mon originated either in India or Mongolia, travelling south to settle on the western banks of the Chao Phraya valley in the first century BC. Here they founded the **Dvaravati kingdom** (sixth to eleventh centuries AD), building centres at U Thong, Lopburi and Nakhon Pathom and later consolidating a northern kingdom in Haripunchai (modern-day Lamphun). They probably introduced Theravada Buddhism to the region, and produced some of the earliest Buddhist monuments, particularly Wheels of Law and Buddha footprints.

Over on the Burmese side of the border, the Mon kingdom had established itself around the southern city of Pegu well before **the Burmese** filtered into the area in the ninth century, but by the mid-eighteenth century they'd been stripped of their homeland and were once again relocating to Thailand. The Thais welcomed them as a useful source of labour, and in 1814 the future Rama IV arrived at the Kanchanaburi border with three royal warboats and a guard of honour to chaperone the exiles. Swathes of undeveloped jungle were given over to them, many of which are still Mon-dominated today.

The **persecution** of Burmese Mon has abated somewhat in recent years, though there are still sporadic outbursts of violence, and the Mon continue to struggle for the right to administer their own independent Mon State in their historical homelands opposite Kanchanaburi province in lower Myanmar. As one commentator has described it, while some of Myanmar's ethnic minority groups seek to *establish* autonomy, the Mon are attempting to *reclaim* it, and they still celebrate their national day on February 4 in the town of Ye each year. Though the New Mon State Party (NMSP) entered into a ceasefire agreement with the Burmese junta in June 1995, international human-rights organizations continue to report violations against civilian Mon living in Myanmar. Thousands of Mon men, women and children have been press-ganged into unpaid labour, and soldiers have occupied some Mon villages and confiscated farmland and livestock. In an attempt to wipe out Mon culture, the military leaders also banned the teaching of Mon language, literature and history in government schools, though since 2013 some brave teachers have been teaching it outside school hours.

Not surprisingly, Mon fled these atrocities in droves, the majority ending up in five **resettlement camps** in a Mon-controlled area along the Thai–Myanmar border, the biggest being Halockhani near Sangkhlaburi; the eleven thousand Mon estimated to be living in these camps as of October 2011 have no right of entry into Thailand, though since 2013, many have resettled in the USA. For more information, see the website of the Human Rights Foundation of Monland (HURFOM; ⓦrehmonnya.org).

Like Thais, the Mon are a predominantly Buddhist, rice-growing people, but they also have strong animist beliefs. All Mon families have totemic **house spirits**, such as the turtle, snake, chicken or pig, which carry certain taboos; if you're of the chicken-spirit family, for example, the lungs and head of every chicken you cook have to be offered to the spirits, and although you're allowed to raise and kill chickens, you must never give one away. Guests belonging to a different spirit group from their host are not allowed to stay overnight. Mon **festivals** also differ slightly from Thai ones – at Songkhran (Thai New Year), the Mon spice up the usual water-throwing and parades with a special courtship ritual in which teams of men and women play each other at bowling, throwing flirtatious banter along with their wooden discs.

and contains a much-prized Buddha relic (said to be a piece of his skeleton) brought to Ban Waeng Ka from Sri Lanka. It's a focal point for the Mon community on both sides of the Thai–Myanmar border, particularly at Mon New Year in April. There's a **tourist market** in the covered cloisters at the chedi compound, with plenty of reasonably priced Burmese woodcarvings, checked *longyis* and jewellery.

The wat is spread over two compounds (you might want to hail a motorbike taxi to get here from the bridgehead), with the bot, **viharn** and monks' quarters about 1km away from the chedi, at the end of the left-hand fork in the road. The interior of the viharn is decorated with murals showing tableaux from the five hundred lives of the Buddha, designed to be viewed in anticlockwise order.

Three Pagodas Pass and the Burmese border

24km north of Sangkhlaburi • Songthaews leave Sangkhla bus station every 40min from 6.30am until about 6.30pm and take 40min; the last songthaew back to Sangkhla leaves at about 4pm

All border trade for hundreds of kilometres north and south has to come through **Three Pagodas Pass** (signed as **Jadee Sam Ong**), but at the time of writing the border was **closed** to foreigners. Unless you're looking for heavy teak furniture or orchids, that means it's currently not worth making the trip as there's nothing more than a small market on the Thai side, in the village of **Ban Chedi Sam Ong**, plus the three eponymous little **chedis** said to have been erected in the eighteenth century by the kings of Myanmar and Thailand as a symbolic peace gesture. If and when full border operations resume, foreigners will probably once again be allowed access to the Burmese border village of **Payathonzu**, whose main attraction is the Mon temple **Wat Sao Roi Ton**, known in Burmese as **Tai Ta Ya temple**, or the Temple of One Hundred Teakwood Posts.

ARRIVAL AND DEPARTURE   SANGKHLABURI

By bus A/c buses run from Bangkok's Northern Mo Chit bus terminal via Kanchanaburi to Thanon Tessaban 1, opposite the bus station on the western edge of Sangkhla (2 daily; 7hr). Buses from Kanchanaburi take about 5 hours.

By minibus The fastest way to get to Sangkhlaburi from Kanchanaburi is by a/c minibus (every 20min, 7am–5pm; 4hr; reserve a few hours ahead and be prepared to buy an extra seat if you have luggage); they also pick up from Thong Pha Phum. Minibuses terminate on Thanon Tessaban 1, with services in the opposite direction departing from

the same spot.

By car or motorbike Driving from Kanchanaburi to Sangkhlaburi can be tiring as the road is full of twists after Thong Pha Phum; the last 25km are particularly nerve-wracking due to the switchback bends. Nonetheless, the scenery is fabulous, particularly at the lakeside viewpoint just north of kilometre-stone 35 (about 40km south of Sangkhlaburi). As this is a border area, there are several police checkpoints en route – after a quick look at your passport, the officers should wave you through.

GETTING AROUND AND SERVICES

Sangkhlaburi itself is small enough to walk round in an hour, but if the sun is beating down hard, you might want to look for an alternative.

ORGANIZED TRIPS OUT OF SANGKHLABURI

Sangkhlaburi is a good base from which to explore the surrounding countryside, and two guesthouses in town run organized trips. *P Guest House* does good-value packages featuring various combinations of elephant-riding, bamboo-rafting and boat trips on the lake (from B1100/person, including accommodation). *Burmese Inn* does one-day rafting excursions on the Songkalia River (B850) and two- and three-day treks in the Thung Yai Naresuan Wildlife Sanctuary, around the Karen village of Ban Sane Pong (B1500–3500; prices based on a minimum of 5 people). They also keep a book of useful information on **motorbike routes** in the area, including to Takianthong waterfall and Sawan Badan cave, both accessed via the road to Three Pagodas Pass.

By motorbike taxi or songthaew Motorbikes usually charge B20 from the bus station to the guesthouses and around B100 for a ride from the guesthouses to Wat Wang Wiwekaram across the water.

By bicycle or motorbike *P Guest House* rents out bicycles (B20/hr; B100/day) and motorbikes (B50/hr; B200/day).

By kayak Decent kayaks are available by the hour (B150)

and half-day (B300) at *P Guest House*.

By pick-up truck *Burmese Inn* or *P Guest House* should be able to arrange a pick-up truck and driver; prices depend on the length of hire and distances travelled.

Services Travellers' cheques and dollars can be changed at Siam Commercial Bank, on the edge of the market in the town centre, which also has an ATM.

ACCOMMODATION

2

Reservations are essential at all accommodation for weekends and national holidays.

Burmese Inn Soi 1 ☎ 086 168 1801, ⓦ burmese-inn .com. This rambling, traveller-oriented guesthouse overlooks the northeastern spur of the lake just behind the newer bridge, offering easy access to the Mon village, but hardly any rooms have lake views. Most of the rooms and bungalows feel run-down, but there's a decent restaurant and they arrange tours too (see box opposite). Fan B500, a/c B1000

★ J Family Bed and Breakfast (Kumsai Soonploy) 17/1 Soi 2 ☎ 034 595511. A genuine homestay offering four big rooms with fan and shared bathroom in the large family home of the Mon woman, Kumsai Soonploy, who runs the Baan Unrak shop and bakery (see p.208).

There are also a few tents to rent at the same price if rooms are full. Kumsai speaks great English, is very welcoming, and is the person to speak to about volunteering with refugees. B150

P Guest House West of soi 3 ☎ 034 595061, ⓦ p-guesthouse.com. Large, popular, efficiently run and clued-up Mon-owned place that sits prettily on the banks of the lake. There are rather run-down, stone-studded rooms with shared bathrooms that have partial lake views, or much more luxurious en-suite rooms with a/c that are much bigger and brighter and have sweeping views. Reservations strongly advised. Fan and shared bathroom B300, a/c B950

EATING AND DRINKING

Day and night, the cheapest places to eat are at and around the **market** in the town centre. If you're hankering after a decent latte, however, drop into one of the new a/c coffee shops that have popped up across town. Note that most places close quite early.

Bakery Opposite Soi 3. The sociable *Bakery* does brownbread sandwiches, hot veggie meals (B60–90), pizzas and banana cake, and is staffed by volunteers from the nearby Baan Unrak orphans' home. Daily 7am–8pm.

Birdland 13/1 Thanon Si Sawan Khiri ☎ 086 8016738. Run by long-time resident Jimmy, who's passionate about books, and his wife, who's passionate about cooking, this open-sided place in front of a secondhand bookstore is a great place to feed both your body and mind. Everything from pancakes to Burmese curry, and portions are very generous. Go for the yummy potato balls (B90), and ask Jimmy to recommend a book. Daily 7am–8pm.

Blend Tessaban 1, just across from the bus station. A handy place to wait before catching a bus, this diddy

café serves scrummy home-baked cakes and good, strong Arabica coffee (B40). Daily 8am–6pm.

Blue Rock 307 Thanon Si Sawan Khiri ☎ 087 1529030. If you're looking for nightlife in Sangkhlaburi, here's your spot. This farang-managed place serves a range of beers and cocktails (around B150) as well as big breakfasts and steaks. Daily 10am till late.

P Guest House West of soi 3 ☎ 034 595061. The large restaurant at *P Guest House* offers fine lake views from its terrace and serves a short menu of Thai and Burmese food (most dishes around B120), as well as a few Western dishes, such as an American breakfast (B150). Daily 7am–8.30pm.

Bang Pa-In

Little more than a roadside market, the village of **BANG PA-IN**, 60km north of Bangkok, has been put on the tourist map by its extravagant and rather surreal **Royal Palace**, even though most of the buildings can be seen only from the outside. King Prasat Thong of Ayutthaya first built a palace on this site, 20km downstream from his capital, in the middle of the seventeenth century, and it remained a popular country residence for the kings of Ayutthaya. The palace was abandoned a century later when the capital was moved to Bangkok, only to be revived in the middle of the nineteenth century when the advent of steamboats shortened the journey time upriver. Rama IV (1851–68) built a modest residence here, which his son Chulalongkorn (Rama V), in his passion for westernization, knocked down to make room for the eccentric melange of European, Thai and Chinese architectural styles visible today.

The palace

Daily 8am–4pm, ticket office closes 3.30pm • B100 • Electric cart rental B400 first hour, B100 subsequent hours • Ⓦ palaces.thai.net • Visitors are asked to dress respectfully, so no vests, shorts or sandals

Set in manicured grounds on an island in the Chao Phraya River, and based around an ornamental lake, the **palace** complex is flat and compact, and easy to see on foot. The best approach is to explore slowly, following walkways that crisscross the lake.

The lakeside and covered bridge

On the north side of the lake stand a two-storey, colonial-style residence for the royal relatives and the Italianate **Varobhas Bimarn** (**Warophat Phiman**, "Excellent and Shining Heavenly Abode"), which housed Chulalongkorn's throne hall and still contains private apartments where the present royal family sometimes stays, though the lavishly furnished rooms by the entrance are usually open to the public. A covered bridge links this outer part of the palace to the **Pratu Thewarat Khanlai** ("The King of the Gods Goes Forth Gate"), the main entrance to the inner palace, which was reserved for the king and his immediate family. The high fence that encloses half of the bridge allowed the women of the harem to cross without being seen by male courtiers.

Aisawan Thiphya-art

You can't miss the glittering **Aisawan Thiphya-art** ("Divine Seat of Personal Freedom") in the middle of the lake: named after King Prasat Thong's original palace, it's the only example of pure Thai architecture at Bang Pa-In. The elegant tiers of the pavilion's roof shelter a bronze statue of Chulalongkorn.

The inner palace

In the inner palace, the **Uthayan Phumisathian** ("Garden of the Secured Land"), recently rebuilt by Queen Sirikit in grand, neocolonial style, was Chulalongkorn's favourite house. After passing the candy-striped **Ho Withun Thasana** ("Sage's Lookout Tower"), built so that the king could survey the surrounding countryside, you'll come to the main attraction of Bang Pa-In, the **Phra Thinang Wehart Chamrun Residential Hall** ("Palace of Heavenly Light"). A masterpiece of Chinese design, the mansion and its contents were shipped from China and presented as a gift to Chulalongkorn in 1889 by the Chinese Chamber of Commerce in Bangkok. The sumptuous interior gleams with fantastically intricate lacquered and gilded wooden screens, hand-painted porcelain floor tiles and ebony furniture inlaid with mother-of-pearl.

The obelisk

The simple marble **obelisk** behind the Uthayan Phumisathian was erected by Chulalongkorn to hold the ashes of Queen Sunandakumariratana, his favourite wife. In 1881, Sunanda, who was then 21 and expecting a child, was taking a trip on the river here when her boat capsized. She could have been rescued quite easily, but the laws concerning the sanctity of the royal family left those around her no option: "If a boat founders, the boatmen must swim away; if they remain near the boat [or] if they lay hold of him [the royal person] to rescue him, they are to be executed." Following the tragedy, King Chulalongkorn became a zealous reformer of Thai customs and strove to make the monarchy more accessible.

ARRIVAL AND EATING | | **BANG PA-IN**

Bang Pa-In can easily be visited on a day-trip from Bangkok or Ayutthaya; many day-trips from both destinations feature a stop here (see p.216).

By train The best route from Bangkok is by train from Hualamphong station, which takes just over an hour to reach Bang Pa-in (on arrival, note the separate station hall built by Chulalongkorn for the royal family). All trains continue to Ayutthaya, with half going on to Lopburi. Note that trains from Ayutthaya are more frequent than the English-language timetable implies (most Ayutthaya guesthouses keep the full Thai timetable). From Bang Pa-In's train station it's a 2km hike to the palace, or you can take a motorbike taxi for about B40. Returning to the station, catch a motorized samlor from the market, about 300m southwest of the palace entrance.

Destinations Ayutthaya (12 daily; 15min); Bangkok

Hualamphong (12 daily; 1hr 30min).

By bus Slow buses leave Bangkok's Northern Mo Chit terminal (roughly every 30min; 2hr) and stop at Bang Pa-In market, about 300m southwest of the palace entrance. This is also the easiest place to catch a bus back to Bangkok.

By songthaew From Ayutthaya, large songthaews leave Thanon Naresuan roughly every half hour for the 20min journey to Bang Pa-In market, returning from the same spot.

Eating There are food stalls just outside the palace gates, and at Bang Pa-In market, plus a couple of well-appointed riverside restaurants (no English signs) between the railway station and the palace, opposite Wat Chumpol Nikarayam.

Ayutthaya

In its heyday as the booming capital of the Thai kingdom, **AYUTTHAYA**, 80km north of Bangkok, was so well-endowed with temples that sunlight reflecting off their gilt decoration was said to dazzle from 5km away. Wide, grassy spaces today occupy much of the atmospheric site, which now resembles a graveyard for temples: grand, brooding red-brick ruins rise out of the fields, satisfyingly evoking the city's bygone grandeur while providing a soothing contrast to more glitzy modern temple architecture. A few intact buildings help form an image of what the capital must have looked like, while three fine museums flesh out the picture.

The core of the ancient capital was a 4km-wide **island** at the confluence of the Lopburi, Pasak and Chao Phraya rivers, which was once encircled by a 12km-long wall, crumbling parts of which can be seen at the Phom Petch fortress in the southeast corner. A grid of broad roads now crosses the island, known as **Ko Muang**: the hub of the small modern town occupies its northeast corner, around the Thanon U Thong and Thanon Naresuan junction, but the rest is mostly uncongested and ideal for exploring by bicycle.

There is much pleasure to be had, also, from soaking up life on and along the encircling **rivers**, either by taking a boat tour or by dining at one of the waterside restaurants. It's very much a working waterway, busy with barges carrying cement, rice and other heavy loads to and from Bangkok and the Gulf and with cross-river ferry services that compensate for the lack of bridges. In addition, places like the Million Toy

---

VISITING AYUTTHAYA – ORIENTATION AND TEMPLE PASS

The majority of Ayutthaya's ancient remains are spread out across the western half of the island in a patchwork of parkland: **Wat Phra Mahathat** and **Wat Ratburana** stand near the modern centre, while a broad band runs down the middle of the parkland, containing the **Royal Palace** (Wang Luang) and temple, the most revered Buddha image, at **Viharn Phra Mongkol Bopit**, and the two main **museums**. To the north of the island you'll find the best-preserved temple, **Wat Na Phra Mane**, and **Wat Phu Khao Thong**, the "Golden Mount"; to the west stands the Khmer-style **Wat Chai Watthanaram**, while to the southeast lie the giant chedi of **Wat Yai Chai Mongkol** and **Wat Phanan Choeng**, still a vibrant place of worship. The city's main temples can be visited for a reduced rate when you buy the special six-in-one **pass** (B220; valid for 30 days), which is available from most temple ticket offices.

2

Suphanburi

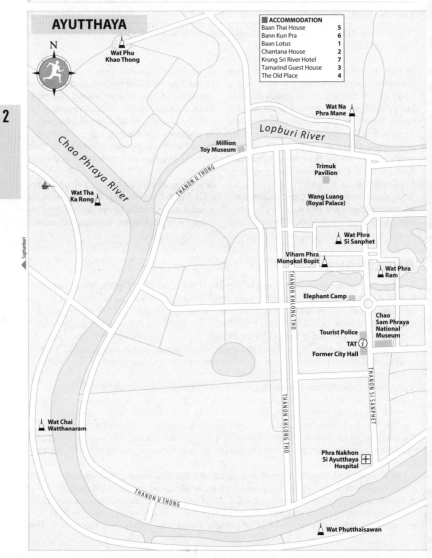

AYUTTHAYA

N

Wat Phu
Khao Thong

■ACCOMMODATION	
Baan Thai House	5
Bann Kun Pra	6
Baan Lotus	1
Chantana House	2
Krung Sri River Hotel	7
Tamarind Guest House	3
The Old Place	4

Wat Na
Phra Mane

Lopburi River

Chao Phraya River

Million
Toy Museum

THANON U THONG

Trimuk
Pavilion

Wang Luang
(Royal Palace)

Wat Tha
Ka Rong

Wat Phra
Si Sanphet

Viharn Phra
Mongkol Bopit

Wat Phra
Ram

THANON KHLONG THO

Elephant Camp

Chao
Sam Phraya
National
Museum

Tourist Police

TAT ⓘ

Former City Hall

THANON SI SANPHET

Wat Chai
Watthanaram

Phra Nakhon
Si Ayutthaya
Hospital

THANON U THONG

Wat Phutthaisawan

Museum are also worth a visit, providing a balance to the sombre mood of all the ancient culture.

Ayutthaya comes alive each year for a week in mid-December, with a **festival** that commemorates the town's listing as a **World Heritage Site** by UNESCO on December 13, 1991. The highlight is the nightly *son et lumière* show, featuring fireworks and elephant-back fights, staged around the ruins.

Brief history

Ayutthaya takes its name from the Indian city of Ayodhya (Sanskrit for "invincible"), the legendary birthplace of Rama, hero of the *Ramayana* epic. It was founded in

1351 by U Thong – later **Ramathibodi I** – after Lopburi was ravaged by smallpox, and it rose rapidly through exploiting the expanding trade routes between India and China. Stepping into the political vacuum left by the decline of the Khmer empire at Angkor and the first Thai kingdom at Sukhothai, by the mid-fifteenth century Ayutthaya controlled an empire covering most of the area of modern-day Thailand. Built entirely on canals, few of which survive today, Ayutthaya grew into an enormous amphibious city, which by 1685 had one million people – roughly double the population of London at the same time – living largely on houseboats in a 140km network of waterways.

Ayutthaya's golden age

Ayutthaya's great wealth attracted a swarm of **foreign traders**, especially in the seventeenth century. At one stage around forty different nationalities, including Chinese, Persians, Portuguese, Dutch, English and French, were settled here, many of whom lived in their own ghettos and had their own docks for the export of rice, spices, timber and hides. With deft political skill, the kings of Ayutthaya maintained their independence from outside powers, while embracing the benefits of their cosmopolitan influence: they employed foreign architects and navigators, used Japanese samurai as royal bodyguards, and even took on outsiders as their prime ministers, who could look after their foreign trade without getting embroiled in the usual court intrigues.

In decline

In 1767, this four-hundred-year-long golden age of stability and prosperity came to an abrupt end. After more than two centuries of recurring tensions, the Burmese captured and ravaged Ayutthaya, taking tens of thousands of prisoners back to Myanmar. With

AYUTTHAYA TOURS AND CRUISES

Ayutthaya is relatively spread out, so if you're pushed for time and want to make the most of its historic ruins and busy waterways, consider joining one of the **day-trips** from Bangkok. With more time, you can explore by tuk-tuk, bicycle or boat.

FROM BANGKOK

The most popular **day-trips** to Ayutthaya from Bangkok feature only the briefest whizz around the old city's two or three main temples, making a stop at the Bang Pa-In summer palace en route (see p.211) and rounding the day off with a three-hour river cruise back down the Chao Phraya from the northern Bangkok suburb of Nonthaburi; Grand Pearl Cruise is one of the main operators (ⓦgrandpearlcruise.com; B1900). You can also cruise the river in more style, spending one or more nights on plushly converted teak rice-barges such as the *Mekhala* (ⓦasian-oasis.com) or the two owned by the *Anantara Riverside Hotel* (ⓣ02 477 0770, ⓦbangkok-cruises.anantara.com).

BY TUK-TUK, BICYCLE, BOAT OR ELEPHANT

If you're pushed for time you could hire a **tuk-tuk** for a whistle-stop tour of the old city for around B200 an hour (or B500 for three hours), either from the train station or from Chao Phrom market. **Sunset tuk-tuk tours** organized by guesthouses (about 2hr; B300/vehicle) are also popular, taking in some of the illuminated ruins (the five main ruins are lit nightly 7–9pm) and ending at the night market, or there are the guided **bicycle tours** run by Ayutthaya Boat & Travel (ⓣ081 733 5687, ⓦayutthaya-boat.com), whose itineraries include the ruins by day or night, a combination cycle and boat tour and a dinner cruise. For a serious **guided tour** of the ruins, local expert Professor Monton at Classic Tour (ⓣ081 832 4849; about B2000/person/day, depending on group size) comes highly recommended.

Circumnavigating Ayutthaya by boat is a very enjoyable way to take in some of the outlying temples, and possibly a few lesser-visited ones too; many of the temples were designed to be approached and admired from the river, and you also get a leisurely look at twenty-first-century riverine residences. All guesthouses and agencies offer **boat tours**, typically charging B200–300 per person for a two-hour trip; boats can also be chartered from the pier outside the Chantharakasem Palace museum.

It's also possible to take a brief **elephant ride** (B400/person for 20min, B500 for 30min) past a couple of the central ruins from the roadside elephant "camp" on Thanon Pathon. The elephants and their mahouts are photogenically clad in period costume and you can buy the elephants bananas while they wait for custom, or simply watch them return home after 6pm when they rumble across to the northeast side of town to bathe and bed down in the restored sixteenth-century kraal. Wild elephants were formerly driven to the kraal for capture and taming, but these days it's the headquarters of Elephantstay (ⓦelephantstay.com), an organization that runs three- to fourteen-day residential packages for visitors who want to ride, feed, water and bathe the ninety resident elephants.

even the wats in ruins, the city had to be abandoned to the jungle, but its memory endured: the architects of the new capital on Ratanakosin island in Bangkok perpetuated Ayutthaya's layout in every possible way.

On the island

Most of Ayutthaya's main sights, as well as most accommodation and restaurants, are located on the island, so it makes sense to begin your exploration here, then branch out to sights off the island if you have time.

Wat Phra Mahathat

1km west of the new town centre along Thanon Naresuan • Daily 8am–6pm • B50, or included with the B220 six-in-one pass

Heading west out of the new town centre brings you to the first set of ruins – a pair of temples on opposite sides of the road. The overgrown **Wat Phra Mahathat**, on the left, is the epitome of Ayutthaya's nostalgic atmosphere of faded majesty. The name "Mahathat" (Great Relic Chedi) indicates that the temple was built to house remains of the Buddha himself: according to the royal chronicles – never renowned for historical accuracy – King Ramesuan (1388–95) was looking out of his palace one morning when ashes of the Buddha materialized out of thin air here. A gold casket containing the ashes was duly enshrined in a grand 38m-high prang. The prang later collapsed, but the reliquary was unearthed in the 1950s, along with a hoard of other treasures, including a gorgeous marble fish, which opened to reveal gold, amber, crystal and porcelain ornaments – all now on show in the Chao Sam Phraya National Museum (see p.218).

You can climb what remains of the prang to get a good view of the broad, grassy complex, with dozens of brick spires tilting at impossible angles and headless Buddhas scattered around like spare parts in a scrapyard; look out for the serene (and much photographed) head of a stone Buddha that has become nestled in the embrace of a bodhi tree's roots.

Wat Ratburana

Across the road from Wat Phra Mahathat • Daily 8am–6pm • B50, or included with the B220 six-in-one pass

The towering **Wat Ratburana** was built in 1424 by King Boromraja II to commemorate his elder brothers, Ay and Yi, who managed to kill each other in an elephant-back duel over the succession to the throne, thus leaving it vacant for Boromraja. Here, four elegant Sri Lankan-style chedis lean outwards as if in deference to the main prang, on which some of the original stuccowork can still be seen, some of which has been restored, including fine statues of garudas swooping down on nagas. It's possible to descend steep steps inside the prang to the crypt, where on two levels you can make out fragmentary murals of the early Ayutthaya period.

Wat Phra Ram

West of Wat Phra Mahathat • Daily 8am–6pm • B50, or included with the B220 six-in-one pass

West of Wat Phra Mahathat you'll see a lake, now surrounded by a popular park, and the slender prang of **Wat Phra Ram**, built in the late fourteenth century on the site of Ramathibodi's cremation by his son and successor as king, Ramesuan. Sadly, not much of the prang's original stuccowork remains, but you can still get an idea of how spectacular it would have looked when the city was at its zenith.

Wat Phra Si Sanphet and the Wang Luang (Royal Palace)

Both sites lie to the northwest of Thanon Si Sanphet from Wat Phra Ram • Both daily 7am–6pm • B50, or included with the B220 six-in-one pass

Wat Phra Si Sanphet was built in 1448 by King Boromatrailokanat as a private chapel, and was formerly the grandest of Ayutthaya's temples. Even now, it's one of the best preserved.

The wat took its name from one of the largest standing metal images of the Buddha ever known, the **Phra Si Sanphet**, erected here in 1503. Towering 16m high and covered in 173kg of gold, it did not survive the ravages of the Burmese, though Rama I rescued the pieces and placed them inside a chedi at Wat Pho in Bangkok. The three remaining grey chedis in the characteristic style of the old capital were built to house the ashes of three kings, and have now become the most familiar image of Ayutthaya.

The site of this royal wat was originally occupied by Ramathibodi I's wooden palace, which Boromatrailokanat replaced with the bigger **Wang Luang** (Royal Palace; same hours and ticket as Wat Phra Si Sanphet), stretching to the Lopburi River on the north side. Successive kings turned the Wang Luang into a vast complex of pavilions and halls, with an elaborate system of walls designed to isolate the inner sanctum for the king and his consorts. The palace was destroyed by the Burmese in 1767 and plundered by Rama I for its bricks, which he needed to build the new capital at Bangkok. Now you can only trace the outlines of a few walls in the grass and inspect an unimpressive wooden replica of an open pavilion – better to consult the model of the whole complex in the Historical Study Centre (see below).

Viharn Phra Mongkol Bopit

On the south side of Wat Phra Si Sanphet • Daily 8am–5pm • Free

Viharn Phra Mongkol Bopit attracts tourists and Thai pilgrims in about equal measure. The pristine hall – a replica of a typical Ayutthayan viharn, with its characteristic chunky lotus-capped columns around the outside – was built in 1956, with help from the Burmese to atone for their flattening of the city two centuries earlier, in order to shelter the revered **Phra Mongkol Bopit**, which, at 12.45m high (excluding the base), is one of the largest bronze Buddhas in Thailand. The powerfully austere image, with its flashing mother-of-pearl eyes, was cast in the fifteenth century, then sat exposed to the elements from the time of the Burmese invasion until its new home was built. During restoration, the hollow image was found to contain hundreds of Buddha statuettes, some of which were later buried around the shrine to protect it.

The Million Toy Museum

In the northwest corner of the island, just west of the Royal Palace and the westernmost bridge over the Lopburi River • Tues–Sun 9am–4pm • B50 • ⓦ milliontoymuseum.com

After a few hours gazing at the ruins of ancient temples, it comes as a welcome relief to enter the quirky, private **Million Toy Museum**, where cabinets on two floors are packed not only with toys, but also with odd items like Queen Elizabeth II coronation mugs from 1953. Kids love it, and even adults will recognize a few favourites from childhood, such as Superman, Minnie Mouse, Donald Duck and Goofy. There's a café out front that is also full of toy characters, and seats in a shady garden where you can rest your legs.

Chao Sam Phraya National Museum

10min walk south of Viharn Phra Mongkol Bopit • Wed–Sun 8.30am–4pm, last admission 3.30pm • B150

The largest of the town's three museums is the **Chao Sam Phraya National Museum**, where most of the moveable remains of Ayutthaya's glory – those that weren't plundered by treasure-hunters or taken to the National Museum in Bangkok – are exhibited. Apart from numerous Buddhas and some fine woodcarving, the museum is bursting with **gold treasures**, including the original relic casket from Wat Mahathat, betel-nut sets and model chedis, and a gem-encrusted fifteenth-century crouching elephant found in the crypt at Wat Ratburana.

Historical Study Centre

Thanon Rotchana, a 5min walk from Chao Sam Phraya National Museum • Daily 8.30am–4.30pm • B100

It's worth paying a visit to the **Historical Study Centre**, if only to check out its scale model of the Royal Palace before you set off to wander around the real thing. The visitors' exhibition upstairs puts Ayutthaya's ruins in context, dramatically presenting a broad social history of the city through videos, sound effects and reconstructions of temple murals. Other exhibits include model ships and a peasant's wooden house.

Chantharakasem Palace Museum

In the northeast corner of the island • Wed–Sun 8.30am–4pm • B100

The **Chantharakasem Palace** was traditionally the home of the heir to the Ayutthayan throne. The Black Prince, Naresuan, built the first *wang na* (palace of the front) here in about 1577 so that he could guard the area of the city wall that was most vulnerable to enemy attack. Rama IV (1851–68) had the palace restored and it now houses a **museum** displaying many of his possessions, including a throne platform overhung by a white *chat*, a ceremonial nine-tiered parasol that is a vital part of a king's insignia. The rest of the museum features beautiful ceramics and Buddha images, and a small arsenal of cannon and musketry.

Off the island

It's easy enough to visit places off the island via various bridges across the river, especially if you're travelling around on a bike. If you're pushed for time, the two main sights are Wat Chai Watthanaram to the west, and Wat Yai Chai Mongkol to the southeast of the island.

Wat Na Phra Mane

On the north bank of the Lopburi River, opposite the Wang Luang • Daily 8.30am–5pm • B20

Wat Na Phra Meru is in some respects Ayutthaya's most rewarding temple, being the only one from the town's golden age that survived Burmese attacks, though frequent refurbishments make it appear quite new.

The main **bot**, built in 1503, shows the distinctive features of Ayutthayan architecture – outside columns topped with lotus cups, and slits in the walls instead of windows to let the air circulate. Inside, underneath a rich red-and-gold coffered ceiling that represents the stars around the moon, sits a powerful 6m-high Buddha in the disdainful, over-decorated royal style characteristic of the later Ayutthaya period.

In sharp contrast is the dark-green **Phra Khan Thavaraj** Buddha, which dominates the tiny viharn behind to the right. Seated in the "European position", with its robe delicately pleated and its feet up on a large lotus leaf, the gentle figure conveys a reassuring serenity. It's advertised as being from Sri Lanka, the source of Thai Buddhism, but more likely is a seventh- to ninth-century Mon image from Wat Phra Mane at Nakhon Pathom.

Wat Phu Khao Thong

2km northwest of Wat Na Phra Mane • Daily dawn–dusk • Free

Head northwest of Wat Na Phra Mane and you're in open country, where the 50m-high chedi of **Wat Phu Khao Thong** rises steeply out of the fields. In 1569, after a temporary occupation of Ayutthaya, the Burmese erected a Mon-style chedi here to commemorate their victory. Forbidden by Buddhist law from pulling down a sacred monument, the Thais had to put up with this galling reminder of the enemy's success until it collapsed nearly two hundred years later, when King Borommakot promptly built a truly Ayutthayan chedi on the old Burmese base – just in time for the Burmese to return in 1767 and flatten the town. This "Golden Mount" has recently been restored, with a colossal equestrian statue of King Naresuan, conqueror of the Burmese, to keep it company. You can climb 25m of steps up the side of the chedi to look out over the countryside and the town, with glimpses of Wat Phra Si Sanphet and Viharn Phra Mongkok Bopit in the distance.

Wat Tha Ka Rong

Opposite the northwest corner of the island, near the confluence of the Chao Phraya and Lopburi rivers • Daily dawn–dusk • Free

This modern temple is wild – think Buddha goes to Disneyland. Highlights include a room full of enormous statues of famous monks, motion-activated skeletons, robots and other mannequins that *wai* as you pass and ask for a donation, and the plushest bathrooms you'll see in town. There's also a floating market on the riverside selling souvenirs, and an interesting display of Buddha images from neighbouring countries.

Wat Chai Watthanaram

Across the river, southwest of the island • Daily 8am–6pm • B50, or included with the B220 six-in-one pass

It's worth the bike or boat ride to reach the elegant brick-and-stucco latticework of Khmer-style stupas at **Wat Chai Watthanaram**. Late afternoon is a popular time to visit, as the sun sinks photogenically behind the main tower.

King Prasat Thong built Wat Chai Watthanaram in 1630, possibly to commemorate a victory over Cambodia, designing it as a sort of Angkorian homage, around a towering central Khmer corncob **prang** encircled by a constellation of four minor prangs and eight tiered and tapered chedis. Most of the stucco facing has weathered away to reveal the red-brick innards in pretty contrast, but a few tantalizing fragments of stucco relief remain on the outside of the chedis, depicting episodes from the Buddha's life. Around the gallery that connects them sits a solemn phalanx of 120 headless seated Buddhas, each on its own red-brick dais but showing no trace of their original skins, which may have been done in black lacquer and gold-leaf. To the east a couple of larger seated Buddhas look out across the river from the foundations of the old bot.

Wat Yai Chai Mongkol

Southeast of the island, about 2km from the station • Daily 8am–5pm • B20 • If cycling here, avoid the multi-laned Pridi Damrong/Naresuan Bridge and Bangkok road by taking the river ferry across to the train station and then heading south 1.5km before turning east to the temple

Across the Pasak River southeast of the island, you pass through Ayutthaya's new business zone and some rustic suburbia before reaching the ancient but still functioning **Wat Yai Chai Mongkol**. Surrounded by formal lawns, flowerbeds and much-photographed saffron-draped Buddhas, the wat was established by Ramathibodi I in 1357 as a meditation site for monks returning from study in Sri Lanka. King Naresuan put up the beautifully curvaceous **chedi** to mark the decisive victory over the Burmese at Suphanburi in 1593, when he himself had sent the enemy packing by slaying the Burmese crown prince in an elephant-back duel. Built on a colossal scale to outshine the Burmese Golden Mount on the opposite side of Ayutthaya, the chedi has come to symbolize the prowess and devotion of Naresuan and, by implication, his descendants right down to the present king. By the entrance, the **reclining Buddha** was also constructed by Naresuan. A huge modern glass-walled shrine to the revered king dominates the back of the temple compound.

Wat Phanan Choeng

Near the confluence of the Chao Phraya and Pasak rivers, to the west of Wat Yai Chai Mongkol • Daily 8am–5pm • B20

In Ayutthaya's most prosperous period, the docks and main trading area were located near the confluence of the Chao Phraya and Pasak rivers, to the west of Wat Yai Chai Mongkol. This is where you'll find the oldest and liveliest working temple in town, **Wat Phanan Choeng**. The main viharn is often filled with the sights, sounds and smells of an incredible variety of merit-making activities, as devotees burn huge pink Chinese incense candles, offer food and rattle fortune sticks. It's even possible to buy tiny golden statues of the Buddha to be placed in one of the hundreds of niches that line the walls, a form of votive offering peculiar to this temple. If you can get here during a festival, especially Chinese New Year, you're in for an overpowering experience.

CLOCKWISE FROM TOP LEFT WAT PHU KHAO THONG, AYUTTHAYA (P.219); WAT YAI CHAI MONGKOL, AYUTTHAYA; AISAWAN THIPHYA-ART, BANG PA-IN (P.211) >

The 19m-high Buddha, which almost fills the hall, has survived since 1324, shortly before the founding of the capital, and tears are said to have flowed from its eyes when Ayutthaya was sacked by the Burmese. However, the reason for the temple's popularity with the Chinese is to be found in the early eighteenth-century shrine by the pier, with its image of a beautiful Chinese princess who drowned herself here because of a king's infidelity: his remorse led him to build the shrine at the place where she had walked into the river.

Baan Hollanda

Just south of Wat Phanan Choeng • Wed–Sun 9am–5pm • B50 • ⓦ baanhollanda.org

During Ayutthaya's heyday in the sixteenth and seventeeth centuries, foreign merchants were attracted here to trade with the Siamese, and were permitted to set up trading posts on either side of the Chao Phraya River to the southeast of the island. Three settlements have now been turned into museums recounting foreign relations with Siam, and of these, **Baan Hollanda** (the Dutch settlement) is the most interesting (the others are those of the Japanese and Portuguese). Established in 2013 in order to inform visitors about the history of the Dutch in Siam, the exhibition covers Siamese–Dutch relations from the first arrival of the Dutch East India Company in 1604. The Dutch bought rice, tin, deerskins and wood from Siam and in return sold Japanese silver and Indian printed textiles to the Siamese. The centre also demonstrates how the Dutch have mastered the art of flood protection in their own country so that a large percentage of its population lives below sea level without fear, and there's an opportunity for visitors to pick up a pair of ceramic clogs or a windmill at the museum shop.

ARRIVAL AND DEPARTURE   AYUTTHAYA

BY TRAIN

The best way of getting to Ayutthaya from Bangkok is by train (with departures mostly in the early morning and evening); trains continue on to Nong Khai and Ubon Ratchathani in the northeast, and to the north and Chiang Mai. The station is on the east bank of the Pasak; to get to the centre of town, take a ferry from the jetty 100m west of the station (last ferry around 8pm; B5) across and upriver to Chao Phrom pier; it's then a 5min walk to the junction of Thanon U Thong and Thanon Naresuan, near most guest-houses (if you're going to stay at *Bann Kun Pra*, however, take the ferry from the neighbouring jetty, which runs directly across the river and back). The station has a useful left-luggage service (24hr; B30 per piece per day).

Destinations Bangkok Hualamphong (around 35 daily; 1hr 30min–2hr); Chiang Mai (6 daily; 10hr 45min–13hr 10min); Lopburi (18 daily; 45min–1hr 30min); Nong Khai (5 daily; 9hr 30min); Phitsanulok (12 daily; 3hr 30min–6hr 20min); Ubon Ratchathani (7 daily; 7hr 20min–10hr 30min).

BY BUS OR MINIBUS

From/to Bangkok Frequent buses to Ayutthaya depart Bangkok's Northern Mo Chit terminal. Most pull in at the bus stop on Thanon Naresuan, near the main accommodation area, though some long-distance services only stop at Ayutthaya's bus terminal, 5km to the east of the centre on Highway 1, from where you'll need a tuk-tuk to get into

town (B150–200). Private a/c minibuses from Bangkok's Victory Monument and Southern Bus Terminal finish their routes opposite the Thanon Naresuan bus stop (both about every 20min during daylight hours). Services in the opposite direction, returning to Bangkok, leave from all the above-mentioned drop-off points. There are also tourist minibuses that connect Ayutthaya with Suvarnabhumi Airport and Thanon Khao San.

From/to Kanchanaburi Travelling from Kanchanaburi, it's possible to bypass the Bangkok gridlock, either by hooking up with an a/c tourist minibus (daily; 3hr) arranged through guesthouses in Kanchanaburi or, under your own steam, by taking a public bus to Suphanburi (every 20min; 1hr 30min), then changing to an Ayutthaya bus, which will drop you off on Thanon Naresuan. To travel from Ayutthaya to Kanchanaburi, the easiest option is to book a seat on a minibus through one of the guesthouses.

Other services Fast but cramped tourist minibuses serve Sukhothai, and there are also connecting minibuses for Ko Samet and Ko Chang, an overnight bus service to Chiang Mai and another to Siem Reap in Cambodia. These depart from the bus terminal to the east of the city centre.

Destinations Bangkok (every 20min; 1hr 30min–2hr); Chiang Mai (12 daily; 9hr); Chiang Rai (10 daily; 12hr); Kamphaeng Phet (6 daily; 5hr); Lampang (12 daily; 8hr); Lamphun (12 daily; 9hr); Lopburi (every 20min; 2hr); Phitsanulok (10 daily; 5hr); Sukhothai (12 daily; 4hr 30min–6hr); Suphanburi (every 30min; 1hr); Tak (6 daily; 6hr).

AYUTTHAYA EXHIBITIONS

While visiting the branch of the Tourist Information Centre on the site of the former city hall, it's well worth heading upstairs to the smartly presented multi-media **exhibition** on Ayutthaya (daily 8.30am–4.30pm; free), which provides an engaging introduction to the city's history, an overview of all the sights, including a scale-model reconstruction of Wat Phra Si Sanphet, and insights into local traditional ways of life. Also on this floor, there's the **Ayutthaya National Art Museum** (Mon, Tues & Thurs–Sun 8.30am–4.30pm; free), which has depictions of animals, people and landscapes by Thai artists including a drawing in black ink by former Prime Minister Chuan Leekpai.

2

GETTING AROUND

Busloads of tourists descend on Ayutthaya's sights during the day, but the area covered by the old capital is large enough not to feel swamped. Distances are deceptive, so it's not a good idea to walk everywhere.

By bicycle or motorbike Bicycles can be rented at guesthouses, around the train station and from the tourist police. Watch out, though, as some places try to charge up to B100 per day – double the usual rate. Some guest-houses and a few cheaper outlets in front of the station rent small motorbikes.

By tuk-tuk Tuk-tuks are easy enough to flag down on the street. Their set routes for sharing passengers are more useful for locals than for tourists, but a typical journey in town on your own should only cost B50. If you want to hire a tuk-tuk for the day, it's best to head for the ferry landing at Chao Phrom Pier or the area around Naresuan Soi 2 (see below).

By motorbike taxi Motorbikes charge around B40 for medium-range journeys.

INFORMATION

Tourist information TAT's helpful Ayutthaya Tourist Information Centre (daily 8.30am–4.30pm; ☏ 035 246076, ✉ tatyutya@tat.or.th) is split between a room on the ground floor of the former city hall (on the west side of the street, opposite the Chao Sam Phraya National Museum), and an ornate wooden building a short walk further north on the same stretch of road.

ACCOMMODATION

Ayutthaya offers a good choice of accommodation, including a small ghetto of **budget guesthouses** on and around the soi that runs north from Chao Phrom market to Thanon Pamaphrao; it's sometimes known as Soi Farang but is actually signed as Naresuan Soi 2 at the southern end and Pamaphrao Soi 5 at the northern.

Baan Lotus 20 Thanon Pamaphrao ☏ 035 251988. Two large wooden buildings set in a huge overgrown compound with a pond and pavilion for relaxing out back. One building consists of fan rooms and the other with a/c; rooms are a good size but sparsely furnished. It's a wonderfully restful location just a few steps from the restaurants and bars on Soi Farang. Fan B450, a/c B600

Baan Thai House 199 Moo 4, Sri Krung Villa, 600m east of the train station ☏ 035 245555, ⓦ baanthai house.com. Twelve immaculate a/c villas with sloping pitched roofs, set around manicured tropical gardens and a huge artificial pond with its own wooden water wheel and rowing boats (free for guests to use). Rooms have flatscreen TVs, wooden floors and delicately carved furnishings, plus classy outdoor showers. Perks include personal service, a spa, an outdoor pool and an excellent restaurant. B2400

Bann Kun Pra 48/2 Thanon U Thong, just north of Pridi Damrong Bridge ☏ 035 241978, ⓦ bannkunpra.com. The best rooms in the rambling, hundred-year-old teak house here have shared bathrooms and gorgeous river-view balconies. There are also two newer and slightly noisier blocks near the road, where you can choose between cheap, single-sex dorm rooms with individual lockable tin trunks, or newly renovated en-suite doubles with a/c, attractive wooden floors and private terraces overlooking the waterway. They also offer river tours and a warm welcome. Dorms B250, fan doubles B600, a/c doubles B1100

Chantana House 12/22 Naresuan Soi 2 ☏ 035 323200, ✉ chantanahouse@yahoo.com. At the quieter end of the travellers' soi, this low-key guesthouse has simple, boxy but spotlessly clean en-suite fan and a/c rooms, though not all have outward-facing windows. Kind, friendly staff, but not much English spoken. Fan B400, a/c B600

Krung Sri River 27/2, Thanon Rojana ☏ 035 244333, ⓦ krungsririver.com. Ayutthaya's most prominent central hotel occupies nine storeys in a prime if noisy position beside the Pridi Damrong Bridge, with some standard rooms and all suites enjoying river views. Furnishings aren't exactly chic, but there's a/c and TVs throughout, an attractive third-floor pool and a car park. B2100

The Old Place Guest House 102 Thanon U Thong, just south of the Chao Phrom Pier ☎ 035 211161. Plain fan and a/c rooms with stark white walls and en-suite bathrooms, in a good location near the pier and markets. Fan B350, a/c B500

★ **Tamarind Guest House** On a lane off Thanon Chikul

in front of the entrance to Wat Mahathat ☎ 081 6557937. Tucked away from the main road, this quirky guesthouse has bags of character and its seven rooms are all different in design, though all have attractive wooden floors and bright colour schemes. There's a great, multi-level family room and the owner can help with sightseeing plans. Free coffee, tea and cookies. B646

EATING AND DRINKING

Other than the restaurants listed below, the *roti* (Muslim pancake) stalls near the hospital around the southern end of Thanon Si Sanphet are good for daytime snacks and after dark there are a couple of **night markets**. There's an excellent one with a wide range of food beside the river at Hua Raw, about ten minutes' walk north of Naresuan Soi 2, and another at the west end of Thanon Bang Laen, 150m south of Wat Phra Mahathat. Competing singers at the clutch of **bar-restaurants** can make Soi Farang a bit of a battle of the bands after 9pm but it's fun and lively, and free with your beer.

Bann Kun Pra Thanon U Thong, just north of Pridi Damrong Bridge ☎ 035 241978, ⓦ bannkunpra.com. The riverside dining terrace here is just as atmospheric as the lovely guesthouse upstairs, and enjoys fine views. It specializes in reasonably priced fish and seafood, notably prawns, and the red curry with beef and jackfruit (B140) is good too. Most mains around B150. Daily 7am–10.30pm.

Kankitti 7/1 Moo 2, Thanon U Thong, on the south side of town ☎ 035 241971. Congenial spot where, on a river-bank terrace or a moored boat with views of Wat Phutthaisawan's white prang, you can dine on Ayutthaya's most famous delicacy, river prawns (around B1600 per kilo), or on less expensive but nevertheless very tasty dishes such as green curry with fishballs (B120). Daily 9am–9.30pm.

★ **Saithong** 45 Moo 1 Thanon U Thong ☎ 035 241449. On the south side of the island, just east of Kankitti, this place has an attractive riverside terrace and a cosy a/c

room, and its seafood is especially popular among Thais, so it's often full on weekend evenings. Try the seabass with spicy lemon sauce (B150) or the *yum Saithong* – a spicy salad with shrimp, chicken, squid and ham (B150). Live music from 6pm each evening. Daily 10am–10pm

Street Lamp Bar Naresuan Soi 2. One of the most popular bars on the street, with regular live music, ranging from country to rock and blues, and cheap, ice-cold beer. Simple dishes like fried rice from B55. Daily 7am–midnight.

Tony's Place 12/18 Naresuan Soi 2 ☎ 035 252578, ⓦ tonyplace-ayutthaya.com. The size of this cavernous timbered restaurant on the ground floor of the guesthouse, plus its cushioned chill-out areas and blasting music, makes this a popular travellers' meeting place; the typical food (most dishes B80–120) and beer are cheap enough but nothing special, and staff are rather disinterested. Daily 7am–midnight.

DIRECTORY

Banks and ATMs There are plenty of banks with exchange services and ATMs around the junction of Thanon Naresuan and Naresuan Soi 2.

Hospital The government Phra Nakhon Si Ayutthaya

hospital is at the southern end of Thanon Si Sanphet (☎ 035 241888).

Tourist police Based just to the north of the TAT office on Thanon Si Sanphet (☎ 035 242352 or ☎ 1155).

Lopburi and around

Mention the name **LOPBURI** to a Thai and the chances are that he or she will start telling you about monkeys – the central junction in the old town of this unexceptional provincial capital, 150km due north of Bangkok, swarms with **macaques**. So beneficial are the beasts to the town's tourist trade that a local hotelier treats six hundred of them to a sit-down meal at Phra Prang Sam Yod temple every November, complete with menus, waiters and napkins, as a thank you for their help. In fact, the monkeys can be a real nuisance, so make sure to close your windows at night and take care with bags while out and about.

The town's central **Khmer buildings** give a good idea of the architecture of the Ayutthaya period, though the number of monuments is far fewer than in Ayutthaya itself. However, all sites are within walking distance of each other, so Lopburi makes a good scaled-down

LOPBURI

*Map labels:*
THANON PRANG SAM YOD
Ban Vichayen
Phra Prang Sam Yod
San Phra Karn
THANON VICHAYEN
Prang Khaek
Minivans to Bangkok
THANON NARAI MAHARAT
Lopburi River
RUE DE FRANCE
Wat Sao Thong Thong
Tesco Lotus
THANON NA PHRA KARN
THANON RATCHADAMNERN
Night Market
Phayakkha Gate
THANON PHRAYA KAMCHAT
SOI 1
SOI 2
Police Station
THANON PHRA RAM
Phra Narai Ratchanivet & Narai National Museum
Minivans to Bangkok
THANON NA PHRA THAT
Wat Choeng Tha
THANON PHETRACHA
THANON SORASAK
Wat Phra Si Ratana Mahathat
Train Station
THANON BAN PRATU CHAI
THANON KANCHANAKHOM
THANON BAN PRATU CHAI
N
0   250   metres

TAT Office, Bus Terminal (1.5km), Phra Phutthabat & Bangkok

alternative if you'd like to avoid the crowds of Ayutthaya. Particularly interesting are the **Somdet Phra Narai National Museum**, housed in a partly reconstructed seventeenth-century palace complex, and **Ban Vichayen**, once home to the Greek adventurer Constantine Phaulkon. Lopburi's main festival is the five-day **King Narai Reign Fair** in February, which commemorates the seventeenth-century king's birthday with costumed processions, cultural performances, traditional markets and a *son et lumière* show at Phra Narai Ratchanivet.

The old centre of Lopburi sits on an egg-shaped island between canals and the Lopburi River, with the railway line running across it from north to south. **Thanon Vichayen**, the main street, crosses the rail tracks at the town's busiest junction before heading east – now called Thanon Narai Maharat – through the newest areas of development, via Sakeo roundabout and the bus station, towards Highway 1. Most of the town's accommodation and restaurants are set within the quiet, partly residential core between Phra Narai Ratchanivet to the west and Thanon Na Phra Karn to the east.

Brief history

Originally called Lavo, Lopburi is one of the longest-inhabited towns in Thailand, and was a major centre of the Mon (Dvaravati) civilization from around the sixth century. It maintained a tenuous independence in the face of the advancing Khmers until as late as the early eleventh century, when it was incorporated into the empire as the provincial capital for much of central Thailand. Increasing Thai migration from the north soon tilted the balance against the Khmers, and Lopburi was again independent from some time early in the thirteenth century until the rise of Ayutthaya in the middle of the fourteenth. Thereafter, Lopburi was twice used as a second capital, first by King Narai of Ayutthaya in the seventeenth century, then by Rama IV of Bangkok in the nineteenth, because its remoteness from the sea made it less vulnerable to European expansionists. Rama V downgraded the town, turning the royal palace into a provincial government office and museum; Lopburi's modern role is as the site of several huge army barracks.

Wat Phra Si Ratana Mahathat

Just south of Thanon Na Phra That • Daily 8.30am–4.30pm • B50

The impressive centrepiece of the sprawled grassy ruins of **Wat Phra Si Ratana Mahathat** is a laterite prang in the Khmer style of the twelfth century, decorated with finely detailed stuccowork and surrounded by a ruined cloister. Arrayed in loose formation around this central feature are several more rocket-like Khmer prangs and a number of graceful chedis in the Ayutthayan style, among them one with a bulbous peak and faded bas-reliefs of Buddhist saints. King Narai added to the mishmash of styles by building a "Gothic" viharn on the eastern side of the main prang, now roofless, which is home to a lonely, headless stone Buddha, often draped in photogenic saffron.

Phra Narai Ratchanivet (King Narai's palace)

Sandwiched between Thanon Ratchadamnern and Thanon Phetracha; main entrance on Thanon Sorasak • Wed–Sun 8am–5pm • B150 • Museum Wed–Sun 9am–4pm

The imposing gates and high crenellated walls of the **Phra Narai Ratchanivet** make it easy to imagine how visitors from afar would have been in awe of the palace in its seventeenth-century heyday. The extensive grounds are a pleasant place to stroll, and the informative museum in the centre of the complex is a good place to begin a tour of Lopburi. King Narai, with the help of French architects, built the heavily fortified palace in 1666 as a precaution against any possible confrontation with the Western powers, and for the rest of his reign he was to spend eight months of every year here, entertaining foreign envoys and indulging his love of hunting. After Narai's death, Lopburi was left forgotten until 1856, when Rama IV – worried about British and French colonialism – decided to make this his second capital and lavishly restored the central buildings of Narai's palace.

Phayakkha Gate

The main entrance to the palace complex is through the **Phayakkha Gate** on Thanon Sorasak. You'll see the unusual lancet shape of this arch again and again in the seventeenth-century doors and windows of Lopburi – just one aspect of the Western influences embraced by Narai. Around the **outer courtyard**, which occupies the eastern half of the complex, stand the walls of various gutted buildings – twelve warehouses for Narai's treasures, stables for the royal hunting elephants and a moated reception hall for foreign envoys. With their lily ponds and manicured lawns, these well-shaded grounds are ideal for a picnic or a siesta.

Somdet Phra Narai National Museum

Straight ahead from the Phayakkha Gate another arch leads into the **central courtyard**, where the three buildings of the museum are located. The typically Ayutthayan **Chanthara Phisan Throne Hall** contains a fascinating exhibition on Narai's reign – check out the pointed white cap typical of those worn by noblemen of the time, which increased their height by no less than 50cm. The colonial-style **Phiman Mongkut Pavilion** houses exhibits that show the development of Lopburi from prehistory to the present, spread across three floors. On the first floor are artefacts unearthed in excavations around town, mostly dating to the Dvaravati era. On the second floor are objects of Khmer art, as well as objects from the Ayutthaya and Rattanakosin era, while the top floor is dedicated to **King Mongkut**, filled with his furniture and assorted memorabilia of his reign, including his very short and uncomfortable-looking bed and eerie painted statues of his equally vertically challenged near-contemporaries, Napoleon and Queen Victoria. The final building is the **Phra Pratiep Building**, which contains examples of local arts and crafts and gives a taste of local culture.

Dusit Sawan Hall

On the south side of the museum lies the shell of the **Dusit Sawan Hall**, where foreign dignitaries came to present their credentials to King Narai. Inside you can still see the niche, raised 3.5m above the main floor, where the throne was set; beneath the niche, a modern plaque showing Narai receiving the French envoy, the Chevalier de Chaumont, in 1685 is revered as an icon of the king, with offerings of gold leaf, joss sticks and garlands. The whole building is divided in two around the throne: the front half has "foreign" doors and windows with pointed arches; the rear part, from where the king would have made his grand entrance, has traditional Thai openings. The hall used to be lined with French mirrors in imitation of Versailles, with Persian carpets and a pyramidal roof of golden glazed tiles rounding off the most majestic building in the palace.

Wat Sao Thong Thong

Rue de France

Halfway along Rue de France is a building whose plain terracotta roof tiles and whitewashed exterior give it a strangely Mediterranean look. This is in fact the viharn of **Wat Sao Thong Thong**, and is typical of Narai's time in its combination of Thai-style tiered roof with "Gothic" pointed windows. Erected as either a Christian chapel or a mosque for the Persian ambassador's residence, it was later used as a Buddhist viharn and has now been tastefully restored, complete with brass door-knockers and plush red carpet. Inside there's an austere Buddha image of the Ayutthaya period and, in the lamp niches, some fine Lopburi-style Buddhas.

Ban Vichayen

Thanon Vichayen • Daily 8.30am–4.30pm • B50

The complex of **Ban Vichayen** was originally built by Narai as a residence for foreign ambassadors, with a Christian chapel incongruously stuccoed with Buddhist flame and lotus-leaf motifs. Though now just a nest of empty shells, it still conjures up the atmosphere of court intrigue and dark deeds which, towards the end of Narai's reign, centred on the colourful figure of its most famous resident, **Constantine Phaulkon**, a Greek adventurer who came to Ayutthaya with the English East India Company in 1678. He entered the royal service as interpreter and accountant, rapidly rising to the position of prime minister. It was chiefly due to his influence that Narai established close ties with Louis XIV of France, a move that made commercial sense but also formed part of Phaulkon's secret plan to turn Narai and his people to Christianity, with the aid of the French. (It was around this time that the word for Westerner, *farang*, entered the Thai language, from the same derivation as *français*, which the Thais render *farangset*.) In 1688, a struggle for succession broke out, and leading officials persuaded the dying Narai to appoint as regent his foster brother, Phetracha, a great rival of Phaulkon's. Phetracha promptly executed Phaulkon on charges of treason, and took the throne himself when Narai died. Under Phetracha, Narai's open-door policy towards foreigners was brought to a screeching halt and the Thai kingdom returned to traditional, smaller-scale dealings with the outside world.

Prang Khaek

The junction of Thanon Vichayen and Thanon Sorasak is marked by an unusual traffic island on which perch the three stubby red-brick towers of **Prang Khaek**, a well-preserved Hindu shrine, possibly to the god Shiva, dating from as early as the eighth century. The three towers, which face east and are aligned in a row, have been restored on several occasions – most notably in the seventeenth century under the auspices of King Narai.

Phra Prang Sam Yod and San Phra Karn

On the corner of Thanon Prang Sam Yod and Thanon Vichayen • Daily 6am–6pm • B50

Like nearby Prang Khaek, **Phra Prang Sam Yod**, at the top of Thanon Na Phra Karn, seems to have originally been a Hindu temple, later converted to Buddhism under the Khmers. The three chunky prangs, made of dark laterite with some restored stuccowork, and symbolizing the Hindu triumvirate of Brahma, Vishnu and Shiva, are Lopburi's most photographed sight, though they'll only detain you for a minute or two – while you're here, check out some carved figures of seated hermits at the base of the door columns.

The shrine's grassy knoll is a good spot for **monkey-watching** – monkeys run amok all over this area, so keep an eye on your bags and pockets. Across the railway line at the modern red-and-gold shrine of **San Phra Karn**, there's even a monkey's adventure playground for the benefit of tourists, beside the base of what must have been a huge Khmer prang.

Wat Phra Phutthabat (Temple of the Buddha's Footprint)

17km southeast of Lopburi, off Highway 1 • Any of the frequent buses to Saraburi or Bangkok from Lopburi's Sakeo roundabout will get you there (30min)

The most important pilgrimage site in central Thailand, **Wat Phra Phutthabat** is believed to house a footprint made by the Buddha.

The **legend** of Phra Phutthabat dates back to the beginning of the seventeenth century, when King Song Tham of Ayutthaya sent some monks to Sri Lanka to worship the famous Buddha's footprint of Sumankut. To the monks' surprise, the Sri Lankans asked them why they had bothered to travel all that way when, according to the ancient Pali scriptures, the Buddha had passed through Thailand and had left his footprint in their own backyard. As soon as Song Tham heard this he instigated a search for the footprint, which was finally discovered in 1623 by a hunter named Pram Bun, when a wounded deer disappeared into a hollow and then emerged miraculously

---

THE FESTIVAL OF THE HOLY FOOTPRINT

During the dry season in January, February and March, a million pilgrims from all over the country flock to Wat Phra Phutthabat for the **Ngan Phrabat** (**Festival of the Holy Footprint**). During the fair, which reaches its peak in two week-long lunar periods, one usually at the beginning of February and the other at the beginning of March, stalls selling souvenirs and traditional medicines around the entrance swell to form a small town, and traditional entertainments, magic shows and a Ferris wheel are laid on. The fair is still a major religious event, but before the onset of industrialization it was the highlight of social and cultural life for all ages and classes; it was an important place of courtship, for example, especially for women at a time when their freedom was limited. Another incentive for women to attend the fair was the belief that visiting the footprint three times would ensure a place in heaven – for many women, the Phrabat Fair became the focal point of their lives, as Buddhist doctrine allowed them no other path to salvation. Up to the reign of Rama V (1868–1910) even the king used to come, performing a ritual lance dance on elephant-back to ensure a long reign.

healed. The hunter pushed aside the bushes to discover a foot-shaped trench filled with water, which immediately cured him of his terrible skin disease. A temple was built on the spot, but was destroyed by the Burmese in 1765 – the present buildings date from the Bangkok era.

A staircase flanked by nagas leads up to a marble platform, where an ornate mondop with mighty doors inlaid with mother-of-pearl houses the **footprint**, which in itself is not much to look at. Sheltered by a mirrored canopy, the stone print is nearly 2m long and obscured by layers of gold leaf presented by pilgrims; people also throw money into the footprint, some of which they take out again as a charm or merit object. The hill behind the shrine, which you can climb for a fine view over the gilded roofs of the complex to the mountains beyond, is covered in shrines. The souvenir village around the temple includes plenty of **food stalls**.

ARRIVAL AND GETTING AROUND   LOPBURI

BY TRAIN

Lopburi is on the main line north to Chiang Mai and is best reached by train from Bangkok's Hualamphong Station (most departures early morning and evening), via Ayutthaya. A popular option is to arrive in Lopburi in the morning, leave your bags at the conveniently located station while you look around the old town, then catch one of the night trains to the north.

Destinations Ayutthaya (16 daily; 45min–1hr 30min); Bangkok Hualamphong Station (16 daily; 2hr 30min–3hr); Chiang Mai (5 daily; 10–12hr); Phitsanulok (12 daily; 3hr–5hr 15min).

BY BUS OR MINIBUS

The long-distance bus terminal is on the southwest side of the huge Sakeo roundabout, 2km east of the old town: any blue city bus or red songthaew heading west on Thanon Narai Maharat to Narai's Palace will take you there (B10).

From/to Bangkok Besides regular buses from the Northern Mo Chit terminal, a couple of companies operate fast a/c minibuses between Bangkok's Victory Monument (west side, near Ratchawithi Hospital) and Lopburi, which leave when full (5am–8pm) and terminate outside their offices on Thanon Na Phra Karn, 200m north of the Lopburi train station. They depart from the same location.

From/to Kanchanaburi Coming from Kanchanaburi, it's possible to bypass Bangkok by taking a public bus to Suphanburi (every 20min; 1hr 30min), then changing to a Lopburi bus; the same applies heading in the opposite direction.

Destinations Ayutthaya (every 20min; 2hr); Bangkok (every 20min; 2–3hr); Chiang Mai (5 daily; 9hr); Khorat (6 daily; 3hr 30min); Phitsanulok (3 daily; 4hr); Suphanburi (hourly; 3hr).

GETTING AROUND

By motorbike Lopburi is easily explored on foot, but if you want to get further afield, *Noom Guesthouse I* rents out automatic motorbikes for B250/day.

INFORMATION AND TOURS

Tourist information The TAT office is east of San Phra Karn on Highway 311 (Thanon Narai Maharat) near the city hall (daily 8.30am–4.30pm; ☎036 422768–9, ✉tatlobri @tat.or.th); it's too far from the city's main sights to be of much use, though they can provide a good map of the town and a booklet of nearby attractions.

Tours *Noom Guesthouse I* runs rock-climbing trips to the cliff-face at Khao Chin Lae, about 20km east of town, behind Wat Pa Suwannahong (from B1000 excluding equipment), while a trip to swim in a nearby lake and see a cave packed with bats (also with *Noom I*) costs B600 for up to five people.

ACCOMMODATION

Benjatara Boutique Place Resort 123/33 Moo 1, Tambon Khao Sam Yod (just east of the Phra Narai roundabout, on a lane to the north immediately after the Ford dealership) ☎036 422 608, ⓦbenjatara lopburi.com.com. This smart, modern place offers the town's most comfortable lodging, with large, well-equipped rooms, some of which have balconies. Breakfast is included in the price, but it's a bit of a trek from the town centre. B550

Nett Hotel 17/1-2 oi 2, Thanon Ratchadamnern ☎036 411738. The best alternative to *Noom* (see below) is this clean and friendly place, announced by a multicoloured mosaic of a dragon and a cockerel. It offers unadorned en-suite fan or a/c rooms, the latter with hot water, TVs and fridges, though don't expect a view. Fan B200, a/c B350

★Noom Guesthouse I 15-17 Thanon Praya Kumjud ☎036 427693, ⓦnoomguesthouse.com. Most travellers make a beeline for the rooms at *Noom Guesthouse I*, whose centrally located old wooden house is fronted by a street-side restaurant and bar. There's a good mix of teak-floored rooms in the main house, with shared bathrooms, or you can stay in one of the en-suite bungalows out back. Facilities are very good and include TV in the bungalows. Fan B300, a/c B500

Noom Guesthouse II Soi 2, Thanon Ratchadamnern ☎036 427693, ⓦnoomguesthouse.com. Offering clean and quiet fan rooms in the town centre, this is a good alternative if the main Noom Guesthouse is full. B350

EATING AND DRINKING

Lopburi's dining scene is pretty limited, but the **night market**, which sets up all along the west side of the railway tracks, is a reliable choice for cheap eats. The most popular places for a **beer**, day or night, are *Ma Tini* and the sociable pavement tables at *Noom Guesthouse I*.

Coffee House Thanon Ratchadamnern ☎081 587 7606. Good espressos, lattes and cappuccinos (around B30) in this fairly comfortable little café near the northern end of Soi 1. Noodles (around B15) and Western breakfasts (around B40) are also on offer. Daily 8am–5pm.

Ma Tini 18 Thanon Praya Kumjud ☎088 6807335. *Ma Tini*, meaning "come here", is run by Tee, a musician who sometimes plays with his band and other times puts on classic rock songs. Seating is on a shady outdoor terrace, and though the menu covers a wide range of Thai, Western and vegetarian dishes (mostly B70–90), it's more bar than restaurant, and a cool place to hang out in the evening, enjoying the music over a beer or a cocktail. Daily 8.30am–midnight.

Namaste India 2-3 Soi Surasak, near the southwest corner of the palace ☎083 776 5050. Also known as "Naan Stop Curry", this Indian restaurant offers a change from Thai food, with thali, tandoori chicken and several vegetarian dishes on offer (most main dishes around B100–150), in a cosy and welcoming environment. Buffet (B190) available on Saturday evening from 6–10pm. Daily 10.30am–10.30pm.

★**Noom Guesthouse I** 15-17 Thanon Praya Kumjud ☎036 427693, ⓦnoomguesthouse.com. This classic travellers' café serves a great range of Thai and Western dishes in its cosy, ground-floor restaurant, with tables spilling on to the street in the evening. They serve a filling English breakfast (B130) and plenty of beers and cocktails in the evening. Owner Noom is the man to ask if you have any queries about attractions near Lopburi or onward travel. Restaurant daily 7.30am–9pm (bar often stays open later).

Pae Ban Rim Nam 57/68 Soi Wat Choeng Tha, off Thanon Phetracha ☎036 618005. This floating restaurant, located just south of King Narai's Palace, makes a good spot for lunch after exploring the palace grounds and the museum. Dishes are a bit expensive but portions are huge (they cater mostly to Thai groups), with lots of seafood and classics like green curry (B120) on the menu. They sometimes host karaoke parties in the evening, when it's not such a pleasant experience. Daily 10am–10pm.

Sahai Pan Ta Near the northwest corner of Wat Mahathat ☎036 414604. Lit up outside by neon lights, this is a typical Thai night club with a very dark interior and very loud live music from 8.30pm. There's no English sign, but look out for the huge *Ben More* billboard. No cover charge but drinks are a bit pricier than elsewhere to cover entertainment costs. Daily 6pm–2am.

DIRECTORY

ATMs There are several ATMs on Thanon Ratchadamnern, east of Thanon Sorasak.

Market Lopburi's busy market sets up on Thanon Praya Kumjud every Wednesday from 3–9pm, selling everything from sunglasses and Thai pop CDs to freshly made doughnuts.

Phitsanulok

Handily located midway up the railway line between Bangkok and Chiang Mai, the likeable provincial capital of **PHITSANULOK** makes a useful and pleasant stopover with reasonable hotels and good transport connections, especially to the historical centres of Sukhothai and Kamphaeng Phet. The main sight in town is the country's second-most important Buddha image, enshrined in historic **Wat Mahathat** and the focus of pilgrimages from all over Thailand; it is complemented by one of the best ethnology collections in Thailand, at the **Sergeant Major Thawee Folklore Museum**. There are also several potentially rewarding national parks within an hour or two's drive along Highway 12, the so-called "**Green Route**".

Typically for a riverside town, "Phit'lok" as it's often nicknamed, is long and narrow. The heart of the city, which occupies the east bank of the Nan River, is easily walkable and still feels quite old-fashioned with its shophouses, traditional restaurants and food stalls, particularly along Thanon Boromtrailoknat between the police station and the *Pailyn Hotel*. The two main sights, however, lie at opposite extremities: Wat Mahathat to the north, and the folklore museum 2.5km south.

Brief history

Huge swathes of Phitsanulok were destroyed by fire in 1957, but the town's history harks back to a heyday in the late fourteenth and early fifteenth centuries when, with

PHITSANULOK

● EATING
Ban Mai	3
Café Veggie	5
Cake by Lithai	4
Coffee Mania	2
Italy: The Restaurant	7
Kwaytiaw Hoy Kha Rim Nan	1
Tui Pochana	6

■ NIGHTLIFE
| Amarin in Town | 1 |

■ ACCOMMODATION
Bon Bon Guest House	5
Lithai Guest House	6
London Hotel	3
Pailyn Hotel	2
Pattara Resort	4
Yodia Heritage Hotel	1

Nan River

THANON PHAYASUEA
Tourist Police
THANON AKKHATASAROTH
Wat Phra Si Ratana Mahathat (Wat Yai)
THANON JAKARNBOON
NARESUAN BRIDGE
THANON SINGAWAT
Topland Plaza
Anusorn Tour
12
Wat Rajburana
Buses to Sukhothai
THANON BOROMTRAILOKNAT
THANON BHUDHABUCHA (PUTTABUCHA)
THANON AKITWONG
Kamalasom Massage
Provincial Tourism Office
TOT
THANON WANGCHAN
SOI 1
SOI 3
THANON AKKATHASAROTH (EKATHOSAROT)
THANON THAMMABUCHA
Rama 1 Monument
Police Station
AKKATHASAROTH BRIDGE
THANON NARESUAN
Train Station
Night Market
Market
SOI 1
TH. SAIRUTHAI
City Bus Stands
Asia Hotel
Night Bazaar
THANON CHAO PHRAYA
Pharmacy
THANON PHYALITHAI
Clocktower
Sumalee Bakery
THANON WISUT KASAT
Night Market
Day Market
THANON SURASRI
THANON BOROM TRAILOKNAT
Day Market
TAT
Able Tour & Travel
THANON BOROMTRAILOKNAT
THANON RAMESUAN

N

0 100 metres

Airport   Buddha Chinnarat Hospital   Folk Museum (450m), Garden Birds of Thailand (500m) &   Buddha Foundry (500m)

Sukhothai
Bus Station, "Green Route" & Lom Sak
Rattanavej Hospital

2

FESTIVALS AND EVENTS IN PHIT'LOK

Phitsanulok hosts two lively **food festivals** every year, once during the Western New Year period (Dec 25–Jan 1) and again at Songkhran, the Thai New Year (April 9–15). Almost every restaurant in town participates, selling their trademark dishes from special stalls set up along the east bank of the river, and there's traditional Thai dance and other entertainments. In February, Phitsanulok honours the **Phra Buddha Chinnarat** with a **week-long festival**, which features *likay* folk-theatre performances and dancing (see p.48) Then, later in the year, on the third weekend of September, traditional **longboat races** are staged on the Nan River, in front of Wat Mahathat.

Sukhothai waning in power, it rose to prominence as the favoured home of the crumbling capital's last rulers. After supremacy was finally wrested by the emerging state of Ayutthaya in 1438, Phitsanulok was made a provincial capital, subsequently becoming a strategic army base during Ayutthaya's wars with the Burmese, and adoptive home to Ayutthayan princes. The most famous of these was **Naresuan**, a famously courageous warrior who was governor of Phitsanulok before he assumed the Ayutthayan crown in 1590. The foundations of Naresuan's Chandra Palace, where both he and his younger brother Akkathasaroth were born, have been excavated in the grounds of a former school northwest of the bridge that bears his name; the tramway tour makes a stop there.

Wat Phra Si Ratana Mahathat (Wat Yai)

Entrances on Thanon Buddhabucha on the east bank of the Nan River, and on Thanon Jakarnboon; **Wat Mahathat** Daily 6.30am–6pm • B50 • **Gallery of Buddha Images** Wed–Sun 9am–4pm • Free • Can be reached on city buses #1, #5, #8, #12 and #13 • No shorts or skimpy clothing

Officially called **Wat Phra Si Ratana Mahathat** (and known locally as **Wat Yai**, meaning "big temple"), this fourteenth-century temple was one of the few buildings miraculously to escape Phitsanulok's great 1957 fire. It receives a constant stream of worshippers eager to pay homage to the highly revered Buddha image inside the viharn. Because the image is so sacred, a **dress code** is strictly enforced here, forbidding shorts and skimpy clothing. When you're done with the temple, take a look at the riverside stalls outside, which offer visitors the chance to make merit by buying live **eels**, **fish** and **baby turtles** (kept in plastic bags) and releasing them into the Nan River.

Phra Buddha Chinnarat

Delicately inlaid mother-of-pearl doors mark the entrance to the viharn, opening onto the low-ceilinged interior, painted mostly in dark red and black, with gold leaf motifs, and dimly lit by narrow slits along the upper walls. In the centre of the far wall sits the much-cherished **Phra Buddha Chinnarat**: late Sukhothai in style and probably cast in the fourteenth century, this gleaming, polished-bronze Buddha is one of the finest of the period and, for Thais, second in importance only to the Emerald Buddha in Bangkok. Tales of the statue's miraculous powers have fuelled the devotion of generations of pilgrims – one legend tells how the Buddha wept tears of blood when Ayutthayan princes arrived in Phitsanulok to oust the last Sukhothai regent. The Phra Buddha Chinnarat stands out among Thai Buddha images because of its *mandorla*, the flame-like halo that symbolizes extreme radiance and frames the upper body and head like a chair-back, tapering off into nagas at the arm rests. There's an almost perfect replica of the Phitsanulok original in Bangkok's Marble Temple (see p.115), commissioned by Rama V in 1901. Visitors are asked not to photograph this image in a standing position, but to kneel respectfully in front of it as locals do.

THE BUDDHA'S FOOTPRINT, WAT PHRA PHUTTHABAT, NEAR LOPBURI (P.228) >

The prang

Behind the viharn, the gilded mosaic **prang** houses the holy relic that gives the wat its name (Mahathat means "Great Relic Stupa") – though which particular remnant lies entombed here is unclear – and the cloister surrounding both structures contains a gallery of Buddha images of different styles.

The river bank

South of Wat Mahathat and Naresuan Bridge, **the east and west banks** of the Nan River have been landscaped into a pleasant riverside park and jogging track that runs all the way down to Akkathasaroth (Ekathosarot) Bridge. There are no exceptional attractions along its course, but you may want to make a stop at Wat Rajburana, or join the locals who come out in their thousands each evening to exercise in this area. South of Akkathasaroth Bridge, the east bank of the river is dominated by the permanent stalls of the **night bazaar**, the place for locals and tourists to shop for bargain-priced fashions and a cheap meal.

Wat Rajburana

Just south of Naresuan Bridge • Daily 6am–8.30pm

Like Wat Mahathat, **Wat Rajburana** survived the 1957 fire. Recognizable by the huge brick-based chedi that stands in the compound, the wat is chiefly of interest for the *Ramakien* **murals** (see p.88) that cover the interior walls of the bot. Now fading, they were probably painted in the mid-nineteenth century. Other interesting features are a scripture library raised on concrete piles, a bo tree surrounded by support sticks, and a boat once used by King Rama V that is protected by a shelter and bedecked with floral garlands.

The Sergeant Major Thawee Folk Museum

26/138 Thanon Wisut Kasat, 1.3km southeast of the train station • Daily 8.30am–4.30pm • B50 • Local bus #1 will drop you close by

The **Sergeant Major Thawee Folk Museum** (Jatawee Buranaket) displays a variety of exhibits on the region's culture and its fascinating look at traditional rural life makes this one of the best ethnology museums in the country. The collection, which is housed in a series of wooden pavilions, belongs to former sergeant major Dr Thawee, who has pursued a lifelong personal campaign to preserve and document a way of life that's gradually disappearing. Highlights include the reconstructed kitchen, veranda and birthing room of a typical village house, known as a "tied house" because its split-bamboo walls are literally tied together with rattan cane; and an exceptionally comprehensive gallery of traps: dozens of specialized contraptions designed to ensnare everything from cockroaches to birds perched on water buffaloes' backs. There's also a display on weaving and natural dyes, a collection of traditional toys and some fearsome-looking wooden implements for giving yourself a massage. A recent addition to the museum is an aquarium of fish found in local rivers.

Buddha Foundry

26/43 Thanon Wisut Kasat, 1.35km southeast of the train station, about 50m south of the Folk Museum • Daily 8am–5pm • Free • ☎ 055 301668 • Local bus #1 will drop you close by

For a rare chance to see Buddha images being forged, head to the **Buranathai Buddha Bronze-Casting Foundry**. Anyone can drop in to see the fairly lengthy procedure, which is best assimilated from the illustrated explanations along the entrance lane. Images of all sizes are made here, from 30cm-high household icons to mega models destined for wealthy temples. The Buddha business is quite a profitable one: worshippers can earn a great deal of merit by donating a Buddha statue, particularly a precious one, to their local wat, so demand rarely slackens. There's a gift shop on site.

Garden Birds of Thailand

Behind the Buddha Foundry on Thanon Wisut Kasat, 1.35km southeast of the train station • Daily 8.30am–5pm • B50 • Accessible from the foundry or via Soi 17

Garden Birds of Thailand (Suan Nok) is another of Dr Thawee's enthusiasms: a zoo containing hundreds of breathtakingly beautiful Thai birds, each one segregated and informatively described. It's an astonishing collection that offers a unique chance to admire at close range such beauties as the blue magpie, the Eurasian jay and the common hoopoe, though it's sad to see the hornbills trying to saw their way out of the cage with their beaks.

2

ARRIVAL AND DEPARTURE   PHITSANULOK

Phitsanulok stands at the hub of an efficient transport network that works well as a transit point between Bangkok, the far north and Isaan. Nearly every Bangkok–Chiang Mai **train** stops here, and assorted **buses** head east towards the Isaan towns of Loei and Khon Kaen.

BY PLANE

Phitsanulok airport (☎055 301010) is 7km south of town and about B150 by taxi (☎089 7031098) from the centre. The airport is served by Air Asia and Nok Air flights to and from Bangkok (around 5 daily; 50min), and Kan Air services to Chiang Mai (4 weekly; 1hr).

BY TRAIN

Phitsanulok train station (☎055 258005) is in the town centre; tuk-tuk rates from here to hotels and attractions are posted outside (mostly B60).
Destinations Ayutthaya (11 daily; 4hr 30min–5hr 30min);

Bangkok Hualamphong (11 daily; 5hr 30min–8hr); Chiang Mai (6 daily; 5hr 50min–8hr 15min); Lamphun (6 daily; 5hr 40min–7hr 20min); Lopburi (11 daily; 3hr–5hr 15min).

BY BUS

The new regional bus station (☎055 986187) is 7km east of the city on Highway 12 (near the junction with Highway 11), from where it's B130 by tuk-tuk to the centre or a ride on local bus #1 or #6 (see p.236). If coming from Sukhothai or the north, you should be able to get off somewhere more central, near Topland Plaza, before the bus continues to the terminus. If you've arrived at the train station and want to make an

---

THE GREEN ROUTE

East of Phitsanulok, Highway 12 has been tagged "**the Green Route**" by TAT because it gives access to several national parks and rapids, and provides an excuse for a pleasant day or two's excursion from the city. Their local office can provide a map outlining routes.

The first highlight is the chance to go **whitewater rafting** on the Class 1–5 rapids of the Khek River; the *Sappraiwan Resort* (☎055 293293, ⊛sappraiwan.com; doubles B1600) at kilometre-marker 53 on Highway 12 arranges an overnight trip (June–Nov; B1995/person including three meals and one night's accommodation). The resort also has an elephant sanctuary where you can watch the pachyderms playing together.

Next up is **Phu Hin Rongkla National Park** (B500; ☎055 233527, ⊛dnp.go.th), about 100km northeast of Phitsanulok: turn north off Highway 12 at kilometre-stone 68 onto Route 2013, then east onto Route 2331 to reach the visitor centre. Formerly the notorious stronghold of the insurgent Communist Party of Thailand from 1967 to 1982, the park still contains some relics from that period, though its short trails through montane forests and natural rock gardens are now the main point of interest. Should you want to stay, the park offers accommodation (dorms B100, doubles B800).

Also on the Green Route is **Thung Salaeng Luang National Park** (B200–500 depending on which areas you want to visit; ☎055 268019, ⊛dnp.go.th/parkreserve), 82km east of Phitsanulok (turn south off Highway 12 at kilometre-stone 79). Thung Salaeng is famous for the flowers that carpet its grasslands at Thung Nonson for a brief period after the end of the rainy season (November is the best time to go) and has two designated mountain-bike trails as well as rafting opportunities. Bungalows are available in the park from B1000.

The Dhamma Abha Vipassana meditation centre (☎081 8277331, ⊛abha.dhamma.org), which follows the teachings of S.N. Goenka, holds frequent ten-day **meditation** courses every month (sign up on the website), and is also in this area, in Ban Huayplu; turn north off Highway 12 at kilometre-stone 49.

2

TOURS OF PHITSANULOK

For a cheap whizz around some of the town's main sights you could take the thirty-minute **tramway tour** that starts in front of the tourist information booth on Thanon Singawat, just east of the Naresuan Bridge (9am–3pm; departs when full, approximately every 30min on busy days; B40). Commentary is in Thai but there's a printed English-language summary available and the route takes in a couple of excavated ruins across the river – King Naresuan's place of birth, Chandra Palace, plus the Sukhothai-era Wat Wihanthong – neither of which is really worth making the effort to walk to.

At night a fleet of samlors twinkling with fairy lights takes tourists on an hour-long **evening tour** of Phitsanulok and its night bazaar; arrange the trip (around B250) through any hotel.

immediate bus connection to Sukhothai, you can either take a samlor or local bus to the regional bus station, where the Sukhothai buses originate, or join the bus at a pick-up point opposite the Topland Plaza shopping centre on Thanon Singawat (B60 by samlor, or take a/c local bus #5 – non-a/c #5 goes elsewhere – to the Plaza, then cross the road).

Destinations Bangkok (over 70 daily; 5–6hr); Chiang Mai (about 50 daily; 5–6hr); Chiang Rai (about 30 daily; 6–7hr); Kamphaeng Phet (hourly; 3hr); Khon Kaen (16 daily; 5–6hr); Khorat/Nakhon Ratchasima (14 daily; 6–7hr); Loei (6 daily; 5hr); Lomsak (hourly; 2hr); Mae Sot (8 daily; 3hr 15min–5hr); Phrae (17 daily; 2–3hr); Sukhothai (hourly; 1hr); Tak (10 daily; 3hr); Ubon Ratchathani (9 daily; 12hr); Udon Thani (5 daily; 7hr).

GETTING AROUND

BY BUS

Several local city bus routes (roughly every 30min 5am–9pm) crisscross the city, most running via the city-centre bus stands on Thanon Akkathasaroth, 150m south of the train station, where southbound buses pick up outside the *Asia Hotel* and northbound ones from across the road.

Useful routes #1, from the regional bus station to Wat Mahathat, the train station and the Folk Museum; #5 and #11, from the train station to Topland Plaza (for Sukhothai buses) and Wat Mahathat; #6, from the regional bus station

to the *Pailyn Hotel*.

BY CAR OR MOTORBIKE

Avis (☎ 089 9698672) and Budget (☎ 055 301020) have desks at the airport. Motorbike rental is available for around B200 per day at Anusorn Tour (☎ 055 214453), opposite Topland Plaza on Thanon Akkathasaroth.

BY TAXI

For a metered taxi, call ☎ 055 338888.

INFORMATION

Tourist information The helpful and well-informed TAT office (daily 8.30am–4.30pm; ☎ 055 252742, ✉ tatphlok @tat.or.th) is on the eastern arm of Thanon Boromtrailoknat

(known to local taxi drivers as Surasi Trade Centre). They can provide a good map of the town.

ACCOMMODATION

Bon Bon Guest House 77 Thanon Phayalithai ☎ 055 219058. The only genuine guesthouse in town, this place is set back from the road with three storeys of rooms, all with small balconies. The twenty rooms are all en suite and kept nice and clean; some have a/c. They rent bicycles too, but no breakfast included in the room rate. Fan B350, a/c B450

Lithai Guest House 73/1–5 Thanon Phayalithai ☎ 055 219626–9, Centrally located, this is a good budget option, used mainly by salespeople so it feels more like a hotel than a guesthouse. The big, clean rooms come with either fan or a/c. Breakfast included. Fan B350, a/c B580

London Hotel 21–22 Soi Buddhabucha (Puttabucha) 1 ☎ 055 225145. The cheapest and most basic place in town, this converted family home has just eight small, bare-bones, fan rooms upstairs, all sharing bathrooms. B100

Pailyn Hotel 38 Thanon Boromtrailoknat ☎ 055 252411-5. Central, long-running three-star tourist and business hotel that's old-fashioned and unstylish but offers good-sized a/c rooms with comfortable beds. Upper-floor rooms in the twelve-storey tower enjoy long-range river views from their balconies. Has a massage centre, restaurant and nightclub and runs tours to Sukhothai. Breakfast included for superior and deluxe rooms. B700

Pattara Resort 349/40 Thanon Chaiyanupap, 2km west of the town centre ☎ 055 282966, ✆ pattararesort.com. Situated out of town in a residential area, this rambling resort is the best place in Phitsanulok to really relax. All rooms, from the superior rooms up to the very large pool villas, are surrounded by greenery and furnished with thick-mattress beds, flatscreen TVs and subtle lighting. There's also a spa, good restaurant and free pick-up from the airport. B3800

Yodia Heritage Hotel 89/1 Thanon Buddhabucha (Puttabucha), 250m north of Wat Phra Si Ratana Mahathat ☎ 055 214677, ⓦ yodiaheritage.com. This classy boutique hotel beside the river has just 25 contemporary-styled rooms, all with a/c, wooden floors, elegantly restrained decor, bathtubs and a balcony overlooking the small garden. The on-site *Amore* restaurant enjoys river views, and there's also a library. **B2300**

EATING AND DRINKING

In the evening, **night market** stalls set up south of the night bazaar along the east bank of the river, south of Akkathasaroth Bridge. *Phat thai* and *hawy thawt* (omelette stuffed with mussels) are popular choices, but the most famous dish is "flying vegetables", in which strong-tasting morning-glory (*phak bung*) is stir-fried before being tossed flamboyantly in the air towards the plate-wielding waiter or customer. Also famous in Phit'lok are *kwaytiaw hoy kha*, or dangling leg noodles, so named for the style of eating noodles while sitting with legs dangling over the side of a raised pavilion.

Amarin In Town 50–52 Thanon Phayalithai ☎ 090 1021533. This bar is something of a beer drinker's paradise, with a huge range of brews on offer, including Czech, German, Belgian and Japanese, and even Fuller's London Pride (B110 small bottle). There are several draught beers (B220–250) and a few snacks. Daily 6pm–midnight.

Ban Mai 93/30 Thanon Wisut Kasat ☎ 055 303122. It's worth heading east across the railway tracks to this smart restaurant in a residential lane off Thanon Wisut Kasat (opposite the *Ayara Grand Palace*). Expect starched tablecloths, sturdy furnishings and attentive service, complementing classic Thai dishes, such as *tom kha kai* (chicken, coconut and galangal soup, B150). Daily 11am–10pm.

Café Veggie 93/2 Thanon Phayalithai ☎ 089 7070399. This modern a/c restaurant features an appetizing menu of salads (B135–165), soups and sandwiches, but, despite the name, it's not exclusively vegetarian, and you can indulge in burgers and fish and chips (B159) too, along with delicious juices to wash it down. Cooking classes also on offer. Daily 10.30am–8pm.

Cake by Lithai 73/1-5 Thanon Phayalithai ☎ 055 219626-9. On the ground floor of the *Lithai Guest House*, this restaurant-cum-bakery offers comfortable seating, swift service and a wide range of dishes at reasonable prices. These include spaghetti (B70–200), steaks (from B120) and many Thai dishes, mostly B60–120. Daily 7am–9pm.

Coffee Mania Thanon Buddhabucha, just south of the Provincial Tourism Office ☎ 055 251133. This laidback café enjoys an excellent riverside location, with seating in and around an attractive wooden building. They serve delicious milky cappuccinos (B40), as well as a few snacks such as cakes and biscuits. Daily 8am–7pm.

Italy: The Restaurant Thanon Boromtrailoknat Soi 7 ☎ 055 219 177. Offers a huge choice of pizzas (B140–260), calzones and pastas, plus wines, in a slightly quieter part of town, away from the worst of the traffic noise. Daily 11am–10pm.

Kwaytiaw Hoy Kha Rim Nan 100m north of Wat Mahathat ☎ 081 379 3172. The "dangling leg" noodles here are so famously tasty they've been featured on several TV channels. Choose from *phat thai*, Sukhothai noodles with red pork in chilli-hot broth, *tom yam* soup with noodles, or yellow noodles with pork; tofu versions are also available (B30–50). There's no English sign but it's got a brown awning, and customers eat from bowls on a shelf while dangling their legs from the open-sided pavilion. Daily 9am–4pm.

Tui Phochana 90 Thanon Phayalithai. One of several cheap and cheerful Thai curry shops on this road, where you just point to a dish that takes your fancy. This one is famous for its tasty *phanaeng muu* (pork curry with coconut; B25–40). Daily 8am–8.30pm.

DIRECTORY

ATMs ATMs are found across town, including at the corner of Soi 7 and Thanon Boromtrailokanat and outside most convenience stores.

Hospitals Rattanavej Hospital on Thanon Phra Ong Dam (☎ 055 210820–1) is private, and Buddha Chinnarat Hospital, Thanon Sithamtraipidok (☎ 055 219842-4), is government-run.

Left luggage At the train station (7am–11pm; B30/ item).

Massage Kamalasom Massage on Thanon Akitwong (Mon–Fri 8.30am–8.30pm, Sat & Sun 8.30am–4.30pm; B250/90min; ☎ 055 252600).

Pharmacy There are several pharmacies in the town centre, including at 175/6 Thanon Akkathasaroth (daily 5–10pm).

Tourist police For all emergencies, call the tourist police on the free 24hr phoneline ☎ 1155, or contact them at their office north of Wat Mahathat on Thanon Akkathasaroth (☎ 055 253009).

Travel agent Able Tour and Travel (Mon–Fri 8am–6pm, Sat 8am–4pm; ☎ 055 242206, ⓔ ablegroup@hotmail .com), near the TAT office on Thanon Boromtrailoknat, sells air tickets and can arrange minibuses to Sukhothai or Kamphaeng Phet (B1800 excluding petrol).

Sukhothai

For a brief but brilliant period (1238–1376), the walled city of **SUKHOTHAI** presided as the capital of Thailand, creating the legacy of a unified nation of Thai peoples and a phenomenal artistic heritage. Some of Thailand's finest buildings and sculpture were produced here, but by the sixteenth century the city had been all but abandoned to the jungle. Now an impressive assembly of elegant ruins, the Old City, 58km northwest of Phitsanulok, has been preserved as **Sukhothai Historical Park** and is one of Thailand's most visited ancient sites.

There are several accommodation options near the historical park, but travellers looking for urban comforts tend to stay in so-called **NEW SUKHOTHAI**, a modern market town 12km to the east, which has good travel links with the Old City and is also better for restaurants and long-distance bus connections. It's a small, friendly town, used to seeing tourists but by no means overrun with them. The town straddles the Yom River, which burst its banks and caused serious flooding in 2011, since when an ugly flood wall has been erected along its course through town.

Sukhothai makes a peaceful and convenient base for visiting Ramkhamhaeng National Park, as well as the ruins of Si Satchanalai and Kamphaeng Phet, which, while not as extensively renovated, are still worth visiting – if only for their relative wildness and lack of visitors. Most of these outlying places can be reached fairly easily by public

NEW SUKHOTHAI

ACCOMMODATION

At Home	3
Ban Thai Guest House	8
J&J Guest House	5
Lotus Village	4
Ruean Thai Hotel	2
Sawasdipong Hotel	6
Sukhothai Heritage Resort	1
TR Guest House	7

EATING

Dream Café	4
Hong Rama Tearoom	3
Kru Iew	2
May Klang Kroong	1
Pai Restaurant	6
Poo Restaurant	5

DRINKING

Chopper Bar	1

THE SUKHOTHAI BUDDHA

The classic Buddha images of Thailand were produced towards the end of the Sukhothai era. Ethereal, androgynous figures with ovoid faces and feline expressions, they depict not a Buddha meditating to achieve enlightenment – the more usual representation – but an already **enlightened Buddha**: the physical realization of an abstract, "unworldly" state. Though they produced mainly seated Buddhas, Sukhothai artists are renowned for having pioneered the **walking Buddha**, one of four postures described in ancient Pali texts but without precedent in Thailand.

2

transport, but for trips to Wat Thawet and Ramkhamhaeng National Park you'll need to rent your own vehicle or arrange a driver through your accommodation.

The Historical Park (Muang Kao Sukhothai)

12km west of New Sukhothai • Daily 6.30am–6pm, floodlit Sat 6.30–9pm • B100 per zone (central, north and west), plus B20–50 per vehicle

In its prime, the Old City boasted around forty separate temple complexes and covered an area of about seventy square kilometres between the Yom River and the low range of hills to the west. At its heart stood the walled royal city, protected by a series of moats and ramparts. **SUKHOTHAI HISTORICAL PARK**, or **Muang Kao Sukhothai**, covers all this area and is divided into five **zones**: all the most important temples lie within the central zone, with the Ramkhamhaeng Museum just outside it; the ruins outside the city walls are spread out over a sizeable area and divided into north, south, east and west zones.

With the help of UNESCO, the Thai government's Fine Arts Department has restored the most significant ruins and the result reveals the original town planners' keen aesthetic sense, especially their astute use of water to offset and reflect the solid monochrome contours of the stone temples. Although there is a touch of the too perfectly packaged theme park about the central zone (and, in some critics' opinions, too liberal an interpretation of thirteenth-century design), it's a serene and rewarding site, with plenty to investigate should you want to look more closely. It does, however, take a determined imagination to visualize the ancient capital as it must once have looked, not least because houses and palaces would have filled the spaces between the wats – like their Khmer predecessors, the people of Sukhothai constructed their secular buildings from perishable materials such as wood, only using expensive, durable stone for their sacred structures. The **central zone** covers three square kilometres so a bike is recommended, or you could join one of the regular tram tours (B40), which take about an hour and visit the three main temples in the central zone (Wat Mahathat, Wat Sri Sawai and Wat Sa Si). Of the eleven ruins here, Wat Mahathat is the one that should definitely not be missed.

There's a much less formal feel to the ruins in the **outer zones**, where you're as likely to find cows trampling through the remains as tourists; with some clever planning, you could visit several lesser-known ruins without paying the zone fee. You'll need a bicycle or car to get around, but all sites are clearly signposted from the gates encircling the central zone. The **north** zone is the closest and most rewarding, followed by the **east** zone (no fee) just off the road to New Sukhothai. If you're feeling energetic, head for the **west** zone, which requires a much longer bike ride and some hill climbing. The ruins to the **south** (no fee) are rarely visited, but Wat Chetuphon and Wat Chedi Si Hong are definitely worth a look.

Brief history

Prior to the thirteenth century, the land now known as Thailand was divided into a collection of petty principalities, most of which owed their allegiance to the Khmer

SUKHOTHAI HISTORICAL PARK:
THE OLD CITY

ACCOMMODATION
Old City Guest House   1
Orchid Hibiscus Guest House   3
Tharaburi Resort   2

empire and its administrative centre Angkor (in present-day Cambodia). With the Khmers' power on the wane, two Thai generals joined forces in 1238 to oust the Khmers from the northern plains, founding the kingdom of **Sukhothai** ("Dawn of Happiness" in Pali) under the regency of one of the generals, Intradit. In short order they had extended their control over much of present-day Thailand, as well as parts of Myanmar and Laos.

King Ramkhamhaeng

The third and most important of Sukhothai's eight kings, Intradit's youngest son **Ramkhamhaeng** (r.1279–98) laid the foundations of a unique Thai identity by establishing Theravada (Hinayana) Buddhism as the common faith and introducing the forerunner of the modern Thai alphabet; of several inscriptions attributed to him, the most famous, found on what's known as Ramkhamhaeng's Stele and housed in Bangkok's National Museum (with a copy kept in Sukhothai's Ramkhamhaeng Museum), tells of a utopian land of plenty ruled by a benevolent monarch.

Ramkhamhaeng turned Sukhothai into a vibrant spiritual and commercial centre, inviting Theravada monks from Nakhon Si Thammarat and Sri Lanka to instruct his people in the religion that was to supplant Khmer Hinduism and Mahayana Buddhism, and encouraging the growth of a ceramics industry with the help of Chinese potters. By all accounts, Ramkhamhaeng's successors lacked his kingly qualities, and so, by the second half of the fourteenth century, Sukhothai had become a vassal state of the newly emerged kingdom of Ayutthaya; finally, in 1438, it was forced to relinquish all vestiges of its independent identity.

Ramkhamhaeng National Museum
Just outside the main entrance to the central zone • Daily 9am–4pm • B150

The well-presented **Ramkhamhaeng National Museum** features several illuminating exhibitions and contains some of the finest **sculptures** and reliefs found at the temples of Sukhothai's Old City and nearby Si Satchanalai. Outstanding artefacts in the downstairs gallery of the main building include the fourteenth-century bronze statue of a walking Buddha, and the large Buddha head that was found at Wat Phra Phai Luang in the north zone of Sukhothai Historical Park. Also here is a useful guide to the many different **stucco motifs** that once decorated every Sukhothai-era temple, along with a copy of one of the finest local examples of stucco relief, depicting the Buddha being sheltered by a naga, whose original is still *in situ* at Si Satchanalai's Wat Chedi Jet Taew. The wide-ranging section on Ramkhamhaeng's famous **stele** features a complete translation of the inscription, plus a detailed look at the origins and evolution of the original "Tai" script. The upstairs gallery concentrates on **Sangkhalok ceramics** and provides a much more informative introduction than the kiln museum in Si Satchanalai.

Statue of King Ramkhamhaeng

A modern **statue** of King Ramkhamhaeng sits to the right inside the main entrance to the central zone, just beyond the ticket office. Cast in bronze, he holds a palm-leaf book in his right hand – a reference to his role as founder of the modern Thai alphabet. Close by stands a large bronze **bell**, a replica of the one referred to on the famous stele (also reproduced here), which told how the king had the bell erected in front of his palace so that any citizen with a grievance could come by and strike it, whereupon the king himself would emerge to investigate the problem.

Wat Mahathat
Central zone

Your first stop in the central zone should be Sukhothai's most important site, the enormous **Wat Mahathat** compound. It's packed with the remains of scores of

2

LOY KRATHONG

Every year on the evening of the full moon of the twelfth lunar month (usually in November), Thais all over the country celebrate the end of the rainy season with **Loy Krathong**, also known as the Festival of Light. One of Thailand's most beautiful festivals, it's held to honour and appease the spirits of the water at a time when all the fields are flooded and the canals and rivers are overflowing their banks. The festival is said to have originated seven hundred years ago, when **Nang Noppamas**, the consort of a Sukhothai king, adapted an ancient Brahmin tradition of paying homage to the water goddess.

At this time, nearly everyone makes or buys a **krathong** and sets it afloat (*loy*) on the nearest body of water, to cast adrift any bad luck that may have accrued over the past year. *Krathongs* are miniature basket-boats made of banana leaves that have been elegantly folded and pinned, origami style, and then filled with flowers, three sticks of incense and a lighted candle; the traditional base is a slice of banana tree trunk, but it's increasingly popular to buy your *krathong* ready-made from the market, sometimes with an eco-unfriendly polystyrene bottom. Some people slip locks of hair and fingernail clippings between the flowers, to represent sinful deeds that will then be symbolically released along with the *krathong*; others add a coin or two to persuade the spirits to take away their bad luck (swiftly raided by opportunist young boys looking for small change). It's traditional to make a wish or prayer as you launch your *krathong* and to watch until it disappears from view: if your candle burns strong, your wishes will be granted and you will live long.

Chiang Mai goes to town over Loy Krathong (see p.285), but **Sukhothai Historical Park** is the most famous place in Thailand to celebrate the festival, and the ruins are the focus of a spectacular festival held over several nights around the full moon. The centrepiece is a charming *son et lumière* performance at Wat Mahathat, complemented by firework displays, the illumination of many Old City ruins, thousands of candles floating on the shimmering lotus ponds, a parade of charming Nang Noppamas (Miss Loy Krathong) lookalikes and all sorts of concerts and street-theatre shows. All accommodation gets packed out during the festival, so book ahead if possible.

monuments and surrounded, like a city within a city, by a moat. This was the spiritual focus of the city, the king's temple and symbol of his power; successive regents, eager to add their own stamp, restored and expanded it so that by the time it was abandoned in the sixteenth century it numbered ten viharns, one bot, eight mondops and nearly two hundred small chedis. Looking at the wat from ground level, it's hard to distinguish the main structures from the minor ruins. Remnants of the viharns and the bot dominate the present scene, their soldierly ranks of pillars, which formerly supported wooden roofs, directing the eye to the Buddha images seated at the far western ends.

The principal chedi complex, which houses the Buddha relic, stands grandly, if a little cramped, at the heart of the compound, built on an east–west axis in an almost continuous line with two viharns. Its elegant centrepiece follows a design termed **lotus-bud chedi** (after the bulbous finial ornamenting the top of a tower), and is classic late Sukhothai in style. This lotus-bud reference is an established religious symbol: though Sukhothai architects were the first to incorporate it into building design – since when it's come to be regarded as a hallmark of the era – the lotus bud had for centuries represented the purity of the Buddha's thoughts nudging through the muddy swamp and finally bursting into flower. The chedi stands surrounded by eight smaller towers – some with their stucco decoration partially reapplied, and some with a Buddha image in one of their four alcoves – on a square platform decorated with a procession of walking Buddha-like monks, another artistic innovation of the Sukhothai school, here depicted in stucco relief. Flanking the chedi platform are two square mondops, built for the colossal standing Buddhas still inside them today.

The grassy patch across the road from Wat Mahathat marks the site of the former palace, of which nothing now remains.

Wat Sri Sawai
300m southwest of Wat Mahathat, central zone

The triple corn-cob-shaped prangs of **Wat Sri Sawai** make for an interesting architectural comparison with Wat Mahathat. Just as the lotus-bud chedi epitomizes Sukhothai aspirations, the prang represents Khmer ideals: Wat Sri Sawai was probably conceived as a Hindu shrine several centuries before the Sukhothai kingdom established itself here. The stucco reliefs decorating the prangs feature a few weatherworn figures from both Hindu and Buddhist mythology, which suggests that the shrine was later pressed into Buddhist service; the square base inside the central prang supported the Khmer Shiva lingam (phallus), while the viharn out front is a later, Buddhist, addition.

Wat Trapang Ngoen
Just west of Wat Mahathat, central zone

The particularly fine lotus-bud chedi of **Wat Trapang Ngoen** rises gracefully against the backdrop of distant hills. Aligned with the chedi on the symbolic east–west axis are the dilapidated viharn and, east of that, on an island in the middle of the "silver pond" after which the wat is named, the remains of the bot. Walk the connecting plank to the bot to appreciate the setting from the water. North of the chedi, notice the fluid lines of the walking Buddha mounted onto a brick wall – a classic example of Sukhothai sculpture.

Wat Sa Si
North of Wat Trapang Ngoen, central zone

Entirely surrounded by water, **Wat Sa Si** commands a fine position on two connecting islands north of Wat Trapang Ngoen. The bell-shaped chedi with a tapering spire and square base shows a strong Sri Lankan influence, and the metallic replica of a freestanding walking Buddha is typical Sukhothai.

Wat Phra Phai Luang
North zone, about 500m north of the old city walls: exit the central zone north of Wat Sa Si

About 500m north of the earthen ramparts of the old city walls, a footbridge (also accessible to bicycles and motorbikes) leads you across to **Wat Phra Phai Luang**, one of the ancient city's oldest structures. The three prangs, only one of which remains intact, were built by the Khmers before the Thais founded their own kingdom here, and, as at the similar Wat Sri Sawai, you can still see some of the stucco reliefs showing both Hindu and Buddhist figures. Others are displayed in Ramkhamhaeng National Museum (see p.241). It's thought that Wat Phra Phai Luang was at the centre of the old Khmer town and that it was as important then as Wat Mahathat later became to the Thais. When the shrine was converted into a Buddhist temple, the viharn and chedi were built to the east of the prangs: the reliefs of the (now headless and armless) seated Buddhas are still visible around the base of the chedi. Also discernible among the ruins are parts of a large reclining Buddha and a mondop containing four huge standing Buddhas in different postures.

Wat Sri Chum
About 750m southwest from the Wat Phra Phai Luang compound, north zone

Wat Sri Chum boasts Sukhothai's largest surviving Buddha image, the Phra Achana. This enormous, heavily restored brick-and-stucco seated Buddha, measuring more than 11m from knee to knee and almost 15m high, peers through the slit in its custom-built mondop. Check out the elegantly tapered fingers, complete with gold-leaf nail varnish. A passageway – rarely opened up, unfortunately – runs inside the mondop wall, taking you from ground level on the left-hand side to the Buddha's eye level and then up again to the roof, affording a bird's-eye view of the image.

Wat Chang Lom
East zone, about 1.5km east of the main entrance

The only temple of interest in the **east zone** is canalside **Wat Chang Lom**, beside the bicycle track to New Sukhothai and just off the road to the new city. Chang Lom means "surrounded by elephants" and the main feature here is a large Sri Lankan-style, bell-shaped chedi encircled by a frieze of elephants.

Wat Saphan Hin
West zone, almost 5km west of the Ramkhamhaeng National Museum

Be prepared for a long haul out to the **west zone**, in the forested hills off the main road to Tak. Marking the western edge of the Old City, the hilltop temple of **Wat Saphan Hin** should – with sufficiently powerful telescopic lenses – give a fantastic panorama of the Old City's layout, but with the naked eye conjures up only an indistinct vista of trees and stones. The wat is reached via a steep 300m-long pathway of stone slabs (hence the name, which means "Stone Bridge") that starts from a track running south from the Tak road.

Wat Chetupon and Wat Chedi Si Hong
South zone; follow Route 1272 south from just southwest of Wat Chang Lom

Surrounded by a narrow moat that is smothered with pink water lilies which open for a few hours every morning, **Wat Chetupon**'s main feature is a headless walking Buddha framed by laterite columns of what was once the viharn. Behind it is a headless standing Buddha, and the mondop that once protected them also housed a sitting and reclining Buddha. Just opposite, **Wat Chedi Si Hong** is largely overgrown, though it's possible to make out a few stucco elephants round the base of the chedi and the crossed legs of a large Buddha image that is also framed by laterite columns.

Sangkhalok Museum
2km east of New Sukhothai on Highway 101, close to the junction with Highway 12, the road to Phitsanulok • Daily 8am–5pm • B100 • Samlor ride from central New Sukhothai should cost no more than B40–50

If you have a serious interest in ceramics you'll probably enjoy the Sukhothai-era exhibits at the privately owned **Sangkhalok Museum** – ask for one of the informative museum booklets at the ticket desk to get the most out of a visit. The ground floor of the museum displays ceramic artefacts from twelfth- to sixteenth-century Sukhothai, including **water pipes** used in the city's widely admired irrigation system, and the lotus-bud **lamps** whose gracefully shaped perforations both shield the flame and diffuse its light and are still popular in Thailand today. Some of the finest pieces are the **bowls** with scalloped rims and bluish-green patterns and the characteristically expressive **figurines**; unusually, many of these works are signed by the potter. This style of pottery has become known as Sangkhalok, after the prosperous city of Sawankhalok, near Si Satchanalai (see p.252), which was part of the kingdom of Sukhothai at that time. Also on show are some of the most exquisite ceramics produced in northern Thailand during the Lanna era (thirteenth to sixteenth centuries). Upstairs, the focus is on the cultural significance of certain artefacts and their recurring motifs.

Wat Thawet
8km north of New Sukhothai along the River Yom • Donation requested • Best reached by bicycle (taking a tuk-tuk would mean having to travel along the busy main road)

Famous for its one hundred different, brightly painted, concrete statues depicting morality tales and Buddhist fables, **Wat Thawet** makes a stark contrast to the temples in the historical park. The main attraction is a **sculpture park** that was conceived by a local monk in the 1970s, with the aim of creating a "learning garden" where visitors could learn about the Buddhist ideas of hell and karmic retribution. For example, people who have spent their lives killing animals are depicted here with the head of a buffalo, pig, cock or elephant, while those who have been greedy and materialistic stand naked and undernourished, their ribs and backbones sticking out. Then there's the alcoholic who is forced to drink boiling liquids that make his concrete guts literally explode on to the ground.

Part of the appeal of Wat Thawet is that it makes a good focus for a very pleasant **bicycle trip** from Sukhothai, a 16km round-trip that is almost entirely along peaceful canalside tracks. It's a bit tricky to find, but the friendly folks at *Lotus Village* can direct you there, and Cycling Sukhothai leads bike trips here too (see p.246).

Ramkhamhaeng National Park

Around 30km southwest of Sukhothai • B100 • ☎ 055 910000, ⓦ dnp.go.th/parkreserve • To get to the main park entrance from New Sukhothai, follow Highway 101 towards Kamphaeng Phet for 19km, then take side road 1319 (signed to Khao Luang) for the final 16km to park headquarters; Kamphaeng Phet-bound buses will take you to the junction, but you'll have trouble hitching to the park from here, so renting private transport is advised

The forested area immediately to the southwest of Sukhothai is protected as **Ramkhamhaeng National Park** and makes a pleasant day-trip on a motorbike. The park is home to waterfalls and herbal gardens and, if you're feeling sufficiently energetic, there's the possibility of a challenging mountain climb.

The headquarters stands at the foot of the eastern flank of the highest peak, **Khao Luang** (1185m), which can be climbed in around four hours, but only safely from November to February. Several very steep trails run up to the summit from here, but they are not very clearly marked; the first couple of kilometres are the worst, after which the incline eases up a little. From the top you should get a fine view over the Sukhothai plains. If you want to camp on the summit, simply alert the rangers at the park headquarters, and they will arrange for their colleague at the summit to rent you a tent; you need to take your own food and water. Fan-cooled **bungalows** in the area around the park headquarters can be rented for B1200.

Thung Luang Pottery Village

16km south of New Sukhothai on Highway 101

En route to or from Ramkhamhaeng National Park you could make a detour to **Thung Luang Pottery Village** (signposted), where nearly every household is involved in the production of earthenware pots, vases and statuary. Their lamps and table decorations are often purchased by Thai resort hotels and used to add colour to outdoor restaurants. Once you've turned off the main road, you'll pass a line of roadside stalls, but to enter the heart of the pottery neighbourhoods continue for another kilometre or so, past a school and two temples.

ARRIVAL AND DEPARTURE   **SUKHOTHAI**

BY PLANE

The tiny airport is about 25km north of town (halfway to Si Satchanalai) and is served by two daily Bangkok Airways' flights in each direction between Bangkok and Sukhothai (1hr 20min). Shuttle buses transfer passengers to or from New Sukhothai hotels for B180 per person and to or from the Old City for B300; call ☎ 055 647220 one day in advance to arrange a pick-up to the airport. The local Bangkok Airways office (☎ 055 647224) is at the airport, though you can also buy air tickets from the more central Sukhothai Travel Agency (see p.249).

BY BUS

New Sukhothai has direct bus connections with many major provincial capitals and makes a good staging point between Chiang Mai and Bangkok, as well as an easy day-trip from Phitsanulok. All buses use the Sukhothai bus terminal, located about 3km west of New Sukhothai's town centre, just off the bypass (note that buses from Mae Sot and Tak pass the Old City en route). To get from the bus station to the New Sukhothai guesthouses, you can either use the public songthaew (B30) and get off by the river, which puts you less than a 10min walk from most

2

CYCLING AROUND SUKHOTHAI

You can **cycle** from New Sukhothai to the historical park along a peaceful canalside track. To pick up the track, start from the bridge in New Sukhothai, cycle west along the main road to the historical park for about 3km (beyond Sukhothai Hospital, just before the Big C hypermarket) until you reach a temple with an impressive gold-and-white-decorated gateway on the right-hand side. A narrow track between this temple and the adjacent petrol station takes you via a small bridge to a track that runs along the north bank of Khlong Maerampan, nearly all the way to the Old City. It's an easy 14km ride. Near the end you cross a major road to pick up the final stretch of track; then, after reaching the elephant statues at the ruins of Wat Chang Lom (see p.244), cross the bridge on your left to regain the main road into the historical park, about 1.5km away. **Bicycle rental** is available from a few guesthouses in New Sukhothai and in great numbers at the historical park where outlets near the songthaew stop rent them out for B30.

Alternatively, join a **guided cycle tour** around the historical park (B990) with Belgian–Thai-run Cycling Sukhothai (☏085 083 1864, ⓦcycling-sukhothai.com). They also offer recommended **sunset bicycle tours** around local villages and countryside most afternoons from 4pm (B400) plus longer half-day tours (B750). All trips include mountain bike and transfers, and are bookable through most guesthouses.

accommodation, or you can charter a motorbike taxi, tuk-tuk, samlor or songthaew (B50–60/vehicle); rates are posted in the bus terminal. Otherwise, many guesthouses will pick you up for free – just ring ahead.

Destinations Ayutthaya (hourly; 6hr); Bangkok (every 30min; 6–7hr); Chiang Mai (every 30min; 5–6hr); Chiang Rai (3 daily; 8–9hr); Kamphaeng Phet (hourly; 1hr–1hr 30min); Khon Kaen (12 daily; 6–7hr); Lampang (hourly; 4hr); Mae Sot (3 daily; 2hr 30min–3hr); Nan (daily; 5hr); Phitsanulok (hourly; 1hr); Phrae (daily; 4hr); Si Satchanalai (every 30min; 1hr–1hr 45min); Tak (6 daily; 1hr 30min).

BY TRAIN AND BUS

If you're coming from Bangkok, Chiang Mai or anywhere in between, one option is to take the train to Phitsanulok and then change onto one of the hourly buses to New Sukhothai (1hr). For details on getting from the train station to the bus pick-up point, see the Phitsanulok "Arrival and departure" section (p.235).

GETTING AROUND

By bus Public buses from the bus terminal pass by the Old City (approximately hourly 6.30am–6.20pm).

By songthaew Songthaews from New Sukhothai (every 15min; 15min; B30; see map, p.238 for location) terminate at the central zone entrance point, beside a couple of cycle-rental outlets.

By tuk-tuk New Sukhothai guesthouses can organize a tuk-tuk to drop you in Old Sukhothai for B200. Tuk-tuks at the New Sukhothai bus station and in the town offer a 4hr tour of the ruins plus return transport for about B600.

By bicycle Cycling makes a peaceful and pleasant way to see Sukhothai and its surroundings (see box above).

By tram During busy times, a tram takes visitors round the central zone for B40 per person, starting from the ticket office and passing three of the main sites.

By motorbike For getting around the wider area, motorbike rental (around B200/day) is available at several places on Thanon Pravetnakorn and at nearby *Poo Restaurant*.

INFORMATION

Tourist information The TAT office at 200 Thanon Charodvithitong (daily 8.30am–4.30pm; ☏055 616228, ⓔtatsukho@tat.or.th) in the new city is the best place to go to for maps and information on the historical park. Alternatively, friendly tour guide Naa offers free information and advice by phone or in person at her cookery school (see p.248).

Guidebook Dawn F. Rooney's lively and beautifully photographed *Ancient Sukhothai* is a great guidebook, not only to Sukhothai's Old City but also to those of Si Satchanalai and Kamphaeng Phet; you'll need to buy it before you arrive, though.

ACCOMMODATION

There's plenty of attractive accommodation in Sukhothai; just be wary of commission-hungry tuk-tuk drivers falsely claiming places are full, no good or no longer in business.

NEW SUKHOTHAI

At Home 184/1 Thanon Wichien Chamnong ☎055 610172, ⓦathomesukhothai.com. Delightful, genuinely welcoming guesthouse that's been converted from a fifty-year-old family home to accommodate eleven large, attractive rooms, some en suite and others sharing bathrooms. The most atmospheric are upstairs in the teak-walled, teak-floored part of the house, which is set back from the road in a garden with a large pond, where there are a few smart new bungalows too. Fan B400, a/c B650, bungalows B850

Ban Thai Guest House 38 Thanon Pravetnakorn ☎055 610163, ⓔbanthai_guesthouse@yahoo.com. On the west bank of the Yom River, this comfortable, traveller-oriented budget option comprises several attractive wood-floored rooms in a single-storey house with shared bathrooms, plus some wooden bungalows with private bathroom at the back. Bicycle tours and motorbike rental too. Doubles B250, fan bungalows B350, a/c bungalows B500

J&J Guest House 12 Soi Wat Kuhasuwan, around 100m north of the bridge ☎055 620095, ⓦjjguest-house .com. Located on the west side of the River Yom, *J&J* has eight furnished bungalows with en-suite bathrooms, TVs, and handbasins in the shape of blooming flowers. The rooms are set around a quiet lawned area. Fan B600, a/c B700

★**Lotus Village** 170 Thanon Ratchathani, also accessible from Thanon Rajuthit ☎055 621484, ⓦlotus-village.com. Elegantly simple mid-priced accommodation in a relaxing Thai compound of beautiful teak houses set around a mature tropical garden with lotus ponds. All but the superior rooms have polished teak floors: some are in detached bungalows, others have either fan or a/c and there's also a family house that can sleep six. The Lotus bungalows (B1700) are particularly appealing. There's a charming spa here too (see p.249). Reception shuts at 9pm. Fan B900, a/c B1300

Ruean Thai Hotel 181/20 Soi Praharuammit, off Thanon Charodvithitong ☎055 612444, ⓦrueanthai hotel.com. This idiosyncratic thirty-room hotel has been painstakingly assembled from ten century-old teak houses from the Sukhothai area. The main two-storey complex is built around a central swimming pool, its attractive facades fashioned from salvaged teak walls, windows and doors, and steeply gabled roofs; room interiors are modern, individually furnished and with good-quality contemporary bathrooms. Those with most character are the deluxe and family rooms. All rooms have a/c and fridges; price depends on the size. There is a restaurant, free bicycle use and free transfers from the bus station. Rates include a good buffet breakfast. B1480

Sawasdipong Hotel 56/2-5 Thanon Singhawat ☎055 611567, ⓦsawasdipong.com. A good budget option in a

central location, with good-value rooms that all have a/c, TV and en-suite bathrooms, set back from the busy main road so it's reasonably quiet. B390

TR Guest House 27/5 Thanon Pravetnakorn ☎055 611663, ⓦsukhothaibudgetguesthouse.com. Large a/c doubles in a spotlessly clean concrete block, plus slightly less stylish but otherwise identical fan. There's also a handful of en-suite bungalows out back, reached through a car park; these have mozzy nets but not much else in the way of decoration. Toh and Long, the helpful and knowledgable couple who run the place, can provide you with an excellent map of the area, and can help out with travel plans. Motorbikes for rent (B250–300/day). Fan B250, a/c B400, bungalows B600

THE OLD CITY AREA

Old City Guest House Thanon Charodvithitong, a few metres from the access road to the museum and central zone ☎081 8864886; map p.240. Good-value guesthouse offering a range of options in two-storey buildings around a yard (with parking), set back from the road. Choose between small, rather dark but very cheap rooms with shared bathrooms; attractive, well-priced, en-suite fan rooms; and large, quite plush, a/c doubles with TV. Possibly the best location for seeing the main ruins. Fan B200, a/c B500

Orchid Hibiscus Guest House Just off Route 1272, about 1km southeast of the main entrance to the historical park ☎081 962 7698, ⓦorchidhibiscus -guesthouse.com; map p.240. Tranquil Italian–Thai-managed garden haven within easy cycling reach of the Old City. The brick bungalows are furnished with four-poster beds, a/c and mosquito nets and are ranged around a pretty tropical flower garden and swimming pool. They also have a couple of more private teak bungalows, plus, in a compound across the road, three- and four-bed family houses for rent. Email for cheapest rates. Doubles B900, bungalows B1300, houses B1500

Tharaburi Resort 321/3 Thanon Muangkao-Napoh, on Route 1272, just south of the junction with Highway 12 ☎055 697132, ⓦtharaburiresort.com; map p.240. Probably the best of several luxury resorts near the historical park, the *Tharaburi* oozes style and character. The twenty rooms and suites are in two separate one-storey buildings and a two-storey Thai house. Most rooms have teak walls and floors and are decorated with traditional Thai interior design. There's also a pool, free airport pick-up service, bicycles for guests' use and cookery courses. Big discounts for internet bookings. B3823

SUKHOTHAI AIRPORT

Sukhothai Heritage Resort Just outside the airport compound ☎055 647567, ⓦsukhothaiheritage.com; map p.238. Tastefully designed four-star hotel set in lovely

2

rural surrounds of organic rice fields (where guests can learn about rice farming), an orchid farm and lotus ponds. The hotel garden is artfully planted with shrubs and hedges and there are two pools, a restaurant and a library.

Rooms are modern with verandas overlooking the pool, flatscreen TVs and DVD players. Bicycles are available for guests' use. It's about halfway between Sukhothai and Si Satchanalai, so well placed for a visit to both. **B2500**

EATING AND DRINKING

The local speciality is a pungent bowl of **Sukhothai noodles**: thin rice noodles served in a dark, slightly sweet broth flavoured with soy sauce, coriander and chilli and spiked with chunks of pork crackling, green beans and peanuts. In New Sukhothai you can find them at *May Klang Kroong* and at the **hot-food stalls** and streetside tables that set up every evening in front of Wat Ratchathani on Thanon Charodvithitong and further west near *Poo Restaurant*. There's also a permanent covered area for night-market-style **restaurants** on the soi between Thanon Ramkhamhaeng and Thanon Nikhon Kasem. In the Old City, there is a string of restaurants serving hot food and fresh coffee on the street beside the Old City Guest House, just east of the main central zone entrance.

Chopper Bar 95/1-2 Thanon Pravetnakorn ☎ 055 611190. Upstairs terrace and bar with great music and a huge range of cocktails (from B85), as well as an extensive menu of Thai dishes (mostly B90–120). A good place to meet locals and other travellers. Daily 2.30pm–midnight.

★ **Dream Café** 86/1 Thanon Singhawat ☎ 055 612081. Dark and cosy, with walls and windowsills full of curios and Thai antiques, this rather cool, long-running Sukhothai institution serves great food (two courses for around B300–400) and is very popular. Highlights include *tom yam* with pork spare ribs and young tamarind leaves (B200), fresh Vietnamese-style spring rolls, and deep-fried banana-flower fritters. Choose also from several different ice-cream sundaes and a range of stamina-enhancing herbal drinks (B75) – plus gin-and-tonics. Daily 5–11pm.

Hong Rama Tearoom Nakorn de Sukhothai, 35/1 Thanon Prasertpong ☎ 095 6794949. On the ground floor of a boutique hotel, this welcoming restaurant is right opposite the covered night market, yet still tempts plenty of diners in with its smart design and eager-to-please staff. Mostly Thai cuisine (B80–180), but several Western dishes too such as pizza and spaghetti carbonara (B120), beer served in chilled glasses and yummy chocolate lava dessert. Daily 11am–9pm.

Kru Iew 203/25 Thanon Wichien Chamnong, corner of Soi Mahasaranon 1, about 75m north of At Home

guesthouse. This award-winning, folksy lunch spot is famous locally for its aromatic parcels of *phat thai* wrapped in thin omelette (from B35), its fresh Vietnamese-style *naem nueng* herb and pork spring rolls (B110–200) – and its Sukhothai noodles. Watch the white-capped cooks in their open-plan kitchens. Daily 9am–3.30pm.

May Klang Kroong 139 Thanon Charodvithitong ☎ 055 621882. No Roman-script sign but look out for the shopfront festooned with ferns. This is a great place to sample Sukhothai noodles (B35) and other local specialities from the short menu (in English), and soak up the mood of a bygone era. Staff wear traditional dress and there's also a small gift shop selling traditional clothing. Daily 8am–9pm.

Pai Restaurant 3 Thanon Pravetnakorn ☎ 080 8988848. Small but smart restaurant in the budget district, serving a range of Thai favourites like green curry with chicken (B60), as well as cakes and coffee. Good spot to sit back and watch the world go by. Daily 7.30am–10pm.

Poo Restaurant 24/3 Thanon Charodvithitong ☎ 086 9392085. Streetside travellers' bar-restaurant that serves all the standard Thai dishes plus cheap draught Chang beer, Belgian beer (from B120) and cocktails (from B100). Also rents motorbikes. Daily 7am–10pm.

SHOPPING

In the Old City, several shops just outside the park entrance sell reproduction antique furniture and ceramics.

Usa Sungkalok Sukhothai 357/1 Moo 3, just outside the central zone ☎ 081 9537604; map p.240. Visit this friendly ceramics factory for the best range of

traditional-style ceramics, especially copies of historic Sangkhalok and Sukhothai designs and glazes. Daily 8am–6pm.

DIRECTORY

Banks, exchange and ATMs In the Old City there's a currency exchange booth (daily 8.30am–12.30pm) next to the museum, and several ATMs on the approach road. New Sukhothai has many banks and ATMs.

Cookery courses One- and two-day courses led by

excellent tour guide Naa at her cooking school in the Old City (423/6 Moo 3, 300m south of the museum; ☎ 089 858 9864, ✉ ninetynine_gh@yahoo.com; B800/person/day). Accommodation is available for those on two-day courses.

Hospital The government-run Sukhothai Hospital (☎055 616403) is west of New Sukhothai on the road to Sukhothai Historical Park; there's a more central 24hr clinic on Thanon Singhawat.

Massage and spa treatments The most luxurious option is at *Lotus Village* (🌐lotus-village.com/spa; see p.247), where treatments take place in a lovely teak house and include turmeric body scrubs, herbal saunas, waxing and Thai massage (B600/1hr). There are many other cheaper massage places at guesthouses in the New City.

Post office Thanon Nikhon Kasem, about 1km south of the bridge in New Sukhothai (Mon–Fri 8.30am–4.30pm).

Tourist police For all emergencies, call the tourist police on ☎1155, or go to the local police station on Thanon Singhawat or the police box on Thanon Wichien Chamnong in New Sukhothai.

Travel agent Domestic and international air tickets can be bought through Sukhothai Travel Service, 10–12 Thanon Singhawat (Mon–Sat 8am–5pm; ☎055 613075, ✉sukhothai_travel@hotmail.com).

Si Satchanalai

In the mid-thirteenth century, Sukhothai cemented its power by establishing several satellite towns, of which the most important was **SI SATCHANALAI**, 57km upriver from Sukhothai on the banks of the Yom. Now a UNESCO-listed **historical park**, the partially restored ruins of **Muang Kao Si Satchanalai** have a quieter ambience than the grander models at Sukhothai Historical Park, and the additional attractions of the riverside wat in nearby **Chalieng**, the **Sangkhalok pottery kilns** in Ban Ko Noi, the **Sathorn Textile Museum** in New Si Satchanalai and **Boon Lott's Elephant Sanctuary** combine to make the area worth exploring.

The Historical Park (Muang Kao Si Satchanalai)

Just across the Yom River from Route 101 • Daily 8am–4.30pm • B100, which includes entry to Wat Phra Si Ratana Mahathat; vehicles B10–50, depending on size

Si Satchanalai Historical Park, or **Muang Kao Si Satchanalai**, is where you'll find most of the main monuments. At the entrance on the park's eastern side, there are food stalls, bicycle rental and a trolley bus (see p.253).

Muang Kao Si Satchanalai Information Centre

South of Wat Nang Phya, on the road that skirts around the central area of ruins • Daily 8am–5pm

Once inside the park it's worth heading to this friendly information centre, set around tranquil gardens, which provides useful background information on the area and shows how its location, on a plain between the Yom River and the Khao Phra Sri ridge, made it ideal for human habitation. Exhibits include shards of pottery from the excavation at nearby Wat Chom Chuen and some polished stone tools from Tha Chai subdistrict. There's also a large-scale model of the entire UNESCO World Heritage Site, showing how the temples hug the bend in the river.

Wat Chang Lom

Towards the centre of the park, southwest of the main entrance

Most circuits begin with the most striking set of ruins, the elephant temple of **Wat Chang Lom**, whose centrepiece is a huge, Sri Lankan-style, bell-shaped chedi set on a square base studded with 39 life-sized elephant buttresses (those in Sukhothai and Kamphaeng Phet are smaller). A mahout and his elephant sometimes hang out here to prove the point. Many of the elephant reliefs are in good repair, with much of their stucco flesh still intact; others now have their bulky laterite-brick innards exposed.

Wat Chedi Jet Taew

Just across from Wat Chang Lom

Wat Chedi Jet Taew has seven rows of small chedis thought to enshrine the ashes of Si Satchanalai's royal rulers, which makes it the ancient city's most important

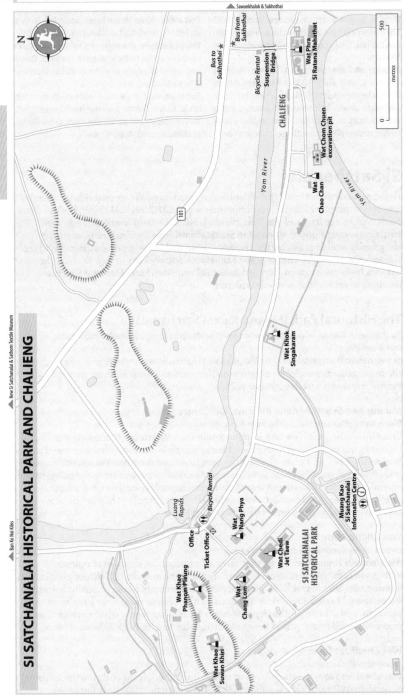

SI SATCHANALAI HISTORICAL PARK AND CHALIENG

▲ Sawankhalok & Sukhothai

▲ Ban Ko Noi Kilns
▲ New Si Satchanalai & Sathorn Textile Museum

Bus from Sukhothai

Wat Phra Si Ratana Mahathat

Bicycle Rental
Suspension Bridge

CHALIENG

Bus to Sukhothai

Wat Chom Chuen excavation pit

Yom River

Wat Chao Chan

Yom River

101

Wat Khok Singakaram

Luang Rapids

Bicycle Rental

Office

Ticket Office

Wat Nang Phya

Muang Kao Si Satchanalai Information Centre

Wat Chedi Jet Taew

SI SATCHANALAI HISTORICAL PARK

Wat Khao Phanom Pleung

Wat Chang Lom

Wat Khao Suwan Khiri

N

0   500
metres

temple. One of the 34 chedis is an elegant scaled-down replica of the hallmark lotus-bud chedi at Sukhothai's Wat Mahathat (see p.241). Several have fine stucco-covered Buddha images in their alcoves, including a famously beautiful one of the Buddha sheltered by a naga (now with restored head), also reproduced in Ramkhamhaeng National Museum.

Wat Nang Phya
A few hundred metres south of Wat Chedi Jet Taew

Wat Nang Phya is remarkable for the original stucco reliefs on its viharn wall, which remain in fine condition; stucco is a hardy material that sets soon after being first applied, and becomes even harder when exposed to rain – hence its ability to survive seven hundred years in the open. The balustraded wall has slit windows and is entirely covered with intricate floral motifs.

Wat Khao Phanom Pleung and Wat Khao Suwan Khiri
About 600m north of Wat Chang Lom

The hilltop ruins of Wat Khao Phanom Pleung and nearby Wat Khao Suwan Khiri afford splendid aerial views of different quarters of the ancient city. The sole remaining intact chedi of **Wat Khao Phanom Pleung** sits on top of the lower of the hills and used to be flanked by a set of smaller chedis built to entomb the ashes of Si Satchanalai's important personages – the ones who merited some special memorial, but didn't quite make the grade for Wat Chedi Jet Taew. The temple presumably got its name, which means "mountain of sacred fire", from the cremation rituals held on the summit.

Wat Khao Suwan Khiri's huge chedi, which graces the summit 200m northwest, has definitely seen better days, but the views from its platform – south over the main temple ruins and north towards the city walls and entrance gates – are worth the climb.

Wat Phra Si Ratana Mahathat
Just over 2km southeast of the Historical Park • B100, which includes entry to Si Satchanalai Historical Park; vehicles B10–50, depending on size

Before Sukhothai asserted control of the region and founded Si Satchanalai, the Khmers governed the area known as **Chalieng**, which is cradled in a bend in the Yom River. Just about all that now remains of Chalieng is **Wat Phra Si Ratana Mahathat**, whose compound, aligned east–west and encircled by a now sunken wall of laterite blocks, contains structures thought to date back to the Khmer era, but with later additions by Sukhothai and Ayutthayan builders.

If you approach from the wooden suspension bridge you'll enter via the semi-submerged eastern gateway, passing beneath a hefty Khmer-style carved lintel that was hewn from a single block of stone. Inside, the compound is dominated by a towering corncob prang, the main shrine, which was likely remodelled during the Ayutthayan era and whose exterior has been renovated with all-over stucco decorations. The ruined viharn in front of the prang enshrines a large seated Buddha sculpted in typical Sukhothai style, with hand gestures symbolizing his triumph over temptation. The tall stucco relief of a walking Buddha to the left is also classic Sukhothai and is regarded as one of the finest of its genre. Immediately to the west of the prang, the remains of the octagonal laterite platform and its bell-shaped chedi are believed to date from a different era, possibly considerably earlier. A mondop containing a large standing Buddha guards one side and looks towards the River Yom; a second viharn, containing two Buddha images, occupies the other flank.

Ban Ko Noi kilns

Endowed with high-quality clay, the area around Si Satchanalai – known as Sawankhalok or Sangkhalok during the Ayutthaya period – commanded an international reputation as a ceramics centre from the mid-fourteenth to the end of the fifteenth century, producing pieces still rated among the finest in the world. More than two hundred **kilns** have been unearthed in and around Si Satchanalai to date, and it's estimated that there could once have been a thousand in all. One of the main groups of kilns is in the village of **BAN KO NOI**, which is about 5km upstream from the park entry point and can be reached by bicycle by following the very pleasant, almost traffic-free road beside the river (not the one going into the park) through hamlets fringed with flowering shrubs and fruit trees. If you continue another kilometre or so beyond Ban Ko Noi, there is another set of kilns that has been excavated and is now protected by an open-sided pavilion.

Sangkhalok Kiln Preservation Centre

Daily 8.30am–4.30pm • B100

Four excavated kilns at Ban Ko Noi have been roofed and turned into the **Sangkhalok Kiln Preservation Centre**. Two of the kilns are up-draught kilns and two are cross-draught kilns, the latter generating a greater and more consistent heat, which enabled the production of glazed ware. Most Sangkhalok ceramics were glazed – the grey-green celadon, probably introduced by immigrant Chinese potters, was especially popular – and typically decorated with fish or chrysanthemum motifs. A small display of **Sangkhalok ceramics** gives a hint of the pieces that were fired here: domestic items such as pots, decorated plates and lidded boxes; decorative items like figurines, temple sculptures and temple roof tiles; and items for export, particularly to Indonesia and the Philippines, where huge Sangkhalok storage jars were used as burial urns.

At busy times, stalls across the road from the Preservation Centre sell reproduction ceramics and "antiques". Several of Thailand's major museums feature collections of ceramics from both Si Satchanalai and Sukhothai under the umbrella label of Sangkhalok, and there's a dedicated collection of Sangkhalok wares just outside New Sukhothai (see p.244).

Sathorn Textile Museum

11km north of the Historical Park, at the northern end of the modern town of Si Satchanalai, on the east side of Highway 101 • Daily 9am–5pm • Free • Any Sukhothai guesthouse can include a visit to the museum in a Si Satchanalai day-trip, or you can come here on the bus from New Sukhothai, getting off in modern Si Satchanalai rather than at the ruins

The **Sathorn Textile Museum** houses the private collection of Khun Sathorn, who also runs the adjacent textile shop, and he or his staff open up the one-room exhibition for anyone who shows an interest.

Most of the **textiles** on show come from the nearby village of Hat Siew, whose weavers have long specialized in the art of *teen jok*, or hem embroidery, whereby the bottom panel of the sarong or *phasin* (woman's sarong) is decorated with a band of supplementary weft, usually done in exquisitely intricate patterns. Some of the textiles here are almost a hundred years old and many of the *teen jok* **motifs** have symbolic meaning showing what the cloths would have been used for – a sarong or *phasin* used for a marriage ceremony, for example, tends to have a double image, such as two birds facing each other. Elephants also feature quite a lot in Hat Siew weaving, probably a reference to the village custom in which young men who are about to become monks parade on elephants to their ordination ceremony. The tradition continues to this day and elephant parades are held at the mass ordination ceremony every year on April 7. Modern Hat Siew textiles are sold at the adjacent Sathorn **shop** and at other outlets further south along the main road.

Boon Lott's Elephant Sanctuary (BLES)

304 Moo 5, Ban Na Ton Jan, Tambon Ban Tuek (about 30km northeast of Si Satchanalai, on the way to Uttaradit; arrange pick-up at Sukhothai Airport) • B5000/person/night (advance booking necessary) • ⓦ blesele.org

Named after a baby elephant that succumbed to various injuries, **Boon Lott's Elephant Sanctuary (BLES)** was started by Katherine Connor in 2004 and is now one of the most popular sanctuaries in the country, home to around twenty elephants that have been saved from abuse and sickness. The sanctuary is only open to guests staying overnight; accommodation consists of three teak cottages and prices are inclusive of all meals. Guests are involved in every aspect of caring for the elephants, from collecting food for them to repairing elephant pens and bathing the pachyderms. Typically people stay around three to five days, but at the time of writing it was fully booked a year ahead, so this is one experience that needs some advance planning.

ARRIVAL AND DEPARTURE   SI SATCHANALAI

A visit to Si Satchanalai Historical Park works best as a day-trip from Sukhothai (60km away). The easiest option is to travel with a **car** or **motorbike** from New Sukhothai, or join an **tour** from there, which can be organized through many of the guesthouses.

By bus The fastest way to get here by public transport from Sukhothai is on one of the a/c buses bound for Chiang Rai; these depart New Sukhothai bus station at 6.40am, 9am and 11.30am and take just over an hour. Local buses depart about every half-hour (also from the bus station), but take almost two hours and sometimes require a change of bus in Sawankhalok. All buses drop passengers on Highway 101 at the signpost for Wat Phra Si Ratana Mahathat, beside a pink archway gate. Pass through it, follow the narrow road and cross the suspension bridge to the temple, from where it's a further 2km to Si Satchanalai Historical Park. Heading back, the last conveniently timed a/c bus to New Sukhothai passes Old Si Satchanalai at about 4.30pm.

GETTING AROUND

By bicycle If arriving by bus, the best place to rent a bike (B30) is the shop at the end of the suspension bridge, close to Wat Phra Si Ratana Mahathat. Bikes are also available for rent for the same price in front of the entrance to the historical park.

By trolley bus At busy times, a trolley bus takes visitors on a tour of the main temples from the entrance, lasting around an hour, for B20 per person.

Kamphaeng Phet

KAMPHAENG PHET, 77km south of Sukhothai, was probably founded in the fourteenth century by the kings of Sukhothai as a buffer city between their capital and the increasingly powerful city-state of Ayutthaya. Strategically sited 100m from the east bank of the Ping, the ruined old city has, like Sukhothai and Si Satchanalai before it, been partly restored and opened to the public as a **historical park** and is similarly listed as a UNESCO World Heritage Site. The least visited of the three, it rivals both Sukhothai and Si Satchanalai for your attention mainly because of the untamed setting and the gracefully weathered statues of its main temple.

A new city has grown up on the southeastern boundaries of the old, the usual commercial blandness offset by a riverside park, plentiful flowers and an unusual number of historic wooden houses dotted along the main thoroughfares. You can even swim off an island in the middle of the river, accessible via a footbridge near Soi 21, a few hundred metres south of the night market. With a few days in the area, you can spend time bird-watching or rafting in the nearby national parks.

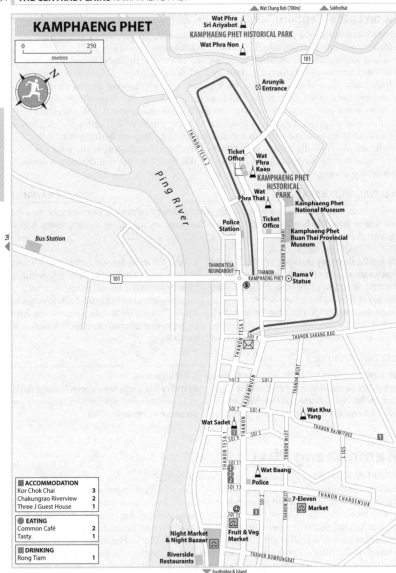

Historical Park (Muang Kao Kamphaeng Phet)

Daily 6am–6pm • B150 for both main zones or B100 for one zone • vehicles B10–50 • Bicycle rental B30–50 • Tram tours (when enough people) B20

Ruins surround modern Kamphaeng Phet on all sides, but the **Historical Park** – or **Muang Kao Kamphaeng Phet** – takes in the two most interesting areas: the oblong zone inside the old city walls, and the forested ("*arunyik*") area just north of that. A tour of both areas involves a 5km round-trip, so you'll need transport; a bicycle or tram tour are the best options. The ruins that dot the landscape across the Ping River, west of the Thanon Tesa roundabout, belong to the even older city of Nakhon Chum, but are very dilapidated.

Parts of the **city walls** that gave Kamphaeng Phet its name are still in good condition, though Highway 101 to Sukhothai now cuts through the enclosed area and a few shops have sprung up along the roadside, making it hard to visualize the fortifications as a whole. Approaching from the Thanon Tesa roundabout, you can either head up Thanon Pin Damri and start your tour at **Wat Phra That** and the **Provincial Museum**, or you enter the compound from the western gate and come in at the back end of **Wat Phra Kaeo**.

The dozen or so ruins in the forested area north of the city walls – east 100m along Highway 101 from behind Wat Phra Kaeo, across the moat and up a road to the left – are all that remains of Kamphaeng Phet's **arunyik** (forest) temples, built here by Sukhothai-era monks in a wooded area to encourage meditation. It's an enjoyably tranquil and atmospheric area to explore, with the tumbledown structures peeking out of the thinly planted groves that line the access road; the road winds around a fair bit before eventually rejoining the Sukhothai–Kamphaeng Phet highway to the north of the walled city.

Wat Phra Kaeo

Inside the city walls

Built almost entirely of laterite and adorned with laterite Buddhas, **Wat Phra Kaeo** was the city's central and most important structure, and given the name reserved for temples that have housed the kingdom's most sacred image: the Emerald Buddha, now in the wat of the same name in Bangkok (see p.84), is thought to have been set down here to rest at some point. Seven centuries later, the Buddha images have been worn away into attractive abstract shadows, often aptly compared to the pitted, spidery forms of Giacometti sculptures, and the slightly unkempt feel to the place makes a perfect setting. Few tools have been unearthed at any of the Kamphaeng Phet sites, giving weight to the theory that the sculptors moulded their statues from the clay-like freshly dug laterite before leaving it to harden. Small, overgrown laterite quarry pits are still visible all over the old city. The statues would originally have been faced with stucco, and restorers have already patched up the central tableau of one reclining and two seated Buddhas. The empty niches that encircle the principal chedi were once occupied by statues of bejewelled lions.

Wat Phra That

Adjoining Wat Phra Kaeo, inside the city walls

Just east of Wat Phra Kaeo is Kamphaeng Phet's second-biggest temple, **Wat Phra That**. Together, Wat Phra That and Wat Phra Kaeo represented the religious centre of the ancient city. Here the central bell-shaped chedi, now picturesquely wreathed in lichen and stray bits of vegetation, is typical of the Sri Lankan style and was built to house a sacred relic.

Kamphaeng Phet National Museum

Just east of Wat Phra That, inside the city walls • Wed–Sun 9am–4pm • B100 • ⓦ thailandmuseum.com

Kamphaeng Phet National Museum takes a look at the fascinating development of the ancient city. The prize exhibit in its upstairs sculpture gallery is the bronze standing **Shiva**: cast in the sixteenth century in Khmer-Ayutthayan style, the statue has had a chequered history – including decapitation by a nineteenth-century German admirer. Also on this floor is an unusual wooden, seventeenth- or eighteenth-century Ayutthayan-style standing Buddha, whose diadem, necklace and even hems are finely carved.

Kamphaeng Phet Ruan Thai Provincial Museum

Next to Kamphaeng Phet National Museum, inside the city walls • Daily 9am–4.30pm • B10

While you're at the National Museum you can't miss the alluring group of recently built traditional-style teakwood *salas* in the adjacent compound. This is the **Kamphaeng Phet Ruan Thai Provincial Museum**, whose captivating exhibits and scale models introduce the history, traditions and contemporary culture of Kamphaeng Phet province.

Wat Phra Non

Arunyik area: the first temple on the left once through the entrance

Wat Phra Non is otherwise known as the Temple of the Reclining Buddha, though you need a good imagination to conjure up the indistinct remains into the once enormous Buddha figure. Gigantic laterite pillars support the viharn that houses the statue; far more ambitious than the usual brick-constructed jobs, these pillars were cut from single slabs of stone from a nearby quarry and would have measured up to 8m in height.

Wat Phra Sri Ariyabot

Arunyik area: immediately to the north of Wat Phra Non

The four Buddha images of **Wat Phra Sri Ariyabot** are in better condition than Wat Phra Non's reclining Buddha. With cores of laterite and skins of stucco, the restored standing and walking images tower over the viharn, while the seated (south-facing) and reclining (north-facing) Buddhas have been eroded into indistinct blobs. The full-grown trees rooted firmly in the raised floor are evidence of just how old the place is.

Wat Chang Rob

Arunyik area: 1km from the entrance gate • Follow the road around the bend from Wat Phra Sri Ariyabot

Wat Chang Rob is crouched on top of a laterite hill. Built to the same Sri Lankan model as its sister temples with a similar name in Sukhothai and Si Satchanalai (Wat Chang Lom; see p.244 & p.249 respectively), this "temple surrounded by elephants" retains only the square base of its central bell-shaped chedi. Climb one of its four steep staircases for a view out over the mountains in the west, or just for a different perspective of the 68 elephant buttresses that encircle the base. Sculpted from laterite and stucco, they're dressed in the ceremonial garb fit for such revered animals; floral reliefs can just be made out along the surfaces between neighbouring elephants – the lower level was once decorated with a stucco frieze of flying birds.

ARRIVAL AND DEPARTURE   **KAMPHAENG PHET**

Most people visit Kampheng Phet as a **day-trip** from Sukhothai, either on one of the direct buses or by arranging a tour and driver through their guesthouse – though there are buses here from other towns, too.

By bus Arriving by bus from Sukhothai or Phitsanulok, you'll enter Kamphaeng Phet from the east and should get off either inside the old city walls or at the Thanon Tesa roundabout rather than wait to be deposited across the river at the terminal, 2km west of town on Highway 101. From the bus station, you'll need to hop on a red town songthaew, which will take you to the Thanon Tesa roundabout just east of the river (the most convenient disembarkation point for the ruins), or further into the town centre for most of the hotels and restaurants.

Destinations Bangkok (hourly; 6hr 30min); Chiang Mai (hourly; 6hr); Phitsanulok (hourly; 3hr); Sukhothai (hourly; 1hr–1hr 30min); Tak (hourly; 1hr).

GETTING AROUND AND TOURS

By songthaew From the Thanon Tesa roundabout, songthaews do a clockwise circle around the new town, running south along Thanon Rajdamnoen (get off at the intersection with Rajdamnoen Soi 4 for *Three J Guest*

CLOCKWISE FROM TOP LEFT WAT MAHATHAT, SUKHOTHAI (P.241); DON RAK CEMETERY, KANCHANABURI (P.190); THI LAW SU FALLS (P.265) >

House), then west along Bumrungrat, north up Thanon Tesa 1 and west out to the bus station.

By bicycle or motorbike Bicycles are available for rent (B30–50/day) at the entrance to both sections of the historical park. *Three J Guest House* is the only place that rents out motorbikes (B200/day) – not very convenient for day-trippers, however.

Tours *Three J Guest House* can arrange day-trips to nearby waterfalls, hot springs and a glass-blowing village.

ACCOMMODATION

Kor Chok Chai 19/43 Rajdamnoen Soi 8, east of the fruit and veg market ☎ 055 711247. The main budget alternative to *Three J Guest House*, with decent fan and a/c rooms, this hotel is recognizable by its pair of Chinese stone lions guarding the door. It's centrally located, comfortable (though a bit run-down) and friendly. Fan **B280**, a/c **B340**

Chakungrao Riverview 149 Thanon Tessa 1 ☎ 055 714900-4, ⓦ chakungraoriverview.com. The best hotel in central Kamphaeng Phet, though it's seen better days. Rooms are a decent size and all have a/c, TV and en-suite bathrooms. Those out front have river views, and those out back look over a temple. Staff are very helpful and breakfast

is included. **B1000**

Three J Guest House 79 Thanon Rajwithee, 600m east of the main drag ☎ 081 887 4189, ⓦ three jguesthouse.com. The most traveller-oriented place in Kamphaeng Phet, this pleasant, secluded homestay with a dozen comfortable bungalows is built from rough-cut logs and set in a Chinese-style rock garden at the back of a family home. All rooms have cosy verandas; the cheapest options share bathrooms and the priciest have a/c, and there are family rooms sleeping four people (B800). There's bicycle and motorbike rental (B50/B200 per day), and day-trips to nearby attractions (see above). Fan **B300**, a/c **B500**

EATING AND DRINKING

From late afternoon the **night market** is the most enjoyable place to eat. Occupying a covered area in the southern part of the new town between the river and Thanon Tesa 1, it offers a mouthwateringly wide selection of specialist sweet and savoury stalls; ask for the special local noodle dish, *kway tiaw cha kang rao*, made with cowpeas and pork.

Common Café 141 Thanon Tessa 1 ☎ 088 1155916. This cool coffee shop serves not only all kinds of coffee, but also imported beers, cocktails (B129–149), smoothies and a few snacks like croissants and cakes. Daily 10am–11pm.

Rong Tiam Rajdamnoen Soi 9. This welcoming bar is the place to head if you're looking for nightlife; it's full of character and very popular among locals. There's live

music every evening from 9pm, played by talented local musicians. Daily 6pm–midnight.

Tasty 115–119 Thanon Tessa 1 ☎ 055 712594. If you'd rather eat in a/c comfort than in the night market, head for this cosy spot, where prices are only marginally higher (most dishes B45–60). The Thai and a few Western dishes are well prepared and presented, and there are seats upstairs if it's full downstairs. Daily 10.30am–10.30pm.

Mae Sot and the border

Located just 6km from Myanmar, and 100km west of Tak, **MAE SOT** is very much a border town, populated by a rich ethnic mix of Burmese, Karen, Hmong and Thai. It is dependent on its thriving trade in Burmese gems and teak as well as, reportedly, on an even more lucrative cross-border black market in drugs, labourers and sex workers. For the casual visitor, however, it's a relaxed place to hang out, with several good restaurants to enjoy, although there are no unmissable sights. The short ride to the border market provides additional, if low-key, interest, and there are several caves and waterfalls within day-tripping distance.

For many people, Mae Sot is just an overnight stop on the way to **Umphang** (see p.263), a remote village 164km further south. Since the road to Umphang is full of twists and bends and the journey takes at least four hours, it is advisable to set out in the morning, either in a bumpy songthaew or with your own wheels.

In Mae Sot the Burmese influence is palpable in everything from food to fashions; many of the guesthouses are run by Burmese staff, who often speak good English, and the only real sights in the town are its handful of glittering Burmese-style temples.

MAE SOT

ACCOMMODATION	
Bai Fern	5
Ban Thai	2
Centara Mae Sot Hill Resort	1
Duang Kamol (D.K.) Hotel	6
Green Guest House	3
Irawadee Resort	4
J2 Hotel	7

SHOPS	
Borderline	1
Weave	2

EATING	
Bai Fern	5
Borderline Tea Garden	4
Casa Mia	3
Khao-Mao Khao-Fang	1
Krua Canadian Restaurant	6
The Passport	2

Rim Moei market

Frequent songthaews (B25) ferry Thai traders and a meagre trickle of tourists the 6km from Mae Sot's government bus station to the border at **RIM MOEI**, where a market for Burmese goods has grown up along the high street and beside the banks of the Moei River. It's a bit tacky, and not as fun to browse as Mae Sot's markets, but it's not a bad place to pick up Burmese **handicrafts**, particularly wooden artefacts such as boxes and picture frames, woven Karen shoulder-bags and checked *longyis*. The best buys are chunky teak tables and chairs, most of them polished up to a fine, golden brown sheen; vendors will arrange shipping.

Wat Thai Wattanaram and Wat Phra That Doi Hin Kiu

Both temples are located on a turn to the north of the Asian Highway about 500m east of the Friendship Bridge; Wat Thai Wattanaram is signposted just 100m up this road, while Wat Phra That Doi Hin Kiu is 7km further north on the same road – take the right fork at a police checkpoint along this road and look for the temple on the hill to the right (no English sign). You'll need your own transport to get here

If you're heading out to the Rim Moei market, it's worth taking a look at nearby **Wat Thai Wattanaram**, a Shan temple built in 1857. The main attractions here are a 45m reclining Buddha with bright red lips that's protected by an open-sided shelter, and a cloister of 28 sitting Buddha images just beyond this. The viharn has a display of Shan musical instruments on the second floor. If you're not heading into Myanmar where you can visit the Kyaiktiyo Pagoda (Golden Rock), you can see Thailand's smaller equivalent at **Wat Phra That Doi Hin Kiu** on a hill that looks out over the Moei River – an idyllic pastoral scene. A 5m-tall standing Buddha marks the beginning of the steep stairway that leads up to the gold-painted rock, which is surmounted by a small chedi surrounded by Burmese figurines. The rock is precariously balanced and seems about to tumble down the mountain, and its gleaming gold colour makes a stark contrast with the lush green background.

Waterfalls, springs and caves near Mae Sot

There are several minor caves and waterfalls around Mae Sot, which are easy enough to explore if you have your own transport, though none can compare with Umphang's far

2

HELPING MAE SOT'S BURMESE REFUGEES

There are currently five camps for **refugees** from Myanmar along the border to the north and south of Mae Sot, and Mae Sot itself was the headquarters for many related international **aid projects**, though many have now relocated to Yangon. Some of these organizations welcome donations and some are happy to receive visitors and even short-term volunteers; ask at *Ban Thai* guesthouse, Borderline shop and at *Krua Canadian* and *Bai Fern* restaurants. One of the most famous organizations in Mae Sot is the **Mae Tao clinic**, which provides free medical care for around 150,000 Burmese migrants and refugees a year, focusing on those who fall outside the remit of the camps and cannot use the Thai health system. The clinic was founded in 1989 by a Karen refugee, Dr Cynthia, who has won several prestigious international awards for her work; her clinic also trains and equips "backpack teams" of mobile medics who spend months travelling through the Burmese jungle providing healthcare to internally displaced peoples. To help the clinic by giving blood or financial aid, visit the office inside the clinic compound on Thanon Indharakiri (mornings are preferable but the office opens Mon–Sat 9am–4pm; ☎055 544655, ⓦmaetaoclinic.org); it's about 1km west of *Ban Thai*, or 350m east of the bus station. The clinic also runs a primary and secondary school and welcomes volunteer health-workers and teachers who can commit for several months.

---

mightier Thi Law Su Falls. Borderline shop (see p.263) should be able to provide you with route maps and information.

To reach the three-tier **Mae Kasa Falls** (rainy season only) and hot springs (around 14km from town) head north out of Mae Sot, along Highway 105 towards Mae Ramat, then take a side road at around kilometre-stone 13 for 7km. Much further north, just after kilometre-stone 95 on Highway 105, a sign directs you the 2km off the highway to the enormous 800m-deep bat-cave, **Tham Mae Usu** (inaccessible July–Oct because of flooding).

South out of town, off Route 1090 to Umphang, the 97 tiers of **Pha Charoen Falls** are 41km from Mae Sot; take any songthaew bound for Umphang. The falls drop down through the jungle like a wonky staircase, and are a popular photo spot for day-tripping Thais.

Highland Farm Gibbon Sanctuary

A couple of kilometres on from Pha Charoen Falls, 43km south of Mae Sot at kilometre-stone 42.8 on Route 1090 to Umphang • ☎089 958 0821, ⓦ gibbonathighlandfarm.org • Take any songthaew bound for Umphang • Free for brief visits

Highland Farm Gibbon Sanctuary cares for over sixty injured and abandoned gibbons, most of which have been rescued from abusive owners and are unable to live in the wild. They also take care of around twenty monkeys, a couple of jackals and an Asiatic bear. The sanctuary welcomes day-trippers and homestay visitors (minimum stay five nights; US$45 per person per day full-board), and also offers one-month placements ($1100 all-inclusive), but you'll need to book months in advance as it's often full with volunteers.

ARRIVAL AND DEPARTURE   MAE SOT

By plane Nok Air operates flights from Bangkok (Don Muang; 2–3 daily; 1hr 15min) to Mae Sot's airport, 3km west of town, as does Kan Air (Don Muang; daily; 1hr 15min). Motorbike taxis and metered taxis are on hand for the run into the centre. Domestic and international air tickets can be bought at SE Southeast Express internet centre and shipping agent, 522/3 Thanon Indharakiri (☎055 547048, ⓔjoenew2006@gmail.com).

By bus, minibus or songthaew Buses for Bangkok, Chiang Mai, Chiang Rai, Mae Sai, Phitsanulok and Sukhothai leave from government bus station west of town at the Thanon Indharakiri/Highway 105 intersection; a motorbike taxi into town costs around B50. Minibuses to Tak and songthaews to Mae Sariang and Mae Ramat leave from Soi Rongchai; songthaews to Pha Charoen and Rim Moei leave from Thanon Banthung; and songthaews to Umphang leave from Mae Sot Villa, a housing development to the east of the town centre.

Destinations Bangkok (12 daily; 8hr 30min); Chiang Mai (2 daily; 6hr 30min–7hr 30min); Chiang Rai (2 daily; 11hr); Mae Ramat (songthaews every 30min; 45min); Mae Sai (2 daily; 12hr); Mae Sariang (songthaews hourly 6am–noon; 5hr); Phitsanulok (9 daily; 4–5hr); Sukhothai (9 daily; 2hr 30min–3hr); Tak (minibuses every 30min; 2hr); Umphang (songthaews hourly 7.30am–noon; 4–5hr).

GETTING AROUND AND INFORMATION

By bicycle or motorbike Several guesthouses such as *Bai Fern* rent motorbikes (around B200/day) and bicycles (around B50/day).

By car Thai Rent a Car (☏ 089 4567890, ⍟ thairentacar .com) has an office at the airport and rents cars from B1100 per day.

2

REFUGEES FROM MYANMAR: THE KAREN

With a population of five to seven million, the **Karen** are Myanmar's largest ethnic minority, but their numbers have offered no protection against persecution by the Burmese. This mistreatment has been going on for centuries, and entered a new phase after the country won its independence from Britain in 1948. Unlike many other groups in Myanmar, the Karen had remained loyal to the British during World War II and were supposed to have been rewarded with autonomy when Britain pulled out; instead they were left to battle for that themselves. Fourteen years after the British withdrawal, the **Burmese army** took control, setting up an isolationist state run under a bizarre ideology compounded of militarist, socialist and Buddhist principles. From that time, the military were engaged in armed conflict with all ethnic minority groups in the country until 2011, when a new government, consisting of military and civilians, brought about a fragile stability.

However, despite positive steps in a nationwide peace process, which has seen numerous ceasefires signed since late 2011, clashes continue to erupt between government forces and armed factions of some minority groups. The Karen people, whose homeland state of Kawthulay borders northwest Thailand from Mae Sariang down to Three Pagodas Pass, are among those affected. Despite signing a ceasefire, the Karen National Union (KNU), which has an armed wing, was still involved in skirmishes with Burmese government troops at the time of this update. (The Karen are distinct from the Karenni, or Red Karen, whose homeland is north of Kawthulay and borders Thailand's Mae Hong Son province.)

As a result of these conflicts, many Karen continue to flee across the Thai border. For many years **Thai government policy** has been to admit only those who are fleeing active fighting, not human rights violations. Thailand is not a signatory to the 1951 Convention Relating to the Status of Refugees and has no legal framework for processing asylum seekers. The hundreds of thousands who have left their homeland because of politically induced economic hardship – forced labour, theft of their land and livestock, among other factors – must therefore either try to enter the refugee camps illegally, or attempt to make a living as **migrant workers**. There are between two and three million migrants from Myanmar currently in Thailand. Without refugee status, these exiles are extremely vulnerable to abuse, both from corrupt officials and from exploitative employers. In Mae Sot, for example, where Burmese migrants are a mainstay of the local economy, many of them are reportedly paid as little as B100 a day (less than half the national minimum wage) to work in the worst jobs available, in gem and garment factories, and as prostitutes. Demands for better wages and improved conditions, however, nearly always result in deportation.

Reactions in the **Thai press** to Burmese refugees are mixed, with humanitarian concerns tempered by economic hardships in Thailand and by high-profile cases of illegal Burmese workers involved in violent crimes and drug-smuggling (Myanmar is now one of the world's leading producers and smugglers of methamphetamines, also known as *ya baa*, or Ice, much of which finds its way into Thailand).

For recent **news** and archive reports on the situation in Myanmar and on its borders, see ⍟ bnionline.net. For information on how to offer **support** to refugees from Myanmar, see the website of the Thai Burma Border Consortium (TBBC; ⍟ tbbc.org), and further leads on p.58. A good book about the Karen struggle and the refugee situation in Mae Sot is *Restless Souls: Rebels, Refugees, Medics and Misfits* by Phil Thornton, a Mae Sot-based journalist.

By taxi Mae Sot has a small fleet of metered taxis; call ☎ 055 030357 to book one (B50). Rates are B30 for the first two kilometres, and B4 per kilometre after that. There are only a few in town and you can't pick them up on the street.

Tourist information There is no TAT office here, but both Borderlines shop and *Krua Canadian* restaurant are good sources of local information (see opposite), as are the guesthouses.

ACCOMMODATION

Because of the many volunteers in town, most guesthouses offer weekly and monthly discounts.

★ **Ban Thai** 740/1 Thanon Indharakiri ☎ 055 531590, ✉ banthai_mth@hotmail.com. The most appealing guesthouse in Mae Sot occupies several traditional-style, wooden-floored houses in a peaceful garden compound at the west end of town. All rooms are tastefully and comfortably furnished; those in the main house share bathrooms, while those in the more expensive compound houses are en suite and have cable TV. It's often full so advance bookings are recommended. Fan B280, a/c B850

Centara Mae Sot Hill Resort 100 Asia Highway/ Highway 105 ☎ 055 532601, ⊛ centarahotelsresorts .com. The top business hotel in the area has tennis courts and a pool, though rooms are unexceptional and it's a 10min drive from the town centre. B1500

Duang Kamol (D.K.) Hotel 298/2 Thanon Indharakiri ☎ 055 531699. The nicest and best value of the town-centre hotels has huge, clean rooms, many of them with little balconies and some with a/c and TVs. The entrance is on the first floor, above a series of shops. Fan B250, a/c B380

Irawadee Resort 758/1-2 Thanon Indharakiri ☎ 055 535430, ⊛ irawadee.com. The rooms here definitely have character, though you might find the gold-painted furnishings, red walls and canopied beds a bit over the top. The "resort" tag is a bit of a misnomer – it's more like a boutique hotel – but it has a good central location and helpful staff. B1200

J2 Hotel 149/8 Thanon Indharakiri ☎ 055 546999, ✉ j2hotel@hotmail.com. This is probably the best of several new mid-range options in town, although the location is about 1km east of the centre. The good-sized rooms have tiled floors, stylish furnishings and flatscreen TVs, and breakfast is included in the price. B850

EATING AND DRINKING

Thanon Prasat Vithi is well stocked with noodle shops and **night-market stalls**, there's lots of Muslim and Burmese food for sale in the market, and there are several bars and restaurants on the new ring road east of town between Thanon Indharakiri and the Asian Highway; this is the best area to go looking for nightlife.

Bai Fern 660/2 Thanon Indharakiri ☎ 055 533343. Welcoming restaurant which serves some of the most imaginative food in the region. The menu includes pepper steak (B220), salmon salad (B150), authentic Italian carbonara (B120), traditional Thai curries and lots of vegetarian options, as well as brownies, chocolate cake and mixed-grain bread. Daily 8.30am–11pm.

Borderline Tea Garden 674/14 Thanon Indharakiri ☎ 055 546584, ⊛ borderlinecollective.org. In the garden behind their fair-trade handicrafts shop, this very relaxed café serves cheap Burmese snacks – including vegetable pakoras (B50) and potato curry with flat bread (B50) – washed down with Burmese tea (B25), lemon grass and other juices (B35). Everything on the menu is vegetarian and no alcohol is served. They also have a book exchange and run cookery classes (see opposite). Daily 7.30am–9pm.

Casa Mia Thanon Don Kaew, 5min walk past Ban Thai guesthouse ☎ 087 2044701. Popular for its home-made pizzas and pastas, including an especially delicious spicy tortellini pomodoro. Also does a big range of Thai dishes,

---

CROSSING THE MYANMAR BORDER AT MAE SOT

If you have a visa arranged in advance, you can enter Myanmar via the international border crossing (daily 6am–6pm) at the Thai-Myanmar Friendship Bridge, just 7km west of Mae Sot. Regular songthaews go there from the bus station west of town (see p.260), and from the bridge it's just 1km to the town of Myawaddy in Myanmar. There's a separate window for foreigners, so the process of crossing the border is fairly rapid. From Myawaddy, it's possible to travel on to popular tourist destinations like the Kyaiktiyo Pagoda (the Golden Rock) and Mawlamyine. Before the opening of the border to foreigners, this border post was used mostly by long-stay visitors to Thailand on visa runs, but now that the Thai government has clamped down on visa extensions it's becoming more popular as the starting point for an exploration of Myanmar.

salads, veggie options and a daily roster of cakes and desserts – cheesecake, banoffee pie and the like. Most mains B40–120. Mon–Fri & Sun 8am–10pm.

★**Khao-Mao Khao-Fang** 382 Moo 9, Thanon Mae Sot-Mae Ramat (about 2km north of town on the west side of Highway 105) ☎055 532483, ⍟khaomaokhaofang .com. A garden restaurant extraordinaire, where the artfully landscaped cascades, rivulets, rock features and mature trees make you feel as if you're sitting in a primeval forest film set, especially at night when sea-green lighting adds to the effect. Even the chairs and tables are carved from tree trunks and branches. A popular spot for dates and VIP lunches, it serves a fantastic range of food, including some unusual Thai dishes, such as banana blossom and coconut milk spicy salad (B120). Everything is beautifully prepared and presented, and there are some yummy desserts too, like banana fritters with sesame glaze (B140). Don't miss the bathrooms, which are something special. During the day you could use the Mae Ramat/Mae Sariang songthaew service, but after dark you'll need to call a taxi or use your own transport. Daily 11am–3pm & 5–10pm.

Krua Canadian Restaurant 3 Thanon Sripanich ☎055 534659. There's a great menu of delicious dishes (mostly B90–140) at this simple restaurant, including the best Western breakfasts in town, plus bangers and mash, steaks and a good range of Thai, Mexican and vegetarian dishes. Also serves several blends of local hill-tribe coffee, and owner Dave is a mine of local information. Daily 7am–10pm.

The Passport at HCTC 507 Moo 10, Maepa, about 2km northwest of the town centre ☎080 1182651, ⍟thehctc.org. This excellent restaurant is a training school (the Hospitality & Catering Training Centre) for underprivileged Karen, and the students are enthusiastic and charming. Choose one of the three-course menus (Thai or Western), which change weekly, for around B200–250, and enjoy the attractive, minimalist decor. Fri & Sat 6.30–9pm.

SHOPPING

For fashions, Burmese sarongs and daily necessities, you can't beat the well-stocked **day market** that runs south off Thanon Ruamchit. Mae Sot is most famous, however, as a good place to buy jewellery: the **gem and jade shops** on central Thanon Prasat Vithi offer a larger and less expensive selection than the stalls at the Rim Moei border market, and even if you don't intend to buy, just watching the theatrical haggling is half the fun.

Borderline 674/14 Thanon Indharakiri (next to Wat Arunyaket) ☎055 546584, ⍟borderlinecollective.org. This place stocks an eye-catching range of Karen crafts, such as sarongs, scarves, slippers, cushion covers, yoga mats and laptop bags. They also sell an excellent hand-painted map of the town for B90, and their most popular item is the bags of tea from Myanmar (B150 for 250g). Most items are made by Karen women living in refugee camps along the border. Tues–Sun 9am–7pm.

Weave 541 Thanon Indharakiri (opposite Bai Fern restaurant) ☎055 546754, ⍟weave-women.org. A similar operation to Borderline, with a name that's short for "Women's Education for Advancement and Empowerment". Traditional patterns, dyes and colour combinations are used to create a variety of woven products, such as traditional Karen shifts, thus helping to preserve Karen culture and give local refugee women an income. Daily 9am–8pm.

DIRECTORY

Cookery lessons Learn how to rustle up Shan, Karen and Burmese dishes at *Borderline Tea Garden*. Three-hour classes run at 9am, noon and 3pm, costing B1000 for one person, B600 for two, and B500 for three to six people.

Hospitals Mae Sot Hospital is on the southeastern edge of town (☎055 531970) and Phawo Hospital is on the southwestern edge (☎055 533912).

Immigration office At Rim Moei border crossing (see box opposite).

Language lessons Thai lessons are available through *Krua Canadian Restaurant*, while Burmese lessons are available through most guesthouses and several restaurants.

Massage Herbal saunas (3–7pm) at Wat Mani, on Thanon Indharakiri.

Tourist police For all emergencies, call the tourist police on the free, 24hr phoneline ☎1155, or contact them at the police station on Thanon Indharakiri (☎055 533523).

Umphang

Surrounded by mountains and situated at the confluence of the Mae Khlong and Umphang rivers, the small and very quiet village of **UMPHANG** is made up of little more than a thousand or so wooden houses and a wat. It won't take long to explore the minute grid of narrow roads that bisects the village, and although it's popular

UMPHANG

ACCOMMODATION
Baan Farang	1
Phu Doi Campsite	2
Suan Boonyaporn Garden Huts	3
Tu Ka Su Guest House	4

RESTAURANTS & CAFÉS
Ban Krusun Souvenir Shop	2
Krua Klang Doi	3
Phu Doi	1

among Thai visitors, foreign tourists are still relatively rare here, so communication could be a challenge. Coming here is all about trips to **Thi Law Su Waterfall**, which many believe to be the most beautiful in the country, with a drop of around 200m and a width of around 400m during the rainy season. Even if you don't fancy trekking or rafting to the falls, it's worth making the spectacular trip 164km south from Mae Sot to Umphang, both for the stunning mountain scenery you'll encounter along the way, and for the buzz of being in such an isolated part of Thailand. Bring some warm clothes as it can get pretty cool at night and in the early mornings – and the songthaew ride along the Sky Highway from Mae Sot is often windy.

Riding the Sky Highway

The drive from Mae Sot to Umphang generally takes about four hours and for the first hour proceeds in a fairly gentle fashion through the maize, cabbage and banana plantations of the Moei valley. The fun really begins when you start climbing into the mountains and the road – accurately dubbed the "**Sky Highway**" – careers round the edges of steep-sided valleys, undulating like a fairground rollercoaster (there are 1219 bends in all). The scenery is glorious, but if you're prone to car sickness, dose up on preventative tablets as the ride can be very unpleasant: the songthaews (see p.266) get so crammed with people and produce that there's often no possibility of distracting yourself by staring out of the window.

Karen, Akha, Lisu and Hmong people live in the few hamlets along the route, many growing cabbages along the cleared lower slopes with the help of government incentives (part of a national campaign to steer upland farmers away from the opium trade). The **Hmong** in particular are easily recognized by their distinctive embroidered jackets and skirts edged in bright pink, red and blue bands (see p.771). In 2000, the local **Karen** population mushroomed when three refugee camps from the Rim Moei area were relocated to the purpose-built village of Umpiem Mai alongside the Sky Highway midway between Mae Sot and Umphang (see box, p.261). Umpiem Mai is currently home to around thirteen thousand Karen refugees.

In fact the Umphang region was inhabited by Karen hill tribes before the Thais came to settle in the area in the early twentieth century; later, when the Thais began trading in earnest with their neighbours across the Burmese border, the Karen traders from

EXPLORING THE UMPHANG WILDLIFE SANCTUARY

Most people who visit Umphang sign up for a trip of two to three days (see Tour Operators, p.266) to the three-tiered **Thi Law Su Waterfall** (Nam Tok Thilawsu), star feature of the Umphang Wildlife Sanctuary (entry B200), which, unusually for Thailand, flows all year round. These trips usually involve rafting along spectacular rivers, often passing through narrow gorges (which many find the highlight of the trip), as well as trekking and camping near the base of the falls. The waterfall is at its most impressive just after the rainy season in November, when it extends to a dramatic 400m across. During this period you can swim in the beautifully blue lower pool, but trails can still be muddy, which makes for tough going; trek leaders often recommend wearing rubber boots (best bought in Mae Sot as they're hard to find in Umphang). One stretch of the route becomes so muddy during and just after the rainy season that it's impassable to human feet and needs to be done on elephant-back, a pretty uncomfortable ride of three to four hours. Nonetheless, the best **season** for trekking is November to February, even if the nights get pretty chilly. From December to April (the dry season), it's usually possible to climb to one of the waterfall's upper tiers, mud permitting. By contrast, at the height of the rainy season (July–Sept), it's often impossible to trek anywhere, the access road (unsealed) is frequently impassable and the falls are hidden behind a sea of mist. Around the falls, the vegetation is mainly montane forest, home to numerous varieties of orchid, and plenty of commonly encountered monkeys and hornbills, plus an elusive band of wild elephants.

Access to the falls is strictly controlled by national park rangers, who forbid people from taking food or plastic water bottles beyond the ranger station and campsite, from where it is a comfortable 1.5km walk along a raised wooden walkway to the falls. As yet, the number of visitors is reasonably small – except on public holidays, during school holidays and on some weekends, when Thai trippers flood the area.

A **typical tour** to Thi Law Su lasts three days and follows something like this increasingly standard itinerary. Day one: rafting down the Mae Khlong River via Thi Law Jor Falls and some striking honeycomb cliffs; then a 9km trek (3hr) to the official campsite near Thi Law Su Falls. Day two: morning at the falls, then a two-hour trek to a homestay at the Karen village of Khotha. Day three: a three-hour elephant ride (or trek) to Mae Lamoong junction; return to Umphang by car. Some trekkers find the three-day itinerary too baggy, with quite a lot of empty time at day's end (bring a book), so if you want a more challenging experience try to persuade your trekking agency to cover the same itinerary in two days. **Prices** start at about B3000 per person for the two-day Thi Law Su trek (minimum two people) or B4000 for three days. Some tour operators offer a one-day trip from Umphang (around B2000/person), rafting halfway to the falls, driving the rest of the way, walking to the falls and back from the campsite, then driving all the way back in the afternoon. Prices do vary between operators: smaller outfits can't afford to undercut the big operators and cost savings can mean lower wages – and morale – for guides. If you haven't pre-arranged a tour, the best time to contact **trek leaders** at the smaller outfits in Umphang is often after about 4pm, when they've returned from their last trip. Guides should provide tents, bedrolls, mosquito nets and sleeping bags, plus food and drinking water; trekkers may be asked to help carry some of the gear.

Although Thi Law Su is the most famous destination in the Umphang area, other programmes are available on request. From June to October there's **whitewater rafting** from the Karen village of **Umphang Khi** via the forty-plus rapids of the Umphang River, which can also include a fairly long trek and a night in the village. Alternatively, there are one- and two-day rafting trips to **Thi Law Leh Falls**, which involve four to eight hours' rafting (depending on water levels) via a series of cataracts along the Mae Khlong River, and the possibility of a seven-hour trek on the second day. For bird-spotting, ask about trips to Thung Yai Naresuan.

Myanmar used to carry their identification documents into Thailand in a bamboo container which they called an "umpha" – this is believed to be the origin of the name Umphang.

ARRIVAL AND DEPARTURE UMPHANG

When it comes to public transport, Umphang is effectively a dead end, so the only way to travel on from here is to go back to **Mae Sot** first.

By songthaew The only public transport access to Umphang is by songthaew along the Sky Highway from Mae Sot (hourly 7.30am–noon; 4–5hr; B120, or B160 if you're lucky enough to get the front seat). Heading back to Mae Sot, songthaews leave at least hourly until noon from the top of the town, which is also where they drop off passengers, though it's usual for guesthouses to phone ahead and get the songthaew to pick you up. After noon you'll probably need to charter the whole vehicle.

GETTING AROUND AND TOUR OPERATORS

Just about every guesthouse and resort in Umphang can help arrange a trip to Thi Law Su, but many cater exclusively to Thais. Those listed below have English-speaking guides and a reputation for reliability. Some tour operators offer a pick-up in Mae Sot; contact individual companies for details. *Tu Ka Su Guest House* can arrange a 4WD with driver for exploring the area (price dependent on destination). There's no official motorbike rental in Umphang, but it's worth asking around as guesthouse owners may be able to help you.

BL Tour 438 Thanon Umphang-Palata ☎055 561021, ⓦ boonlumtour.com. Ask for English-speakers Oi or Johnny. Very low-priced two- and three-day visits to Thi Law Su, including all extras such as food and sleeping bags; happy to do the two-day version, omitting the Khotha homestay.

Mr Boonchuay 360 Moo 1 ☎055 561020, ⓦ boonchuay tour.net. Umphang-born and bred, Mr Boonchuay knows the area well and has a good reputation; his English is not perfect, but he has English-speaking guides. Offers standard Thi Law Su programme. Trekkers can stay in the basic concrete rooms behind his office (B300/double) or in nicer bungalows down by the river (B400/double).

Tu Ka Su At Tu Ka Su Cottage, 40 Moo 6 ☎055 561295, ⓦ tukasu.webs.com. One of the best organized tour operators in Umphang, Tu Ka Su offers three- and four-day trips to Thi Law Su with prices ranging from B3200 to B4500. Unfortunately most of their website is in Thai, but you can email them for details.

Umphang Hill At Umphang Hill Resort, 59 Moo 6 ☎055 542942, ⓦ umphanghill.com. The biggest outfit in the area offers eleven itineraries and tailor-made permutations, ranging from three-day trips to Thi Law Su (B6650/person for 2–4 people) to seven-day trips to Umphang Khi and Thi Law Su, including elephant riding (B17,000/person for 2–4 people).

Umphang House 214 Moo 1 ☎089 5685273, ⓦ umphanghouse.webs.com. Offers one-, two- and three-day tours with prices starting at B2000 per person; the three-day tours include an elephant ride. Ask to speak with Dac.

ACCOMMODATION

As most of the accommodation in Umphang is geared towards trekkers in transit, room prices are usually included in the tour price, though not all guesthouses run tours themselves.

Baan Farang 109 Moo 4, Tambon Mae Klong ☎080 115 5678. This place has just half a dozen comfortable fan-cooled bungalows in a large riverside garden, including a large one for families. Breakfast is included in the price and staff can help arrange tours. It's located about 4km north of town. **B500**

Phu Doi Campsite and Resort Thanon Pravitpaiwan Soi 4 ☎055 561049, ⓦ phudoi.com. Decent set of en-suite fan rooms in a couple of wooden houses with verandas overlooking a pond. They also run tours but cater mostly to Thais. **B400**

Suan Boonyaporn Garden Huts 8/1 Thanon Umphang-Palata ☎055 561093, ⓦ boonyapornresort .com. A spread of accommodation options, all with fans, set around a pretty riverside flower garden, ranging from fairly simple wooden huts to attractive wooden bungalows fronted by decks and with partial river views. **B300**

Tu Ka Su Cottage 40 Moo 6, Umphang ☎055 561295, ⓦ tukasu.webs.com. In a pretty garden up the hill from the river, this quite stylish place is the most attractive in Umphang and offers nicely designed en-suite wooden cabins, with TV and fans; some have cute, semi-garden-style bathrooms. **B600**

EATING

The town's best places to eat are located on Thanon Umphang-Palata, and there are cheap **food stalls** that set up close to the temple at dusk.

Ban Krusun Souvenir Shop Thanon Sukomwattana. Along with CDs and local arts and crafts, this souvenir shops sells good cappuccinos and lattes (B40). Daily 6.30am–8.30pm.

Krua Klang Doi 19/1 Moo 6, Umphang (just east of Tu Ka Su) ☎ 081 2847926. Popular with locals and visitors, this simple restaurant serves good cheap Thai standards (from B50), including some fresh and spicy salads. Daily 8am–9pm.

Phu Doi Adjacent to Phu Doi Campsite, Thanon Pravitpaiwan Soi 4. Popular with Thais, this place has an English-language menu of curries and meat-over-rice dishes (around B80). Sept–May daily 7am–8pm.

2

The north

SUNRISE, CHIANG MAI PROVINCE

The north

Travelling up by rail through the central plains, there's no mistaking when you've reached the north of Thailand: somewhere between Uttaradit and Den Chai, the train slows almost to a halt, as if approaching a frontier post, to meet the abruptly rising mountains that continue largely unbroken to the borders of Myanmar (Burma) and Laos. Beyond this point the climate becomes more temperate (downright cold at night between December and February), nurturing the fertile land that gave the old kingdom of the north the name of Lanna, "the land of a million rice fields". Although only one-tenth of the land can be used for rice cultivation, the valley rice fields here are three times more productive than those in the dusty northeast, and the higher land yields a great variety of fruits, as well as beans, groundnuts and tobacco.

Until the beginning of the last century, Lanna was a largely independent region. On the back of its agricultural prosperity, it developed its own styles of art and architecture, which can still be seen in its flourishing temples and distinctive handicraft traditions. The north is also set apart from the rest of the country by its exuberant festivals, a cuisine that has been heavily influenced by Myanmar and a dialect quite distinct from central Thai. Northerners proudly call themselves *khon muang*, "people of the principalities", and their gentle sophistication is admired by the people of Bangkok, whose wealthier citizens build their holiday homes in the clean air of the north's forested mountains.

Chiang Mai, the capital and transport centre of the north, is a great place just to hang out or prepare for a journey into the hills. For many tourists, this means joining a trek

Highlights

❶ Hill-tribe trekking A chance to visit the diverse hill tribes of northern Thailand and explore dramatic countryside along the way. **See p.55**

❷ Chiang Mai Old-town temples, the best of Thai crafts, cookery courses and fine restaurants – the north's sophisticated capital is a great place to hang out. **See p.275**

❸ Festivals Exuberant Songkhran, glittering Loy Krathong and colourful Poy Sang Long are the pick of many. **See p.285 & p.341**

❹ Khao soi Delicious, spicy, creamy noodle soup, the northern Thai signature dish. See p.293

❺ Wat Phra That Doi Suthep Admire the towering views from this stunning example of temple architecture, just outside Chiang Mai. **See p.302**

❻ Nan A welcoming riverside town offering fascinating temple murals, attractive handicrafts and dramatic mountainscapes. **See p.322**

❼ The Mae Hong Son loop A rollercoaster journey – with a chill-out break in laidback Pai – through the country's wildest mountain scenery. **See p.329**

❽ Whitewater rafting on the Pai River Well-organized excitement taking in rapids, gorges and beautiful waterfalls. **See p.347**

HIGHLIGHTS ARE MARKED ON THE MAP ON PP.272–273

HIGHLIGHTS

1. Hill-tribe trekking
2. Chiang Mai
3. Festivals
4. Khao soi
5. Wat Phra That Doi Suthep
6. Nan
7. The Mae Hong Son loop
8. Whitewater rafting on the Pai River

MYANMAR

(see p.55) to visit one or more of the **hill tribes**, who comprise one-tenth of the north's population and are just about clinging onto the ways of life that distinguish them from one another and the Thais around them (see p.769). For those with qualms about the exploitative element of this ethnological tourism, there are plenty of other, more independent, options.

A trip eastwards from Chiang Mai to the ancient city-states of Lampang, Phrae and Nan can be highly rewarding, not only for the dividends of going against the usual flow of tourist traffic, but also for the natural beauty of the region's upland ranges – seen to best effect from the well-marked trails of **Doi Khun Tan National Park** – and for its eccentric variety of Thai, Burmese and Lao art and architecture. Congenial **Lampang** contains wats to rival those of Chiang Mai for beauty – in Wat Phra That Lampang Luang the town has the finest surviving example of traditional northern architecture anywhere – while little-visited **Phrae**, to the southeast, is a step back in time to a simpler Thailand. Further away but a more intriguing target is **Nan**, with its heady artistic mix of Thai and Lao styles and steep ring of scenic mountains.

To the west of Chiang Mai, the trip to **Mae Hong Son** takes you through the most stunning mountain scenery in the region into a land with its roots across the border in Myanmar, with the option of looping back through **Pai**, a laidback, sophisticated hill station that's become a popular hub for treks and activities. Bidding to rival Chiang Mai as a base for exploring the countryside is **Chiang Rai** to the north; above Chiang Rai, the northernmost tip of Thailand is marked by the Burmese border crossing at **Mae Sai** and the junction of Thailand, Laos and Myanmar at **Sop Ruak**. Fancifully dubbed the "Golden Triangle", Sop Ruak is a must on every bus party's itinerary – but you're more likely to find peace and quiet among the ruins of nearby **Chiang Saen**, set on the leafy banks of the Mekong River.

East of Chiang Saen on the Mekong River, **Chiang Khong** is an important crossing point to Houayxai in Laos, from where boats make the scenic two-day trip down the Mekong to Luang Prabang.

GETTING THERE AND AROUND   THE NORTH

As elsewhere in Thailand, buses are by far the most important form of transport for getting to and around the north. However, the mountainous topography makes **getting around** the region necessarily roundabout, with bus routes divided into three main areas: east from Chiang Mai, through Lampang and Phrae to Nan, which is almost a dead end (though one very slow bus a day winds its way over some spectacular hills to Chiang Rai); west from Chiang Mai around the Mae Hong Son loop through Mae Sariang and Pai; and north of Chiang Rai, an area that is well served by buses along the main routes, fed by songthaews on the minor roads. To get between Chiang Mai and Chiang Rai, you can either take a fast, direct service along Highway 118 or catch a bus to Tha Ton, followed by a boat down the Kok River to Chiang Rai.

By plane There are domestic flights to the airports at Chiang Mai, Lampang, Phrae, Nan, Mae Hong Son, Pai and Chiang Rai. In addition, Chiang Mai is served by international flights from and to dozens of cities in China, East Asia and Southeast Asia. There are also flights between Kunming in China and Chiang Rai (China Eastern Airlines).
By train The Northern Rail Line offers several daily services, mostly overnight, between Bangkok and Chiang Mai. Although trains are generally slower than buses, the stations at Den Chai (from where buses and songthaews run to Phrae and Nan) and Lampang are useful if you're coming up from Bangkok.

By motorbike To fully appreciate the mountainous landscape of the north, many people take to the open roads on rented motorbikes, which are available in most northern towns (Chiang Mai offers the best choice) and are relatively inexpensive. You should be cautious about biking in the north, however, especially if you're an inexperienced rider, and avoid riding alone on any remote trails – for expert advice on motorbike travel, check out ⓦ gt-rider .com, the website of Chiang Mai resident David Unkovich, who also produces good maps of the Mae Hong Son loop and "The Golden Triangle" (available locally and online).

Brief history

The first civilization to leave an indelible mark on the north was **Haripunjaya**, the Mon (Dvaravati) state that was founded at Lamphun in the late eighth or early ninth century. Maintaining strong ties with the Mon kingdoms to the south, it remained the cultural and religious centre of the north for four centuries. The Thais came onto the scene after the Mon, migrating down from China between the seventh and the eleventh centuries and establishing small principalities around the north.

King Mengrai and the founding of Chiang Mai

The prime mover for the Thais was **King Mengrai** of Ngon Yang (around present-day Chiang Saen), who, shortly after the establishment of a Thai state at Sukhothai in the middle of the thirteenth century, set to work on a parallel unified state in the north. By 1296, when he began the construction of Chiang Mai, which has remained the capital of the north ever since, he had brought the whole of the north under his control, and at his death in 1317 he had established a dynasty which was to oversee a two-hundred-year period of unmatched prosperity and cultural activity.

The Burmese occupation

After the expansionist reign of Tilok (1441–87), who hosted the eighth world council of Theravada Buddhism in Chiang Mai in 1477, a series of weak, squabbling kings came and went, while Ayutthaya increased its unfriendly advances. But it was the **Burmese** who finally snuffed out the Mengrai dynasty by capturing Chiang Mai in 1558, and for most of the next two centuries they controlled Lanna through a succession of puppet rulers. In 1767, the Burmese sacked the Thai capital at Ayutthaya, but the Thais soon regrouped under King Taksin, who with the help of **King Kawila** of Lampang gradually drove the Burmese northwards. In 1774 Kawila recaptured Chiang Mai, then deserted and in ruins, and set about rebuilding it as his new capital.

The colonial period

Kawila was succeeded as ruler of the north by a series of incompetent princes for much of the nineteenth century, until colonialism reared its head. After Britain took control of Upper Burma, **Rama V** of Bangkok began to take an interest in the north – where, since the Bowring Treaty of 1855, the British had established lucrative logging businesses – to prevent its annexation. He forcibly moved large numbers of ethnic Thais northwards, in order to counter the British claim of sovereignty over territory occupied by Thai Yai (Shan), who also make up a large part of the population of Upper Burma. In 1877 Rama V appointed a commissioner over Chiang Mai, Lamphun and Lampang to better integrate the region with the centre, and links were further strengthened in 1921 with the arrival of the railway from Bangkok.

The north today

Since the early twentieth century, the north has built on its agricultural richness to become relatively prosperous, though the economic booms of the last thirty years have been concentrated, as elsewhere in Thailand, in the towns, due in no small part to the increase in tourism. The eighty percent of Lanna's population who live in rural areas – of which the vast majority are subsistence farmers – are finding it increasingly difficult to earn a living off the soil, due to rapid population growth and land speculation for tourism and agro-industry.

Chiang Mai

Although rapid economic progress in recent years has brought problems such as pollution and traffic jams, **CHIANG MAI** still manages to preserve some of the atmosphere of an ancient village alongside its modern urban sophistication. It's the kingdom's second city, with a youthful population of about 400,000 (more than 60,000 of them are students), and the contrast with the maelstrom of Bangkok is pronounced: the people here are famously easy-going and even speak more slowly than their cousins in the capital, a lilting dialect known as *kham muang*. Chiang Mai's moated old quarter, where new buildings are limited to a height of four storeys, has retained many of its traditional wooden houses and quiet, leafy gardens, as well as the most famous and interesting **temples** in the city – Wat Phra Singh, Wat Chedi Luang and Wat Chiang Man – clustered conveniently close to each other. These elegant wats

CHIANG MAI

1 , Tha Ton, Huay Tung Tao & Mae Sa Valley

National Museum

PRACHA UTHIT

Chetawan
Massage School

Wat Jet Yot

SOI VIENGBUA

Main entrance
to University

Maya
Shopping
Centre

THANON HUAI KAEO

Chang Phuak
Bus Station

BARS & CLUBS

Drunken Flower	
(Mao Dok Mai)	**7**
Fabrique	**4**
Good View	**8**
Infinity	**2**
Myst	**1**
North Gate Jazz Co-op	**5**
The Riverside	**9**
Sangdee	**6**
Warm Up	**3**
Writer's Club	
and Wine Bar	**10**

Computer
Plaza

Chang
Phuak
Gate

THANON MANEE NOPARAT

THANON SI PHUM

Cacti

Thai Airways

Lanna
Folklife Museum

City Arts and Cultural
Centre and Historical Centre

Kad Suan Kaew
Shopping Mall

Chiang Mai
Ram Hospital

THANON INTHRAWARAROT

Three Kings
Monument

Maharaj
Hospital

THANON SUTHEP

Suan
Dork
Gate

Wat
Phra
Singh

THANON RATCHADAMNOEN

JHABAN

Wat
Chedi
Luang

Chiang Mai
University
Art Museum

Wat
Suan Dork

Wat
Umong

Yoga Tree

Wat Mengrai

THANON

Buak
Hat
Public
Park

Wat
Ram Poeng

Bus to
Chom Thong

THANON BAMRUNGBURI

Suan Prung
Gate

THANON CHANGLO

ACCOMMODATION

Anantara Chiang Mai	**19**
Baan Kaew Guest House	**20**
Baan Orapin	**5**
Bon Ça Va	**4**
Chiang Mai Gate Hotel	**21**
D2 Hotel	**11**
Dhara Dhevi	**15**
Duangtawan	**17**
Eco Resort	**6**
Elliebum	**12**
Four Seasons	**1**
Galare Guest House	**10**
Gerard Habitat	**3**
Green Tulip	**16**
Hollanda Montri	**2**
Rachamankha	**8**
Riverside House	**14**
River View Lodge	**13**
Royal Princess	**18**
Tri Yaan Na Ros	**22**
U Chiang Mai	**7**
Wanasit	**9**

Chinese
Consulate

Documentary
Arts Asia

N

Chiang Mai
Airport

Old Medicine
Hospital

THANON MAHIDOL

SUPERHIGHWAY

Immigration
Office

Airport Plaza &
Northern Village

Old Chiangmai
Cultural Centre

108   1141

Hang Dong, Ban Tawai & Doi Inthanon

may be Chiang Mai's primary tourist sights, but they're no pre-packaged museum pieces – they're living community centres, where you're quite likely to be approached by monks keen to chat and practise their English. Inviting handicraft **shops**, some interesting **museums**, good-value accommodation, rich cuisine and riverside bars further enhance the city's allure, making Chiang Mai a place that detains many travellers longer than they expected. These days, increasing numbers of travellers are

SHOPS

Adorn by Studio Naenna	**3**
Boots	**10**
Doi Tung Lifestyle	**2**
HQ	**9**
Kritiya	**8**
Mengrai Kilns	**12**
Shinawatra	**4**
Sop Moei Arts	**6**
Studio Naenna	**1**
Suriwong	**13**
Thai Tribal Crafts	**5**
Vila Cini	**7/11**

RESTAURANTS & CAFÉS

Amazing Sandwich	**5**
Arcobaleno	**9**
Ba Mii Kiaw Stall	**7**
Café de Nimman	**12**
The Duke's	**20**
Elliebum	**18**
Hinlay	**11**
Hong Tauw Inn	**4**
Huan Soontaree	**1**
Huen Phen	**19**
iberry	**10**
Imoya	**22**
Khao Soi Samoe Jai	**2**
Khun Churn	**23**
Kiat Ocha	**14**
Lamduon Faharm Khao Soi	**3**
Love at First Bite	**17**
Pattana	**6**
Rachamankha	**15**
Samsen Villa	**8**
SP Chicken	**16**
Tengoku de Cuisine	**21**
Wan Lamun	**13**

3

TREKKING AND OTHER OUTDOOR ACTIVITIES IN CHIANG MAI

The **trekking** industry in Chiang Mai offers an impressive variety of itineraries, with dozens of agencies covering nearly all trekkable areas of the north – see Basics (p.55) for general advice on how to choose an agency. Most treks include a ride on an elephant and a bamboo-raft excursion, though the amount of actual walking included can vary greatly. Below we have listed a couple of operators who offer something a little different. Most of the companies detailed below include free pick-ups and drop-offs in the price of their tours, which can easily be arranged through your accommodation.

GENERAL ADVENTURE TOURS

Contact Travel Tasala, to the east of town ☎053 850160, ⓦactivethailand.com. Long-standing, general agency that offers a wide range of adventure tours, including whitewater rafting, trekking, cycling and kayaking.

TREKKING

Eagle House See p.291. This well-run guesthouse runs the standard type of trek, with elephants and rafting available, but to carefully chosen quiet areas and with an educational bent, and passes on a proportion of costs towards funding projects in hill-tribe villages.
The Trekking Collective 3/5 Soi 1, Thanon Loi Khro ☎053 208340, ⓦtrekkingcollective.com. This upmarket outfit arranges pricey but high-quality customized treks from one to six days and can cater for specific interests such as animal-watching; it too is involved in community programmes to help tribal people.

CYCLING AND KAYAKING

Chiang Mai Mountain Biking 1 Thanon Samlarn, opposite Wat Phra Singh ☎081 024 7046, ⓦmountainbikingchiangmai.com. Mountain-biking tours, ranging from single-track downhill rides, mostly on Doi Suthep, to cross-country leisure or hike-and-bike trips. The same company offers one- and multi-day kayaking trips on the north's lakes and rivers, including whitewater trips and paddles on the Ping River through Chiang Mai (ⓦchiangmaikayaking.com).
Chiang Mai Sunday Bicycle Club ⓦcmcycling.org. Interesting rides (part of a local cycling campaign) every Sunday morning from Tha Phae Gate that are open to all.

Click and Travel 158/40 Thanon Chiang Mai–Hod ☎053 281553, ⓦclickandtravelonline.com. Belgian–Thai company that runs cycling tours of Chiang Mai and the north, lasting from a few hours to four days, and maintains a useful website, ⓦchiangmaicycling.org, full of all manner of information for cyclists.

WHITEWATER RAFTING

Siam Rivers Kona Café, 17 Thanon Ratchawithi ☎089 515 1917, ⓦsiamrivers.com. Chiang Mai's longest-standing whitewater rafting outfit, with high standards of safety (trips run roughly late May to Feb/March), which also offers full-moon trips and whitewater kayaking.

ROCK-CLIMBING

Chiang Mai Rock Climbing Adventures 55/3 Thanon Ratchaphakinai ☎053 207102 or ☎086 911 1470, ⓦthailandclimbing.com. Climbing trips and courses to Crazy Horse Buttress, a limestone outcrop in the San Kamphaeng area, 50km east of town, which offers highly varied climbing with more than a hundred routes. Also caving courses and trips, bouldering trips and a bouldering wall, as well as equipment rental and sales, private guides and a partner-finding service.

ZIPLINING

Flight of the Gibbon ☎053 010660, ⓦtreetopasia .com. Full-day rainforest canopy tours on zip lines and sky bridges in the hills to the east of town, with an excellent reputation and high standards of safety.
Jungle Flight ☎053 208666, ⓦjungleflightchiang mai.com. The first, and probably the best, of Flight of the Gibbon's several imitators, offering similar ziplining trips at cheaper prices.

---

also taking advantage of the city's relaxed feel to indulge in a burst of self-improvement, enrolling for **courses** in **cookery**, **massage** and the like (see box, p.281).

Many colourful **festivals** (see box, p.285) attract throngs of visitors here too: Chiang Mai is one of the most popular places in Thailand to see in the Thai New Year – Songkhran – in mid-April, and to celebrate Loy Krathong at the full moon in November, when thousands of candles are floated down the Ping River in lotus-leaf boats. And a pilgrimage to **Doi Suthep**, the mountain to the west of town, should not be missed, to see the sacred, glittering temple and the towering views over the valley of the Ping River, when weather permits. Beyond the city limits (see p.302), a number of other day-trips can be made, such as to the ancient temples of Lamphun – and, of course, Chiang Mai is the main centre for hill-tribe **trekking**, as well as all sorts of other outdoor activities (see box opposite).

Orientation is simple in central Chiang Mai, which divides roughly into two main parts: the **old town**, surrounded by the well-maintained moat and occasional remains of the city wall, where you'll find most of the temples, and the **new town centre**, between the moat and the Ping River to the east, the main market and shopping area. The biggest concentration of guesthouses and restaurants hangs between the two, centred on the landmark of **Tha Pae Gate** (*Pratu Tha Pae*) in the middle of the east moat. Also noteworthy is the area around **Thanon Nimmanhaemin**, near the university to the west of the old town, which is home to an ever-expanding choice of bars and restaurants, especially in the sois on its east side. On the outskirts, the town is bounded to the north, east and south by the Superhighway and two further huge but incomplete ring roads, with Thanon Chon Prathan (Canal Road) providing a western bypass.

Brief history

Founded as the capital of Lanna in 1296, on a site indicated by the miraculous presence of deer and white mice, Chiang Mai – "New City" – has remained the north's most important settlement ever since. Lanna's golden age under the Mengrai dynasty, when most of the city's notable temples were founded, lasted until the Burmese captured the city in 1558. Two hundred years passed before the Thais pushed the Burmese back beyond Chiang Mai to roughly where they are now, and the **Burmese influence** is still strong – not just in art and architecture, but also in the rich curries and soups served here. After the recapture of the city, the *chao* (princes) of Chiang Mai remained nominal rulers of the north until 1939, but, with communications rapidly improving from the beginning of the last century, Chiang Mai was brought firmly into Thailand's mainstream as the region's administrative and service centre.

Wat Phra Singh

At the far western end of Thanon Ratchdamnoen in the old town

If you see only one temple in Chiang Mai it should be **Wat Phra Singh**, perhaps the single most impressive array of buildings in the city. Just inside the gate to the right, the wooden scripture repository is the best example of its kind in the north, inlaid with glass mosaic and set high on a base decorated with stucco angels. The largest building in the compound, a colourful modern viharn fronted by naga balustrades, hides from view a rustic wooden bot, a chedi with a typical northern octagonal base constructed in 1345 to house the ashes of King Kam Fu, and – the highlight of the whole complex – the beautiful **Viharn Lai Kam**. This wooden gem is a textbook example of Lanna architecture, with its squat, multi-tiered roof and exquisitely carved and gilded

---

CHIANG MAI BOAT TRIPS

A pleasant way to get a feel for the city and its layout is to take a **boat trip** on the Ping River. Frequent two-hour cruises operated by Mae Ping River Cruises (☎053 274822 or ☎081 884 4621, ⊛maepingrivercruise.com) depart from Wat Chaimongkol on Thanon Charoen Prathet, sailing 8km upstream through lush countryside to a riverside farmhouse for a look around the fruit, herb and flower gardens, plus refreshments and fruit-tasting (B500/person; minimum two people, includes pick-up from your accommodation). Mae Ping River Cruises also offer trips to Wiang Kum Kam (see p.304). Another alternative is to take a trip on a scorpion-tailed boat (currently at 9am, 11am, 1pm, 3pm and 5pm; 1hr 30min; B500/person, minimum two people; ☎081 960 9398, ⊛scorpiontailedrivercruise.com), a reconstruction of vessels that plied the river a century ago. This cruise heads downriver from a pier on Thanon Charoenrat, north of Nakhon Ping Bridge, and includes a commentary (in English) on historic places beside the river.

3

MENGRAI MANIA

The spirit of **King Mengrai**, the heroic founder of the Lanna kingdom (see p.723), is still worshipped at dozens of shrines in Chiang Mai and the north seven hundred years after his death, but three in the old city stand out. About halfway between Wat Phra Singh and Wat Chedi Luang, Wat Kawt Kala was the second temple founded by the king in Chiang Mai (after Wat Chiang Man) and had its name changed to **Wat Phra Chao Mengrai** (or just **Wat Mengrai**) in the 1950s. The standing Buddha in its own *sala* just to the right of the main viharn here is said to replicate exactly King Mengrai's dimensions – and no wonder he was capable of such heroic deeds, as the image is 4m tall. By the beautiful, stately *bo* tree at the back of the compound stands a more plausible life-size modern statue of the king himself holding an elephant hook, where people leave all kinds of offerings, including swords.

Between Wat Chedi Luang and Chiang Mai City Arts and Cultural Centre stand two further monument-shrines to the great king. The site where he was killed by lightning in 1317, aged 79, is marked by a glittering, much-venerated **shrine** in its own small piazza on the corner of Thanon Ratchdamnoen and Thanon Phra Pokklao. A few minutes on up Thanon Phra Pokklao, Mengrai features again in the bronze **Three Kings Monument** in front of the arts and cultural centre, showing him discussing the auspicious layout of his "new city", Chiang Mai, with his allies, Ramkhamhaeng of Sukhothai and Ngam Muang of Phayao. The three kings had studied together under a religious teacher in Lopburi, but when they met up again, things were actually rather different from the harmonious picture portrayed by the monument: on a visit to Phayao, Ramkhamhaeng had an affair with Ngam Muang's wife, and Mengrai had to step in and mediate.

---

pediment: if you feel you're being watched as you approach, it's the sinuous double arch between the porch's central columns, which represents the Buddha's eyebrows.

Inside sits one of Thailand's three **Phra Singh** (or Sihing) Buddha images (see p.97), a portly, radiant and much-revered bronze in a fifteenth-century Lanna style. Its setting is enhanced by the partly damaged but colourful **murals** of action-packed tableaux, which give a window on life in the north a hundred years ago. The murals illustrate two different stories: on the right-hand wall is an old folk tale, the *Sang Thong*, about a childless king and queen who are miraculously given a beautiful son, the "Golden Prince", in a conch shell. The murals on the left show the story of the mythical swan Suwannahong, who forms the magnificent prow of the principal royal barge in Bangkok. Incidentally, what look like Bermuda shorts on the men are in fact **tattoos**: in the nineteenth century, all boys in the north were tattooed from navel to kneecap, an agonizing ordeal undertaken to show their courage and to enhance their appeal to women. On one side of the wat is a high school for young yellow-sashed novices and schoolboys in blue shorts, who all noisily throng the temple compound during the day. Dally long enough and you'll be sure to have to help them with their English homework.

Wat Chedi Luang

Main entrance on Thanon Phra Pokklao, 10min walk east along Thanon Ratchdamnoen from Wat Phra Singh, with side entrances on Thanon Ratchamanka, Thanon Jhaban and Thanon Ratchdamnoen • Monk Chat daily 9am–6pm

At **Wat Chedi Luang**, an enormous chedi, built in 1421 to house the ashes of King Ku Na but toppled from its present 90m to its present 60m by an earthquake in 1545, is the temple's most striking feature. You'll need a titanic leap of the imagination, however, to picture the beautifully faded pink-brick chedi, in all its crumbling grandeur, as it was in the fifteenth century, when it was covered in bronze plates and gold leaf, and housed the Emerald Buddha (see p.86) for eighty years. Recent attempts to rebuild the entire chedi to its former glory, now abandoned, have nevertheless led to modern replacements of the elephants at the base, the nagas that line the lengthy staircases and the Buddha images in its four niches, including an oversized replica of the Emerald Buddha, funded by the present king for Chiang Mai's seven-hundredth anniversary in 1996, in its old spot on the eastern side. A cup on a wire stretching to the pinnacle is used to bless the chedi during major Buddhist festivals: it's filled with water, and a pulley draws it to the spire where the water is tipped out over the sides of the chedi.

COURSES IN CHIANG MAI

The most popular course on offer is how to **cook** Thai food (especially at the cluster of small schools on and around Soi 5, Thanon Ratchdamnoen), followed by **Thai massage**. Chiang Mai is also a popular place for meditation retreats (see p.286), while other skills to be tackled, besides rock-climbing (see p.278), include: **t'ai chi**, on eight- to ten-day programmes or in two-hour private lessons, at Naisuan House, off Thanon Doi Saket Kao (☎085 714 5537, ⦿taichithailand.com); **yoga**, and other classes, at the Yoga Tree, 65/1 Thanon Arak (☎081 724 7308, ⦿theyogatree.org); **Thai boxing** at Lanna Muay Thai (Kiat Busaba), 161 Soi Changkhian, Thanon Huai Kaeo (☎053 892102 or ☎081 951 3164, ⦿lannamuaythai.com); **Thai dance** at the Thai Dance Institute, 53 Thanon Kohklong, Nong Hoi (☎053 801375–6, ⦿thaidance institute.com); one- to five-day workshops in **jewellery-making** through Nova, 179 Thanon Tha Pae (☎053 273058, ⦿nova-collection.com); and **Lanna arts and culture** with Origin Asia (see p.26).

COOKERY COURSES

Asia Scenic 31 Soi 5, Thanon Ratchdamnoen ☎053 418657–8. This much-recommended school covers all the bases, with an organic farm outside of town (B1200/day) and an organic garden at its in-town school, where you can take full- (B1000) or half-day classes (morning or evening; B800). Transfers included.

Chiang Mai Thai Cookery School Office at 47/2 Thanon Moonmuang ☎053 206388, ⦿thaicookery school.com. The original – and still the best – offering courses of one to five days (on-site accommodation available), as well as more advanced evening masterclasses. Each day begins with either an introduction to Thai ingredients, shopping in the market, making curry pastes or vegetable carving. Courses are held at the owners' house, a 30min drive out of town (transport provided). B1450–6700, including a recipe book.

Thai Farm Cooking School 38 Soi 9, Thanon Moonmuang ☎081 288 5989, ⦿thaifarmcooking .com. Offers the chance to pick your own organic vegetables, herbs and fruits for cooking on its farm, a 30min drive from town (transport provided). B1300/day; vegetarian, vegan and three-day courses also possible.

THAI MASSAGE COURSES

We give details on having a massage in Chiang Mai later in the chapter (see p.289).

Baan Hom Samunprai 9km south of town beyond Wiang Kum Kam ☎053 817362, ⦿homprang.com. Live-in massage courses out in the countryside costing B2100/day, including accommodation in a traditional village-style house with full board and the use of a pool, steam baths and bicycles; live-out courses from B1400/day.

Chetawan Massage School 7/1–2 Soi Samud Lanna, Thanon Pracha Uthit, off Thanon Chotana ☎053 410360–1, ⦿watpomassage.com. A branch of the massage school at Bangkok's Wat Pho (see p.91), which is considered to be the best place to study Thai massage in Thailand. Thirty-hour courses (6hr/day for 5 days) in traditional Thai (B9500) or foot (B7500) massage.

Old Medicine Hospital Off Thanon Wualai, opposite the Old Chiangmai Cultural Centre ☎053 201663, ⦿thaimassageschool.ac.th. The longest-established centre in Chiang Mai, aka Shivagakomarpaj after the Indian hermit who is said to have founded the discipline over two thousand years ago. Highly respected five-day courses (B5000) with dorm accommodation available; foot, oil and herbal compress courses are also offered.

Sunshine Network ☎089 835 5312, ⦿thaiyoga massage.infothai.com. An international group of practitioners and teachers founded by the highly respected German teacher, Harald Brust, aka Asokananda, who died in June 2005. Asokananda emphasized the spiritual aspect of what he called Thai yoga massage or Ayurvedic bodywork. Led by one of Asokananda's followers, twelve-day beginners' courses (B19,500, including basic accommodation, simple vegetarian rice meals and transport) are held at a rural retreat in a Lahu village between Chiang Mai and Chiang Rai, often with optional yoga, t'ai chi and Vipassana meditation classes.

Thai Massage School of Chiangmai Northeast of town on the Mae Jo road, 2km beyond the Super-highway ☎053 854330, ⦿tmcschool.com. Accredited by the Ministry of Education and highly recommended by past pupils. Five-day courses (B7500), as well as longer professional courses. All courses include transport.

3

In a modern building (which women are not allowed to enter) by the main entrance stands the city's *lak muang* or foundation pillar, here called the **Sao Inthakin** (Pillar of Indra), a brick structure covered in coloured glass and topped by a Buddha. Built by King Mengrai at Wat Sadeu Muang (on Thanon Inthrawarorot) when he established Chiang Mai, the pillar was moved here to the city's geographical centre by King Kawila in 1800, while he was re-founding the city after the ravages of the wars with the Burmese. The building has recently been renovated, with colourful murals depicting the foundation legends of Wat Chedi Luang and the *Sao Inthakin*, including guardian angels brandishing assault rifles and other twenty-first-century weaponry. Above, the *Sao Inthakin* building is sheltered by a stately gum tree which, the story has it, will stand for as long as the city's fortunes prosper.

On the northeast side of the chedi, **Monk Chat** is advertised, giving you a chance to meet and talk to the monks in English. There's a mildly diverting museum on the chedi's north side, while on the southwest side, a couple of small viharns shelter astonishingly lifelike waxworks of two much-revered but recently deceased monks.

Wat Pan Tao

Thanon Phra Pokklao, next door to Wat Chedi Luang on the north side

While you're in the vicinity, pop in on **Wat Pan Tao** to see the recently renovated, fourteenth-century, all-teak viharn. Constructed of unpolished panels, it's supported on enormous pillars and protected by carved wooden bars on the windows, a classic of graceful Lanna architecture. The teak panels apparently came from a royal palace and still sport a beautiful carved peacock over the main door, the emblem of the Chiang Mai kings. With a very active abbot, this temple is a good place to catch festivals, especially Songkhran, when it's filled with enormous sandcastles planted with coloured flags.

The city museums

Thanon Phra Pokklao • Tues–Sun 8.30am–5pm • B90 for each or B180 combined ticket • ☎ 053 217793, ⓦ cmocity.com

Around the landmark Three Kings Monument (see p.280) and its tree-lined piazza, the municipality has recently opened three museums of varying levels of interest.

Chiang Mai City Arts and Cultural Centre

Immediately behind the monument, the elegant 1920s former provincial office has been turned into the main **Chiang Mai City Arts and Cultural Centre** – essentially a museum with the aim of conveying the identity of the city and the region through its history, customs and culture. To this end, scale models and plenty of high-quality English-language audiovisuals are thoughtfully deployed, with some nice touches such as vivid reminiscences by Chiang Mai's older inhabitants about what the city was like in the early twentieth century. Upstairs, the interest tails off, though there is an engaging audiovisual and exhibit on the hill tribes. The courtyard in the back half of the building shelters temporary exhibitions, a souvenir shop and a small café.

Lanna Folklife Museum

Across Thanon Phra Pokklao, the colonial-style former courthouse is now the smartly designed **Lanna Folklife Museum**, with an attractive coffee shop in the grounds. An anthropological survey of Lanna culture and traditions, it's a bit listy and would benefit from more contextual information, but the curators have persuaded some notable local collectors to lend some beautiful artefacts: ceramics, lacquerware, ceremonial wooden betel sets (see box opposite) and textiles. You'll also learn about local styles of mural painting and Buddhist ritual, as well as the *fon lep* (nail dance), a Lanna women's dance that's enhanced by the wearing of 20cm brass fingernail extensions.

BETEL

Betel-chewing today is popular only among elderly Thais, particularly country women, but it used to be a much more widespread social custom, and a person's betel tray set was once a Thai's most prized possession and an indication of rank: royalty would have sets made in gold, the nobility's would be in silver or nielloware, and poorer folk wove theirs from rattan or carved them from wood. A set comprises at least three small covered receptacles, and sometimes a tray to hold these boxes and the knife or nutcracker used to split the fruit.

The three essential ingredients for a good chew are betel leaf, limestone ash and areca palm fruit. You chew the coarse red flesh of the narcotic fruit first (best picked when small and green-skinned), before adding a large heart-shaped betel leaf, spread with limestone-ash paste and folded into manageable size; for a stronger kick, you can include tobacco and/or marijuana at this point. An acquired and bitter taste, betel numbs the mouth and generates a warm feeling around the ears. Less pleasantly, constant spitting is necessary – which is why you'll often see spittoons in old-fashioned hotels in Thailand, re-used as waste baskets. It doesn't do much for your looks either: betel-chewers are easily spotted by their rotten teeth and lips stained scarlet from the habit.

3

Chiang Mai Historical Centre

Behind the City Arts and Cultural Centre, with its entrance on Thanon Ratchawithi, the **Chiang Mai Historical Centre** is the most disappointing of the three museums – you'll get little more out of it than you would from reading a half-decent history of the region, and it's probably most notable as the site of the Friday afternoon farmers' market (see p.299).

Wat Chiang Man

Thanon Ratchaphakinai

Erected by Mengrai on the site where he first pitched camp, **Wat Chiang Man** is the oldest temple in Chiang Mai and most notable for two dainty and very holy Buddha images housed in the viharn to the right of the entrance: the **Phra Sila**, a graceful marble bas-relief carved in northern India, supposedly in the sixth century BC, stands in the typical *tribunga*, or hip-shot stance; its partner, the **Phra Setangamani** (or Crystal Buddha), made four centuries later, probably in Lavo (modern Lopburi), is much revered by the inhabitants of Chiang Mai for its rainmaking powers and is carried through the streets during the Songkhran festival to help the rainy season on its way. Neither image is especially beautiful, but a powerful aura is created by making them difficult to see, high up behind two sets of iron bars.

Thailand Creative and Design Centre (TCDC)

1/1 Thanon Muang Samut, behind Muang Mai market • Tues–Sun 10.30am–6pm • Free • ☎ 052 080500, ⓦ tcdc.or.th

The Chiang Mai branch of this resource centre for designers occasionally hosts interesting temporary shows that are worth looking out for. In December 2014, it was one of the hubs for the ambitious new Chiang Mai Design Week (ⓦ chiangmaidesign week.com), which will hopefully be repeated in the coming years.

Chiang Mai National Museum

On the northwestern outskirts on the Superhighway • Wed–Sun 9am–4pm • Currently free, normally B100

In telling the history of Lanna art and culture, the **National Museum** has far fewer bells and whistles than its rival, the Chiang Mai Arts and Cultural Centre, but in terms of the quality of artefacts on display, it wins hands down. Inside, the airy rooms are cool enough for a long browse, and the collection is mostly labelled in English. However,

> **LANNA BUDDHA IMAGES**
>
> In the golden age of the Lanna kingdom, from the fourteenth to the sixteenth centuries, Buddha images were produced in the north in two contrasting styles. One group, which resembles images from northern India, has been called the **lion-type**, after the Shakyamuni (Lion of the Shakyas) archetype at the great Buddhist temple at Bodh Gaya, the site of the Buddha's enlightenment. It's been conjectured that a delegation sent by King Tilok to Bodh Gaya in the 1450s brought back a copy of the statue, which became the model for hundreds of Lanna images. These broad-shouldered, plump-bellied Buddhas are always seated with the right hand in the touching-the-earth gesture, while the face is well rounded with pursed lips and a serious, majestic demeanour. The second type is the **Thera Sumana** style named after the monk Mahathera Sumana, who came from Sukhothai in 1369 to establish his Sri Lankan sect in Lanna. The Chiang Mai National Museum is well stocked with this type of image, which shows strong Sukhothai influence, with an oval face and a flame-like *ushnisha* on top of the head.

3

the museum has for several years been under renovation, which may finish in 2017. At the moment, they're working on the first floor, with a temporary exhibition of Lanna artefacts on show on the ground floor, including local Buddha images, scripture cabinets and some lovely ceramics from San Kamphaeng. Once they have finished the first floor, that should be open to the public, with the ground floor closed for renovation. There's an excellent spot for lunch, a branch of *Lamduon Faharm Khao Soi* (see p.296), just east of the museum on the north side of the Superhighway.

Wat Jet Yot

Set back from the Superhighway, a 5min walk west of the National Museum

The peaceful garden temple of **Wat Jet Yot** is named after the "seven spires" of its unusual chedi. It was built in 1455 by King Tilok, after a model of the great temple at Bodh Gaya in India, and represents the seven places around Bodh Gaya which the Buddha visited in the seven weeks following his enlightenment; it also houses the king's ashes. Around the base of the chedi, delicate stuccos portray flowers and cross-legged deities serenely floating in the sky, whose faces are said to be those of Tilok's relatives. They represent the angels who gathered to rejoice at the Buddha's enlightenment, showering him with heavenly flowers.

Chiang Mai Zoo and Aquarium

Thanon Huai Kaeo

About 1km beyond Wat Jet Yot, the Superhighway meets Thanon Huai Kaeo, a broad avenue that runs from the northwest corner of the moat to the foot of Doi Suthep, where it becomes the winding road up to the summit. Heading out up Thanon Huai Kaeo, past the sprawling campus of Chiang Mai University (CMU or "*Mor Chor*"), brings you to **Chiang Mai Zoo and Aquarium**, in an attractive park at the base of the mountain.

The zoo

Daily 8am–5pm • B150 • ⓦ chiangmaizoo.com

Originally a menagerie of a missionary family's pets, the **zoo** now houses an impressive collection of about eight thousand animals, including rare Thai species, in modern, relatively comfortable conditions. There's a children's zoo and a colourful aviary, while larger mammals include elephants, giraffes, Humboldt penguins, koalas, a rhino and the current favourites, two **giant pandas** on an extended loan from China (B100 extra, children B50). Despite a disorientating layout, it makes a diverting visit, especially for kids, though visitors from temperate countries can probably do without entering the new Snow Dome. Feeding and activity times for animals are posted clearly (including on the website), and refreshment stalls for humans are never far away.

The zoo is better visited in the morning to avoid the afternoon heat. The grounds are too big to walk round, but "**panorama buses**" (small open-sided buses; B20, children B10) and a **monorail** (B150, children B100) are available to take you around.

The aquarium

Mon–Fri 10am–4pm, Sat & Sun 9am–4.30pm • B520 (includes admission to zoo) • ⓦ chiangmaiaquarium.com

Towards the western side of the zoo (linked to the entrance by shuttle bus), the recently built **aquarium** is the biggest in Southeast Asia, with what's said – at 130m – to be the longest underwater viewing tunnel in the world. With the aim of showing landlocked Chiang Mai some rarely seen species, the huge edifice is strictly divided in half: in the freshwater section, you can see not only the Mekong giant catfish (see p.372), but also *thae pha*, the Chao Phraya giant catfish; while the salty half displays rare white-tip reef sharks, rays and moray eels. There's a saltwater touch pool, and a long menu of feeding times, detailed on the website; it's also possible to snorkel (B1000) and scuba-dive (B4290) with the fishes.

3

CHIANG MAI FESTIVALS

Chiang Mai is the best and busiest place in the country to see in the Thai New Year, **Songkhran**, which takes over the city between April 13 and 15 and during the preceding days. The most obvious role of the festival is as an extended "rain dance" in the driest part of the year, when huge volumes of canal water are thrown about in a communal water-fight that spares no one a drenching. The other elements of this complex festival are not as well known but no less important. In the temple compounds, communities get together to build sandcastles in the shape of chedis, which they cover with coloured flags – this bestows merit on any ancestors who happen to find themselves in hell and may eventually release them from their torments, and also shows an intent to help renovate the wat in the year to come. Houses are given a thorough spring-clean to see out the old year, while Buddha images from the city's main temples are cleaned, polished and sprinkled with lustral water, before being ceremonially carried through the middle of the water-fight to give everyone the chance to throw water on them and receive the blessing of renewal. Finally, younger family members formally visit their elders during the festival to ask for their blessings, while pouring scented water over their hands.

Loy Krathong, on and around the night of the full moon in November, has its most showy celebration at Sukhothai (see box, p.242), but Chiang Mai – where it is also known as **Yipeng** – is not far behind. While a spectacular but unnerving firework fiesta rages on the banks, thousands of candles are gently floated down the Ping River in beautiful lotus-leaf boats. As well as floating krathongs, people release **khom loy**, paper hot-air balloons that create a magical spectacle as they float heavenward, sometimes with firecrackers trailing behind. As with krathongs, they are released to carry away sins and bad luck, as well as to honour the Buddha's topknot, which he cut off when he became an ascetic (according to legend, the topknot is looked after by the Buddha's mother in heaven).

Chiang Mai's brilliantly colourful **flower festival**, centred on Buak Hat Park at the southwest corner of the old town usually on the first weekend of February, also attracts huge crowds. The highlight is a procession of floats, modelled into animals, chedis and even scenes from the *Ramayana*, and covered in flowers. In early April, the **Poy Sang Long** festival, centred around Wat Pa Pao near the northeast corner of the old city, is an ordination ritual for young Shan men, who are paraded round town on the shoulders of relatives. The boys are dressed in extravagant, colourful clothing with huge floral headdresses, which they symbolically cast off at the end of the festival to don a saffron robe – its most elaborate manifestation in Thailand is in Mae Hong Son (see box, p.341). In late May or early June, the week-long **Inthakin Festival**, a life-prolonging ceremony for the city of Chiang Mai, using holy water from Doi Luang Chiang Dao, is focused around the city foundation pillar at Wat Chedi Luang, which is thronged with market stalls and local people making offerings.

3

MEDITATION IN CHIANG MAI

The peace and quiet of the northern capital make it ideally suited to **meditation** sessions, short courses and longer retreats, many of which are conducted in English. General information and advice about meditation is given in Basics (see p.51), where you'll also find details of the retreats at Wat Phra That Chom Thong, 60km south of Chiang Mai.

Green Papaya Sangha ⓦ greenpapayasangha.org. Offers meditation in the tradition of Vietnamese Zen Master, Thich Nhat Hanh, on Thursday evenings at 7.30pm at the Yoga Tree (see p.281). It also hosts dhamma talks from teachers of other Buddhist traditions. By donation.

International Buddhist Meditation Centre Wat Phra That Doi Suthep ⊕ 053 295012, ⓦ fivethousand years.org. A variety of Vipassana meditation courses for beginners and experienced students, from five to 21 days. Registration must be made in advance (courses are often full). By donation.

Mahachulalongkorn Buddhist University Wat Suan Dork ⓦ monkchat.net. Introductory retreat courses on meditation and Thai Buddhist culture, for which you need to wear white clothes, available for B300. Including yoga, chanting and almsgiving, they begin at about 1pm on a Tuesday, before departure to the training centre on Doi Suthep, returning to Wat Suan Dork at about 3pm the next day (B500). Courses are sometimes cancelled so check the schedule on the website.

Northern Insight Meditation Centre Wat Ram Poeng (aka Wat Tapotaram), off Thanon Chon Prathan near Wat Umong ⊕ 053 278620, ⓦ palikanon.com /vipassana/tapotaram/tapotaram.htm. Disciplined Vipassana courses (with a rule of silence, no food after noon and so on), taught by Thai monks with translators. The minimum stay is ten days, with a basic course lasting 26 days, and payment is by donation.

Wat Suan Dork

Thanon Suthep • Monk Chat Mon–Fri 5–7pm • ⓦ monkchat.net

Wat Suan Dork, the "Flower Garden Temple", is surrounded by walls as part of Chiang Mai's fortifications. Legend says that Mahathera Sumana, when he was invited to establish his Sri Lankan Buddhist sect here in 1369, brought with him a miraculous glowing relic. Ku Na, the king of Chiang Mai, ordered a huge chedi – the one you see today – to be built in his flower garden, but as the pea-sized relic was being placed inside the chedi, it split into two parts: one half was buried here, the other found its way to Doi Suthep, after further adventures (see p.302).

The brilliantly whitewashed chedi now sits next to a garden of smaller, equally dazzling chedis containing the ashes of the Chiang Mai royal family; framed by Doi Suthep to the west, this makes an impressive and photogenic sight, especially at sunset. At the back of the dusty compound, the bot is decorated with lively *Jataka* murals and enshrines a beautifully illuminated, 500-year-old bronze Buddha image. Nearby signs point the way to **Monk Chat**, organized by the Mahachulalongkorn Buddhist University based at the temple, which gives the monk-students the opportunity to meet foreigners and practise their English, and you the chance to talk to monks about anything from Buddhism to the weather – or about the university's overnight Buddhist culture and meditation courses (see box above).

Chiang Mai University Art Museum

Thanon Nimmanhemin, near the corner of Thanon Suthep • Tues–Sun 9am–5pm • Free • ⊕ 053 944833 or ⊕ 053 218280, ⓦ cmumuseum.org

The modern **Chiang Mai University Art Museum** is not only confirmation of the city's growing importance, but also a boon to the large local artistic community. The large, purpose-built exhibition areas are well designed and lit, and the exhibitions generally change each month, giving visitors an insight into modern Thai art, as well as anything from Japanese lacquerware sculpture to Iranian carpetry art. There's a café and shop, and films and concerts are regularly put on here.

Wat Umong

Off Thanon Suthep: turn left (south) after Wang Nam Gan (a royal agricultural produce project), then follow the signs to the wat for about 1km along a winding lane

More of a park than a temple, **Wat Umong** makes an unusual, charming place for a stroll in the western suburbs. According to legend, the wat was built by King Mengrai, but renovated in the 1380s by King Ku Na for a brilliant but deranged monk called Jan, who was prone to wandering off into the forest to meditate. Because Ku Na wanted to be able to get Jan's advice at any time, he founded this wat and decorated the tunnels (*umong*) beneath the chedi with paintings of trees, flowers and birds to simulate the monk's favoured habitat. Some of the old tunnels can still be explored, where obscure fragments of paintings and one or two small modern shrines can be seen. Above the tunnels, frighteningly lavish nagas guard the staircase up to the bell-shaped, Sri Lankan-style **chedi** and a grassy platform that supports a grotesque black statue of the fasting Buddha, all ribs and veins: he is depicted as he was during his six years of self-mortification, before he realized that he should avoid extremes along the Middle Path to enlightenment. Behind the chedi, the ground slopes away to a **lake** inhabited by hungry carp, where locals come to relax and feed the fish. On a tiny island here, reached by a concrete bridge, stands a statue of the late Buddhadasa Bhikkhu (see p.532), a famous southern Thai monk who re-established the monastic community here in the 1960s.

Throughout the tranquil wooded grounds, the temple's diverse education-focused philosophy comes vividly alive: as you enter the compound you pass through a shady grove where signs are pinned to nearly every tree, displaying simple Buddhist maxims in Thai and English and the botanical name of the species. There's a library, in the centre of the temple grounds, with some books in English, and an adjacent bookshop; outside at tables and covered seating areas local people read, study and conduct discussions.

ARRIVAL AND DEPARTURE
CHIANG MAI

On arrival at the train station or one of the bus stations, you can either flag down a red songthaew out on the road or charter a tuk-tuk or songthaew (see p.288) to get to the centre. To **book tickets** for departure, there are several ways to dodge a long, extra trip out to Arcade (see p.28 & p.288), including just asking your guesthouse or hotel. Queen Bee, 5 Thanon Moonmuang (☎053 275525, ⓦqueenbeetours.com), is a reliable **travel agent** for train tickets and all manner of minibus, bus and domestic plane tickets, as well as for a wide range of tours. Global Union Express, near Warorot Market at 35 Thanon Chang Moi (☎053 234400 ⓦguetravel.com), is a good agent for domestic and international plane tickets.

BY PLANE

Chiang Mai Airport is 3km southwest of the centre. Its busiest route is Bangkok, which is served by all six of the main Thai carriers (only Thai and Bangkok Airways fly to Suvarnabhumi from here). Meanwhile Bangkok Airways does Ko Samui and Phuket, Thai Smile Phuket, Air Asia Hat Yai, Krabi, Phuket, Surat Thani and Ubon Ratchathani, and Nok Air Udon Thani. There are also dozens of international routes from China, East and Southeast Asia, while Kan Airlines (ⓦkanairlines.com) operates mostly small propeller planes out of Chiang Mai on a constantly changing schedule of domestic routes.

Airport facilities You'll find currency exchange booths and ATMs, cafés, a tourist police booth and car rental offices such as Avis (☎02 251 1131, ⓦavisthailand.com).

Getting to/from the centre Two licensed a/c taxi companies have booths in the domestic baggage hall and in the arrivals hall, charging from B150 to Tha Pae Gate, for example (they don't use their meters). From the exit by the international arrivals hall, at the south end of the terminal, a/c minibuses run to hotels in town every half-hour (B40/person). Tuk-tuks and red songthaews can bring departing passengers to the airport (around B120 from the city centre), but are not allowed to pick up fares there.

Destinations Bangkok (25 daily; 1hr); Chiang Rai (2 weekly; 35min); Hat Yai (daily; 2hr); Hua Hin (3 weekly; 1hr 50min); Khon Kaen (1 daily; 1hr 10min); Khorat (4 weekly; 1hr 50min); Ko Samui (1 daily; 1hr 50min); Krabi (2 daily; 2hr); Mae Hong Son (3–4 daily; 35min); Nan (2 weekly; 45min); Pai (5 weekly; 30min); Phitsanulok (4 weekly; 1hr); Phuket (5 daily; 2hr); Surat Thani (1 daily; 2hr); Ubon Ratchathani (1 daily; 1hr 45min); Udon Thani (1 daily; 1hr).

BY TRAIN

Many people arrive – often an hour or two later than scheduled – at the train station (which has a left-luggage office) on Thanon Charoen Muang, just over 2km from Tha Pae Gate on the eastern side of town. There's usually a welcoming committee of guesthouse staff, plugging their accommodation and offering free lifts.

Destinations Bangkok (5 daily; 12hr–14hr 30min); Den Chai (for Phrae and Nan; 6 daily; 4–5hr); Doi Khun Tan (5 daily; 1hr 30min); Lampang (6 daily; 2hr–2hr 30min).

BY BUS

Arcade bus station Chiang Mai's main bus station is off the south side of Thanon Kaeo Nawarat, about 3km from Tha Pae Gate to the northeast.

Chang Phuak bus station This small station off the east side of Thanon Chotana handles services from the rest of Chiang Mai province (including Chom Thong and Tha Ton); buses from Lamphun also end up here.

Bus companies The main Chiang Mai-based long-distance bus company, Green Bus (☎053 242214–5, ⓦgreenbusthailand.com), maintains a ticket office in the centre of town, on Thanon Inthrawarorot, just east of Wat Phra Singh. If you insist on travelling here with one of the low-cost tourist bus companies on Bangkok's Thanon Khao San despite our warnings (see p.136), try to find out exactly where you'll be dropped in Chiang Mai before making a booking: these companies' buses have been known to stop on a remote part of the Superhighway, where they "sell" their passengers to various guesthouse touts.

Destinations Bangkok (30 daily; 10–11hr); Chiang Khong (3 daily; 5–6hr); Chiang Rai (every 30min; 3–4hr); Chiang Saen (2 daily; 5hr); Chom Thong (every 30min; 1hr); Fang (every 30min; 3hr 30min); Khon Kaen (9 daily; 12hr); Khorat (11 daily; 12hr); Lampang (every 30min; 1hr 30min); Lamphun (every 20min; 1hr); Luang Prabang, Laos (1 daily; 18hr); Mae Hong Son (5 daily via Mae Sariang, 8hr; roughly hourly via Pai, 6–8hr); Mae Sai (6–8 daily; 4hr 40min–5hr 15min); Mae Sot (2 daily; 6hr 30min); Nan (8–9 daily; 5–6hr); Pai (hourly; 3hr 30min); Phitsanulok (over 30 daily; 5–6hr); Phrae (11 daily; 4hr); Sukhothai (up to 22 daily; 5–6hr); Tha Ton (7 daily; 4hr); Udon Thani (2 daily; 12hr).

GETTING AROUND

BY BICYCLE

Although you can comfortably walk between the most central temples, bicycles are the best way of getting around the old town and, with a bit of legwork, out to the attractions beyond the moat too. Sit-up-and-beg models and basic mountain bikes are available at many outlets around the old town, especially on the roads along the eastern moat, for about B50/day, while Cacti, 94/1 Thanon Singharat, near the corner of Si Phum (☎053 212979 or ☎089 757 9150), rents good-quality, well-maintained road and mountain bikes (B80–450/day), as well as selling new and used bikes and doing repairs.

BY SONGTHAEW

There's been talk about setting up a comprehensive bus system in Chiang Mai for years, but for now people make do with red songthaews (*rot daeng*), which act as shared taxis within the city, picking up a number of passengers headed in roughly the same direction and taking each to their specific destination (songthaews of other colours serve outlying villages and suburbs). A journey in the centre of town, for example from Tha Pae Gate to Wat Phra Singh, will set you back B20, but it'll naturally cost more to go somewhere off the beaten track or if the driver thinks you want to charter (*mao*) the whole vehicle.

BY TAXI, TUK-TUK OR SAMLOR

Chiang Mai's so-called "meter taxis" never switch on their meters, they only quote flat fares, typically B150 for a 2km journey. You can't flag them down on the street – ask at your accommodation or call ☎053 262878 for a pick-up. More prevalent are tuk-tuks, for which heavy bargaining is expected – allow around B60 for a short journey, say from the Night Bazaar to Tha Pae Gate. The town still has a few samlors, which are cheap when used by locals to haul produce home from the market, but not so cheap when chartered by groups of upmarket tourists on sightseeing tours from their hotel.

BY MOTORBIKE

Motorbikes – most useful for exploring places outside of Chiang Mai – are available to rent in all shapes and sizes around Tha Pae Gate, costing around B200/day for a 125cc automatic. Among reliable rental outlets, Queen Bee, 5 Thanon Moonmuang (☎053 275525, ⓦqueen-bee.com), and Mr Mechanic, Thanon Moonmuang, near the corner of Thanon Ratchawithi (☎053 214708, ⓦmr-mechanic1994 .com), who has bikes of all sizes, can also offer insurance.

BY CAR

Many outlets in the Tha Pae Gate area rent out cars and 4WDs, from as little as B800/day: reliable companies offering insurance and breakdown recovery include Avis, at Chiang Mai airport (☎02 251 1131, ⓦavisthailand.com; delivery and collection anywhere in Chiang Mai); Journey, 283 Thanon Tha Pae (☎053 208787, ⓦjourneycnx.com); North Wheels, 70/4–8 Thanon Chaiyapoom (☎053 874478, ⓦnorthwheels.com); Mr Mechanic and Queen Bee (see p.287).

INFORMATION

Tourist information The TAT office (daily 8.30am–4.30pm; ☎053 248604) is on Thanon Chiang Mai–Lamphun, on the east bank of the river south of Nawarat Bridge. It's not to be confused with TAD Travel and Tours on Thanon Ratchaphakinai and other similarly named outlets prominently displaying "INFORMATION" signs, which pretend to be government information offices but are in fact private travel agents.

Maps *Nancy Chandler's Map of Chiang Mai*, sold in many outlets in the city (B275), is very handy for a detailed exploration: like her brightly coloured Bangkok map, it gives a personal choice of sights, shops, restaurants and various oddities. Regular updates are posted at ⓦ nancychandler.net.

Listings Several free, monthly, locally published magazines such as *Citylife* contain information about upcoming events in town and articles about local culture; they're distributed in spots where tourists tend to congregate, including hotel lobbies. *Citylife* also has a website at ⓦ chiangmainews.com and produces a fortnightly map with events listings, *City Now*.

ACCOMMODATION

Chiang Mai is well stocked with every kind of accommodation to suit all budgets, though places may fill up from December to February and are very busy at festival time, particularly during Songkhran (April), Loy Krathong (Nov) and around New Year's Eve. **Basic guesthouses**, often friendly, quiet affairs with their own outdoor cafés, are gathered on the narrow sois inside the old city. Situated close to the eastern side of the moat and Tha Pae Gate, **Thanon Moonmuang's Soi 9** and the **south end of Thanon Ratchaphakinai** almost warrant being called travellers' ghettoes (though nothing like on the scale of Bangkok's Thanon Khao San), but there are plenty of other, quieter options within the moat where you can better soak up the old town's charm. In the moderate price range, by far the best options are the **upmarket guesthouses and lodges**, which, as well as good facilities, generally offer much more appealing decor and atmosphere than similarly priced hotels. At the top end, there has been a recent explosion of **luxury accommodation** in Chiang Mai, ranging from small boutique hotels to massive projects like the Mandarin Oriental's *Dhara Devi*, most of them enhanced by traditional Lanna architectural touches.

3

ESSENTIALS

Scams Beware of tuk-tuk and songthaew drivers at the bus and train stations offering a free ride if you stay at a particular guesthouse – perhaps adding, falsely, that the place you had planned to stay is full or closed – as you'll probably find that the price of a room is bumped up to pay for your ride. To get around this, some guesthouses send their own staff to the stations, who will genuinely give you a free ride; and many places will offer a free pick-up when you book.

Trekking hassles Many of the least expensive places in Chiang Mai make their money from trekking and tours, which can be convenient as a trek often needs a lot of organizing beforehand, but can equally be annoying if you're in Chiang Mai for other reasons and are put under pressure to trek; most of the guesthouses we've listed can arrange trekking, but at none of them should you get this kind of undue hassle.

MASSAGES AND SPAS IN CHIANG MAI

Many of Chiang Mai's top hotels now have full-service **spas**, and there are several upmarket stand-alones. However, some of the best traditional **massages** in town – no frills but highly skilled and good value – are likely to be had at schools such as the Old Medicine Hospital, which offers consistently good Thai (B300/90min), herbal and foot massages; and out in the countryside Baan Hom Samunprai offers great two-hour massages for B600, as well as foot massages, herbal compress massages and steam baths (for both, see p.281).

Chiangmai Oasis Spa 4 Thanon Samlan, just south of Wat Phra Singh, & 102 Thanon Sirimuangkarajan ☎053 920111, ⓦchiangmaioasis.com. Upmarket spa with a good reputation (B1990 for a 2hr traditional massage).

Let's Relax Night Bazaar Pavilion, Thanon Chang Klan ☎053 818498, ⓦletsrelaxspa.com. Part of a nationwide chain, this reasonably priced spa lays on a few more frills, longer opening hours and a wider range of treatments than the basic massage centres (from B500 for a 1hr Thai massage).

The Peak Spa & Beauty Salon Twin Peaks Condo, 187/13 Thanon Chang Klan ☎053 818869, ⓦpeak -spa.com. Excellent choice, offering a wide range of treatments at moderate prices, but with service and facilities comparable to an upmarket hotel spa (from B800 for 90min Thai massage). Free transfers included.

Thai Massage Conservation Club 99 Thanon Ratchamankha, near Wat Chedi Luang ☎053 904452. Basic setup with traditional massages by extremely competent, blind masseurs (B180/hr), who focus on vigorous acupressure rather than stretching.

THA PAE GATE AREA
GUESTHOUSES

Awana House 7 Soi 1, Thanon Ratchdamnoen ☎053
419005, ⓦawanahouse.com; map p.290. This helpful,
Thai–Dutch guesthouse has a tiny, covered pool and large,
nicely furnished rooms (most with balconies), complete

with colourful trompe l'oeil paintings, a/c, hot water, cable
TV and fridge. There's also a pleasant, mostly covered
rooftop terrace, which shelters two fan rooms with double
beds, sharing a hot-water bathroom. Fan B475, a/c B640
Chiang Mai Thai House 5/1 Soi 5, Thanon Tha Pae
☎053 904110, ⓦchiangmaithaihouse.com; map

THA PAE GATE AREA

● SHOPS	
Backstreet Books	3
Boots	5
Fair Trade Shop	7
Gecko Books	4
Ginger	1
The Lost Bookshop	8
Neramit	2
Nova Collection	6

● RESTAURANTS & CAFÉS	
Aroon Rai	6
Blue Diamond	2
La Fontana	8
Miguel's	1
Mit Mai	7
Pho Vieng Chane	5
Ratana's Kitchen	3
Ruen Tamarind	4

■ ACCOMMODATION	
Awana House	10
Chiang Mai Thai House	13
Diva Guesthouse	15
Eagle House	6
Gap's House	12
Giant Guesthouse	4/17
Jonadda Guest House	5
Kavil Guest House	8
Libra House	3
Mini Cost	9
Pha Thai House	16
SK House	1
Supreme Guest House	2
Tamarind Village	11
Three Sis	14
Your House	7

■ BARS & CLUBS	
Brasserie	1
Jack Van Bar	2
THC (The Hemp Collective)	4
UN Irish Pub	3

p.290. There's a choice of smallish but well-furnished rooms with fan and cable TV, or bigger ones with a/c and mini-bar (some with cute mini-gardens on the ground floor), in this centrally located but fairly quiet place, which also has a tiny pool. Fan B600, a/c B1200

Diva Guesthouse 84/13 Thanon Ratchaphakinai ☏053 273851, ⓦ divaguesthouse.com; map p.290. Helpful spot with richly coloured murals on the walls, a sociable ground-floor café and a wide choice of clean rooms with en-suite showers: six-bed, fan-cooled dorms and fan and a/c private rooms of all sizes. Success has spawned two overspill branches nearby. Dorms B110, doubles B300

★ **Eagle House** 16 Soi 3, Thanon Chang Moi Kao ☏053 235387, ⓦ eaglehouse.com; map p.290. Run by an Irishwoman and her Thai husband who are keen to promote ethical ecotourism, this friendly, quiet, well-maintained guesthouse offers a spacious garden terrace area with a good café and well-organized treks, as well as Thai cookery courses. Choose from a wide variety of en-suite rooms of different sizes, most with hot water, some with a/c. Phone for a free pick-up. Fan B220, a/c B370

Gap's House 3 Soi 4, Thanon Ratchdamnoen ☏053 278140, ⓦ gaps-house.com; map p.290. Set around a relaxing, leafy compound strewn with objets d'art is a wide range of a/c rooms with antique furniture and hot showers. The room price includes a simple cooked breakfast, and a vegetarian buffet is served in the evening (not Sun); one- or two-day cookery courses available. No reservations are taken, though you can call on your proposed arrival date to check availability. Decent rates for singles. B470

Giant Guesthouse Soi 6, Thanon Moonmuang ☏053 227338, ⓦ giantguesthouse.com; map p.290. This popular option is right next to the market and has its own kitchen – ideal if you fancy practising your Thai cooking. The staff are helpful and offer free bicycles and free pick-ups from the airport or bus station, and also put on films in the comfortable lounge. Rooms come with fan (shared or en-suite bathrooms) or a/c. There's another, fan-only branch at the bottom of Thanon Ratchaphakinai with dorm beds (B120). Fan B180, a/c B400

Jonadda Guest House 23/1 Soi 2, Thanon Ratchawithi ☏053 227281, ⓔ jonadda@hotmail.com; map p.290. Friendly place with a variety of bright, clean, comfortable fan rooms (including triples) with strong hot showers, in a modern, multistorey building. Good prices for singles and big discounts in low season. Fan B600, a/c B800

Kavil Guest House 10/1 Soi 5, Thanon Ratchdamnoen ☏053 224740 or ☏089 852 1875; map p.290. Friendly place in a modern four-storey building on a quiet soi. All twelve rooms have en-suite hot-water bathrooms; the rooms with fans are small, plain and clean, while those with a/c are pleasantly decorated and more spacious (the a/c can be switched off to turn these into fan rooms).

The downstairs café is at the front, which means there's no noisy courtyard effect. Fan B250, a/c B350

Libra House 28 Soi 9, Thanon Moonmuang ☏053 210687, ⓦ librahousechiangmai.com; map p.290. Excellent, family-run, trekking-oriented guesthouse with keen, helpful service and 24hr check-in. Forty large, plain but well-maintained rooms, spread across five buildings with some quiet sitting areas, are en suite, some with hot water. Free daytime pick-ups for advance bookings. Fan B250, a/c B600

Mini Cost 19–19/4 Soi 1, Thanon Ratchdamnoen ☏053 418787–8, ⓦ minicostcm.com; map p.290. Smart ochre-painted guesthouse and apartment block with helpful staff, offering comfortable rooms with some colourful modern Thai decorative touches, as well as a/c, hot water, fridges and cable TV. B1000

Pha Thai House 48/1 Thanon Ratchaphakinai ☏053 278013 or ☏081 998 6933, ⓦ phathaihouse.com; map p.290. Wide variety of rooms, all with en-suite hot showers and a/c, in a leafy garden setting with a small swimming pool: some boast balconies, colourful decor, fridges, TVs and antique-style furniture, while plainer rooms at the front of the compound by the road are much cheaper. Family rooms also available. B800

SK House 30 Soi 9, Thanon Moonmuang ☏053 210690, ⓦ theskhouse.com; map p.290. Efficient, brick-built high-rise with a ground-floor café, a small, shaded swimming pool and a slightly institutional feel. Fan rooms come with hot-water bathrooms, while the a/c rooms are much more colourful and attractive, with cable TV. Fan B250, a/c B600

Supreme Guest House 44/1 Soi 9, Thanon Moonmuang ☏053 222480, ⓦ facebook.com/supremehouse; map p.290. Friendly, laidback, basic guesthouse in a modern concrete block with a pleasant roof veranda. The rooms are comfortable and have TVs and solar-heated showers. Fan B350, a/c B550

Three Sis 1 Soi 8, Thanon Phra Pokklao ☏053 273243, ⓦ 3sisbedandbreakfast.com; map p.290. Genteel B&B opposite Wat Chedi Luang with lots of attractive open-plan public areas to loll about in. Rooms in the new building have wooden floors and tasteful furnishings that also feature a lot of dark wood, while those in the original building are almost as spacious but less stylish; all have a/c, hot water, cable TV and fridge. Breakfast included. B1700

★ **Your House** 8 Soi 2, Thanon Ratchawithi ☏053 217492, ⓦ yourhouseguesthouse.com; map p.290. Very welcoming, old-town atmosphere (though some rooms get a bit of noise from nearby bars) and a wide choice of accommodation: in the attractive, original teak house, six airy rooms share three bathrooms with hot showers; the two modern annexes across the lane, both with hot water en suite, include lovely, big rooms with polished teak floors, small balconies and well-equipped bathrooms. Optional a/c in most rooms. The attractive restaurant

3

serves good Thai and French food, with buffalo steak and chips a speciality. Good for treks, day-trips and train, plane and bus tickets. Discounts for singles. Fan B250, a/c B450

HOTELS

Tamarind Village 50/1 Thanon Ratchdamnoen ☎053 418896, ⓦtamarindvillage.com; map p.290. Named for a huge, 200-year-old tamarind tree that shades the compound, this small, tranquil boutique resort in the heart of Chiang Mai's old city is designed in Lanna style, though the extremely comfortable rooms, which all enjoy lovely garden views, have modern touches. Good-sized pool, attractive spa, an interesting programme of cultural activities and excellent restaurant (see p.294) too. B5530

REST OF CHIANG MAI

GUESTHOUSES

Baan Kaew Guest House 142 Thanon Charoen Prathet ☎053 271606, ⓦbaankaew-guesthouse.com; map p.276. Set back from the road in a quiet, pretty garden, this attractive modern building has twenty large, simple but well-equipped and well-maintained rooms with hot water, mini-bars and a/c. B800

★**Baan Orapin** 150 Thanon Charoenrat ☎053 243677, ⓦbaanorapin.com; map p.276. Delightful compound overshadowed by tall longan trees, offering big, comfy and characterful rooms with teak and rattan furnishings and wooden floors. Some rooms come with four-poster beds and balconies. Breakfast included; minimum stay two nights. B2100

Bon Ça Va 252/13–14 Thanon Phra Pokklao ☎053 418266, ⓦfacebook.com/boncavahotel; map p.276. Small, friendly guesthouse with a tasteful antique look, just south of Chang Puak Gate, offering large, clean rooms with a/c, hot showers, fridges and cable TV. B900

Eco Resort 109 Thanon Bamrungrat ☎053 247111, ⓦecoresortchiangmai.com; map p.276. This former school in huge, lush, quiet gardens has been tastefully transformed into a modern, eco-friendly hostel-cum-hotel, with a/c and hot water throughout. Choose between well-equipped dorms (some with only two beds) with smart, white bedding, and attractive rooms with large bathrooms in a subtle contemporary style. There's a lovely, 25m pool surrounded by hanging plants and stylish common rooms. Simple breakfast included. Dorm B450, double B1980

★**Elliebum** 114/3 Thanon Ratchamanka ☎053 814723 or ☎085 018 7400, ⓦelliebum.com; map p.276. Sociable and very helpful home-from-home right in the centre of the old town, with lots of advice and information about the area available. The huge, fresh, modern rooms are more like junior suites (big enough for a family), with a/c, walk-in hot showers, sofas, fridges, TV and DVD, above a café (see p.296). Also on offer are culinary walking tours (see p.294). Tasty à la carte breakfasts included. B1700

Galare Guest House 7 Soi 2, Thanon Charoen Prathet ☎053 818887 or ☎053 821011, ⓦgalare.com; map p.276. Near Narawat Bridge, this long-standing, well-run upmarket guesthouse is justly popular. Plain a/c rooms, each with hot-water bathroom, TV and fridge, overlook a shady lawn that gives way to a riverside terrace restaurant. B1200

Gerard Habitat 2/8 Soi 3, Thanon Nimmanhaemin ☎053 227272, ⓦgerardhabitat.com; map p.276. On a relatively quiet Nimman soi, this place is a beautiful showcase for the designer-owner's contemporary bamboo furniture (which is on sale in the ground-floor shop). The large, balconied rooms feature a/c, TV, DVD, hot showers, fridges and microwaves, and there's a stylish little garden. Breakfast included. B1700

Green Tulip 85 Thanon Samlarn ☎053 275858, ⓦgreentuliphouse.com; map p.276. In a good location down the road from Wat Phra Singh, with a bar-restaurant offering good food downstairs, a pleasant roof garden and a loud colour scheme. Clean, bright, basic rooms with fan or a/c and en-suite hot showers. Dorms B150, doubles B500

★**Hollanda Montri** 365 Thanon Charoenrat ☎053 242450, ⓦhollandamontri.com; map p.276. North of the centre by the busy Rama IX Bridge, in a modern building by the river, this Dutch–Thai guesthouse has large, comfortable and attractive fan or a/c rooms with TVs and hot-water bathrooms, and cheerful staff. A very pleasant, terraced riverside bar-restaurant offers a long menu of Thai and European dishes. Free daytime bicycles. Fan B500, a/c B600

Riverside House 101 Thanon Chiang Mai–Lamphun ☎053 241860, ⓦriversidehousechiangmai.com; map p.276. Welcoming place with a lush garden on the east bank of the river, though just a short walk from the night bazaar, with plain but clean and cosy a/c rooms with cable TV and hot showers, plus a small swimming pool. B700

River View Lodge 25 Soi 4, Thanon Charoen Prathet ☎053 271109–10, ⓦriverviewlodgch.com; map p.276. Tasteful, well-run and good-value alternative to international-class hotels, with a beautiful riverside garden, a small swimming pool and neat decorative touches in the rooms; the most expensive have balconies overlooking the river. Breakfast included. B1800

Wanasit 6 Soi 8, Thanon Ratchamanka ☎053 814042; map p.276. Tranquil and popular for longer stays, this three-storey guesthouse by the south wall of Wat Phra Singh is showing its age a little but offers bright, clean rooms with small, hot-water bathrooms, most with balconies, and a roof terrace. B400

HOTELS

Anantara Chiang Mai 123 Thanon Charoen Prathet ☎053 253333, ⓦanantara.com; map p.276. Occupying a prime riverside site, though hemmed in by noisy Charoen Prathet, this luxury place offers high-concept minimalist design in its spacious rooms, along with balconies and river views. There's a good-looking spa and a 34m riverside swimming pool, while a renovated teak house – formerly the British Consulate, built in 1905 – serves afternoon teas and tapas and the restaurant dishes up excellent Indian, Thai and Western food. Breakfast included. B10,200

Chiang Mai Gate Hotel 11/10 Thanon Suriyawong ☎053 203895–9, ⓦchiangmaigatehotel.com; map p.276. Located just to the south of the old city, this place has 120 well-equipped rooms with Lanna touches in the design, a/c and hot water, plus a swimming pool and helpful staff. Breakfast included. B1075

D2 Hotel 100 Chang Klan ☎053 999999, ⓦdusit.com; map p.276. With its muted orange theme and helpful staff in street fashions, plus stunning lighting and minimalist furnishings, this place in the heart of the night bazaar, run by the Dusit Group, is probably the coolest luxury hotel in Chiang Mai. A spa, fitness centre and stylish rooftop pool are among the amenities. B4240

Dhara Dhevi 51/4 Thanon Chiang Mai–Sankamphaeng ☎053 888888, ⓦdharadhevi.com; map p.276. Occupying huge grounds a few kilometres east of the city centre, the *Dhara Dhevi* transports its guests into another era, the heyday of the Lanna Kingdom. Traditional Lanna architecture is complemented by modern touches in the villas, suites and residences, which are equipped with every conceivable comfort and look out over rice fields and vegetable gardens. With a breathtaking spa (modelled on the royal palace of Mandalay), cooking school, a daily programme of crafts demonstrations, shopping centre, library of books and DVDs, two swimming pools, tennis courts, a patisserie and four restaurants, guests need never leave the premises. B21,400

Duangtawan 132 Thanon Loi Khro ☎053 905000, ⓦduangtawanhotelchiangmai.com; map p.276. This five-hundred-room, international-standard hotel by the night bazaar pulls in package groups with attractive rates and an impressive range of facilities: spacious roof-top pool, well-equipped gym, spa and highly regarded 24th-floor Chinese restaurant with fine views of Doi Suthep. B2295

★ **Four Seasons** About 15km north of Chiang Mai on Mae Rim–Samoeng Old Road, at the start of the Mae Sa valley ☎053 298181, ⓦfourseasons.com; map p.276. The last word in Lanna luxury, with superbly appointed rooms and apartments, a swimming pool and a gorgeous spa, all set around a picturesque lake and rice paddies (where you can learn to plant rice) with fine views of Doi Suthep behind. On a long menu of activities, the highlight is a top-quality cooking school. B20,390

★ **Rachamankha** 6 Soi 9, Thanon Ratchamanka ☎053 904111, ⓦrachamankha.com; map p.276. Looking more like a temple than a hotel, this spacious, architect-owned property with just 25 elegant rooms is hidden in the quiet backstreets of the old city. There's a lovely, large pool, a spa, an excellent restaurant (see p.296) and a well-stocked library with sherry laid out for browsers. Breakfast and complimentary mini-bar included. Discounts for stays of three nights or longer. B9730

Royal Princess 111 Thanon Chang Klan ☎053 253900, ⓦdusit.com; map p.276. Tidy, centrally located hotel close to the night bazaar, with two hundred elegant rooms, an attractive swimming pool and fitness centre, fine restaurants and impeccable service. B3060

Tri Yaan Na Ros 156 Thanon Wualai ☎053 273174, ⓦtriyaannaros.com; map p.276. Snuggled away to the south of the old city centre, this renovated colonial building oozes atmosphere, from the four-poster beds to the photos of ancient Lanna on the walls. There's a small library, a swimming pool and free bicycles for guests' use. Breakfast included. B3860

U Chiang Mai 70 Thanon Ratchdamnoen ☎053 327000, ⓦuhotelsresorts.com; map p.276. Innovative hotel that offers 24hr use of room (no matter what time you check in), heritage talks and walks, breakfast (included) available in your bedroom all day, and free bikes. The reading room and spa occupy the hundred-year-old former governor's residence, while some of the rooms – decorated in contemporary Thai style, with daybeds on the balconies, rain showers and iPods – give straight onto the small, black swimming pool in the central courtyard. B6880

EATING

The main difficulty with **eating** in Chiang Mai is knowing when to stop. All over town there are inexpensive and enticing restaurants serving typically northern food, which has been strongly influenced by Burmese cuisine, especially in curries such as *kaeng hang lay* (usually translated on menus as "Northern Thai curry"), made with pork, ginger, garlic and tamarind. At **lunchtime** the thing to do is to join the local workers in one of the simple, inexpensive cafés that put all their efforts into producing just one or two special dishes – the traditional meal at this time of day is *khao soi*, a thick broth of curry and coconut cream, with egg noodles and a choice of meat. The main **night markets** are at the back and front entrances to Chiang Mai University on Thanon Suthep and Thanon Huai Kaeo; along Thanon Bamrungburi by Chiang Mai Gate; along Thanon Manee Noparat by Chang Puak Gate; plus a few stalls in front of Somphet market on Thanon Moonmuang. Also in the evening you'll find restaurants which lay on touristy **cultural shows** with *khan toke* dinners, a selection of northern dishes traditionally eaten on the floor off short-legged lacquer trays. Of these, the Old Chiangmai Cultural Centre, 185/3 Thanon Wualai (B520; ☎053 275097, ⓦoldchiangmai.com), with its show of northern Thai and hill-tribe dancing, has the best reputation. Many of the **bars** listed in "Drinking and nightlife" (see p.297) have good reputations for their food, especially *The Riverside* and *The UN Irish Pub*.

FOOD WALKS AND DINNER CRUISES

In the mornings, *Elliebum Guesthouse* (see p.292) offers fascinating guided **food walks** around the old town (4hr; from B750/person), taking in Chiang Mai Gate Market and the locals' favourite street restaurants and dessert stalls. With plenty of insights about Thai cuisine and culture along the way, they're a great way to get to know the city.

Every evening, *The Riverside* (see p.298) runs a **dinner cruise**, charging B150/person on top of whatever you order from its very good menu. Booking is recommended, but you'll certainly need to get there by 7.15pm to put your orders in (boat departs at 8pm).

THA PAE GATE AREA

THAI

Aroon Rai Thanon Kotchasarn ☎053 276947; map p.290. This basic, long-standing restaurant by Tha Pae Gate serves great northern Thai dishes, such as tasty *kaeng hang lay muu* (B60), *khao soi* and a very good *kaeng khae*, a typical local curry without coconut milk, with lots of herbs and vegetables. They also sell their curry pastes for you to take home. Daily roughly noon–9.30pm.

★Ratana's Kitchen 320–322 Thanon Tha Pae ☎053 874173; map p.290. A good-value favourite among locals and visitors both for northern specialities (B50–100) such as *kaeng hang lay*, *khao soi* and mixed hors d'oeuvres, and for tasty Western breakfasts, sandwiches, cottage pie and steaks. Extensive vegetarian menu, wine and cocktails too. Daily 7.30am–11.30pm.

Ruen Tamarind 50/1 Thanon Ratchdamnoen ☎053 418896–9; map p.290. Overlooking the pool at the *Tamarind Village* hotel (see p.292), this elegant restaurant serves up excellent Thai cuisine, including mainstream fare such as *tom kha thaleh* (coconut soup with seafood) and more creative offerings, as well as a long and interesting selection of northern Thai favourites, for around B200–300 a dish. Also does afternoon tea. Daily 7am–11pm.

INTERNATIONAL

Blue Diamond Soi 9, Thanon Moonmuang; map p.290. Popular, mostly vegetarian restaurant in a quiet neighbourhood of guesthouses, serving very good Thai dishes, Western breakfasts (from B70), home-made bread, shakes, herbal teas and hill-tribe coffee. Mon–Sat 7am–8.30pm.

★La Fontana 39/7–8 Thanon Ratchamanka ☎053 207091, ⓦlafontanachiangmai.com; map p.290. Chiang Mai's best Italian, dishing up great home-made pastas (B150–200), risottos, pizzas, meat and fish dishes, as well as tempting antipasti and panna cotta, ice cream and other desserts, all washed down with imported Italian wine. Daily 11.30am–10.30pm; in low season, sometimes closes Tues and at lunchtimes.

Miguel's Thanon Chaiyapoom ☎053 874148, ⓦfacebook.com/miguelscafechiangmai; map p.290. A warm welcome, a relaxing terrace and good Mexican food: feast on the *nachos grande* with chicken for B220,

perhaps with a side order of guacamole (in season). Daily 9am–11pm.

Mit Mai 42/2 Thanon Ratchamanka ☎053 275033; map p.290. It looks like a simple Thai restaurant from the street, but in fact *Mit Mai* serves up excellent food in large portions from Yunnan province in China, including a zesty chicken salad and snow peas stir-fried with Yunnanese ham (B90), as well as more exotic dishes such as *fong nom thawt* (fried cheese) and white bamboo grubs. Daily 10am–10pm.

Pho Vieng Chane Kad Klang Wieng, Thanon Ratchdamnoen, corner of Ratchaphakinai; map p.290. Specializes in *pho* (pronounced "fur"; from B35), a tasty noodle soup, but serves all manner of excellent, cheap Vietnamese food. At the shared outside tables in the grassy courtyard, you can also order good Italian dishes from the neighbouring restaurant. Daily 11am–9.30pm; closed Mon & Tues in the last week of the month.

REST OF CHIANG MAI

THAI

Ba Mii Kiaw Stall Thanon Manee Noparat, just west of Wat Lok Malee; map p.276. When the DTAC phone shop closes for the night, this pushcart kitchen with plenty of tables turns up on the forecourt and starts serving the best noodle soup in town, stuffed with roast red pork and wonton (*ba mii kiaw*; B35). Mon–Sat 6pm–midnight.

Café de Nimman Soi 13, Thanon Sirimuangkarajan ☎053 218405; map p.276. Excellent food such as squid stuffed with pork in green curry (B120) and creative Thai salads, at this stylish, reasonably priced restaurant with lots of attractive outdoor tables. Daily 11am–11pm.

Hong Tauw Inn 95/17–18 Nantawan Arcade, Thanon Nimmanhemin ☎053 218333; map p.276. Comfortable a/c restaurant done out in "country inn" style, with antiques, plants and old clocks, making for a relaxing environment. The varied menu of home-style cuisine ranges from rice and noodle dishes such as *khanom jiin*, to delicious central and northern Thai main dishes, such as a *phanaeng* curry for B90, and includes a wide range of *nam phrik*, spicy relishes, as well as *lon*, chilli dips with coconut milk. Daily 11am–11pm.

★Huan Soontaree 208 Thanon Patan, 3km north of the Superhighway ☎053 872707, ⓦsaochiangmai .com; map p.276. A convivial riverfront restaurant owned

WAT PHRA THAT DOI SUTHEP, NEAR CHIANG MAI (P.302) >

by the famous northern Thai folk-singer Soontaree Vechanont, who entertains diners from her balcony-level stage (she performs Mon–Sat, but is augmented by other good local musicians nightly). Delicious, very reasonably priced northern Thai specialities such as fried Chiang Mai sausage with whole baby garlic. Split levels allow a choice of seating, including on a leafy riverside terrace hung with paper lanterns, or on a balcony near the stage. Daily 4pm–midnight.

Huen Phen 112 Thanon Ratchamanka; map p.276. One of Chiang Mai's best northern Thai restaurants – and certainly the most famous. Try local specialities such as *sai oua* (sausage), *kaeng hang lay* (pork curry) and *khao soi* (noodle curry; B40). In the evening, the restaurant opens in an old wooden house decorated with antiques around the back (with a pricier menu). Daily roughly 8am–4pm & 5–10pm.

Khao Soi Samoe Jai Thanon Faham, just north of Wat Faham; map p.276. Thick, tasty and very cheap *khao soi* (spiced to order) and other northern specialities, plus delicious satay, *som tam*. No English sign – it's a wooden house with a red, white and blue awning. Daily 7/8am–5pm.

Khun Churn Thanon Thiphanet ☎053 270071, ⓦfacebook.com/khunchurn; map p.276. Sophisticated vegetarian restaurant in the grounds of the Old Chiangmai Cultural Centre, famous for its B169 all-day buffet, mostly consisting of stir-fries and salads; also does vegan options. Daily 8am–9/10pm.

Kiat Ocha 41–43 Thanon Inthrawarorot, off Thanon Phra Pokklao (the English sign says "Hainanese chicken"); map p.276. Delicious and very popular satay and *khao man kai* – boiled chicken breast served with dipping sauces, broth and rice – from around B40 a dish. This and the surrounding cafés are especially handy if you're looking round the old town. Daily 6am–2.30pm, or until the food runs out.

Lamduon Faharm Khao Soi 352/22 Thanon Charoenrat; map p.276. Excellent, very cheap *khao soi* prepared to a secret recipe, which can be spiced according to your taste; delicious crackling with the pork version. Also satay, *khanom jiin*, *som tam*, waffles and an assortment of juices. Daily 8.30am–4/4.30pm.

Pattana Soi 9, Thanon Nimmanhaemin ☎090 804 5658, ⓦfacebook.com/pattanafusionthaisouthern cuisine; map p.276. At this welcoming restaurant, you can feast on excellent, beautifully presented southern Thai dishes such as *nam phrik kung siap* (on the menu as "deep-fried shrimp in chilli sauce") and *khua kling* (minced "spare ribs with red curry and spices"). Most dishes B150–250. Daily 11am–9.30pm.

Rachamankha 6 Soi 9, Thanon Ratchamanka ☎053 904111; map p.276. In the courtyard of the boutique hotel of the same name (see p.293), this is one of Chiang Mai's classiest places to eat, with starched linen tablecloths and elegant cutlery and often with live traditional music in

the evening. From an unusual menu of northern Thai, Shan, Burmese and fusion dishes (mostly B300–400), try the Burmese-style beef curry and finish off with the mango flambé in a papaya bowl. Daily 7am–11pm.

★**Samsen Villa** Rimping Condominium, 201 Thanon Charoenrat ☎053 306588, ⓦsamsenvilla.com; map p.276. The best of several restaurants on the east bank of the Ping River, serving excellent, creative Thai food (most dishes B100–200) in the charming waterfront garden of this prominent condo by Nakhon Ping Bridge. Don't miss the grilled beef with elephant garlic and the *lon* (chilli dip with coconut milk), but avoid the signature "jelly beer" – unless you like your beer flat and frozen like a Slurpie. Daily 11am–10.30pm.

SP Chicken 9/1 Soi 1, Thanon Samlarn ☎080 500 5035; map p.276. Justly famous basic northeastern restaurant that's featured in the *New York Times*. The signature chickens (B80 for a half) are slowly cooked whole on a rotisserie and eaten with *som tam* and sticky rice, but the *laap* is also very good. Daily 11am–9pm.

Wan Lamun Thanon Inthrawarorot (no English sign, but look for the pink flower on its Thai sign); map p.276. Delightful spot purveying excellent lunches such as *khanom jiin* and *phat thai* and delicious Thai and Western desserts, to take away – perhaps to the square in front of the City Arts and Cultural Centre. Daily 7am–3/4pm, though some things will sell out earlier.

INTERNATIONAL

Amazing Sandwich 20/2 Thanon Huai Kaeo ⓦamazing sandwich.com; map p.276. The place to go if you hanker after a sandwich, bagel or baguette made up to order; also serves breakfasts and home-made yoghurts, juices and lassis. Mon–Sat 8.30am–8pm, Sun 8.30am–4pm.

Arcobaleno 60 Thanon Wat Ket ☎053 306254, ⓦarcobaleno-cm.com; map p.276. Tasty Italian food (main dishes from around B200) served in and around an attractive wooden house on a quiet lane near Nakhon Ping Bridge. Try the *spaghetti arcobaleno* (with smoked bacon, mushrooms and tomato sauce) and the delicious panna cotta for dessert. Daily 11am–2pm & 5.30–10pm.

The Duke's 49/4–5 Thanon Chiang Mai–Lamphun ☎053 249231, ⓦwherestheduke.com; map p.276. If you're looking for a decent steakhouse while in northern Thailand, head on down to *The Duke's*, which rustles up imported steaks, ribs, seafood, pizzas, American desserts and the rest. Simple burgers cost around B100, but most other dishes are B200 and up. Everything's big here, from the portions to the chairs. Also has a (more expensive) branch in the Night Bazaar Pavilion on Thanon Chang Klan. Daily 11am–11.30pm.

Elliebum 114/3 Thanon Ratchamanka ☎053 814723; map p.276. This stylish and welcoming café with a shady garden patio serves excellent espresso coffees, made with arabica beans sustainably grown in the nearby mountains, delicious fruit smoothies, top-notch breakfasts such as blueberry pancakes with maple syrup and fresh fruit, plus great sandwiches and Thai dishes for lunch. Mon–Sat 8am–5.30pm, Sun 8am–noon.

Hinlay 8/1 Thanon Na Wat Ket ☎053 242621; map p.276. Appealing garden restaurant dishing up very good Indian as well as Burmese and Thai curries (around B100), accompanied by roti bread and raita. Worth calling ahead as hours are sometimes erratic. Daily 10am–10pm.

iberry Off the south side of Soi 17, Thanon Nimmanhemin; map p.276. Chiang Mai's best and most famous ice-cream shop, owned by comedian "Nose" Udom – who is portrayed as a pink dog in a huge statue in the quirky garden. Also does home-made sorbets and cakes and good coffee. Daily 10am–10pm.

Imoya Thanon Chang Klan ☎053 271451; map p.276. Part of a chain of restaurants exported from Japan, with an appealing retro look, lined with old film posters and photos, as well as manga comics. Popular with expat Japanese, the wide-ranging menu includes good sushi (from B60). Daily 5pm–midnight.

Love at First Bite 28 Soi 1, Thanon Chiang Mai–Lamphun ☎053 242731, ⓦloveatfirstbite-cm.com; map p.276. Head south from the east side of Nawarat Bridge, then turn into the first lane on the left to discover this relaxing haven of home-baked cakes and pies, plus delicious coffee, served in a tiny café or on a neat lawn surrounded by flower beds. Tues–Sun 10am–6pm.

Tengoku de Cuisine Opposite the Dhara Dhevi hotel, south off the San Kamphaeng road ☎053 851133; map p.276. Great Japanese cuisine makes this stylish little restaurant to the east of town worth the trip. The sushi and the tartare (tataki) of New Zealand beef with spring onion are both very good, while the aubergine with miso sauce is not to be missed – all are best sampled on an all-you-can-eat "buffet" menu (though all dishes are prepared to order) for B800. Daily 10am–2pm & 5.30–10pm.

DRINKING AND NIGHTLIFE

Although there's a clutch of hostess bars bordering the east moat and along Loi Khro, and several gay bars offering sex shows, Chiang Mai's **nightlife** generally avoids Bangkok's sexual excesses, but offers plenty of opportunities for a good night out. The main concentrations of **bars** are on the east bank of the Ping River, around Tha Pae Gate and to the west of town around Thanon Nimmanhemin. It's also well worth checking out the strip of good-time bars at **JJ Market** on Thanon Assadatorn on the north side of town, which sport aspirational Bangkok names like *Tha Chang* and *Hualamphong* and which heave at weekends with the youth of Chiang Mai, drinking and watching the live bands.

THA PAE GATE AREA

Brasserie Thanon Chaiyapoom ⓦfacebook.com /brasseriechiangmai; map p.290. Decent restaurant in a surprisingly chilled, rustic haven sheltered by foliage from the busy moat road, but more famous as the venue for some of the city's best live blues and rock, brought to you by Tuk, Nakhon Sawan's answer to Jimi Hendrix. Daily 4/5pm–1/2am.

Jack Van Bar Thanon Chaiyapoom; map p.290. Favourite late-late hangout, where you can sit at outdoor tables on a large forecourt (with a brazier for the cool season) and order up mean cocktails from a Jack Daniels-sponsored camper van. Hours are temperamental: usually around 10pm–very late.

THC (The Hemp Collective) 19/4–5 Thanon Kotchasarn, opposite Tha Pae Gate; map p.290. Laidback crusty place, decorated with paper lanterns and floor cushions in the rooftop bar, where DJs play an eclectic music choice. Daily roughly 6pm–late.

★**UN Irish Pub** 24/1 Thanon Ratchawithi ⓦunirishpub .com; map p.290. Though it hasn't had an Irish owner for a few years now, this is a cordial, well-run pub that serves Guinness on tap, as well as good food, including home-made bread for satisfying breakfasts and sandwiches, home-made pies and pizzas. Appealing beer garden, quiz night on Thursday, and all manner of sports on TV (the schedule is posted weekly on its website). Daily roughly 8am–1am.

REST OF CHIANG MAI

★**Drunken Flower (Mao Dok Mai)** Soi 17, Thanon Nimmanhemin ☎053 894210, ⓦthedrunkenflower .com; map p.276. Laidback and very congenial, this quirky venue is a favourite among university students and 20-somethings, both Thai and farang. Reasonable prices

---

GAY NIGHTLIFE IN CHIANG MAI

For an introduction to the city's **gay scene**, check out the roads off the west side of Thanon Chotana, where there's a clutch of bars around the gay-owned *Lotus Hotel*, which itself has a popular garden bar. At 1/21–22 Soi Viengbua here, the long-running *Adam's Apple* (daily 9pm–1am; ⓦadamsappleclub.com) hosts go-go dancers and cabaret shows. Meanwhile, out on Thanon Chon Prathan (Canal Road) just south of Thanon Huai Kaeo, *See Man Pub* is Chiang Mai's biggest gay dance club, with live bands and Coyote dancers (daily 9pm–late).

3

for drinks and an eclectic range of background music, often with live acoustic music at the weekend. Tues–Sun 5pm–midnight.

Fabrique 226 Thanon Wichayanon; map p.276. The ground floor of the *President Hotel* has been taken over by this highly fashionable club, which features a huge dance hall, a cosier bar area and attractive outdoor terraces for chilling, and occasionally attracts big-name international DJs. Daily 10am–late.

Good View 13 Thanon Charoenrat ☎053 241866, ⓦgoodview.co.th; map p.276. An upmarket clone of the neighbouring *Riverside*, this large venue on the banks of the Ping River appeals to fashionable Thais with its smart staff, extensive menu of Thai, Chinese and Western food, and slick, competent musicians, who play anything middle of the road from country to jazz. Daily 10am–midnight/1am.

Infinity Soi 6, Thanon Nimmanhemin ☎053 400085, ⓦfacebook.com/infinity.chiangmai; map p.276. At the end of Soi 6 in what's known as Prasertland or Kad Cherng Doi (a huge car park and loosely designated entertainment zone), this stylish and spacious venue, with live bands, DJs and lots of outdoor tables, is one of the clubs of the moment in Chiang Mai. Daily roughly 7pm–1am.

Myst Floor 6, Maya Shopping Centre, Thanon Huai Kaeo ⓦmystmaya.com; map p.276. Chiang Mai branch of a venue on Bangkok's Soi Thong Lo, this sophisticated rooftop bar offers creative cocktails – what they call "molecular mixology" – imported beers such as Hoegaarden on draught and cool night-time views. Daily 4pm–1/2am.

North Gate Jazz Co-op Thanon Si Phum ⓦfacebook .com/northgate.jazzcoop; map p.276. Chilled, open-fronted bar with pavement tables overlooking Chang

Phuak Gate, featuring high-quality live jazz nightly; Tuesday's open-mike night is the big event of the week. Open most nights roughly 8pm–midnight.

★**The Riverside** Thanon Charoenrat ☎053 243239, ⓦtheriversidechiangmai.com; map p.276. On one side of the road candlelit terraces by the water (best to book if you want a table here) and an often heaving, lively bar for gigs, on the other a spacious complex of rooms, terraces, a stage and a bar area for imported craft beers. Various soloists and bands perform nightly on the two stages, with the tempo increasing as the night wears on. Long, high-quality menu of Western and Thai food (including northern specialities) also on offer, as well as dinner cruises (see p.294). Daily 10am–1am.

Sangdee Gallery and Café 5 Soi 5, Thanon Sirimuang-karajan ☎053 894955, ⓦsangdeegallery.org; map p.276. An all-rounder that's always worth checking out, this non-profit art gallery-café-bar hosts karaoke Tuesday, live music Wednesday, an open mike Thursday and a DJ Friday. Mon–Sat roughly 11am–midnight.

Warm Up 40 Thanon Nimmanhemin ☎053 400677, ⓦfacebook.com/warmupcafe1999; map p.276. Hugely popular venue with students and young locals, offering both live bands and local and international DJs spinning the latest sounds in different indoor and outdoor zones. Daily 6pm–2am.

Writer's Club and Wine Bar 141/3 Thanon Ratchdamnoen ☎053 814187; map p.276. An unofficial foreign correspondents' club for Chiang Mai, this welcoming bar near the centre of the old city is popular among farang residents and visitors, serving a range of beers and wines, plus good Thai and Western food. Daily except Sat noon–midnight.

ENTERTAINMENT

Cinemas All of the city's big shopping centres have top-floor cineplexes. Your best bet for English-soundtrack or English-subtitled films near the centre is the Major Cineplex (ⓦmajorcineplex.com/en/cinema/major-chiangmai) on top of Airport Plaza, southwest of the old town. French-language films with English subtitles are screened at the

Alliance Française, 138 Thanon Charoen Prathet, on Fridays at 8pm (☎053 275277), while Documentary Arts Asia, 12/7 Soi 3, Thanon Wualai (☎088 138 7470, ⓦdoc-arts.asia), a non-profit organization promoting visual literacy in Southeast Asia, shows Asian-themed films on Monday evenings and documentaries on Thursdays.

SHOPPING

Shopping is an almost irresistible pastime in Chiang Mai, whether it be for traditional silver bracelets, chic contemporary lacquerware or even secondhand books. Serious shoppers should get hold of a copy of *Nancy Chandler's Map of Chiang Mai* (see p.289), and of the free, quarterly booklet, *Art and Culture Lanna* (ⓦartandcultureasia.com), which carries adverts for some of the town's leading boutiques and galleries, with maps.

MARKETS AND THE SAN KAMPHAENG ROAD

Two main tourist shopping areas, the San Kamphaeng road and the night bazaar, conveniently operating at different times of the day, sell the full range of local handicrafts, backed up by markets, shopping malls and the weekend walking streets (see box opposite).

THE SAN KAMPHAENG ROAD

The road to San Kamphaeng, which extends due east from the end of Thanon Charoen Muang for 13km, is the main daytime strip, lined with every sort of handicrafts shop and factory, where you can usually watch the craftsmen at work. The biggest concentrations are at Bo Sang, the "umbrella village", 9km from town, and at San Kamphaeng

CHIANG MAI'S WALKING STREETS AND FARMERS' MARKET

If you're in Chiang Mai at the weekend it's worth heading down to **Thanon Wualai**, just south of the old city, on a Saturday between about 5pm and 11pm, or to the larger affair on **Thanon Ratchdamnoen** and part of **Thanon Phra Pokklao** in the old city on a Sunday at the same time. Closed to traffic for the duration, these "**walking streets**" become crowded with vendors selling typical northern Thai items such as clothes, musical instruments and snacks, as musicians busk to the throngs of people. The walking streets have become even more popular than the night bazaar, as they are ideal places to pick up a souvenir and mingle with a very mixed crowd of Thais and farangs.

Meanwhile, on Friday afternoons (roughly noon–6pm), the shady garden beside the Chiang Mai Historical Centre (see p.283) hosts an increasingly popular organic **farmers' market**, which also features handicrafts and live music (from about 3pm).

itself, once important for its kilns but now dedicated chiefly to silk weaving.

Getting there Frequent white songthaews to San Kamphaeng leave Chiang Mai from the central Lamyai market, but it's difficult to decide when to get off if you don't know the area. You could sign up for a tour or hire a tuk-tuk for a few hundred baht, but the catch here is that the drivers will want to take you to the shops where they'll pick up a commission. The best way to go is by bicycle or motorbike, which allows you to stop where and when you please, but take care with the fast-moving traffic on the narrow road.

THE NIGHT BAZAAR

The other main shopper's playground is the night bazaar, sprawling around the junction of Thanon Loi Khro and Thanon Chang Klan (and into the adjacent, quieter Anusarn market). Here bumper-to-bumper street stalls and several indoor areas (including the original Chiang Mai Night Bazaar shopping centre on the west side of Thanon Chang Klan) sell just about anything produced in Chiang Mai, plus crafts from other parts of Thailand and Southeast Asia, as well as counterfeit designer goods; the action starts up at around 5pm, and there are plenty of real bargains.

WAROROT MARKET

During the day, bustling Warorot market on Thanon Chang Moi has lots of cheap and cheerful cotton, linen and ceramics for sale on the upper floors. In the heart of the market, you can watch locals buying chilli paste, sausage and sticky rice from their favourite stalls, and maybe even join the queue. There's also a pungent and colourful flower market just east of here, on Thanon Praisani by the river, while the atmospheric warren of narrow lanes to the south and west of the market is well worth a browse, for everything from silk, cotton and hill-tribe crafts to stationery and plastic.

THE NORTHERN VILLAGE

The Northern Village in the Airport Plaza shopping centre (Mon–Fri 11am–9pm, Sat & Sun 10am–9pm), at the corner of the Superhighway and Highway 108, is like a market of stalls moved into an a/c mall. It has all manner of slightly upmarket handicrafts and contemporary decorative products, ranging from silver and wood to textiles and herbal products.

FABRICS, CLOTHES AND CONTEMPORARY INTERIOR DESIGN

Few visitors leave Chiang Mai without some new item of clothing and, to tempt you to dig deeper into your purse, upmarket silks and cottons often share shelf-space with bold examples of modern interior design.

Silk The silk produced out towards San Kamphaeng, to the east of Chiang Mai, is richly coloured and hard-wearing, with various attractive textures. Bought off a roll, the material is generally cheaper than in Bangkok, and can cost as little as B300/metre for top-quality four-ply (suitable for shirts and suits), for example at Kritiya. Ready-made silk clothes, though inexpensive, are generally staid and more suited to formal wear.

Cotton In Chiang Mai you'll also see plenty of traditional, pastel-coloured cotton, which is nice for furnishings, most of it from the village of Pa Sang southwest of Lamphun. Outlets in the basement of the main Chiang Mai night bazaar shopping centre on Thanon Chang Klan have good, cheap selections of this sort of cloth at around B200–300/metre, plus hand-painted and batik-printed lengths, and ready-made tablecloths and the like.

Fashion and interior design You'll find some stunning contemporary design in Chiang Mai, often fusing local crafts with modern, minimalist elements. A fruitful place for this kind of shopping is Thanon Nimmanhemin, on the west side of the city, which savvy locals sometimes tag Chiang Mai's Sukhumvit for its services to well-to-do expats. Its northern end towards Thanon Huai Kaeo, particularly on and around Soi 1, has a concentration of interesting fashion and decor boutiques. Thanon Charoenrat, on the east side of the river, also hosts several stylish outlets for clothes and interior design between Nawarat and Nakhon Ping bridges, while Ban Tawai (see p.300) boasts some creative decor shops.

3

CHIANG MAI'S TRADITIONAL CRAFTS

Chiang Mai is the best place in Thailand to buy handicrafts, and it's a hotbed of traditional cottage industries offering generally high standards of workmanship at low prices.

WOODCARVING

The city has a long tradition of **woodcarving**, which expresses itself in everything from salad bowls to half-size elephants. In the past the industry relied on the cutting of Thailand's precious teak, but manufacturers are now beginning to use other imported hardwoods, while bemoaning their inferior quality.

Wooden objects are sold all over the city, but the most famous place for carving is **Ban Tawai**, a large village of shops and factories where prices are low and where you can watch the woodworkers in action. One of Thailand's most important woodcarving centres, Ban Tawai relied on rice farming until forty years ago, but today virtually every home here has carvings for sale outside and each back yard hosts its own cottage industry. To get there, you'll need your own transport: follow Highway 108 south from Chiang Mai 13km to Hang Dong, then head east for 2km. A regularly updated, free **map** of Ban Tawai's outlets, which now include all manner of antiques and interior decor shops, is available around town (or go to ⓦ ban-tawai.com).

LACQUERWARE

Lacquerware can be seen in nearly every museum in Thailand, most commonly in the form of **betel sets**, which used to be carried ceremonially by the slaves of grandees as an insignia of rank and wealth (see box, p.283). Betel sets are still produced in Chiang Mai according to the traditional technique, whereby a woven bamboo frame is covered with layers of rich red lacquer and decorated with black details. A variety of other objects, such as trays and jewellery boxes, is also produced, some decorated with gold leaf on black gloss. Lacquerware makes an ideal choice for gifts, as it is both light to carry, and at the same time typically Thai, and is available in just about every other shop in town.

CELADON

Celadon, sometimes known as greenware, is a delicate variety of stoneware which was first made in China over two thousand years ago, and later produced in Thailand, most famously at Sukhothai and Sawankhalok.

Mengrai Kilns at 79/2 Soi 6, Thanon Samlarn (☎053 272063, ⓦ mengraikilns.com; daily 8am–5pm), is the best of several kilns in Chiang Mai that have revived the art of celadon. Sticking to the traditional methods, Mengrai produces beautiful and reasonably priced vases, crockery and larger items, thrown in elegant shapes and covered with transparent green, blue and purple glazes.

UMBRELLAS AND PAPER

The village of **Bo Sang** bases its fame on souvenir **umbrellas** – made of silk, cotton or mulberry (*sa*) paper and decorated with bold, painted colours – and celebrates its craft with a colourful **umbrella fair** every January. The artists who work here can paint a small motif on your bag or camera in two minutes flat.

The grainy **mulberry paper**, which makes beautiful writing or sketching pads, is sold almost as an afterthought in many of Bo Sang's shops. The best place to buy it is **HQ**, down a small soi opposite Wat Phra Singh at 3/31 Thanon Samlarn (☎053 814717–8, ⓦ hqpapermaker.com; daily 9am–6pm), which sells sheets of beautifully coloured mulberry paper, along with a huge range of other specialist papers.

SILVER AND JEWELLERY

Chiang Mai's traditional **silversmiths'** area is on **Thanon Wualai**, on the south side of the old town, though the actual smithing is now done elsewhere. If you're serious about buying silver, however, this is still the place to come, with dozens of small shops on Wualai itself and on Soi 3 selling repoussé plates, bowls and cups, and attractive, chunky jewellery. For sterling silver, check the stamp that shows the item is 92.5 percent pure; some items on sale in Chiang Mai are only eighty percent pure and sell much more cheaply.

A good general **jewellery** store is **Nova Collection** at 179 Thanon Tha Pae (☎053 273058, ⓦ nova-collection.com; Mon–Sat 9am–8pm & Sun 12.30–8pm), which has some lovely rings and necklaces blending gold, silver, platinum, steel and precious stones in striking and original designs.

Doi Tung Lifestyle Thanon Nimmanhemin, opposite Soi 1 ☎053 217981, ⓦdoitung.org; map p.276. Part of the late Princess Mother's development project based at Doi Tung, selling very striking and attractive cotton and linen in warm colours, made up into clothes, cushion covers, rugs and so on. Daily 10am–7pm.

Ginger 199 Thanon Moonmuang ☎053 419014; 6/21 Thanon Nimmanhemin; ⓦthehousethailand.com; maps p.290 & p.276. Chichi boutiques selling striking and original women's and men's wear, accessories and contemporary home decor, especially cushion covers. Thanon Moonmuang daily 10am–9.30pm; Thanon Nimmanhemin Mon–Thurs 10am–7pm, Fri–Sun 10am–9pm.

Kritiya 46 Thanon Khwang Men, the lane that runs south from the west side of Warorot Market ☎053 234478; map p.276. This small, atmospheric shop is probably the best place in town to buy bolts of high-quality local silk at competitive prices. Mon–Sat 9/10am–4.30/5pm.

Neramit Off Thanon Chang Moi at 91/2 Thanon Ratchawong ☎053 234353, ⓦneramit-custom-tailoring .com; map p.290. Has a good reputation for men's tailoring. Mon–Sat 9am–7pm, Sun 4–7pm.

Shinawatra 7km out on the San Kamphaeng road ☎053 338053–5, ⓦshinawatrathaisilk.co.th (with a shop at 18/1 Thanon Huai Kaeo ☎053 223264); map p.276. Century-old silk factory and showroom, which has entertained luminaries such as Princess Diana and is a good place to follow the silk-making process right from the cocoon. Daily 9am–6pm.

Sop Moei Arts 150/10 Thanon Charoenrat ☎053 306123, ⓦsopmoeiarts.com; map p.276. Gorgeous fabrics – scarves, wall-hangings, bags and cushion covers – and stylish basketware, with part of the profits going back to the eponymous Karen village and nearby refugee camp near Mae Sariang, where they're made. Mon–Fri & Sun 10am–6pm, Sat noon–4pm.

Studio Naenna 138/8 Soi Changkhian, Thanon Huai Kaeo ☎053 226042; & Adorn by Studio Naenna, 22 Soi 1, Thanon Nimmanhemin ☎053 895136; ⓦstudio -naenna.com; map p.276. If you're interested in the whole process of traditional fabric production, particularly the use of natural dyes, this is an excellent place to begin. If you phone for an appointment, you can see a demonstration of dyeing, including the plants from which the dyes are extracted, and watch the weavers in action at the main studio on Soi Changkhian (where full-on workshops in the use of indigo and other dyes are also held). It's part of an eco-friendly, sustainable project set up by Patricia Cheesman, an expert on Thai textiles. Adorn is the main outlet for their products, which consist of top-quality, ready-made silk and cotton garments, accessories and art pieces. Studio Naenna April–Sept Mon–Fri 9am–5pm, Oct–March Mon–Sat 9am–5pm; Adorn daily 10am–6pm.

Vila Cini 30–34 Thanon Charoenrat ☎053 246246; OP Place, Le Meridien Hotel, corner of Thanon Chang Klan and Thanon Loi Khro ☎053 252233, ⓦvilacini.com; map p.276. Sumptuously coloured silk scarves, bags, shirts, ties and cushion covers, as well as bolts of silk by the metre (Thanon Charoenrat only). The century-old teak shophouse on Charoenrat is an attraction in itself. Thanon Charoenrat daily 8.30am–10.30pm; OP Place daily 11am–11pm.

HILL-TRIBE CRAFTS

Thai Tribal Crafts 208 Thanon Bamrungrat ☎053 241043; 25/9 Thanon Moonmuang, near Thanon Ratchamanka (Fair Trade Shop); Northern Village, Airport Plaza; ⓦttcrafts.co.th; map p.276 & p.290. Long-running, non-profit, fair-trade shops, sponsored by a Christian charity, with a huge range of products made by seven of the region's hill tribes, from bags, scarves, home furnishings and silverware to musical instruments and bamboo basketry. Bamrungrat Mon–Sat 9am–5pm; Moonmuang Mon–Sat 10am–7pm; Northern Village daily 10am–8pm.

BOOKS

Backstreet Books 2/8 Thanon Chang Moi Kao ☎053 874143; map p.290. Large, well-organized secondhand bookshop near Tha Pae Gate, where you can buy or exchange books, with a smaller branch, The Lost Bookshop, at 34/3 Thanon Ratchamanka (☎053 206656; map p.290). Daily 8am–9pm.

Gecko Books 2/6 Thanon Chang Moi Kao ☎053 874066, ⓦgeckobooks.net; map p.290. Similar to Backstreet Books, with a long-standing rivalry – and, very conveniently for book-buyers, they're located right next door to each other – but Gecko has the edge in that the database of its stock is searchable online. Also has several other branches around town. Daily 8am–9pm.

Suriwong 54/1 Thanon Sri Dornchai ☎053 281052; map p.276. The best place for new English-language publications, stocking a wide selection of novels, books about Thailand and maps in an organized display; it also features newspaper and stationery sections. Daily 10am–7pm.

COMPUTERS

For sales and repairs, either Panthip Plaza, corner of Chang Klan and Sri Dornchai roads, or Computer Plaza, Thanon Manee Nopparat on the north side of the moat.

DIRECTORY

Banks, ATMs and exchange Dozens of banks with ATMs are dotted around Thanon Tha Pae and Thanon Chang Klan, and many exchange booths here stay open for evening shoppers.

Consulates Canada, 151 Superhighway ☎ 053 850147; China, 111 Thanon Chang Lo ☎ 053 280380; India, 33/1 Thanon Thung Hotel ☎ 053 243066; US, 387 Thanon Witchayanon ☎ 053 107700.

Hospitals Lanna, at 103 Superhighway (☎ 053 999777, ⓦ lanna-hospital.com), east of Thanon Chotana, has a 24hr emergency and ambulance service and dentistry department; McCormick (☎ 053 921777) is cheaper, used to farangs and is nearer, on Thanon Kaeo Nawarat; Chiang Mai Ram, at 8 Thanon Boonruangrit (☎ 053 920300), also has a very good reputation.

Immigration office By the airport, but probably moving to Promenada Mall, 5km southeast of the old city on H1141 – check ⓦ thaivisa.com (Mon–Fri 8.30am–4.30pm).

Pharmacies Boots branches include Thanon Tha Pae, opposite Tha Pae Gate, and Thanon Chang Klan, in front of the Chiang Inn Plaza.

Post offices The GPO is way out of the centre on Thanon Charoen Muang near the train station, but there's a far more convenient post office at 43 Thanon Samlarn (Phra Singh PO), near Wat Phra Singh (Mon–Fri 8.30am–4pm, Sat 9am–noon), which offers a packing service and sells cheap phonecards, amulets, you name it. There are also post offices on Thanon Phra Pokklao at the junction with Thanon Ratchawithi (Sri Phum PO), plus a small post office agent with longer hours on Thanon Ratchdamnoen by Tha Pae Gate, both in the old town, as well as on Thanon Wichayanon near Nawarat Bridge (Mae Ping PO), and at the airport.

Thai language courses AUA (American University Alumni), 73 Thanon Ratchdamnoen (☎ 053 277951 or ☎ 053 278407, ⓦ learnthaiinchiangmai.com), is the longest-established and best place to learn Thai, certified by the Ministry of Education. Several levels of classes are offered, starting with spoken Thai for beginners (60hr over about six weeks; B4800), with class sizes limited to five to twelve students. Individual and small-group instruction can also be arranged.

Tourist police At the far end of Thanon Huai Kaeo, at the start of the road up Doi Suthep, opposite the zoo ☎ 1155.

Around Chiang Mai

You'll never feel cooped up in Chiang Mai, as the surrounding countryside is dotted with day-trip options in all directions. Dominating the skyline to the west, **Doi Suthep** and its eagle's-nest temple are hard to ignore, and a wander around the pastoral ruins of **Wiang Kum Kam** on the southern periphery has the feel of fresh exploration. Much further south, the quiet town of **Lamphun** offers classic sightseeing in the form of historically and religiously significant temples and a museum. To the north, the **Mae Sa valley** may be full of tour buses, but its highlight, the **Queen Sirikit Botanic Gardens**, as well as the nearby lake of **Huay Tung Tao** and **Darapirom Palace**, merits an independent jaunt. Distinctly missable, however, is the Chiang Mai **Night Safari** to the southwest of the city, which has encroached on land belonging to Doi Suthep National Park, and even announced as an opening promotion when it was launched in 2006 that the meat of all the animals on display would also be available in its restaurant (though the offer has now been withdrawn) – much better to spend your money at Chiang Mai Zoo (see p.284).

All the excursions described here can be done in half a day; not all of them are covered by public **transport**, but a car with driver arranged through a Chiang Mai guesthouse should cost you around B800 for a half-day local trip. There are also some good options for longer jaunts that could be done in a day out of Chiang Mai, notably to Doi Inthanon National Park (see p.329), to Lampang and the Thai Elephant Conservation Centre (see p.309) and to the Elephant Nature Park (see p.351).

Doi Suthep

A jaunt up **DOI SUTHEP**, the mountain which rises steeply at the city's western edge, is the most satisfying brief trip you can make from Chiang Mai, chiefly on account of beautiful **Wat Phra That Doi Suthep**, which dominates the hillside and gives a towering view over the goings-on in town. This is the north's holiest shrine, its pre-eminence deriving from a magic relic enshrined in its chedi and the miraculous legend of its founding. The original chedi was built by King Ku Na at the end of the fourteenth century, after the glowing relic of Wat Suan Dork had self-multiplied just before being enshrined. A place had to be found for the clone, so Ku Na put it in a travelling shrine on the back of a white elephant and waited to see where the sacred animal would lead: it eventually climbed Doi Suthep, trumpeted three times, turned round three times, knelt down and died, thereby indicating that this was the spot. Ever since, it's been northern Thailand's most important place of pilgrimage, especially for the candlelit processions on **Makha Puja**, the anniversary of the sermon to the disciples, and **Visakha Puja**, the anniversary of the Buddha's birth, enlightenment and death, when thousands of people walk up to the temple through the night from Chiang Mai.

Doi Suthep-Pui National Park
Park headquarters are about 1km beyond the wat • B100 • ☎ 053 210244, ⓦ dnp.go.th

A signpost halfway up the road to the temple is about the only indication that you're in **Doi Suthep-Pui National Park**, which also encompasses the 1685m peak of Doi Pui to the northwest of Doi Suthep; however, an entry fee is not levied if you are only visiting the wat, Phuping Palace and Ban Doi Pui, a highly commercialized Hmong village near the palace that's worth avoiding. Despite the nearness of the city, its rich mixed forests support 330 species of bird, and the area is a favoured site for nature study, second in the north only to the larger and less-disturbed Doi Inthanon National Park.

About 5km from the base of the mountain road, a road on the right leads 3km to **Mon Tha Than Falls**, a beautiful spot, believed by some to be home to evil spirits. The higher fall is an idyllic 5m drop into a small bathing pool, completely overhung by thick, humming jungle.

Wat Phra That Doi Suthep
B30, or B50 including the cable car • ⓦ doisuthep.com • Meditation courses are held here (see p.286)

Opposite a car park and souvenir village, 16km from the base of the mountain road, a flight of three hundred naga-flanked steps – or the adjacent cable car – is the last leg on

---

KHRUBA SRIVIJAYA

Khruba Srivijaya, widely regarded as the "patron saint" of northern Thailand, was born in 1878 in a small village 100km south of Chiang Mai. His birth coincided with a supernatural thunderstorm and earthquake, after which he was given the auspicious nickname Faa Rawng (Thunder) until he joined the monkhood. Appointed abbot of his local temple by the age of 24, he came to be regarded as something of a rebel – though a hugely popular one among the people of Lanna. Despite the suspicions of the Sangha, both locally and in Bangkok, he became abbot of Lamphun's Wat Chama Thevi, which he set about restoring with gusto. This was the beginning of a tireless campaign to breathe life into Buddhist worship in the north by renovating its religious sites: over a hundred temples got the Khruba treatment, including Chiang Mai's Wat Phra Singh, Wat Phra That Haripunjaya in Lamphun and Wat Phra That Doi Tung near Mae Sai, as well as bridges, schools and government buildings. His greatest work, however, was the construction in 1935 of the paved road up to Wat Phra That Doi Suthep, which beforehand could only be reached after a climb of at least five hours. The road was constructed entirely by the voluntary labour of people from all over the north, using the most primitive tools. The project gained such fame that it attracted donations of B20 million, and on any one day as many as four thousand people were working on it. So that people didn't get in each other's way, Khruba Srivijaya declared that each village should contribute 15m of road, but as more volunteers flocked to Chiang Mai, this figure had to be reduced to 3m. The road was completed after just six months, and Khruba Srivijaya took the first ride to the temple in a donated car.

When Khruba Srivijaya died back in his native village in 1938, Rama VIII was so moved that he sponsored a royal cremation ceremony. The monk's relics were divided up and are now enshrined at Wat Suan Dork in Chiang Mai, Wat Phra Kaeo Don Tao in Lampang and at many other holy places throughout the north. There's a statue of him at the end of Thanon Huai Kaeo, where the road to Wat Phra That Doi Suthep starts, and you'll see photos of him in temples, shops and restaurants all over the north, where Khruba amulets are still hugely popular, over seventy years after his death.

the way to **Wat Phra That Doi Suthep**. From the temple's **lower terrace**, the magnificent views of Chiang Mai and the surrounding plain, 300m below, are best in the early morning or late afternoon in the cool season, though peaceful contemplation of the view is frequently shattered by people sounding the heavy, dissonant bells around the terrace – they're supposed to bring good luck. At the northwestern corner is a 2m-high statue of the elephant, which, so the story goes, expired on this spot.

Before going to the **upper terrace** you have to remove your shoes – and if you're showing a bit of knee or shoulder, the temple provides wraps to cover your impoliteness. This terrace is possibly the most harmonious piece of temple architecture in Thailand, a dazzling combination of red, green and gold in the textures of carved wood, filigree and gleaming metal – even the tinkling of the miniature bells and the rattling of fortune sticks seem to keep the rhythm. A cloister, decorated with gaudy murals, tightly encloses the terrace, leaving room only for a couple of small minor viharns and the altars and ceremonial gold umbrellas which surround the central focus of attention, the **chedi**. This dazzling gold-plated beacon, a sixteenth-century extension of Ku Na's original, was modelled on the chedi at Wat Phra That Haripunjaya in Lamphun – which previously had been the region's most significant shrine – and has now become a venerated emblem of northern Thailand. Look out for an old black-and-white photograph opposite the northeastern corner of the chedi, showing a cockerel that used to peck the feet of visitors who entered with their shoes on.

Phuping Palace

4km up the paved road from the wat • Daily 8.30am–4.30pm, tickets on sale 8.30–11.30am & 1–3.30pm; usually closed between Jan and early March when the royals are in residence • B50 • ⓦ bhubingpalace.org • Dress politely – no shorts or bare shoulders (clothes rental available)

Phuping Palace is the residence for the royals when they come to visit their village development projects in the north. There's a viewpoint over the hills to the south, rose and fern gardens and some pleasant trails through the grounds, but the buildings themselves are off-limits.

ARRIVAL AND DEPARTURE   DOI SUTHEP

The best way to get up the mountain is in a rented vehicle, allowing you to stop along the way to admire the views. The road, although steep in places, is paved and well suited for motorbikes.

By shared songthaew Red shared songthaews to Doi Suthep leave from Thanon Huai Kaeo in front of the zoo or Chiang Mai University, but will only set off once they have a complement of at least six passengers (B40 one-way to the wat; at least B70 one-way to Phuping Palace, for which you're likely to have to wait a bit longer for a full complement of passengers). Some Doi Suthep shared songthaews also hang out on Thanon Manee Noparat near Chang Puak Gate, but you're probably going to have to wait longer for enough passengers to show up here and/or have to pay the driver a bit more money to get him to go.

By chartered vehicle It costs around B600 to charter a whole songthaew, about B800 to arrange a car and driver through your guesthouse.

ACCOMMODATION

Bungalows and camping On the higher slopes near the national park headquarters, there are national park bungalows with hot-water bathrooms (from B400 for two people) and campsites, for which tents can be rented (from B150 for two people). There's a campsite and bungalows with hot-water bathrooms (B1500 for six people) beside Mon Tha Than Falls.

Wiang Kum Kam

5km south of Chiang Mai city centre, beyond the Superhighway, on the east bank of the Ping River

The well-preserved and little-visited ruins of the ancient city of **WIANG KUM KAM** – traditionally regarded as the prototype for Chiang Mai – are hidden away in the picturesque, rural fringe of town. According to folklore, Wiang Kum Kam was built by King Mengrai as his new capital of the north, but was soon abandoned because of inundation when the Ping River changed course. Recent excavations, however, have put paid to that theory: Wiang Kum Kam was in fact established much earlier, as one of a cluster of fortified satellite towns that surrounded the Mon capital at Lamphun. After Mengrai had conquered Lamphun in 1281, he resided at Kum Kam for a while, raising a chedi, a viharn and several Buddha statues before moving on to build Chiang Mai. Wiang Kum Kam was abandoned some time before 1750, probably as a result of a Burmese invasion.

About half of Wiang Kum Kam's 22 known temple sites have now been uncovered, along with a stone slab (now housed in the Chiang Mai National Museum) inscribed in a unique forerunner of the Thai script. A recently opened **museum** (daily 8.30am–5pm; B10) gives a dry, basic introduction to the temples, but it's inconveniently located on the far southern edge of Wiang Kum Kam: if you head east on Chiang Mai's second ring road, it's on the left, just after the first permissible left turn after the river bridge.

Chedi Si Liam
1km south of the Superhighway on the east bank of the river

Head first for **Chedi Si Liam**, which provides a useful landmark: this Mon chedi, in the shape of a tall, squared-off pyramid with niched Buddha images, was built by Mengrai in memory of his dead wife. Modelled on Wat Kukut in Lamphun, it was restored in 1908 by a wealthy Mon resident of Chiang Mai using Burmese artisans and is still part of a working temple.

Wat Kan Thom
About 2km from Chedi Si Liam: backtrack along the river road you've travelled down from Chiang Mai, take the first right turn, turn right again and keep left through a scattered farming settlement

Wat Kan Thom (aka Wat Chang Kham) lay at the centre of the old city and is still an important place of worship. Archeologists were only able to get at the site after much of it had been levelled by bulldozers building a playground for the adjacent school, but they have managed to uncover the brick foundations of Mengrai's viharn. The modern shrine next to it is where Mengrai's soul is said to reside. Also in the grounds are a white chedi and a small viharn, both much restored, and a large new viharn displaying fine craftsmanship.

If you have your own transport, from here you can head off along the trails through the thick foliage of the longan plantations to the northwest of Wat Kan Thom, back towards Chedi Si Liam. On this route, you come across surprisingly well-preserved chedis and the red-brick walls of Wiang Kum Kam's temples in a handful of shady clearings set between rural dwellings.

ARRIVAL AND DEPARTURE   WIANG KUM KAM

By boat and horse carriage A nice way of seeing Wiang Kum Kam is on a trip with Mae Ping River Cruises (2–4 daily; 2hr altogether; B800/person including pick-up from your accommodation), which involves a 20min cruise down the river followed by a carriage ride around six of the temples (see p.279).

By motorbike or bicycle About 3km square, the ancient city can be explored on a bicycle or a motorbike, though it's easy to get lost in the maze of lanes connecting the ruins. If you're happy to look around under your own steam, the best way to approach Wiang Kum Kam is by heading down Thanon Chiang Mai–Lamphun, then forking right at Nong Hoi market (a short way after the *Holiday Inn*) onto Thanon Koh Klang, which will bring you under the Superhighway to Chedi Si Liam.

Lamphun

Though capital of its own province, **LAMPHUN** lives in the shadow of the tourist attention (and baht) showered on Chiang Mai, 26km to the north. Yet for anyone interested in history, a visit to this former royal city is a must and, if you have your own transport, combines very well with a trip to Wiang Kum Kam. The town's largely plain architecture is given some character by the surrounding waterways, beyond which stretch lush rice-fields and plantations of *lamyai* (longan); the sweetness of the local variety is celebrated every year in early August at the **Ngan Lamyai** (Longan Festival), when the town comes alive with processions of fruity floats, a drum-beating competition and a Miss Lamyai beauty contest. Lamphun also offers a less frantic alternative to Chiang Mai during the Songkhran and Loy Krathong festivals, the Khuang River being a far less congested place to float your *krathong* than Chiang Mai's Ping River. Though the streets of the town are usually sleepy, the ancient working **temples** of Wat Phra That Haripunjaya and Wat Kukut are lively and worth aiming for on a half-day trip from Chiang Mai.

Lamphun claims to be the oldest continuously inhabited town in Thailand, and has a history dating back to the late eighth or early ninth century when the ruler of the major Dvaravati centre at Lopburi sent his daughter, Chama Thevi, to found the Theravada Buddhist city-state of **Haripunjaya** here. Under the dynasty she established, Haripunjaya flourished as a link in the trade route to Yunnan in southwest China and managed to resist coming under the suzerainty of the Khmers at Angkor, who absorbed Lopburi and the other Dvaravati cities in central Thailand in the eleventh century. In 1281, after a decade of scheming, the great Lanna king Mengrai conquered Lamphun and brought it under his control.

Chama Thevi's planners are said to have based the **layout** of the town on the shape of an auspicious conch shell. The rough outcome is a rectangle, narrower at the north end than the south, with the Khuang River running down its kilometre-long east side, and moats around the north, west and south sides. The main street, Thanon Inthayongyot, bisects the conch from north to south, while the road to Wat Kukut (Thanon Chama Thevi) heads out from the middle of the west moat.

Wat Phra That Haripunjaya

Easiest access through the rear entrance on Thanon Inthayongyot

One of the north's grandest and most important temples, **Wat Phra That Haripunjaya** has its bot and ornamental front entrance facing the Khuang River. Its main festival is Visakha Puja, the anniversary of the Buddha's birth, enlightenment and death, which is said to coincide with the anniversary of the temple's establishment, when the main chedi is bathed in holy water donated by the king. However, the date of its founding is actually hard to fathom: the earliest guess is 897, when the king of Haripunjaya is said to have built a chedi to enshrine a hair of the Buddha. More certain is the date of the main rebuilding of the temple, under King Tilok of Chiang Mai in 1443, when the present ringed chedi was erected in the then-fashionable Sri Lankan style (later copied at Doi Suthep and Lampang). Clad in brilliant copper plates, it has since been raised to a height of about 50m, crowned by a gold umbrella.

The plain open courtyards around the chedi contain a compendium of religious structures in a wild mix of styles and colours. On the north side, the tiered Haripunjaya-style pyramid of **Chedi Suwanna** was built in 1418 as a replica of the chedi at nearby Wat Kukut. You get a whiff of southern Thailand in the open space beyond the Suwanna chedi, where the **Chedi Chiang Yan** owes its resemblance to a pile of flattened pumpkins to the Srivijayan style. On either side of the viharn (to the east of the main chedi) stand a dark red **bell tower**, containing what's claimed to be the world's largest bronze gong, and a weather-beaten **library** on a raised base. Just to add to the temple's mystique, an open pavilion at the southwest corner of the chedi shelters a stone indented with four overlapping **footprints**, believed by fervent worshippers to confirm an ancient legend that the Buddha once passed this way. Next to the pavilion is a small **museum** which houses bequests to the temple, including some beautiful

Buddha images in the Lanna style. Finally, beside the back entrance, is the **Phra Chao Tan Jai**, a graceful standing Buddha, surrounded by graphic murals that depict a horrific version of Buddhist hell.

Hariphunchai National Museum

Thanon Inthayongyot, across the road from Wat Phra That Haripunjaya's back entrance • Wed–Sun 8.30am–4pm • B100

The **Hariphunchai National Museum** contains a well-organized but not quite compelling collection of religious finds, and occasionally stages some interesting temporary exhibitions. The terracotta and bronze Buddha images here give the best overview of the distinctive features of the Haripunjaya style: large curls above a wide, flat forehead, bulging eyes, incised moustache and enigmatic smile.

Wat Chama Thevi

Thanon Chama Thevi

Art-history buffs will get a thrill out of **Wat Chama Thevi** (also known as Wat Kukut), where the main brick chedi, Suwan Chang Kot, which was built around 1150 and repaired in 1218, is the only complete example of Haripunjaya architecture.

Queen Chama Thevi is supposed to have chosen the site by ordering an archer to fire an arrow from the city's western gate – to retrace his epic shot, follow the road along the National Museum's southern wall to the west gate at the city moat, and keep going for nearly 1km along Thanon Chama Thevi. Chedi Suwan Chang Kot is five-tiered and rectangular, inset with niches sheltering beautiful, wide-browed Buddha images in stucco, typical of the Haripunjaya style. Believed to enshrine Chama Thevi's ashes, it lost its pinnacle at some stage, giving rise to the name Wat Kukut, the temple with the "topless" chedi. On your way back to the town centre from Wat Chama Thevi, you might like to pop in at **Wat Mahawan**, famous for the Buddha image amulets on sale here.

<table>
<tr><td>**ARRIVAL AND DEPARTURE**</td><td>**LAMPHUN**</td></tr>
</table>

It's not worth considering catching the train from Chiang Mai to Lamphun as schedules are unreliable and the station there is way out to the northeast of the town centre.

By songthaew or bus Blue songthaews from Thanon Chiang Mai–Lamphun in Chiang Mai, a couple of hundred metres south of Nawarat Bridge, or buses from Chang Puak bus station, via Lamyai market on Thanon Praisani, will put you off outside the back entrance of Wat Haripunjaya.

By motorbike or car The direct (and scenic) route from Chiang Mai to Lamphun is Thanon Chiang Mai–Lamphun, which becomes Highway 106, for much of the way a stately avenue lined with 30m-tall *yang* trees that makes for a pleasant motorbike or car ride.

ACCOMMODATION AND EATING

Lamphun Ice 6 Thanon Chaimongkol ☎ 053 511452. Among the few restaurants in Lamphun with an English-language menu, this place serves tasty Thai food at reasonable prices; it's conveniently situated on the road that runs along the south wall of Wat Haripunjaya. Daily 10am–midnight.

Lamphun Will Hotel Thanon Chama Thevi opposite

Wat Kukut ☎ 053 534865–6, ⓦ lamphunwillhotel.com. It's unlikely you'll want to stay overnight in Lamphun, but this stylish, contemporary hotel is a decent choice. There's a swimming pool, a restaurant, and en-suite, hot-water bathrooms, a/c, fridges and cable TV in all the bedrooms. **B1500**

Huay Tung Tao

Signed off Highway 107 (the continuation of Thanon Chotana) about 10km north of Chiang Mai; it's then 2km west from the turn-off to the paved road around the lake

With your own transport, **Huay Tung Tao**, a large man-made lake at the base of Doi Suthep, is a great place to cool off during the hot season; it's safe to swim in, with canoes and inner tubes to rent, and is also used by anglers and windsurfers. Floating bamboo shelters along the water's edge provide shade from the sun, and you can order simple food such as sticky rice, grilled chicken and *som tam*.

Darapirom Palace

16km north of Chiang Mai in Mae Rim: look out for a sign on the left of Highway 107 just before Mae Rim police station • Tues–Sun 9am–5pm • B20 • ☎ 053 299175

In **Mae Rim**, a small market town that's now almost a suburb of Chiang Mai, the **Darapirom Palace** is a gorgeous colonial-style building from the early twentieth century. The palace was once the home of Princess Dara Rasamee (1873–1933), daughter of Chao Inthanon, the lord of Chiang Mai, who became the favourite concubine of King Chulalongkorn (Rama V) in the days before Chiang Mai was fully integrated into the Siamese state. Extremely proud of her northern heritage – and now something of a heroine to lovers of Lanna culture – the princess had this residence built in 1914, a few years after Chulalongkorn's death, when she returned from Bangkok to live out her later years in her homeland. Bangkok's Chulalongkorn University has opened the palace as a museum, featuring period furnishings and many items that once belonged to the princess. Photographs of her show her knee-length hair – which contrasted strongly with the fashion among Siamese women of the time to sport short-cropped hair – and the various rooms of the museum display her wardrobe and personal effects including musical instruments.

The Mae Sa valley

About 1km north of central Mae Rim on Highway 107, Route 1096, a good sealed road, heads west up the valley

Running west from Mae Rim, the **Mae Sa valley** has the atmosphere of a theme park, sheltering a menagerie of snake farms, monkey shows, elephant camps, tiger sanctuaries, "adventure sports" venues, and orchid and butterfly farms, but its highlight, the lovely botanic gardens, is well worth the trip. The main Route 1096 through the valley also passes the unspectacular **Mae Sa Waterfall** (part of Doi Suthep-Pui National Park; B100), where you can walk up a peaceful trail passing lots of little cascades along the way. Once you've seen all you want to in the valley, you have the option of continuing west for a scenic drive in the country: turn left on to Route 1269 before Samoeng, and follow this road as it swoops up and down over hills, skirting all the way round Doi Suthep to join Highway 108 8km south of Chiang Mai, a two-hour drive in all.

Queen Sirikit Botanic Gardens

12km up Route 1096 from the Mae Rim turn-off • Daily 8.30am–5pm, Natural Science Museum daily 9.30am–3.45pm • B100, plus B100 per car • Shuttle buses B30 (unlimited rides) • ⓦ qsbg.org

The magnificent **Queen Sirikit Botanic Gardens**, which offer fine views across the mountain valley, are the main reason for coming to Mae Sa. If you are at all botanically inclined, you could easily spend half a day here, exploring the four nature trails that link its arboretum, ornamental beds, rock garden, orchid nursery, areas of climbers and medicinal plants and a complex of a dozen glasshouses. There's also an interesting and attractive Natural Science Museum, with English labels, to put things in context, and a café. Hop-on, hop-off shuttle buses run around the steep, extensive grounds, if the heat gets too much; cars are also allowed to drive round, but motorbikes must park at the entrance.

ACCOMMODATION AND EATING   **MAE SA VALLEY**

Pong Yang Angdoi Resort 2km beyond the botanic gardens on the south side of the road ☎ 053 879151, ⓦ pongyangangdoi.com. Set in a steep, tree-covered valley with a view of an attractive waterfall, this resort might tempt you to spend a night out of Chiang Mai. It boasts cosy, well-equipped bungalows, all with a/c, hot water and balconies, as well as a very good, scenic restaurant. B2000

Doi Khun Tan National Park

Around 50km southeast of Chiang Mai · B100 · ☎ 053 546335, ⓦ dnp.go.th

One of three major national parks close to Chiang Mai, along with Suthep and Inthanon, **DOI KHUN TAN NATIONAL PARK** is accessible by train from Chiang Mai: a 1352m-long rail tunnel, the longest in Thailand, built between 1907 and 1918 by German engineers and Thai workers (of whom over a thousand died due to accidents, malaria and tigers), cuts through the mountain that gives the park its name. Despite this, and the fact that the king has famously holidayed here, the park remains unspoiled, but has enough infrastructure to encourage overnighting. The park is most popular on weekends, when groups of Thai schoolchildren visit, and during the cool season.

Covering 255 square kilometres, the park's vegetation varies from bamboo forest at an altitude of 350m to tropical evergreen forest between 600m and 1000m; the 1373m summit of Doi Khun Tan is known for its wild flowers, including orchids, gingers and lilies. Most of the small mammal species in the park are squirrels, but you're more likely to see some birds, with over 182 species found here.

3

Trails through the park

The park's **trails** are clearly marked, running from short nature trails around the park headquarters (where maps are available) to three major trails that all eventually lead to the summit of **Doi Khun Tan** – with impressive views of the surrounding countryside, it's clear how it fulfilled its role as a World War II military lookout. The main 8.3km trail from the train station to the Doi Khun Tan summit, though steep, is very easy, divided into four quarters of approximately 2km each, with each quarter ending at a resting place. While you shouldn't have a problem getting to the summit and back in a day, a more rewarding option is to do the walk in two days, staying overnight in the bungalows or at one of the campsites along the trail. Alternatively, you can take a circular route to the summit and back, forsaking a large chunk of the main trail for the two subsidiary trails that curve around either side, taking in two **waterfalls**.

ARRIVAL AND DEPARTURE   DOI KHUN TAN NATIONAL PARK

By train There are currently two morning and three afternoon trains daily from Chiang Mai to Khun Tan station on their way to Lampang and beyond, but there's no longer an evening train back (the last one's at 1.35pm), ruling out a day-trip by rail from the city (though it might be worth checking the latest timetables, just in case the evening service is reinstated). The park headquarters is a 1300m walk up the summit trail from the train station.
Destinations Bangkok (4 daily; 11–13hr); Chiang Mai (5 daily; 1hr 30min); Lampang (5 daily; 50min).
By car or motorbike A car or motorbike can take you to the park headquarters, though no further: from Chiang Mai follow Highway 11 to the turn-off to Mae Tha and head northeast for 18km, following signs for the park.

ACCOMMODATION AND EATING

If you want to stay in the park, consider booking in advance through the Department of National Parks website (ⓦ dnp.go.th). There's a basic **restaurant** at the headquarters and beside the bungalows.

Bungalows The park's bungalows, scattered about 1km up the main trail from the headquarters, are mostly spacious and well-appointed log cabins with hot-water bathrooms, sleeping up to six people. Some have outside seating areas with great views over the rolling hills. **B500**
Camping There's a well-equipped (and often very busy) campsite at the park headquarters; if you don't have your own tent you can rent one here. **B150**

Lampang and around

A high road pass and a train tunnel breach the narrow, steep belt of mountains between Chiang Mai and **LAMPANG**, the north's second-largest town, 100km to the southeast.

Lampang is an important transport hub – Highway 11, Highway 1 and the Northern Rail Line all converge here – and given its undeniably low-key attractions, nearly all travellers sail through it on their way to the more trumpeted sights further north. But unlike most other provincial capitals, Lampang has the look of a place where history has not been completely wiped out: houses, shops and temples survive in the traditional style, and the town makes few concessions to tourism. Out of town, the beautiful complex of **Wat Phra That Lampang Luang** is the main attraction in these parts, but while you're in the neighbourhood you could also stop by to watch a show at the **Elephant Conservation Centre**, on the road from Chiang Mai.

The modern centre of Lampang sprawls along the south side of the Wang River, with its most frenetic commercial activity taking place along Thanon Boonyawat and Thanon Robwiang near Ratchada Bridge. Here, you'll find stalls and shops selling the famous local **pottery**, a kitsch combination of whites, blues and browns, made from the area's rich and durable kaolin clay. On all street signs around town, and in

LAMPANG

■ **ACCOMMODATION**
Akhamsiri Home	2
Auangkham Resort	1
Riverside Guest House	5
R Lampang	4
Wienglakor	1

● **RESTAURANTS & CAFÉS**
Aroy One Baht	5
Escape Bistro & Café	1
Grandma's Café	4
Mae Hae	6
Riverside	3
Wienglakor	2

CENTRAL LAMPANG

larger-than-life statues at key intersections, is a **white chicken**. This symbol of Lampang relates to a legend concerning the Buddha, who sent down angels from Heaven in the form of chickens to wake up the local inhabitants in time to offer alms to the monks at the end of Buddhist Lent. Perhaps the town's image as a laidback, sleepy place is justified in the light of this tale.

Brief history

Founded as Kelang Nakhon by the ninth-century Haripunjaya queen Chama Thevi, Lampang became important enough for one of her two sons to rule here after her death. After King Mengrai's conquest of Haripunjaya in 1281, Lampang suffered much the same ups and downs as the rest of Lanna, enjoying a burst of prosperity as a **timber** town at the end of the nineteenth century, when it supported a population of twenty thousand people and four thousand working elephants. Many of its temples are financially endowed by the waves of outsiders who have settled in Lampang: refugees from Chiang Saen (who were forcibly resettled here by Rama I at the beginning of the nineteenth century), Burmese teak-loggers and, more recently, rich Thai pensioners attracted by the town's sedate charm.

Wat Phra Kaew Don Tao

Thanon Phra Kaeo, 1km northeast of the Ratchada Bridge

Lampang's few sights are well scattered; the best place to start is on the north side of the river (the site of the original Haripunjaya settlement), whose leafy suburbs today contain the town's most important and interesting temple, **Wat Phra Kaew Don Tao**. An imposing, rather forbidding complex, the temple was founded in the fifteenth century to enshrine the Phra Kaew Don Tao image, now residing at Wat Phra That Lampang Luang (see p.314). For 32 years it also housed the Emerald Buddha (local stories aver this to be a copy of Phra Kaew Don Tao), a situation that came about when an elephant carrying the holy image from Chiang Rai to Chiang Mai made an unscheduled and therefore auspicious halt here in 1436. The small **museum** at the back of the compound displays some dainty china among its exhibits, but its main focus is woodcarving, a craft at which Burmese artisans excel.

The chedi and mondop

The clean, simple lines of the white, gold-capped **chedi**, which is reputed to contain a hair of the Buddha, form a shining backdrop to the wat's most interesting building, a Burmese **mondop** stacked up in extravagantly carved tiers; it was built in 1909 by craftsmen from the local Burmese community, employed for the task by a Thai prince (whose British-style coat of arms can be seen on the ceiling inside). All gilt and gaudy coloured glass, the interior decoration is a real fright, mixing Oriental and European influences, with some incongruously cute little cherubs on the ceiling. The mondop's boyish bronze centrepiece has the typical features of a Mandalay Buddha, with its jewelled headband, inset black and white eyes, and exaggerated, dangling ears, which denote the Buddha's supernatural ability to hear everything in the universe. In front of the Buddha is an image of Khruba Srivijaya, the north's most venerated monk (see box, p.303).

Ban Sao Nak

6 Thanon Ratwattana • Daily 10am–5pm • B50

Not far from Wat Phra Kaew Don Tao can be found **Ban Sao Nak** ("house of many pillars"), a private museum containing a fine display of ceramics, lacquerware and teak furnishings. Built in 1895 in a mixture of Burmese and Lanna styles, this sprawling wooden mansion is supported by a maze of 116 teak pillars and contains some interesting fading photographs of its former occupants, who were local notables. Here and outside, in the carefully landscaped grounds, you'll get a sense of how life would have been for the north's wealthier residents at the turn of the twentieth century.

Wat Sri Chum

Thanon Sri Chum, a 5min walk south of Thanon Robwiang

The Burmese who worked on Wat Phra Kaew Don Tao were brought to Lampang in the late nineteenth century when, after the British conquest of Upper Burma, timber companies expanded their operations as far as northern Thailand. Fearing that the homeless spirits of fallen trees would seek vengeance, the Burmese loggers often sponsored the building of temples, most of which still stand, to try to appease the tree spirits and gain merit. Though the spirits had to wait nearly a century, they seem to have got their revenge: due to a short circuit in some dodgy wiring, the viharn of **Wat Sri Chum**, which is the biggest Burmese temple in Thailand as well as the most important and beautiful Burmese temple in town, was damaged by fire in 1992. Now restored to its former glory, with fresh carvings and murals by Burmese craftsmen, it's sited in a small grove of bodhi trees.

Wat Sri Rong Muang

Towards the west end of Thanon Takrao Noi

To get more of a flavour of Myanmar, head for 100-year-old **Wat Sri Rong Muang**, which presents a dazzling ensemble: the crazy angles of its red-and-yellow roof shelter Mandalay Buddhas and several extravagantly carved gilt sermon-thrones, swimming in a glittering sea of coloured-glass wall tiles.

Thanon Talat Kao

Behind the south bank of the river • Walking street Sat & Sun roughly 5–10pm

When you've had your fill of temples, **Thanon Talat Kao**, the "Old Market Street", is good for a quiet stroll in the early morning. It has some very old shophouses and mansions, with intricate balconies and gables and unusual sunburst designs carved over some of the doors, showing a mixture of European, Burmese and Chinese influences – it used to be known as Talat Jiin, "Chinese market", or in northern dialect, Kad Kong Ta, which means "Pier Street Market", but went into decline with the advent of the railway in 1916. On Saturday and Sunday evenings, Talat Kao comes to life as a "**walking street**", similar to those in Chiang Mai, with food, silk and other crafts for sale and musicians playing. (There's a smaller walking street market on Friday early evening just across the river on Thanon Wang Nuea.)

Lampang Medicinal Plants Conservation Assembly

3km northwest of the town centre on Thanon Kunmuang • Daily 8am–5pm • ☎ 054 350787 • Traditional massage from B130/hr • A songthaew from the centre of Lampang costs around B60; if driving yourself, follow Thanon Chammathewi towards Haeng Chat for about 2km, then turn right and left, following signs for Lampang Herbs Conservation

Though the **Lampang Medicinal Plants Conservation Assembly** (Rak Samoonprai) sounds like the kind of place where botanists might hold seminars, it is in fact a traditional health centre set in a shady compound. If you feel like pampering your body, head out here for a strong traditional massage, herbal sauna or even a bare-footed health walk over a path of rounded pebbles designed to provide a natural foot massage. The facilities are spotless, the grounds are full of labelled herbs, and a huge range of medicinal plant products is on sale.

FROM TOP KHAO SOI (P.293); MURAL IN WAT PHUMIN, NAN (P.322) >

Wat Phra That Lampang Luang

18km southwest of Lampang • Blue songthaews to Kor Kha from Lampang's Thanon Robwiang will continue to the wat on request (B70), but on the way back, you'll probably have to catch a motorbike taxi to Kor Kha (B30) and then a blue songthaew into Lampang (B40); otherwise you could charter a blue songthaew to take you there and back (about B300 for the vehicle)

A grand and well-preserved capsule of Lanna art and design, **Wat Phra That Lampang Luang** is one of the architectural highlights of northern Thailand. The wat was built early in the Haripunjaya era as a *wiang* (fortress), one of a satellite group around Lampang – you can still see remains of the threefold ramparts in the farming village around the temple. Outside the wat, simple snacks, handicrafts and antiques can be bought from market stalls. If you're driving yourself to the temple, head south from Lampang on Highway 1, then cross the bridge over the Wang River at Kor Kha and turn right, heading north for about 3km on Route 1034; if you're coming from Chiang Mai or the elephant centre, just after Hang Chat (before you reach Lampang) turn right off Highway 11 onto Route 1034.

The main viharn

At the main entrance, a naga staircase leads you up to a wedding cake of a gatehouse, richly decorated with stucco, which is set in the original brick boundary walls. Just inside, the oversized fifteenth-century **viharn** is open on all sides in classic Lanna fashion, and shelters a spectacular centrepiece: known as a *ku*, a feature found only in the viharns of northern Thailand, this gilded brick tower looks like a bonfire for the main Buddha image sitting inside, the Phra Chao Lan Thong. Tall visitors need to mind their heads on the panels hanging from the low eaves, which are decorated with attractive, though fading, early nineteenth-century paintings of battles, palaces and nobles in traditional Burmese gear.

The rest of the main compound

The temple's main walled compound is home to no fewer than four other viharns. In front of the murky, beautifully decorated viharn to the left, look out for a wooden *tung chai* carved with flaming, coiled nagas, used as a heraldic banner for northern princes. The battered, cosy **Viharn Nam Tame**, second back on the right, dates to the early sixteenth century. Its drooping roof configuration is archetypal: divided into three tiers, each of which is divided again into two layers, it ends up almost scraping the ground. Under the eaves you can just make out fragments of panel paintings, as old as the viharn, illustrating a story of one of the exploits of the Hindu god Indra.

The wat's huge central **chedi** enshrines a hair of the Buddha and ashes from the right side of his forehead and neck. By its northwest corner, a sign points to a drainage hole in the wat's boundary wall, once the scene of an unlikely act of derring-do: in 1736, local hero Thip Chang managed to wriggle through the tiny hole and free the *wiang* from the occupying Burmese, before going on to liberate the whole of Lampang.

At the chedi's southwest corner, the **Haw Phra Phuttabhat** (no entry for women) is a small chamber that acts as a camera obscura. If you close the door behind you, an image of the chedi is projected through a small hole in the door onto a sheet hung from the ceiling.

Phra Kaew Don Tao

A gate in the south side of the main compound's boundary wall leads first to a spreading **bodhi tree** on crutches: merit-makers have donated hundreds of supports to prop up its drooping branches. The tree, with its own small shrine standing underneath, is believed to be inhabited by spirits, and the sick are sometimes brought here in search of a cure.

The path beyond the bodhi tree will bring you to a small, unimpressive viharn to the west of the main compound, which is the home of **Phra Kaew Don Tao**, the much-revered companion image to Bangkok's Emerald Buddha, and the wat's main focus of pilgrimage. Legend has it that the statuette first appeared in the form of an emerald found in a watermelon presented by a local woman to a venerated monk. The two of them tried to carve a Buddha out of the emerald, without much success, until the god Indra appeared and fashioned the marvellous image, at which point the ungrateful townsfolk accused the monk of having an affair with the woman and put her to death, thus bringing down upon the town a series of disasters which confirmed the image's awesome power. In all probability, the image was carved at the beginning of the fifteenth century, when its namesake wat in Lampang was founded. Peering through the rows of protective bars inside the viharn, you can just make out the tiny meditating Buddha, which is actually made of jasper, not emerald. Like the Emerald Buddha in Bangkok, Phra Kaew Don Tao has three costumes, one for each season of the year (see p.86).

Thung Kwian market

21km from Lampang on Highway 11, en route to the Thai Elephant Conservation Centre

If you have your own vehicle, the **Thung Kwian market** (open daily) offers not only a useful stop for refreshments near the elephant centre, but also a chance to view the panoply of products on sale – rabbits and birds, honeycombs, bugs and creepy-crawlies of every description. This is a favourite spot for city Thais to pick up some exotic taste to take back home with them.

The Thai Elephant Conservation Centre

30km west of Lampang on Highway 11 • Shows daily at 10am, 11am & 1.30pm, with the chance to see the elephants bathing at 9.40am & 1.10pm • B200 • ☏ 054 829333, ⓦ thailandelephant.org • The centre is on the bus route between Chiang Mai and Lampang; from the gates, there are regular shuttle buses into the elephant showground 2km away

The **Thai Elephant Conservation Centre** (aka the National Elephant Institute) is the most authentic and worthwhile place in Thailand to see elephants displaying their skills. Entertaining **shows** put the elephants through their paces, with plenty of loud trumpeting for their audience. After some photogenic bathing, they walk together in formation and go through a routine of pushing and dragging logs, then proceed to paint pictures and play custom-made instruments. You can feed them bananas and sugar cane after the show, and even take a **ride** on one (available daily 8am–3.30pm) – B500 gets you thirty minutes, while B1000 gives you an hour's ride, with a chance to get out into the nearby forest (longer day-trips, overnight treks and mahout training programmes are also on offer – see the website). Visitors are also free to look around the hospital, but not the royal stables, where six of Rama IX's ten white elephants are kept.

Run by the Thai government, the conservation centre was originally set up in 1969 in another nearby location as a young elephant-training centre, the earliest of its kind in Thailand. However, since the ban on logging, the new centre, opened in 1992, emphasizes the preservation of the elephant in Thailand (see box, p.316). By promoting ecotourism the centre is providing employment for the elephants and enabling Thai people to continue their historically fond relationship with these animals. Money raised from entrance fees and donations helps to finance the **elephant hospital** here, which cares for sick, abused, ageing and abandoned elephants. The centre has three simple **restaurants** on site, and offers the possibility of **homestays** and bungalow **accommodation** (from B1000; see the website for more details).

ARRIVAL AND DEPARTURE   LAMPANG

By plane Bangkok Airways (Suvarnabhumi Airport; 3 daily; 1hr 30min) and Nok Air (Don Muang Airport; 2 daily; 1hr 15min) run flights from Bangkok. The airport is just south of town, and songthaews and a/c taxis are on hand for the short ride to the centre.

By train The train station lies less than 1km southwest of the town centre. A shared yellow-and-green songthaew from here to the guesthouses costs B20/person.

THE ELEPHANT IN THAILAND

To Thais the **elephant** has profound **spiritual significance**, derived from both Hindu and Buddhist mythologies. Carvings and statues of **Ganesh**, the Hindu god with an elephant's head, feature on ancient temples all over the country and, as the god of knowledge and remover of obstacles, Ganesh has been adopted as the symbol of the Fine Arts Department – and is thus depicted on all entrance tickets to historical sites. The Hindu deity Indra rarely appears without his three-headed elephant mount **Erawan**, and miniature devotional elephant effigies are sold at major Brahmin shrines, such as Bangkok's Erawan Shrine. In Buddhist legend, the future **Buddha's mother** was able to conceive only after she dreamt that a white elephant had entered her womb: that is why elephant balustrades encircle many of the Buddhist temples of Sukhothai, and why the rare white elephant is accorded royal status (see p.115) and featured on the national flag until 1917.

The **practical** role of the elephant in Thailand was once almost as great as its symbolic importance. The kings of Ayutthaya relied on elephants to take them into battle against the Burmese – one king assembled a trained elephant army of three hundred – and during the nineteenth century King Rama IV offered Abraham Lincoln a male and a female to "multiply in the forests of America" and to use in the Civil War. In times of peace, the phenomenal strength of the elephant has made it invaluable as a beast of burden: elephants hauled the stone from which the gargantuan Khmer temple complexes of the northeast were built, and for centuries they have been used to clear forests and carry timber.

The traditional cycle for domestic elephants born in captivity is to spend the first three years of their lives with their mothers (who are pregnant for 18–22 months and get five years' maternity leave), before being separated and raised with other calves in training schools. Each elephant is then looked after by a **mahout** (*kwan chang*), a trainer, keeper and driver rolled into one. Traditionally the mahout would have stayed with the elephant for the rest of its life, but nowadays this rarely happens, as being a mahout is seen as a low-status job.

Training begins with mahouts taking months to earn the trust of their charge; over the next thirteen years the elephant is taught about forty different commands, from simple "stop" and "go" orders to complex instructions for hooking and passing manoeuvres with the trunk. By the age of 16, elephants are ready to be put to work and are expected to carry on working until they reach 50 or 60, after which they are retired and may live for another twenty years.

Ironically, the **timber industry** was the animal's undoing. Mechanized logging destroyed the wild elephant's preferred river-valley grassland and forest habitats, forcing them into isolated upland pockets. As a result, Thailand's population of wild elephants is now thought to be under two thousand, while there are around 2500 domesticated animals – down from a roughly estimated total population of a hundred thousand in 1900 (the Asian elephant is now officially classified as an endangered species). With the 1989 **ban on commercial logging** within Thai borders – after the 1988 catastrophe when the effects of deforestation killed a hundred people and wiped out villages in Surat Thani province, as mudslides swept down deforested slopes carrying cut timber with them – elephants and their mahouts were faced with the further problem of **unemployment**. Though a small number of elephants continue to work in the illegal teak-logging trade along the Burmese border, most mahouts struggle to find the vast amount of food needed to sustain their charges – about 125kg per beast per day.

Tourism has stepped into the breach, mostly in the form of elephant shows and trekking, though it's been a mixed blessing to say the least, as the elephants are often poorly treated, overworked or downright abused. In town streets and on beaches, you'll often see mahouts charging drunk tourists for the experience of handfeeding their elephants bananas or sugar cane, and Thais for the chance to stoop under their trunks for good luck. Towns, however, are simply not the right environment for them – they're regularly involved in road accidents, for example, despite the red reflectors that many sport on their tails; overall, it's best not to feed town elephants in this way. Demand from the tourism industry is now outstripping supply, and it's feared that captive beasts – which have a lower birth rate than elephants in the wild – may disappear in the next ten years or so, which in turn will mean that wild elephants will again be under threat (see p.759). According to recent reports, the number of baby elephants being registered exceeds the number of births, suggesting many are being taken from the wild.

Destinations Bangkok (5 daily; 10–12hr); Chiang Mai (6 daily; 2hr–2hr 30min).
By bus The bus station is southwest of the town centre, just off the bypass, though some buses also make a stop on Thanon Phaholyothin in the centre. Yellow-and-green songthaews wait at the edge of the terminal, departing when full up (B20/person within the city).

Destinations Bangkok (at least hourly, with a concentration of overnight buses leaving around 8–9pm; 8hr); Chiang Mai (at least every 30min; 1hr 30min–2hr); Chiang Rai (roughly every 30min; 4–5hr); Mae Sai (4 daily; 4–5hr); Nan (7 daily; 4hr); Phitsanulok (roughly hourly; 4hr); Phrae (roughly every 30min; 2hr–2hr 30min); Sukhothai (roughly hourly; 4hr); Tak (roughly every 30min; 2hr 30min).

GETTING AROUND

Most of the town can be covered on foot, but there are alternatives, including the town's horse-drawn carriages (see box below).

By songthaew There are plenty of shared yellow-and-green songthaews that cruise the streets looking for custom (B20/person within the city).
By bicycle, motorbike or car Bicycles (B50–60/day)

can be rented at *Akhamsiri Home*, R-Lampang and *Riverside Guest House*; motorbikes (B250/day) and cars (B900/day) at Pornpitak Tour, 363/1 Thanon Tipchang (☎054 226774, ⓦ pornpitaktour.com).

3

INFORMATION AND TOURS

Tourist information The small, helpful municipal tourist information centre (Mon–Fri 9am–4.30pm, plus Sat & Sun 9am–4.30pm in high season, though sometimes closing for lunch; ☎054 237229), just west of the clocktower and next to the fire station on Thanon Takrao Noi, can provide a map of the town, which shows horse-drawn carriage routes.

Tours Staff at the tourist information centre can book day-trips to the Thai Elephant Conservation Centre and Wat Phra That Lampang Luang (B1200 in an a/c taxi, B600–800 in a songthaew). Another good bet is Pornpitak Tour, 363/1 Thanon Tipchang (☎054 226774, ⓦ pornpitaktour.com), where staff can organize local sightseeing tours.

ACCOMMODATION

Akhamsiri Home 54/1 Thanon Pamaiket ☎054 228791, ⓦ akhamsirihome.com. Set around a garden café in a quiet part of town, attractive, slightly cutesy rooms in modern Thai style, with balconies upstairs and small gardens downstairs; all have a/c, hot water, TVs and fridges. B̲5̲9̲0̲
Auangkham Resort Thanon Wang Nuea ☎054 221305–6, ⓦ auangkhamlampang.com. At this friendly, leafy haven on the peaceful north bank of the river, the public areas have a colourful, retro feel while the large, bright bedrooms all have French windows and verandas overlooking the lovely garden, as well as a/c and hot showers. B̲1̲1̲0̲0̲
★**Riverside Guest House** 286 Thanon Talat Kao ☎054 227005, ⓦ theriverside-lampang.com. This

peaceful, traditional compound of teak houses with a small, attractive garden offers tasteful en-suite rooms decorated with antiques and traditional textiles, all with access to hot showers (a few sharing) and many with a/c; some boast balconies or terraces overlooking the river. Varied breakfasts and all-day drinks are served on the relaxing terraces of the riverside café (not to be confused with the *Riverside* restaurant, further west). Fan B̲3̲5̲0̲, a/c B̲6̲0̲0̲
R Lampang Talat Kao, just east of Riverside Guest House ☎054 225278, ⓦ r-lampang.com. Part guest-house, part doll's house, *R Lampang* occupies a prime spot on the riverfront, with shades of pastel green and soft pink providing the backdrop for a weird and wonderful collection of corridor curios – from white-painted samlors

---

LAMPANG'S HORSE-DRAWN CARRIAGES

If you want to get out to Wat Phra Kaew Don Tao you might want to employ the services of a **horse-drawn carriage**, which, along with white chickens, is a prevalent symbol of Lampang (in fact, Thais often refer to the city as *muang rot mah*, or "horse-cart city"). These colourfully decked-out carriages, complete with Stetson-wearing driver, can be hired at several stops around town, including towards the east end of Thanon Boonyawat and opposite the tourist office. There are two "standard routes" around town; the shorter one (3km) costs B200 (carrying two people), while the longer one (4km) costs B300. An alternative is the B400, one-hour city tour, which includes a brief stop at Wat Phra Kaew Don Tao, plus a handful of other city sights.

to clapped-out old TV sets. The fan rooms are too small, but the a/c rooms with TV and fridge are worth the investment. Fan **B350**, a/c **B650**

Wienglakor 138/38 Thanon Phaholyothin ☎054 316430–5, ⓦlampangwienglakor.com. Of several big and expensive hotels in town, this one has the cosiest rooms and the most tasteful decor, with coffered ceilings, parquet floors and ornamental ponds in traditional Thai style, as well as a good restaurant (see below). Breakfast included. **B1500**

EATING AND DRINKING

Along with the riverfront, the stretch of **Thanon Takrao Noi** between the clocktower and Thanon Wienglakon is a lively part of town after dark, featuring many simple restaurants and the Atsawin **night market** running off its side streets to the south, as well as **pubs** and **karaoke bars**.

★**Aroy One Baht** Thanon Tipchang ☎089 700 9444. Cheap eats in a nice old wooden house with outdoor terraces, staffed by happy young Thais. The spicy snakehead fish soup, served in coconut milk, is a bargain at B40. Highly recommended. Daily 4pm–midnight.

Escape Bistro & Café 357/37 Thanon Duangrat ☎054 322622. The most refined snack-stop on broad and busy Thanon Duangrat, this chilly a/c café is spread over two floors and a sunny outdoor terrace area. Try the delicious chocolate lava cake (B90) as you flick through the huge selection of magazines. Daily 8.30am–8pm.

Grandma's Café Thanon Tipchang ☎054 322792. Conveniently located coffee hangout that's popular with artsy young Lampangers, especially in the early evening. Serves good espressos and lots of noodle and rice dishes. Mon–Sat 10am–7pm.

Mae Hae Thanon Uparaj. This nondescript sky-blue shophouse, 10m from Thanon Boonyawat, serves some of the best *sai oua* (spicy pork sausage) you're likely to encounter, bursting with flavour, as well as other excellent northern Thai dishes such as *tam khanun* (jackfruit salad). There's no English sign and no menu – just choose and point at the tempting ready-made dishes, which cost around B50 each. Daily 9am–7pm.

★**Riverside** 328 Thanon Tipchang ☎054 221861. Cosy, relaxing bar-restaurant-bakery on rustic wooden terraces overlooking the water, serving a wide variety of excellent Thai dishes, including northern specialities, and Western food, to the sounds of live music (quality variable) in the evenings. A wood-fired pizza oven is stoked up four nights a week (Tues, Thurs, Sat & Sun; evenings only; from B150) and produces interesting fusion offerings such as pizza *sai oua* (with spicy northern Thai sausage). Daily 11am–midnight.

Wienglakor 138/38 Thanon Phaholyothin ☎054 316430–5. The best hotel restaurant in town with a wide choice of well-prepared, good-value northern dishes and an inviting ambience, overlooking the landscaped gardens. Dinner on Friday and Saturday nights is accompanied by live Thai music (6–8pm). Daily 10am–midnight.

Phrae

Heading east out of Lampang on your way to the small city of **PHRAE**, you'll pass through the tobacco-rich Yom valley, dotted with distinctive brick curing-houses. Phrae province is famous for woodcarving and the quality of its *seua maw hawm*, the deep-blue, collarless working shirt seen all over Thailand (produced and sold in abundance in the village of Ban Thung Hong, 4km north of central Phrae on Highway 101). The main reason to stop here, however, is to explore Phrae's old town, with its peaceful lanes filled with temples and traditional teak houses – as in Lampang, the former logging industry attracted Burmese workers and the influence is evident – and to enjoy the old-fashioned and friendly nature of a place still virtually untouched by tourism.

Sited on the southeast bank of the Yom River, Phrae is clearly divided into old and new towns; an earthen wall surrounds the roughly oval-shaped old town, with a dry moat on its southeastern side and the new town centre beyond that. At the centre of the **old town**, a large roundabout is the main orientation point; running northwest–southeast through the roundabout, through Pratuchai (the main gate on the southeastern side of the old town), and into the **new town** is Thanon Charoen Muang, where several shops sell the trademark deep-indigo shirts. The main street in the new town, Thanon Yantarakitkoson, intersects Thanon Charoen Muang about 300m southeast of the old town.

Vongburi House

Thanon Khamlue • Daily 10am–5pm • B30

The white-and-pink **Vongburi House** (Baan Wongburi) is a good place to begin an exploration of the old town. Built of teak between 1897 and 1907 in Thai–European style for the wife of the last lord of Phrae, it's smothered in elaborate, lace-like woodcarving on all the eaves, gables and balconies, and around doors and windows. Inside the house, exhibits include fine silverware, antique furniture, undershirts with magic spells written on them to ward off danger, and various documents such as elephant identity papers and artefacts that shed light on the history of the family, who still live in part of the complex.

Wat Luang

Just south of Thanon Rob Muang, around 100m from Vongburi House

Phrae's oldest temple complex, **Wat Luang**, dates from the town's foundation around the twelfth century; it contains the only intact original brick entrance gate to the city, though unfortunately it has been closed up and turned into an ugly shrine to Chao Pu, an early Lanna ruler. Apart from the gate, the oldest component of the wat is the crumbling early Lanna-style **chedi** called Chang Kham after the four elephants – now mostly trunkless – which sit at its octagonal base; these alternate with four niches containing Buddha images and some haphazardly leaning, gilded bronze parasols.

Over the years, Wat Luang has been added to and parts of it have been quite spoiled in a gaudy modernization process; until recently, a dishonest monk was even taking down parts of the temple to sell. Apart from the ruined entrance gate, this meddling is most evident in the **viharn**, opposite, where an ugly and very out-of-place laterite brick facade has been placed in front of the original Lanna-style sixteenth-century entrance.

Opposite the chedi on the north side of the compound, a **museum** (irregular hours; free) on two floors houses some real treasures, the most important being a collection of sixteenth-century bronze Buddhas and several glass cases containing old manuscripts with beautifully gilded covers, which are located upstairs.

Wat Phra Non

About a block west of Wat Luang along Thanon Rob Muang

In the far northwestern corner of the old city is **Wat Phra Non**, established three centuries ago, whose name comes from the 9m-long reclining Buddha housed in a small viharn; look out for the Lanna-style bot's finely carved wooden pediment showing scenes from the *Ramayana*.

Ban Prathup Jai

Beyond the old town's west gate • Daily 8am–5pm • B40

Signposted among the tranquil lanes out beyond the old town's west gate lies the massive two-storey teak house of **Ban Prathup Jai**, constructed out of nine old houses in the 1970s. A visit here allows you to appreciate the beauty and strength of the wood, even if the overall effect is a bit over the top. The lower floor has an impressive interior of 130 pillars of solid teak carved with jungle scenes; huge wooden elephants wander among the columns, and solid teak walls provide a backdrop for ornately carved furniture. There's also a souvenir shop where you can buy all things wooden. Upstairs has the feel of a traditional house, and the furniture and objects are those that you might find in a well-to-do Thai home: ornately carved cabinets crammed with bowls and other ordinary household objects, tables displaying framed family portraits, wall carvings and even a teak bar.

Wat Chom Sawan

Around 200m north of the bus station on Thanon Yantarakitkoson

Built in 1894 under the reign of King Rama V, **Wat Chom Sawan** is a fine example of Burmese-style architecture. Recently restored, the main teak structure (notable for its impressive multi-tiered roof) houses the ordination hall and the monks' residence. Inside, the ceiling and columns are beautifully carved and dotted with glittering stained glass. Treasures include an ivory image of the Buddha in Burmese style, scripture slabs and Luang Pho San, a seated Buddha figure made of woven bamboo.

Free Thai Movement Museum

Tucked behind the Phrae Paradorn hotel • Daily dawn–dusk • Free • Enter via the hotel's reception area (ask at reception if doors are locked)

This fascinating little museum tells the story of Thailand's struggles during World War II, when the country was obliged to ally itself with Japan, having been invaded and effectively occupied by the Japanese. Among the exhibits on show are photos and newspaper articles from the era, plus weapons used by **Seri Thai** (the Free Thai Movement) during their clandestine resistance against Japanese forces.

Wat Phra That Cho Hae

9km east of town (1km beyond the village of Padang) • Without your own transport, you'll need to charter a songthaew (about B300) from the bus station

Wat Phra That Cho Hae is an important pilgrimage centre sited on a low hill, approached by two naga stairways through a grove of teak trees. One staircase leads to a shrine where a revered Buddha image, Phra Chao Tan Chai, is said to increase women's fertility. The small grounds also house a gilded 33m-high **chedi**, traditionally wrapped in the yellow satin-like cloth, *cho hae* (which gives the wat its name), in March or April, and a brightly decorated viharn with an unusual cruciform layout. To the north of the main compound, a new viharn houses a shiny Buddha and some well-crafted murals and window carvings.

Phae Muang Phi

18km northeast of Phrae off Highway 101

Out of town are the so-called ghost pillars at **Phae Muang Phi**, a geological quirk of soil and wind erosion. Overzealous reports describe this as Thailand's Grand Canyon, but it's not a fair comparison, and it's probably only worth visiting if you're going on through to Nan with your own transport. Some locals believe the place is haunted, which may explain the lack of development in the area.

3

ARRIVAL AND DEPARTURE

PHRAE

By plane Nok Air runs a daily flight from Bangkok's Don Muang to Phrae's airport, 3km southeast of town. If you're staying at one of the fancier hotels, ask them to pick you up from the airport; otherwise, you might have to walk about 200m out of the airport to the main road, to catch a songthaew.

By bus or minibus Buses and a/c minibuses stop at the main bus station off Thanon Yantarakitkoson, towards the northeast of town.

Destinations Bangkok (13 daily; 8hr); Chiang Mai (11 daily; 4hr); Chiang Rai (at least hourly; 4hr); Den Chai

(hourly; 30min); Lampang (roughly every 30min; 2hr–2hr 30min); Nan (hourly; 2hr); Phitsanulok (at least hourly; 3hr).

By train Den Chai train station, just 20km to the southwest, is on the main Bangkok–Chiang Mai line. Frequent songthaews run from Den Chai (30–40min) to a stand south of Phrae's old town, returning from the same spot.

By car If you're driving here from Lampang, turn left from Highway 11 at Mae Khaem onto Route 1023 and approach the town via Long and some lovely scenery.

GETTING AROUND

By songthaew To charter a songthaew from the bus station to Wat Luang, for example, will cost around B60 for the vehicle.

By bicycle or motorbike The *Mae Yom Palace Hotel* rents

out bicycles (B100/day). Motorbikes can be rented for B200/day at Saeng Fa (☎ 054 521598), next to the Bank of Ayudhaya on Thanon Yantarakitkoson.

INFORMATION

Tourist information For information about the town and a clutch of handy maps, try the new TAT office at 2

Thanon Baan Mai (daily 8.30am–4.30pm; ☎ 054 521127, ✉ tatphrae@tat.or.th).

ACCOMMODATION

Huern Na Na 7/9 Thanon Sasibutr ☎ 054 524800, ⊛ huernnana.com. New thirty-room hotel with an impressive Lanna-style exterior, an attractive swimming pool, a spa and sauna. Bright, luxurious bedrooms with an appealing contemporary style that blends dark wood with occasional splashes of colour and feature espresso machines. Breakfast included. B2600

Mae Yom Palace Hotel 181/6 Thanon Yantarakitkoson ☎ 054 521028–35, ✉ wccphrae@hotmail.com. Good upmarket hotel, with a handy central location near the bus station. Facilities include a large, attractive swimming pool, a restaurant with a pleasant outdoor terrace and bicycle rental. Rooms are carpeted and air-conditioned, with hot showers, fridges and cable TV. Breakfast included

in the price. B1500

Phoomthai Garden Hotel 31 Thanon Sasibutr ☎ 054 627359, ⊛ phoomthaigarden.com. Attractive, low-rise fifty-room hotel to the south of the old town, featuring a lot of teak and earth tones in its decor and furniture. The bedrooms have balconies overlooking the leafy garden. Free pick-ups from airport and bus station and free bicycles for guests' use. Breakfast included. B1200

Phrae Paradorn 177 Thanon Yantarakitkoson ☎ 054 511177. Not as "absolutely clean" as the sign outside proclaims, but still a very good budget choice, with a simple breakfast thrown in. The a/c rooms include fridges, the fan rooms balconies, and all have hot water and TV. Fan B380, a/c B590

EATING AND DRINKING

To get a cheap and varied dinner in the town centre, your best bet is to head for the lively **night market** that convenes each evening just outside Pratuchai, the main gate on the southeastern side of the old town, towards the western end of Thanon Charoen Muang.

Baan Klang Wiang Thanon Wichairacha. Simple restaurant in a covered yard that serves some of the best *khao soi* (see p.293) in town, either with chicken or pork. Daily from 10am until they run out (usually about 2pm).

★**Ban Fai** A couple of kilometres south out of town at the junction of the Den Chai road and the bypass towards Nan. This open-sided barn-like place is the best restaurant around, serving very good Thai food including northern specialities such as *nem* (spiced pork sausages), the typical Lanna pork curry, *kaeng hang lay*,

and a tasty *kaeng ho*, a rich curry (originally from leftovers) mixing *kaeng hang lay*, glass noodles and aubergines. Daily 8am–10pm.

Gingerbread House Corner of Thanon Charoen Muang and Thanon Rong Sor ☎054 523671. In a two-storey, teak former hotel, this friendly, civilized café and art gallery offers tasty dishes such as *kaeng hang lay* (B120), as well as Western breakfasts, coffees and cakes. High season daily 8.30am–9pm; low season Mon–Thurs 8.30am–6pm, Fri–Sun 8.30am–8pm.

Nan

After leaving the Yom River, Highway 101 gently climbs through rolling hills of cotton fields and teak plantations to its highest point, framed by limestone cliffs, before descending into the high, isolated valley of the **Nan River**, the longest in Thailand (740km) and one of the tributaries of the Chao Phraya. Ringed by high mountains, the small but prosperous provincial capital of **NAN**, 225km northeast of Lampang, rests on the grassy west bank of the river. Few Western visitors make it out this far, but it's a likeable place with a thriving handicrafts tradition, a good museum and some superb temple murals at **Wat Phumin**, as well as at Wat Nong Bua out in the countryside (see p.326). Nan's centre comprises a disorientating grid of crooked streets, around a small core of shops and businesses where Thanon Mahawong and Thanon Anantaworarichides meet Thanon Sumondhevaraj.

NAN

0 — 100 metres

■ **ACCOMMODATION**
Dhevaraj Hotel	5
Fah Place	3
Nan Boutique Hotel	1
Pukha Nanfa Hotel	4
SP Guest House	2

● **SHOPS**
| Jangtrakul | 1 |
| Ngennan | 2 |

● **RESTAURANTS & CAFÉS**
Heuan Jao Nang	3
Hot Bread	4
Poom Sam	1
Tanaya Kitchen	2

The town comes alive for the **Lanna boat races**, usually held in late October or early November, when villages from around the province send teams of up to fifty oarsmen to race in long, colourfully decorated canoes with dragon prows. It's now also popular on cool-season weekends with tourists from Bangkok, for whom an art festival is laid on over a weekend in February. The lush surrounding valley is noted for its cotton-weaving, sweet oranges and the attractive grainy paper made from the bark of local *sa* (mulberry) trees.

Brief history

Although it has been kicked around by Myanmar, Laos and Thailand, Nan province has a history of being on the fringes, distanced by the encircling barrier of mountains. Rama V brought Nan into his centralization programme at the start of the twentieth century, but left the traditional ruling house in place, making it the last province in Thailand to be administered by a local ruler (it remained so until 1931). During the troubled 1970s, Communist insurgents holed up in this twilight region and proclaimed Nan the future capital of the liberated zone, which only succeeded in bringing the full might of the Thai Army down on them; the insurgency faded after the government's 1982 offer of amnesty. Today, energies are focused on development, and the province has become less isolated with the building of several new roads.

The National Museum

Just off Thanon Phakong in the southwest part of town • Wed–Sun 9am–4pm • B100

The best place to start an exploration is at the **National Museum**, located in a tidy, century-old palace with superb teak floors, which used to be home to the rulers of Nan. Its informative, user-friendly displays give you a bite-sized introduction to Nan, its history and its peoples, the prize exhibit being a talismanic elephant tusk with a bad case of brown tooth decay, which is claimed to be magic black ivory. The tusk was presented to the lord of Nan by the ruler of Keng Tung (now in Myanmar) over three hundred years ago and now sits on a colourful wooden *khut*, a mythological eagle. The museum also houses elegant pottery and woodcarving, gorgeously wrought silverware and some rare Lao Buddhas.

Wat Phumin

Thanon Phakong

Wat Phumin will grab even the most over-templed traveller. Its 500-year-old centrepiece is an unusual cruciform building, combining both the bot and the viharn, which balances some quirky features in a perfect symmetry. Two giant nagas pass through the base of the building, with their tails along the balustrades at the south entrance and their heads at the north, representing the sacred oceans at the base of the central mountain of the universe. The doors at the four entrances, which have been beautifully carved with a complex pattern of animals and flowers, lead straight to the four Buddha images arranged around a tall altar in the centre of the building – note the Buddhas' piercing onyx eyes and pointed ears, showing the influence of Laos, 50km away. What really sets the bot apart are the **murals**, whose bright, simple colours seem to jump off the walls. Executed in the late nineteenth century – though occasionally retouched – the paintings take you on a whirlwind tour of heaven, hell, the Buddha's previous incarnations, local legends and incidents from Nan's history, and include stacks of vivacious, sometimes bawdy, detail, which provides a valuable pictorial record of that era.

Wat Chang Kham

Thanon Phakong

Like Wat Phumin, **Wat Chang Kham** is over five hundred years old, though the two viharns that stand side by side are unexceptional in design. The main feature here is a gorgeous, gold-capped chedi, supported by elephants on all sides; those on the corners are adorned with gold helmets and straps. The temple is attached to a school, a reminder that temples were once the only source of education in the country.

Wat Phra That Chae Haeng

2km southeast of town, just off Highway 1168

Wat Phra That Chae Haeng is a must, as much for its setting on a hill overlooking the Nan valley as anything else. The wat was founded in 1300, at a spot determined by the Buddha himself when he passed through this way – or so local legend would have it. The nagas here outdo even Wat Phumin's: the first you see of the wat across the fields is a wide driveway flanked by monumental serpents gliding down the slope from the temple. A magnificent gnarled bodhi tree with hundreds of spreading branches and roots guards the main gate, set in high boundary walls. Inside the walls, the highlight is a slender, 55m-high golden chedi, surrounded by four smaller chedis and four carved and gilded umbrellas, as well as small belfries and stucco lions. Close competition comes from the viharn roof, which has no fewer than fifteen Lao-style tiers, stacked up like a house of cards and supported on finely carved *kan tuei* (wood supports) under the eaves.

ARRIVAL AND DEPARTURE

NAN

BY PLANE

Nok Air (4 daily; 1hr 40min) and Air Asia (2 daily; 1hr 10min) run flights between Bangkok's Don Muang Airport and Nan, while Kan Air provides a link with Chiang Mai (2 weekly; 45min). The airport is 2km northwest of town, and is served by a/c taxis (about B100 to the centre; ☎ 054 773555 or ☎ 084 617 0777).

BY BUS

The bus station is in the southwest corner of town, off the main road to Phrae; songthaews to the centre cost around B20/person.

From/to Chiang Mai The bus journey to Nan from Chiang Mai takes around 6hr, so it might be worth catching one of the more comfortable first-class or VIP vehicles that serve this route, shaving a little off the journey time.

From/to Chiang Rai One bus a day winds its tortuous way over the mountains from Chiang Rai, via Chiang Kham; if you're prone to motion sickness and want to avoid the worst of the twisting roads, change buses in Phrae instead.

Destinations Bangkok (12 daily; 10–11hr); Chiang Mai (8–9 daily; 5–6hr); Chiang Rai (1 daily; 6–7hr); Den Chai (hourly; 2hr 30min); Phitsanulok (12 daily; 8hr); Phrae (hourly; 2hr).

INFORMATION, TOURS AND GETTING AROUND

Tourist information There's a municipal tourist information booth and a national parks information booth opposite Wat Phumin (daily 8.30am–4.30pm, usually closing 1hr for lunch; ☎ 054 751169 or ☎ 054 750247), or visit helpful Fhu Travel at 453/4 Thanon Sumondhevaraj (see p.327), for local information or to find out about their tours.

Tourist police Thanon Suriyapong (☎ 054 710216 or ☎ 1155).

Bicycle and motorbike rental If you want to explore the area on two wheels, Oversea, a bike and motorbike retailer on Thanon Sumondhevaraj near the corner of Thanon Mahawong (☎ 054 710258 or ☎ 081 882 9362), rents out decent bicycles (B100/day) and motorbikes (B250/day).

ACCOMMODATION

Despite being a small town with few visitors, Nan has some attractive accommodation options, ranging from family-run guesthouses to clean, reasonably priced hotels. The only times of year when finding somewhere to stay might be a problem are during the Lanna boat races (late Oct or early Nov) and over Christmas and New Year.

Dhevaraj 466 Thanon Sumondhevaraj ☎ 054 751577, ⊕ dhevarajhotel.com. Large, centrally positioned hotel, popular with tour groups, which has a slightly institutional feel but is a hub of Nan social life. There's an outdoor pool and a wide range of well-maintained accommodation, all with hot water and nice cosy beds. Breakfast included. **B1200**

Fah Place Soi Kha Luang 1, 237/8 Thanon Sumondhevaraj ☎ 054 710222. Just down a small soi off the main road, this striking, modern, cream block contains spacious, very good-value a/c rooms, done out with attractive tiles, tasteful wooden furniture and large hot-water bathrooms. **B500**

Nan Boutique Hotel North of the centre at 1/11 Thanon Kha Luang ☎054 775 532, ⊕tazshotels.com. At this central, thirty-room hotel, the handsome and well-equipped bedrooms are good value for money, with lots of extras like bathrobes, slippers and herbal toiletries to help you unwind. On-site facilities include a restaurant and a small gift shop, and guests are given free access to bikes. Free airport transfers. Breakfast included. B1800

Pukha Nanfa Hotel 369 Thanon Sumondhevaraj ☎054 771111, ⊕pukhananfahotel.co.th/en. An eye-catching wooden building on the city's main street, with an imposing chalet-like facade that sparkles with fairy lights.

Inside, ornate carvings and wall hangings lead the way to a massive wooden staircase, which twists up towards the elegant, panelled bedrooms. There's a wonderful first-floor terrace with views over the street, and a restaurant downstairs. Breakfast included. B2500

★**SP Guest House** 233 Thanon Sumondhevaraj ☎054 774897. Actually on Trok Hua Wiangtai, a narrow alley off the main road, this well-maintained, friendly guesthouse offers spacious a/c rooms, with hot-water bathrooms, fridges and TVs. The owners are extremely helpful, and there are big family rooms available. B600

EATING AND DRINKING

Plenty of restaurants cluster around Thanon Anantaworarichides, while the **night market** is just around the corner on Thanon Phakong. The liveliest drinking scene in Nan is on **Kad Nan**, an alley of cool bars, boutiques and gift shops, about 1km up Thanon Mahayot from Thanon Anantaworarichides on the right.

Heuan Jao Nang East bank of the Nan River, about 500m north of the bridge. The attractive tables on an embankment above the river are good for sunset-watching, and the food's great, too (most dishes B150–250): lots of river fish – try the *pla khang patcha*, fish stir-fried with green peppercorns, lady-finger roots and other herbs – and northern specialities, including delicious, tongue-tingling (literally) deep-fried chicken with Vietnamese mint (*kai thawt makhwen*). Daily 11am–11pm.

Hot Bread Thanon Suriyapong. This friendly café near Wat Phumin bakes its own white and wholewheat bread and cakes, and serves Western breakfasts, lots of vegetarian dishes and good espresso coffees (from B45). The same owner has a popular *khao soi* place next door if you'd prefer

a northern Thai breakfast. Daily 7am–4pm.

★**Poom Sam (Poom 3)** Thanon Anantaworarichides ☎054 772100. It may look like any other streetside restaurant, but *Poom Sam* prepares excellent Thai and Chinese food with great service at reasonable prices, and there's a comfy a/c room as well. Try the *tom yam kung* (B120) or the chicken *matsaman* curry with apple and pineapple. Daily 5.30pm–2am.

Tanaya Kitchen Thanon Anantaworarichides ☎054 710930. Right next door to *Poom Sam*, this tiny, homely and friendly café serves tasty Thai dishes such as *phat thai* and can do good vegetarian versions using tofu and mushrooms. Daily 10am–7.30pm.

SHOPPING

Loyalty to local traditions ensures the survival of several good **handicrafts shops** in Nan, most of which are found on Thanon Sumondhevaraj north of the junction with Anantaworarichides. On Saturday evenings (roughly 6–9/10pm), the same stretch of street hosts a "**walking street**", similar to those in Chiang Mai, with crafts and food for sale.

Jangtrakul 304–6 Thanon Sumondhevaraj ☎054 771357 or ☎054 710016. The best all-rounder among the crafts shops on the street, selling local woodcarving, silks and cottons, including colourful Thai Lue weaving and hill-tribe clothing. Daily 8am–7pm.

Ngennan (Ngern Nan) 430/1 Thanon Sumondhevaraj ☎054 773063, ⊕ngennan.com. Centrally located silver shop stocking a wide range of well-made bracelets, necklaces, earrings and bowls. Daily 7.30am–6pm.

Around Nan

The remote, mountainous countryside **around Nan** runs a close scenic second to the precipitous landscape of Mae Hong Son province, but its remoteness means that Nan has even worse transport and is even more poorly mapped. This does, of course, make it an exciting region to explore, where you may encounter the province's ethnic minorities: the Thai Lue (see p.326); the **Htin**, an upland Mon-Khmer people, most of whom have migrated since the Communist takeover of Laos in 1975; the **Khamu**, skilled metalworkers who have moved to Nan over the last 150 years from southwest China and Laos; and the little-known Mrabri (see box below) – a good place to organize excursions is Fhu Travel (see box opposite). More straightforward targets include the temple at **Nong Bua**, with it superb murals, and beautiful **Doi Phukha National Park**.

Nan Riverside Art Gallery

20km north of Nan up Route 1080 · Daily except Wed 9am–5pm · B20 · ☎ 081 989 2912 · Served by buses (roughly hourly) from Nan bus station en route to Tha Wang Pha

The impressive **Nan Riverside Art Gallery** was founded by local, nationally famous artist, Winai Prabripu, in a lovely setting by the banks of the Nan River. Various exhibition spaces display his paintings – many of them local landscapes focusing on details of plants in season and paintings inspired by the Wat Phumin murals – as well as rotating exhibitions by other contemporary Thai artists, sculptures and photos. A visit to the gallery combines well with Ban Nong Bua.

3

Ban Nong Bua

About 40km north of Nan off the west side of Route 1080 · Roughly hourly services from Nan bus station to Tha Wang Pha, from whose southern outskirts signs in English point you left across the Nan River to Wat Nong Bua, 3km away (coming by bus, either hire a motorbike taxi in the centre of Tha Wang Pha, or walk the last 3km)

BAN NONG BUA, site of a famous muralled **temple** of the same name, makes a rewarding day-trip from Nan. The village and surrounding area are largely inhabited by **Thai Lue** people, distant cousins of the Thais, who've migrated from China in the past 150 years. They produce beautiful cotton garments in richly coloured geometric patterns; just behind the wat, you can watch **weavers** at work and buy the opulent fabrics. The quality of design and workmanship is very high here, and prices, though not cheap, are reasonable for the quality.

Wat Nong Bua

Built in 1862 in typical Lanna style, **Wat Nong Bua**'s beautifully gnarled viharn has low, drooping roof tiers surmounted by stucco finials – here you'll find horned nagas and tusked makaras (elephantine monsters), instead of the garuda finial which invariably crops up in central Thai temples. The viharn enshrines a pointy-eared Lao Buddha, but its most outstanding features are the **murals** that cover all four walls. Executed between 1867 and 1888, probably by the Wat Phumin painters, they depict with much humour

---

SPIRITS OF THE YELLOW LEAVES

Inhabiting the remote hill country west of Nan, the population of about three hundred **Mrabri** represents the last remnants of nomadic hunter-gatherers in Thailand, though their way of life is rapidly passing. Believing that spirits would be angered if the tribe settled in one place, grew crops or kept animals, the Mrabri traditionally built only temporary shelters of branches and wild banana leaves, moving on to another spot in the jungle as soon as the leaves turned yellow; thus they earned their poetic Thai name, **Phi Tong Luang** – "Spirits of the Yellow Leaves". They eked out a hard livelihood from the forest, hunting with spears, trapping birds and small mammals, digging roots and collecting nuts, seeds and honey.

In recent decades, however, deforestation by logging and slash-and-burn farming has eaten into the tribe's territory, and the Mrabri were forced to sell their labour to Hmong and Mien farmers, often under slave-like conditions. But in the last few years, salvation for many Mrabri has come in the form of weaving **hammocks**: foreign visitors noticed their skill at making string bags out of jungle vines and helped them to set up a small-scale hammock industry. The hammocks are now exported to countries around the world, and the Mrabri weavers have the benefits of education, free healthcare and an unemployment fund. For more information, go to ⓦ jumbohammock.com.

TOURS AROUND NAN

Nan is a pleasant spot to spend a day or two, but if you fancy doing something a bit more energetic, it's worth heading out to the countryside. With or without your own vehicle, your best option is to head for the reliable Fhu Travel at 453/4 Thanon Sumondhevaraj (☎054 710636 or ☎081 287 7209, ⊛fhutravel.com). As well as dispensing advice about the region, Fhu and Ung, his wife, organize popular and enjoyable guided **tours** and **trekking** trips. One-day tours to Wat Nong Bua, including a visit to the local weavers, as well as to silversmiths and rattan furniture makers, cost B3400 for two people or B900/person for five people, including lunch. Treks (for three days, B4000/person in a group of two, B2500 in a group of five) head west, through tough terrain of thick jungle and high mountains, visiting Mrabri, Htin, Hmong and Mien villages. As well as offering **cycling** tours around town, Fhu can also arrange one- or two-day **whitewater-rafting** excursions on the Wa River to the east of town and one-day **kayaking** trips on the Nan River near town.

and vivid detail scenes from the *Chanthakhat Jataka* (the story of one of the Buddha's previous incarnations, as a hero called Chanthakhat). This is a particularly long and complex *Jataka* (although a leaflet outlining the story in English is sometimes available, in return for a small donation to temple funds), wherein our hero gets into all kinds of scrapes, involving several wives, other sundry liaisons, some formidably nasty enemies and the god Indra transforming himself into a snake. The crux of the tale comes on the east wall (opposite the Buddha image): in the bottom left-hand corner, Chanthakhat and the love of his life, Thewathisangka, are shipwrecked and separated; distraught, Thewathisangka wanders through the jungle, diagonally up the wall, to the hermitage of an old woman, where she shaves her head and becomes a nun; Chanthakhat travels through the wilderness along the bottom of the wall, curing a wounded naga-king on the way, who out of gratitude gives him a magic crystal ball, which enables our hero to face another series of perils along the south wall, before finally rediscovering and embracing Thewathisangka in front of the old woman's hut, at the top right-hand corner of the east wall.

Doi Phukha National Park

Around 80km northeast of Nan off Route 1256 • B200 • ☎054 701000, ⊛dnp.go.th

East of Tha Wang Pha, Route 1080 curves towards the town of **Pua**, on whose southern outskirts Route 1256, the spectacular access road for **Doi Phukha National Park**, begins its journey eastwards and upwards. The paved road climbs up a sharp ridge, through occasional stands of elephant grass and bamboo, towards Doi Dong Ya Wai (1939m), providing one of the most jaw-droppingly scenic drives in Thailand. Across the valleys to the north and south stand rows of improbably steep mountains (including the 1980m Doi Phukha itself, far to the south), covered in lush vegetation with scarcely a sign of human habitation.

From the park headquarters, 24km up the road from Pua, there's a self-guided, 4km **trail**, but to hike up any of the park's many peaks, you'll need to hire a guide (about B200/day) from the headquarters.

ARRIVAL AND DEPARTURE	**DOI PHUKHA NATIONAL PARK**

It's difficult to get into the park on public transport, and you'll usually have to stay the night. The trip is most exciting if tackled on a motorbike (though watch out for loose chippings on the bends).

By bus and songthaew Hourly buses from Nan's main station run to Pua (2hr), from where irregular songthaews from the market (best in the mornings, though you may find school songthaews in the late afternoon) serve the handful of villages along Route 1256 towards Bo Kleua.

CROSSING THE LAO BORDER AT HUAI KON

In the far north of Nan province, the **border crossing** at **Huai Kon** is open to foreigners, with Lao visas available on arrival. However, there's no public transport between the Thai and Lao border posts, necessitating a 1km walk over a hill. Of several air-conditioned minibuses that run each day to Huai Kon (starting from Den Chai), the best one to catch leaves Nan bus station around 7.45–8am, arriving at the border at about 10–10.30am. On the Lao side, you can catch a public songthaew to Muang Ngern and on to Pak Huai Khaen, about 40km away on the Mekong River; then charter a longtail boat for the short journey (about B300) to Pak Beng, where you can stay overnight and catch a morning boat to Luang Prabang.

ACCOMMODATION AND EATING

Food is available at the park's simple **restaurant**, and there are also several food stalls serving basic snacks.

Bo Klua View About 20km beyond the park headquarters towards Bo Kleua ☏054 778140 or ☏081 809 6392, ⚁bokluaview.com. This mid-range resort has a dozen stylish a/c bungalows with large verandas set around a terraced rice field and a restaurant serving good Thai and Western food. B̲1̲6̲5̲0̲

National park bungalows Park headquarters, 24km up the road from Pua ☏054 701000, ⚁dnp.go.th. Accommodation ranges from large chalets sleeping six or seven through rooms for four (all the above with hot showers and fridges), to small, basic bungalows for two. B̲3̲0̲0̲

National park camping There's a large, open, grassy campsite near the park headquarters.

Sao Din

60km south of Nan; head south on Highway 101 to Wiang Sa, then turn left and follow Route 1026 to Na No, just after which a turning on the right leads into the site

One of several brief excursions from Nan possible with your own transport, **Sao Din** ("earth pillars") provides a more intriguing example of soil erosion than the better-known site at Phae Muang Phi near Phrae. Here the earth pillars cover a huge area and appear in fantastic shapes, the result of centuries of erosion by wind and rain. There's little in the surrounding area, which makes wandering among the formations a peaceful experience. If you come here, be sure to wear long trousers and boots, especially in the cool season, as a thorny plant that grows in the region can cause discomfort.

The Mae Hong Son loop

Two main roads head in opposite directions from Chiang Mai over the western mountains, meeting each other in Mae Hong Son, at the heart of Thailand's most remote province – and offering the irresistible prospect of tying the highways together into a 600km **loop**. The towns en route give a taste of Myanmar to the west, but the journey itself, winding over implausibly steep forested mountains and through tightly hemmed farming valleys, is what will stick in the mind.

The **southern** leg of the route, **Highway 108**, first passes **Doi Inthanon National Park**, with its twisting curves, lofty views over half of northern Thailand and enough waterfalls to last a lifetime; from here, with your own vehicle you could shortcut the southernmost part of the loop by taking the paved but very winding Routes 1088 and 1263 from Mae Chaem to Khun Yuam. Sticking to the main loop, however, you'll next reach **Mae Sariang**, an important town for trade across the Burmese border and a gentle, low-key base for trekking and trips on the Salween River. The provincial capital, **Mae Hong Son**, roughly at the midpoint of the loop, is a more developed hub for exploring the area's mountains, rivers and waterfalls, though it can become frantic with tour groups in the cool season, especially on November and December weekends when the sunflowers are out.

The **northern** leg follows **Route 1095**, much of which was established by the Japanese army to move troops and supplies into Myanmar after its invasion of Thailand during World War II. The road heads northeast out of Mae Hong Son towards the market town of **Soppong**, whose surroundings feature beautiful caves (notably **Tham Lot**), appealing accommodation and stunning scenery to trek, cycle or kayak through. Halfway back towards Chiang Mai from Mae Hong Son is **Pai**, a cosy, cosmopolitan and hugely popular tourist hangout with plenty of activities and some gentle walking trails in the surrounding valley.

GETTING THERE AND AROUND   **MAE HONG SON LOOP**

We've covered the loop in a **clockwise** direction here, in part because Doi Inthanon is best reached direct from Chiang Mai, but you could just as easily go the other way round. Travelling the loop is straightforward, although the mountainous roads go through plenty of bends and jolts. The labour-intensive job of **paving** every hairpin bend was completed in the 1990s, but ongoing repair work can still give you a nasty surprise if you're riding a motorbike.

By plane From Chiang Mai, there are Nok Air and Kan Air flights to Mae Hong Son and Kan Air flights to Pai.

By bus Mae Hong Son is about eight hours' travelling time from Chiang Mai by a/c or ordinary bus, although services along the shorter but even more winding northern route are now augmented by faster, hourly a/c minibuses, which cover the ground via Pai in about six hours.

By motorbike or jeep Above all the loop is made for motorbikes and jeeps: the roads are generally quiet (but watch out for huge, speeding trucks) and you can satisfy the inevitable craving to stop every five minutes and admire the mountain scenery. A useful piece of equipment for this journey is the 1:375,000 map of the Mae Hong Son loop, with useful insets of Pai's and Mae Hong Son's environs, published by Golden Triangle Rider (Ⓦ gt-rider .com) and available in local bookshops.

Doi Inthanon National Park

Traversed by Route 1009 to the west of Chom Thong and Highway 108 • A checkpoint by Mae Klang Falls collects the B300 entrance fee • Ⓣ 053 286728, Ⓦ dnp.go.th

Covering a huge area to the southwest of Chiang Mai, **DOI INTHANON NATIONAL PARK**, with its Karen and Hmong hill-tribe villages, dramatic waterfalls and panoramas over rows of wild, green peaks to the west, gives a pleasant, if slightly sanitized, whiff of northern countryside, its attractions and concrete access roads kept in good order by the national parks department. The park, named after the

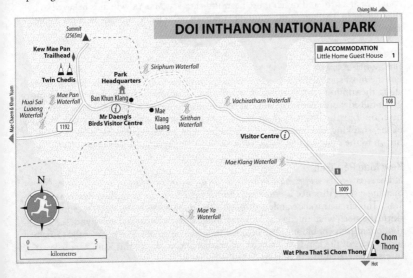

DOI INTHANON NATIONAL PARK

Summit (2565m)

Kew Mae Pan Trailhead

Twin Chedis

Siriphum Waterfall

Park Headquarters

Mae Pan Waterfall Ban Khun Klang

Huai Sai Luang Waterfall

Mae Chaem & Khun Yuam

1192

Mr Daeng's Birds Visitor Centre

Mae Klang Luang

Sirithan Waterfall

Vachiratharn Waterfall

108

Visitor Centre

Mae Klang Waterfall

1

1009

Mae Ya Waterfall

Wat Phra That Si Chom Thong

Chom Thong

Hot

Chiang Mai

■ ACCOMMODATION
Little Home Guest House   1

N

0   5
kilometres

3

highest mountain in the country and so dubbed the "Roof of Thailand", is geared mainly to wildlife conservation but also contains hill-tribe agricultural projects producing strawberries, apples and flowers for sale. Often shrouded in mist, Doi Inthanon's temperate forests shelter a huge variety of flora and fauna, which make this one of the major destinations for naturalists in Southeast Asia. The park supports about 380 **bird species**, the largest number of any site in Thailand – among them the ashy-throated warbler and a species of the green-tailed sunbird, both unique to Doi Inthanon – as well as, near the summit, the only red rhododendrons in Thailand and a wide variety of ground and epiphytic orchids. The waterfalls, birds and flowers are at their best in the cool season, but night-time temperatures sometimes drop below freezing, making warm clothing a must.

Wat Phra That Si Chom Thong
Chom Thong, 58km southwest of Chiang Mai on Highway 108

The gateway to the park is **CHOM THONG**, a market town with little to offer apart from the attractive **Wat Phra That Si Chom Thong**, whose impressive brass-plated chedi dates from the fifteenth century. The nearby bo tree has become an equally noteworthy architectural feature: dozens of Dalí-esque supports for its sagging branches have been sponsored by the devoted in the hope of earning merit. Inside the renovated sixteenth-century viharn, a towering, gilded *ku* housing a Buddha relic (supposedly from the right side of his skull) just squeezes in beneath the ceiling, from which hangs a huge, sumptuous red-and-green umbrella. Weaponry, gongs, umbrellas, thrones and an elephant-tusk arch carved with delicate Buddha images all add to the welcoming clutter. The temple is also famous for its meditation retreats (see p.51).

The main waterfalls
Four sets of waterfalls provide the main roadside attractions along Route 1009 from Chom Thong to the park headquarters: overrated **Mae Klang Falls**, 8km in, which with its picnic areas and food vendors gets overbearingly crowded at weekends; **Vachiratharn Falls**, the park's most dramatic, with a long, misty drop down a granite escarpment 11km beyond; **Sirithan Falls**, which looks like a smaller version of Vachiratharn and is just a couple of kilometres further up the hill; and finally the twin cascades of **Siriphum Falls**, backing the park headquarters a further 9km on. With your own wheels you could reach a fifth and much more beautiful cataract, **Mae Ya**, which is believed to be the highest in Thailand – the winding, 14km paved track to it heads west off Route 1009, 2km north of Highway 108.

The chedis
11km beyond the headquarters

For the most spectacular views in the park, continue 11km beyond the headquarters along the summit road to the sleek, twin chedis looming incongruously over the misty green hillside: on a clear day you can see the mountains of Myanmar to the west from here. Built by the Royal Thai Air Force, the chedis commemorate the sixtieth birthdays of the Thai king and queen; the king's monument, **Napamaytanidol Chedi** (1987), is brown to the more feminine lilac of the queen's **Napapolphumsiri Chedi** (1992).

Kew Mae Pan Trail
Trailhead a short way up the summit road from the chedis • 2hr; open Nov–May • B200 for compulsory guide

Starting a short distance up the road from the chedis is the rewarding **Kew Mae Pan Trail**. This circular walk wanders through sun-dappled forest and open savanna as it skirts the steep western edge of Doi Inthanon, where violent-red epiphytic rhododendrons (in bloom Dec–Feb) are framed against open views over the canyoned headwaters of the Pan River, when the weather allows. To do this walk, you have to hire a local Karen or Hmong guide at the trailhead.

The summit and around

Doi Inthanon's **summit** (2565m), 6km beyond the chedis, is a big disappointment – from the car park you can see little beyond the radar installation. For many people, after a quick shiver and a snapshot in front of a board proclaiming this the highest point in Thailand, it's time to hop in the car and get back to warmer climes. A small, still-revered stupa behind this board contains the ashes of King Inthanon of Chiang Mai (after whom the mountain was renamed): at the end of the nineteenth century he was the first to recognize the importance of this watershed area in supplying the Ping River and ultimately the Chao Phraya, the queen of Thailand's rivers. A hundred metres back down the road, it's an easy stroll along a raised walkway to the bog known as **Ang Ka** (Crow's Pond), which is the highest source of these great waterways and one of the park's best bird-watching sites. The cream and brown sphagnum mosses that spread underfoot, the dense ferns that hang off the trees and the contorted branches of rhododendrons give the place a creepy, primeval atmosphere.

The Mae Chaem road

Around 7km after it turns off the main summit road, the paved **Mae Chaem road** skirts yet another set of waterfalls: look for a steep road to the right, leading down to a ranger station and, just to the east, the dramatic long drop of **Huai Sai Luaeng Falls**. A 2.5km circular walking trail from the ranger station takes in **Mae Pan Falls**, a series of short cascades in a peaceful, shady setting.

ARRIVAL AND DEPARTURE   DOI INTHANON NATIONAL PARK

The main road through the park, Route 1009, turns west off Highway 108, 1km north of the gateway town of Chom Thong, winding generally northwestwards for 48km to the top of Doi Inthanon, passing the park headquarters about 30km in. A second paved road forks left 10km before the summit, affording breathtaking views as it helter-skelters down for 20km to the sleepy, riverside weaving village of Mae Chaem, southwest of the park.

By bus Frequent non-a/c blue buses to Chom Thong from Chiang Mai's Chang Puak bus station can be picked up at the southern end of Thanon Phra Pokklao (Chiang Mai Gate). At Chiang Mai Gate, it should also be possible to pick up a yellow songthaew (slower and only slightly cheaper) for the journey to Chom Thong. Once there, you can charter a whole songthaew or a/c minibus to explore the park for around B1000–1500 for the day.
By motorbike or jeep You could do the park justice in a day with an early start from Chiang Mai, or treat it as the

first stage of a longer trip to Mae Hong Son: from Mae Chaem, either follow Route 1088 south to pick up Highway 108 again towards Mae Sariang, 25km west of Hot; or take Route 1088 north then Route 1263 west through remote countryside, joining Highway 108 just north of Khun Yuam.
With a tour Most tour operators in Chiang Mai (see p.287) offer day-trips to the national park (around B1500–3000/person, depending on group size) – if you don't have your own transport, this is the easiest way to visit.

INFORMATION

Park information For information on the park, stop at the visitor centre 1km beyond the Mae Klang checkpoint, or at the park headquarters, a further 22km on.
Birding information Two hundred metres beyond the headquarters on the left-hand side of Route 1009, at Mr

Daeng's Birds Visitor Centre (☎053 286731–2 or ☎081 884 8108, ⊛mrdeang.com), bird-watchers can consult a useful logbook of recent sightings, pick up a simple, photocopied map of birding sites, or hire a guide for B1000–3000/day for up to five people.

ACCOMMODATION AND EATING

In the daytime, **food stalls** operate at Mae Klang, Vachiratharn and Mae Ya falls, while the **restaurants** beside the park headquarters and at the Birds Visitor Centre are open daytime and evening. The following places are listed in order of distance from the park's headquarters.

National park bungalows ☎053 286730, ⊛dnp .go.th. Park accommodation comes in standard log-cabin or concrete varieties, with electricity, mattresses or beds

and bedding. Three- to 23-berth bungalows, set among dense stands of pine near the headquarters, have hot-water bathrooms, while simpler, fifteen-person bungalows at Huai Sai Luaeng Falls cost B1500/night. Accommodation is often fully booked at weekends and national holidays, but at other times you should be OK to turn up on the day. B1000–6500

Birds Visitor Centre 200m west of the headquarters on Route 1009 ☎053 286732 or ☎081 884 8108, ⓦmrdeang.com. Uncle Daeng offers pleasant, colourful, tile-floored rooms with hot water and TV at his Birds Visitor Centre (see p.331). B500

National park camping Camping, an often chilly

alternative, is permitted on a site about 500m from the park headquarters and another site at Huai Sai Luaeng Falls. Two- to three-person tents can be rented at headquarters for B225/night (bedding extra).

Little Home Guest House & Restaurant 7km from Chom Thong along the main park road ☎053 033555, ⓦlittlehomeinthanonresort.com. This cutesy place has clean, well-maintained, fan or a/c bungalows and rooms with hot-water bathrooms. Fan B800, a/c B1000

West towards Mae Sariang

Heading south from Chom Thong, the road flattens out a little, passing dusty and seldom-visited weaving villages as it follows the Ping River downstream. Just after Hot the road bends west, climbing up once again towards the **Ob Luang Gorge National Park**, where attractions include whitewater rafting down the Chaem River.

Pa-Da Cotton Textile Museum

On the east side of Highway 108 between kilometre-stones 68 and 69, in Ban Rai Pai Ngarm ☎053 361231 • Daily roughly 8am–5pm • Free • All buses between Chiang Mai and Hot or Mae Sariang pass Ban Rai Pai Ngarm

Among several weaving villages to the south of Chom Thong, the **Pa-Da Cotton Textile Museum** at Ban Rai Pai Ngarm is well worth a look; it's reached down a beautiful avenue of bamboo trees. The museum is dedicated to the work of Saeng-da Bansiddhi, a local woman who started a cooperative practising traditional dyeing and weaving techniques using only natural products and was made a National Artist in 1986. Saeng-da died in 1993, and the museum, which displays some of her personal effects as well as looms, fabrics and plants used in dyeing, was established to honour her efforts to revive these disappearing skills. It's situated on the upper floor of a large wooden building, while on the ground floor weavers can be seen busy at work (not Thurs). Lovely bolts of cloth and a small range of clothes and scarves in earthy and pastel colours are on sale at reasonable prices.

Ob Luang Gorge National Park

17km west of Hot on Highway 108 • B200 • ☎053 315302, ⓦdnp.go.th

Weaving through pretty wooded hills up the valley of the Chaem River for 17km from Hot will bring you to **Ob Luang Gorge National Park**, which is billed with wild hyperbole as "Thailand's Grand Canyon". A wooden bridge over the short, narrow channel lets you look down on the Chaem River bubbling along between sheer walls 30m below. The park is also tagged "Land of Prehistoric Human" because of the discovery of Bronze Age graves here, containing seashell bracelets and other decorative items, as well as rock paintings of elephants and human figures. Upstream from the bridge near the park headquarters, you can relax at the roadside food stalls and swim in the river when it's not too fast. At the headquarters you can arrange hour-long 5km **whitewater-rafting** trips in the cool season on the river's class II–III rapids (from B1800 for four people up to B2500 for eight, including guides, transport, life jackets and helmets; ☎093 242 3458 or ☎089 263 5055).

West of Ob Luang, the highway gradually climbs through pine forests, the road surface bad in patches and the countryside becoming steeper and wilder.

ARRIVAL AND DEPARTURE   **OB LUANG GORGE NATIONAL PARK**

By bus Buses travelling between Chiang Mai and Mae Sariang pass by the park headquarters, as do buses travelling between Bangkok and Mae Hong Son.

3

ACCOMMODATION

National park bungalows ☎ 053 315302, ⊛ dnp.go.th. There are a few large bungalows with three bedrooms and two bathrooms with hot water, sleeping ten people, in which you can usually rent a room for two. Bungalow B2100,

room B700

Campsite The shady riverbank shelters a campsite; you can rent a two- to three-person tent for B225 (bedding extra).

Mae Sariang and around

After its descent into the broad, smoky valley of the Yuam River, Highway 108's westward progress ends at **MAE SARIANG**, 191km from Chiang Mai, a quietly industrious market town showing a marked Burmese influence in its temples and rows of low wooden shophouses. Halfway along the southern route between Chiang Mai and Mae Hong Son, this is an obvious place for a stopover. From here you can make an intriguing day-trip to the trading post of **Mae Sam Laeb** on the border with Myanmar and out onto the Salween River.

Soaking up the atmosphere is the main activity in this border outpost, which is regularly visited by local hill tribes and dodgy traders from Myanmar. If you want something more concrete to do, stroll around a couple of temples off the north side of the main street, whose Burmese features provide a glaring contrast to most Thai temples. The first, **Wat Si Boonruang**, sports a fairytale castle of a bot with an intricate, tiered, corrugated roof in green and white piled high above. Topped with lotus buds, the unusual *sema* stones, which delineate the bot's consecrated area, look like old-fashioned street bollards. The open viharns here and next door at **Wat Utthayarom** (aka Wat Jong Sung) are mounted on stilts, with broad teak floors that are a pleasure to get your feet onto. Both wats enshrine Burmese-style Buddhas, white and hard-faced.

Mae Sam Laeb

46km southwest of Mae Sariang and accessible by hourly songthaews from the market in the morning (1hr 30min)

MAE SAM LAEB lies on the mighty Salween (or Salawin) River, which, having descended from Tibet through Myanmar, forms the Thai–Burmese border for 120km here, before emptying into the Andaman Sea. The village is little more than a row of bamboo stores and restaurants, but with its Thai, Chinese, Karen and Burmese inhabitants, it has a classic frontier feel about it. The best way to get a feel for Mae Sam Laeb's relaxed vibe is to sign up for one of the highly recommended **boat trips** organized by Tukta at *Northwest Guest House* in Mae Sariang (B1500/person, based on a group of four, including transport from Mae Sariang). The boat cruises down the Salween through

MAE SARIANG

▲ Khun Yuam & Mae Hong Son

Yuam River

Bus Terminal

Wat Utthayarom   Wat Si Boonruang

THANON WIANG MAI

THANON LAENG PHANIT

◄ Mae Sam Laeb

1194

THANON WAI SEUKSA

THANON MAE SARIANG

Police Station

N

105

Mae Sariang River

Chiang Mai ►

▼ Mae Sot

0   250
metres

■ ACCOMMODATION	
Mae Loegyi	5
Northwest Guest House	3
River Bank Guest House	1
River House Hotel	2
River House Resort	4

● RESTAURANTS	
Intira	2
Sawatdee	1

TREKS AND TOURS FROM MAE SARIANG

Mae Sariang's location close to the Burmese border makes it an ideal base for exploring some lesser-travelled areas. The centrally located *Northwest Guest House* organizes local **tours**, such as **boat trips** on the Salween River (see opposite) and three-day **treks** into the wild countryside along the Burmese border (B2500/person based on a group of two; cheaper in a larger group), including 4–5hr of walking a day and visits to waterfalls (not in the hot season) and hot springs. The friendly and helpful owner, Tukta, can arrange visits or several days of volunteering in a rural school between Mae Sariang and Sop Moei and can organize trips to suit your needs.

idyllic countryside for an hour to the small unspoilt Karen village of Sop Moei, right on the confluence of the Moei River with the Salween, where lunch is taken before sailing back to Mae Sam Laeb.

ARRIVAL AND DEPARTURE

MAE SARIANG

By bus Mae Sariang is on the Chiang Mai–Mae Hong Son bus route, with a/c and non-a/c buses departing from Chiang Mai's Arcade bus station, from where there are also several a/c minibuses a day. Buses from Bangkok's Northern Mo Chit terminal also pass through on the way to Mae Hong Son.

Destinations Bangkok (3 daily; 12hr); Chiang Mai (10–11 daily; 4hr); Mae Hong Son (5 daily; 4hr).
By songthaew Scenic Highway 105 up from Mae Sot (see p.258) is covered by songthaews (5–6 daily; 6hr), though the journey's really too long to make on a rattling bench seat.

GETTING AROUND

By bicycle or motorbike Bicycles (B50–100/day), motorbikes (B200) and 4WDs (B1500), handy for exploring

temples and Karen weaving villages in the surrounding Yuam valley, can be rented from *Northwest Guest House*.

ACCOMMODATION

Mae Sariang has a good range of accommodation for such a tiny town. In addition, **homestays** in a Lawa village near Mae La Noi to the north of town, where you can learn to make jewellery and weave, as well as several multi-day tours in northern Thailand, can be arranged through Thailand Hilltribe Holidays (☎085 548 0884, ⓦ thailandhilltribeholidays.com).

Mae Loegyi Thanon Wiang Mai ☎086 920 2835 or ☎089 637 8899. A little away from the riverside action, such as it is, this pleasant and welcoming place offers very clean, creeper-clad, ochre bungalows with a/c, hot showers and TVs, some with separate sitting rooms. B600
Northwest Guest House 81 Thanon Laeng Phanit ☎089 700 9928, ⓦ northwestgh.blogspot.com. Clean, friendly spot with plenty of local information and tidy, polished-wood rooms; hot-water bathrooms are either shared (fan rooms) or en suite (a/c). Fan B250, a/c B450
River Bank Guest House Thanon Laeng Phanit ☎053 682787, ⓔ riverbankmaesariang@gmail.com. Classy rooms decked out all over in golden teak and equipped with a/c, cable TV, spotless hot-water bathrooms, fridges, crisp white linen and lovely balconies overlooking

the river. B800
River House Hotel Thanon Laeng Phanit ☎053 621201, ⓦ riverhousehotels.com. Modern all-teak hotel in traditional open-plan style, where the rooms have simple, tasteful furnishings, fine river views, verandas, a/c and en-suite hot-water bathrooms. Breakfast included. B1000
River House Resort Thanon Laeng Phanit ☎053 683066, ⓦ riverhousehotels.com. Run by the owner of *River House Hotel*, this is Mae Sariang's fanciest place to stay. All rooms come with a/c, hot water, mini-bars and smart teak furnishings; some have river-view balconies, while the more expensive ones boast bathtubs, and there's also an attractive garden overlooking the river. Breakfast included. B1800

EATING AND DRINKING

Intira Thanon Wiang Mai. The locals' favourite, a slightly scruffy roadside restaurant with an a/c room, which does a good chicken with cashew nuts (B100) and some interesting local specialities such as boar in red curry. Daily 8am–8.30pm.
Sawatdee Thanon Laeng Phanit. Popular with local NGO

workers, *Sawatdee* bar-restaurant offers Thai and Isaan food, sandwiches and a few other Western dishes, on a terrace overlooking the river, with some low tables, hammocks and axe cushions for chilling out. The view is superb. For something cheap and filling, try the tasty fried rice (B40). Daily roughly 5pm–2am.

Khun Yuam

North of Mae Sariang, wide, lush valleys alternate with tiny, steep-sided glens – some too narrow for more than a single rice paddy – turning Highway 108 into a winding rollercoaster. The market town of **KHUN YUAM**, 95km from Mae Sariang, is a popular resting spot, especially for those who've taken the direct route here (Route 1263) over the mountains from Mae Chaem.

Thai–Japan Friendship Memorial Hall

Daily 8am–noon & 1–5pm • B100

The **Thai–Japan Friendship Memorial Hall**, on the left of the main thoroughfare, Thanon Rajaburana, at the north end of town, hosts a curious collection of rusting relics from the Japanese World War II occupation – old trucks, rifles, water canisters and uniforms – though there's no mention of the thousands of Thais who died building the Death Railway (see p.188), or indeed the road west from Chiang Mai to Mae Hong Son, for the Japanese. Lining the walls, hundreds of black-and-white photos document the later period of the war, when after their retreat from Myanmar in 1944, some of the Japanese rested here with the sick and wounded for two years and longer.

ACCOMMODATION AND EATING
KHUN YUAM

Ban Farang Just off Thanon Rajaburana, north of the museum and well signposted ☎ 053 622086, ⓦ banfarang-guesthouse.com. In a leafy setting on the edge of town, each of the smart, very clean rooms here has duvets and a hot-water bathroom; there are cheap dorm beds, too (B150). The restaurant serves up good Thai and Western food, at reasonable prices. Fan **B500**, a/c **B600**

The Buatong fields

Just north of Khun Yuam, Route 1263 branches off to the east over the hills towards Mae Chaem; after about 20km, a side road leads north towards Ban Mae U-Khor and the **Buatong fields** on the slopes of Doi Mae U-Khor, where Mexican sunflowers make the hillsides glow butter-yellow in November and early December. You'll often see the same flowers by the roadside at this time of year, but the sheer concentration of blooms at Mae U-Khor, combined with sweeping views over endless ridges to the west, draws dozens of tour groups in air-conditioned minibuses.

Mae Surin Waterfall

On the spur road that branches north from Route 1263 to the Buatong fields, around 15km beyond Ban Mae U-Khor • B200 • ☎ 053 061073, ⓦ dnp.go.th

Mae Surin Waterfall in Nam Tok Mae Surin National Park is arguably the most spectacular waterfall in the whole country, the waters hurtling over a cliff and plunging almost 100m before crashing on huge boulders and foaming down a steep gorge. The kind topography of the region allows a great view of the falls from directly in front, but the best view, from below, requires a steep and at times precarious three-hour hike down and back from the park's well-appointed campsite.

Mae Ko Vafe and Ban Pha Bong

Back on Highway 108, 35km north of Khun Yuam, a right turn leads up to **Mae Ko Vafe** – a Thai rendition of "microwave", referring to the transmitters that grace the mountain's peak; the paved road climbs for 10km to a Hmong village, where the fantastic view west stretches far into Myanmar. Around 15km beyond this turn-off, Highway 108 climbs to a roadside **viewing area**, with fine vistas, this time to the east, of the sheer, wooded slopes and the Pha Bong Dam in the valley far below. Subsequently the road makes a dramatic, headlong descent towards Mae Hong Son, passing the **Ban Pha Bong** hot springs,

7km north of the viewing area (11km before Mae Hong Son). These have been turned into a small spa complex with hot spring-water baths, traditional masseurs, private treatment rooms and a restaurant.

Mae Hong Son and around

MAE HONG SON, capital of Thailand's northwestern-most province, sports more nicknames than a town of ten thousand people seems to deserve. In Thai, it's Muang Sam Mok, the "City of Three Mists": set deep in a mountain valley, Mae Hong Son is often swathed in mist, the quality of which differs according to the three seasons (in the hot season it's mostly composed of unpleasant smoke from burning fields). In former times, the town, which wasn't connected to the outside world by a paved road until 1968, was known as "Siberia" to the troublesome politicians and government officials who were exiled here from Bangkok. Nowadays, thanks to its mountainous surroundings, it's increasingly billed as the "Switzerland of Thailand": eighty percent of Mae Hong Son province is on a slope of more than 45 degrees.

3

● RESTAURANTS & CAFÉS
Alawaa	6
Ban Pleng	8
Fern	7
Kai Mook	3
Khai Kata Restaurant	1
Khao Soi Panoon	2
Salween River	4
Sunflower	5

■ BAR
Crossroads	1

■ ACCOMMODATION
Baiyoke Chalet	7
Fern Resort	12
Friend House	4
Imperial Mae Hong Son Resort	11
Johnnie House	5
Mountain Inn	10
Pana Huts	1
Pen Porn House	6
Piya Guest House	8
The Residence	3
Romtai House	9
Sang Tong Huts	2

MAE HONG SON

0   250
metres

3

"LONG-NECK" WOMEN

The most famous – and notorious – of the Mae Hong Son area's spectacles is its contingent of **"long-neck" women**, members of the tiny **Kayan Lahwi** tribe of Myanmar (sometimes called Padaung) who have come across to Thailand to escape Burmese repression. Though the women's necks appear to be stretched to 30cm and more by a column of brass rings, the "long-neck" tag is a technical misnomer: a *National Geographic* team once X-rayed one of the women and found that instead of stretching out her neck, the pressure of eleven pounds of brass had simply squashed her collarbones and ribs. Girls of the tribe start wearing the rings from about the age of 6, adding one or two each year up to the age of 16 or so. Once fastened, the rings are generally for life, for to remove a full stack may eventually cause the collapse of the neck and suffocation – in the past, removal was a punishment for adultery.

The **origin** of the ring-wearing ritual remains unclear, despite an embarrassment of plausible explanations. Kayan Lahwi legend says that the mother of their tribe was a dragon with a long, beautiful neck, and that their unique custom is an imitation of her. Tour guides will tell you the practice is intended to enhance the women's beauty. In Myanmar, where the practice is now discouraged, it's variously claimed that ring-wearing arose out of a need to protect women from tiger attacks or to deform the wearers so that the Burmese court would not kidnap them for concubines.

In spite of their handicap (they have to use straws to drink, for example), the women are able to carry out some kind of an ordinary life: they can marry and have children, and they're able to weave and sew, although these days they spend most of their time posing like circus freaks for photographs. Only half of the Kayan Lahwi women now lengthen their necks; left to follow its own course, the custom would probably die out, but the influence of **tourism** may well keep it alive for some time yet. The villages in Mae Hong Son, and now also in Chiang Mai and Chiang Rai provinces, where they live, are set up by Thai entrepreneurs as a money-making venture (visitors are charged B250–500 to enter these villages). At least, contrary to many reports, the "long necks" are not held as slaves: they are each paid a very basic wage of about B1500 per month, supplemented by whatever they can make selling handicrafts to tourists. However, their plight as refugees is certainly precarious and vulnerable; those in Mae Hong Son are in theory allowed to move around the province, but those in Chiang Mai and Chiang Rai are confined to their villages.

To match the hype, Mae Hong Son has become a hugely popular destination, sporting, alongside dozens of backpacker guesthouses, several upmarket hotels and resorts for Thai and farang tourists. Many visitors come here for **trekking** in the beautiful countryside, others just for the cool climate and lazy upcountry atmosphere. The town is still small enough and sleepy enough to hole up in for a quiet week, though in the high season (Nov–Feb) swarms of minibuses disgorge tour groups who hunt in packs through the souvenir stalls and fill up the restaurants. At this time of year, lakeside Thanon Pradit Jongkham and the small road that runs up to the post office become a pedestrianized "walking street" in the evening, allowing vendors to sell souvenirs, handicrafts and clothes and to serve food at low tables on the waterfront.

Running north to south, Mae Hong Son's main drag, **Thanon Khunlumprapas**, is intersected by Thanon Singhanat Bamrung at the traffic lights in the centre of town. Beyond the typical concrete boxes in the centre, Mae Hong Son sprawls lazily across the valley floor and up the lower slopes of Doi Kong Mu to the west, trees and untidy vegetation poking through at every possible opportunity to remind you that open country is only a stone's throw away.

Brief history

Mae Hong Son was founded in 1831 as a training camp for elephants captured from the surrounding jungle for the princes of Chiang Mai (Jong Kham Lake, in the southeastern part of the modern town, served as the elephants' bathing spot). The hard work of hunting and rearing the royal elephants was done by the **Thai Yai** (aka Shan), who account for half the population of the province and bring a strong Burmese flavour to

Mae Hong Son's temples and festivals. The other half of the province's population is made up of various hill tribes (a large number of Karen, as well as Lisu, Hmong and Lawa), with a tiny minority of Thais concentrated in the provincial capital. The latest immigrants to the province are **Burmese refugees** (see box, p.261), based in camps between Mae Hong Son and the border, who generally do not encourage visitors as they've got quite enough on their plates without having to entertain onlookers.

Wat Chong Kham

Towards the southeast of the town centre, just south of the lake

Mae Hong Son's classic picture-postcard view – either by day or when illuminated at night – is its twin nineteenth-century Burmese-style temples, Wat Chong Kham and Wat Chong Klang, from the opposite, north, shore of Jong Kham Lake (Nong Jong Kham), their gleaming white and gold chedis and the multi-tiered roofs and spires of their viharns reflected in the water. In the viharn of **Wat Chong Kham** is a huge, intricately carved sermon throne, decorated with the *dharmachakra* (Wheel of Law) in coloured glass on gold; the building on the left has been built around the temple's most revered Buddha image, the benign, inscrutable Luang Pho To.

Wat Chong Klang

Next to Wat Chong Kham, just south of the lake

Wat Chong Klang, the other of the two lakeside temples, is famous for its paintings on glass, which are said to have been painted by artists from Mandalay more than a hundred years ago; they're displayed over three walls on the left-hand side of the viharn. The first two walls behind the monks' dais (on which women are not allowed to stand) depict *Jataka* stories from the Buddha's previous incarnations in their lower sections, and the life of the Buddha himself in their upper, while the third wall is devoted entirely to the Buddha's life. A room to the left houses an unforgettable collection of **teak statues**, brought over from Myanmar in the middle of the nineteenth century. The dynamically expressive, often humorous figures are characters from the *Vessantara Jataka*, but the woodcarvers have taken as their models people from all levels of traditional Burmese society, including toothless emaciated peasants, butch tattooed warriors and elegant upper-class ladies.

Mae Hong Son Living Museum Co-ordination Centre

Thanon Singhanat Bamrung • Daily 8.30am–4.30pm

It's well worth calling in on the **Mae Hong Son Living Museum Co-ordination Centre**, the welcoming information office for an interesting project to open up Mae Hong Son as a living cultural showcase – not least because, at the time of visiting, they were about to open an on-site museum devoted to the hill tribes. You'll certainly get some useful information (and a map) about good local restaurants and about the remaining examples of Thai Yai teak architecture in town.

The morning market

Between Thanon Nivetpisarn and Thanon Panishwattana • Daily from dawn until around 9am

The town's vibrant, smelly **morning market** is worth dragging your bones up at dawn to see. People from the local hill tribes often come down to buy and sell, and the range of produce is particularly weird and wonderful, including, in season, porcupine meat, displayed with quills to prove its authenticity.

Wat Hua Wiang

Thanon Panishwattana

The many-gabled viharn of 150-year-old **Wat Hua Wiang** shelters, under a lace canopy, one of the most beautiful Buddha images in northern Thailand, the **Chao Palakeng**. Copied from a famous statue in Mandalay, the strong, serene bronze has the regal clothing and dangling ears typical of Burmese Buddhas.

TOURS AND TREKKING AROUND MAE HONG SON

Once you've exhausted the few obvious sights in town, the first decision you'll have to grapple with is whether to visit one of the three villages of "long-neck" women around Mae Hong Son (see p.338). Our advice is don't: they're effectively human zoos for snap-happy tourists, offering no opportunity to discover anything about Kayan culture. Less controversially, the roaring **Pha Sua Falls** and the villages of **Mae Aw** and **Ruam Thai** to the north of town make a satisfying day out. Other feasible targets include the hot springs at **Ban Pha Bong** (see p.336) and, further out, **Mae Surin Waterfall** (see p.336) and **Tham Lot** (see p.344). If all that sounds too easy, Mae Hong Son is Thailand's third-largest centre for **trekking**.

There's no getting away from the fact that trekking up and down Mae Hong Son's steep inclines is tough, though the scenery is magnificent. Most of the hill-tribe villages here are Karen, interspersed with indigenous Thai Yai (Shan) settlements in the valleys. Heading east, where many villages are very unspoilt, having little contact with the outside world, is preferable to the more populous, less traditional west; to the southeast, you'll be able to visit Hmong and Karen, to the northeast, Lisu also. In the latter direction, if you're very hardy, you might want to consider the five- to six-day routes to Soppong or Pai, which have the best scenery of the lot. About a dozen guesthouses and travel agencies in Mae Hong Son run multi-day treks, on which guides can often build a camp of natural materials while overnighting in the forest.

Chakraphan (Chan) Prawinchaikul ☎ 053 611040 or ☎ 089 552 6899, ⓦ trekkingthailand.com. Chan is a highly recommended, currently independent guide, who speaks good English, specializes in flowers and insects and offers everything up to a six-day trek to Pai (one-day treks from B1500/person).

Rose Garden Tours 86/4 Thanon Khunlumprapas ☎ 053 611681, ⓦ rosegarden-tours.com. A reliable company for guided tours around the area, with day-long excursions starting from B900. For a standard one-day trek, including bamboo-rafting on the Pai River, elephant riding and a relatively easy 3hr walk, Rose

Garden charges B1450/person (cheaper in a big group).
Tour Merng Tai 89 Thanon Khunlumprapas ☎ 053 611979, ⓦ tourmerngtai.com. Among a wide variety of trips, including cycling tours around town, Tour Merng Tai offers several community-based tourism programmes, employing village guides and cooks and contributing part of the profits to local communities. They're mostly one-day treks, visiting Lahu, Thai Yai and Karen villages (from B1700/person, including 4WD transport where necessary, English-speaking guide and lunch), though longer treks and homestays are possible.

Wat Doi Kong Mu

On the hill to the west of town

For a godlike overview of the area, drive or climb up to **Wat Doi Kong Mu** on the steep hill to the west. From the temple's two chedis, which enshrine the ashes of respected nineteenth-century Thai Yai monks, you can look down on the town and out across the sleepy farming valley north and south. Behind the chedis, the viharn contains an unusual and highly venerated white marble image of the Buddha, surrounded in gold flames. If you've got the energy, trek up to the bot on the summit, where the view extends over the Burmese mountains to the west.

Pha Sua Falls, Mae Aw and Ban Ruam Thai

North of Mae Hong Son: if driving yourself, turn left off Route 1095 10km north of town, following signposts for Pha Sua

North of Mae Hong Son, a trip to **Pha Sua Falls** and the border villages of **Mae Aw** and **Ruam Thai** takes in some spectacular and varied countryside. Your best options are to rent a vehicle or join a tour (B900–1200/person for a one-day excursion, including a visit to the highly overrated Fish Cave). With your own wheels, you can stop off en route at the Phu Klon Country Club (☎ 053 282579, ⓦ phuklon.co.th), more commonly known as the **mud spa**, where you can get a face or body mask or bathe in the hot spring water.

Pha Sua Falls

About 20km from the turn-off from Route 1095 you'll reach **Pha Sua Falls**, a wild, untidy affair, which crashes down in several cataracts through a dark overhang cut in the limestone. The waterfall is in full roar in October after the rainy season, but has plenty of water all year round. Take care when swimming, as several people have been swept to their deaths here.

Mae Aw

Above the falls the paved road climbs precipitously, giving glorious, broad vistas of both Thai and Burmese mountains, before reaching the unspectacular half-Hmong, half-Thai Yai village of **Naphapak** after 11km. From here, a largely flat stretch of tarmac (built by the Thai military to help the fight against the opium trade) heads north for 7km to **MAE AW** (aka Ban Rak Thai), a settlement of Kuomintang anti-Communist Chinese refugees (see p.362), right on the Burmese border. The tight ring of hills around the village heightens the feeling of being in another country: delicate, bright-green tea bushes line the slopes, while Chinese ponies wander past long, unstilted bamboo houses. In the central marketplace on the north side of the village reservoir, shops sell great bags of Oolong and Chian Chian teas, as well as dried mushrooms.

Ban Ruam Thai

Heading 6km west from Naphapak along a fairly rough paved road, you'll come to **BAN RUAM THAI**, a Thai Yai settlement where a royal project has had a lot of success in substituting coffee for opium. At the western end of the village lies **Pang Oung**, a large reservoir surrounded by pine-clad slopes that's very popular with Thai tourists and has been dubbed "Switzerland in Mae Hong Son" – the locals have even put bells on their cows.

ARRIVAL AND DEPARTURE

MAE HONG SON

By plane Mae Hong Son airport is close to the centre (about B60 in a tuk-tuk), towards the northeast of town. Kan Airlines runs direct flights from and to Chiang Mai three or four times a day (35min).

By bus Buses to Mae Hong Son (most of which are a/c) depart from Chiang Mai's Arcade bus station, travelling mostly via Mae Sariang or via Pai. Daily buses also run from Mae Sariang and, to meet tourist demand, there are also regular a/c minibuses from Chiang Mai and Pai. Minibuses coming into Mae Hong Son via Pai go past the *Crossroads* bar, so ask the driver to drop you there if you're staying in town. From the new bus station, tuk-tuks run north into the centre for about B60.

Destinations Bangkok (2–3 daily; 16hr); Chiang Mai (hourly; 6–8hr); Mae Sariang (5 daily; 4hr); Pai (hourly; 3–4hr).

POY SANG LONG

Mae Hong Son's most famous and colourful festival is **Poy Sang Long**, held over the first weekend of April, which celebrates the ordination into the monkhood, for the duration of the schools' long vacation, of Thai Yai boys between the ages of 7 and 14. Similar rituals take place in other northern Thai towns at this time, but the Mae Hong Son version is given a unique flavour by its Thai Yai elements. On the first day of the festival, the boys have their heads shaved and are anointed with turmeric and dressed up in the colours of a Thai Yai prince, with traditional accessories: long white socks, plenty of jewellery, a headcloth decorated with fresh flowers, a golden umbrella and heavy face make-up. They are then announced to the guardian spirit of the town and taken around the temples. The second day brings general merry-making and a spectacular **parade**, headed by a drummer and a richly decorated riderless horse, which is believed to carry the town's guardian spirit. The boys, still in their finery, are each carried on the shoulders of a chaperone, accompanied by musicians and bearers of traditional offerings. In the evening, the novices tuck into a sumptuous meal, waited on by their parents and relatives, before the ordination ceremony in the temple on the third day.

GETTING AROUND

Local transport, in the form of songthaews from the north side of the morning market, is thinly spread and unreliable, so for all excursions it's best to rent your own vehicle or join an organized tour through your guesthouse or one of the many travel agents in town.

By motorbike or four-wheel drive PA Motor on Thanon Pradit Jongkham opposite *Friend House* (see below) rents out motorbikes for B150/day, as well as cars and 4WDs from B1500.

By bicycle The internet shop next to Bangkok Bank on Thanon Khunlumprapas (☎ 084 372 3515) rents out bikes for around B100/day.

INFORMATION

Tourist information The TAT office is on Thanon Ratchathumpitak, towards the northeast of the city centre (daily 8.30am–4.30pm; ☎ 053 612982–3, ⓦ travelmae hongson.org).

ACCOMMODATION

Mae Hong Son has a healthy roster of **guesthouses**, many of them being good-value, rustic affairs built of bamboo or wood and set in their own quiet gardens; most huddle together around Jong Kham Lake or spread themselves out on the northern slopes of Doi Kong Mu on the northwestern edge of town, which greatly adds to their scenic appeal. If you've got a little more money to spend, you can get out into the countryside to one of several self-contained **resorts**, though staying at most of these is not exactly a wilderness experience – they're really designed for weekending Thais travelling by car. Finally, several **upmarket hotels** have latched onto the area's meteoric development, offering all the usual international-standard facilities.

Baiyoke Chalet Thanon Khunlumprapas, just across from the post office ☎ 053 613132–9, ⓦ baiyokehotel .com. The standard rooms here are small and simple, with plain white walls, bedside lamps, a desk, a mini-bar, TV, a/c and hot shower. Upgrading to a superior room buys you much more space, plus a balcony overlooking a topiary-filled courtyard. Breakfast included. B1380

★**Fern Resort** 6km south of town on Highway 108, then signposted 2km east on a paved minor road ☎ 053 686110–1, ⓦ fernresort.info. By far the best resort around Mae Hong Son, this eco-friendly and sustainable place employs local villagers as much as possible. In a peaceful, shady valley, a brook runs through the beautiful, spacious grounds, past rice fields and stylish, large cottages with hot water, a/c and verandas (no phones or TV). There's an attractive swimming pool, nature trails in the surrounding Mae Surin National Park and mountain bikes for guests' use; free pick-ups from town and regular free shuttle buses to the *Fern Restaurant* in town. Breakfast included. B2500

Friend House 20 Thanon Pradit Jongkham ☎ 053 620119. Decent, clean, modern teak-and-concrete house with upstairs balcony giving views of the lake. Larger rooms have hot-water bathrooms, smaller ones share hot showers and have mattresses on the floor. B200

Imperial Mae Hong Son Resort 149 Moo 8, Tambon Pang Moo ☎ 053 684444–5, ⓦ imperialhotels.com. On the south side of the town by the turn-off for Huai Deua, this low-rise building is set in pretty, sloping landscaped gardens, overlooked by spacious, bright rooms featuring satellite TV, balconies and mini-bars; there's a large swimming pool, sauna and fitness centre, too. Breakfast included. B2175

Johnnie House Thanon U-Domchaonitesh ☎ 053 611667. In a small compound near the lake, this clean, friendly place has airy rooms, sharing hot showers, in a nice, old, wooden house, as well as bright, concrete affairs with en-suite hot-water bathrooms. B200

Mountain Inn 112 Thanon Khunlumprapas ☎ 053 611802–3, ⓦ mhsmountaininn.com. Large, neat and tasteful rooms with a/c, hot-water bathrooms, carpeting, mini-bars and TVs, set round a flower-strewn garden and swimming pool. Look out for the stencilled wall art and quirky smiling statues in the lobby. B1800

Pana Huts Signposted 300m south off Thanon Makkasandi ☎ 053 614331 or ☎ 086 772 8502, ⓦ panahuts.com. Congenial spot in a quiet, lush valley in the shadow of Doi Kong Mu that feels a lot further from town than it actually is. Made from woven bamboo, the rooms and bungalows have well-equipped hot-water bathrooms, mosquito nets and nice touches like pot plants and bedside lights. B600

Pen Porn House 16/1 Thanon Padungmuaytaw ☎ 053 611577. The smart, clean and well-maintained rooms at this motel-like place come with hot showers, and are set around a small, shady garden. Fan B400, a/c B500

★**Piya Guest House** 1/1 Soi 3, Thanon Khunlumprapas ☎ 053 611260, ⓔ piyaguesthouse@hotmail.com. Friendly, well-run, hotel-like guesthouse, boasting large, brightly painted, clean bungalows with spacious, hot-water bathrooms and a/c in a lush garden dotted with fruit trees beside the lake. B600

The Residence 41/4 Thanon Nivetpisarn ☎ 053 614100, ⓦ theresidence-mhs.com. Tasteful three-storey guesthouse furnished throughout with golden teak.

The a/c rooms boast smart, hot-water bathrooms, crisp, white linen and duvets on the beds, mini-bars and even proper desks with reading lamps. Bicycles available to guests. B1300

Romtai House 22 Thanon Chamnansathit ☎053 612437, ⊛maehongson-romtai.com. There's a wide choice of spacious, well-kept rooms and bungalows with hot water at this tranquil place that's set around a rambling, colourful garden and a big lotus pond. B400

Sang Tong Huts Down a small lane off Thanon Makkasandi ☎053 611680, ⊛sangtonghuts.info.

Upmarket, German-run guesthouse with a cute swimming pool, offering rustic chic on a steep, jungly slope on the edge of town. Roofed with traditional, thatched *tong teung* leaves and equipped with mosquito nets on the beds, accommodation ranges from simple huts with split-bamboo walls to posh cottages with verandas, rugs and tapestries, and large, attractively tiled bathrooms with hot water. Home-baked bread, cakes and jam for breakfast, and Thai dinners, are served in a simple, open-sided seating area around an open fire. B350

EATING AND DRINKING

In addition to *Khao Soi Panoon* and the *khai kata* place listed below, you could head to the Mae Hong Son Living Museum Co-ordination Centre (see p.339) for information about other traditional restaurants favoured by locals. There's also a small, popular, takeaway-only **evening market** on Thanon Panishwattana, along from the day market, that closes around 8pm.

3

Alawaa South side of Jong Kham Lake, across from Wat Chong Klang ☎053 620688. Stylish, a/c, polished-concrete café with a small garden patio, serving good espresso coffees, teas, smoothies and cakes. Mon–Sat 9am–6pm, Sun 11am–5pm.

Ban Pleng 108/5 Thanon Khunlumprapas ☎053 612522. With its traditional roofs of *tong teung* leaves, this restaurant specializes in northern Thai and local Thai Yai dishes; try the crunchy fern salad with sesame seeds and oil (B60) or the very tasty *pla lung*, minced fish balls with tomato, garlic and ginger. Mon–Sat 9am–10pm.

Crossroads 16 Thanon Singhanat Bamrung ☎053 612500. This welcoming, aptly named bar – located at the junction of the town's two main roads – serves up Thai and Western food, including American breakfasts (B120), great shakes, good coffee and cocktails. Set in a lovely old Thai Yai teak house that's now filled with retro knick-knacks, it's a cool place to chill out in the evenings. Daily 9am–midnight.

Fern 87 Thanon Khunlumprapas ☎053 611374. Large, justly popular eating place, with a nice terrace and a good reputation for its Thai food (from B80), such as spicy coconut shoot salad and river fish with spicy mango salad. It also serves a few Thai Yai, northern Thai and Western dishes. Daily 10.30am–10pm.

Kai Mook Thanon U-Domchaonitesh. Friendly and congenial old-timer with lots of interesting menu choices: chilli dips (*nam phrik*), *lon* – a kind of chilli dip with coconut milk – and northern Thai dishes including hors d'oeuvres. The zingy peanut salad (B80; on the menu as bean salad) is tasty and refreshing. Daily 10am–10pm.

Khai Kata Just off Thanon Singhanat Bamrung, immediately inside the gate to the morning market opposite Krung Thai Bank. Mae Hong Son's best breakfast – which may well leave you asking for seconds – is the Vietnamese-style *khai kata* here (fried eggs with minced pork), served with mini-baguettes and traditional coffee. Daily 5am–1pm.

★Khao Soi Panoon Thanon Padungmuaytaw, next to Kadkam Plaza. This simple housefront restaurant does a superb version of the northern breakfast and lunch soup with egg noodles, *khao soi*, creamy and toothsome, served with either chicken or beef (B35). Daily roughly 8am–5pm.

★Salween River 23 Thanon Pradit Jongkham ☎053 613421, ⊛salweenriver.com. English- and Thai-run restaurant and bar with a book exchange. The kitchen serves up a wide variety of Western favourites (main dishes B100 and up), as well as northern Thai, Thai Yai and Burmese food (mostly B50–90), including a delicious green tea salad, and Arabica coffee produced by local hill tribes. Sells Golden Triangle Rider's good map of the Mae Hong Son loop. Daily 7.30am–10pm.

Sunflower Thanon Pradit Jongkham ⊛maehongson travel.com/sunflower. A good place for breakfast, lunch, dinner or just a drink, on a large terrace overlooking the lake and the temples behind. Home-made bread and pizzas, espresso coffees, and some tasty Thai dishes, including Lanna and Thai Yai specialities. In high season you're likely to catch some live music either here or next door at *The Meeting*. Daily roughly 8am–10pm.

DIRECTORY

ATMs and exchange You'll find an ATM just across from *Baiyoke Chalet* in the heart of town, plus several banks and exchange booths along Thanon Khunlumprapas.

Hospital Sri Sangwarn, Thanon Singhanat Bamrung ☎053 611378 or ☎053 611907.

Immigration office Thanon Khunlumprapas, north of the town centre (Mon–Fri 8.30am–4.30pm; ☎053 612106).

Pharmacy Paaset, Thanon Singhanat Bamrung.

Tourist police Thanon Singhanat Bamrung ☎053 611812 or ☎1155.

Soppong and Tham Lot

The small market town of **SOPPONG**, 68km from Mae Hong Son on Route 1095 in the district of Pang Ma Pha (which is sometimes used on signposts), gives access to the most famous of over two hundred known caves in the area, **Tham Lot**, 9km north in **BAN THAM**. Due to its proximity to Pai, Soppong has become popular for day-trippers, and now even supports several ATMs.

Tham Lot

Ban Tham, 9km north of Soppong; Thai Yai guide with lantern B150 per group (up to three people), bamboo raft B300–400 for up to three people

Turn right in Ban Tham to find the entrance to the **Tham Lot Nature Education Station**, set up to look after the cave. A short walk through the forest brings you to the entrance of Tham Lot, where the Lang River begins a 600m subterranean journey through the cave. Access to the various parts of the cave depends on the time of year and how much rain there has been, and may involve hiring a bamboo raft for some or all of your journey: for most of the year you'll need to raft from Doll to Coffin Cave, while at the driest times it may be possible to wade, and at the highest water levels it may be necessary to walk around to the exit and get to the last part, Coffin Cave, from there. Normally two hours should allow you enough time for travelling through the broad, airy tunnel, and for the main attraction, climbing up into the sweaty caverns in the roof.

The first of these, **Column Cavern**, 100m from the entrance on the right, is dominated by a 20m-high cave stalagmite snaking up towards the ceiling – be sure not to touch any of the cave formations. Another 50m on the left, bamboo ladders lead up into **Doll Cave**, which has a glistening, pure white wall and a weird red and white formation shaped like a Wurlitzer organ; deep inside, stalagmites look like dolls. Just before the vast exit from the cave, wooden ladders on the left lead up into **Coffin Cave**, named after the remains of a dozen crude log coffins discovered here, one of them preserved to its full length of 5m. Hollowed out from teak trunks about 1700 years ago, they are similar to those found in many of the region's caves: some are raised 2m off the ground by wooden supporting poles, and some still contained bones, pottery and personal effects when they were discovered. It's worth hanging round the cave's exit at sunset, when hundreds of thousands of tiny black chirruping swifts pour into the cave in an almost solid column, to find their beds for the night.

ARRIVAL AND DEPARTURE   **SOPPONG AND BAN THAM**

By bus All buses connecting Mae Hong Son with Pai and Chiang Mai pass through Soppong. From the bus stop in the centre of Soppong, it's possible to pick up a motorbike taxi (B70) or pick-up truck (B300) for the gentle run along the paved forest road to Ban Tham.

ACCOMMODATION AND EATING

SOPPONG
Little Eden Guest House A short walk east of Soppong's bus stop ☎ 053 617054, ⍟ littleeden -guesthouse.com. This tranquil spot has a variety of neat, attractive bungalows and plush rooms, each with a private hot-water bathroom. The pretty garden has an attractive swimming pool and slopes down towards the Lang River, which is flanked by a relaxing pavilion and crossed by a

---

TOURS FROM CAVE LODGE

The owners of *Cave Lodge* (see opposite) can provide plenty of useful information about Tham Lot and other robust, active **caves** that can be explored in the region (many of which they themselves discovered), and organize **guided trips** (from B600/person, including equipment and lunch). They also offer **kayaking**, including trips through Tham Lot, plus 6km of fun rapids (roughly June–Jan; from B650). Maps for self-guided walking from the lodge to local Thai Yai, Karen, Lahu and Lisu villages are available, as well as local, English-speaking guides for one-day hikes and full-on **trekking** (typically B2500 for 3 days).

suspension bridge that leads to a short loop walk through the forest. Services here include motorbike rental, and there are plenty of tours and treks on offer. **B450**

★**Soppong River Inn** At the west end of town ☏ 053 617107, ⓦ soppong.com. On this extensive, densely foliated, quiet plot you'll find a handful of cottage-style rooms, tastefully decorated and thoughtfully designed, all with hot showers, many with outdoor bathrooms and some with luxuries such as a/c, DVD players and iPod docks. As well as a good café serving Western, Thai and Thai Yai food, there's a lovely, partly thatched deck over the Pai River, which here runs swiftly through a craggy, jungly defile. Thai massage and treks available. **B700**

BAN THAM

★**Cave Lodge** On the other side of Ban Tham from the cave ☏ 053 617203, ⓦ cavelodge.com. This long-established guesthouse makes an excellent, friendly base

for exploring the area. The owners can arrange local sightseeing trips and activities (see box opposite) and there's a good range of accommodation, from dorms to wooden rooms and bungalows, some with shared hot showers and others with their own bathrooms. There's also a herbal steam sauna and a relaxing communal area around an open fire for hanging out and eating Thai, Thai Yai and Western food, including home-baked bread and muffins. Dorm **B120**, double **B300**

BAN NONG TONG

Lisu Homestay In the village of Ban Nong Tong, a 10min motorbike ride from Soppong ☏ 085 721 1575, ⓦ lisuhilltribe.com. A genuine Lisu homestay where you can go trekking, have a massage and herbal steam bath and learn the hill tribe's crafts, music, dance, massage and cooking (courses extra at B700/day). Full board per person **B300**

Pai

Set in a broad, gentle, mountain-ringed valley 43km beyond Soppong, **PAI** was once just a small-town stopover on the tiring journey to Mae Hong Son, but in recent years has established itself as a major tourist destination in its own right. There's nothing special to see here, but you can partake of all manner of outdoor activities, courses – there's even a circus school – and holistic therapies, not to mention retail therapy at the art studios, bookshops and jewellery shops. The guesthouses, out-of-town resorts and restaurants have tailored themselves to the flood of Westerners who make the journey out from Chiang Mai, some of whom settle into the town's full-on traveller culture and

PAI

Airport & Mae Hong Son

0 — 250 metres

N

THANON CHAISONGKHRAM

THANON KHETKELANG

THANON BUNGSOAN

THANON WAT NGAM

THANON RATCHADAMRONG

THANON TESARAN

Pai River

PT House
North Wheels
Wat Luang
District Office
Thom's Elephant Camp Office
Bus Station
Thai Adventure Rafting
Back Trax
Pai Cookery School
Thai Adventure Rafting
Aya Service
Wat Pa Kham
PTTM
Pai High School

Mo Paeng Falls

Tourist Police

1095

Chiang Mai

Swimming Pool, Wat Mae Yen & Hot Springs

■ ACCOMMODATION	
Breeze of Pai	4
Duang Guest House	5
Golden Hut	2
Hotel des Artists	6
Li Lu Hotel	11
Mr Jan's	9
Pai Fah Boutique Hotel	10
Pai Nai Fun	3
Pai River Corner	7
Pai Village Boutique Resort	8
The Quarter	1

● RESTAURANTS & CAFÉS		
Baan Benjarong	11	
Big's Little Café	5	
Burger House	9	
Canteen	2	
Chew Xin Jai	10	
Madame Ju Coffee	3	
Nong Beer	4	
Nong Best	1	
Som Tam Na Amphoe	6	
TTK	8	
Witching Well	7	

■ BARS	
Be-Bop	3
Edible Jazz	1
Thien Art Space	2

● SHOP	
Siam Books	1

3

PAI HOT SPRINGS, SPAS AND TRADITIONAL MASSAGE

Just because you're hundreds of kilometres from the nearest beach, that doesn't mean you can't enjoy a good soak. The Pai area is home to some natural hot springs and a clutch of decent spas, all of which offer massages.

Accessible from the minor road south from Wat Mae Yen, about 7km southeast of town (or by turning left off the main Chiang Mai road straight after the bridge over the Pai River), are some **hot springs** (B300), part of Huai Nam Dang National Park, which have one or two very hot, rough pools that aren't really up to much. Much better than the pools, however, are the nearby **spas**, which put the piped hot water from the springs to more productive use. *Pai Hotsprings Spa Resort* (☎ 053 065748, ⓦ paihotspringssparesort.com), down a side road about 1km north of the springs, has a large, shady mineral pool that's open to non-guests (B100), as well as offering various massages and accommodation with spa-water bathrooms.

Massages are available at several notable spots in town, including *Mr Jan's* guesthouse (see p.348), famous for its Thai and Burmese/Shan massages (from B150/hr) and saunas using herbs from their own garden. Having trained at the Old Medicine Hospital in Chiang Mai, the staff at Pai Traditional Thai Massage (PTTM) on Thanon Tessaban 1 (☎ 053 699121) have a good reputation for traditional massages (B180/hr), and run government-approved, three-day **massage courses** (B2500).

laidback, New-Agey feel for weeks or even months. Meanwhile, Pai is now firmly on the radar of Thai tourists, so in high season, especially on weekends when the sunflowers near Mae Hong Son are out (see p.336), the narrow through-streets get clogged with air-conditioned minibuses. It can be an odd mix, but an evening promenade along the "walking street" of Thanon Chaisongkhram, with its Thai-style galleries and gift shops in the traditional buildings at the western end and more traveller-oriented outlets to the east – plus a sprinkling of local hill-tribe people and shrouded Thai Muslims – is undoubtedly pleasant and *sanuk*.

Wat Mae Yen and the swimming pool

Fluid: daily 9am–sunset • B60 • ⓦ fluidswimmingpool.com

Several undemanding walks can be made around Pai's broad, gently sloping valley. The easiest – a round-trip of about an hour – takes you across the river bridge on the east side of town and up the hill to **Wat Mae Yen**, which commands a great view over the whole district. On the way to the wat, you'll pass Fluid, the town's large open-air 25m **swimming pool**, with food and drink available, as well as fitness equipment, a steam room and monthly pool parties.

Towards Mo Pang Falls

To the west of town, beyond Pai Hospital, the continuation of Thanon Chaisongkhram will bring you, after 3km, to **Wat Nam Hu**, supposedly founded by sixteenth-century nationalist hero, King Naresuan, and housing a Buddha image with an unusual topknot containing miraculous holy water. A kilometre further on, you'll pass the Kuomintang village of **Ban Santichon** and its Chinese theme park of thatched adobe buildings, housing tea and souvenir shops and several popular Yunnanese restaurants – which appeal mostly to Pai's many Chinese visitors. As you continue, the road gradually climbs through comparatively developed Thai Yai, Lisu and Lahu villages to **Mo Pang Falls**, with a pool for swimming, about 10km west of Pai.

ARRIVAL AND DEPARTURE   PAI

Aya Service, a travel agency on Thanon Chaisongkhram (☎ 053 699888, ⓦ ayaservice.com), offers bus (including Bangkok, Chiang Rai and visa runs to Mae Sai and Nong Khai), air and train tickets. It also organizes overnight minibuses directly to Chiang Khong, arriving in time to take the morning boat to Luang Prabang (B1750 for a through-package including the slow boat).

By plane Kan Air flies to Pai from Chiang Mai (25min) five times a week, landing at the airstrip on the north side of town.

By bus As well as public, non-a/c buses, faster, more comfortable, more expensive, hourly a/c minibuses run to Pai from both Chiang Mai and Mae Hong Son: Prempracha (☎053 064307) covers both routes, using the respective bus stations, while Aya Service (☎053 699888 in Pai, ☎053 247663 in Chiang Mai) runs from Chiang Mai only, but offers pick-ups from your accommodation.

Destinations Chiang Mai (hourly; 3–4hr); Mae Hong Son (hourly; 3–4hr); Soppong (hourly; 1hr 30min).

GETTING AROUND

By car If you're driving yourself, note that the eastern part of Thanon Chaisongkhram, the north end of Rungsiyanon and Thanon Tessaban 1 are pedestrianized, at least in the tourist season. Wat Luang on Thanon Khetkalang is a handy place to park. North Wheels on Thanon Khetkalang rents out cars (☎053 698066, ⒲northwheels.com; from B1300/day).

By motorbike taxi Yellow-vested motorbike taxis wait on Thanon Chaisongkhram opposite the bus station, but if you're staying in one of the more central guesthouses it's easy enough to walk.

By rented motorbike Aya Service, on Thanon Chaisongkhram, rents motorbikes, charging from B100/day, not including insurance, which is an extra B40–80.

By bicycle Bikes can be rented from PT House on Thanon Khetkalang (B50/day).

3

OUTDOOR ACTIVITIES AND COURSES IN PAI

Pai makes a good base for **trekking**, which can be arranged through the guesthouses or trekking agents, among which *Duang Guest House* (who can arrange one-way treks to Mae Hong Son over 5–7 days), Thai Adventure Rafting (see below) and Back Trax at 17 Thanon Chaisongkhram (☎053 699739, Ⓔbacktraxinpai@yahoo.com) are reliable. With all of these agencies, the cost starts at around B800/day (in a large group), with bamboo rafting and elephant riding extra. Thai Adventure Rafting's two-day trek, for example, heads off to friendly, hassle-free Karen and Lahu villages to the north near the Myanmar border, taking in caves and some beautiful scenery. Its one-day treks take in Lisu and Lahu villages and a three-tiered waterfall, and it also offers combination tours of one day trekking and one day rafting (from B2800/person), as well as afternoon **mountain-biking** tours (from B850/person).

As well as trekking, agencies in town can arrange bamboo-rafting, kayaking and tubing on the Pai River. Pai also offers massage courses (see opposite).

COOKERY SCHOOL

Pai Cookery School Thanon Wan Chalerm ☎081 706 3799, ⒲paicookeryschool.com. Thai cooking courses of 2hr (B500), 4hr, including a trip to the market to learn about ingredients (B750), or up to three days; vegetarians catered for.

ELEPHANT CAMP

Thom's Office in town on Thanon Runsiyanon ☎053 065778, ⒲thomelephant.com. Among several elephant camps about 5km south of town on the minor road from Mae Yen towards the hot springs, Thom's offers rides that include going into the river with the elephant and a free bathe in a hot spring pool (B1200 for 2hr, including transport from town), as well as mahout training courses (on-site accommodation is available).

WHITE-WATER RAFTING

Thai Adventure Rafting Two branches on Thanon Chaisongkhram ☎053 699111, ⒲thairafting.com (not to be confused with the imitative Pai Adventure Rafting). The reliable and experienced, French-run Thai Adventure Rafting specializes in rubber-raft trips. Heading down the Pai River to Mae Hong Son, you'll pass through gorges and sixty rapids (up to class IV) and take in waterfalls and hot springs. The full journey lasts two days, including a night at a comfortable jungle camp by the river, and costs B3500/person, though one-day trips (B1800) are also available; the season normally runs from early June to the middle of February, with the highest water from August to early September, and participants must be able to swim.

YOGA RETREAT

Xhale Yoga In Pai Resort ☎089 758 3635, ⒲xhaleyogapai.com. Certified tutor Bhud runs highly recommended, five-night yoga retreats (starting every other Mon; from B12,500 including vegetarian meals, accommodation and tuition).

INFORMATION

Events listings and maps The free, monthly, English-language *Pai Events Planner*, widely available in restaurants and guesthouses, has news about what's on. Aya Service, on Thanon Chaisongkhram, can also provide you with an excellent map of the area.

ACCOMMODATION

The streets in the centre of town teem with places to stay, and there are dozens of hotels, resorts and "treehouse retreats" in the quiet countryside around Pai. However, you'll have to put up with guesthouse owners' penchant for Pai-based puns: think *Pai in the Sky*, *Pai Chart* and so on.

CENTRAL PAI

Breeze of Pai Just off Thanon Chaisongkhram near Wat Pa Kham ☎ 081 998 4597, ⓦ facebook.com/breezeofpai. Congenial, well-maintained place with large, simple but chic, ochre bungalows and single-storey rooms with nice parquet floors and hot showers. The compound's a little crowded but lent privacy by plenty of rich foliage, enhanced by seasonal flowers and fountains. Book exchange. B800

Duang Guest House 5 Thanon Rungsiyanon ☎ 053 699101. Opposite the bus station, this is a clean and reliable place to stay, with hot showers throughout, whether shared or en suite, and a good restaurant, though it all feels a little cramped; the best rooms have a fridge and TV. Good rates for singles. B200

Golden Hut 107 Moo 3, north of Edible Jazz ☎ 053 699949. Very cheap bamboo fan rooms with shared hot showers, in a quiet garden set back from the river, or riverside bungalows on stilts. B200

Hotel des Artists (Rose of Pai) Thanon Chaisongkhram, across from Pai River Corner ☎ 053 699539, ⓦ hotelartists.com. On a corner plot near the river and centred around an attractive glass-sided living room, this stylish hotel has just fourteen bedrooms, the best of which have fantastic terraces that face out across the water. In the spacious rooms, bell-shaped lanterns illuminate the beds (which are raised off the ground on platforms made from local wood) while facilities include a/c, TVs, DVD players, and artfully tiled en-suite bathrooms. Breakfast included. B4400

Li Lu Hotel Thanon Rungsiyanon, close to the junction with Thanon Ratchadamrong ☎ 053 064351–2, ⓦ lilu hotel.com. With a sister property in Chiang Mai, this is a comfortable if slightly stark hotel in a central part of town. The plain a/c rooms have an almost industrial feel, with swathes of distressed concrete, dark wood and white paint, and the en-suite, hot-water bathrooms are sparkly clean. Facilities include a library and a chic restaurant. B1400

Mr Jan's Thanon Sukhaphibun 3 (Tessaban) ☎ 053 699554. On one of a mess of small streets behind and to the east of Thanon Chaisongkhram, these quiet, comfy concrete rooms with hot showers are set in a delightfully overgrown and fragrant medicinal herb garden. Also offers on-site sauna and massages (see p.346). B250

Pai Fah Boutique Hotel Thanon Tessaban 1 ☎ 088 409 1151, ⓦ paifahhotel.com. Terracotta-coloured walls wrapped by foliage separate this good-looking hotel from the road, creating a surprisingly quiet little enclave. Inside, the a/c rooms are small but tastefully pieced together, with spacious private bathrooms, and there are plenty of shady public areas to relax in on sunny afternoons. B900

Pai Nai Fun East bank of the river ☎ 081 641 5493, ⓦ painaifun.com. Meaning "Pai in a Dream", this spot has prime position among several resorts with bamboo bathing platforms that line the river here. The cheapest rooms are simple, thatched, bamboo A-frames sharing hot showers in the scrappy garden at the back (you'll have to fork out B900 for an A-frame with a terrace right on the riverbank). B200

■ ACCOMMODATION	
Baan Krating	1
Belle Villa	2
Mountain View	3
Spicypai	4

AROUND PAI

Pai River Corner Eastern end of Thanon Chaisongkhram, by the river ☎053 699049, ⓦpairivercorner.com. Elegant, Mediterranean-style resort with beautifully furnished, balconied rooms, some of which have their own large jacuzzi in a private courtyard, set around an attractive garden and swimming pool. Breakfast included. B3900

Pai Village Boutique Resort South off Thanon Chaisongkhram, by the river ☎053 698152, ⓦpaivillage.com. In the heart of Pai, rural simplicity – bamboo and teak huts with roofs of *tong teung* leaves, traditional sunburst-design gables and golden-teak furniture – with plenty of home comforts, including verandas and large bathrooms with hot showers and Western loos. About B500 more gets you a/c and more living space in a "Deluxe Village" bungalow. Clustered rather closely together in a lush garden strewn with ponds, but with seductive corners for sitting out. Fan B1560, a/c B2080

The Quarter Thanon Chaisongkhram, just west of Pai Hospital ☎053 699423, ⓦthequarterhotel.com. Chic luxury hotel in a central but quiet location. Set in two-storey houses around a lovely contemporary Thai garden and a smart pool with jacuzzi, the modern minimalist rooms feature distressed concrete, dark wood and splashes of dark silk, as well as DVD players. Free mountain bikes. Breakfast included. B4800

OUT OF TOWN

Baan Krating About 2km north of town on the east bank of the river, signposted to the right off the Mae Hong Son road. Set in spacious, grassy grounds with a swimming pool overlooking the river, the tasteful stilted villas are decorated with plenty of dark wood and equipped with a/c, hot showers and large verandas. They're showing their age but offer good value for the setting and facilities. B1600

Belle Villa About 1km north of town, signposted to the right off the Mae Hong Son road ☎053 698226–7, ⓦbellevillaresort.com. Elegant luxury rooms and villas on stilts, all with balconies, mini-bars and safes. Traversed by a stream and decorated with rice fields, the grounds sport two stylish pools. Breakfast included. B2850

Mountain View 500m up a side road by the tourist police at the south end of town ☎086 180 5998, ⓦthemountainviewpai.com. Laidback, old-style resort of wood and woven bamboo bungalows, some with private bathrooms and some with shared facilities, set in ten acres of hilltop land among a small arboretum of flowering trees, with a sociable campfire burning in the cool season. Call for free pick-up from the centre. Free access to Fluid swimming pool (see p.346). B200

★**Spicypai** Around 700m east of the Thanon Ratchadamrong bridge; keep right at the junctions you pass along the way and then follow the signs to the hostel ☎088 294 2004, ⓦspicyhostels.com. Ultra-cheap and ultra-sociable dorm beds with mosquito nets, in a series of lofty, stilted bamboo huts thatched with *tong teung* leaves, surrounded by vivid green paddy fields. Facilities include shared hot showers, a self-catering kitchen and lockers for your valuables, and there's a big BBQ every Saturday evening. Breakfast included. Dorm B150

EATING

Baan Benjarong South end of town on Thanon Rungsiyanon ☎053 698010. In a town where you can get everything from sushi to falafel, this is one of the few places to offer a wide variety of authentic and tasty Thai dishes – the banana-flower salad (*yam hua plee*) is especially delicious. Small, often full on busy nights (no reservations) and service can be a little begrudging. Daily approximately 11am–1.30pm & from 5pm until they get "tired", sometimes about 7.30pm.

Big's Little Café Thanon Chaisongkhram ⓦfacebook.com/bigslittlecafepai. Run by Big, who has worked as a chef in England, this tiny streetside café is renowned for its tasty and keenly priced burgers, sandwiches and Western breakfasts. Customers sit around on bar stools while their food is prepared right in front of them. A good spot for meeting other travellers. Daily roughly 9am–7pm.

Burger House Thanon Rungsiyanon ☎053 699093, ⓦburgerhousepai.com. Surprisingly tasty burgers in various forms using imported beef (B75–105), plus breakfasts and other Western dishes, in a good central location. For something different, try the tasty chicken and avocado burger (B89). Daily 8.30am–9pm.

Canteen Thanon Chaisongkhram, just beyond the Quarter Hotel ☎086 302 7672. Under a canopy of beautiful, mature lychee trees, concrete sofas and tables on a lawn around an old teak house form the setting for some tasty fusion food, such as squid with salted egg and bell peppers (B155). Mon–Sat 10am–8pm.

Chew Xin Jai On the next soi down from Thanon Ratchadamrong. Chinese vegetarian and vegan restaurant, offering tasty buffet food such as green curry with tofu on brown rice (B30) and pricier made-to-order dishes like tempura. Daily 8am–7pm.

Madame Ju Coffee Corner of Chaisongkhram and Khetkalang. One for lovers of kitsch: pink and purple walls, all manner of sentimental paintings and statuettes and a plinky-plinky soundtrack straight from a music box. Whatever the ambience, the espressos are excellent, and there's a huge range of milk and yoghurt fruit smoothies, fruit shakes, Western- and Chinese-style teas and ice cream. Daily 9am–8pm.

Nong Beer Corner of Chaisongkhram and Khetkalang ☎053 699103. One of Pai's longest-standing and most popular places for cheap eats dishing up great *khao soi*, pork satay and a wide range of buffet stir-fries and curries, including northern pork belly curry (*kaeng hang lay*). Daily 8am–9pm.

Nong Best Thanon Khetkalang, just south of Pai Flora Resort. This bare-bones restaurant with an open streetside kitchen doesn't look like much from the outside but it's justifiably very popular with locals, and you can taste why – excellent pork with basil and chillies (B50) and crispy pork with snow peas (B60). Daily 9am–9pm.

Som Tam Na Amphoe Thanon Ratchadamrong, next to Payi Resort ☎053 698087. The green papaya salad here (B30) is a must-eat for Thai visitors to Pai, served with grilled chicken (B70), or available in the Khorat version, *tam sua*, with rice noodles and crab (B60). The sign's in Thai,

but includes the phone number. Daily 10am–4.30pm.

TTK Thanon Ratchadamrong, next to TTK Guesthouse ☎053 698093. Famous for its falafel (B150 for a plate with pitta, chips, hummus and pickles) and other Middle Eastern dishes, this large, welcoming indoor-outdoor restaurant also serves reasonably priced beer, espresso coffees and Western and Middle Eastern breakfasts. Daily 8.30am–9.30pm.

★ **Witching Well** Thanon Tessaban 1, opposite Pai River Corner ⓦwitchingwellrestaurant.com. Cosy and popular, this little café-restaurant attracts free-thinking backpackers from around the world. There's a distinctly witchy theme – from the drinkable potions (herbal teas, B50) to the magical home-made cakes. Daily 8am–9.30pm.

DRINKING AND NIGHTLIFE

Several **bars** around town offer live music and DJs: as well as those listed below, look out for posters around town, which sometimes announce one-off parties too. There are also a couple of simple, open-air bars on the east bank of the river, just over the main bridge, that stay open late.

Be-Bop South end of town, beyond the junction of Khetkalang and Rungsiyanon ☎053 699128. Among a clutch of nightspots, this large, well-designed bar hosts live jazz, funk, blues and rock in the evenings (from about 10pm) and is a popular spot for travellers to congregate. Open mike Wed. Daily 8/9pm–1am.

★ **Edible Jazz** Just off Thanon Chaisongkhram near Wat Pa Kham ☎087 177 7455. This ramshackle and laid-way-back garden café and bar on a quiet, leafy lane is a mellow, sociable spot for a cheap drink. It offers an acoustic

set roughly 8.30–10.30pm and an open mike night on Sunday. Daily roughly noon–midnight.

Thien Art Space East of the Thanon Ratchadamrong bridge, just before the swimming pool. Very cool new bar-restaurant-gallery in a lovely geodesic structure, with pillars and vaulting made entirely of woven bamboo, and booths and floor cushions for chilling out. There's a good range of beers and cocktails and a mellow soundtrack – except when the live acoustic music's on (most nights). Daily 8.30am–midnight.

DIRECTORY

ATMs You'll find ATMs in the centre, on Thanon Chaisong-khram and Thanon Rungsiyanon.

Hospital Thanon Chaisongkhram ☎053 699211.

Bookshop Siam Books, Thanon Chaisongkhram (☎053

699075), has a good selection of used paperbacks.

Tourist police South end of town, on the road to Chiang Mai ☎053 611812–3 or ☎1155.

From Pai to Chiang Mai

Once out of the Pai valley, Route 1095 climbs for 35km of hairpin bends, with beautiful views north to 2175m Doi Chiang Dao near the top. In the cool season, with your own transport, you can witness – if you get started from Pai an hour before dawn – one of the country's most famous views of the sun rising over a sea of mist at **Huai Nam Dang National Park** (B300). The viewpoint is signposted on the left 30km out of Pai; take this turning and go on 6km to the park headquarters. Back on Route 1095, once over the 1300m pass, the road steeply descends the south-facing slopes in the shadow of Doi Mae Ya (2005m), before working its way along the narrow, more populous lower valleys. After 55km (at kilometre-stone 42), a left turn leads 6.5km over some stomach-churning hills to **Pong Duet hot springs**, where scalding water leaps up to 4m into the air, generating copious quantities of steam in the cool season. A few hundred metres downstream of the springs, a series of pools allows you to soak in the temperature of your choice. The last appealing detour of the route is to **Mokfa Falls** (part of Doi Suthep-Pui National Park; B100), where a cascade tumbles about 30m into a sand-fringed pool that is ideal for **swimming**, making an attractive setting for a break – it's 2km south of the main road, 76km from Pai. Finally, at **Mae Malai**, turn right onto the busy Highway 107 and join the mad, speeding traffic for the last 34km across the wide plains to Chiang Mai.

To Chiang Rai via Tha Ton

If you're coming up from Chiang Mai, the quickest and most obvious **route to Chiang Rai** is Highway 118, a fast, 185km road that swoops through rolling hill country. A much more scenic approach, however, is to follow Highway 107 and Highway 1089; a two-day trip along this route will leave you enough time for a longtail boat trip along the **Kok River** and an overnight stay in **Tha Ton**, which boasts several appealing riverside resorts and a wide variety of outdoor activities. There are other diversions en route, including the admirable **Elephant Nature Park** and a couple of good guesthouses that can arrange trekking in the countryside near **Chiang Dao**.

The Elephant Nature Park

12km beyond Mae Taeng • Full-day trip costs B2500/person • Best to book your visit online as far in advance as possible, though they have an office in Chiang Mai at 1 Thanon Ratchamanka • ☎ 053 818932, ⊚ elephantnaturepark.org

From Chiang Mai the route towards Tha Ton heads north along Highway 107, retracing the Mae Hong Son Loop as far as Mae Malai. About 3km after Mae Taeng, a signposted left turn leads 9km to the **Elephant Nature Park**, which is essentially a rescue centre and hospital for sick, orphaned and neglected elephants, but hands-on educational visits by the public are encouraged. On a daytime visit, you'll get to feed, bathe and learn about the elephants close up, but it's also possible to stay for two days or sign up as a paying volunteer for a week or longer. The park's owner, Sangduan ("Lek") Chailert, has become something of a celebrity in recent years, being featured on the BBC and in *Time* magazine for her conservation efforts. Visits must be booked in advance and include transport from and to your accommodation in Chiang Mai.

Chiang Dao

Around kilometre-stone 72, **CHIANG DAO**, which hosts an interesting hill-tribe fresh market on Tuesday mornings, stretches on and on along the old main road as the dramatic limestone crags and forests of Thailand's third-highest peak, Doi Luang Chiang Dao (or Doi Luang, "Great Mountain"; 2240m), loom up on the left. A new bypass sweeps round to the west of town, carrying traffic heading straight for Fang and Tha Ton.

Tham Chiang Dao

5km northwest of Chiang Dao, across the bypass • Daily roughly 8am–4pm • Admission to the caves is B40 and guides ask around B100 to take a group of up to four people on a roughly 30min tour • Access from Chiang Dao by yellow songthaews and motorbike taxis

An extensive complex of interconnected caverns, **Tham Chiang Dao** has an attached monastery (the caves were given religious significance by the local legend of a hermit

---

> **TREKS UP DOI LUANG CHIANG DAO**
>
> Guided treks to the **summit of Doi Luang Chiang Dao**, famous for its many rare alpine plants and birds, can be arranged by both *Malee's* and *Chiang Dao Nest* (see p.352) during the cool season, roughly from November to March. There's an altitude difference of 1100m from the trailhead to the summit: fit hikers can do it in one day (from B1000/person in a large group), though it's more pleasurable to spend two days (from B2200/person in a large group, including camping below the summit).

sage who is said to have dwelt in them for a millennium). Several of the caverns can be visited; a couple have electric light but others need the services of a guide with a lantern; guides will point out unusual rock formations and keep you on the right track – it's said the deepest parts of the cave are 12km underground, and just a few of the caverns are considered safe to visit.

ARRIVAL AND GETTING AROUND CHIANG DAO

By bus Take one of the buses from Chiang Mai's Chang Phuak bus station bound for Fang or Tha Ton. You'll need to tell the driver or ticket seller that you want to stop in Chiang Dao otherwise they might plough straight past.

By motorbike taxi or songthaew From the junction at the southern end of town, where bus drivers are most likely to make a stop, you can take a motorbike taxi (B60) or songthaew (B150) to the guesthouses.

ACCOMMODATION AND EATING

Chiang Dao Nest About 1500m further north along the road from the caves ☎ 053 456242, ⓦ chiang daonest.com. There are two branches of this farang favourite, one on each side of *Malee's*, with around twenty bungalows in total – all with attached hot-water bathrooms and verandas. The one nearer to the caves has a/c and serves Thai food, while the further one – which has a small swimming pool – turns out gourmet Western dishes (mains at around B300–400). **B995**

Malee's Nature Lovers Bungalows About 1500m further north along the road from the caves ☎ 081 961 8387, ⓦ maleenature.com. In this cosy garden compound, delightfully set in the shadow of the mountain, you'll find comfy bungalows of varying size, all with hot showers, as well as camping facilities (B100/person), a saltwater plunge pool and good food. They can arrange treks and bird-watching trips; mountain-bike and motorbike rental is available. **B850**

Doi Angkhang

Back on Highway 107, the road shimmies over a rocky ridge marking the watershed between the catchment areas of the Chao Phraya River to the south and the Mekong River ahead, before descending into the flat plain around Fang and the Kok River. Branching off to the left some 60km from Chiang Dao (at kilometre-stone 137), a steep and winding 25km road, Route 1249, for which you'll need your own transport, leads up to the mountain known as **Doi Angkhang** (1928m; map of the mountain available from Chiang Mai TAT office). Besides a royal agricultural project that produces peaches, raspberries and kiwis in the cool season, the mountain is home to a luxurious resort, where you can stop for food and spend a couple of hours soaking up the scenery.

ACCOMMODATION DOI ANGKHANG

★**Angkhang Nature Resort** 1/1 Moo 5 Baan Khum ☎ 053 450110, ⓦ mosaic-collection.com/angkhang. At this gorgeous hillside resort, the luxurious teak pavilions have balconies with great views, the restaurant uses organic produce from the royal project, and bird-watching, trekking, mule riding or mountain biking to nearby hill-tribe villages are the main activities. Breakfast included. **B2500**

Tha Ton and around

The tidy, leafy settlement of **THA TON**, nearly 180km north of Chiang Mai, huddles each side of a bridge over the Kok River, which flows out of Myanmar 4km to the north upstream. Life in Tha Ton revolves around the bridge – buses and boats pull up here, and most of the accommodation is clustered nearby. The main attractions here are longtail-boat and bamboo-raft rides downstream to Chiang Rai.

Wat Tha Ton

On the west side of the bridge • ⓦ wat-thaton.org

The over-the-top ornamental gardens of **Wat Tha Ton**, endowed with colossal golden and white Buddha images and an equally huge statue of Kuan Im, the Chinese

BOAT AND RAFT TRIPS ALONG THE KOK RIVER

Travelling down the 100km stretch of the **Kok River** to Chiang Rai gives you a chance to soak up a rich diversity of typical northern landscapes, which you never get on a speeding bus. Heading out of Tha Ton, the river traverses a flat valley of rice fields and orchards, where it's flanked by high reeds inhabited by flitting swallows. After half an hour, you pass the 900-year-old **Wat Phra That Sop Fang**, with its small hilltop chedi and a slithering naga staircase leading up from the river bank. Beyond the large village of **Mae Salak**, 20km from Tha Ton, the river starts to meander between thickly forested slopes. From among the banana trees and giant wispy ferns, kids come out to play, adults to bathe and wash clothes, and water buffalo emerge simply to enjoy the river. About two hours out of Tha Ton the hills get steeper and the banks rockier, leading up to a half-hour stretch of small but feisty rapids, where you might well get a soaking. Beyond the rapids, crowds of boats suddenly appear, ferrying tour groups from Chiang Rai to the Karen village of **Ruammid**, 20km upstream, for elephant-riding. From here on, the landscape deteriorates as the bare valley around Chiang Rai opens up.

LONGTAIL BOATS

The best time of year to make this trip is in the cool season (roughly Nov–Feb), when you'll get both lush vegetation and exciting rapids. Canopied **longtail boats** (B350/person) leave from the south side of the bridge in Tha Ton every day at 12.30pm for the trip to Chiang Rai, which takes around four rather noisy hours. The slower, less crowded journey upriver gives an even better chance of appreciating the scenery – the longtails leave Chiang Rai at 10.30am. However, if there are fewer than four passengers, these public boats won't depart – though there's always the option of buying up the extra seats. If you can get a group of up to six people together (up to twelve when the river's deeper in the rainy season), it's better to charter a longtail from the boat landing in Tha Ton (B2500; ☏053 459427), which will allow you to stop at the hill-tribe villages and hot springs en route.

BAMBOO RAFTS

If you have more time, the peaceful **bamboo rafts** which glide downriver to Chiang Rai in three days almost make you part of the scenery. Each party is accompanied by two steersmen who dismantle the rafts in Chiang Rai and bring the bamboo back to be recycled in Tha Ton. *Garden Home Nature Resort*, for example (see p.354), charges B4250/person in a group of two (less if there are more people), including soft drinks and food, staying at a Lahu village and the hot springs along the way. It also offers two-day versions, starting at Ban Pa Tai, east of Tha Ton (B3500/each for two people), as well as one-day trips downriver from Tha Ton, returning by car.

ACCOMMODATION

A peaceful **guesthouse** between Mae Salak and Ruammid, from which you can go trekking (guided or self-guided), might tempt you to break your river journey. *Akha Hill House* (☏089 997 5505, ⓦakhahill.com; fan B250, a/c B900), on the south bank of the Kok, 3km on foot from the riverside hot springs near Huai Kaeo waterfall, offers lofty views, comfortable rooms and bungalows, some with en-suite hot showers (with decent rates for singles), and free transport daily to and from Chiang Rai, as well as to the hot springs and elephant camp.

bodhisattva of mercy, are well worth the short climb. From any of the statues, the views up the narrow green valley towards Myanmar and downstream across the sun-glazed plain are heady stuff.

ARRIVAL AND DEPARTURE	THA TON AND AROUND
By bus or songthaew Regular services run between Chiang Mai's Chang Phuak bus station and Tha Ton (4hr). Otherwise, you could take one of the half-hourly buses to the ugly frontier outpost of Fang, 153km from Chiang Mai, then change onto a roughly half-hourly songthaew to Tha Ton. From Tha Ton, it's also possible to move on to Mae	Salong by songthaew (see p.364) or Mae Sai by a/c minibus (1 daily; 1hr 30min). **By car or motorbike** If you're coming up Highway 107 with your own transport, you can give Fang a miss altogether by branching west on a bypass signposted to Mae Ai.

ACCOMMODATION AND EATING

There are several simple **restaurants** opposite the boat landing; in addition, all of the following resorts have good restaurants open to non-guests.

The Coffee Mug Opposite the boat landing. Run by an enthusiastic local lad and handy for morning boat departures, this simple café serves breakfasts such as muesli, fruit and yoghurt (B100) and decent espresso coffees. Mon–Sat 8.30am–3/4pm.

Garden Home Nature Resort On the east bank of the river, 300m north of the bridge ☎ 053 373015, ✉ gardenhome14@hotmail.com. A very appealing riverside option, with friendly, clued-up staff and attractive en-suite rooms and bungalows (all with hot showers) sheltering in plenty of space under an orchard of lychees. The restaurant serves Western breakfasts, coffee and a good choice of Thai food – at lovely, thatched *salas* on stilts over the river if you like – and they offer motorbike rental and trekking (from B900/person for one day, in a group of two), as well as various journeys down the Kok River (they can even arrange for the 12.30pm boat to Chiang Rai to pick you up from the resort). Fan $\overline{\text{B500}}$, a/c $\overline{\text{B800}}$

★**Mae Kok River Village Resort** About 1km east of the bridge on the right-hand side of Highway 1089 ☎ 053 053628, ⒲ maekok-river-village-resort.com. An excellent upmarket choice, set in extensive gardens, with well-designed, stylish, a/c rooms set around a swimming pool (which includes a pool for toddlers). A huge range of activities – from Thai cooking to kayaking – is on offer. Breakfast included. $\overline{\text{B3500}}$

Thaton River View Resort About 200m beyond Garden Home ☎ 053 373173–5, ⒲ thaton-riverview -resort.chiangmai-chiangrai.com. With an even better location than *Garden Home* on a bend in the river that's hemmed in by densely forested hillside. You can enjoy great views of it all from the well-equipped a/c rooms and bungalows and the excellent Thai terrace restaurant. Rates include breakfast. $\overline{\text{B1400}}$

Ban Lorcha

Beyond Tha Ton, Route 1089 heads east towards Mae Chan and Highway 1; about 20km out of town, at Ban Kew Satai, a dramatic side road leads north for 16km to Mae Salong (see p.362). On the way, it's worth breaking your journey (about 1km west of Kew Satai on Route 1089, and accessible by songthaews from Tha Ton and Mae Salong) at **BAN LORCHA**. As part of a community-based tourism development project, owned and managed by the villagers, with technical assistance from the PDA in Chiang Rai (see p.358), this Akha settlement has been opened to visitors, who pay an entrance fee of B50 (income goes into a village development fund). A guide leads you on a 1km walk through the village, which is strategically dotted with interesting display boards in English, and you'll get a chance to have a go on an Akha swing (not the ceremonial one), see a welcome dance and watch people weaving and tool-making, for example.

Chiang Rai

Sprawled untidily over the south bank of the Kok River, **CHIANG RAI** continues to live in the shadow of the local capital, Chiang Mai, but in the last few years has acquired several genuine sights of interest, notably the **Mae Fah Luang Art & Cultural Park**, a beautiful storehouse of Lanna art. There's now also a good choice of guesthouses and upmarket riverside hotels in which to lay your head, and from here you can set up a wide range of trekking, day-trips and other outdoor activities in the surrounding countryside. The town quietly gets on with its own business during the day, when most of its package tourists are out on manoeuvres, but at night the neon lights flash on and souvenir stalls and ersatz Western restaurants are thronged. Meanwhile, Chiang Rai keeps up its reputation as a dirty-weekend destination for Thais, a game given away by just a few motels with carports – where you drive into the garage and pay for a discreet screen to be pulled across behind you.

Brief history

Chiang Rai is most famous for the things it had and lost. It was founded in 1263 by King Mengrai of Ngon Yang who, having recaptured a prize elephant he'd been chasing

CHIANG RAI

N

ACCOMMODATION			
Baan Bua Guest House	10	Golden Triangle Inn	9
Baan Bua Homestay	13	Imperial River	
Baan Rub Aroon		House Resort	1
Guest House	8	Jitaree Guest House	5
Baan Warabordee	12	The Legend	2
Ban Lotus	4	Moon & Sun	7
Chat House	6	Tourist Inn	14
Dusit Island Resort Hotel	3	Wiang Inn	11

SHOPS	
Boots	2
Orn's Bookshop	3
Thai Tribal Crafts	1

RESTAURANTS & CAFÉS	
Aye's	5
Baan Chivit Mai	6
Cabbages & Condoms	3
Chivit Thammada	2
Doi Chaang	4
Muang Thong	7
Salungkham	1

New Bus Station, Wat Rong Khun & Chiang Mai ▼

around the foot of Doi Tong, took this as an auspicious omen for a new city. Tradition has it that Chiang Rai then prevailed as the capital of the north for thirty years, but historians now believe Mengrai moved his court directly from Ngon Yang to the Chiang Mai area in the 1290s. Thailand's two holiest images, the Emerald Buddha (now in Bangkok) and the Phra Singh Buddha (now either in Bangkok's National Museum, Chiang Mai or Nakhon Si Thammarat, depending on which story you believe), also once resided here before moving on – at least replicas of these can be seen at Wat Phra Kaeo and Wat Phra Singh.

Doi Tong

Northwest of the centre

A walk up to **Doi Tong**, the hummock to the northwest of the centre, is the best way to get your bearings in Chiang Rai and, especially at sunset, offers a fine view up the Kok River as it emerges from the mountains to the west. On the highest part of the hill stands a kind of phallic Stonehenge centred on the town's new **lak muang** (city pillar) representing the Buddhist layout of the universe. Historically, the erection of a *lak muang* marks the official founding of a Thai city, precisely dated to January 26, 1263 in the case of Chiang Rai; the new *lak muang* and the elaborate stone model around it

3

TOURS AND TREKKING FROM CHIANG RAI

Communities from all the hill tribes have settled around **Chiang Rai**, and the region offers the full range of terrain for **trekking**, from reasonably gentle walking trails near the Kok River to tough mountain slopes further north towards the Burmese border; elephant riding is included in most treks. However, this natural suitability has attracted too many tour and trekking agencies, and many of the hill-tribe villages, especially between Chiang Rai and Mae Salong, have become weary of the constant toing and froing; the south side of the river to the west of town is generally a better bet. Sizes of group treks from Chiang Rai tend to be smaller than those from Chiang Mai, often with just two or three people, with a maximum of about seven in a group. Nearly all guesthouses in Chiang Rai can fit you up with a trek – *Chat House* is responsible and reliable, typically charging around B2500–3500 per person for three days and two nights in a group of between two and six people. One place to avoid is the village of "long-neck" women (see p.338), just north of Chiang Rai's airport, who are virtual prisoners living in an artificial village for the convenience of tourists.

More expensive treks are offered by several nonprofit foundations promoting **community-based tourism** that are based in and around Chiang Rai, as detailed below.

Natural Focus ☎ 053 758658 or ☎ 085 888 6869, ⓦ naturalfocus-cbt.com. Set up by the Hill Area and Community Development Foundation, this CBT initiative offers one- to five-day tours to learn about mountain life, as well as youth, community development and volunteer skills programmes.

PDA At the Hill Tribe Museum (see p.358) ☎ 053 719167, ⓦ pdacr.org. This development agency offers one- or multi-day jungle treks to non-touristy areas,

usually including elephant riding and a longtail-boat trip. It also lays on a wide range of guided tours, to its Akha project at Ban Lorcha (see p.354), Mae Salong and other places of interest.

Thailand Ecotour ⓦ thailandecotour.org. Part of the excellent Mirror Foundation (see p.58), with an interesting and well-received programme that includes one-day bicycle tours and one- to seven-day treks.

were erected 725 years later to the day, as part of the celebrations of King Bhumibol's sixtieth birthday. The *lak muang* itself represents Mount Sineru (or Meru), the axis of the universe, while the series of concentric terraces, moats and pillars represent the heavens and the earth, the great oceans and rivers, and the major features of the universe. Sprinkling water onto the garlanded *lak muang* and then dabbing your head with the water after it has flowed into the basin below brings good luck. The old wooden *lak muang* can be seen in the viharn of **Wat Phra That Doi Tong**, the city's first temple, which sprawls over the eastern side of the hill.

Wat Phra Kaeo

Thanon Trairat • Temple daily dawn–dusk • Sangkaew Hall daily 9am–5pm • Free • ⓦ watphrakaew-chiangrai.com

Thailand's most important image, the Emerald Buddha, which had supposedly been sculpted by the gods in Patna, India, in 234 BC, was placed in the chedi at **Wat Phra Kaeo** by King Mahaprom of Chiang Rai in 1390. However, lightning destroyed the chedi 44 years later, allowing the image to continue its perambulations around Southeast Asia, finally settling down in Bangkok. A beautiful replica can now be seen here in a tiny, Lanna-style pavilion, the **Hor Phra Yok**. Carved in China from milky green Canadian jade, the replica was presented by a Chinese millionaire to mark the ninetieth birthday of the Princess Mother, Mae Fah Luang, in 1990, and consecrated by King Bhumibol himself. At 47.9cm wide and 65.9cm tall, it's millimetres smaller than the actual Emerald Buddha, as religious protocol dictated that it could not be an exact copy of the original. There's much else of interest in the temple complex, which has recently been renovated to a high standard, notably the **Sangkaew Hall**. Distinguished by its informative labels on Thai religious practice in English, this museum houses all sorts of Buddhist paraphernalia, including the belongings of famous monks from Chiang Rai.

FROM TOP WAT CHONG KLANG AND WAT CHONG KHAM, MAE HONG SON (P.337); LANTERNS DURING LOY KRATHONG (P.285) >

The Hill Tribe Museum and Handicrafts Shop

620/25 Thanon Tanalai • Mon–Fri 8.30am–6pm, Sat & Sun 10am–6pm • Museum B50

The **Hill Tribe Museum and Handicrafts Shop** stocks an authentic selection of tasteful and well-made hill-tribe **handicrafts**. The shop, on the second floor, was started by the country's leading development campaigner, Meechai Viravaidya, under the auspices of the PDA (Population and Community Development Association), and all proceeds go to village projects. The museum is a great place to learn about the hill tribes before going on a trek, and includes a slick, informative slide show (20min). You can donate old clothes or money for jumpers and blankets, and the PDA also organizes treks and tours themselves (see p.356).

Mae Fah Luang Art & Cultural Park (Rai Mae Fah Luang)

5km west of the city centre in Ban Pa Ngio • Tues–Sun 8.30am–5.30pm; Dec & Jan open till 10pm by candlelight, with dance shows on Sat & Sun • B200 • ⓦ maefahluang.org • To get here, charter a songthaew for about B100 one-way, or B200 return; with your own transport, head west on Thanon Tanalai for 1.7km from Thanon Trairat, turn right at the traffic lights onto Thanon Hong Lee and follow the road for 2–3km until you see the entrance on the left-hand side

By far Chiang Rai's most compelling attraction is the **Mae Fah Luang Art and Cultural Park**, a beautiful showcase of Lanna art and architecture, and its influences from Myanmar, Laos and China. In particular, the museum displays the consummate skills of local woodcarvers, with a focus on teak, which in Thailand is associated with concepts of dignity. It's set in lovely parkland, including a young teak garden that holds 43 varieties from northern Thailand.

The main reason for coming here is to see the **Haw Khum**, an amazing, multi-tiered barn of a building on massive stilts. It took five years to construct in the 1980s, in honour of the Princess Mother, Mae Fah Luang, using materials from 32 old houses in Chiang Rai province. Look out especially for the *ben grit* (fish scales) roof tiles, which inevitably are also made of teak. Lit by candles, the interior's dramatic centrepiece is a huge, slender, wooden prasat, representing the centre of the universe, Mount Meru, set in a sunken white sandpit – which not only symbolizes the Ocean of Milk, but also soaks up moisture to protect the teak. Dozens of very fine wooden artefacts surround the prasat, including a beautifully serene Burmese Buddha in a delicate, many-frilled robe that looks as if it's moving. Standouts among the displays in the nearby **Haw Kaew** – which is also made entirely of teak – are some ornate *oop*, or ceremonial alms bowls, and a bed headboard and footboard that sport scary carvings of Rahoo: the monster eating the moon connotes not only eclipses, but also a good night's sleep.

Wat Rong Khun

13km south of Chiang Rai on the west side of Highway 1 • Mon–Fri 8am–noon & 1–5pm, Sat & Sun 8am–noon & 1–5.30pm • Catch a Phayao-bound bus from the old bus station or a light-blue songthaew from the day market on Thanon Uttarakit

Wat Rong Khun almost defies description. Begun in 1997, it's the life's work of local contemporary artist, **Chalermchai Kositpipat** (see p.751), who has rediscovered Buddhism in a big way since spending time as a monk in 1992; he is also training dozens of "disciples", as he calls them, to finish the temple long after his death. Taking traditional Buddhist elements such as nagas and lotus flowers, and Lanna features such as long, slender *tung kradan* banners, Ajarn Chalermchai has enlarged and elaborated them, adding all sort of frills, layers and tiers. Surrounded by ponds, fountains and bridges (as well as a burgeoning village of souvenir shops and cafés for tourists), the temple is all white (to stand for the Buddha's purity), inlaid with clear glass tiles (to represent his wisdom); the end result is like a frosted wedding cake. Inside the bot, which houses an eerily lifelike waxwork of the wat's former abbot, you can often watch Chalermchai's disciples painting the golden-toned murals; an earthquake in 2014 damaged the plasterwork and toppled the temple's uppermost spire, but the work goes on. In the adjacent Hall of Masterwork, some of the artist's original paintings are on display, while reproductions are on sale (to raise money for the project) in the souvenir shop, along with a useful B100 booklet on the temple in English, which explains the meaning of the complex design.

If you're a fan of Chalermchai's work, you'll want to check out his new **clocktower**, back in Chiang Rai at the junction of Banphaprakan and Jet Yot roads, which hosts a mini *son et lumière* for ten minutes every night at 7, 8 and 9pm. His designs can also be seen in the florid lampposts all over town.

ARRIVAL AND DEPARTURE
CHIANG RAI

By plane Bangkok Airways, Thai Smile, Nok Air and Air Asia each fly between Bangkok and Chiang Rai 3–4 times daily (1hr 15min). The airport is 8km north of town on Highway 1 – about a B120 taxi ride.

By bus Chiang Rai's new bus station is about 6km south of the centre on Highway 1. It handles inter-provincial routes (including a/c and some non-a/c services from/to Lampang), while the old bus station on Thanon Phaholyothin serves Chiang Rai province (Mae Sai, Chiang Saen, Chiang Khong and buses and a/c minibuses to Sop Ruak), plus Nan and most non-a/c buses to Lampang; some services, to Chiang Mai and Mae Sot for instance, stop at both, however. Shared songthaews shuttle between the two bus stations for B20.

Destinations Bangkok (24 daily; 11–12hr); Bo Kaeo, Laos (4 daily; 4hr); Chiang Mai (every 20min; 2–3hr); Chiang Khong (every 20min; 3hr); Chiang Saen (every 20min; 1hr 30min); Khon Kaen (6 daily; 12hr 30min); Khorat (6 daily; 12hr 30min); Lampang (roughly every 30min; 4hr–5hr 30min); Luang Prabang, Laos (1 daily; 17hr); Mae Sai (every 20min; 1hr–1hr 30min); Mae Sot (2 daily; 10hr); Nakhon Phanom (3 daily; 19hr); Nan (1 daily; 6hr); Phitsanulok (1 daily; 7hr); Phrae (6 daily; 4–5hr); Rayong (4 daily; 19hr); Sukhothai (4 daily; 7hr 30min); Udon Thani (3 daily; 13hr).

By boat Longtails from/to Tha Ton dock at the boat station, northwest of the centre on the north side of the Mae Fah Luang Bridge.

GETTING AROUND

By metered taxi or tuk-tuk The city's new a/c metered taxis charge from B35 (plus a B20 call-out fee; ☎053 773477), while tuk-tuks start at around B50.

By bicycle Fat Free, 542/2 Thanon Banphaprakan (☎053 752532), has good sit-up-and-begs for B60, hybrids for B150 and mountain bikes for B200–250.

By car or motorbike Car rental is available through North Wheels – who also have motorbikes with insurance – at 591 Thanon Phaholyothin (☎053 740585, ⊛north wheels.com), or through Avis at the airport (☎02 251 1131, ⊛avisthailand.com). Motorbikes can also be rented at ST on Thanon Jet Yot (☎053 713652).

INFORMATION AND MAPS

Tourist information TAT has a helpful office at 448/16 Thanon Singhaklai (daily 8.30am–4.30pm; ☎053 717433 or ☎053 744674–5, ✉tatchrai@tat.or.th) with some useful free maps and brochures. Ask here about the renovated old provincial office opposite, which may be turned into a museum, and about Baan Dam (the Black

House Museum), a gothic collection of fantastical buildings and artefacts, 13km north of town off Highway 1 – the National Artist, Thawan Duchanee, who gathered the hoard as inspiration for his works, died in late 2014, but the museum may have reopened by the time you read this.

ACCOMMODATION

A wide choice of good **guesthouses** is within walking distance of central Chiang Rai, while several very appealing **hotels** hug the tranquil banks of the Kok River on the town's fringes.

Baan Bua Guest House 879/2 Thanon Jet Yot ☎053 718880, ⊛baanbua-guesthouse.com. Congenial and well-run establishment arrayed around a surprisingly large, quiet and shady garden, set back off the road. The very clean and attractive concrete, single-storey rooms all come with hot showers. Fan **B300**, a/c **B500**

Baan Bua Homestay 1047/2 Thanon Jet Yot ☎053 717952, ⊛baanbuahomestay.com. Despite being painted in lurid shades of pink and green, this wooden house is hard

to spot, as it's nestled in a quiet side street, tucked away behind *Tourist Inn*. The a/c rooms are quiet and fresh; some have private bathrooms outside the room (washbasins inside) while others are en suite. There's also a fan-cooled dorm on the ground floor sleeping three people who share a hot-water bathroom. Dorm **B220**, double **B580**

★**Baan Rub Aroon Guest House** 65 Thanon Ngam Muang ☎053 711827, ⊛baanrubaroon.net. In a pretty, quiet garden, this lovely early twentieth-century mansion has polished teak floors, lots of houseplants and immaculate hotel-style rooms with a/c and clean white sheets. The downside is that rooms share hot-water bathrooms, but there's also a very well-equipped kitchen and a nice terrace for eating breakfast (included). There's a six-bed dorm, too. Dorm B300, double B550

Baan Warabordee 59/1 Thanon Sanpanard ☏053 754488, ⊚facebook.com/warabordeechiangrai. Among a number of similar, slightly upmarket guesthouses on this surprisingly quiet, dead-end street in the town centre, a traditional wooden gate welcomes you into the pleasant, fountain-cooled garden here. The surrounding rooms are large and tastefully decked out in natural tones, with a/c, hot showers, TVs and fridges; some have their own balconies. Simple breakfast included. B500

Ban Lotus Soi Santirat Singhaklai, next to Jitaree Guest House ☏080 879 9242. Around a tranquil lawn dotted with fruit trees, a quadrangle of simple, one-storey, fan-cooled bedrooms with soft mattresses and hot showers in their good-sized bathrooms. B200

Chat House 3/2 Soi Sangkaew, Thanon Trairat ☏053 711481, ⊚chatguesthouse.com. Located behind its own garden restaurant and bakery on a quiet soi, this is Chiang Rai's longest-running travellers' hangout, with a laidback, friendly atmosphere and backpacker-oriented facilities. The cheaper rooms (including a dorm for B100/bed and three singles for B150) are in an old, mostly wooden house with shared hot showers, while a concrete row of garden rooms have en-suite hot water, some with a/c. Fan B200, a/c B400

Dusit Island Resort Hotel 1129 Thanon Kaisornrasit ☏053 607999, ⊚dusit.com. Set on an expansive island in the Kok River offering unbeatable views of the valley, this is one of the swankiest places to stay in town, with high standards of service. The huge rooms are lavishly furnished, with fancy bathrooms, mini-bars and big TVs. Hotel facilities include a rooftop steakhouse, fitness centre, steam rooms, jogging track and swimming pool. Discounts and packages available on the website. B2600

Golden Triangle Inn 590 Thanon Phaholyothin ☏053 713918 or ☏053 740478. Large, comfortable, tastefully decorated rooms with a/c and hot water in a garden compound in the heart of town. B600

Imperial River House Resort 482 Moo 4, Thanon Mae Kok ☏053 750830–4, ⊚imperialriverhouse.com. Opposite *The Legend* on the north bank of the Kok, this four-storey resort has elegantly designed and sumptuously furnished rooms with lovely wooden floors, all overlooking the large swimming pool and landscaped riverside gardens. Extremely relaxing location and excellent service. B2300

Jitaree Guest House 246/3 Soi Santirat Singhaklai, the first soi on the right north of the traffic lights at the Singhaklai/Rattanakhet intersection, behind the police dormitory blocks ☏053 719348, ⊚jitaree .house.tripod.com. Welcoming place in a quiet street, offering big, clean rooms with hot showers in a concrete block with hanging plants, set around a large courtyard. B300

The Legend 124/15 Thanon Kohloy ☏053 910400, ⊚thelegend-chiangrai.com. Describing itself as a "boutique river resort", this place offers large luxury rooms decorated in contemporary Lanna style with verandas and outdoor bathrooms. Hugging the south bank of the Kok, the compound also features a huge infinity pool and a top-class spa. Breakfast included. B4400

Moon & Sun 632 Thanon Singhaklai ☏053 719279. Good-value, welcoming small hotel, with decent-sized, comfortable a/c rooms with fridges, TVs and hot showers, plus attractive furnishings and fittings in cream and light brown. Simple breakfast included. B600

Tourist Inn 1004/4–6 Thanon Jet Yot ☏053 752094, ⊗touristinn1@hotmail.com. Clean guesthouse in a modern four-storey building run by a Japanese–Thai team. The reception area downstairs has books for guests' use and a European-style bakery, serving good breakfasts, while bright, light rooms upstairs come with hot-water bathrooms. There are cheaper, older rooms in attached buildings at the back, with en-suite cold showers. Fan B250, a/c B400

Wiang Inn 893 Thanon Phaholyothin ☏053 711533, ⊚wianginn.com. Set back off the main road, this 260-room hotel has a bright and spacious lobby, an attractive pool and comfortably furnished rooms equipped with all facilities and decorated with Thai murals. Breakfast included. B2400

EATING AND DRINKING

Chiang Rai's **restaurants**, including a growing number of Western places, congregate mostly along Thanon Phaholyothin near the night bazaar, which itself shelters a huge but indifferent food centre. You need never go without a good **coffee** fix in Chiang Rai: the stuff grown on the nearby mountains of Doi Wawee and Doi Chaang is served up at several cafés around the main Rattanakhet–Phaholyothin junction. Meanwhile, Thanon Jet Yot is lined with hostess and hippie **bars**.

Aye's 479 Thanon Phaholyothin ☏053 752534. A spacious, popular restaurant with a relaxing atmosphere, live music in the evenings and a wide menu of international and Thai dishes – try the *kaeng hang lay* (B300), a delicious, northern pork and ginger curry. Daily 11.30am–11.30pm.

Baan Chivit Mai 172 Thanon Prasobsuk, opposite the old bus station ☏053 712357. Scandinavian bakery run by a Swedish charity that helps children in Chiang Rai and Bangkok slums (see ⊚baanchivitmai.com). Very clean, a/c café serving excellent sandwiches, cakes, breakfasts and coffees, plus pastas, Swedish meatballs (B200) and simple Thai dishes. Mon–Fri 8am–7pm, Sat & Sun 8am–6pm.

Cabbages and Condoms At the Hill Tribe Museum (see p.358). Proudly proclaiming "our food is guaranteed not to cause pregnancy", this restaurant covers its walls with paraphernalia devoted to family planning and HIV/AIDS prevention. The Thai food, including some traditional northern dishes and a few dishes suitable for vegetarians, is a bit hit and miss, but it's for a good cause. Live band every night. Daily 10am–midnight.

Chivit Thammada On the north bank of the Kok River, immediately west of the Highway 1 bridge – turn left at the first traffic lights over the bridge, then second left down a (signposted) soi ☎ 081 984 2925, ⓦ chivitthammada.com. A destination café for visiting Thais, with leafy riverside terraces and a day spa. Sustainably run, with high standards of service, it uses local, organic and seasonal produce whenever possible, in Thai fusion and Western dishes such as decadent and tasty eggs Benedict with truffle hollandaise, bacon and smoked salmon (B220). The home-made cakes are also very tempting, as well as a

huge range of very good coffees, smoothies, detox drinks and imported beers. Daily 8am–8pm.

Doi Chaang Thanon Rattanakhet. Amid fountains, waterfalls, a small forest of plants and classical music, this café offers very good espresso coffees and welcoming service. Daily 7am–9pm.

Muang Thong 889/1–2 Thanon Phaholyothin, just south of the Wiang Inn Hotel. This clean, no-frills and inexpensive place does a wide range of Thai and Chinese dishes and displays a huge selection of ingredients outside its open-sided eating area. Popular with Thais and foreigners alike. Daily 24hr.

★ **Salungkham** 834/3 Thanon Phaholyothin, between King Mengrai's statue and the river ☎ 053 717192, ⓦ salungkham.com. Justifiably rated by locals as serving the best Thai food in town (main dishes around B150), with a garden for evening dining; try the superb *kaeng hang lay*, a northern Thai pork-belly curry, or stir-fried white cabbage with home-smoked ham. There's no sign in English, but look out for the PT petrol station on the opposite side of the road. Daily 11am–10pm.

SHOPPING

As well as the outlets detailed below, there's a good handicrafts shop at the Hill Tribe Museum (see p.358). At weekends, Chiang Rai's **walking streets**, similar to those in Chiang Mai, come alive with musicians and all manner of stalls, including lots of food and local crafts and products such as coffee and macadamias. There's one on Thanon Tanalai, around the junction with Wisetwiang, on Saturday evening; and another on Thanon San Khong Noi, to the southwest of the centre, on Sunday evening (aka "Happy Street").

Boots Thanon Phaholyothin. Well-stocked chemist with English-speaking staff. Daily 11am–10pm.

Night bazaar Off Thanon Phaholyothin next to the old bus station. Sells cheap DVDs and all sorts of handicrafts, some of good quality and competitively priced – though it's usually crowded with tour groups. Daily 8am–8pm.

Orn's Bookshop 1051/61 Thanon Jet Yot, off Soi 1 ☎ 081 022 0818. Secondhand fiction and travel books to

buy or exchange. Daily roughly 5–11pm.

Thai Tribal Crafts 528/8 Thanon Banphaprakan ⓦ ttcrafts.co.th. Non-profit, fair-trade shop, sponsored by a Christian charity, with a huge range of products made by seven of the region's hill tribes, from bags, scarves, home furnishings and silverware to musical instruments and bamboo basketry. Mon–Sat 9am–6pm.

DIRECTORY

Cookery classes *Chat House* runs one-day cookery classes including transfers from your accommodation and a trip to the local market (B950/person).

Tourist police The tourist police (☎ 1155 or ☎ 053 717779) have a temporary office opposite the tourist office, but are planning to move to an undecided, out-of-town location.

North of Chiang Rai

The northernmost tip of Thailand, stretching from the Kok River and Chiang Rai to the border, is split in two by Highway 1, Thailand's main north–south road. In the western half, rows of wild, shark's-tooth mountains jut into Myanmar, while to the east, low-lying rivers flow through Thailand's richest rice-farming land to the Mekong River, which forms the border with Laos here.

At a push, any one of the places described in this section could be visited in a day from Chiang Rai, while hardly anyone visits **Mae Sai** on the Burmese border except on a visa-run day-trip. If you can devote two or three days, however, you'd be better off moving camp to **Mae Salong**, a mountain-top Chinese enclave, or **Chiang Saen**, whose atmospheric ruins by the banks of the Mekong contrast sharply with the ugly commercialism of nearby **Sop Ruak**, the so-called Golden Triangle. Given more time and patience, you could also stop over at the palace, temple and arboretum of **Doi Tung** to look down over Thailand, Laos and Myanmar, and continue beyond Chiang Saen to **Chiang Khong** on the banks of the Mekong, which is now a popular crossing point to Laos.

For hopping around the main towns here by **public transport**, the setup is straightforward enough: frequent buses to Mae Sai run due north up Highway 1; to Chiang Saen, they start off on the same road before forking right onto Highway 1016; for most other places, you have to make one change off these routes onto a songthaew.

Hill Tribe Culture Centre and Ban Therd Thai

For driving to Mae Salong from Chiang Rai, locals recommend heading west from Mae Chan towards Tha Ton along Route 1089, then turning north at Ban Kew Satai along Route 1234, a longer journey but on better roads. The old, more direct approach is on Route 1130, a dizzying, narrow rollercoaster of a road that ploughs its way westwards up to Mae Salong for 36km from **Ban Pasang**, 32km north of Chiang Rai on Highway 1. With your own transport, a few marginally interesting attractions might tempt you to stop along this route, notably the **Hill Tribe Culture Centre**, 12km from Ban Pasang, where there's a small hill-tribe handicrafts market, and a couple of Mien and Akha souvenir villages. At Sam Yaek, 24km from Ban Pasang, a paved side-road heads north for 13km to **Ban Therd Thai** ("Village to Honour Thailand"). In its former incarnation as Ban Hin Taek ("Village of Broken Stone"), this mixed village was the opium capital of the notorious Khun Sa (see box opposite): the Thai army drove Khun Sa out after a pitched battle in 1983, and the village has now been renamed and "pacified" with the establishment of a market, school and hospital.

Mae Salong (Santikhiri)

Perched 1300m up on a ridge, commanding fine views of sawtoothed hills, stands the Chinese Nationalist outpost of **MAE SALONG** – the focal point for the area's fourteen thousand **Kuomintang**, who for two generations now have held fast to their cultural identity, if not their political cause. Though it has temples, a church and a mosque, it's the details of Chinese life in the backstreets – the low-slung bamboo houses, the pictures of Chiang Kai-shek, ping-pong tables, the sounds of Yunnanese conversation – that make the village absorbing.

Mae Salong straggles for several kilometres along a roughly east–west road, with a central junction near the morning market and the steps for the Princess Mother Pagoda. It gets plenty of Thai visitors, especially at weekends in the cool season, when they come to admire the cherry blossoms and throng the main street's souvenir shops to buy such delicacies as sorghum whisky (pickled with ginseng, deer antler and centipedes) and locally grown Chinese tea, coffee, mushrooms and herbs. Free cups of tea are offered nearly everywhere, and it's possible to visit, for example, **Mae Salong Villa**'s own estate and factory – ask at the resort for directions and tea-processing times. It might also be worth braving the dawn chill to get to the **morning market**, held in the middle of town near *Shin Sane Guest House* (before 8am, best around 7am), which pulls shoppers and vendors in from the surrounding Akha, Lisu and Mien villages.

Brief history

The ruling party of China for 21 years, the **Kuomintang** (Nationalists) were swept from power by the Communist revolution of 1949 and fled in two directions: one group, under party leader Chiang Kai-shek, made for Taiwan, where it founded the Republic of China; the other, led by General Li Zongren, settled in northern Thailand and

DRUGS AND THE GOLDEN TRIANGLE

Opium will always be associated with the Far East in the popular imagination, but the opium poppy actually originated in the Mediterranean. It arrived in the East, however, over twelve centuries ago, and was later brought to Thailand from China with the hill tribes who migrated from Yunnan province. Opium growing was made illegal in Thailand in 1959, but during the 1960s and 1970s rampant production and refining of the crop in the lawless region on the borders of Thailand, Myanmar and Laos earned the area the nickname **the Golden Triangle**. Two main "armies" operated most of the trade within this area. The ten-thousand-strong **Shan United Army** (SUA), set up to fight the Burmese government for an independent state for the Shan (Thai Yai) people, funded itself from the production of heroin (a more refined form of opium). Led by the notorious warlord Khun Sa, the SUA attempted to extend their influence inside Thailand during the 1960s, where they came up against the troops of the **Kuomintang** (KMT). These refugees from China, who fled after the Communist takeover there, were at first befriended by the Thai and Western governments, who were pleased to have a fiercely anti-Communist force patrolling this border area. The Kuomintang were thus able to develop the heroin trade, while the authorities turned a blind eye.

By the 1980s, the danger of Communist incursion into Thailand had largely disappeared, and the government was able to concentrate on the elimination of the crop, putting the Kuomintang in the area around Mae Salong on a determined "**pacification**" programme. In 1983 the Shan United Army was pushed out of its stronghold at nearby Ban Hin Taek (now Ban Therd Thai), over the border into Myanmar, and in 1996, Khun Sa cut a deal with the corrupt Burmese military dictatorship. The man once dubbed the "Prince of Death", who had a US$2 million bounty on his head from the United States, was able to live under Burmese army protection in a comfortable villa in Rangoon until his death in 2007.

The Thai government has succeeded in reducing the size of the opium crop within its borders to an insignificant amount, but Thailand still has a vital role to play as a conduit for heroin; most of the production and refinement of opium has simply moved over the borders into Myanmar and Laos. And in the last few years, opium growing within northern Thailand, although still at a very low level, has apparently started to increase again, based on small patches in remote mountains and using a high-yield, weather-resistant breed supplied by the Burmese drug barons.

The destruction of huge areas of poppy fields has had far-reaching repercussions on the **hill tribes**. In many cases, with the raw product not available, opium addicts have turned to injecting heroin from shared needles, leading to a devastating outbreak of AIDS. The Thai government has sought to give the hill tribes an alternative livelihood through the introduction of legitimate cash crops, yet these often demand the heavy use of pesticides, which later get washed down into the lowland valleys, incurring the wrath of Thai farmers.

The dangers of the heroin trade have in recent years been eclipsed by the flood of **methamphetamines** – either *yaa baa* (literally "crazy medicine") or Ice (crystal meth) – that is infiltrating all areas of Thai society, but most worryingly the schools. Produced in vast quantities in factories just across the Burmese border, mostly by former insurgents, the United Wa State Army, *yaa baa* and Ice are the main objective of vehicle searches in border areas, with perhaps a billion tablets smuggled into Thailand each year. It's estimated that three million Thais are methamphetamine users, prompting the Thaksin government into a fierce crackdown in the first half of 2003 which, much to the consternation of human rights watchers, led to two thousand extra-judicial deaths and 51,000 arrests. Things have quietened down since then, but the frequent busts of methamphetamine dealers show that the problem has not gone away.

Myanmar. The Nationalists' original plan to retake China from Mao Zedong in a two-pronged attack never came to fruition, and the remnants of the army in Thailand became major players in the **heroin trade** and, with the backing of the Thai government, minor protagonists in the war against Communism.

In the 1980s, the Thai government began to work hard to "pacify" the Kuomintang by a mixture of force and more peaceful methods, such as **crop programmes** to replace opium. Around Mae Salong at least, its work seems to have been successful, as

---

HORSE TREKS AND HIKES FROM MAE SALONG

The Kuomintang live up to their Thai nickname – *jiin haw*, meaning "galloping Chinese" – by offering **treks on horses**, a rare sight in Thailand. Trips to Akha, Lahu and other Chinese villages can be arranged at the *Shin Sane Guest House* from B500 for three hours, but it's worth meeting your guide and checking out the itinerary and the horses before you hand over any money. Note that the horses are small and won't take anyone over around 80kg.

Armed with a sketch map from one of the guesthouses, it would be possible to **walk** to some of the same villages yourself – or better still, in high season you can hire a **guide** from *Little Home Guest House* for B600 per day.

---

evidenced by the slopes to the south of the settlement, which are covered with a carpet of rich green tea bushes. Since its rehabilitation, Mae Salong is now officially known as **Santikhiri** (Hill of Peace).

The Princess Mother Pagoda

Towering above the village on top of a hill, the **Princess Mother Pagoda**, a huge, gilt-topped chedi, is so distinctive that it has quickly become Mae Salong's proud symbol. It's a long and steep climb up 718 steps from near the morning market to get there, but with a rented vehicle you can follow the road to the western end of the village and branch right beyond the bank on a road that carries you heavenward, revealing some breathtaking views on the way.

Chinese Martyrs Memorial Museum

At the western edge of the village, on the way out towards Tha Ton • Daily 8am–5pm • B20

The **Chinese Martyrs Memorial Museum** recounts the origins of the Kuomintang in Thailand, giving details of battles such as the famous one fought against Thai and Lao Communists and Hmong at Phu Chi Fa near Chiang Khong, and depicting the Kuomintang as heroic protectors of the Kingdom of Thailand. The huge complex encompasses a shrine to the KMT martyrs who fell in the fighting.

ARRIVAL AND DEPARTURE   MAE SALONG

From Chiang Rai Buses (every 20min; 45min) leave Chiang Rai's old bus station for Pasang, 32km to the north on Highway 1. You'll then need to change to a green songthaew for the 1hr–1hr 30min chug up to Mae Salong (4–5 daily, originating in Mae Chan market; last departure about 1.30pm).

From Tha Thon There are four direct yellow songthaews a day between Tha Ton and Mae Salong, via the interesting

Akha village of Ban Lorcha (see p.354).

Leaving Mae Salong When it's time to depart Mae Salong, you'll find the songthaews for Tha Ton and Ban Pasang by *Little Home* and *Shin Shane* guesthouses, just west of the central junction.

By rented motorbike *Shin Sane Guest House* rents out motorbikes for B200/day.

ACCOMMODATION

You'll appreciate Mae Salong best if you spend the night here, after the day-trippers have left. Fortunately, there's a wide range of **accommodation**, including half a dozen budget guesthouses clustered around the central junction. Rates are significantly lower out of season, when the village feels wonderfully peaceful.

★**Little Home Guest House** Central junction ☎053 765389, ⓦmaesalonglittlehome.com. This friendly hillside spot offers smart bungalows in a pretty garden, with nice views from its verandas and hot-water en-suite bathrooms. The staff bend over backwards to help guests in their explorations and make them feel at home. At the time of writing, they were rebuilding their good Yunnanese restaurant with guest bedrooms above. **B500**

Mae Salong Villa On the main road towards the eastern end of the village ☎053 765114–5, ⓦmaesalong-villa.com. Choose between large, comfortable rooms in a two-storey block and Chinese-style family bungalows with better views from their picture windows, all with hot showers and fridges. In a pretty, sloping garden facing the Princess Mother Pagoda and Burmese mountains. Breakfast included **B1000**

Osmanthus House (Ban Hom Meun Li) Between the central junction and Mae Salong Villa ☎053 765271, ⓦfacebook.com/osmanhouse. Boutique hotel done out in ochre and black paint and polished concrete, where the spacious rooms provide fantastic views northwards from their large balconies and even from their bathrooms; they're equipped with platform beds, big-screen TVs, mini-bars and hot showers. Noodles for breakfast included. **B1500**

Shin Sane Guest House Central junction ☎053 765026, ⓦmaesalong-shinsane.blogspot.com. Welcoming place with plenty of local information, offering small, very cheap bedrooms with shared hot-water bathrooms in a funky wooden building and well-kept bungalows (with hot showers; B300 double, B200 single) in the garden behind. Free use of washing machine. **B100**

EATING AND DRINKING

The choice of restaurants in Mae Salong is narrower than its hotel selection, but there are some excellent places to sample Yunnanese dishes.

Mae Salong Villa On the main road towards the eastern end of the village ☎053 765114–9. Has great views and cooks up some of the best food in town, including delicious but expensive Chinese specialities like roast pork, *het hawm* (wild mushrooms) and *kai dam* (black chicken), which is usually served in soup with Chinese herbs (B300). Daily 7am–8pm.

Salema A short way west of the central junction before the bank. Welcoming Muslim-Chinese restaurant that rustles up delicious Yunnanese specialities such as deep-fried mushrooms in soy sauce (B80) and stir-fried chicken with ginger, as well as cheaper dishes on rice. Daily 7.30am–8pm.

Sweet Mae Salong Between the central junction and Mae Salong Villa, opposite Osmanthus House ☎083 096 7777. This place hits the spot with delicious, home-baked cakes, excellent espresso, mellow sounds and lovely views from the rear terraces; they'll also rustle up a green curry with *roti*, if you're more peckish. Daily 8am–5pm.

Doi Tung

Steep, wooded hills rise abruptly from the plains west of Highway 1 as it approaches the Burmese border. Crowned both by a thousand-year-old wat and by the country retreat of the Princess Mother (the present king's late mother), the central peak here, 1322m **DOI TUNG**, makes a worthwhile outing just for the journey. A broad, new road, Route 1149, runs up the mountainside, beginning 43km north of Chiang Rai on Highway 1, just before the centre of **Ban Huai Khrai**.

Cottage Industries Centre and Outlet

Around 1km from Ban Huai Khrai • Daily 8am–5pm

The old road to the mountain from the centre of Ban Huai Khrai passes after 1km or so the **Cottage Industries Centre and Outlet**, set up by the Princess Mother, where you can watch crafts such as paper-making from the bark of the *sa* (mulberry) tree in progress and buy the finished products in the on-site shop.

The Royal Villa complex

12km up the main summit road, then left up a side road • Royal Villa: daily 7am–5.30pm; closed if royals in residence • Villa B90; combined ticket to villa, Hall of Inspiration & garden B190; all three plus access to the arboretum (see p.366) B220

The largely Swiss-style **Royal Villa** on Doi Tung was built for the Princess Mother (the mother of the present king, she was never queen herself, but was affectionately known as *Mae Fah Luang*, literally "royal sky mother"). She took up residence here on several occasions to work on development projects in the area, before her death in 1995.

Detailed English-language leaflets are available to help visitors guide themselves around. In the Grand Reception Hall, which also features some beautiful floral wall panels made of embroidered silk, the positions of the planets and stars at the time of the Princess Mother's birth in 1900 have been carved into the ceiling. You can also visit her living room, bedroom and study, all left as when she lived here.

The Hall of Inspiration and the gardens

Hall of Inspiration Daily 8am–5pm • B50 **Mae Fah Luang Garden** Daily 6.30am–6pm • B90

On the access road to the Royal Villa, a few hundred metres back down the hill, the **Hall of Inspiration** contains hagiographical displays on the Princess Mother and her family and is strictly for royal-watchers. Next door, the immaculate ornamental **Mae Fah Luang Garden** throngs with snap-happy day-trippers at weekends. The Princess Mother's hill-tribe project has helped to develop local villages by introducing new agricultural methods: the slopes which were formerly blackened by the fires of slash-and-burn farming and sown with opium poppies are now used to grow teak and pine, and crops such as strawberries, macadamia nuts and coffee, which, along with pottery, *sa* paper, rugs and clothes, are sold in the shops and stalls near the entrance to the gardens. There's also an information booth that has simple maps of the mountain here.

Wat Phra That Doi Tung

Beyond the turn-off for the Royal Villa, a paved road heads northeast, climbing over a precarious saddle with some minor temple buildings and passing through a tuft of thick woods, before reaching **Wat Phra That Doi Tung** on top of the mountain. Pilgrims to the wat earn themselves good fortune by clanging the rows of dissonant bells around the temple compound and by throwing coins into a well, which are collected for temple funds. For non-Buddhist travellers, the reward for getting this far is the stunning view out over the cultivated slopes and half of northern Thailand. The wat's most important structures are its twin **chedis**, erected to enshrine relics of the Buddha's collarbone in 911. When the building of the chedis was complete, King Achutaraj of Ngon Yang ordered a giant flag (*tung*), reputedly 2km long, to be flown from the peak, which gave the mountain its name.

Mae Fah Luang Arboretum

Daily 8am–5pm • B50

A very steep, sometimes rough, paved **back road** runs right along the border with Myanmar to Mae Sai (22km), via two army checkpoints and the Akha village of Ban Pha Mee, beginning near the saddle beneath the peak of Doi Tung. After about 4km of asphalt, you reach the delightful **arboretum** at the pinnacle of **Doi Chang Moob** (1509m), a landscaped garden planted with rhododendrons, azaleas, orchids and ferns and furnished with fantastic terrace viewpoints looking east to Chiang Saen, the Mekong and the hills of Laos beyond, and west to the mountains around Mae Salong. For the most awesome view, however, continue a short way up the Mae Sai road to the Thai military checkpoint, to gaze at the opposing Burmese camp and seemingly endless layers of Burmese mountain stacked up to the north.

ARRIVAL AND DEPARTURE   DOI TUNG

By bus and songthaew Any bus between Chiang Rai and Mae Sai can put you off in Ban Huai Khrai, where you can charter a lilac songthaew (B600) to take you up the mountain and back.

ACCOMMODATION AND EATING

Cafés and restaurants There's a Doi Tung coffee shop, an excellent restaurant and a self-service café on the access road to the Royal Villa, in the complex of shops near Mae Fah Luang Garden.

Doi Tung Lodge In the woods below the Royal Villa ☏ 053 767015–7, ⌨ doitung.org. The spacious, simply furnished rooms at this upmarket tourist lodge are rather institutional and overpriced, but all come with a/c, hot water, balcony, TV and fridge. Breakfast included. B2100

Mae Sai

With its bustling border crossing into Myanmar and kilometres of tacky souvenir stalls, **MAE SAI** can be an interesting place to watch the world go by, though most foreigners only come here on a quick visa run. Thailand's most northerly town lies 61km from Chiang Rai at the dead end of Highway 1, which forms the town's single north–south street. Wide enough for an armoured battalion, this ugly boulevard still has the same name – **Thanon Phaholyothin** – as at the start of its journey north in the suburbs of Bangkok. The road ends at the Mae Sai River, which here serves as the Thailand–Myanmar border.

For a lofty perspective on the comings and goings, climb up through the market stalls to the chedi of **Wat Phra That Doi Wao**, five minutes' walk from the bridge on the west side of Phaholyothin, behind the *Top North Hotel*. As well as Doi Tung to the south and the hills of Laos in the east, you get a good view up the steep-sided valley and across the river to Thachileik.

ARRIVAL AND DEPARTURE   MAE SAI

By bus From Chiang Rai, frequent green buses to Mae Sai run due north up Highway 1. They stop 4km short of the frontier at the bus station, from where shared red songthaews shuttle into town. Returning to the bus station, the songthaews head off from the corner of Soi 2 on the east side of Thanon Phaholyothin, about 50m south of the border bridge, or you should be able to flag one down further along its route. If you're heading to Doi Tung,

you could take a yellow and blue songthaew from near the corner of Soi 10 to Ban Huai Khrai, saving you a journey out to Mae Sai's bus station.

Destinations Bangkok (12 daily; 13hr); Chiang Mai (6–8 daily; 4hr 40min–5hr 15min); Chiang Rai (every 20min; 1hr 30min); Khorat (6 daily; 14–15hr); Lampang (4 daily; 4–5hr); Mae Sot (1 daily; 11hr); Phitsanulok (6 daily; 9hr); Sukhothai (1 daily; 8hr); Tha Ton (1 daily; 1hr 40min).

GETTING AROUND

By motorbike Motorbikes can be rented from Pornchai, about 500m south of the bridge on the west side of Thanon

Phaholyothin, for B250/day.

ACCOMMODATION AND EATING

The huge night market that stretches far down Thanon Phaholyothin from the border is the best place to eat in the evening.

Navy Home About 1km south of the bridge on the east side of Thanon Phaholyothin ☎053 732929, ⓦnavyhome.com. Owned by a retired admiral, this hotel greets guests with a gangway over a pond, a display of his ceremonial uniforms and "Welcome aboard" signs, not to mention spent naval missile casings. It's even shaped like a ship and, although some of the rooms are cabin-like in size, they're all neat, clean and, well, shipshape, with a/c, hot showers, fridges and TVs. B600

Piyaporn Pavilion Just off the west side of Thanon Phaholyothin about 500m south of the bridge ☎053 731395. Mae Sai's best hotel is this imposing seven-storey block, with well-equipped rooms in a smart,

contemporary style, plus a/c, hot-water bathtubs, TVs and fridges. B1300

Rim Nam (Riverside) Right under the western side of the bridge, down a slip road to the left of the border checkpoint. A popular, reasonably priced restaurant with a riverside terrace, which gets crowded during the day with tourists watching the border action and serves cheap one-dish meals as well as its speciality, crab with curry powder (B300). Daily 7/8am–8/9pm.

Yeesun 5min walk west of the bridge along the river bank at 816/13 Thanon Sailomjai ☎053 733455. This is a good budget option, with neat, carpeted rooms with a/c, hot water, TV and fridge. B500

CROSSING THE BURMESE BORDER TO THACHILEIK

Thanon Phaholyothin ends at a short pedestrianized **bridge** over the Mae Sai River, which forms the border with Myanmar. Armed with a Burmese visa, you can enter the country here, notably for trips to the historic Thai Yai (Shan) town of Keng Tung. Even without a visa, you can have the dubious pleasure, during daylight hours, of crossing over to **Thachileik**, the Burmese town opposite, for yet more tacky shopping. You'll first be stamped out by **Thai immigration** at the entrance to the bridge, then on the other side of the bridge, you pay US$10, or an exorbitant B500, to Burmese immigration for a one-day stay. Coming back across the bridge, unless you already have a multiple-entry Thai visa or re-entry permit, you'll be given a new fifteen-day entry stamp – thirty days for UK, US, Canadian and other G7 citizens – by Thai immigration.

Sop Ruak

The "**Golden Triangle**", a term originally coined to denote a huge opium-producing area spreading across Myanmar, Laos and Thailand (see box, p.363), has, for the benefit of tourists, been artificially concentrated into the precise spot where the borders meet, 70km northeast of Chiang Rai. Don't come to the village of **SOP RUAK**, at the confluence of the Ruak (Mae Sai) and Mekong rivers, expecting to come across sinister drug-runners or poppy fields – instead you'll find souvenir stalls, pay-toilets, a huge, supremely tacky golden Buddha shrine, two opium museums and lots of signs saying "Golden Triangle" which pop up in a million photo albums around the world.

Hall of Opium

At the Mae Sai end of the village • Tues–Sun 8.30am–5.30pm, last ticket sale 4pm • B200 • ⓦ maefahluang.org

Under the auspices of the Mae Fah Luang Foundation based at Doi Tung (see p.365), the ambitious **Hall of Opium** took B400 million and nine years to research and build, with technical assistance from the People's Republic of China. It provides a well-presented, largely balanced picture, in Thai and English, of the use and abuse of opium, and its history over five thousand years, including its spread from Europe to Asia and focusing on the nineteenth-century **Opium Wars** between Britain and China. Dioramas, games and audiovisuals are put to imaginative use, notably in a reconstruction of a nineteenth-century Siamese opium den, playing the interactive "Find the Hidden Drugs", and, most movingly, watching the personal testimonies of former addicts and their families.

House of Opium

On the main through-road near Wat Phra That Phu Khao • Daily 7am–7pm • B50

The **House of Opium** is smaller and cheaper than the similarly named Hall of Opium, which it imitates, and it tends more to glorify opium use. All the paraphernalia of opium growing and smoking is housed in several display cases, including beautifully carved teak storage boxes, weights cast from bronze and brass in animal shapes, and opium pipes.

The meeting of the waters

The confluence of the Ruak (Mae Sai) and Mekong rivers is undoubtedly monumental, but to get an unobstructed view of it you'll need to climb up to **Wat Phra That Phu Khao**, a 1200-year-old temple perched on a small hill above the village. To the north, beyond the puny Ruak River, you'll see the mountains of Myanmar marching off into infinity, while eastwards across the mighty Mekong are the hills and villages of Laos. This pastoral scene has now been marred, however, by the appearance of a Thai luxury hotel, which is actually over on an uninhabited strip of Burmese land immediately upstream of the confluence. The attached casino bypasses Thai laws against gambling, and the usually strict border formalities are waived for visitors coming from Thailand.

ARRIVAL AND DEPARTURE   SOP RUAK

By songthaew from Mae Sai Regular blue songthaews make the 45min trip in the morning to Sop Ruak's main river road from the corner of Soi 8 on the east side of Thanon Phaholyothin, about 300m south of the bridge in Mae Sai (they leave when they're full).

By songthaew or bicycle from Chiang Saen You can take a blue songthaew from (and back to) Thanon Phaholyothin in Chiang Saen (frequent in the morning; 15min) or rent a bike and cycle there (it's an easy 10km ride on a paved road, though not much of it runs along the river bank).

A QUICK TRIP TO LAOS

Sop Ruak puts you tantalizingly close to Laos and, even if you don't have time to spend exploring the country properly, you can still have the thrill of stepping on Lao soil. A **longtail boat** from next to *Siwan Restaurant*, for example, will give you a kiss-me-quick tour of the "Golden Triangle" (B500), including a stop at a souvenir market on the Lao island of Done Xao (B30 admission).

ACCOMMODATION

There's nowhere decent to stay in Sop Ruak for budget travellers, but for those willing to splurge, there are some excellent options on the outskirts of the village, including a couple of places that offer great views of the Mekong River.

Anantara Entrance off the main road, at the Mae Sai end of the village ☎053 784084, ⓦgoldentriangle .anantara.com. Tastefully designed in a blend of traditional and contemporary styles and set in extensive grounds, this palatial luxury hotel is one of the finest in northern Thailand. The balconies of all its rooms and its swimming pool offer breathtaking views over the country-side to the Mekong, Myanmar and Laos. Among many amenities available to guests are a spectacular spa, a Thai cookery school, yoga classes and a well-run elephant camp that rescues street elephants (ⓦhelpingelephants.org). Rates include round-trip transfers from Chiang Rai airport, full-board meals and a range of activities. **B43,080**
Greater Mekong Lodge In the Golden Triangle Park,

next to the Hall of Opium ☎053 784450. Decent-value if slightly institutional rooms, all with a balcony, fridge, hot water and a/c. You can choose between rooms in the main hotel building or stilted chalets (where the views are better). Includes breakfast. **B1200**
Serene at Chiang Rai About 500m south of the House of Opium, on the riverside ☎053 784500, ⓦserene atchiangrai.com. As well as good service, a handy location and an elegant poolside terrace right by the river, this place offers big, clean and contemporary a/c rooms, whose attached bathrooms impress with freestanding tubs. There's a café on site serving breakfasts, lunches and dinners, and guests can use bikes free of charge. Special offers on "city view" rooms often available. Breakfast included. **B3000**

EATING

As well as the places listed below, there's a row of ramshackle **restaurants** by the waterfront, serving up basic Thai food and some decent fruit shakes.

Baan Dhalia At the Anantara ☎053 784084, ⓦgoldentriangle.anantara.com. This magnificent but pricey Italian restaurant has a menu that includes decadent delights such as spaghetti served in a wheel of Parmesan, and tiger prawns sautéed with white wine and garlic. The wine list is excellent. Daily 6.30–11pm.

Siwan In front of the Imperial Golden Triangle Hotel, along the main river road. The best of the riverfront restaurants, welcoming *Siwan* specializes in *tom yam pla* (spicy and sour soup with river fish), but also offers cheaper dishes such as *phat thai* (B80), as well as great views of the Mekong. Daily 7am–9pm.

Chiang Saen

Combining dozens of tumbledown temple ruins with sweeping Mekong River scenery, **CHIANG SAEN**, 60km northeast of Chiang Rai, is a good base camp for the border region east of Mae Sai. The town's focal point, where the Chiang Rai road (Thanon Phaholyothin) meets Thanon Rim Khong (the main road along the banks of the Mekong), is a lively junction thronged by buses, songthaews and longtails and lined with market stalls selling goods from China. Turning left at this T-junction soon brings you to Sop Ruak, and you may well share the road with the tour buses that sporadically thunder through (though most of them miss out the town itself by taking its western bypass). Very few tourists turn right in Chiang Saen, passing the busy port for cargo boats from China, along the road to Chiang Khong, even though this is the best way to appreciate the slow charms of the Mekong valley.

The layout of the old, ruined city is defined by the Mekong River running along its east flank; a tall rectangle, 2.5km from north to south, is formed by the addition of the ancient ramparts, now fetchingly overgrown, on the other three sides. The grid of leafy streets inside the ramparts is now too big for the modern town, which is generously scattered along the river road and across the middle on Thanon Phaholyothin.

Brief history

Originally known as Yonok, the region around Chiang Saen seems to have been an important Thai trading crossroads from some time after the seventh century. The city of Chiang Saen itself was founded around 1328 by the successor to the renowned King Mengrai of Chiang Mai, Saen Phu, who gave up his throne to retire here. Coveted for its strategic location guarding the Mekong, Chiang Saen had multiple allegiances, paying tribute to Chiang Mai, Keng Tung in Myanmar and Luang Prabang in Laos, until Rama I razed the place in 1804. The present village was established only in 1881, when Rama V ordered a northern prince to resettle the site with descendants of the old townspeople mustered from Lamphun, Chiang Mai and Lampang, to reinforce the extent of Thai rule in the face of increasing colonial interest.

National Museum

Thanon Phaholyothin, just inside the old city walls • Wed–Sun 8.30am–4.30pm • B100

The **National Museum** makes an informative starting point for a visit, housing some impressive architectural features rescued from the surrounding ruins, with good labelling in English, as well as a plethora of Buddha images – the two typical northern Thai styles of Buddha are sometimes referred to jointly as the "Chiang Saen style", though most academics instead use the more helpful term "Lanna style" (see p.284). As in many of Thailand's museums, the back end is given over to exhibits on folk culture, one of many highlights being the beautiful wooden lintel carved with *hum yon* (floral swirls representing testicles), which would have been placed above the front door of a house to ward off evil and for ventilation.

Wat Phra That Chedi Luang

Thanon Phaholyothin, next door to the museum

Wat Phra That Chedi Luang, originally the city's main temple, is worth looking in on for its imposing octagonal chedi, said to house a relic of the Buddha's breastbone and now decorated with a huge yellow ribbon, while handicraft stalls in the grounds sell Thai Lue cloths among their wares. In March 2011, a 6.8-magnitude earthquake rocked Myanmar, and the aftershocks (felt strongly in Chiang Saen) caused the top of the spire to break off. It and the other surrounding buildings that suffered damage, including Wat Pa Sak, are gradually being rebuilt.

Wat Pa Sak

Just beyond the ramparts to the west • Open access, but there's a B50 admission fee if the custodian's around

Wat Pa Sak's brick buildings and laterite columns have been excavated and restored by the Fine Arts Department, making it the most accessible and impressive of Chiang Saen's many temples. The wat's name is an allusion to the hundreds of teak trees that Saen Phu planted in the grounds when he built the chedi in 1340 to house relics of the Buddha's right ankle from India. The chedi's square base is inset with niches housing alternating Buddhas and *deva* (angels) with flowing skirts, and above rises the tower for the Buddha relic, topped by a circular spire. Beautiful carved stucco covers much of the structure, showing intricate floral scrolls and stylized lotus patterns as well as a whole zoo of mythical beasts.

Wat Phra That Chom Kitti

Outside the northwest corner of the ramparts

The open space around modern Chiang Saen, which is dotted with trees and another 140 overgrown ruins (both inside and outside the ramparts), is great for a carefree wander. A spot worth aiming for is the gold-topped, crooked chedi of **Wat Phra That Chom Kitti**, which houses yet another relic of the Buddha himself and gives a good view of the town and the river from a small hill outside the ramparts.

Wat Phra That Pha Ngao

3km southeast along the river road – look out for the tall brick gate on the right

Wat Phra That Pha Ngao, well worth the short detour from the centre, is thought to have been built originally in the sixth century. The temple contains a supposedly miraculous chedi perched on top of a large boulder, but the real attraction is the **new chedi** on the hillside above: take the 1km track which starts at the back of the temple and you can't miss the gleaming, white-tiled Phra Borom That Nimit, designed by an American, with attractive modern murals and built over and around a ruined brick chedi. From here, though you have to peer through the trees, the views take in Chiang Saen, the wide plain and the slow curve of the river. To the east, the Kok River, which looks so impressive at Chiang Rai, seems like a stream as it pours into the mighty Mekong. On the way down from the chedi, have a look at the new Lao-style bot, which was inaugurated by Princess Sirindhorn in 1999 and is covered from tip to toe in beautiful woodcarving.

3

ARRIVAL AND DEPARTURE
CHIANG SAEN

By bus or songthaew Buses from Chiang Rai (every 20min; 1hr 30min) and, in the morning, regular blue songthaews from Sop Ruak (15min) and Mae Sai (1hr) stop by the market on Thanon Phaholyothin, while songthaews from Chiang Khong (2hr; best done in the morning, usually involving a change at Ban Hat Bai) stop on the river road to the south of the T-junction; motorized samlors wait to ferry people around town.

By slow boat to China Armed with a Chinese visa (available in Bangkok or Chiang Mai), you can catch a boat up the Mekong from Chiang Saen to Guanlei in China.

Passenger boats, run by Maekhong Delta Travel, 230/5 Thanon Phaholyothin, Mae Sai (☎053 642517–9), are scheduled to run weekly in high season (10hr), but will only depart if they have enough takers. Cargo boats with two-person cabins depart most days and provide better views of the lovely scenery than the passenger boats, but take at least two days and one night, sometimes four days and three nights (B3000–4000/person including cabin and full board). Both kinds of boat can be booked through *Gin's Guest House* and *Maekhong View Resort*.

GETTING AROUND

By longtail boat Longtail boats congregate around the riverside near the central T-junction, offering local tours of the "Golden Triangle" lasting a couple of hours, including the Lao souvenir market on Done Xao island (B30 admission). The smaller boats slightly north of the junction charge B600/boat one-way, B800 return, while trips to Chiang Khong (approximately 1hr 30min downriver) cost

B3000 one-way, B3500 return.
By bicycle or motorbike To get around the ruins and the surrounding countryside, bicycles (B80/day) and motor-bikes (B200/day) can be rented from the no-name barber shop opposite the Bangkok Bank on Thanon Phaholyothin. Motorbikes are also available for B200 at *Gin's Guest House* and *Maekhong View Resort*.

INFORMATION

Tourist information There's a municipal tourist office (Mon–Fri 8am–4pm; ☎053 777084) on Thanon

Phaholyothin, opposite the National Museum, which houses exhibits on the architecture and conservation of the city.

ACCOMMODATION

Gin's Guest House Outside the ramparts, 2km north of the T-junction ☎053 650847. At this attractive guesthouse – by far the best of a small handful in Chiang Saen – there's a choice between bungalows with

en-suite hot showers and TVs in the garden, and spacious, well-furnished rooms in the main house, with polished wood floors and a/c. The owner organizes local trekking and tours, and breakfast is available at the same owners'

Maekhong View Resort across the road. Fan B300, a/c B600

★ **Gin's Maekhong View Resort and Spa** Outside the ramparts, about 2km north of the T-junction ☎053 650847 or ☎053 650857, ⊛ginmaekhongview.com. Set around a pretty lawn and an attractive, small swimming pool on the river side of Thanon Rim Khong, the a/c rooms and pricier bungalows here are bright, tasteful and well equipped, all with verandas/balconies that offer views of the Mekong and a dry-season field of sunflowers. Breakfast included. B1500

Pak Ping Rim Khong About 500m north of the T-junction ☎053 650151, ⊛facebook.com/pakping

rimkhong. Friendly new boutique hotel with a pleasant garden area, where the bright, contemporary rooms are decked out with dark wooden furniture, crisp white linen and a few splashes of colour, and equipped with a/c, hot showers and fridges. Breakfast included. B800

Siam Triangle By the river, 1km south of the T-junction on the continuation of Thanon Rim Khong (Route 1129) ☎053 651115–7, ⊛siamtriangle.com. A swanky, high-end place that has an infinity-edge swimming pool overlooking the river, a sauna and gym, as well as polished a/c rooms – "Deluxe" rooms have their own balconies with views across to Laos, while "Superior" rooms face inland. Breakfast included. B2500

EATING AND DRINKING

Food in Chiang Saen is nothing special; you could do worse than try the **street-food stalls** on the riverfront promenade just north of the T-junction, where you can sprawl on mats at low tables in the evening, followed by a drink at one of the small, lively bars opposite.

Samying Thanon Phaholyothin, beside the Krung Thai bank ☎053 777040. Popular with locals, this is a cheap, clean, well-run restaurant serving river fish in various preparations and good Thai salads. Daily 6am–5pm.

Siam Triangle By the river, 1km south of the T-junction

on the continuation of Thanon Rim Khong (Route 1129) ☎053 651115–7, ⊛siamtriangle.com. There's a good range of Thai and international dishes at the *Siam Triangle's* riverside restaurant, which has gorgeous views across the river. An expensive choice. Daily 6am–midnight.

Chiang Khong and around

As one of the jumping-off points into Laos from Thailand, **CHIANG KHONG** is constantly bustling with travellers waiting to go over the river to the Lao town of Houayxai and embark on the lovely Mekong boat journey down to Luang Prabang. On a high, steep bank above the water, Chiang Khong is strung out along a single, north–south street, Thanon Sai Klang, which runs down to the fishing port of Ban Hat Khrai. Once you've admired the elevated view of the traffic on the Mekong and glimpsed the ruined, red-brick turrets of the French-built Fort Carnot in Houayxai, there's little to do in the town itself, though several local excursions might tempt you to stay a little longer. On Fridays, there's a bustling **market** around the bridge to the south of central Chiang Khong, while Saturdays see a night market, mostly for food, on the main street in front of *Nam Khong Riverside Hotel*.

Village excursions

If you'd like to explore the area around Chiang Khong more fully, the best option is to put yourself up at *Baan Tam-Mi-La* guesthouse (see p.374), where Khun Wat has

---

GIANT CATFISH

The **Mekong giant catfish** (*pla buk*) is the largest scaleless freshwater fish in the world, measuring up to 3m in length and weighing up to 300kg. Chiang Khong has traditionally been the catfish capital of the north, attracting fish merchants and restaurateurs from Chiang Rai, Chiang Mai and Bangkok – the mild, tasty meat of the *pla buk* is prized for its fine, soft texture, and one fish can fetch up to B100,000. The **catfish season** is officially opened at the port of Ban Hat Khrai on April 18 with much pomp, including an elaborate ceremony to appease Chao Por Pla Buk, the giant catfish god. The season's haul used to be between thirty and sixty fish all told, but recent years have been so disappointing (some with no catches at all) that Thailand's Fishery Department has begun an artificial spawning programme.

BOAT TRIPS ON THE MEKONG

If you're twiddling your thumbs in Chiang Khong while waiting to cross to Laos, or simply want to spend some time out on the water, ask at your guesthouse about one-hour **boat trips** on the Mekong (B500) or full-day voyages up to Chiang Saen and back (around B3000) from a pier near Wat Luang. As you leave Chiang Khong itself and chug past sandy outcrops, it's likely you'll catch glimpses of villagers fishing, playing or washing in the river (usually met with big smiles and lots of frantic waving).

simple local maps and lots of information. **Thung Na Noi**, a Hmong village 8km west, with a market every Friday, makes a good cycling trip, with the possibility of returning by a more circuitous, 12km route through the forest. Pupils from the village school can guide you to an attractive waterfall, Huai Tong, 3km away. At the Thai Lue village of **Si Dornchai**, 14km south of Chiang Khong on Route 1020, you can watch weavers at work at shops near the bridge – this would also make a good trip by bike, returning via back roads along the river. With your own car or motorbike, you could push on from Si Dornchai for 50km to the interesting Kuomintang village of **Ban Pha Tang** and the precipitous mountain viewpoint at **Phu Chi Fa**, 25km beyond.

3

ARRIVAL AND DEPARTURE

CHIANG KHONG

By bus or a/c minibus Direct buses between Chiang Khong and Chiang Rai follow three different routes taking roughly 2hr, 2hr 30min or 3hr (each route approximately hourly, from Chiang Rai's old bus station); be sure to ask for the quickest time, *sawng chuamohng*. All buses arriving in Chiang Khong stop on the main road at the south end of town, except the service between Chiang Mai and Luang Prabang, which uses the Baw Khaw Saw terminal on Route 1020, 4km south of town towards the new Mekong bridge. Because of the popularity of the border crossing here, there are now direct a/c minibuses from and to Chiang Mai and Pai; you can arrange tickets through travel agents such as Queen Bee (see p.287) and Aya Service (see p.346) and guesthouses, including *Baan Tam-Mi-La* (see p.374).

Destinations Bangkok (9 daily; 13hr); Chiang Mai (3 daily; 5–6hr); Chiang Rai (every 20min; 2–3hr); Luang Prabang, Laos (1 daily; 15hr).

By songthaew from/to Chiang Saen The town is served by songthaews from and to Chiang Saen; the 2hr journey is best done in the early morning and usually involves a change of vehicle at Ban Hat Bai. In Chiang Khong, songthaews drop off and leave from the roadside near the post office.

By car from/to Chiang Saen If you're driving yourself between Chiang Saen and Chiang Khong, it's best to branch off the direct Route 1129 onto the winding, scenic, paved roads that hug the northward kink in the Mekong River.

GETTING AROUND

By tuk-tuk If you need transport from the bus to the centre of town, the local version of a tuk-tuk, a

CHIANG KHONG

N

■ **ACCOMMODATION**
Baan Fai	5
Baan Tam-Mi-La	2
Funky Box Hostel	3
Nam Khong Riverside Hotel	6
Ruanthai (Huanthai) Sopaphan Resort	4
Sopaphan Homestay	1

● **RESTAURANTS & CAFÉS**
Baan Fai	3
Baan Tam-Mi-La	2
Bamboo	1
Fai Nguan (Fai Ngern)	4

■ **BAR**
The Hub	1

Chiang Saen

Wat Phra Kaew

Songthaews to Chiang Saen

Wat Luang

Mekong River

Police Station

Sob Som River

Buses to Bangkok
Buses to Chiang Rai
Buses to Chiang Mai
Buses to Bangkok

1020

0   250
metres

Chiang Rai (137km), Thai–Lao Friendship Bridge,   Si Dornchai & Phu Chi Fa   Ban Hat Khrai converted motorbike known as a "skylab", should take you there for around B30.

By mountain bike Good hybrid bikes (B100/day) can be rented from *The Hub* (see opposite).

By motorbike or car *Baan Fai* rents motorbikes for B250/day, cars for B1200/day.

ACCOMMODATION

Baan Fai 27 Thanon Sai Klang ☎053 791394. A wide variety of rooms, from singles with shared hot showers (B200) to newly renovated doubles with a/c, fridges and attached hot-water bathrooms, in some funky old wooden houses on a small plot of land in front of *Nam Khong Riverside Hotel* – with further refurbishment under way. Breakfast included with the a/c rooms. Fan B350, a/c B800

★**Baan Tam-Mi-La** Soi 1, Thanon Sai Klang (signposted down a lane in the middle of town among a cluster of shops) ☎053 791234, ⓦbaantammila .com. With helpful, clued-up staff and a scenic, easy-going riverfront location, this place has tasteful, well-designed rooms and wooden bungalows on a leafy slope, with en-suite hot showers, and sells good hammocks. Basic bicycles free for guests to use. Fan B450, a/c B700

Funky Box Hostel Soi 2, Thanon Sai Klang ☎082 765 1839, ⓦfacebook.com/thehubpub. This hostel owned by *The Hub* (see opposite) does what it says on the tin: one large, fan-cooled, shed-like dormitory, decorated in bright, funky colours, is equipped with comfy beds, lockers and three hot-water bathrooms. Good breakfasts can be had at the pub or to "grab-and-go". Dorm B100

Nam Khong Riverside Hotel Thanon Sai Klang ☎053 791796, ⓦnamkhongriverside.com. The town's top spot to stay, a huge, low-rise hotel set around a pretty riverside garden with a river-view restaurant, karaoke facilities and smartly furnished rooms, all with a/c, hot water, fridges, balconies and Mekong views. Accordingly, ground-floor rooms tend to be cheapest. Breakfast included. B1300

Ruanthai (Huanthai) Sopaphan Resort Right next to Ban Tam-Mi-La ☎053 791023, ⓔsukatungka @gmail.com. The smart rooms in this large, homely teak house, hung with textiles and sporting lovely polished floors, have en-suite hot showers, and the best face across a common wooden terrace to the river. Fan B450, a/c B800

Sopaphan Homestay Thanon Sai Klang ☎053 792022. A more basic guesthouse than *Ruanthai Sopaphan* opposite, though also sporting a small forest's worth of highly polished teak. The warren-like premises contain a huge variety of rooms with hot showers, either shared or en suite. There's little in the way of charm or service, or anything to justify the tag "homestay", but it's hard to argue with the price; may change name soon. B150

EATING AND DRINKING

Baan Fai 27 Thanon Sai Klang ☎053 791394. With some nice, shady streetside tables, this welcoming guesthouse café serves decent espresso coffees, fruit shakes, breakfasts, sandwiches and a few simple Thai dishes. Daily 7am–10pm.

Baan Tam-Mi-La 113 Thanon Sai Klang ☎053 791234. Excellent guesthouse terrace restaurant with a sweeping view of the river, making it an ideal spot to while away the time. Very good Thai food, lots of vegetarian options and

---

CROSSING TO LAOS

Tourists cross the border via the new Fourth Thai-Lao Friendship Bridge, 8km downstream from Chiang Khong, where thirty-day **visas for Laos** are available on arrival (US$30 or B1500 and up, depending on nationality, plus $1 overtime fee after 4pm and at weekends) – for information about other means of getting a Lao visa, see Basics (see p.28). As paying in baht at the border is so unfavourable, banks and gold shops in Chiang Khong sell dollars.

From Houayxai, the Lao town opposite Chiang Khong, there are buses to Luang Prabang, Vientiane, Luang Namtha and Oudomxai, for example, but by far the most popular option is to catch a **passenger boat to Luang Prabang**. Generally departing between 10am and noon every morning, these glide down the scenic Mekong in two days, with an overnight and usually a change of boat at Pakbeng. An alternative is to take one of the early-morning **speedboats** (6–7hr), on which passengers should be provided with helmets and life jackets, but they're cramped, noisy and dangerous.

From Chiang Khong, you'll need to catch a tuk-tuk to the bridge, then a shuttle bus across the bridge, then a songthaew on the Lao side to the pier for Luang Prabang boats in Houayxai – your best option is to book a passenger boat ticket through a travel agent or guesthouse such as *Baan Tam-Mi-La* in Chiang Khong for B1250, which will include all transport from your guesthouse to the pier in Houayxai.

a few Western dishes, plus espressos, home-baked cakes and bread, and hearty breakfasts. Daily 7am–8pm.

Bamboo Thanon Sai Klang ☎053 791621. Small, eclectic bakery, juice bar and restaurant that turns out good espressos, a wide choice of breakfasts, sandwiches (from B70) and Thai, Indian and Mexican food. Daily 7.30am–8.30pm.

Fai Nguan (Fai Ngern) Nam Khong Riverside Hotel, Thanon Sai Klang ☎053 791796. Well-appointed hotel restaurant with great views of the river and a wide range of Thai dishes, notably salads (from B90) and northern specialities, plus a few pizzas and steaks. Daily 7am–midnight.

The Hub Soi 2, Thanon Sai Klang. Fun, lively bar run by a Liverpudlian who holds the world record for going round the world on a bike (106 days), with a fascinating small museum of biking paraphernalia. Customers get to choose the music themselves, happy hour lasts from 4 to 9pm and activities range from yards-of-ale drinking to toe-wrestling. Daily 4pm–midnight or "on demand".

3

The east coast

LONELY BEACH, KO CHANG

The east coast

Just a few hours' drive from the capital, the east-coast resorts attract a mixed crowd of weekending Bangkokians and sybaritic tourists. Transport connections are good and, for overlanders, there are several Cambodian border crossings within reach. Beautiful beaches aren't the whole picture, however, as the east coast is also crucial to Thailand's industrial economy, its natural gas fields and deep-sea ports having spawned massive development along the first 200km of coastline, an area dubbed the Eastern Seaboard. The initial landscape of refineries and depots shouldn't deter you though, as offshore it's an entirely different story, with beaches as glorious as more celebrated southern retreats and enough peaceful havens to make it worth packing your hammock.

The first worthwhile stop comes 100km east of Bangkok at the town of **Si Racha**, which is the point of access for tiny **Ko Si Chang**, whose dramatically rugged coastlines and low-key atmosphere make it a restful retreat. In complete contrast, nearby **Pattaya** is Thailand's number one package-tour destination, its customers predominantly middle-aged European men enticed by the resort's sex-market reputation, or snap-happy groups, all undeterred by its lacklustre beach. Things soon look up, though, as the coast veers sharply eastwards towards Ban Phe, revealing the island of **Ko Samet**, the prettiest of the beach resorts within comfortable bus-ride range of Bangkok.

East of Ban Phe, the landscape becomes lusher and hillier around **Chanthaburi**, the dynamo of Thailand's gem trade and one of only two eastern provincial capitals worth visiting. The other is **Trat**, 68km further along the highway, and an important hub both for transport into **Cambodia** via Hat Lek – one of this region's two main border points, the other being Aranyaprathet (see box, p.381) – and for the forty islands of the Ko Chang archipelago. The most popular of this island group is large, forested **Ko Chang** itself, whose long, fine beaches have made it Thailand's latest resort destination. A host of smaller, less-developed islands fills the sea between Ko Chang and the Cambodian coast, most notably temptingly diverse **Ko Mak** and **Ko Kood**.

GETTING AROUND | THE EAST COAST

By bus Highway 3 extends almost the entire length of the east coast, beginning in Bangkok as Thanon Sukhumvit, and known as such when it cuts through towns, and hundreds of buses ply the route, connecting all major mainland destinations. It's also possible to travel between the east coast and the northeast and north without doubling back through the capital: the most direct routes into Isaan start from Pattaya, Rayong and Chanthaburi.

By plane Bangkok's Suvarnabhumi Airport (see p.133) is less than 50km from Si Racha, and there are two domestic airports along the east coast itself: at U-Tapao naval base, southeast of Pattaya, and just west of Trat.

KO SAMET

Highlights

❶ Ko Samet This pretty little island, fringed with a dozen or so beaches of fine, dazzlingly white sand, is easy to get to and offers a wide choice of accommodation, though it's suffering a little for its popularity these days. **See p.394**

❷ Trat Welcoming guesthouses and restaurants and an atmospheric old quarter make for a worthwhile stopover on the way to the islands or Cambodia. **See p.404**

❸ Ko Chang Head for Lonely Beach if you're in the mood to party, or to Hat Khlong Phrao,

Ao Bang Bao or Hat Khlong Gloi for progressively more tranquil scenes. **See p.409**

❹ Ko Mak Lovely, lazy, palm-filled island with peaceful white-sand beaches, a welcoming atmosphere and some stylish accommodation. **See p.422**

❺ Ko Kood The real beauty of the east, with some great beaches, Thailand's fourth-largest island is untamed and as yet largely undeveloped. **See p.425**

HIGHLIGHTS ARE MARKED ON THE MAP ON P.380

By train Though a rail line connects Bangkok with Si Racha and Pattaya, it is served by just one slow train a day in each direction; a branch line makes two journeys a day to Aranyaprathet near the Cambodian border.

Si Racha

The eastbound journey out of Bangkok is not at all scenic, dominated initially by traffic-choked suburban sprawl and then by the industrial landscape of the petrochemical and shipping industries that power Thailand's Eastern Seaboard. The first major

THE EAST COAST

KHAO YAI NATIONAL PARK

Nakhon Nayok

Prachin Buri

Sa Kaew

Aranyaprathet · Poipet

Sisophon

Suvarnabhumi Airport

Chachoengsao

Ancient City

Phanat Nikhom

Chonburi

Bang Saen

CAMBODIA

Si Racha

Ko Si Chang

Laem Chabang

Nong Yai

KHAO CHAMAO KHAO WONG NATIONAL PARK

KHAO SOI DAO

Soi Dao · Ban Laem

Khao Soi Dao Tai ▲

Pong Nam Ron

Ban Pakkard

Ko Phai · Ko Larn

Pattaya

Jomtien

Ko Klung

Ko Man Wichai

Ko Lin

KHAO KHACHAKUT NATIONAL PARK

Pailin

Klaeng

Bang Saray

Sattahip

Rayong

Ban Phe

Ko Samet

Khung Wiman

Laem Sadet

Ao Khung Kraben

Chanthaburi

KHAO SA BAP NATIONAL PARK

Bo Rai

Khram Yai Island

Laem Singh

Khlung

Ban Khlong Phlu

Trat

Ban Dan Kao

GULF OF THAILAND

Ban Nam Chiao

Laem Ngop

Ko Chang

Khao Lan

Laem Sok

N

Ko Wai

Ko Mak

Khlong Yai

Hat Lek

Cham Yeam

Pak Khlong

Ko Kood

HIGHLIGHTS

1 Ko Samet
2 Trat
3 Ko Chang
4 Ko Mak
5 Ko Kood

0   50
kilometres

CROSSING THE CAMBODIAN BORDER VIA ARANYAPRATHET

The most commonly used overland crossing into **Cambodia** from Thailand is at **Poipet**, which lies just across the border from the Thai town of **Aranyaprathet**, 210km due east of Bangkok. It's best to arm yourself in advance with an e-visa for Cambodia (see p.27) and to make the journey by regular public transport from Bangkok to Siem Reap and beyond. It's also possible to travel via Aranyaprathet and get a thirty-day visa on arrival at the border, though this can expose you to possible **scams**, including a fake "Cambodian Consulate" in Aranyaprathet and rip-off currency exchange (it's not compulsory to buy riel before entering Cambodia, despite what some touts may say). For further details, see ⓦthaivisa.com for its visa-run forum; and ⓦtalesofasia.com/cambodia-overland.htm for a very detailed description of the crossing and advice on onward transport into Cambodia. Once you've walked across the border and entered Cambodia, it's about two hours in a taxi or bus to reach Siem Reap, 150km away. If you have the deep misfortune of getting stuck in dusty, dirty Aranyaprathet, where local transport comes in the form of tuk-tuks, try the comfortable fan and a/c rooms at *Inter Hotel* at 108/7 Thanon Chatasingh (☎037 231291, ⓦourweb.info/interhotel; fan B300, a/c B550).

From **Bangkok**, you can travel to Aranyaprathet Station, 4km from the border post, by **train** (2 daily; 6hr); you'll need to catch the 5.55am if you want to get across the border the same day. Return trains depart Aranyaprathet at 6.40am and 1.55pm (5hr 25min–6hr). Alternatively, take a **bus** from Bangkok's Northern (Mo Chit) Bus Terminal to Aranyaprathet (at least hourly; 4hr 30min), or a faster, more expensive a/c minibus from Victory Monument. If you have an e-visa, you can catch one of Baw Khaw Saw's public buses that run from Mo Chit via Aranyaprathet all the way to Siem Reap and Phom Penh. To reach Aranyaprathet from east-coast towns, the easiest route is to take a bus from **Chanthaburi** to the town of **Sa Kaew**, 130km to the northeast, and then change to one of the frequent buses for the 55km ride east to Aranyaprathet.

It's also possible to buy a **through ticket to Siem Reap** from Trat and Ko Chang, or from Thanon Khao San in Bangkok (B250–400), but this option is dogged by scams (including a visa "service charge", described in detail at ⓦtalesofasia.com/cambodia-overland-bkksr-package.htm and on the forum at ⓦthaivisa.com), can take longer than doing it independently, and often uses clapped-out buses or even pick-ups on the Cambodian side, despite the promised "luxury bus".

population centre is the provincial capital of **Chonburi**, whose only notable attraction is its annual October bout of buffalo racing. Twenty kilometres on, you reach the fast-growing town of **SI RACHA**, a prosperous residential and administrative hub for the Eastern Seaboard's industries and home to a sizeable population of expat families. The town is best known though as the source of *nam phrik Si Racha* (commonly known as Sriracha), the chilli-laced ketchup found on every kitchen table in Thailand, and as the departure point for the island of **Ko Si Chang** (see p.382). Si Racha's only sight is the Sino–Thai "island temple" of **Wat Ko Loy**, a gaudy hexagon presided over by a statue of the Chinese Goddess of Mercy, Kuan Im, and located on an islet at the end of a 1500m causeway, adjacent to the pier for boats to Ko Si Chang.

ARRIVAL AND DEPARTURE   SI RACHA

BY BUS

Frequent buses pass through Si Racha on their journeys between Bangkok's Eastern (Ekamai) and Northern (Mo Chit) bus terminals, and Pattaya and Trat further east. They all drop off and pick up passengers near the huge Robinsons/Pacific Park shopping centre on Thanon Sukhumvit in Si Racha's town centre.

First-class terminal Fast, first-class, dedicated Si Racha–Bangkok buses have their own small terminal a couple of hundred metres south of Robinsons, on the east side of Thanon Sukhumvit, set back slightly from the road

next to Tops supermarket; from here, there are also a/c minibuses to Suvarnabhumi Airport.

Destinations Bangkok (Eastern/Northern bus terminals; every 40min; 1hr 30min–2hr 30min); Chanthaburi (6 daily; 3hr 30min); Pattaya (every 20min; 50min); Trat (6 daily; 5hr).

BY TRAIN

Though a rail line connects Bangkok with Pattaya and Sattahip via Si Racha, it is served by just one slow, third-class, often late, train a day in each direction. The train

station is on the far eastern edge of town, a tuk-tuk ride from the pier for Ko Si Chang.
Destinations Bangkok (daily; 3hr 30min); Pattaya (daily 6.55am; 30min).

BY BOAT
Ko Si Chang pier, known as Tha Wat Ko Loy, is 2.5km from

Robinsons shopping centre; a motorbike taxi or tuk-tuk will drive you there for B40–60 or, if walking, take any road west towards the sea as far as Thanon Chermchompon (also spelt Jermjompol), then head north up Chermchompon until you reach the junction for the Ko Si Chang pier and Wat Ko Loy. Boats run to Ko Si Chang between 7am and 8pm (hourly; 40–50min).

ACCOMMODATION AND EATING

For **food**, Thanon Si Racha Nakhon 3 is a good place to browse, lined with restaurants and night-time food stalls, or there's an official night market by the day market and clocktower further south down Thanon Chermchompon.

City Hotel 6/126 Thanon Sukhumvit ☎038 322700, ⓦ citysriracha.com. This high-rise, two hundred-room hotel, 300m south of Pacific Place, offers smart a/c digs, with a gym, a spa, a tennis court, Japanese and international restaurants and a pool on site. B2825
Sri Wattana Soi Sri Wattana, directly across Thanon

Chermchompon from Thanon Si Racha Nakhon 3, about 500m south of the pier junction ☎038 311037. Very simple, cabin-like en-suite fan rooms, built on a jetty jutting out over the atmospheric but sometimes smelly waterfront, with a pleasant sea-view terrace though no wi-fi. B300

Ko Si Chang

4

The unhurried pace and absence of consumer pressures make small, dry, rocky **KO SI CHANG** an engaging place to get away from it all for a day or two. Unlike most other east-coast destinations, it offers no real beach life – it's a populous, working island with a deep-sea port, rather than a tropical idyll – and there's little to do here but explore the craggy coastline by kayak or ramble up and down its steep, scrubby contours on foot or by motorbike. The island is famous as the location of one of Rama V's summer palaces, a few parts of which have been restored, and of a popular Chinese pilgrimage temple, as well as for its rare white squirrels, which live in the wooded patches inland.

Rama V's Palace

Hat Tha Wang • Tues–Sun 9am–5pm • Free

The most famous sight on the island is **Rama V's Palace**, which occupies a large chunk of gently sloping land midway down the east coast, behind pebbly **Hat Tha Wang**. It's an enjoyable place to explore and can be reached on foot from the middle of Thanon Asadang in about half an hour.

Built in the 1890s as a sort of health resort for sickly royals, the palace (also known as **Phra Judhadhut Ratchathan**) formed the heart of an extensive complex comprising homes for royal advisers, chalets for convalescents, quarters for royal concubines and administrative buildings. By the turn of the twentieth century, however, Rama V (King Chulalongkorn) had lost interest in his island project and so in 1901 his

---

KO SI CHANG FESTIVALS

Ko Si Chang celebrates three particularly interesting festivals. **Songkhran** is marked from April 17 to 19 with sandcastle building, greasy-pole-climbing and an exorcism ritual for any islanders who have suffered unpleasant deaths over the previous year. At **Visakha Puja**, the full moon day in May when the Buddha's birth, death and enlightenment are honoured, islanders process to the old palace with hand-crafted Chinese lanterns. And on September 20, Ko Si Chang honours its royal patron **King Chulalongkorn**'s birthday with a sound and light show in the palace grounds and a beauty contest staged entirely in costumes from the Chulalongkorn era.

golden teak palace was moved piece by piece to Bangkok, and reconstructed there as Vimanmek Palace; its foundations are still visible just south of the palace's Saphan Asadang pier. Following modern renovations, the elegant design of the palace grounds is apparent once more. They fan out around an elaborate labyrinth of fifty interlinked ponds and a maze of stone steps and balustrades that still cling to the shallow hillside. Close to the shore, four of the original Western-style **villas** have been reconstructed to house displays, of varying interest, on Chulalongkorn's relationship with Ko Si Chang; one of them also doubles as a weekend coffee shop. Inland, signs direct you up the hillside to the palace's unusual whitewashed shrine, **Wat Asadang**, whose circular walls are punctuated with Gothic stained-glass windows and surmounted by a chedi.

Hat Tham Pang and Ko Khang Khao

The main beach on the west coast, and the most popular one on the island, is **Hat Tham Pang**. It's a tiny patch of sand, backed by shoulder-to-shoulder umbrellas and deckchairs belonging to the basic beach restaurants; you can rent snorkels and kayaks here too. The best **snorkelling** spots are further south, around the tiny islands off Ko Si Chang's southern tip, particularly off the north coast of **Ko Khang Khao**, forty minutes by kayak from Hat Tham Pang.

Wat Tham Yai Prik

Accessible via a fork off Thanon Asadang opposite *Tiew Pai* (10min walk)

The **Wat Tham Yai Prik** temple and meditation centre is open to interested visitors and meditators, who can meditate in caves set into the mountain. Unusually, nuns as well as monks here wear brown (rather than white) and everyone participates in the upkeep of the splendid monastery: you can see some of the fruits of their labour in the extensive roadside orchard. Just west of the wat lies the pretty, rocky cove known as **Hat Tham** or **Hat Sai**, which is only really swimmable at low tide.

Khao Khat

On the northwest trajectory of the ring road, you'll pass beneath the gaze of a huge yellow Buddha before reaching the rocky northwest headland of **Khao Khat**, a few hundred metres further on. The uninterrupted panorama of open sea makes this a classic sunset spot, and there's a path along the cliffside.

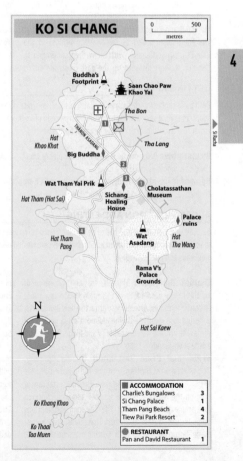

4

KO SI CHANG

0 ———— 500
metres

Buddha's Footprint
Saan Chao Paw Khao Yai
Tha Bon
THANON ASADANG
Hat Khao Khat
Tha Lang
Big Buddha
Wat Tham Yai Prik
Hat Tham (Hat Sai)
Sichang Healing House
Cholatassathan Museum
Palace ruins
Hat Tham Pang
Wat Asadang
Hat Tha Wang
Rama V's Palace Grounds
N
Hat Sai Kaew
Ko Khang Khao
Ko Thaai Taa Muen

Si Racha

■ **ACCOMMODATION**
Charlie's Bungalows 3
Si Chang Palace 1
Tham Pang Beach 4
Tiew Pai Park Resort 2

● **RESTAURANT**
Pan and David Restaurant ... 1

Saan Chao Paw Khao Yai

The showy, multi-tiered Chinese temple of **Saan Chao Paw Khao Yai** (Shrine of the Father Spirit of the Great Hill) is stationed at the top of a steep flight of steps and commands a good view of the harbour and the mainland coast. Established here long before Rama V arrived on the island, the shrine was dedicated by Chinese seamen who saw a strange light coming out of one of the **caves** behind the modern-day temple. The caves, now full of religious statues and related paraphernalia, are visited by boatloads of Chinese pilgrims, particularly over Chinese New Year. Continue on up the cliffside to reach the small pagoda built for Rama V and enshrining a **Buddha's Footprint**. Two very long, very steep flights of stairs give access to the footprint: the easternmost one starts at the main waterfront entrance to the Chinese temple and takes you past a cluster of monks' meditation cells, while the westerly one rises further west along the ring road and offers the finest lookouts.

ARRIVAL AND INFORMATION

KO SI CHANG

By boat Ferries to Ko Si Chang leave from Tha Wat Ko Loy in Si Racha (see p.382) from 6am to 8pm (hourly; 40–50min; B50, later ferries B60), wending their way past the congestion of international cargo boats and Thai supply barges that anchor in the protected channel between the mainland and Ko Si Chang. On arrival, boats dock first at Tha Lang (also signed as Tateawavong Bridge) in the island's main settlement, with many then continuing to Tha Bon a short distance up the east coast. Motorized

samlor drivers meet the boats and charge B50 to most accommodation, or B80 to Hat Tham Pang; as they are paid commission by some hotels and restaurants, be wary of any opinionated remarks. Boats to the mainland leave Tha Lang between 6am and 7pm (hourly; 40–50min); the same boats depart Tha Bon 15min earlier.

Tourist information Ⓦko-sichang.com, a useful website compiled by David at *Pan and David Restaurant* (see below), offers detailed coverage of the island.

GETTING AROUND

Both piers connect with Thanon Asadang, a small, concrete ring road on which you'll find the market, a bank and many shops. In town it's easy enough to walk from place to place, but to really enjoy what Ko Si Chang has to offer you'll need to either rent a motorbike or charter a samlor for the day.

By motorbike Bikes can be rented from the pier or from *Charlie's Bungalows* for B300 a day.
By samlor The island's trademark samlors are driven by distinctive, elongated 1200cc motorbikes and virtually

monopolize the roads, as there are barely any private cars; a tour of the island will set you back around B350, or B60 an hour.

ACCOMMODATION AND EATING

Because water on the island has to be bought from a private desalination company at six times the price it costs on the mainland, **accommodation** on Ko Si Chang is expensive and disappointingly poor value. Booking ahead is advisable for weekends and public holidays.

Charlie's Bungalows Thanon Asadang, 2min walk south of Tiew Pai Park Resort in town ☎085 191 3863, Ⓦkohsichang.net. A dozen or so attractive new bungalows, done out in a maritime theme around a small garden; all come with a/c, hot water, satellite TV and fridge. Prices go up a little at weekends. B1000

★**Pan and David Restaurant** Thanon Asadang, 200m before the entrance to the old palace grounds ☎038 216075, Ⓦko-sichang.com. The only restaurant of note on the island, run by a sociable and well-informed American expat and his Thai wife. The long and delicious menu includes authentically fiery Thai salads, tasty home-made fettuccine (B295 with porcini mushroom sauce),

fillet steak, Thai curries (B180 with free-range chicken), and home-made fresh strawberry ice cream. Mon, Tues, Thurs & Fri roughly 10am–10.30pm, Sat & Sun 8.30am–10.30pm.
Si Chang Palace Thanon Asadang, across from Tha Bon in town ☎038 216276–9, Ⓦsichangpalace.com. The most upmarket place on the island has good a/c rooms with balconies, the best of them enjoying fine eastward sea views; all have hot water, TV and fridge. There's a pool here too. Breakfast included. B1260
Tham Pang Beach Hat Tham Pang ☎038 216179, Ⓦtampangbeach.com. The busiest west-coast accommo- dation, whose twenty fairly rudimentary concrete

bungalows – all with bathroom, fans and TVs, some with sea views – are stacked in tiers up the cliffside behind Ko Si Chang's only beach. There's a restaurant, plus beach equipment for rent, though no wi-fi. Reservations essential for weekends. **B700**

Tiew Pai Park Resort Thanon Asadang, in town near Tha Lang ☎ 038 216084, ⊛ tiewpai.net. Very central and

cheaper than the competition, this is most backpackers' first choice. Bungalows and rooms are crammed around a scruffy garden across the road from the restaurant and many are pretty basic; the best value are the en-suite fan bungalows, some of which have TV and fridge, and there are also some cheap single rooms with shared bathrooms. No wi-fi. Fan **B650**, a/c **B950**

DIRECTORY

Massage The charming little Sichang Healing House (☎ 038 216467; Mon, Tues & Thurs–Sun 9am–6pm, ⊛ ko-sichang.com/spa_welcome.html), west off Thanon Asadang on the way to the old palace, offers Thai massage

(B500 for 90min) and herbal treatments, as well as five-day massage courses (B6000), at its cute little garden retreat. There's a small branch on Hat Tham Pang too.

Pattaya

With its streets full of high-rise hotels and hustlers on every corner, **PATTAYA** is the epitome of exploitative tourism gone mad, but most of the two million annual visitors don't mind that the place looks like the Costa del Sol bathed in smog because what they are here for is sex. The city swarms with male and female **prostitutes**, spiced up by Thailand's largest population of *katoey* (transgender females), involved in sex work, and plane-loads of Western men flock here to enjoy their services in the rash of hostess bar-beers, go-go clubs and massage parlours for which "Patpong-on-Sea" is notorious. The signs trumpeting "Viagra for Sale" say it all. Pattaya also has the largest number of **gay services** (targeted mainly at foreigners) in Thailand, with several exclusively gay hotels and an entire zone devoted to gay sex bars.

Pattaya's evolution into sin city began with the Vietnam War, when it got fat on selling sex to American servicemen. When the soldiers and sailors left in the mid-1970s, Western tourists were lured in to fill their places, and ex-servicemen soon returned to run the sort of joints they had once blown their dollars in. These days, at least half the bars and restaurants in Pattaya are Western-run. More recently, there has been an influx of criminal gangs from Germany, Russia and Japan, who reportedly find Pattaya a convenient centre for running their rackets in passport and credit-card fraud, as well as child pornography and prostitution; expat murders are a regular news item in the *Pattaya Mail*.

Local tourism authorities try hard to improve Pattaya's **image**, and with surprising success now entice families and older couples with a catalogue of more wholesome entertainments such as theme parks, golf courses, shopping plazas and year-round diving. Russian, Chinese and Korean holidaymakers seem particularly keen, and Cyrillic and Chinese script are now a common sight. A recent flush of more sophisticated boutique hotels and restaurants is also starting to bring in a younger Thai crowd, which has brightened the picture a little. But in truth the beach here is far from pristine – way outshone by Ko Samet just along the coast – so after-hours "entertainment" is still the primary inducement.

Pattaya Beach

At the heart of this ever-expanding adult playground is 4km-long **Pattaya Beach**, the noisiest, most unsightly zone of the resort, crowded with yachts and tour boats and fringed by a sliver of sand and a paved beachfront walkway. The densest glut of hotels, restaurants, bars, fast-food joints, souvenir shops and tour operators is halfway down Pattaya Beach Road (also signed as Pattaya Saineung), in **Central Pattaya** (Pattaya Klang),

PATTAYA BEACH

ACCOMMODATION

Areca Lodge	8
Centara Nova Hotel	5
The Cottage	3
Diana Dragon Apartment	7
Dusit Thani Pattaya	2
Ice Inn	6
Pattaya Marriott	9
Sandalay Resort	4
Woodlands Hotel and Resort	1

RESTAURANTS & CAFÉS

Ali Baba	6
Italia	7
Khao Suay	4
Ko Khun Pon Yang Kham	1
Mantra	3
PIC Kitchen	5
Seoul Grill	2

BARS & CLUBS

The Blues Factory	5
Heineken Beer Garden	1
Hopf Brew House	4
Jazz Pit	2
Minus Five Ice Bar	3

SHOPS

Asia Books	1
Thais4Life	2

between sois 6 and 13, but after dark the action moves to the neon zone south of Soi 13/2. Here, in **South Pattaya**, and specifically along ultra-sleazy **Walking Street**, sex is peddled in hundreds of go-go bars, discos, massage parlours and open-sided bar-beers, and the hordes of visitors treat it as a tourist sideshow. The gay district is also here, in the lanes known as **Pattayaland** sois 1, 2 and 3 (or **Boyz Town**), but actually signed as sois 13/3, 13/4 and 13/5.

Jomtien Beach and Buddha Hill

South around the headland from South Pattaya, **Jomtien Beach** (sometimes spelt Chom Tian) is also fronted by enormous high-rises, many of them condominiums. Though the atmosphere here is not as frantic as in Pattaya, Jomtien also flounders under an excess of bar-beers and shops flogging tacky souvenirs and, like its neighbour, is forever under construction. The nicest stretch of sand is shady **Dongtan Beach**, beyond the northern end of Jomtien Beach Road, which is also Pattaya's main gay beach, though used by all. The bulge of land behind Dongtan Beach, separating Jomtien from South Pattaya, is Khao Phra Tamnak, variously translated as **Buddha Hill** or **Pattaya Hill**, site of several posh hotels and the Pattaya Park waterpark and funfair.

Underwater World

Thanon Sukhumvit, just south of the Thep Prasit junction near Tesco Lotus, behind Jomtien Beach • Daily 9am–6pm • B5000 • ⓦ underwaterworldpattaya.com

If you've been disappointed with local reef life, the small and expensive but rather beautiful aquarium at **Underwater World** might make up for it, with its trio of long

JOMTIEN BEACH & BUDDHA HILL

fibreglass tunnels that transport you through shallow rockpools to the ocean floor. There are touch pools and masses of reef fish, as well as a long roster of feeding times, detailed on the website.

Sanctuary of Truth (Wang Boran)

Off the west end of Soi 12, Thanon Naklua, close to the Garden Sea View hotel, beyond the north end of Pattaya Beach • Daily 8am–6pm • B500 • ⓦ sanctuaryoftruth.com • From Central Pattaya take a Naklua-bound songthaew as far as Soi 12, then a motorbike taxi

The hugely ambitious **Sanctuary of Truth**, or **Wang Boran**, stands in a dramatic seaside spot behind imposing crenellated walls. Conceived by the man behind the Muang Boran Ancient City complex near Bangkok (see p.132), it's a majestic 105m-high temple-palace built entirely of wood and designed to evoke the great ancient Khmer sanctuaries of Angkor. Though begun in 1981, it is ever-changing, its external walls covered in a growing gallery of beautiful, symbolic woodcarvings inspired by Cambodian, Chinese, Thai and Indian mythologies.

ACTIVITIES IN PATTAYA

DIVING AND SNORKELLING

Though Pattaya's reefs are far less spectacular than those along the Andaman coast, they can be dived year-round, and underwater visibility is consistent. Most **dive trips** focus on the group of "outer islands" about 25km from shore, which include Ko Rin, Ko Man Wichai and Ko Klung Badaan where you have a reasonable chance of seeing barracuda, moray eels and blue-spotted stingrays. There are also three rewarding wreck dives in the Samae San/Sattahip area. Be careful when choosing a dive operator as there are plenty of charlatans around. All tour agents sell **snorkelling** trips to nearby islands, the majority of them going to the reefs and beaches of **Ko Larn**. You can also make your own way to Ko Larn by public boat from the Bali Hai pier at the far southern end of Walking Street (roughly hourly 7am–6pm; 45min; B30).

Mermaid's Dive Centre Thanon Tabphaya in Jomtien, plus 3 branches elsewhere in Pattaya ⓣ 038 303333, ⓦ mermaiddive.com. One of the most reputable dive shops in Pattaya, with a PADI Five-Star Career Development Centre. It charges B3000 for two dives, with accompanying snorkellers paying B1000, and the four-day Openwater course costs B14,000.

WATERSPORTS

Beachfront stalls in Pattaya and Jomtien offer **waterskiing**, **parasailing** and **jet-skiing**, but you should avoid the last-mentioned: the jet-ski jockeys are notorious for finding scratches on the machine at the end of the rental and trying to charge an exorbitant amount in damages.

Amara Watersports Blue Lagoon Watersports Club, Soi 14 Naa Jomtien, at the far south end of Jomtien Beach ⓣ 038 233276, ⓦ amarawatersports .com. Windsurfing courses, rental and sales, as well as paddleboards, catamarans and kayaks.

Kiteboarding Asia Blue Lagoon Watersports Club, Soi 14 Naa Jomtien, at the far south end of Jomtien Beach ⓣ 085 134 9588, ⓦ bluelagoonpattaya.com. Kitesurfing courses, rental and sales.

MASSAGE

Thai Massage Development School Soi Yodsak, Central Pattaya ⓣ 038 414115–6, ⓦ tmdmassage .com. In among the full-body soaps and "full-service" massage joints, you'll find this traditional place, where you can have a proper Thai massage (B300/60min), or a herbal compress, oil or foot massage; it also offers two-week massage training courses.

COOKING CLASSES

Happy Home Soi 14, off the north side of Central Pattaya Rd, out towards Pattaya 3 Rd ⓣ 084 417 5258, ⓦ happyhome-thaicookingschool.com. Morning (including a market visit) and afternoon classes, with vegetarian versions of all dishes available, and including a weekly dessert class. B1250 including a recipe booklet. Local hotel pickup B50.

ARRIVAL AND DEPARTURE

PATTAYA

By plane Pattaya's U-Tapao Airport (☎038 245599) is inconveniently located at the naval base near Sattahip, about 25km south of the resort, from where a taxi will cost you about B800; you're probably better off using Bangkok's Suvarnabhumi Airport (see p.133), which is linked to Pattaya by bus. The Bangkok Airways office is at Fairtex Arcade, North Pattaya Rd (☎038 412382).

Destinations Ko Samui (1–2 daily; 1hr); Phuket (1 daily; 1hr 35min).

By bus All first-class and VIP Bangkok buses, and some Suvarnabhumi Airport buses, arrive at and depart from the bus station on North Pattaya Rd. Slower second-class Bangkok buses and some Suvarnabhumi Airport buses use the station on Thanon Chaiyapruk in Jomtien, and there are also airport buses from a terminal on Thanon Tabphaya in Jomtien. It's also possible to get to Pattaya direct from Isaan and the north: Nakorn Chai buses to and from Chiang Mai, Chiang Rai, Khorat and Ubon use a terminus on Thanon Sukhumvit, across from the Central Pattaya Rd intersection (☎038 424871); other Isaan buses can be found at two terminals on the opposite side of Thanon Sukhumvit and at the first-class bus station on North Pattaya Rd, which has songthaews that take you south along one-way Pattaya Beach Road (B25), returning along Pattaya 2 Road. Coming by bus from Si Racha, Rayong or Trat, you'll probably get dropped on Thanon Sukhumvit, the resort's eastern limit, from where songthaews will ferry you into town (B30). If heading on to these towns, you need to pick up your bus from one of the drops on Thanon Sukhumvit (easiest at the junctions with North, Central and South Pattaya roads).

Destinations Bangkok (Eastern/Northern bus terminals; every 30min; 2hr 30min–4hr); Bangkok (Southern Bus Terminal; every 2hr; 3hr 30min); Bangkok (Suvarnabhumi Airport; 7 daily; 2hr); Chanthaburi (6 daily; 3hr); Chiang Mai (8 daily; 12–14hr); Chiang Rai (2 daily; 15–17hr); Khorat (4 daily; 5hr); Rayong (every 30min; 1hr 30min); Si Racha (every 20min; 30min); Trat (6 daily; 4hr 30min); Ubon Ratchathani (6 daily; 10–12hr).

By a/c minibus In Bangkok, hostels near Khao San Rd can arrange an a/c minibus service to the beach near Walking Street for B400/person; drivers pick you up from your accommodation but may charge B100 to drop you off at your hotel or before the last stop. You can catch an a/c minibus to Bangkok's Victory Monument for B250 from several spots, including the east end of Central Pattaya Rd near Foodland and South Pattaya Rd in front of the Family Mart near Krung Thai Bank. Any hotel can arrange a ticket on a shared a/c minibus to Suvarnabhumi Airport for around B250/person (or about B800/car for a metered taxi). There are also tourist minibus services to Ko Samet and Ko Chang (tickets can also be booked through most tour agents): Samet Island Tour on Soi Yamato (☎038 427277, ⓦmalibu-samet.com) runs to the Ban Phe pier (for Ko Samet; B400 including transfer and boat but not B200 national park fee); and Pattaya 35 Group, opposite Big C on South Pattaya Rd (☎038 423447) goes to Ko Chang (B700 including ferry), via Ban Phe and Chanthaburi.

By train Pattaya is on a branch of the eastern rail line, and there's one slow train a day in each direction between the resort and Bangkok. Pattaya has two stations, both off the east side of Thanon Sukhumvit: the main one is about 500m north of the Central Pattaya Rd intersection, while Pattaya Tai Station is in South Pattaya near the Thanon Thep Prasit junction. Songthaews (B30) wait at the main station to take passengers to Pattaya Beach Road; from Pattaya Tai Station a songthaew (B10) can take you along Thanon Thep Prasit to Jomtien Beach Road.

Destinations Bangkok (daily; 4hr); Si Racha (daily; 30min).

4

INFORMATION

Tourist information There are municipal tourist service booths (daily roughly 8.30am–4pm) on the beach at the mouth of Walking Street, at City Hall on North Pattaya Rd, at the north end of Jomtien Beach Rd and opposite Thanon Chaiyapruk on Jomtien Beach. Note that private tour companies also pose as "tourist information". The TAT office is inconveniently located at 609 Thanon Pratamnak between South Pattaya and Jomtien (daily 8.30am–4.30pm; ☎038 428750, ⓔtatchon@tat.or.th).

GETTING AROUND

By songthaew Public songthaews – known locally as baht buses, and also available to charter – circulate continuously around the resort from dawn until at least 11pm. Most follow a standard anticlockwise route up Pattaya 2 Rd as far as North Pattaya Rd and back down Pattaya Beach Rd, for a fixed fee of B10/person; others run along the main east–west arteries of North, Central and South Pattaya roads. Songthaews to Jomtien start from next to the school on the south side of the junction of Pattaya 2 Rd and South Pattaya Rd and cost B10–20. Songthaews to Naklua, beyond north Pattaya, start from the north side of the same junction and head up Pattaya 2 Rd (also B10–20).

By mototaxi Drivers in red or green vests are everywhere and offer a very open-air ride from the centre of Pattaya Beach Road to Walking Street for about B50. Helmet not necessarily included; hold on to the rack behind you.

By motorbike Motorbike rental is available everywhere from B250/day, but beware of faulty vehicles, and of scams – sometimes rented bikes get stolen by touts keen to keep the customer's deposit, so you may want to use your own lock. Unpredictable drivers and a disregard for road rules makes Pattaya potentially dangerous for inexperienced riders, with frequent accidents and fatalities. Avoid wearing expensive-looking jewellery while riding a motorbike as ride-by snatchings sometimes occur.

By car Avis car rental (ⓦavisthailand.com) has an office inside the *Dusit Resort* (ⓣ038 361627); many of the motorbike touts also rent out jeeps for about B1300/day.

ACCOMMODATION

The quietest and least sleazy end of town to stay in is **North Pattaya**, between Central Pattaya Road and North Pattaya Road (Thanon Hat Pattaya Neua). There's no travellers' scene in Pattaya and hotels offering doubles under B450 outside low season are almost impossible to find; the cheapest alternatives are often rooms above the bars on sois 6, 13/2, 13/3 and 13/4.

PATTAYA BEACH

Areca Lodge 198/21 Soi Saisong 13 (aka Soi Diana Inn), Central Pattaya ⓣ038 410123, ⓦarecalodge .com; map p.386. An unusually stylish place for Pattaya, with pleasantly furnished a/c rooms in three wings built around two swimming pools, most of them with balconies, all with king beds and hot showers. Buffet breakfast included. B2100

Centara Nova Hotel Soi 12 (aka Soi A.R. or Soi Sukrudee), Central Pattaya Rd ⓣ038 725999, ⓦcentarahotelsresorts.com; map p.386. Central, quiet and welcoming boutique hotel, done out in a plush contemporary style that features a lot of burnished gold. There's a large, attractive pool fed by an artificial waterfall, a spa that uses Dead Sea mud and salt, and a fitness centre. Breakfast included. B4500

The Cottage Off Pattaya 2 Rd, North Pattaya ⓣ038 425650, ⓦthecottagepattaya.com; map p.386. Good-value, simply furnished semi-detached brick bungalows, all with a/c, hot water, TV and fridge, pleasantly set among tall trees within a mature tropical garden away from the main road but opposite the Central Centre. Facilities include two small swimming pools. B1200

Diana Dragon Apartment 198/16 Soi Saisong 13 (aka Soi Diana Inn), Central Pattaya ⓣ038 423928, ⓦdianapattaya.co.th; map p.386. This long-running Pattaya institution has some of the cheapest doubles in town, and they're good value considering the competition: huge and quite light, with a breakfast buffet included, plus use of the pool at *Diana Inn*, 100m away. Guests are left to their own devices, so expect a mild level of neighbour noise. Fan B450, a/c B750

Dusit Thani Pattaya 240/2 Pattaya Beach Rd, North Pattaya ⓣ038 425611, ⓦdusit.com; map p.386. In the less sleazy part of town, this luxury Thai chain hotel is one of only a few Beach Road hotels to be actually on the beach (the others are at the southern end). Sea-view rooms are worth paying extra for as the impressive panoramas take in the whole bay. Also on offer are two swimming pools, a spa and tennis courts, as well as good-value transfers from their hotel on Thanon Silom in Bangkok. B4000

Ice Inn Corner of Saisong 12 and Pattaya 2 Rd, Central Pattaya ⓣ038 720671, ⓦiceinnpattaya.com; map p.386. Cheap fan-cooled singles and reasonably priced a/c doubles in this small thirty-room hotel behind a handicrafts shop, a few metres from the busier bar-beer sois. Rooms are simple but are all en suite. B790

Pattaya Marriott 218 Pattaya Beach Rd, Central Pattaya ⓣ038 412120, ⓦmarriotthotels.com; map p.386. Located in the heart of the resort (attached to the Royal Garden Plaza shopping centre), and across the road from the beach, this international chain hotel is both very central and refreshingly calm, not least because it's designed around a huge swimming pool and tropical garden full of palms. Not surprisingly, it's the first choice for anyone in Pattaya on business. Rooms are capacious and comfortable and have either pool- or sea views. Facilities include two restaurants, a fitness centre and kids' yoga. B6900

Sandalay Resort Between sois 1 and 2, Pattaya Beach Rd, North Pattaya ⓣ038 422660, ⓦsandalayresort .com; map p.386. This hundred-room hotel with swimming pool is in the quieter northern part of town, just across the road from the beach. It has contemporary-styled, well-designed, though quite small, standard a/c rooms plus impressively large deluxe versions. Both options are available with sea view and tiny balcony at extra cost. Good discounts often available. Breakfast included. B3200

Woodlands Hotel and Resort 164 Thanon Pattaya-Naklua, North Pattaya ⓣ038 421707, ⓦwoodland -resort.com; map p.386. A quiet, unpretentious and welcoming family-friendly garden resort 100m north of the Dolphin Circle roundabout, and 400m from a scruffy but quiet thread of beach. The elegant, a/c rooms are in two storeys set round the pools and garden; the most expensive have direct access to the pool from ground-floor balconies. B3060

JOMTIEN AND BUDDHA HILL

★ **Rabbit Resort** Dongtan beachfront, Jomtien ⓣ038 303303, ⓦrabbitresort.com; map p.387. Beautiful place that's the most appealing option in Jomtien, and located on the nicest stretch of beach, the predominantly but not exclusively gay Dongtan Beach. Most accommodation is in teakwood cottages that are elegantly furnished with Thai fabrics and antiques and have garden-style bathrooms;

there are also some "forest rooms" in a two-storey block. All are set around a tropical garden and pool just metres off the beach. Breakfast included. Rooms B4900, cottages B5900

Sheraton Pattaya Resort 437 Thanon Pratamnak (Cliff Rd), South Pattaya ☎038 259888, ⓦstarwood hotels.com; map p.387. Pattaya's most upmarket hotel is smaller and more intimate than most in its class and offers five-star rooms and private pavilions, all with balconies, rain showers and DVD players, for which you pay extra. The beautiful series of freeform swimming pools and the spa are set within lush gardens – compensating for the minuscule private beach – though it's built on a hill so be

prepared for lots of steps. There is a shuttle bus to the shops and restaurants of downtown Pattaya. B6944

Sugar Hut 391/18 Thanon Tabphaya, midway between South Pattaya and Jomtien ☎038 251686, ⓦsugar-hut .com; map p.387. The most characterful accommodation in Pattaya comprises a charming collection of Ayutthaya-style traditional wooden bungalows set in a fabulously profuse garden with three swimming pools, saunas and steam rooms. The bungalows are in tropical-chic style, with low beds, open-roofed shower rooms, mosquito nets and private verandas. There's a few eating options nearby, but you'll need your own transport for the five-minute drive to Jomtien Beach Road or Pattaya Beach Road. B4500

EATING

In among the innumerable low-grade Western cafés that dominate Pattaya's **restaurant scene** are a few much classier joints serving good, sophisticated cuisine – at top-end prices. For the cheapest, most authentic Thai food, just head for the nearest of Pattaya's myriad building sites and you'll find street stalls catering to the construction-site workers.

PATTAYA BEACH

Ali Baba 1/13–14 Central Pattaya Rd ☎038 361620; map p.386. Look beyond the name and the wonderfully kitsch decor and waiters' uniforms, and you'll find some very good Indian food, which keeps many of Pattaya's visitors from the subcontinent happy. There's an authentically long menu of vegetarian dishes, featuring plenty of cheese and some interesting starters with okra; in addition, the butter chicken's a real winner (B260). Daily 11am–midnight.

Italia Walking St, South Pattaya; map p.386. This very Italian café is an incongruously swish little haven with outdoor tables for watching the sleazy cabaret show that is Walking Street. Delicious home-made ice creams (B95 for 2 scoops), espressos, Sambuca and the like. Daily 9am–4am.

Khao Suay Ground Floor, Central Centre, Pattaya 2 Rd, North Pattaya; map p.386. A long menu of good modern Thai food (most mains B120–180) draws Thai families to this tiny café inside the shopping centre. The varied English menu includes *kaeng tai pla* (southern Thai fish stomach curry) and *nam prik pla thuu* (chilli relish with mackerel). The tasty one-meal rice dishes (B70) make for great solo dining. Daily 11am–9.45pm.

★**Ko Khun Pon Yang Kham** North Pattaya Rd, at Soi 6 ☎038 420571, ⓦko-khun.com; map p.386. This garden restaurant offers Thailand's equivalent of wagyu beef, from pampered Pon Yang Kham cows that are bred (from French, Swiss and Thai breeds) and reared in Isaan. It's served northeastern-style too, so no chips or mustard, but it goes well with *som tam*, and the red wine is decent (B100/ glass). B145 for a small but delicious portion of sirloin on a sizzling-hot plate. Daily 5.30pm–midnight.

★**Mantra** Amari Orchid Hotel, Beach Rd, North Pattaya ☎038 429591, ⓦmantra-pattaya.com; map p.386. Setting the standard unexpectedly high for Pattaya,

this large, beautifully designed bar-restaurant creates an ambience somewhere between a contemporary Shanghai hotel and a maharaja's palace. Downstairs there's an open-plan view of the seven different, equally eclectic kitchens specializing in Japanese, Chinese, Indian, Mediterranean and Western food, grills and seafood. A meal might begin with avocado sushi (B410), supplemented with bite-sized Peking duck (B260), continue with coq au vin (B410), and end with a baked mango and glutinous rice parcel with coconut ice cream (B310). The walk-in wine cellar keeps over 160 imported wines. Mon–Sat 5pm–1am, Sun 11am–3pm & 5pm–1am.

PIC Kitchen Soi 5, North Pattaya ☎038 428374, ⓦpic-kitchen.com; map p.386. One of Pattaya's top traditional Thai restaurants, set in a stylish series of teak buildings with the option of Thai-style cushion seating. Elegantly presented curries, lots of different seafood platters, spicy salads and lots of vegetarian dishes (B140). Most mains B220–280. Daily 11am–2pm & 5–11pm.

Seoul Grill The One Patio, next to Burger King, Pattaya 2 Rd, North Pattaya ☎038 411982; map p.386. Long streams of Korean visitors to Pattaya keep the dishes authentic at this clean, two-level spot with classics such as bibimbap (meat and vegetable rice bowls), hot pots and Korean barbecue. There are half a dozen other Korean and Japanese restaurants in the same outdoor plaza. Daily 11am–10pm.

JOMTIEN BEACH

Bruno's 306/63 Chateau Dale Plaza, Thanon Tabphaya, Jomtien ☎038 364600–1, ⓦbrunos-pattaya.com; map p.387. A local institution that's a favourite with expats celebrating special occasions. The food is upmarket, expensive and European – Provençal-style rack of lamb, sirloin steak, dark-chocolate mousse – and there's a cellar

4

of some 150 wines. Main dishes from B250. Daily noon–2.30pm & 6pm–late.

Sugar Hut 391/18 Thanon Tabphaya, Jomtien; map p.387. Attached to the charming hotel of the same name (see p.391), this restaurant gives you the chance to soak up the ambience and enjoy the tropical gardens without shelling out for a bungalow (though the food's not cheap either, with mains starting at B180). Meals are served in an open-sided *sala* and the menu is mainly classy Thai; recommendations include roast duck in red curry (B280). Daily 7am–midnight.

DRINKING AND NIGHTLIFE

Pattaya's **nightlife** revolves around sex (see box below). It is, however, just about possible to have a night out without getting entangled in sleaze, at one of the growing number of hostess-free **bars** listed below, a few of which are surprisingly style-conscious. However you choose to spend your evening, be warned that Pattaya is notorious for female and *katoey* (transgender female) **pickpockets**, who target drunk men walking home in the early hours: while one "distracts" the victim from the front, the other extracts the wallet from behind.

The Blues Factory Soi Lucky Star, Walking St, South Pattaya ⒲thebluesfactorypattaya.com; map p.386. Considered to be the best live-music venue in Pattaya, with sets most nights (Tues–Sat) from the famously charismatic rock guitarist Lam Morrison and his band, and (except on Tues & Wed) from the house blues band as well. Daily 8.30pm–late.

Heineken Beer Garden Central Centre, Pattaya 2 Rd, North Pattaya; map p.386. Outdoor tables, draught Heineken and live music nightly (from about 8pm) from Thai singers and bands, doing mostly Thai pop and country. Also serves a full menu of Thai food (dishes from about B120), with Isaan and seafood specialities. Daily 5pm–2am.

Hopf Brew House Pattaya Beach Rd, between sois 13/1 (Yamato) and 13/2 (Post Office), Central Pattaya; map p.386. Cavernous and very popular a/c beer hall that brews its own Pilsener and wheat beer, serves generous wood-fired pizzas and other Italian dishes, and stages live music nightly. Attracts a youngish crowd, including vacationing couples. Daily 2pm–1/2am.

Jazz Pit Soi 5, North Pattaya ⒲jazzpitpub.com; map p.386. Nightly live jazz (from 8pm) in the cosy lounge-bar adjacent to the *PIC Kitchen* restaurant, and occasional high-profile celeb jamming sessions. Daily 7pm–midnight.

Minus Five Ice Bar Amari Nova Suites, Soi 12 (Soi Sukrudee), Central Pattaya Rd ☏038 426768, ⒲amari.com/novasuites; map p.386. Your chance to literally chill out at this cube of a bar sculpted entirely from ice, right down to the draught beer kegs on the ice-cold counter. For B500 you get lent a winter coat and mittens and are given 20min to down as many vodka shots as you can, then it's back out into the warmth of the trendy Bangkok-style bar adjacent. Tricky to find, it's easier to ask for the large white hotel that it is in, *Amari Nova Suites*. Daily 6pm–late.

PATTAYA'S SEX INDUSTRY

Of the thousand-plus bars in Pattaya, the vast majority are staffed by women and men whose aim is to get bought for the night – depending on whom you believe, there are between six thousand and twenty thousand Thais (and quite a few Russians) working in Pattaya's **sex industry**; most depressing of all is that this workforce includes children as young as 10, despite fairly frequent high-profile paedophile arrests. The vast majority of Pattaya's bars are open-air "**bar-beers**", which group themselves in neon clusters all over North, Central and South Pattaya so that there's barely a 500m stretch of road without a rowdy enclave. The setup is the same in all of them: from mid-afternoon the punters – usually lone males – sit on stools around a brashly lit circular bar, behind which the hostesses (and their high-end versions, the "coyotes") keep the drinks, bawdy chat and well-worn jokes flowing. Where prices aren't established, this is open to a well-known scam of demanding an inflated bill at the end, with threats if the client doesn't cough up.

Drinks are a lot more expensive in the bouncer-guarded **go-go bars** on Walking Street in South Pattaya, where near-naked hostesses serve the beer and live sex shows keep the boozers hooked through the night. The scene follows much the same pattern as in Patpong, Nana and Soi Cowboy in Bangkok, with the women dancing on a small stage in the hope they might be bought for the night – or the week. Go-go dancers, "modelling competitions", shower shows and striptease are also the mainstays of the **gay scene**, centred on Pattayaland Soi 3 (Soi 13/5), South Pattaya.

ENTERTAINMENT

CINEMAS

There are several English-language screenings a day at the multiplexes.

Major Cineplex The Avenue shopping centre, Pattaya 2 Rd, Central Pattaya ⓦ majorcineplex.com.

SF Cinema City Central Festival Centre, Pattaya Beach Rd, Central Pattaya ⓦ sfcinemacity.com.

KATOEY CABARETS

Tour groups – and families – constitute the main audience at Pattaya's *katoey* cabarets. Glamorous and highly professional, each theatre has a troupe of sixty or more transgender women who run through twenty musical-style numbers in fishnets and crinolines, ball gowns and leathers, against ever more lavish stage sets. Any tour agent can organize tickets or you can book at the venue.

Alcazar Opposite Soi 4 on Pattaya 2 Rd in North Pattaya ⓦ alcazarthailand.com. From B600. Daily 5pm, 6.30pm, 8pm & 9.30pm.

Tiffany's North of Soi 1 on Pattaya 2 Rd in North Pattaya ⓦ tiffany-show.co.th. Also hosts an annual international *katoey* beauty pageant over five days in early Nov, Miss International Queen (ⓦ missinternationalqueen.com). From B600. Daily 6pm, 7.30pm & 9pm.

SHOPPING

Asia Books Floor 3, Central Festival Centre, between Pattaya Beach and Pattaya 2 rds. Good selection of English-language books. Daily 11am–11pm.

Thais4Life 504 Soi Yensabai Condotel, off Soi 17 (Soi VC), South Pattaya. One of Pattaya's best secondhand bookshops, this charity sells all its books for B80 (exchanges for B40) and donates profits to medical and other needy projects including Baan Jing Jai orphanage. Mon–Sat noon–6pm.

DIRECTORY

Emergencies For all emergencies, call the tourist police on ☏ 1155 (free, 24hr) or contact them at their office beside TAT on Buddha Hill, between South Pattaya and Jomtien; in the evenings, they also set up a post at the north end of Walking Street.

Hospitals and dentists The best-equipped hospital is the private Bangkok-Pattaya Hospital (☏ 1719 or ☏ 038 259999, ⓦ bangkokpattayahospital.com) on Thanon Sukhumvit, about 400m north of the intersection with North Pattaya Rd, which also has dental services.

Immigration office Soi 5, off Jomtien Beach Rd, Jomtien (Mon–Fri 8.30am–4.30pm; ☏ 038 252750).

Ban Phe

The small coastal town of **BAN PHE**, which lies 17km east of Rayong, its provincial capital, and about 200km from Bangkok, is the port for Ko Samet. Several piers for Samet boats compete for attention here, along with minimarkets, internet centres and tour desks selling onward bus tickets and private transfers. Ban Phe's main street runs from west to east behind the seafront, passing in turn the Chok Krisda pier and the nearby Taruaphe pier, before petering out a few hundred metres later at the municipal pier, Tha Reua Tessaban.

ARRIVAL AND INFORMATION   BAN PHE

When the time comes to leave Ko Samet, you can book tickets for any of the following direct buses and minibuses from Ban Phe at tour agencies on the island.

By bus There are direct a/c buses operated by Cherdchai between Bangkok's Eastern (Ekamai) Bus Terminal and Ban Phe; on departure from Ban Phe, you can easily find them near the municipal pier. Coming by bus from Chanthaburi or Trat, you'll be dropped at a T-junction on Highway 3, from where a songthaew or motorbike taxi will take you the remaining 5km to the Ban Phe piers. Rayong has a wider choice of buses, including services to Chiang Mai and Isaan; the Ban Phe piers are served by frequent songthaews (about 30min) from Rayong bus station.

Destinations Bangkok (14 daily; 3hr); Chanthaburi (from Highway 3; 6 daily; 1hr 30min); Trat (from Highway 3; 6 daily; 3hr).

By a/c minibus A/c minibuses run between many locations in Bangkok, including Thanon Khao San (3–4hr; B250), Victory Monument (about 3hr 30min; B200) and Suvarnabhumi Airport (about 3hr; B400), and Ban Phe. There are also services from Pattaya (see p.389) and Ko Chang (see p.409). On departure, you'll find numerous a/c minibus companies in Ban Phe, including some at the municipal pier and in the two sois opposite Taruaphe (including Pattaya and Ko Chang services), on either side of

4

a 7-Eleven; a frequent Victory Monument service runs from 200m west of the municipal pier; and the helpful RMT at the front of the Chok Krisda pier (☎ 086 344 4026) runs minibuses which serve all three bus terminals in Bangkok, as well as Victory Monument.

By boat Frequent boats run from Ban Phe to Ko Samet,

leaving from various piers – Tha Reua Tessaban has the widest choice. Details are given in our Ko Samet coverage (see p.398).

Tourist police At the municipal pier ☎ 038 651669 or ☎ 1155.

ACCOMMODATION

Christie's Prominent green building, next to a 7-Eleven and opposite the Taruaphe pier ☎ 089 834 9103, ⓦ christiesbanphe.com. This is a good choice for accommodation if you get stuck in Ban Phe, offering homely, attractive rooms, some on the back away from the

main road, all with a/c, hot water, TV and fridge. Downstairs is a restaurant and Irish bar, which organizes visa runs to Cambodia and trips to Siam Reap, and next door is a secondhand bookshop. **B600**

Ko Samet

B200 national park admission fee

Blessed with the softest, squeakiest sand within weekending distance of Bangkok, the tiny island of **KO SAMET**, which measures just 6km from top to toe, is a favourite escape for Thais, expats and tourists. Its fourteen small but dazzlingly white beaches are breathtakingly beautiful, lapped by pale blue water and in places still shaded by coconut palms and occasional white-flowered cajeput (*samet*) trees, which gave the island its name and which are used to build boats. But they are also crowded – although on weekdays there's a lot more room to breathe and relax – and developed to full capacity with over fifty sprawling, albeit low-rise, bungalow developments, a disfiguring number of which pay scant attention to landscaping and rubbish disposal. It's a sobering state of affairs considering that much of the island's coastline has been protected as part of the Khao Laem Ya – Mu Ko Samet **national park** since 1981; all visitors to Ko Samet are required to pay the standard national park fee on arrival, and most hoteliers also pay rent to park authorities, but there's little evidence that this income has been used to improve the island's infrastructure.

Samet's best **beaches** are along the **east coast**, where you'll find nearly all the bungalow resorts, though there's one rather exclusive beach on the otherwise largely inaccessible west coast, and the north-coast shoreline retains a pleasingly village ambience. Most islanders and many resort staff live in the northeast, near the island's main pier, in the ramshackle, badly drained village of **Na Dan**, which has small shops and cheap food stalls as well as Samet's only school, health centre and wat. Na Dan's high street, which runs from the pier down to Hat Sai Kaew, and its other small roads, are paved, as is the road along the north coast to Ao Noi Na. However, from Hat Sai Kaew south, there's only one poorly maintained dirt road (with a branch west to Ao Prao) that runs down the island's forested central ridge, and much of the **interior** is dense jungle, home to hornbills, gibbons and spectacular butterflies. The evergreen

---

WATERSPORTS AND BOAT TRIPS ON SAMET

Samet has no decent coral reefs of its own, so you'll have to take a boat trip to the islands of Ko Kudi and Ko Thalu, off the northeast coast, to get good **snorkelling** (around B700 from most beaches) or **diving**. From the main beaches you can also organize **boat trips** around Samet itself (around B500), rent kayaks and jet skis and arrange banana-boat rides and parasailing.

Samed Resorts Diving Centre Ao Prao ☎ 038 644100–3, ⓦ samedresorts.com. B2000 for one dive, and B17,000 for the four-day PADI Openwater course.

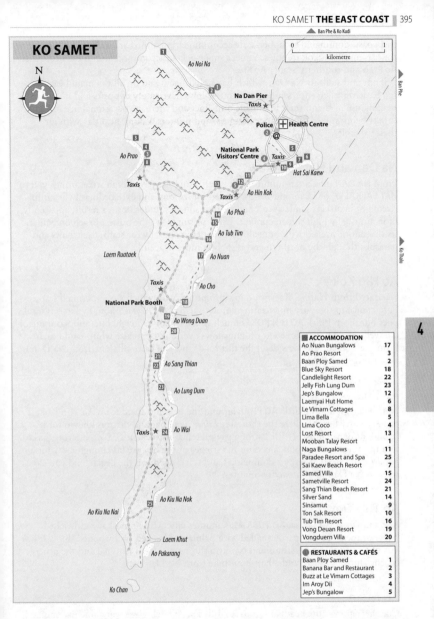

KO SAMET

N

0 _____ 1
kilometre

Ban Phe

Ko Thalu

Ao Noi Na

Na Dan Pier
Taxis ★

Police
2   ╬ Health Centre
@

National Park
Visitors' Centre
4   ★ *Taxis*

Ao Prao

3
4
3
6

Taxis ★

5
10 9 8   7 6
Hat Sai Kaew

13   11 12
3

Taxis ★
Ao Hin Kok

14
Ao Phai

15
Ao Tub Tim

16

Laem Ruataek

17   Ao Nuan

Taxis ★
Ao Cho

National Park Booth

18
Ao Wong Duan

19

20

21
22   Ao Sang Thian

23   Ao Lung Dum

Taxis ★   Ao Wai

24

Ao Kiu Na Nok

25

Ao Kiu Na Nai

Laem Khut

Ao Pakarang

Ko Chan

4

■ ACCOMMODATION	
Ao Nuan Bungalows	17
Ao Prao Resort	3
Baan Ploy Samed	2
Blue Sky Resort	18
Candlelight Resort	22
Jelly Fish Lung Dum	23
Jep's Bungalow	12
Laemyai Hut Home	6
Le Vimarn Cottages	8
Lima Bella	5
Lima Coco	4
Lost Resort	13
Mooban Talay Resort	1
Naga Bungalows	11
Paradee Resort and Spa	25
Sai Kaew Beach Resort	7
Samed Villa	15
Sametville Resort	24
Sang Thian Beach Resort	21
Silver Sand	14
Sinsamut	9
Ton Sak Resort	10
Tub Tim Resort	16
Vong Deuan Resort	19
Vongduern Villa	20

● RESTAURANTS & CAFÉS	
Baan Ploy Samed	1
Banana Bar and Restaurant	2
Buzz at Le Vimarn Cottages	3
Im Aroy Dii	4
Jep's Bungalow	5

vegetation belies the fact that there are no rivers on this unusually dry island, which gets only scant rainfall in an average year. Lack of rain is another plus point for tourists, though it means water is a precious and expensive commodity as it has to be trucked in from the mainland.

The most backpacker-oriented beaches are east-coast **Ao Hin Kok**, **Ao Phai** and **Ao Tub Tim**, with Ao Hin Kok and Ao Phai both quite lively in the evenings; the travellers' vibe at nearby **Ao Nuan** is more alternative, with **Ao Sang Thian** and north-coast **Ao Noi Na** also worth investigating. **Hat Sai Kaew** and **Ao Wong Duan** are the biggest centres on the east coast, dominated by upper-scale accommodation aimed at families, package tourists and Bangkok trendies. Samet's super-deluxe accommodation is on west-coast **Ao Prao** and southern beauty **Ao Kiu**.

Shops and stalls in Na Dan (which has a pharmacy) and on all the main beaches sell basic travellers' necessities. Many bungalows have **safety deposits** and it's worth making use of them: theft is an issue on Samet and there are occasional instances of drinks being spiked by freelance bar-girls, and punters waking next day without their valuables.

Na Dan and Hat Sai Kaew

From **NA DAN** pier, a ten-minute walk south along the paved high street brings you to **HAT SAI KAEW**, or Diamond Beach, named for its long and extraordinarily beautiful stretch of luxuriant sand, so soft and clean it squeaks underfoot – a result, apparently, of its unusually high silicon content. Unsurprisingly, it's the busiest beach on Samet, its shorefront packed with bungalows, restaurants, beachwear stalls, deckchairs and parasols, though the northern end is slightly more peaceful.

Ao Hin Kok

Separated from Hat Sai Kaew by a low promontory on which sits a mermaid statue (a reference to the early nineteenth-century poem, *Phra Abhai Mani*, by famous local poet Sunthorn Phu), **AO HIN KOK** is much smaller than its neighbour, and has more of a travellers' vibe. Just three sets of bungalows overlook the petite white-sand beach from the slope on the far side of the dirt road, and you can walk here from Na Dan in about fifteen minutes.

Ao Phai

Narrow but sparkling little **AO PHAI**, around the next headland from Ao Hin Kok, is Samet's party beach, where the shoreside *Silver Sand* bar and disco is known for its late-night dance music (with a strong gay presence at weekends). Not everyone has to join in though, as the bungalows on the fringes of the bay are far enough away for a good night's sleep. There's a minimarket and travel agent on the beach, and you can walk to Na Dan pier in twenty minutes.

Ao Tub Tim

Also known as Ao Pudsa, **AO TUB TIM** is another cute white-sand bay sandwiched between rocky points, partly shaded with palms and backed by a wooded slope. It has just two bungalow operations and is only a short stroll from Ao Phai and the other beaches further north, and a half-hour hike from Na Dan pier.

Ao Nuan

Clamber up over the headland from Ao Tub Tim (which gives you a fine panorama over Hat Sai Kaew) to reach Samet's smallest and most laidback beach, the secluded **AO NUAN**, effectively the private domain of *Ao Nuan Bungalows* (see p.399). Because it's some way off the main track, the beach gets hardly any through-traffic and feels quiet and private. Although not brilliant for swimming, the rocky shore reveals a good patch of sand when the tide withdraws; the more consistent beach at Ao Tub Tim is only five minutes' walk to the north, and **Ao Cho**, which has some coral, is a five-minute walk south along the footpath.

Ao Wong Duan

The crescent-moon bay of **AO WONG DUAN**, a ten-minute walk round the next-but-one point from Ao Nuan, is Samet's second most popular beach after Hat Sai Kaew, but the mood is calmer and more family oriented while the water is still clear and the backdrop of trees gives plenty of shade. It offers some attractive upmarket accommodation; most guests are either Chinese and Russian package tourists, Pattaya overnighters, or weekending Bangkokians, and there is only one option for shoestring travellers. Although the beach is fairly long and broad, the central shorefront is almost lost under a knot of tiny bars (many with irresistibly comfy armchairs) and tourist shops, and the main stretch of beach all but disappears at high tide. Facilities include minimarkets, ATMs and internet access.

Ao Sang Thian (Candlelight Beach) and Ao Lung Dum

A favourite with Thai students, who relish the beauty of its slightly wild setting, **AO SANG THIAN** ("Candlelight Beach") and contiguous Ao Lung Dum display almost none of the commerce of Wong Duan, a couple of minutes' walk over the hill, though the scenic shorefront is fronted by an unbroken line of bungalows. The narrow, white-sand coastline is dotted with wave-smoothed rocks and partitioned by larger outcrops that create several distinct bays; as it curves outwards to the south you get a great view of the island's east coast. At its southern end, Ao Sang Thian becomes **AO LUNG DUM**, and the various little bungalow outfits fringing the shore here are pretty similar.

Ao Wai

A fifteen-minute walk along the coast path from Lung Dum brings you to **AO WAI**, a very pretty white-sand bay, partially shaded and a good size considering it supports just one (large) **bungalow** operation, *Sametville Resort* (see p.400), which also spills across on to neighbouring little Ao Hin Kleang.

Ao Kiu

Over an hour's walk south of Ao Sang Thian, via a track that begins behind *Vong Deuan Resort* on Ao Wong Duan and can be joined at the southern end of Ao Thian, the gorgeous little twin bays of **AO KIU** – Ao Kiu Na Nok on the east coast and Ao Kiu Na Nai on the west – are separated by just a few hundred metres of land. Both beaches are the domain of Samet's most exclusive hotel, the *Paradee Resort and Spa* (see p.400).

Ao Prao (Paradise Bay)

On the upper west coast, the rugged, rocky coastline only softens into beach once, at **AO PRAO**, also known as Paradise Bay, some 4km north of Ao Kiu Na Nai. This is Samet's most upmarket beach, dominated by two expensively elegant resorts, plus one slightly more affordable option, and nothing else to lower the tone. If you're only visiting for the day, the most direct route from the east-coast beaches is via the inland track from behind *Sea Breeze* on Ao Phai, which takes about twenty minutes on foot. If staying on Ao Prao, your hotel will arrange boat transfers to Ban Phe on the mainland.

Ao Noi Na

West of Na Dan, the island's north coast – known simply as **AO NOI NA** even though it's not strictly a single bay – has a refreshingly normal village feel compared to the rest of Samet. There are an increasing number of places to stay along the narrow coastal road here, offering serene views across the water to the mainland hills behind Ban Phe, and just one white-sand beach of note at the far western end. Though this beach has been hogged by the luxurious *Mooban Talay Resort* (see p.401), it's not private and you can walk there from Na Dan pier in about twenty-five minutes, passing a good **restaurant** (see p.401) en route.

ARRIVAL AND DEPARTURE   KO SAMET

The port of departure for Ko Samet is **Ban Phe** (see p.393). If you want to book your onward travel while on Ko Samet, CP Travel on Hat Sai Kaew (☎ 038 644136), in the beach-access arcade near the national park office, sells **bus** and **minibus** as well as domestic and international **air tickets**; it also has a few new and secondhand books. Malibu Travel on Ao Wong Duan (☎ 038 710676–7) sells Ban Phe to Bangkok Victory Monument **minibus** tickets (B300) that are slightly more expensive than buying in Ban Phe. Note that boat transfers need to be bought separately.

BY BOAT

RESORT BOATS

If you're staying in any of Samet's mid-range or expensive accommodation, ask the resort about boats when you book: many establishments have their own big boats or speedboats to ferry you direct from Ban Phe on reasonably priced shared transfers (usually at set times). Such transfers may be free, but a few resorts make their paid transfers compulsory. You might also want to look into the packages offered by many resorts, which is how most Thais travel to Ko Samet: as well as boats and accommodation, these might include things like dinners and massages.

PUBLIC BOATS

There are half a dozen competing piers in Ban Phe, offering a bewildering variety of speedboats and bigger, slower but much cheaper wooden boats; prices on the latter to Samet's main pier, Na Dan, are fixed (B60 one-way; 40min). Blue wooden boats direct to Ao Wong Duan are run by Malibu Travel (B70 one-way; 70min) from the Taruaphe pier. Watch out for rip-off touts in Ban Phe who try to sell boat tickets at inflated prices or falsely claim that visitors to Ko Samet have to buy a return boat ticket. The first boat from Ko Samet back to Ban Phe leaves Na Dan pier at 7am (from Ao Wong Duan at 8.30am, noon and 4pm), and in theory there's then an hourly service across to Ban Phe until 6pm, but if you have a plane to catch you should allow for boat no-shows and delays.

Tha Reua Tessaban The municipal pier at the east end of Ban Phe has a rather chaotic market hall of a dozen or so private booths which offer the widest choice of speedboats, as well as wooden boats (in high season, hourly to Na Dan, plus three daily to Ao Wong Duan for B70).

Chok Krisda About 500m west of Tha Reua Tessaban, this helpful pier (☎ 081 862 4067) offers speedboats (B1300/boat to Na Dan; 15min) as well as wooden boats hourly to Na Dan (8am–6pm), Ao Noi Na (2 daily; about 40min; B60) and Ao Wong Duan (2 daily, 3 daily in the opposite direction; 70min; B70).

GETTING AROUND

The best way to get up and down the island is by walking along the east-coast beaches and the mostly well-marked paths that connect them. This is impossible at night where overgrown paths, rocks and water often meet indistinguishably in the dark. Samet's principal inland road is a rough, deeply rutted and alternately dusty/muddy dirt track that runs north–south and gives access to all the main beaches.

By songthaew Fleets of green songthaews wait for fares at the Na Dan pier and half a dozen other stands around the island, as marked on our map (see p.395); they will also pick up from accommodation if you get staff to phone them. Rates are fixed and high. You'll generally be charged for chartering the whole vehicle (Na Dan pier to Ao Sang Thian B350; Ao Wong Duan to Hat Sai Kaew B200). Only if there's a large group of people travelling, for example when boats dock at Na Dan, will you get the "shared" rates (B20–40/person). At the time of writing there are plans to introduce public songthaews that would regularly run north–south for a shared rated, regardless of capacity.

By motorbike or ATV You need to be very confident to negotiate the mud and potholes on a motorbike (from B300/day), which is why it's become fashionable to rent a lumbering four-wheeled ATV instead (from B1200/day); both are available for rent at Na Dan pier and on most beaches.

ACCOMMODATION

The trend across the island is upmarket, and in high season you'll be hard pressed to secure an en-suite **bungalow** for under B800, though a few no-frills B300 huts do remain. All beaches get packed on weekends and national holidays, when booking ahead is advisable, though, unusually for Thailand, walk-in guests are often offered the best rates. Many bungalow managers raise their **prices** by sixty percent during peak periods and sometimes on weekends as well: the rates quoted here are typical weekday high-season rates.

HAT SAI KAEW AND NA DAN

Much of the accommodation on Hat Sai Kaew is crammed uncomfortably close together and prices are high. Cheap rooms are sometimes available above the shops and restaurants on the Na Dan road.

Laemyai Hut Home North end of Hat Sai Kaew ☎ 038 644282. The fan bungalows here are the best of the cheapest options on this beach, not least because they're dotted widely around a shaded, sandy, plant-filled garden in one of the prettiest spots, under the Laem Yai headland at the quieter northern end. Fan bungalows are simple but have en suites and feel secluded; a/c versions, some with hot showers, are also available. Fan B800, a/c B1500

Lima Bella Na Dan ☎ 038 644222, ⓦ limasamed.com. This little garden haven occupies a quiet heliconia-filled plot with its own pretty swimming pool, on the semicircular road that arcs round behind and to the east of Na Dan high street. Its 26 design-conscious a/c rooms all have hot water, fridges, TVs and daybeds; some have separate mezzanine bedrooms or living areas and many have bathtubs. The ambience is more intimate and private than most hotels on Samet and it's popular with families. Breakfast included. B3970

Sai Kaew Beach Resort Hat Sai Kaew ☎ 038 644197, ⓦ samedresorts.com. This popular and highly efficient resort has over 150 a/c rooms with hot water, TV and fridge, most of them in distinctive and thoughtfully designed bungalows in bright primary colours. The cheaper "deluxe" cottages and rooms occupy their own grassy area with a separate swimming pool, in front of a pretty but minute little patch of sandy shoreline; they have garden bathrooms and the cottages have private decks. "Premier" rooms are more urban and hotel-like. Rates include national park fee. B6500

Sinsamut Hat Sai Kaew ☎ 038 644134. Initial appearances aren't encouraging here, with rooms stuffed into cheek-by-jowl little blocks behind a restaurant midway down the beach, but most are pleasant inside, with bright, colourful, contemporary decor, and some have outdoor space. Relatively quiet with mild night music from the adjacent beach. The quirky fan-cooled "*katom*" bungalows, set around a grassy little roof garden, enjoy the best outlook. Fan B800, a/c B1500

Ton Sak Resort Hat Sai Kaew ☎ 038 644314, ⓦ tonsak .com. The timbered cabins here are packed very close together, but the surrounding borders of shrubs add a little privacy, and few are more than 100m from the water. Interiors are comfortable if a little old-fashioned, and have a/c and modern hot-water bathrooms. Breakfast included. B3045

AO HIN KOK

Jep's Bungalow Ao Hin Kok ☎ 038 644112–3. A spread of options in unremarkable wooden chalets and concrete bungalows, ranged up the shady, terraced, sandy-soiled

garden: fan-cooled with shared or en-suite bathrooms, or a/c with hot water, TV and breakfast included. It has a tour desk and a good restaurant (see p.401). Fan B300, a/c B1500

Naga Bungalows Ao Hin Kok ☎ 087 958 6206. Long-running, somewhat jaded resort, with a beachfront bar, a Thai boxing ring, a secondhand bookshop, a bakery, currency exchange and internet access. Simple bamboo and wood huts are stacked in tiers up the slope, with decks, mosquito nets and shared bathrooms, as well as pricier concrete a/c rooms with their own adjacent cold-water bathroom. There is bar noise quite late and the compound's a bit scrappy, but the rooms are reasonably well maintained. Fan B600, a/c B1500

AO PHAI

Lost Resort Ao Phai, on the main track to Wong Duan and Ao Prao ☎ 038 644041–2, ⓦ thelostresort.net. A short way inland from *Sea Breeze*, this two-storey block sits peacefully among the hornbills and fruit bats in a grove of tall trees. The ten rooms here have a/c and are of a good standard and fairly priced. B1200

Samed Villa South end of Ao Phai ☎ 038 644094, ⓦ samedvilla.com. The huge rooms and villa-style bungalows at this Swiss-owned resort are packed into a fairly small area along the rocks at the southern end of the bay (good views from the front row) and up the slope behind the restaurant. Interiors are luxurious and well furnished and especially good for families; they all have a/c, hot water, TV and fridges. Buffet breakfast included. B1700

Silver Sand Middle of Ao Phai ☎ 038 644300–1, ⓦ silversandresort.samet.i8.com. This party hub has a spread of well-turned-out rooms, including whitewashed, a/c chalets set around a pretty garden; they all come with safety boxes, verandas and good modern hot-water bathrooms, and some have polished wooden floors. Fan B800, a/c B1200

AO TUB TIM

★**Tub Tim Resort** Ao Tub Tim ☎ 038 644025–9, ⓦ tubtimresort.com. The most popular place to stay on Ao Tub Tim is a sprawling, well-run resort with over a hundred handsome chalet-style wooden bungalows of various sizes and designs, all with classy modern furnishings and outdoor space, plus a good restaurant. Breakfast is included in a/c rooms. Fan B800, a/c B1900

AO NUAN

Ao Nuan Bungalows Ao Nuan ☎ 087 142 7512. The octagonal restaurant and simple, idiosyncratic huts here hark back to a mellower, old-school island vibe, entirely removed from the commercialism, party-goers and even internet of the other beaches (though room rates are definitely modern-day). The nine sturdy timber huts are each built to a slightly different design and dotted across the

4

tree-covered slope that drops down to the bay, with a few hanging right over the beach, making it feel like just yours. Sharing bathrooms, the cheapest are large but spartan, with just a platform bed and a mosquito net; the most expensive boast a/c and hot water. Fan **B800**, a/c **B1500**

AO WONG DUAN

Blue Sky Resort Northern Ao Wong Duan ☎089 936 0842. Perched high above the beach, you'll need to make use of the supplied nets in the fan bungalows here, which let in a fair amount of mosquitoes, though you might be better opting for the more robust a/c huts. Despite this, and the fact that there is no wi-fi, the price is good as all have en suites and sea views, with the beach just down some steps. The *Blue Sky* restaurant is popular for its lofty position and colourful lanterns. Fan **450**, a/c **700**

Vong Deuan Resort Middle of Ao Wong Duan ☎038 651777, ⓦvongdeuan.com. Ideally located in the middle of the beach, with attractive a/c bungalows in various designs set around a pretty tropical garden, including nice white cottages with thatched roofs, contemporary styled interiors and garden bathrooms (with hot showers). Service is efficient, attentive and hotel-like, which makes it a favourite with older guests. Breakfast included. **B2575**

Vongduern Villa Southern Ao Wong Duan ☎038 652300, ⓦvongduernvilla.com. Occupying a big chunk of the bay's southern end, this resort features over fifty rooms, all of them with safes and a/c. "Standard" bungalows are whitewashed timber huts built on stilts, with picture windows, decks and modern furnishings; while "Deluxe" means ornate traditional Thai bungalows kitted out with dark-wood floors, Japanese-style platform beds, hot showers and breakfast. There are also ugly-duckling standard rooms in a block out back that are perfectly fine inside and come with hot showers and balconies. There's also an attractive restaurant deck jutting out over the water, and kayaks and snorkelling equipment for rent. **B1200**

AO SANG THIAN

Candlelight Resort Ao Sang Thian ☎089 247 9597. Very nice wooden bungalows with lots of light and air strung out in a long line, each one facing the water. Most are fan-cooled, with hot showers and TVs; the resort's a/c options are either in these wooden bungalows or in large, very clean concrete rooms with small bathrooms behind the restaurant. Fan **B800**, a/c **B1200**

Sang Thian Beach Resort Towards Ao Sang Thian's northern end ☎038 644255, ⓦsangthianbeachresort .com. This complex comprising a minimart, ATM, massage centre and expansive, waterfront restaurant areas is somewhat institutional, and the welcome lacks the human touch, too. However, the resort boasts tasteful a/c timber chalets built up the cliffside on a series of decks and steps – the decor is navy-and-white maritime chic. There's hot water,

TVs and fridges, and views, mostly encompassing the sea, are pretty. It also has much less interesting compact brick bungalows and concrete rooms up the eastern slope. **B2000**

AO LUNG DUM

Jelly Fish Lung Dum Ao Lung Dum ☎081 458 8430 or ☎081 652 8056. Friendly spot under the bougainvillaea with a decent waterside restaurant. Most of the twenty bungalows with hot showers are right on the rocky shore, practically overhanging the water; a few cheaper rooms and bungalows at the back are also available. Fan **B900**, a/c **B1300**

AO WAI

Sametville Resort Ao Wai ☎038 651681–2, ⓦsametvilleresort.com. At this sizeable resort with a large pool, bungalows in all categories vary in quality, but you've plenty to choose from – including some cute converted boats – unless you come at the weekend, when it tends to fill up with Thai groups. Also on offer are rental motorbikes, snorkelling equipment and Thai massage. Fan **B1260**, a/c **B1800**

AO KIU

Paradee Resort and Spa Ao Kiu ☎038 644104–7, ⓦwww.samedresorts.com. Top of the range on Samet, a very luxurious five-star resort where each of the forty villas stretches over more than 100 square metres and most have their own small private pools. There's also an infinity-edged main pool, a spa and fitness centre, plus lots of nice little extras like DVD players, free kayaks and snorkelling equipment. **B18,960**

AO PRAO (PARADISE BAY)

Ao Prao Resort Ao Prao ☎038 644101, ⓦwww .samedresorts.com. Fifty luxurious wooden chalets and rooms set in a mature tropical garden that slopes down to the beach, all with a/c, TVs and mini-bars. There's an infinity pool, a dive centre, windsurfing and kayaking, among lots of watersports, and a picturesquely sited restaurant with a live band most evenings in high season. The resort runs a shuttle boat from Ban Phe three times a day (B250). **B7400**

Le Vimarn Cottages Ao Prao ☎038 644104, ⓦwww .samedresorts.com. The most indulgent resort on this beach comprises charming, gorgeously furnished cottages, a delightful spa and an infinity pool. Its *Buzz* restaurant (see opposite) is highly regarded. **B10,400**

Lima Coco Ao Prao ☎038 644068, ⓦlimasamed.com. The youngest, trendiest and cheapest choice on the beach, with a Bangkok contemporary chic look and lots of white walls, brightly coloured cushions, day beds and decks. Rooms are built close together in layers up the side of the hill, so that most have some kind of a sea view. There's kayaks, snorkels and sun beds for rent. Breakfast included. **B3030**

AO NOI NA
Baan Ploy Sea Ao Noi Na ☏ 02 438 9771–2, ⓦ www .samedresorts.com. Striking, brown contemporary building with an orange infinity pool, where bedrooms done out in dark wood and orange come with a/c, rain showers, TV and fridge. Pricier options come with a sea-view deck, and there's a good, relaxing seafood restaurant (see below) on the beachfront. Breakfast and boat transfers included. B4800

Mooban Talay Resort Northwestern Ao Noi Na ☏ 081 838 8682, ⓦ moobantalay.com. At the far northwest end of the beach is one of the classiest resorts on the island, a secluded haven at the end of the road, set under the trees on a gorgeous, quiet white-sand beach. Accommodation is in large, attractive a/c bungalows, all with platform beds, garden bathrooms and outdoor seating: the priciest, seafront ones have enormous decks, and there's a beachside pool and a spa. Boat transfers and breakfast included. B6785

EATING AND DRINKING

Most visitors to Ko Samet just eat at their resorts, and in truth there are few restaurants worth making an effort to get to.

HAT SAI KAEW AND NA DAN
Banana Bar and Restaurant Na Dan high street, not far from the police station. Tiny, welcoming establishment serving tastily authentic yellow, green and red curries (B80), as well as *tom yam* and spicy salads. Daily 9am–11.30pm.

Im Aroy Dii Na Dan high street, 10m from the National Park box on Hat Sai Kaew, on the left-hand side of the road (no English sign). There's not much to this basic but clean and bright restaurant, but its name, meaning "Full, Delicious, Good", says it all: tasty, cheap dishes on rice (from B50), as well as more interesting options such as squid with salted egg and chicken with cashew nuts (both B120). Fruit shakes and a cheery chef-owner, too. Daily 7am–9pm.

AO HIN KOK
★**Jep's Bungalow** Ao Hin Kok ☏ 038 644112. Popular all-rounder serving a great menu of authentic Thai dishes (including popular *som tam* sets for B150), seafood, Indian (with chicken tikka for B120 and plenty of veggie dishes), Japanese, Italian and Mexican food at its tables on the

sand, set under trees strung with fairy lights and given extra atmosphere by mellow music. Also does cappuccino and cakes. Daily 7am–12.30am.

AO PRAO (PARADISE BAY)
Buzz at Le Vimarn Cottages Ao Prao ☏ 038 644104, ⓦ www.samedresorts.com. Very refined restaurant serving highly regarded Thai food, including a wide choice of salads, dips and curries (from B290), in its chic modern dining room and upstairs terrace. The attached Italian restaurant, *O*, is just overpriced. Buzz 10am–11pm; O 7am–11pm.

AO NOI NA
Baan Ploy Sea Ao Noi Na ☏ 038 644188–9. Seafood restaurant belonging to the resort of the same name (see above), set in a impressive, open-sided wooden building supported on tree trunks, with axe cushions to recline on. Rock lobster is a speciality (B1500/kg), but there are also more manageable dishes such as a nicely herby shrimp green curry (B200). Daily 7am–10pm.

DIRECTORY

Banks There are ATMs at the Na Dan pier-head, beside the Hat Sai Kaew national park office, on Ao Wong Duan and on Ao Sang Thian; the bigger bungalows also change money.
Emergencies Ko Samet's health centre and police station

(☏ 038 644111) are on Na Dan high street, but for anything serious you should go to the Bangkok-Rayong hospital in Rayong (☏ 038 921999, ⓦ rayonghospital.net).
Post office At *Naga Bungalows* on Ao Hin Kok.

Chanthaburi

For over five hundred years, the seams of rock rich in sapphires and rubies that streak the hills of eastern Thailand have drawn prospectors and traders of all nationalities to the provincial capital of **CHANTHABURI**, 80km east of Ban Phe. Many of these hopefuls established permanent homes in the town, particularly the Shans from Myanmar, the Chinese and the Cambodians. Though the veins of precious stones have now been all but exhausted, Chanthaburi's reputation as a gem centre has continued to thrive and this is still one of the most famous places in Thailand to trade in gems (most of them now imported from Sri Lanka and elsewhere), not least because Chanthaburi is as respected a cutting centre as Bangkok, and Thai lapidaries are considered among the most skilled – and affordable – in the world. Chanthaburi is also an exceptionally

Rayong

THANON THA LUANG

Lak Muang

3153 316

0 250
metres

Bangkok-
Chanthaburi
Hospital

Police

317

Sa Kaew

THANON LEAP NOEN

THANON TETSABARN 1

THANON BENCHAMA-RACHUTIT

Anuban
Chanthaburi
School

SOI RAT MAITRI

Bus Station

THANON SARITDIDECH

THANON SARITDIDECH

Night
Market

Maenam Chanthaburi

N

THANON RIM NAM

Stadium

Thalat
Nam Phu

THANON TETSABARN 2

@

THANON SRI CHAN

THANON KHWANG

Cathedral

THANON TETSABARN 3

Gem
Shop
Area

TROK KACHANG

Gem Shop
Area

THANON SRI CHAN

Taksin
Statue

Taksin Park

2

THANON TRIRAT

Minibuses to
Ban Pakkard

3154

Prapokkao
Hospital

THANON THA CHALAEB

■ ACCOMMODATION	
Kasemsarn Hotel	1
The River Guest House	2

● RESTAURANT	
Chanthorn Pochana	1

CHANTHABURI

3146

Trat

fertile province, renowned for its abundance of orchards, particularly durian, rambutan and mangosteen, which are celebrated with an annual **fruit festival** in the town, held in May or June.

The town is made for low-key exploration, without being particularly compelling. Similarly, the Chanthaburi coastline is barely developed for tourism, though it's popular with Thai visitors for its quiet, shady beaches. However, even if you're not planning a visit to Chanthaburi, you may find yourself stuck here for a couple of hours between **buses**, as this is a major transit point for east-coast services (including most Rayong–Trat buses) and a handy terminus for buses to and from the northeast.

Thanon Rim Nam

Chanthaburi's most interesting neighbourhoods are close to the **river**, particularly along **Thanon Rim Nam**, with its mix of pastel-painted, colonial-style housefronts and traditional wooden shophouses, many displaying finely carved latticework. This district is home to a large Catholic Vietnamese community, most of whom fled here in waves following religious persecution between the eighteenth century and the late 1970s. The earliest refugees constructed what is now, following several revamps, Thailand's largest cathedral, the **Church of the Immaculate Conception**, located across the footbridge from the southern end of Thanon Rim Nam.

The gem dealers' quarter

The **gem dealers' quarter** is centred around Trok Kachang and Thanon Sri Chan (the latter signed in English as "Gem Street") and packed with dozens of gem shops. Most lie empty during the week, but on Fridays, Saturdays and Sunday mornings they come alive as local dealers arrive to sift through mounds of tiny coloured stones and classify them for resale to the hundreds of buyers who drive down from Bangkok.

Taksin Park

Thanon Tha Chalaep

Landscaped **Taksin Park** is the town's recreation area and memorial to King Taksin of Thonburi, the general who reunited Thailand between 1767 and 1782 after the sacking of Ayutthaya by the Burmese. Chanthaburi was the last Burmese bastion on the east coast – when Taksin took the town he effectively regained control of the whole country. The park's heroic bronze statue of Taksin is featured on the back of the B20 note.

ARRIVAL AND DEPARTURE · CHANTHABURI TOWN

By bus Chanthaburi bus station (☏039 311299) is on Thanon Saritdidech, about 750m northwest of the town centre and Thalat Nam Phu market. Seven daily buses make the scenic Chanthaburi–Sa Kaew–Khorat journey in both directions – Sa Kaew is a useful interchange for buses to Aranyaprathet and Cambodia (see box, p.381).

Destinations Bangkok (Eastern Bus Terminal; at least hourly; 4–5hr); Bangkok (Northern Bus Terminal; 13 daily; 3–4hr); Bangkok (Suvarnabhumi Airport; 5 daily; 3hr); Khorat (7 daily; 6hr); Laem Ngop (for Ko Chang; 3 daily; 1hr); Phitsanulok (daily; 11hr); Rayong (8 daily; 2hr); Sa Kaew (for Aranyaprathet; 10 daily; 3hr); Trat (hourly; 1hr 30min).

ACCOMMODATION

Kasemsarn Hotel 98/1 Thanon Benchama-Rachutit ☏039 312340, ⌨hotelkasemsarn.com. Unexpectedly contemporary hotel, whose comfortable a/c rooms, with hot showers, fridges and TVs, are built round a central atrium and done out in whitewash and dark wood; there is a smart coffee shop downstairs. B1300
The River Guesthouse 3/5–8 Thanon Sri Chan ☏039 328211. Shabby traveller-oriented outfit on the edge of the gems quarter, with breakfast served on a riverside terrace next to the road bridge. The cheapest rooms are tiny and windowless and share cold-water bathrooms; better fan and a/c en-suite rooms have narrow beds and TVs, and some boast river-view balconies and hot showers. Fan B190, a/c B490

EATING

Food stalls in Thalat Nam Phu wet market (open dawn to dusk) and at the informal night market off the riverside sois sell Vietnamese spring rolls (*cha gio*) with sweet sauce. Locally made Chanthaburi rice noodles (*sen chan*) are popularly used in *phat thai* throughout Thailand, but in Chanthaburi they're also crucial to the local beef noodle soup, *kway tiaw neua liang*, whose dark broth is flavoured with pungent herbs and spices, including the cardamom that the Chanthaburi mountains are famous for. Thalat Nam Phu is also a popular place to head to for fresh seafood.

CROSSING TO CAMBODIA VIA CHANTHABURI PROVINCE

Most foreigners use the Aranyaprathet–Poipet crossing to get into **Cambodia** (see p.381), with access possible by bus via Chanthaburi. There are also two less used crossings in Chanthaburi province, giving access to the Cambodian town of Pailin, just east of the border. Daung Lem Border Crossing at **Ban Laem** is 88km northeast of Chanthaburi (not served by public transport) and the Phsa Prom border crossing is at **Ban Pakkard** (aka Chong Phakkat), 72km northeast of Chanthaburi. There's a minibus service in the morning from Chanthaburi (just south across the bridge from *The River Guest House*) to Ban Pakkard (1–2hr; B150). It's best to arm yourself in advance with an e-visa for Cambodia, but it's also possible to get a thirty-day visa on arrival at the border; if entering Thailand via this route you'll probably be obliged to show proof of onward travel from Thailand.

★**Chanthorn Phochana** 102/5–8 Thanon Benchama-Rachutit. By far the best of the town's restaurants is this spot a few metres up the road from the *Kasemsarn Hotel*, for which Thai foodies make a beeline. As well as selling Chanthaburi delicacies as souvenirs, it serves regional dishes such as *lon puu* (a kind of salad dip with crab; B120) and *kway tiaw neua liang*, and a delicious range of spicy *yam* salads, Thai curries and stir-fries, many of them using local herbs and vegetables. Daily 8.30am–9pm.

Coastal Chanthaburi

The barely developed **coastline** to the west of Chanthaburi is very pretty, popular with Thai visitors for its empty beaches and shady casuarina trees and worth exploring if you have your own transport.

Hat Khung Wiman and Ao Khung Kraben

Just off Route 3399, about 30km southwest of Chanthaburi, or 80km east of Ban Phe, **HAT KHUNG WIMAN** is a quiet, shady, bronze-sand beach and has two nice places to stay. A couple of kilometres southeast of here and you're at the lip of **AO KHUNG KRABEN**, a deep, lagoon-like scoop of a bay that's occasionally visited by dugongs and is edged by dense mangrove forest. A wide swathe of this mangrove swamp is protected under a royal conservation project and crossed by a kilometre-long boardwalk; you can also rent double kayaks from a hut next to the observation tower for B150 an hour or from *The Pier Resort* (⊕thepier-resort.in.th/en) in the cool season to follow a signed riverine trail. Access is via Laem Sadet on the southern curve of the bay.

4

KKB (Khung Kraben Bay) Aquarium

Across the road from the mangrove project on Laem Sadet's beach road • Tues–Fri 8.30am–4.30pm, Sat & Sun 8.30am–5.30pm • Free • ⊕ aquariumthailand.com

The impressively stocked **KKB Aquarium** is a royal initiative and displays a multicoloured variety of reef fish, some sea horses and a few larger marine creatures, with informative English signage. It's possible to walk here from Chao Lao Beach (3km), and as there's no public transport your only other option would be to drive.

ACCOMMODATION   **KHUNG WIMAN**

Al Medina Beach House Hat Khung Wiman ☎039 417105, ⊕almedinabeach.com. Nine very chic, Moroccan-inspired rooms, all with a/c, hot water and DVD players, some with rain showers and bathtubs. Bicycles and kayaks available. Breakfast included. B4950

★**Faasai Resort** Khung Wiman ☎039 417404, ⊕faasai.com. This New Zealand–Thai owned, environmentally conscious resort is an ideal base from which to explore the coast. Its comfortable, family-friendly, a/c bungalows sit in a tropical garden with views to the Cardamom mountains on the Cambodian border and there's a swimming pool and Wat Pho-trained massage therapists on site. Very unusually, the resort also has its own private little wetland conservation area, where you can sit bird-watching, swim in the natural spring pool or kayak along the rivulet. Hat Khung Wiman is 10min walk away and *Faasai* rents bicycles, motorbikes and cars, and organizes interesting local tours. B1600

Trat

The small and pleasantly unhurried provincial capital of **TRAT**, 68km southeast of Chanthaburi, is the perfect place to stock up on essentials, extend your visa, or simply take a break before striking out again. Most travellers who find themselves here are heading either for Ko Chang, via the nearby port at **Laem Ngop**, for the outer islands, or for Cambodia, via the border at **Hat Lek**, 91km southeast of town. But Trat itself has its own distinctive, if understated, old-Thailand charm and there are lots of welcoming guesthouses to tempt you into staying longer.

Though there are no real sights in Trat, the historic neighbourhood down by Khlong Trat, where you'll find most of the guesthouses and traveller-oriented restaurants, is full

Bangkok-Trat Hospital, Bus Station, Trat Airport, Hat Lek & Chanthaburi

TRAT

■ ACCOMMODATION	
Ban Jaidee	1
Basar Garden	3
Residang House	4
Rimklong Boutique Hotel	2

● RESTAURANTS	
Cool Corner	2
Kluarimklong	3
Raan Ahaan Mangsawirat	1

of old wooden shophouses and narrow, atmospheric sois. The covered market in the heart of town is another fun place to wander. Out-of-town attractions that make enjoyable focuses for a leisurely cycle ride (ask at *Cool Corner* restaurant for detailed directions and other recommended routes; see p.408) include the mangrove forest to the southeast near Ban Dan Kao, and the ornate seventeenth-century **Wat Buppharam**, 2km west of Trat Department Store, and the nearby lake.

Mangrove forest

5.5km southeast of town

In the **mangrove forest** near Ban Dan Kao, a boardwalk with informative English signs takes you through the swamp; after dark it's a good place to see twinkling fireflies too. The boardwalk access is currently unsigned in English; to get here with your own transport, head east from Trat towards Ban Dan Kao and after about 5.4km you'll pass dolphin statues on your left – the track to the mangroves is about 100m further on, on the right (if you get to the estuary and road's end you've gone about 500m too far).

ARRIVAL AND DEPARTURE   TRAT

BY PLANE

Tiny Trat airport (☏ 039 525767–8), served by Bangkok Airways, is about 16km from the Ko Chang piers at Laem

Ngop. There's an airport shuttle minibus direct to Ko Chang hotels for B470/person, including ferry ticket (B700 by speedboat). However, a/c minibuses to Trat town (run by

YELLOW OIL

Trat is famous across Thailand for the **yellow herbal oil** mixture, *yaa luang*, invented by one of its residents, Mae Ang Ki, and used by Thais to treat many ailments: sniff it for travel sickness and blocked sinuses, or rub it on to relieve mosquito and sandfly bites, ease stomach cramps, or sterilize wounds. Ingredients include camphor and aloe vera. It's well worth investing in a lip-gloss-sized bottle of the stuff before heading off to the sandfly-plagued islands; you can buy it for about B70 and upwards at Trat market and at nearby Tratosphere bookshop. There are now several imitations, but Mae Ang Ki's original product (Ⓦ somthawinyellowoil.com) has a tree logo to signify that it's made by royal appointment.

Bangkok Airways) are extortionately high at B500/person, for a ride of less than 30min (though at least you'll be dropped off at your hotel).

Destinations Bangkok (3 daily; 50min); Ko Samui (4 weekly; 1hr 15min); Phuket (4 weekly; 3hr).

BY BUS

All buses terminate at the bus station, 1.5km northeast of central Trat on Highway 318, from where songthaews shuttle passengers into the town centre (B30, or B90 if chartered) or on to the departure points for the islands (see below). A/c minibuses to Bangkok's Victory Monument leave from the 7-Eleven just off Thanon Vivatthana, on the north side of town; there are also minibuses to Hat Lek from the bus station (see box, p.408).

Destinations Bangkok (Eastern Bus Terminal; 6 daily; 4hr 30min–6hr); Bangkok (Northern Bus Terminal; 6 daily; 4hr 30min); Bangkok (Suvarnabhumi Airport; 6 daily; 4hr 10min); Chanthaburi (hourly; 1hr 30min); Pattaya (6 daily; 4hr 30min); Rayong (6 daily; 3hr 30min); Si Racha (6 daily; 5hr).

BY BOAT

Details of boat services to Ko Chang, Ko Mak and Ko Kood are given in the relevant accounts. If you book your boat ticket through your guesthouse in Trat, you should be able to arrange pick-up (usually free) from the guesthouse.

VIA LAEM NGOP

All ferries to Ko Chang and some services to Ko Mak leave from one of three piers to the west of the small port town

of Laem Ngop, 17km southwest of Trat (see map, p.410): Tha Thammachat and Tha Centrepoint for the Ko Chang car ferries, and Tha Kromaluang (Naval Monument Pier) for Ko Mak. These piers are served by songthaew share-taxis from Trat's bus station and by songthaew and a/c minibus share-taxis from Thanon Sukhumvit in the town centre, costing B50/person or B250–300 if chartered; if sharing, allow 60–90min before your boat leaves for the share-taxi to fill up and get you to the pier.

VIA TRAT–SALAK PET SONGTHAEW

If you're going to the east coast of Ko Chang you can take a direct songthaew to Salak Pet (B200, including car ferry) from the temple compound behind *KFC* and Trat Department Store in Trat.

VIA LAEM SOK

Some boats to Ko Mak and nearly all boats to Ko Kood depart from Laem Sok, 30km south of Trat; boat tickets bought in Trat should include free transfers to Laem Sok, but there's also a Laem Sok songthaew service (at least hourly, 8am–1pm; 30–60min) that leaves from the town centre (see map, p.405).

VIA BAN DAN KAO

A few boats to the outer islands depart from Ban Dan Kao, on the river estuary 6km northeast of Trat town; again, your boat ticket should include free transfers to Ban Dan Kao, but otherwise you'll have to charter a songthaew from Trat market.

INFORMATION

Tourist information The Trat and Ko Chang TAT office (daily 8.30am–4.30pm; Ⓣ 039 597259, Ⓔ tattrat@tat .or.th) is out in Laem Ngop, but any guesthouse will help you out with information on transport to the islands or into Cambodia. Alternatively, drop by the Tratosphere bookshop at 23 Soi Kluarimklong (Ⓣ 039 523200) for tips on Trat and the islands from the knowledgeable French owner (he also runs the helpful website, Ⓦ tratmap.com), or visit *Cool Corner* restaurant for a browse through the travellers' comment books.

ACCOMMODATION

Most **guesthouses** in Trat are small and friendly and are well used to fielding travellers' queries about the islands and Cambodia. All those listed here are within a 10min walk of the covered market on Soi Vijit Junya.

CLOCKWISE FROM TOP KO MAK (P.422); LANTERN, SAAN CHAO PAW KHAO YAI, KO SI CHANG (P.382); WAT ASADANG, KO SI CHANG (P.382) >

福如東海
壽比南山

★**Ban Jaidee** 67 Thanon Chaimongkon ☎039 520678 or ☎083 589 0839, ✉maneesita@hotmail.com. Very calm, good-value, inviting and rather stylish guesthouse with a pleasant seating area downstairs and just nine small, simple bedrooms. The nicest rooms are in the original building and have polished wood floors, though those in the modern extension are further from the traffic noise. All rooms share hot-water bathrooms. B200

Basar Garden 87 Thanon Thoncharoen ☎039 523247 or ☎087 402 4620. Decent-sized en-suite rooms in a lovely, atmospheric old wooden house at the greener end of town. Curtains and drapes made from faded batik sarongs add to the faintly bohemian ambience and all rooms have fans and mosquito nets. Free bicycles. B250

Residang House 87/1−2 Thanon Thoncharoen ☎039 530103, �🌐trat-guesthouse.com. Comfortably appointed, good-value three-storey German−Thai-managed guesthouse. Rooms are large, light and clean and all have windows, thick mattresses and hot-water bathrooms; there are family rooms too. Internet access downstairs. Fan B350, a/c B660

★**Rimklong Boutique Hotel** 194 Thanon Lak Muang ☎039 523388, �🌐rimklonghotel.com. The four ground-floor rooms (plus one apartment) at this friendly, popular hotel are done out in a crisp contemporary style and well equipped: a/c, hot water, cable TV and fridge. Those on the side offer a bit more privacy than the two whose doors open right onto Thanon Lak Muang. There is also a nearly half-price single room. The café in reception boasts a serious espresso machine, but you'll have to bring in your own food from outside for breakfast. Doubles B1000, apartment B1400

EATING

Two of the best and cheapest **places to eat** in Trat are at the covered day market on Thanon Sukhumvit, and the night market (daily roughly 5−10pm), between Rai Rung Soi and Soi Vijit Junya, east of Thanon Sukhumvit.

★**Cool Corner** 49−51 Thanon Thoncharoen. Run single-handedly by a local writer/artist, this place has lots of personality, both in its cute hand-painted decor and in its traveller-oriented menu of real coffee, Indian chai, veggie specials, quality breakfasts and great Thai food (including chicken and cashew nuts for B90). A good place to while away an hour or three, listening to the mellow music and perusing the travellers' comment books. Daily roughly 8am−10pm, sometimes closing in the afternoon.

Kluarimklong Soi Kluarimklong. More Bangkok than Trat in its style and menu, this unexpectedly classy little place, under the same ownership as the nearby *Rimklong Boutique Hotel*, has both an indoor and a courtyard dining area. It serves delicious, upmarket Thai food, including steamed *haw mok thalay* seafood curry with coconut (B90) and lots of spicy *yam* salads and *tom yam* soups. Daily 11am−10pm.

Raan Ahaan Mangsawirat No English sign, but follow the soi near Ban Jaidee, off Thanon Chaimongkon. Typical no-frills, very cheap Thai vegetarian place, where you choose two portions of veggie curry, stir-fry or stew from the trays laid out in the display cabinet, and pay about B30 including rice. Daily 7am−1pm.

DIRECTORY

Emergencies Call the tourist police, who have a base at Laem Ngop, on ☎1155 (free, 24hr).

Hospital The best hospital is the private Bangkok−Trat Hospital (☎039 532735 or freephone ☎1719,

---

CROSSING THE CAMBODIAN BORDER VIA HAT LEK

Many travellers use the **Hat Lek−Koh Kong border crossing** for overland travel into Cambodia. It's best to arm yourself in advance with an **e-visa** for Cambodia (see p.27) and to make the journey by regular public transport, but it's also possible to buy a package all the way through to Sihanoukville and Phnom Penh (B750−1000 through travel agents in Trat) and to get a thirty-day visa on arrival at the border, though both of the latter options are more likely to open you up to possible **scams** (see p.381). For a comprehensive guide to the crossing and to the various transport options − and scams − on both sides of the border, see �🌐talesofasia.com/cambodia-overland.htm and the �🌐thaivisa.com forum.

The only way to get to **Hat Lek** under your own steam is by minibus from Trat bus station, 91km northwest (roughly every 45min; 1hr−1hr 30min; B120). Hat Lek (on the Thai side) and Koh Kong (in Cambodia) are on opposite sides of the Dong Tong River estuary, but a bridge connects the two banks. Once through immigration, taxis ferry you into **Koh Kong** town for onward transport to Sihanoukville and Phnom Penh or for guesthouses should you arrive too late for connections (mid-afternoon onwards). **Vans, buses and share-taxis** to Phnom Penh and Sihanoukville take around 4−5hr.

ⓦ bangkoktrathospital.com), part of the Bangkok Hospital group (not to be confused with the Trat Hospital), which has emergency facilities; it's on the Sukhumvit Highway, 1km north of Trat Department Store.

Immigration office Located in Laem Ngop, 100m west of the TAT office (Mon–Fri 8.30am–4.30pm; ☎ 039 597261).

Travel agencies Book international and domestic flights at Koh Chang TT Travel on Thanon Sukhumvit (☎ 039 531420; Mon–Sat 6am–6pm); they also book accommodation on the islands, arrange taxis to Trat airport and transport to Cambodia, and provide local information.

Ko Chang

Edged with a chain of long, mostly white-sand beaches and dominated by a broad central spine of jungle-clad hills that rises sharply to over 700m, **KO CHANG** is developing fast but still feels green. It's Thailand's second-largest island, after Phuket, but unlike its bigger sister has no villages or tourist facilities within its steeply contoured and densely forested **interior**, just a few rivers, waterfalls and hiking trails that come under the auspices of the Mu Ko Chang National Park. Some of its marine environment is also protected, as the national park extends to over forty other islands in the Ko Chang archipelago. Ko Chang's own coast, however, has seen major development over the past decade, and the island is now well established as a mainstream destination, crowded with package tourists and the overspill from Pattaya, and suffering the inevitable inflated prices and inappropriate architecture. That said, it's still possible to find accommodation to suit most budgets, and though the beaches may be busy they're undeniably handsome, with plenty of inviting places to swim, stroll, or snooze under a palm tree.

At 30km north to south, Ko Chang has plenty of coast to explore. The western **beaches** are the prettiest and the most congested, with **White Sand Beach** (**Hat Sai Khao**) drawing the biggest crowds to its mainly upmarket and increasingly overpriced mid-range accommodation; smaller **Hat Kai Bae** is also busy. Most backpackers opt for so-called **Lonely Beach** (officially **Hat Tha Nam**), with its roadside village of travellers' accommodation and famous beachfront party scene; those in search of quiet choose the more laidback **Hat Khlong Phrao**, a long and lovely sweep of sand that caters to most pockets, or **Bang Bao**, which has a village on a jetty with fine views, and its quiet neighbouring beach, **Hat Khlong Gloi**. Every beach has **currency exchange** and most have **ATMs**, along with minimarkets, tour agents, dive shops, internet access, clothes stalls and souvenir shops. White Sand Beach and Hat Kai Bae have the densest concentrations of facilities.

During **peak season**, accommodation on every beach tends to fill up very quickly, so it's worth booking ahead. The island gets a lot quieter (and cheaper) from June to October, when heavy downpours and fierce storms can make life miserable, though sunny days are common too; be especially careful of riptides on all the beaches during the monsoon season.

Sandflies can be a problem on the southern beaches (see p.68); watch out also for **jellyfish**, which plague the west coast in April and May, and for **snakes**, including surprisingly common cobras, sunbathing on the overgrown paths into the interior. The other hazard is **theft** from rooms and bungalows: use your own padlock on bags (and doors where possible) or, better still, make use of hotel safety boxes. After a local eradication programme, Ko Chang is no longer considered to be a malaria-risk area by health authorities in the US and the UK.

ARRIVAL AND DEPARTURE   **KO CHANG**

Access to Ko Chang from the **mainland** is by boat from the Laem Ngop coast, 17km southwest of Trat; details of transport to and from Laem Ngop are given on p.406. Tickets on tourist buses and minibuses to Ko Chang will often include the ferry crossing and transport to your hotel. During high season there are also boats to Ko Chang from Ko Mak and Ko Kood. On Ko Chang, **songthaew share-taxis** meet boats at the Tha Dan Kao and Ao Saparot ferry piers and transport passengers to

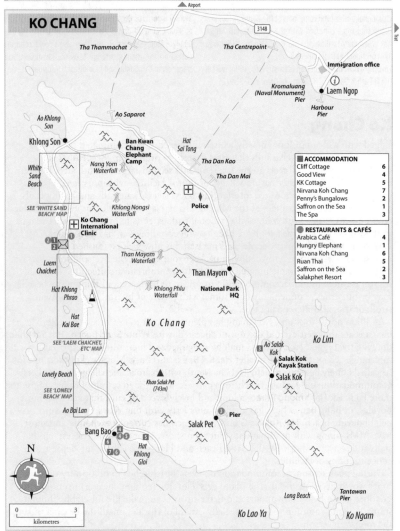

KO CHANG

Airport

3148

Tha Thammachat

Tha Centrepoint

Trat

Immigration office

ⓘ

Kromaluang
(Naval Monument)
Pier

● Laem Ngop

Harbour
Pier

Ao Khlong
Son

Ao Saparot

Khlong Son ●

**Ban Kwan
Chang
Elephant
Camp**

Hat
Sai Tong

White
Sand
Beach

Nang Yom
Waterfall

Tha Dan Kao

Tha Dan Mai

SEE 'WHITE SAND
BEACH' MAP

Khlong Nongsi
Waterfall

Police

▇ ACCOMMODATION	
Cliff Cottage	6
Good View	4
KK Cottage	5
Nirvana Koh Chang	7
Penny's Bungalows	2
Saffron on the Sea	1
The Spa	3

**Ko Chang
International
Clinic**

● RESTAURANTS & CAFÉS	
Arabica Café	4
Hungry Elephant	1
Nirvana Koh Chang	6
Ruan Thai	5
Saffron on the Sea	2
Salakphet Resort	3

Laem
Chaichet

Than Mayom
Waterfall

Than Mayom ●

Hat Khlong
Phrao

Khlong Phlu
Waterfall

**National Park
HQ**

Hat
Kai Bae

SEE 'LAEM CHAICHET,
ETC' MAP

Ko Chang

Ko Lim

Lonely Beach

SEE 'LONELY
BEACH' MAP

▲
Khao Salak Pet
(743m)

Ao Salak
Kok

**Salak Kok
Kayak Station**

● Salak Kok

Ao Bai Lan

Bang Bao ●

N

Hat
Khlong
Gloi

Salak Pet

● Pier

0   3
kilometres

Long Beach

Tantawan
Pier

Ko Lao Ya

Ko Ngam

Ko Mak & Ko Kood

4

west-coast beaches (B50 to White Sand Beach, 25min; B100 to Lonely Beach, 1hr; B150 to Bang Bao, 1hr 15min). On departure, either wait for a songthaew on the main road or ask your accommodation to book one for you (for a small extra fee, usually B20). If you're heading to Ko Chang's east coast, you can make use of the songthaew through service from central Trat (see p.406).

BY BOAT AND PLANE

Bangkok Airways (office in White Sand Beach, ☎039 551654) runs a shuttle-bus service from Ko Chang beaches via the ferry and on to Trat Airport (B470/person, or B700 by speedboat; see p.405), but you can get slightly cheaper prices by pre-booking with ⊛iamkohchang.com.

BY BOAT VIA LAEM NGOP

The main Laem Ngop–Ko Chang boat services are operated by two different car ferry companies from two different piers. Fares are competitive and change frequently: expect to pay B80–120/person one-way, and about B250 for a vehicle, though deals on the latter vary considerably.

Centrepoint Ferry (☎039 538196) runs from Tha Centrepoint, 3km west of Laem Ngop, to Tha Dan Kao; and the more popular Ferry Ko Chang (☎039 518588 or ☎039 555188) runs from Tha Thammachat, 9km west of Laem Ngop, to Ao Saparot. Departures are from 6/6.30am–6/7pm, hourly in high season, every 2hr rest of year. There's plenty of long-distance transport direct to Laem Ngop, bypassing Trat town: a/c buses from Bangkok (5hr 15min–6hr), either from the Eastern (Ekamai) Bus Terminal, via Suvarnabhumi Airport and Chanthaburi (3–4 daily), or from Thanon Khao San and Hualamphong Station (2 daily); and a/c minibuses from Bangkok's Victory Monument, Northern and Eastern bus terminals, Suvarnabhumi Airport and Thanon Khao San.

Destinations Tha Thammachat–Ao Saparot (25min); Tha Centrepoint–Tha Dan Kao (45min).

BY BOAT AND BUS FROM KO CHANG

Every tour agency on Ko Chang offers all manner of bus and a/c minibus packages (including ferries) from the island to other popular tourist destinations – we've listed the key ones. Most (it's worth checking) will include pick-up from your hotel either by songthaew, if you're going by big bus from the mainland ports, or by the minibus itself, which will then board the ferry and take you all the way through.

Destinations Bangkok (big bus to Khao San Rd B400, not including songthaew to the ferry; minibus to Khao San Rd B700; minibus to Sukhumvit Rd hotels B850; 5–6hr); Bangkok Suvarnabhumi Airport (big bus B450; minibus B850; about 5hr); Ko Samet (minibus and ferries B750; about 5hr); Pattaya (minibus B650; about 4hr 30min); Siem Reap (Cambodia, changing at the border; minibus B600; about 10hr).

BY BOAT VIA KO MAK AND KO KOOD

In high season, Bang Bao Boat (☎087 054 4300, ⓦkoh -chang.com/activities/BangBaoBoat.html) runs wooden boats from Bang Bao on Ko Chang to *Koh Mak Resort* on Ao Suan Yai on Koh Mak (roughly Sept–June daily; 1hr 30min–2hr; B550), as well as speedboats to *Koh Mak Resort* (roughly Sept–June 2 daily; 1hr; B700) and on to the west coast of Ko Kood (about 1hr; B900 from Ko Chang). Prices include transfers to or from the west coast of Ko Chang. Several other companies run similar high-season inter-island speedboats (for the same prices including Kai Bae and Leelawadee (ⓦkohmakboat.com), who sail from Hat Kai Bae on Ko Chang, via *Makathanee Resort* on Ao Kao on Ko Mak, to the west coast of Ko Kood. Tour agencies on Ko Chang, as well as guesthouses on Ko Mak and Ko Kood, will have current details.

GETTING AROUND

By songthaew A paved road runs nearly all the way round the island connecting all the beaches, served by plentiful, white songthaew share-taxis. They tend to charge according to how many passengers they have as well as the distance travelled (usually B50–150/person), but sometimes, especially on more remote beaches, you might have to wait until they fill up with enough passengers or the driver will ask you to charter the whole vehicle.

By motorbike or car You can rent motorbikes (from B250) and cars (from B1000) on every beach, but the road is notoriously dangerous, with precipitously steep hills punctuated by sharp, unexpected hairpins, and many reckless, often drunk, drivers, so think twice if you're an inexperienced motorcyclist – accidents happen every day and fatalities are frequent.

By mountain bike Rental available opposite Ko Chang Gym in the VJ Plaza complex in Laem Chaichet (B250/day).

INFORMATION

Tourist information The widely distributed, detailed free maps and quarterly Ko Chang guides published by Whitesands Publications (ⓦkoh-chang-guide.com) are a handy source of information, and the website provides an accommodation-booking service, but for more intelligent insights and opinionated advice, check out ⓦiamkohchang .com, compiled by a Ko Chang resident.

DIRECTORY

Clinic The private 24hr Ko Chang International Clinic (☎1719 or ☎039 532735, ⓦbangkoktrathospital.com) is located beyond the south end of White Sand Beach, 1km south of *Plaloma Cliff Resort*; it has emergency ambulances and a dental service, and will transfer seriously ill patients to its parent Bangkok–Trat Hospital in Trat.

Post office On the main road beyond the southern end of White Sand Beach (Mon–Fri 10am–noon & 1–6pm, Sat 10am–1pm).

Tourist police At the north end of Hat Khlong Phrao (☎1155).

Travel agent A good, helpful agent – for flights, hotel bookings, day-trips, onward transport, car and bike rental, as well as overseas calls and internet access – is Koh Chang Adventure Travel on Hat Sai Khao, between Bangkok Airways and Soi Kert Manee (☎039 551389 or ☎089 247 6834).

4

White Sand Beach (Hat Sai Khao)

Framed by a band of fine white sand at low tide, a fringe of casuarinas and palm trees and a backdrop of forested hills, **Hat Sai Khao**, more commonly referred to as **White Sand Beach**, is, at 2.5km long, the island's longest beach and its most commercial, with scores of mid-range and upmarket hotel and bungalow operations packed together along the shore, plus dozens of shops, travel agents, bars and restaurants lining the inland side of the road. The vibe is much more laidback and traveller-oriented at the far quieter northern end of the beach, however, beyond *KC Grande*, and this is where the most budget-priced accommodation squeezes in, some of it pleasingly characterful and nearly all of it enjoying its own sea view. An extra bonus is that the road is well out of earshot up here, and there's hardly any passing pedestrian traffic. There are some low-key beach **bars** up there too, and more along the shorefront in the central beach area – all of them quite different in feel from the rash of brash, Pattaya-style bar-beers inland from *Plaloma Cliff Resort* in southern Hat Sai Khao. Wherever you stay on White Sand Beach, be careful when swimming as the **currents** are very strong and there's no lifeguard service.

ACCOMMODATION WHITE SAND BEACH

Arunee Resort Just across the road from White Sand Beach ☎039 551075, ⓦfacebook.com/aruneekohchang; map p.413. Built in a partitioned wooden row-house, the sixteen small, very simple terraced rooms here all have a small veranda, mattress, fan and tiny en-suite bathroom and are a good price for central Hat Sai Khao. The friendly owner has a tour desk and internet shop out front. B500

Cookies Hotel White Sand Beach ☎081 861 4227, ⓦcookieskohchang.com; map p.413. If you want hotel-style facilities at affordable prices this is a good option, right in the middle of the beach. Rooms are in two locations, with

the far less interesting site being across the road, with only shops and traffic to look at through the picture windows. Better to pay B500 extra and go for a ground-floor, sea-view "superior" room, set round the shorefront swimming pool. Rooms are large and comfortable and all include breakfast, a/c, hot water, TV, fridge and a veranda. B2000

KC Grande Resort White Sand Beach ☎039 551199, ⓦkckohchang.com; map p.413. The largest and priciest hotel on the beach is able to charge top dollar because it spreads over a huge area of the northern shorefront. Accommodation ranges from rows of a/c bungalows set

---

KO CHANG ACTIVITIES

Tour agents on every beach or at your accommodation should be able to sell you tickets for most of the **activities** described below. There are **spas** at Ao Bai Lan (see p.420) and Ao Salak Kok (see p.422); you can also **snorkel** and **dive** in the archipelago (see p.414).

ELEPHANT CAMPS

Ko Chang or "Elephant Island" is named for its hilly profile rather than its indigenous pachyderms, but there are several **elephant camps** on the island that have brought in their own lumbering forest dwellers so that tourists can ride and help bathe them. However, we can't recommend elephant rides, because in order to be tame enough to be ridden, elephants are put through a cruel process that usually involves separation from their mothers, starvation, beating and sleep deprivation, among other methods. Any elephant that allows you on its back will have been through this process.

KAYAKING

Kayak Chang At Amari Emerald Cove Resort, Hat Khlong Phrao ☎087 673 1923, ⓦkayakchang.com. Well-organized, safety-conscious, British-run company offering half- (B1500) and full-day (B2100) local trips

and expeditions around the archipelago of up to seven days, as well as kayaking lessons and rental. Return transport from your accommodation is included.

COOKING CLASSES

KaTi Culinary Cooking School Hat Khlong Phrao ☎039 557252, ⓦkati-culinary.com. The amiable chef who runs the recommended *KaTi* restaurant

(see p.417) teaches well-regarded cooking classes (Mon–Sat 11am; B1500, including recipe book and transfers as far as White Sand Beach and Hat Kai Bae).

in landscaped gardens fronting the beach to more expensive rooms, some with sea views, in the three-storey hotel block. Facilities are good and include a pool, a spa and a bar with live bands in the evening. Breakfast included. **B4600**

Maylamean Bungalows White Sand Beach ☎ 082 257 6271; map p.413. This stands out among the cluster of funky, north-beach cliffside bungalows, both for its colourful paintwork and because its wooden huts are larger, with en suite and a bit more privacy than many of its neighbours, though no wi-fi. **B450**

Penny's Bungalows Beyond the south end of White Sand Beach, down a lane behind the post office ☎ 039 551122, ⓦ penny-thailand.com; map p.410. Welcoming, helpful, German-run place on what's sometimes called Pearl Beach (Hat Khai Mook), though it's just a rocky extension of Hat Sai Khao. On a compact, flowery plot around a lovely little pool with a kids' pool and jacuzzi, the well-maintained bungalows and hotel-style rooms all have a/c, hot water, TV, fridge and a few decorative touches; the smaller, cheaper ones are near the sea. **B1300**

★Saffron on the Sea Beyond the south end of White Sand Beach, three doors north of Penny's ☎ 039 551253, ⓔ kochangsaffrononthesea@yahoo .com; map p.410. In a lovely, lush garden behind a very good restaurant (see p.414) are seven attractive, homely rooms with a/c, hot water, TV and fridge; the cheaper rooms have no sea view. Management is friendly and there's free kayaks and snorkels. **B1600**

Star Beach White Sand Beach ☎ 087 558 4085; map p.413. Basic, cheerily painted plywood huts cling limpet-like to the rock-face here, just above the sand on the quiet, northern stretch of the beach. Rooms are very simple (no wi-fi) but are all en suite (some with hot showers) and enjoy high-level sea views and breezes. **B550**

White Sand Beach Resort White Sand Beach ☎ 081 863 7737, ⓦ whitesandbeachresort.net; map p.413. Spread across a long, attractive stretch of uncommercialized sand at the far north end of the beach, *White Sand* offers a big range of nicely spaced bungalows, many of them lapping up uninterrupted sea views. Interiors are fairly simple, but boast a/c, wooden floors, hot showers, TVs, fridges and a faintly contemporary style. If you're looking for a proper peaceful beach vibe and a little bit of affordable comfort, within a 10min walk of resort facilities, this is a good option.

**WHITE SAND BEACH
(HAT SAI KHAO)**

GULF OF THAILAND

Police box

7-Eleven

Pharmacy

Ko Saparot & Tha Dan Kao

4

ACCOMMODATION	
Arunee Resort	5
Cookies Hotel	6/7
KC Grande Resort	4
Maylamean Bungalows	2
Star Beach	3
White Sand Beach Resort	1

RESTAURANTS	
15 Palms	2
Norng Bua Seafood	3
Pen's	1
The Spa	4

BARS	
Oodie's Place	1
Sabay Bar	2

BB Divers

Bangkok Airways

Koh Chang Adventure Travel

SOI KERT MANEE

RURAL ROAD

Scuba Zone

V-Mart

Chang Kao Plaza

Ploalma Cliff Resort

0 ——— 500
metres

Ko Chang International Clinic, Post Office & Pearl Beach ▼

Arriving by songthaew, get off at the 7-Eleven beside *KC Grande* and phone for transport. Breakfast included. **B1900**

EATING AND DRINKING

15 Palms White Sand Beach ☎ 039 551095, ⓦ 15palms .com; map p.413. One of the most popular of the row of restaurants that set their tables out on the sand, partly because of its nightly high-season fireshows and *katoey*

shows on Tues & Sat. There's a fresh seafood barbecue every night (B350), plus Thai, Italian and Mexican à la carte, washed down with imported beers and lots of cocktails. Daily 8am–1am.

Hungry Elephant Beyond the south end of the beach, just north of and across the road from the post office; map p.410. The French and Thai food at this unassuming roadside place has a good reputation with local expats. The Thai chef trained at the French Embassy in Bangkok and does toothsome steaks – au poivre, chateaubriand and crème cognac – for B320–350. Daily roughly 10/11am–10pm.

Norng Bua Seafood On the main road, White Sand Beach ⓦnongbuarestaurant.com; map p.413. Popular, bustling basic restaurant, serving noodle soups, fried noodles and fried rice with seafood (B55); other seafood dishes start at B100. Daily 7am–10pm.

Oodie's Place On the main road, White Sand Beach; map p.413. Ko Chang's most famous live-music venue, with live blues, rock, reggae and r'n'b played most nights, plus Thai food (from B80), pizzas (from B200) and French food (from B300). Daily 4pm–2am.

Pen's White Sand Beach; map p.413. Tiny beach restaurant in the northern bungalow cluster that serves exceptionally good home-style Thai food at fairly cheap prices (B80–100 for curries), as well as Western breakfasts. Daily 8.30am–9.30pm.

Sabay Bar White Sand Beach ⓦsabaybarkohchang .com; map p.413. One of Ko Chang's longest-running institutions, where you can choose to sit in the chic a/c bar and watch the nightly live sets from the in-house cover band, or lounge on mats and cushions on the sand and listen in via the outdoor speakers. You pay for the pleasure, however, as drinks are pricey. Also stages fire-juggling shows on the beach and full moon parties. Daily 6pm–2am.

Saffron on the Sea Beyond the south end of the beach, behind the post office three doors north of Penny's (see p.413) ⓣ039 551253; map p.410. On a pretty seafront deck, this restaurant is highly recommended for its Thai food, which doesn't stray too far from the usual suspects, such as green curry (B180) and *nam tok* pork

DIVING AND SNORKELLING IN THE KO CHANG ARCHIPELAGO

Because there's just one main tide a day in the inner Gulf, the **reefs** of the Ko Chang archipelago are much less colourful and varied than Andaman coast dive sites, and they can get very crowded, but they're rewarding enough to make a day-trip worthwhile. The main **dive and snorkel sites** are west of Ko Mak, in the national marine park around **Ko Rang** and its satellite islets. These range from beginners' reefs with lots of hard corals and anemones at depths of 4–6m, frequented by plenty of reef fish – including a resident ten-thousand-strong shoal of yellow fusiliers – and the occasional moray eel, to the more challenging 25m dive at the Pinnacles. There are also some technical wreck dives of Japanese boats from World War II and even some centuries-old Chinese trading ships. The coral around Ko Yuak, off Ko Chang's Hat Kai Bae, is mostly dead, though some operators still sell trips there.

DIVE SHOPS ON KO CHANG

The biggest concentration of **dive shops** is on Ko Chang, though there are also some on Ko Mak and Ko Kood (see p.422 & p.425 respectively). All dive shops on Ko Chang will organize pick-ups from any beach.

Waves permitting, Ko Chang operators run trips year-round, though during the **monsoon season** (June–Sept), visibility can be poor. **Prices** for local dive trips, with two tanks, are about B2900, or from B950 for accompanying **snorkellers**. Dive courses cost about B14,500 for the four-day Openwater, and B4500 for the one-day Discover Scuba introduction.

BB Divers Offices at Lonely Beach, Hat Khlong Phrao and White Sand Beach, main office in Bang Bao ⓣ086 155 6212 or ⓣ039 558040–1, ⓦbbdivers.com. Belgian-run, environmentally minded PADI Five-Star IDC centre and certified Reef Check Facility which uses fishing boats (with sun decks) rather than speedboats.

Accommodation is available at *Barrio Bonito* on Lonely Beach (see p.418).

Scuba Zone Offices at White Sand Beach, Hat Kai Bae and Lonely Beach ⓣ039 619035, ⓦscuba -kohchang.com. British-run PADI Five-Star centre, which also offers technical and wreck diving.

SNORKELLING

From about November to May, several companies run dedicated **snorkelling trips** to reefs and islands around Ko Chang, Ko Wai and Ko Rang. Tickets are sold by tour agents on every beach and prices range from B600 to B1500, depending on the size of the boat (some take as many as a hundred people in high season) and the number of islands visited. In general the more islands "featured" (sailed past), the less time there is for snorkelling, though nearly all the actual snorkelling happens around **Ko Rang**.

salad (B160); also serves baguettes and pastas. Daily roughly 7.30am–9.30pm.

The Spa On the main road, White Sand Beach ⓦ thespakohchang.com; map p.413. Welcoming, environmentally friendly outreach restaurant of *The Spa*

Resort (see p.422). Food is mostly vegetarian, and organic where possible, and includes a delicious "ginger nuts" stir-fry (B140), very good omelettes, seafood, breakfasts and Mexican dishes. There are lots of health drinks and good espressos. Daily 7am–10pm.

Laem Chaichet and Hat Khlong Phrao

Four kilometres south of Hat Sai Khao, the scenic, rocky cape at **LAEM CHAICHET** curves round into sweeping, casuarina-fringed **HAT KHLONG PHRAO**, one of Ko Chang's nicest beaches, not least because it has yet to see the clutter and claustrophobic development of its neighbours. For the moment at least, most of the restaurants, bars and shops are way off the beach, along the roadside, with the shorefront left mainly to a decent spread of accommodation. Laem Chaichet protects an inlet and tiny harbour and offers beautiful views south across the bay and inland to the densely forested mountains. To the south, Hat Khlong Phrao begins with a nice 1km-long run of beach that's interrupted by a wide khlong, whose estuary is the site of some characterful stilt homes and seafood restaurants. You can rent a kayak from almost anywhere along the beach to explore the estuary, and after dark you could paddle upriver to see the fireflies twinkling in the khlongside *lamphu* trees. Beyond the estuary, the long southern beach is partly shaded by casuarinas and backed in places by a huge coconut grove that screens the shore from the road; it's quite a hike to the roadside shops and restaurants from here though, at least 1km along a rutted track.

Both Chaichet and Khlong Phrao have roadside tourist villages with **ATMs**, minimarkets, tour agents, dive centres, internet access, shops and restaurants. The **tourist police** have a post here, and from the southern end of Khlong Phrao it's only a few hundred metres south to the start of the Kai Bae tourist village amenities.

Khlong Phlu Falls

2km east off the main road • B200

Upstream from Hat Khlong Phrao, the khlong that divides the beach in two tumbles into Ko Chang's most famous cascade, **Khlong Phlu Falls** (Nam Tok Khlong Phlu). Signs lead you inland to a car park and some hot-food stalls, where you pay your national park entry fee and walk the last five minutes to the 25m-high waterfall (best in the rainy season) that plunges into an invitingly clear pool defined by a ring of smooth rocks.

ACCOMMODATION   **LAEM CHAICHET AND HAT KHLONG PHRAO**

Amari Emerald Cove Resort Hat Khlong Phrao ☎ 039 552000, ⓦ amari.com; map p.416. Top-of-the-scale hotel from the reliable Thai chain, occupying a lovely, tranquil spot on the southern beach, complete with its own palm-shaded sandy terrace, spa and huge seafront swimming pool with a palatial jacuzzi. The rooms, in low-rise three-storey blocks set around the pool, tropical garden and lagoons, are in luxurious style, with wooden floors and balconies. B4980

Baan Rim Nam Hat Khlong Phrao ☎ 087 005 8575, ⓦ iamkohchang.com; map p.416. Peaceful, scenic and unusual, this converted fishing family's house is built on stilts over the wide, attractive khlong at the end of a walkway through the mangroves. Run by the British author of the best Ko Chang website (see p.411), it has just five comfortable a/c rooms with good hot-water bathrooms, plus decks for soaking up views of the khlongside village,

but no restaurant. You can borrow kayaks and it's a couple of minutes' walk to the beach, or 20min to the main Khlong Phrao facilities. B900

Barali Beach Resort Hat Khlong Phrao ☎ 039 557238, ⓦ baralikohchang.com; map p.416. One of the more elegant spots on the southern beach, with tastefully designed, Balinese-style rooms (some with their own plunge pools), furnished with four-poster beds, sunken baths and lots of polished wood, and set around a beachfront infinity-edge swimming pool and a spa. B4050

Koh Chang Paradise Resort Laem Chaichet ☎ 039 551100–1, ⓦ kohchangparadise.com; map p.416. The biggest and most popular place to stay on the Chaichet end of the beach occupies a huge area between the road and the shore so offers easy access to the beach as well as shops and restaurants. Its generously designed concrete

4

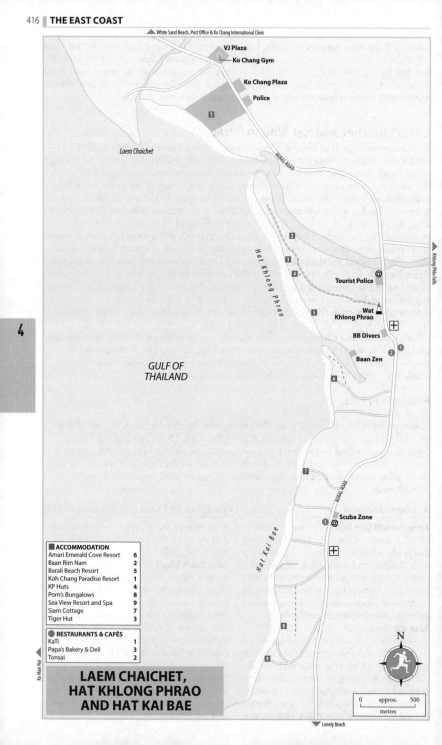

White Sand Beach, Post Office & Ko Chang International Clinic

VJ Plaza

Ko Chang Gym

Ko Chang Plaza

Police

Laem Chaichet

RURAL ROAD

Khlong Phu Falls

Hat Khlong Phrao

Tourist Police

@

Wat
Khlong Phrao

BB Divers

Baan Zen

GULF OF
THAILAND

RURAL ROAD

Scuba Zone

@

Hat Kai Bae

4

Ko Man Nai

ACCOMMODATION

Amari Emerald Cove Resort	6
Baan Rim Nam	2
Barali Beach Resort	5
Koh Chang Paradise Resort	1
KP Huts	4
Porn's Bungalows	8
Sea View Resort and Spa	9
Siam Cottage	7
Tiger Hut	3

RESTAURANTS & CAFÉS

KaTi	1
Papa's Bakery & Deli	3
Tonsai	2

**LAEM CHAICHET,
HAT KHLONG PHRAO
AND HAT KAI BAE**

N

0   approx.   500
metres

Lonely Beach

bungalows have French windows and comfortable, hotel-style, a/c interiors. Some have private plunge pools and there's also a central swimming pool and a spa. B2345
KP Huts Hat Khlong Phrao ☎084 077 5995, ✉kp_huts2599@hotmail.com; map p.416. Though the fifty timber huts here are very simple for the price, they are attractively scattered through the broad, grassy shoreside coconut grove (about 1.5km from roadside amenities) with plenty of sea views. Even some of the cheapest options (with shared bathrooms) are right on the shore, and a few are raised high on stilts for an extra-seductive panorama;

all of the en-suite huts have hot showers and some are designed for families. B400
Tiger Hut Hat Khlong Phrao ☎084 109 9660; map p.416. One of the few budget-minded, old-school travellers' beach bungalows left on Ko Chang, occupying a sandy beachfront garden just south of the khlong and about 2km down a track from the main road. The woven-bamboo and clapboard huts have simple interiors with no wi-fi or towels, but with mosquito nets over the beds and decent-sized bathrooms (some shared), and there's a restaurant deck and bar with pool table. B300

EATING AND DRINKING

KaTi On the main road, Hat Khlong Phrao ☎039 557252; map p.416. Restaurant and cookery school (see p.412) serving very tasty Thai food, slightly adapted for Western tastes, including lots of seafood, *matsaman* chicken curry (B150) and *laap* beef salad (B130), plus delicious home-made ice creams and Thai desserts. Mon–Sat 11am–3pm & 6–10pm, Sun 6–10pm.

Tonsai On the main road, Hat Khlong Phrao; map p.416. The atmosphere at this welcoming restaurant is pleasingly mellow with calm, polite staff, and the menu includes *matsaman* curries (B150), some interesting Thai dips and relishes, pastas, lots of vegetarian options and at least fifty cocktails. Mon 5–10pm, Tues–Sun 11.30am–10pm.

Hat Kai Bae

Narrow, pretty little **HAT KAI BAE** presents a classic picture of white sand, pale blue water and overhanging palms, but in places the shorefront is very slender indeed – and filled with bungalows – and the beach can disappear entirely at high tide. The beach is bisected by a khlong and rocky point, with most of the accommodation to the south. Seaward views from the southernmost end take in the tiny island of Ko Man Nai, whose sandy shores are easily reached by kayak, half an hour offshore from *Porn's Bungalows*. Kai Bae's roadside tourist village is busy and stretches a couple of kilometres. It's got plenty of shops, bars and restaurants, as well as ATMs, currency exchange, dive shops and internet access.

ACCOMMODATION

HAT KAI BAE

Porn's Bungalows Off the access road to Sea View, Hat Kai Bae ☎080 613 9266 or ☎089 099 8757, ⓦpornsbungalows-kohchang.com; map p.416. The most famous of the dwindling number of budget accommodation options on Hat Kai Bae has scores of fan bungalows in various styles, well spaced out under the trees along a huge expanse of the shorefront. The cheapest are concrete huts at the back at the south end; the most luxurious are spacious wooden cabins with hot showers and wraparound decks; all have fans. *Porn's* has two reception areas, at its northernmost and southernmost ends, and a two-storey restaurant, with a bar and pool table, in the middle. Also has kayaks for paddling to offshore Ko Man Nai. B600
Sea View Resort and Spa Hat Kai Bae ☎081 830

7529, ⓦseaviewkohchang.com; map p.416. Swanky and huge beachfront hotel set in lawns and tropical flower gardens, which stretch around the steep headland at the south end of the beach and up to a lighthouse by the main road that shelters tables with good views at the *Lighthouse Restaurant*. A cable car joins up the resort's two swimming pools, pretty spa and its large, light and airy a/c rooms and cottages. B4530
Siam Cottage Hat Kai Bae ☎089 153 6664; map p.416. With cheerily painted interiors, fans, partly outdoor bathrooms and decks, the 36 wooden bungalows (all with a/c) here face each other across a narrow but well-watered, flowery lot that runs down to the sea. There's a cute restaurant and internet access, as well as kayaks for rent. B1100

EATING AND DRINKING

Papa's Bakery & Deli On the main road, Hat Kai Bae; map p.416. Hot pretzels, pizzas, croissants, baguettes and cakes emerge from this friendly German bakery, as well as the bread for some very tasty sandwiches (around B100).

If you're sitting in, you can also tuck into pastas and good espressos; to take away, there are imported cheeses and salamis, too. Free wi-fi. Daily 8am–7pm.

▲ Hat Kai Bae

LONELY BEACH & AO BAI LAN

■ ACCOMMODATION	
Barrio Bonito	7
Easy House	6
Nature Beach	1
Siam Hut	2
The Sunflower	3
Sunset Hut	4
Warapura Resort	5

Siam Beach

Lonely Beach

Minimart

@ Scuba Zone

RURAL ROAD

BB Divers

● RESTAURANTS	
Barrio Bonito	3
Krua Sai Ngam (Sign Ngam Kitchen)	1
The Sunflower	2

N

Ao Bai Lan

Bailan Herbal Sauna

Mercure Resort

0   300
metres

Treetop Adventure Park

▼ Bang Bao

Lonely Beach (Hat Tha Nam)

Hat Tha Nam – dubbed **LONELY BEACH** before it became Ko Chang's top place to party – is small and lively, with a shorefront that's occupied by increasingly expensive accommodation and a hinterland village, ten minutes' walk away, that's the most traveller-oriented on the island. It's at Lonely Beach, overlooking the rocks immediately south of the strand, and along the sandy sois that run inland to the main road, that most backpackers stay, in little bungalows and guesthouses squashed any old how beneath the remaining trees, with every other shop-shack offering tattoos or internet access. Despite the creeping concrete, creatively designed little wood and bamboo bar-restaurants abound, some of them offering chilled, low-key escapes from the loud dance music, all-night parties and buckets of vodka Red Bull that the beachfront places are notorious for.

Day and (especially) night, you should be extremely careful when swimming off Lonely Beach, particularly around *Siam Beach* at the northern end, as the steep shelf and dangerous current result in a sobering number of **drownings** every year, particularly during the monsoon season; do your swimming further south and don't go out at all when the waves are high. Also be careful with your belongings – many a drunken night sees cameras, phones and wallets pilfered unnoticed.

Among the roadside shops you'll find an **ATM**, dive centres, tour agents and motorbike rental and repair.

ACCOMMODATION

LONELY BEACH

Barrio Bonito On the main road, towards the south end of Lonely Beach ☎ 080 092 8208, ⓦ facebook.com /barrio.bonito.5; map p.418. Behind this excellent bar-restaurant (see opposite), the garden shelters some cute, colourful, single-storey rooms, all with fans, bathrooms and armchairs, though they're quite small and tightly packed. Good breakfasts are served in the restaurant, and there's a tiny swimming pool at the front. **B350**

Easy House Inland, up a side road opposite Kachapura Resort, Lonely Beach ☎ 089 116 8191, ⓔ hippeehappy @yahoo.com; map p.418. Laidback place built around polished, dark-wood platforms. The old-style bungalows,

decorated with murals and equipped with mosquito nets, fans and en-suite bathrooms, are quite crowded together, but quiet and cheap. **B500**

Nature Beach Central Lonely Beach ☎ 039 558027 or ☎ 081 803 8933; map p.418. Responsible for Lonely Beach's party reputation, this place's rooms, bar-restaurant (with built-in DJ station) and the beach out front are all hugely popular. It occupies a prime location in the middle of the strand and is at the heart of the action (so if you prefer a quiet night's sleep, head elsewhere). Its 65 shady, closely set bungalows range from attractive, polished-concrete en-suite abodes with verandas at the back by the road, through fan-cooled log cabins, some with hot showers, further forward, to large a/c bungalows at the front with hot water and a bit of chic. There's also a tour desk. Fan B500, a/c B1500

Siam Hut Central Lonely Beach ☎ 086 609 7772, ⓦ siam hutkohchang.com; map p.418. The cheapest place to stay right on the beach, this classic traveller's rest has evening barbecues and movies, a dive school, a tattoo parlour, kayaks for rent and a 24hr kitchen. Accommodation consists of rows and rows of primitive, split-bamboo huts – eighty in total – all en suite (some with hot showers) and with little else but plank floors, mattresses and mozzie nets. Fan B480, a/c B560

The Sunflower Lonely Beach, inland on Soi Sunset ☎ 084 017 9960, ⓦ the-sunflower.com; map p.418. Run by a genial German and his Thai family, the two-dozen bungalows here are set under palm and banana trees 200m or so from the roadside village and equidistant from the rocky coast at *Sunset Hut*, a 5min walk south of the sandy beach. Choose between bamboo or wooden fan bungalows with mosquito nets and open-roofed bathrooms, and concrete bungalows with a/c and hot showers; all have good thick mattresses and are kept very clean. The restaurant is good (see below). Fan B500, a/c B800

Sunset Hut Lonely Beach, 5min walk south beyond Siam Hut, on the rocks ☎ 089 245 4626; map p.418. The concrete en-suite fan bungalows here have hot showers, proper beds and big windows, though no wi-fi; some have perfect, private, over-sea decks too. There are also some big a/c bungalows, but all are tightly packed together in rows running parallel to the shore. The seafront deck-restaurant and bar holds occasional parties. Though you can only swim here at high tide, it's a short walk to the sandy beach and just 400m inland to roadside shops and restaurants. Fan B450, a/c B800

Warapura Resort Lonely Beach, 2min walk south beyond Sunset Hut, on the rocks ☎ 083 987 4777, ⓦ warapuraresort.com; map p.418. Welcoming place with a good dose of Bangkok chic in its twenty gleaming white, balconied rooms and villas, a few of which are on the seafront; all have large bathrooms with hot rain showers, a/c, mini-bars, TVs and DVD players. "Cozy Seaview" rooms are especially stylish, with dark-wood furniture and a large indoor sitting area (B2200). Good-sized, attractive pool and breakfast included. B1400

EATING AND DRINKING

The most intense **partying** on Ko Chang happens down on the beach here, usually at *Nature Beach*, which kicks off most high-season nights with seafood barbecues, live music and fire-juggling shows; there's also a big beach party at *Siam Hut* on Friday nights.

★ **Barrio Bonito** On the main road, towards the south end of Lonely Beach ☎ 080 092 8208, ⓦ facebook.com /barrio.bonito.5; map p.418. Mexican-run bar-restaurant serving excellent Tex-Mex food such as nachos with minced beef (B200) as well as some more unusual dishes, washed down with Corona and lots of tequila cocktails. It's a very congenial place, with lots of places to chill in the landscaped garden, free wi-fi and Latin sounds all the way. Daily 8am–10pm.

Krua Sai Ngam (Sign Ngam Kitchen) On the main road, central Lonely Beach; map p.418. Popular, basic, authentic Isaan restaurant, which even does *som tam* with crab and *pla ra* (fermented fish sauce) – an acquired taste but very northeastern (on the menu as "Som Tam E-sarn";

B50). Also offers catfish and snakehead fish in various soups, curries and salads (try the *yam plaa duk foo*; B140), grilled chicken and simple dishes on rice (B50). No English sign, but look for the corrugated-iron roof and the seafood displayed on ice at the front, directly opposite Soi Sunset. Daily noon–11.30pm.

The Sunflower Lonely Beach, inland on Soi Sunset ☎ 084 017 9960, ⓦ the-sunflower.com; map p.418. Friendly, laidback guesthouse restaurant dishing up very generous set breakfasts (B180), authentically spicy Thai curries (B70), a wide choice of pricier Western food and German beer. Flop on to the axe cushions and soak up the cool sounds or watch a movie. Free wi-fi. Daily 8am–3pm & 5–10pm.

Ao Bai Lan

A fifteen-minute walk along the road and over the hill from the southern end of Lonely Beach village will bring you to **AO BAI LAN**, which hasn't got much of a beach to speak of, but is the site of two of Ko Chang's most interesting attractions, the **Treetop Adventure Park** and the **Bailan Herbal Sauna**.

Treetop Adventure Park

South end of Ao Bai Lan • Daily 9am–5pm • B950/half-day; roundtrip transfer B150 • ☎ 084 310 7600, ⓦ treetopadventurepark.com

If you're happy with heights and like a physical challenge, make an afternoon of it at **Treetop Adventure Park**, an enjoyable and professionally managed jungle activity centre where you get to swing through the trees on a series of trapezes, flying foxes, aerial skateboards, rope ladders and webs. Everyone gets a full safety harness and gloves and starts off with a training session before tackling the two adventure courses (or the special kids' one), which take around two hours in all, though there's no limit to repeat attempts.

Bailan Herbal Sauna

On the main road, Ao Bai Lan • Daily 3–9pm • Sauna B200, treatments from B50, massages B300/hr • ☎ 039 558077, ⓦ bailan-kohchang.com

Bailan Herbal Sauna is the perfect place to tease out any sore muscles. This charming, creatively designed US–Thai-run herbal steam sauna is an alternative little sanctuary of adobe buildings with glass-bottle windows, secluded within a patch of roadside forest. There's a sociable communal sauna, home-made DIY herbal treatments using fresh herbs from their own garden (kaffir lime for hair, white-mud for face and turmeric for skin), and massages are also available, along with fresh juices and herbal teas.

Bang Bao

Almost at the end of the west-coast road, the southern harbour village of **BANG BAO**, much of it built on stilts off a 1km-long central jetty, is the departure point for boat trips and transfers to the outer islands and is also an increasingly popular place to stay. Though it has no beach of its own, you're within a short motorbike ride of both little-developed Hat Khlong Gloi, 2km to the east, and Lonely Beach, 5km up the coast. It's possible to stay on the jetty itself and tuck into seafood at one of its famous restaurants, but you'll probably have to fight your way through vanloads of day-trippers, who clog the narrow path along the jetty as they linger over the trinket shops, clothes stalls and dive shops.

ACCOMMODATION   BANG BAO

Cliff Cottage West side of Ao Bang Bao, next to Nirvana ☎ 085 904 6706, ⓦ cliff-cottage.com; map p.410. British-run resort with a nice deck restaurant on the west-facing cove, and kayaks and snorkels for rent. Basic, thatched, bare-wood huts with decent mattresses, mosquito nets and good sunset views sit up on a small, dusty, shady rise; there's also a row of fan and a/c rooms, all with hot showers, facing in on Bang Bao bay, and a number of "glamping" bell tents that aren't as glamorous as they sound but offer wide cliff-top views. Fan double B700, tents B800, a/c double B900

Good View Bang Bao jetty ☎ 087 927 1357 or ☎ 089 108 0429, ⓦ goodviewbangbao.wordpress.com; map p.410. As the name says, the views from this guesthouse, built over the water halfway down the east side of the jetty, are good, though not great, taking in the shoreline opposite. The bright, clean rooms have wooden floors and

huge hot-water bathrooms, big balconies and a/c – it's worth paying B200 extra for an upstairs room for better views, more privacy and less noise. There's a very large, attractive ground-floor deck with a book corner. B1000

★**Nirvana Koh Chang** West side of Ao Bang Bao ☎ 039 558061–4, ⓦ nirvanakohchang.com; map p.410. Secluded on a narrow neck of land across the bay to the west of the village, this boutique resort is a relaxed and lushly landscaped retreat with two pools and access to good snorkelling in the bay behind (free equipment available); there's no real beach but they run free boats over to Hat Khlong Goi twice a day. Also on offer are cooking classes and free kayaks. Accommodation is in a wide range of chic, Balinese-accented rooms and villas, some with direct sea views, and there's an attractive restaurant too (see below). Good à la carte breakfast included. B3000

EATING AND DRINKING

Arabica Café Opposite 7-Eleven, just before the start of Bang Bao jetty; map p.410. A leafy little café with cute fountains, serving up good espressos (B40), pancakes, sandwiches and Western breakfasts. Daily 8am–9pm.

Nirvana Koh Chang West side of Ao Bang Bao ☎ 039 558061–4, ⓦ nirvanakohchang.com; map p.410. Even if you're not staying at *Nirvana Koh Chang*, you can come

and eat at its dramatically sited *Tantra* restaurant, built on stilts in the bay, or drink at the panoramic, sunset-facing *Sun Deck*, which is reached by a cliffside boardwalk and hosts soothing live music most days. Creatively furnished with woodcarvings from the Indonesian archipelago, the restaurant serves a menu of contemporary Thai and French food (including imported artisan cheeses), as well as tasty fusion dishes created by the French chef, such as beef tournedos in *panaeng* sauce (B350). Very good wine list. Free transfers from anywhere on the west coast of Ko Chang. Sun Deck daily 5–7pm; Tantra daily 6–10pm. **Ruan Thai** Bang Bao jetty ☎ 089 833 5117; map p.410. The best of several neighbouring restaurants, with a deck built on stilts off the west side of the jetty and fresh seafood awaiting its fate in tanks at the front. The fried rice with prawns is very good (B60), or you could upgrade to salads, curries and squid dishes (B120); most other seafood dishes are B200. Daily 9am–10pm.

Hat Khlong Gloi

The nearest swimmable beach to Bang Bao is long, sandy **Hat Khlong Gloi**, 2km east of the village and not far short of the end of the tarmac. It's backed by a lagoon and a long stretch of beach-scrub, but has great views from its small beach cafés and deckchairs. If you're coming by motorcycle, park up at the west end of the beach and walk, as the paved access road then takes a steep, tortuous route around the back of the beach.

ACCOMMODATION   HAT KHLONG GLOI

KK Cottage 100m from the west end of Hat Khlong Gloi ☎ 039 558169, ⓦ on.fb.me/1DZeeHt; map p.410. Friendly, popular spot on a nice stretch of beach, with deckchairs and umbrellas and great views of the bay and the offshore islands. The rather scruffy compound has small, thatched, fan-cooled, en-suite bungalows at the back, concrete ones at the front. The simple bar-restaurant hosts a nightly beach barbecue. Fan B̲5̲0̲0̲, a/c B̲8̲0̲0̲

The east coast

The beaches along the mangrove-fringed **east coast** are less inviting than those in the west, but this side of Ko Chang is much less developed and makes for a fun day-trip; it's about 35km from Ao Khlong Son in the north to Salak Pet in the south.

Than Mayom

South of the piers at Ao Saparot and Tha Dan Kao, the east-coast road runs through long swathes of rubber and palm plantations, with jungle-clad hills to the west and bronze-coloured beaches to the east, passing the national park office and bungalows at **Than Mayom**, where signs direct you inland to the short but lovely Than Mayom falls with two calm pools to swim in, a 45-minute uphill hike away.

Salak Kok and Long Beach

Ao Salak Kok is a deep green bay hedged in with thick mangroves and wooden huts on stilts. To the south, it is at its most charming as the blue boats of the small fishing settlement of **SALAK KOK** bob into view. You can **rent kayaks** from the Salak Kok Kayak Station (B100/hr; run by the Koh Chang Discovery Club, a community tourism venture) to explore a marked route through the mangroves. From Salak Kok, you'll need sturdy motorbike skills to navigate the bumpy, rugged track (25min, or 2.5hr on foot for the adventurous) to the tip of the southeastern headland to reach undeveloped **Hat Sai Yao**, or **LONG BEACH**, the prettiest white-sand beach on this coast, which is good for swimming and has some coral close to shore. There are a few homestays and food stalls here for refuelling.

Salak Pet

The little fishing port of **SALAK PET**, on the south coast, is served by daily songthaews all the way from Trat town (see p.406). There are some white-knuckle moments on the way here, as the road hugs the coast, rewarding you with incredibly clear views of the sea and coast. Still a fairly quiet spot, the village of Salak Pet has a simple temple but is best known for its excellent **seafood restaurant**, *Salakphet Resort* (see p.422). While you are able to rent kayaks here, the port town is a glimpse into life on Ko Chang without the tourists, and you'll often find only the fishermen here to keep you company.

4

★**Salakphet Resort** Salak Pet ☏081 429 9983, ⓦkohchangsalakphet.com; map p.410. The bayside dining deck here offers fine views and seafood so good that people travel all the way from Trat just for lunch; crabs are a speciality – particularly stir-fried with black pepper, or with curry powder – but it's all fresh so the possibilities are infinite. Daily 8am–8pm.

The Spa Ao Salak Kok ☏039 553091, ⓦthespakohchang

.com; map p.410. Beautifully designed wellness and detox retreat that's upmarket but reasonably priced; it also has branches on Ko Samui and in Chiang Mai. The a/c accommodation is set in a lovely mature tropical garden that runs down to the mangrove-ringed bay of western Ao Salak Kok, and there is a good restaurant. Breakfast included. Day visitors are welcome for massage (B500/1hr, B700/90min), herbal saunas and facials, and to eat at its restaurant. **B1555**

Ko Mak

Small, slow-paced, peaceful **KO MAK** (sometimes spelt "Maak") makes an idyllic, low-key alternative to Ko Chang, 20km to the northwest. Measuring just sixteen square kilometres, it's home to little more than four hundred people, divided into five main clans, who work together to keep the island free of hostess bars, jet skis, banana boats and the like, collaborating instead on initiatives such as mountain-bike trails. A couple of narrow concrete roads traverse the island, which is dominated by coconut and rubber plantations; elsewhere a network of red-earth tracks cuts through the trees. Ko Mak is shaped like a star, with fine white-sand beaches along the northwest coast at **Ao Suan Yai** and the southwest coast at **Ao Kao**, where most of the island's (predominantly mid-range and upper-bracket) tourist accommodation is concentrated; the principal village, **Ban Ao Nid**, is on the southeast coast and there's another village at **Ban Laem Son** on the east coast. The main beaches are just about within walking distance of each other, and other parts of the island are also fairly easy to explore on foot, or by mountain bike, motorbike or kayak – the best way to discover the empty, undeveloped beaches hidden along the north and eastern coasts. The **reefs** of Ko Rang are also less than an hour's boat ride away so snorkelling and diving trips are quite popular. There is as yet no major commercial

KO MAK

ACTIVITIES ON KO MAK

The mediocre reefs of Ko Rang (see p.414), part of the Ko Chang National Marine Park, are less than an hour's boat ride west of Ko Mak and are the island's main **diving and snorkelling** destination; they're the main focus of Ko Chang dive and snorkel boats too, so you won't be alone. You can also join a **cookery class**.

Koh Mak Divers On the Ao Kao road just east of Island Hut ☎083 297 7724, ⓦkohmakdivers.com. British-run PADI centre that charges B2400 for two fun dives, B3500 for the beginners' one-day Discover Scuba Diving course and B750 for snorkellers; transfers from your accommodation included.

Smile Koh Mak Next to Koh Mak Seafood restaurant at Ban Ao Nid ☎081 901 9972, ⓦsmilekohmak.com. 4hr cookery classes (B1200, including a recipe book),

with vegetarian options available. Also offers fruit and vegetable carving courses over 2 days (6hr). Transfers from your accommodation included.

Totti On the Ao Kao road opposite the Makathanee Resort ☎081 916 6536 or book through your accommodation. Snorkelling day-trips in a wooden boat to the national marine park. B750, including transfers from your accommodation and lunch box.

development on the island and **no bank or ATM**, and few places accept credit cards, but bungalows on both beaches will change money. There's a small clinic off the Ao Nid road, though for anything serious a speedboat will whisk you back to the mainland.

During the **rainy season** (early June–Sept), choppy seas mean that boat services to Ko Mak are much reduced. Most Ko Mak accommodation stays open – and offers tempting discounts – but the smaller places often don't bother to staff their restaurants. Islanders say that it can be very pleasant during this "green season", though you may be unlucky and hit a relentlessly wet few days.

Ao Kao

Ko Mak's longest and nicest beach is **AO KAO** on the southwest coast, a pretty arc of sand overhung with stooping palm trees and backed in places by mangroves. The beach is divided towards its southern end by a low rocky outcrop that's straddled by *Ao Kao White Sand Beach Resort*, with *Lazy Day Resort* occupying the strand beyond, while the long western beach is shared by a dozen other sets of bungalows, most of them around the pier at the *Makathanee Resort*. The roadside inland from the main accommodation area is where you'll find most of the restaurants and bars: if you're walking from the southern end, by far the easiest access is via the beach, tides permitting.

Ao Suan Yai and around

Long, curvy **AO SUAN YAI** is not quite as pretty a beach as Ao Kao and only has a couple of resorts, but the sand is fine and the outlook is beautiful, with Ko Chang's hilly profile filling the horizon and Ko Kham and other islets in between. You'll need a bicycle or motorbike to access the variety of restaurants on the Ao Kao road.

ARRIVAL AND DEPARTURE   KO MAK

Check ⓦkohmak.com for current routes and schedules for **boat services** from the mainland and the other islands. Boats arrive at one of Ko Mak's three **piers** – at *Koh Mak Resort* on Ao Suan Yai, at the *Makathanee Resort* on Ao Kao or at Ao Nid – and are always met by a modest welcoming committee of accommodation staff offering free transport; similarly, if you book a room in advance, ask your resort for a free pick-up. When it comes to moving on, all hotels keep current boat schedules and can sell you a ticket. Boats to Trat cost roughly B200 (2pm; 3hr); speedboats B450 (2pm & 4pm; 50min).

VIA LAEM SOK

A year-round catamaran service sails to Ao Nid on Ko Mak from Laem Sok pier, 30km south of Trat (☎086 972 4918,

ⓦkohkoodcatamaran.com; daily; 1hr 30min; B400 including transfer to/from Trat bus station or downtown market). Some of the Laem Sok–Ko Kood high-season speedboats will call in at Ao Nid if they have enough customers (see p.429).

VIA LAEM NGOP

A year-round slow boat runs from the Kromaluang (Naval Monument) pier in Laem Ngop, some 20km southwest of Trat (3 weekly; 3hr; B300), to the Makathanee Resort pier on Ko Mak. From approximately October to May, Panan's speedboats also operate from this pier to *Ko Mak Resort* on Ao Suan Yai (2 daily; 45min–1hr; B450); the second of

these is at 4pm, handy if you're arriving from Bangkok. A/c minibuses to Laem Ngop from Bangkok, for example, will sometimes only go as far as the Thammachat or Centrepoint Ko Chang piers, however – check exactly which piers are served when you buy your minibus ticket, or you may be able to pay the driver a little extra to go on to Kromaluang.

VIA KO CHANG OR KO KOOD

Boats run between Ko Chang, Ko Mak and Ko Kood in high season (see p.411).

INFORMATION

Tourist information The best one-stop shop for information about Ko Mak, accommodation bookings and all kinds of transport is the helpful, farang-run Info Point at *Koh Mak Resort* on Ao Suan Yai (Oct–March daily 8.30am–8pm; ☎085 665 3794, ✉kohmakinfopoint @yahoo.com). As well as boat and bus tickets, it offers

currency exchange, Visa cash advances, internet access, motorbike, mountain bike and kayak rental, activity bookings and postal services. There's also a travel agent at *Makathanee Resort* (☎081 870 6287), by the pier on Ao Kao, which offers internet access. ⓦkohmak.com is a useful, fairly comprehensive website about the island.

GETTING AROUND

The island has rough dirt paths, but hardly any traffic, and most visitors rent a mountain bike or motorbike.

By taxi ☎089 752 5292 or ☎089 833 4474. B50/person, minimum charge/vehicle B100; B100/person after 10pm.
By mountain bike or motorbike These (respectively B150/day and B300–350/day) can be rented through accommodation or from *Ko Mak Resort's* Info Point; otherwise, *Food Art Hut* on Ao Kao (see opposite) has a particularly wide

choice of bicycles, including kids' bikes. The island has some long and potentially interesting signed mountain-bike routes – discreet concrete posts enigmatically carved with route numbers A1–C7 – but the explanatory map for navigating them is currently out of print: you should be able to find your way around if you simply go exploring.

ACCOMMODATION

AO KAO

Ao Kao White Sand Beach Resort Ao Kao ☎039 501005, ⓦaokaoresort.com. This welcoming, efficiently managed and lively set of upmarket bungalows occupies an attractive garden fronting the prettiest part of the beach. Its twenty large, comfortable, attractive timber bungalows come with a/c, hot showers and DVD players and most have direct sea views. There are lots of activities, including live bands on Saturday nights, giant chess in the bar, a kids' trampoline, massage, and kayaks and motorbikes for rent. Breakfast included. B2500

★**Baan Koh Mak** Near the pier on Ao Kao ☎089 895 7592, ⓦbaan-koh-mak.com. Arrayed around a clipped lawn, the eighteen bungalows at this chic and welcoming resort are modern, bright and comfortable, cutely done out in futuristically angular white, green and polished concrete, with a/c, hot water, small bedrooms and decent-sized bathrooms; verandas sport either swings or bamboo hammocks. There's a very good restaurant here too. B1690
Goodtime Ao Kao ☎039 501000, ⓦgoodtime-resort .com. Luxurious, tasteful, Thai-style rooms and villas, all with a/c, hot water, TV, fridge, DVD player and use of a pool. They're located on higher ground inland from Ao Kao's *Makathanee Resort*, around a 15min walk from the beach.

Room B1880, villa B4120
Holiday Beach Resort Ao Kao ☎086 751 7668, ⓦholidaykohmak.com. Friendly, well-maintained place, strewn with flowers, facing a large, beachside lawn with deckchairs and tables. White clapboard is the architectural style of choice here, either in cute cottages with cold showers and mosquito nets in the second row, or in large, attractive, hot-water bungalows at the front. Kayaks, mountain bikes and motorbikes for rent. Breakfast included. Fan B800, a/c B1000
Island Hut Ao Kao ☎087 139 5537. This little family-run place has the best-value and most idyllically sited accommodation on the beach, though not always the friendliest welcome. The two-dozen rough-hewn en-suite timber huts are more artfully designed than they might appear: most have cheery stripey doors and idiosyncratic driftwood artwork; all have fans, hanging space and their own deckchairs on decks or private sandy porches, but no wi-fi. Price depends on proximity to the narrow but pretty shore: the most expensive are at the water's edge and catch ocean breezes. Garden hut B300, beach hut B450
Lazy Day Ao Kao ☎081 882 4002, ⓦkohmaklazyday .com. Civilized spot on a huge beachside lawn strewn with flowers and trees. As well as a/c, safes, hot showers and

mini-bars (but no TVs, to preserve the quiet), the spacious, bright, mostly beachfront bungalows sport polished concrete floors, shining white walls and French windows out onto their balconies. Free kayaks, and bikes and motorbikes to rent. Breakfast included. B2500

★ **Monkey Island** Ao Kao ☎ 081 447 8448, �🌐 monkey islandkohmak.com. There's a big range of quality, contemporary-styled bungalows here, all in timber and thatch, and a laidback, hippy-ish vibe. Top-end "Gorilla" seafront villas are huge, with a/c, hot water and the possibility of connecting villas; the large a/c "Chimpanzee" bungalows are also good, while some of the small "Ape" and "Baboon" options share bathrooms. There's also a kids' swimming pool, and a/c room rates include breakfast. Fan B450, a/c B1400

AO SUAN YAI AND AROUND

Bamboo Hideaway Resort A couple of kilometres southeast of Ao Suan Yai, accessed via tracks through the rubber plantations ☎ 039 501085, 🌐 bamboohideaway .com. An idiosyncratic haven, built almost entirely from lengths of polished bamboo. Its comfortable a/c rooms all have mosquito nets on the beds, hammocks and hot showers, and are connected by a raised bamboo walkway. Although the south coast is just a couple of minutes' walk

downhill, Ao Suan Yai has the nearest decent beach. There's an attractive swimming pool on site, as well as a good restaurant. Breakfast included. Closed June–Sept. B2400

★ **Koh Mak Resort** Ao Suan Yai ☎ 039 501013, 🌐 kohmakresort.com. With no less than 1km of shore-line to play with, nearly all of the bungalows here are beachfront (including the "Standard" fan options with hot showers) and enjoy lovely panoramas from their verandas. Among a huge range of accommodation, the most interesting are the very modern, design-conscious rooms and villas – all polished concrete, stacked slate walls, huge picture windows and rain showers, some with private little walled gardens, others with jacuzzis on their rooftop verandas. There's an infinity-edged swimming pool and similarly chic pool bar here too, plus two restaurants and the jack-of-all-trades Info Point (see opposite). Breakfast included. Fan B1500, a/c B1800

Suchanaree Resort Ao Suan Yai ☎ 081 983 2629, ✉ Suchanaree_Tour@hotmail.com. Right next door to *Koh Mak Resort*, but couldn't be more different: it's an intimate, friendly little place in a lush garden, set by a khlong with tables and deckchairs on the shady, beachfront lawn. The small, basic but good-quality, shaggy-thatched wooden bungalows all have fan, mozzie nets and bathrooms, but no wi-fi. B550

EATING AND DRINKING

AO KAO

★ **Beach Café** At Baan Ko Mak, Ao Kao. Coolly done out in black, white and orange with some nice sofas, this restaurant serves exceptionally delicious Thai food, including good *tom kha* soups and great *phanaeng* curries (both B100). Daily 8am–10pm.

Food Art Hut Opposite Monkey Island, Ao Kao. Idiosyncratic all-rounder, offering ice cream, desserts, cakes and espressos, as well as Thai dishes and simple, passable Western food such as spaghetti bolognese (B99), breakfasts, pizzas and sandwiches, washed down with German wheat beer. Daily 8am–3pm & 5–9pm.

Food Garden Opposite Monkey Island, Ao Kao. This popular, cheap and enjoyable garden restaurant serves *phat thai*, various spicy salads and *matsaman* curries (B80), as well as breakfasts and seafood barbecues in the evening. Daily 8am–10pm.

Monkey Bar Monkey Island, Ao Kao. Live music nightly, including jamming sessions, at this bar built

around the beachfront trees. A good place to meet young travellers, if you can hear yourself over the music. Daily 8pm–midnight.

Talay Bar On the beach in front of Beach Café at Baan Ko Mak, Ao Kao. Tables on the sand – with a fire show at 8pm – and great margaritas (B150) plus a long list of other cocktails. Mellow music and evening barbecues. Evenings till late.

BAN AO NID

Ko Mak Seafood Just north of Ao Nid pier ☎ 089 833 4474. Built out into the sea on stilts, with views of the bay and, apparently, of Cambodia on a clear day, this restaurant is mostly true to its name, serving *phat thai* with fresh prawns (B90) and more complex dishes such as tasty squid with salted eggs (B200). (Don't get your hopes up about the advertised Ko Mak Museum next door, though – it's just a collection of old things in an old house.) Free transfers. Daily 10.30am–9.30pm.

Ko Kood

The fourth-largest island in Thailand, forested **KO KOOD** (also spelt Ko Kut and Ko Kud) is still a wild and largely uncommercialized island. Though it's known for its sparkling white sand and exceptionally clear turquoise water, particularly along the west coast, Ko Kood is as much a nature-lover's destination as a beach-bum's. Swathes of its

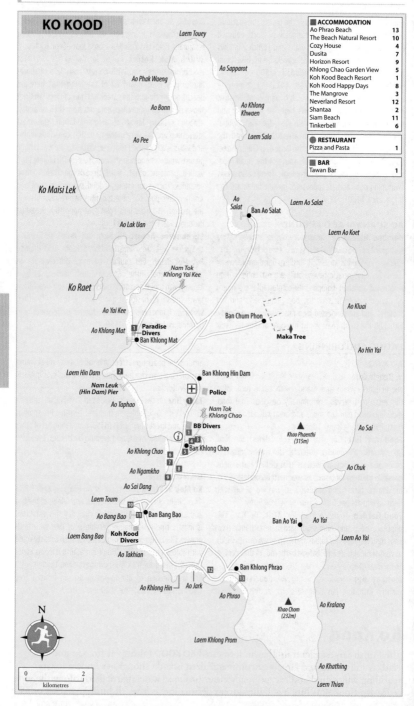

KO KOOD

ACCOMMODATION	
Ao Phrao Beach	13
The Beach Natural Resort	10
Cozy House	4
Dusita	7
Horizon Resort	9
Khlong Chao Garden View	5
Koh Kood Beach Resort	1
Koh Kood Happy Days	8
The Mangrove	3
Neverland Resort	12
Shantaa	2
Siam Beach	11
Tinkerbell	6

RESTAURANT	
Pizza and Pasta	1

BAR	
Tawan Bar	1

DIVING AND SNORKELLING OFF KO KOOD

Ko Kood's three **dive operators** charge around B3000 for two dives, with **snorkellers** paying B1000, and B14,500 for the four-day Openwater Diver course. You might prefer to opt for a local Ko Kood dive as the usual sites around Ko Rang (see p.414) are always packed with dive boats from Ko Chang and Ko Mak.

BB Divers Opposite Away Resort at the north end of Ao Khlong Chao ☎ 082 220 6002, ⓦ bbdivers.com.
Koh Kood Divers Next to Siam Beach Resort at Ao Bang Bao ☎ 085 698 4122, ⓦ kohkooddivers.com.

Paradise Divers Headquarters at Ko Kood Beach Resort at Ao Khlong Mat, with another desk at *Koh Kood Happy Days* on Ao Ngamkho ☎ 087 144 5945, ⓦ kohkood-paradisedivers.com.

shoreline are fringed by scrub and mangrove rather than broad sandy beaches, and those parts of the island not still covered in virgin tropical rainforest are filled with palm groves and rubber plantations. Most of the 25km-long island is penetrated only by sandy tracks and, in places, by navigable khlongs, if at all. All of this makes Ko Kood a surprisingly pleasant place to explore on foot (or kayak), especially as the cool season brings refreshing breezes most days. The interior is also graced with several waterfalls, the most famous of which is Nam Tok Khlong Chao, inland from Ao Khlong Chao and the focus of occasional day-trips from Ko Chang and Ko Mak.

Because of its lack of roads, Ko Kood had been the almost exclusive province of package tourists, but things have become much easier for independent travellers, with a choice of scheduled boat services from the mainland, as well as from Ko Chang and Ko Mak, and the emergence of some budget-minded guesthouses. The island is still pretty much a **one-season destination**, though, as rough seas mean that nearly all the boat services only operate from November through May. An increasing number of places are staying open year-round, however, and offer tempting discounts to those willing to chance the rains and the off-season quiet. There is some **malaria** on the island so be especially assiduous with repellent and nets if you are not taking prophylactics; there's a malaria-testing station in Ban Khlong Hin Dam.

Most of Ko Kood's fifteen hundred residents make their living from fishing and growing coconut palms and rubber trees. Many have Khmer blood in them, as the island population mushroomed at the turn of the twentieth century when Thais and Cambodians resident in nearby Cambodian territory fled French control.

The main settlements are **Ban Khlong Hin Dam**, just inland from the main Nam Leuk (Hin Dam) pier, **Ban Khlong Mat**, a natural harbour-inlet a few kilometres further north up the coast, the stilted fishing village of **Ban Ao Salat** across on the northeast coast and the fishing community of **Ban Ao Yai** on the southeast coast. On the southwest coast, several of the main beaches also have small villages. Of these, the obvious choices for budget travellers are **Ao Khlong Chao** and **Ao Ngamkho**, which both have a wide choice of accommodation and eating options and are within walking distance of each other; **Ao Bang Bao** also has cheapish bungalows and is the longer and arguably better beach but has no village and is more isolated. Seclusion is the thing on all the other west-coast beaches, most of which are the province of just one or two upmarket resorts.

Ao Khlong Chao

About 5km south of the main Nam Leuk (Hin Dam) pier on the west coast, **AO KHLONG CHAO** (pronounced "Jao") is a fun place to stay, boasting both a small sandy beach – no great beauty but a perfectly pleasant "village" beach – and the pretty 2km-long mangrove-lined Khlong Chao, which runs down from the famous Khlong Chao Falls. Close by and upstream of the road-bridge that spans the khlong, just 300m from the palm-fringed beach, is a cluster of little guesthouses, some of them built partially on stilts over the river, which offer the cheapest accommodation on the island.

Nam Tok Khlong Chao (Khlong Chao Falls)

30min walk from Ao Khlong Chao, or kayak 20min upriver from the Khlong Chao bridge to the jetty near the falls, then walk for 10min; you can drive to within 500m of the falls, following the signs from near Khlong Chao Garden View Resort, south of the Khlong Chao bridge

The three-tiered **Nam Tok Khlong Chao** is a pretty if not exceptional waterfall that tumbles down into a large, refreshing pool that's perfect for a dip; it's quietest in the mornings, before the package groups arrive. The track continues beyond the falls through jungle for another few kilometres before terminating at a rubber plantation – if you walk the whole thing it's a pleasant and very quiet four-hour trip there and back, though watch out for snakes, especially cobras.

Ao Ngamkho

Having climbed over the point at the south end of Ao Khlong Chao, the road dips down again to the tiny village at **AO NGAMKHO** and its beach, actually a series of pretty, miniature bays either side of a khlong and between rocky points, with quite rewarding snorkelling and plenty of fish at its southern end.

Ao Bang Bao

From Ao Ngamkho, follow signs for "The Beach" to reach **AO BANG BAO**, about twenty minutes' walk further south (15min west off the main road). This is one of Ko Kood's prettiest beaches, fronted by a longish sweep of bleach-white sand and deliciously clear turquoise water, plus the inevitable fringe of coconut palms, and embraced by a pair of protective promontories.

Ao Jark

On the main southbound road at the Ao Bang Bao turn-off, a 35-minute walk through coconut and rubber plantations brings you to **Ao Khlong Hin**, a wild little bay that's dominated by a small coconut-processing centre and is not really great for swimming. Ten minutes further along the road, which hugs the coast so close here it gets washed by the waves at high tide, remote and breathtakingly lovely little **AO JARK** sits at the mouth of a wide, serene khlong and feels secluded and private.

Ao Phrao

The most southerly bay, **AO PHRAO**, is a long, stunning beach of white sand backed by densely planted palms and the slopes of Khao Chom; to get here, continue for 2km (about a 20min walk) along the pretty coastal road from Ao Jark. Behind Ao Phrao, the tiny fishing village of **Ban Khlong Phrao** occupies the mangrove-lined banks of Khlong Phrao (which extends another kilometre inland). There's a clinic here as well as a few small shops and hot-food stalls.

Ban Ao Yai

A 5km track that's very steep and rough in places connects Ban Khlong Phrao with **Ban Ao Yai**, the southeast coast's main if rather lacklustre fishing village, built entirely on stilts and jetties around the shoreline of a natural harbour. Its main visitors are the crews of anchored fishing boats from Thailand and Cambodia, who come here for drink, supplies, karaoke and the rest.

Ban Khlong Hin Dam and around

The bays of northern Ko Kood, beyond Ao Khlong Chao, are even more thinly populated than the southwest coast, with just a few resorts. Inland is the island's administrative centre, **Ban Khlong Hin Dam**, 3.5km north of Ao Khlong Chao, site of a few shops, the hospital, police station, school and principal island temple. Ko Kood's main west-coast pier is a couple of kilometres to the west, at **Nam Leuk (Laem Hin Dam)**.

About 5km north of Ban Khlong Hin Dam, the small but appealing three-tiered waterfall **Nam Tok Khlong Yai Kee** is basically a miniature version of the famous Nam Tok Khlong Chao (see opposite) and rushes down into a good-sized pool that's ideal for swimming. It's accessible via a five-minute path that's very steep in places, but there are ropes at the crucial points.

Ban Ao Salat and around

The road northeast from Ban Khlong Hin Dam ends after 9km at the tiny stilt village, fishing community and port of **Ban Ao Salat**. Several of the wooden houses strung out along the jetty-promenade serve food and this is a great place for a fresh-seafood lunch, especially crab.

East off this road, in the mature rainforest near Ban Chum Phon, is a locally famous **five-hundred-year-old maka tree** (*Bridelia insulana*), known to islanders as the *ton maai yai*, that's an impressive 35m or more in height and drips with lianas and epiphytes. A kilometre-long path through rubber trees and rainforest will get you there, but you'll need to go with a local to stay on the right track.

4

ARRIVAL AND INFORMATION

KO KOOD

BY BOAT

All boat tickets to Ko Kood from the mainland should include transfers to the pier from Trat, though it's worth double-checking. Mainland and Ko Chang speedboats will drop off at and pick up from most of the west-coast accommodation. All Ko Kood hotels keep current timetables and sell tickets.

FERRIES FROM THE MAINLAND

In all but the worst weather, Koh Kood Princess (⊕ 086 126 7860) runs a year-round boat service to Ko Kood from the Trat mainland, departing from Laem Sok, about 30km south of Trat, occasionally calling at Ao Nid on Ko Mak, and terminating at Ao Salat on the island's northeast coast (1–2 daily; about 1hr 30min; B350 including transfers on Ko Kood). There is also high-season competition from the Ko Kut Express, which sails from Laem Sok to Nam Leuk pier on Ko Kood's west coast (⊕ 084 524 4321, ⊛ kokutexpress .in.th; daily; 1hr 30min–2hr; B350).

SPEEDBOATS FROM THE MAINLAND

There are also several different companies offering high-season speedboat services between the Trat mainland and Ko Kood's western piers and beaches; these are faster and more expensive (up to 4 daily; about 1hr; B600) but can be wet and uncomfortable in all but the flattest seas. Schedules and mainland departure points vary – the usual piers are Laem Sok and Dan Kao, 6km northeast of central Trat – and are best checked with Trat guesthouses or travel agents, the TAT office in Laem Ngop, or guesthouses on Ko Kood.

VIA KO CHANG AND KO MAK

Boats run between Ko Chang, Ko Mak and Ko Kood in high season (see p.411). Speedboats from Ko Chang to Ko Kood (9am; 70–90min; B900) can be caught at the stop-off at Ao Nid on Ko Mak (10am; 45–60min; B400) if there are enough takers. **Tourist information** There's a municipal tourist information office on Ao Khlong Chao, just north of the bridge on the west side of the road (daily 8.30am–6pm).

GETTING AROUND

Exploring the island on foot is both feasible and pleasant, and south of Ao Khlong Chao much of the route is shady. From Ao Khlong Chao to Ao Bang Bao takes about 40min; from Ao Bang Bao to Ao Jark is about 1hr, then another 20min to Ao Phrao.

By songthaew These can be chartered for around B1000/ day.

By motorbike You can rent motorbikes through most guesthouses and resorts (from B250/day), but be warned that the mostly concrete west-coast road is narrow and

steep, and badly rutted in places.

By mountain bike The number of hills may also deter you from getting around by mountain bike – they're available at *Happy Days* on Ao Ngamkho (B150/day) and through some other resorts.

ACCOMMODATION

AO KHLONG CHAO

Cozy House On the south bank of the khlong, Ao Khlong Chao ☎089 094 3650, ⓦkohkoodcozy.com. Has the cheapest rooms in Khlong Chao (with shared bathrooms), in an extended stilt house built around a lovely breezy communal khlongside deck. The pricier rooms and bungalows are not such good value but the home-cooked food is exceptional, especially the fish. Lots of facilities for backpackers, including rental kayaks and motorbikes, petanque and volleyball. **B250**

Khlong Chao Garden View 50m south of the bridge, and about 100m inland from the sea, Ao Khlong Chao ☎087 908 3593. Away from the khlong, this friendly place is set on a lawn dotted with ornamental trees beside the road. Choose between basic, fan-cooled huts with small bathrooms, and larger a/c bungalows with TVs. There's good food at the popular garden restaurant too, especially the *phanaeng* curries. Fan **B400**, a/c **B1000**

★ The Mangrove On the south bank of the khlong, Ao Khlong Chao ☎085 279 0278, ⓦkohkood-mangrove .com. The best of the khlongside options, with nice views of the water and sturdy wooden bungalows spaced around a well-tended lawn, dotted with pretty plants and trees. Interiors are modern and well furnished with TV and hot water. Free kayaks and motorbikes for rent. Includes breakfast. Fan **B1000**, a/c **B1500**

Tinkerbell Ao Khlong Chao ☎081 813 0058, ⓦtinkerbellresort.com. Stylishly designed and landscaped resort at the south end of the beach, which offers a difficult choice. For the same price (including breakfast), you can plump for either a bright, pastel-coloured villa with a/c, hot rain shower, fridge, TV, DVD player and large balcony right on the beach, or an equally attractive two-storey house in the second row, with a plunge pool and a separate large living room and toilet upstairs. There's a small swimming pool fed by an artificial waterfall. **B7500**

AO NGAMKHO

Dusita Ao Ngamkho ☎081 420 4861, ⓦdusitakohkood .com. Directly on the shore, just south of the khlong, this small, friendly outfit offers plainly outfitted fan and a/c wooden cabins, some with nice pebbledash outdoor bathrooms, that all enjoy beautiful sea views and some shade among the sparse coconut grove hung with hammocks. Fan **B1490**, a/c **B1990**

Horizon Resort Ao Ngamkho ☎091 249 4805, ⓦhorizonresortkohkood.com. The large, modern, a/c, hot-water wooden chalets here, some with outdoor bathrooms, sit on a flower-strewn slope atop the little rocky point at the southern end of the bay, with polished floorboards, panoramic sea views and easy access to swimming and snorkelling among the coral off the point.

The French owner also offers the first yoga classes in Ko Kood. **B2200**

Koh Kood Happy Days Ao Ngamkho ☎087 144 5945 or ☎086 018 6012; ⓦkohkood-happydays.com. This backpacker-oriented resort, beside the road, 200m from the northern section of the beach, offers ten en-suite fan and a/c rooms in a little guesthouse block, all with wooden floors, pretty furnishings and a shared veranda. There's also motorbike and mountain-bike rental and internet access, plus a dive shop, a sociable bar and restaurant, and a general store next door. Fan **B450**, a/c **B800**

AO BANG BAO

The Beach Natural Resort Ao Bang Bao ☎086 009 9420, ⓦthebeachkohkood.com. Though it doesn't actually sit on the nicest part of the beach, but behind a rocky area towards the northern end, this resort's diverse, thatched Balinese-style bungalows are tastefully furnished and have garden bathrooms; they're grouped quite closely together so most only offer glimpses of the sea. All have hot showers and a/c (6pm–8am only). Facilities include rental of kayaks, bicycles and motorbikes. Breakfast included. **B2000**

Siam Beach Ao Bang Bao ☎081 899 6200, ⓦsiam beachkohkood.net. This resort occupies almost all of the best part of the beach, sprawling across an extensive area, and is popular with budget travellers, though it's more isolated than similarly priced options on Ao Ngamkho and Ao Khlong Chao. Its big, no-frills huts and bungalows on the seafront nearly all enjoy uninterrupted bay views. Some of the newer a/c rooms are in a less idyllic spot close to a khlong and back from the shore a bit, but they're cheaper than the beachside a/c options and have hot showers. The restaurant cooks up regular seafood barbecues and there's internet access, motorbike and kayak rental. Breakfast included. Fan **B1400**, a/c **B2000**

AO JARK

Neverland Resort Ao Jark ☎081 762 6254, ⓦneverlandresort.com. The only accommodation on this beach is set among the palms between the limpid blue sea and the calm green khlong. It offers comfortable, balconied, log-clad a/c bungalows, some with hot showers, in a pretty garden, as well as fully equipped two-person tents, kayaks and snorkels. Breakfast included. Tents **B500**, bungalows **B1600**

AO PHRAO

Ao Phrao Beach Ao Phrao ☎081 429 7145, ⓦkokut .com. Mainly but not exclusively package-oriented clusters of thatched and more expensive concrete a/c bungalows, all with hot showers and TVs; facilities include free kayaks and a karaoke room. Breakfast included. **B3600**

AROUND BAN KHLONG HIN DAM

★ **Koh Kood Beach Resort** Ao Khlong Mat, about 2km northwest of Ban Khlong Hin Dam ☎081 908 8966, ⓦ visitbeyond.com. This excellent Danish-run resort is set in loads of space on a sweeping, grassy slope above a lovely pool and a nice stretch of sandy beach. Rooms are of two types, all with a/c, outdoor hot showers, mini-bars, TVs, DVD players and sea views from their generous decks: high-roofed, thatched Balinese-style bungalows and slightly more expensive "Thai Twin Houses", very suitable for families, in which two rooms are connected to one terrace with a Jacuzzi. Guests get free rental of mountain bikes, snorkels and kayaks. Breakfast included. B3900

Shantaa North end of Ao Taphao, about 2km west of Ban Khlong Hin Dam ☎081 817 9648, ⓦ shantaa kohkood.com. On a landscaped grassy rise, these nicely decorated villas have a/c and hot rain showers in attractive indoor-outdoor bathrooms. There's not much of a beach but plenty of decks with sunloungers. Breakfast included. B4500

EATING AND DRINKING

Pizza and Pasta South side of Ban Khlong Hin Dam ☎083 297 2860, ⓦ pizzanpasta.info. Genial Italian–Thai roadside restaurant serving a mean bolognese with home-made tagliatelle (B250), pizzas (B220), a few salads, espressos and pastries for breakfast. Also does a delivery service. Daily 8.30am–9pm.

Tawan Bar Ao Khlong Chao. Small roadside bar run by a friendly musician, with live music every night. Daily 3pm–2am.

DIRECTORY

Exchange There's no bank on Ko Kood, but you can change money at the bigger resorts.

Hospital Ban Khlong Hin Dam (☎039 521852).

Pharmacy The shop across from the hospital in Ban Khlong Hin Dam has a small pharmacy section and sells antihistamine tablets for bites from sandflies (see p.68), which can be legion on Ko Kood.

Police Ban Khlong Hin Dam (☎039 521745).

Postal agent In the shop next to *Happy Days* on Ao Ngamkho.

4

The northeast: Isaan

MAIN PRANG, PRASAT PHANOM RUNG

5

The northeast: Isaan

Bordered by Laos and Cambodia on three sides, the scorching-hot tableland of northeast Thailand – known as Isaan, after the Hindu god of death and the northeast – comprises a third of the country's land area and is home to nearly a third of its population. This is the least-visited region of the kingdom, and the poorest: almost three-quarters of Isaan residents are in debt, and the majority still earn less than the national minimum wage of B300 a day. Farming is the traditional livelihood here, despite appallingly infertile soil (the friable sandstone contains few nutrients and retains little water) and long periods of drought punctuated by downpours and intermittent bouts of flooding. As you'd expect, the landscape is mostly flat, but there are plenty of lively festivals and ancient temples to make a visit worth the effort.

Rather than the cities – which are chaotic, exhausting places, with little going for them apart from accommodation and onward transport – Isaan's prime destinations are its **Khmer ruins** and **Khao Yai National Park**. Five huge northeastern **festivals** also draw massive crowds: in May, Yasothon is the focus for the bawdy rocket festival; the end of June or beginning of July sees the equally raucous rainmaking festival of Phi Ta Kon in Dan Sai near Loei; in July, Ubon Ratchathani hosts an extravagant candle festival; in October, strange, pink fireballs float out of the Mekong near Nong Khai; while the flamboyant, though inevitably touristy, "elephant round-up" is staged in Surin in November.

It's rural life that really defines Isaan though, and you can learn a lot about the local residents by staying at one of the family-run **guesthouses** and **homestays** in the region. If you make it this far you should endeavour to see at least one set of Isaan's Khmer ruins: those at **Phimai** are the most accessible, but it's well worth making the effort to visit either **Phanom Rung** or **Khao Phra Viharn** as well, both of which occupy spectacular hilltop locations, though the latter was closed at the time of writing. Relics of an even earlier age, prehistoric cliff-paintings also draw a few tourists eastwards to Pha Taem National Park beside the Mekong River near the little town of **Khong Chiam**.

HAEW SUWAT FALLS, KHAO YAI NATIONAL PARK

Highlights

❶ Khao Yai National Park Easy and tough trails, lots of birds, gibbons and elephants, several waterfalls and night safaris. **See p.437**

❷ Khmer ruins Exquisite Angkor Wat-style temples at Phimai, Phanom Rung and Khao Phra Viharn. **See p.447, p.450 & p.460**

❸ Silk A northeastern speciality, available all over the region but particularly in Khon Kaen. **See p.459**

❹ Yasothon rocket festival Bawdy rainmaking ritual involving ornate home-made rockets. **See p.470**

❺ Phu Kradung Teeming table mountain, the most dramatic of the region's national parks. **See p.483**

❻ The Mekong The best stretch in Thailand for gentle exploration of the mighty riverscape is between Chiang Khan and Nong Khai. **See p.487**

❼ Wat Phu Tok Extraordinary meditation temple on a steep sandstone outcrop. **See p.498**

❽ Wat Phra That Phanom Isaan's most fascinating holy site, especially during the February pilgrimage. **See p.501**

HIGHLIGHTS ARE MARKED ON THE MAP ON P.436

5

Isaan's only mountain range of any significance divides the uninspiring town of **Loei** from the central plains and offers some stiff walking, awesome scenery and the possibility of spotting unusual birds and flowers in the **national parks** that spread across its heights. Due north of Loei at **Chiang Khan**, the **Mekong River** begins its leisurely course around Isaan with a lush stretch where a clutch of guesthouses has opened up the river countryside to travellers. The powerful waterway acts as a natural boundary between Thailand and Laos, but it's no longer the forbidding barrier it once was; with Laos opening further border crossings to visitors, the river is becoming an increasingly important transport link.

At the eastern end of this upper stretch, the border town of **Nong Khai** is surrounded by wonderfully ornate temples, including the bizarre Sala Kaeo Kou. The grandest and most important religious site in the northeast, however, is **Wat Phra That Phanom**, way downstream beyond **Nakhon Phanom**, a town that affords some of the finest Isaan vistas.

In the 1960s, government schemes to introduce hardier crops set in motion a debt cycle that has forced farmers into monocultural cash-cropping to repay their loans for fertilizers, seeds and machinery. For many families, there's only one way off the treadmill: of the twenty-one million people who live in Isaan, an average of two million economic refugees leave the area every year, most of them heading for Bangkok, where northeasterners now make up the majority of the capital's lowest-paid workforce. Children and elderly parents remain in the villages, increasingly dependent on the money sent back every month from the metropolis and awaiting the annual visit in May, when migrant family members often return for a couple of months to help with the rice planting.

ISAAN'S BORDER CROSSINGS

Isaan has six major **border crossings into Laos** (see p.28), all but one (Bueng Kan–Paksan) of which issue Lao visas.

The most popular is at **Nong Khai**, a route that provides easy road access to the Lao capital, Vientiane; the others are Tha Li, Bueng Kan, Nakhon Phanom, Mukdahan and Chong Mek. If you want to avoid possible queues at the border, you can get a Lao visa in advance from the consulate in the central Isaan town of Khon Kaen. Here you'll also find a Vietnamese consulate issuing visas for Vietnam.

It's also possible to travel **overland between Isaan and Cambodia** (see p.27) through two different border crossings: via Chong Chom in Surin province to O'Smach, which has transport to Anlong Veng and then on to Siem Reap; and via Chong Sa Ngam in the Phusing district of Si Saket province to Choam in Anlong Veng.

Brief history

Most northeasterners speak a dialect that's more comprehensible to residents of Vientiane than Bangkok, and Isaan's historic allegiances have tied it more closely to Laos and Cambodia than to Thailand. Between the eleventh and thirteenth centuries, the all-powerful **Khmers** covered the northeast in magnificent stone temple complexes, the remains of which constitute the region's most satisfying tourist attractions. During subsequent centuries the territories along the Mekong River changed hands numerous times, until the present border with Laos was set at the end of World War II. In the 1950s and 1960s, **Communist insurgents** played on the northeast's traditional ties with Laos; a movement to align Isaan with the Marxists of Laos gathered some force, and the Communist Party of Thailand, gaining sympathy among poverty-stricken northeastern farmers, established bases in the region. At about the same time, major US air bases for the **Vietnam War** were set up in Khorat, Ubon Ratchathani and Udon Thani, fuelling a sex industry that has plagued the region ever since. When the American military moved out, northeastern women turned to the tourist-oriented Bangkok flesh-trade instead, and today the majority of prostitutes in the capital come from Isaan.

ARRIVAL AND GETTING AROUND   ISAAN

All towns and cities in Isaan are connected by public transport, as are many of the larger villages, but compared to many other parts of the country, northeastern roads are fairly traffic-free, so hiring your own vehicle is also a good option.

By bus Many travellers approach Isaan from the north, either travelling directly from Chiang Mai to Loei, or going via Phitsanulok, in the northern reaches of the central plains, to Khon Kaen, but you can also take direct buses to Khorat from the east-coast towns of Pattaya, Rayong and Chanthaburi. All major northeastern centres have direct bus services from Bangkok.

By train Two rail lines cut through Isaan, providing useful connections with Bangkok and Ayutthaya.

By plane There are flights between Bangkok and several northeastern cities.

Khao Yai National Park

B400; vehicles B50 extra

About 120km northeast of Bangkok, the cultivated lushness of the central plains gives way to the thickly forested Phanom Dangkrek mountains. A 2166-square-kilometre chunk of this sculpted limestone range has been conserved as **KHAO YAI NATIONAL PARK**, the country's first national park to be established (in 1962) and one of its most popular. Spanning five distinct forest types and rising to a height of 1351m, the park sustains over three hundred bird and twenty large land-mammal species – hence its UNESCO accreditation as a World Heritage Site – and offers a plethora of waterfalls and several undemanding walking trails.

5

KHAO YAI'S WILDLIFE

During the daytime you're bound to hear some of the local wildlife, even if you don't catch sight of it. Noisiest of all are the **white-handed (lar) gibbons**, which hoot and whoop from the tops of the tallest trees, and the bubbling trills of the **pileated (capped) gibbons**. Gibbons generally avoid contact with the ground, unlike the hard-to-miss **pig-tailed macaques**, many of which gather at favoured spots on the road through the park. **Hornbills** also create quite a racket, calling and flapping their enormous wings; Khao Yai harbours large flocks of four different hornbill species, which makes it one of the best observation sites in Southeast Asia. The great hornbill is particularly beautiful, with brilliant yellow and black undersides and a 2m wingspan; the magnificent oriental pied hornbill boasts less striking black and white colouring, but is more commonly seen at close range because it swoops down to catch fish, rats and reptiles. You might also see red-headed trogons, orange-breasted trogons, woodpeckers and Asian fairy-bluebirds, and, if you're very lucky, silver pheasants and Siamese firebacks, endemic only to Thailand and western Cambodia. From November to March Khao Yai hosts several species of **migrant birds**, including the dramatically coloured Siberian thrush and the orange-headed thrush.

A herd of between 200 and 250 Asian **elephants** lives in the park, and its members are often seen at night – it's the only place in Thailand where you have much chance of spotting wild elephants. Khao Yai is also home to a very small number of **tigers**, sightings of which are extremely rare. You're almost certain to spot **civets**, and you might come across a **slow loris**, while barking and sambar **deer** are less nervous after dark. **Wrinkle-lipped bats** assemble en masse at sunset, especially at the cave entrance next to Wat Tham Silathong, just outside the north (main) gate into the park, which every evening disgorges millions of them on their nightly forage.

Rangers discourage visitors from exploring the outer, non-waymarked reaches unguided, partly for environmental reasons, but also because of trigger-happy **sandalwood poachers**. The highly prized sandalwood oil is extracted by making cuts in a mature aloewood tree and collecting chunks of oil-saturated wood – which sells for B20,000–40,000 a kilogram – several months later. Sandalwood trees are indigenous to Khao Yai, and though oil collection does not usually kill the tree, it does weaken it. Guides can point out trees that have been cut in this way along the trails.

For many Thais, however, especially Bangkokians, Khao Yai is not so much a place for wildlife spotting as an easy weekend escape from the fumes. Some have second homes in the area, while others come for the golf and the soft-adventure activities, especially horseriding and off-road driving in ATVs, offered by the increasingly popular "dude-ranch" resorts. The cooler climate here has also made Khao Yai one of Thailand's most productive areas for viticulture and dairy farming.

There's camping and basic accommodation in the park itself, and plenty more comfortable options just beyond the perimeter and in the nearby town of **Pak Chong**. It's quite easy to trek the park trails by yourself, but as some of Khao Yai's best waterfalls, caves and viewpoints are as much as 20km apart, a tour is worth considering. Try to avoid visiting at weekends and holidays, when it's busy; that said, even at peak times, don't expect it to be like a safari park. Bring binoculars if you have them and some warm clothes, as it gets cool at the higher altitudes, especially at night.

The park

Visitor centre daily 7am–6pm

Several well-worn trails radiate from the area around the visitor centre and park headquarters at kilometre-stone 37, and a few more branch off from the roads that traverse the park; a few are signposted en route and some are colour-coded. The **visitor centre** provides brochures showing the more popular trails. Wear good boots, be prepared for some wading through rivers, and take a hat and plenty of water.

You won't spot much wildlife unless you know where to look, which is one reason to join a tour (see p.440), since the guides know which trees the hornbills perch on and where gibbons go to feed. However, if you prefer to go it alone, the following trails are the most popular options.

Kong Kaew Nature Trail

The shortest and least taxing trail is the kilometre-long **Kong Kaew Nature Trail**, which starts just behind the visitor centre. It's paved all the way and takes just thirty minutes in each direction; if it's not too crowded, you could see gibbons, woodpeckers and kingfishers en route.

To Nong Pak Chee observation tower

Of the more adventurous hikes that begin from the park headquarters, the most popular runs from just uphill of the visitor centre restaurant to Nong Pak Chee observation tower in the west of the park. This is a fairly easy walk through forest and grassland that culminates at an observation tower built next to a lake. En route you'll hear white-handed gibbons in the tallest trees, and might spot barking deer in the savanna. If you stay at the tower long enough you could see eagles soaring or needletails dive-bombing the lake; elephants and gaurs sometimes come to drink here, too. The walk takes about two and a half hours to the observation tower (4.5km), from where it's another 900m down a dirt track that meets the main road between kilometre-stones 35 and 36. From the road, you can walk or hitch back either to the headquarters (2km) or down to the checkpoint (12km) and then travel on to Pak Chong. If you just want to spend a few hours at the observation tower and forget the main part of the walk, stop beside the main road between kilometre-stones 35 and 36 (before reaching the park headquarters) and walk the kilometre down the access track to the tower.

Haew Suwat Falls and trail

Another good focus for walks is the area around **Haew Suwat Falls**, east of the visitor centre. These 25m-high falls are a great place for an invigorating shower, and featured in the 1999 film *The Beach*. To get to the falls from the park headquarters, either follow the 8km trail (allow 3–4 hours each way), or walk, drive or hitch the 6km road beyond the headquarters to Haew Suwat – it's a popular spot, so there should be plenty of cars. The **trail** begins on the Nature Trail behind the visitor centre, then veers off it, along a path marked with red flashes. En route to Haew Suwat you'll pass a turn-off to *Pha Kluai/Orchid* campsite and waterfall, 6.1km from the park headquarters (see below). Due to a series of deaths, swimming at Haew Suwat is only allowed in the dry season, when the falls lose some of their power. Even then, it's wise to exercise caution.

To Pha Kluai/Orchid campsite

Day-trippers often do the short walk from Haew Suwat waterfall to **Pha Kluai/Orchid campsite**, which is paved most of the way and takes two hours at most (3.1km). You've a good chance of spotting gibbons and macaques along this route, as well as kingfishers and hornbills. The area around nearby Pha Kluai Falls is famous for its impressive variety of orchids.

LEECHES

If hiking during or just after the rainy season you will almost certainly have some unsolicited encounters with **leeches**; mosquito repellent helps deter them, as do leech socks (canvas gaiters), available from the cafeteria complex opposite the visitor centre, or in the nearby accommodation office (they're also provided free if you join a tour). To get leeches off your skin, burn them with a cigarette or lighter, or douse them in salt; oily suntan lotion or insect repellent can make them lose their grip and fall off.

5

ARRIVAL AND GETTING AROUND   KHAO YAI NATIONAL PARK

There are two access roads to the park – one from the south and another from the north – with checkpoints on both. Everyone travelling by public transport approaches the park from Pak Chong (see p.442), about 25km north of the northern entrance. Some tour companies, like Khao Yai Nature Life & Tours (see opposite), offer pick-up from the airport or hotels in Bangkok.

By shared songthaew The cheapest way to get to Khao Yai from Pak Chong is to take a public songthaew from outside the 7-Eleven shop, 200m west of the footbridge on the north side of the main road near Soi 21 (every 30min 6.30am–4pm, less frequently on Sun; 30min; B40). Public songthaews are not allowed to enter the park itself, so you'll be dropped at the park checkpoint, about 14km short of the Khao Yai visitor centre, park headquarters and most popular trailheads. At the checkpoint (where you pay the national-park entrance fee), park rangers will flag down passing cars and get them to give you a ride up to the visitor centre; this is common practice here. The whole journey from Pak Chong to the visitor centre takes about 1hr.

Chartering a songthaew A quicker but pricier option is to charter a songthaew from Pak Chong: these count as private vehicles and are allowed inside the park. They can be chartered from the corner of Soi 19 in Pak Chong, and cost around B1000 for the ride from Pak Chong to Haew Suwat Falls, or about B1500 for a return trip, including several hours in the park.

Getting back Coming back from the park is often easier, as day-trippers will usually give lifts all the way back to Pak Chong. Otherwise, hitch a ride as far as the checkpoint, or walk to it from the visitor centre – it's a pleasant 3–4hr walk along the fairly shaded park road, and you'll probably spot lots of birds and some macaques, gibbons and deer as well. At the checkpoint you can pick up a songthaew to Pak Chong: the last one usually leaves here at about 5pm. To get back to Pak Chong from one of the resorts on the road to the park, simply ask the owner to call one of the public songthaews. You may have to wait a while, and pay a little extra for them coming to get you, but it still shouldn't be more than B50/person.

Mountain bike rental You can rent mountain bikes from outside the visitor centre (B50/hr; B200/day).

INFORMATION AND TOURS

Tourist information The visitor centre (daily 7am–6pm), by the park office and main trailheads, offers maps and brochures.

Tours Khao Yai's tours are reasonably priced and cater primarily for independent tourists rather than big groups, though it's advisable to book in advance. But be warned: in recent years, the park has been plagued with unscrupulous operators who charge exorbitant up-front fees for tours and then later ask customers to pay the park entry fee separately (including fees for the car, driver and/or guide). As a result, we recommend only reputable outfits, all offering customized trips as well as their own version of the popular, undemanding one-and-a-half-day programme (around B1500/person, including the B400 park entry fee) which typically features a trip to a bat cave just outside the park at dusk, walks along one or two easy trails, a swim in Haew Suwat Falls (dry season only) and some after-dark wildlife spotting; it's usual, though not compulsory, to stay in the tour operator's own accommodation overnight. It's worth booking ahead, especially for overnight expeditions. Prices quoted are for a minimum of two trekkers. Note that it's also possible to hire a park ranger as your personal

---

NIGHT SAFARIS

A much-touted park attraction is the hour-long **night safaris**, or "night-lightings", which take truckloads of tourists round Khao Yai's main roads in the hope of catching some interesting wildlife in the glare of the specially-fitted searchlights.

Night-time **sightings** often include deer and civets, and if you're very lucky you might see elephants too. Opinions differ on the quality of the experience: some find it thrilling to be out on the edges of the jungle after dark, others see it as rather a crass method of wildlife observation, especially at weekends, when the park can feel like a town centre, with four or five trucks following each other round and round the main roads.

All night-lightings are run by the **park rangers**, so tour operators sometimes join forces to hire a truck with ranger and searchlights. If you're on your own, you'll probably need to accompany one of these groups. The safaris depart the park headquarters **every night** at 7pm and 8pm (they can pick you up from the campsite if requested); trucks cost B500 to rent and can take up to ten people: book your place at the national park accommodation office, next to the visitor centre.

guide for the more remote trails, though their command of English is limited; you can arrange this at the park headquarters the night before, but will have to sort out your own transport. There's no set fee, but a fair rate would be B500 for a few hours, or around B1000 for the whole day.

TOUR OPERATORS

Green Leaf Guest House and Tour Kilometre-stone 7.5 on the park road (call for free pick-up from Pak Chong) ☎044 365073 or ☎089 424 8809, ⓦgreen leaftour.com. At this family-run outfit treks are mostly led by owner Nine, who gets good reviews, particularly as a bird-spotter. Accommodation is available at the family guesthouse (see below).

Khao Yai Nature Life & Tours 3km west of Route 2090 (the turn-off is just south of Green Leaf Guest House) ☎081 827 8391, ⓦkhaoyainaturelifetours.com. This

comfy resort offers a variety of programmes, including half-day visits (B600), one-day photography-focused tours (B2000–3500, depending on group size), and tailor-made treks. "Eagle-eye" Tony is a highly accomplished bird-spotter and photographer. For details of their accommodation, see below.

Spice Roads ☎02 381 7490, ⓦspiceroads.com /thailand/khao_yai. Upmarket bicycle tour of Khao Yai and its wineries, departing from Bangkok (2 days B9950/ person all-inclusive).

Wildlife Safari About 2km north of Pak Chong train station at 39 Thanon Pak Chong Subsanun, Nong Kaja (call to arrange free transport from Pak Chong) ☎081 282 8308 or ☎089 628 8224, ⓔjayjungletrek@gmail .com. A good range of bespoke tours, including half-day trips (B300) for those on a tight schedule. Accommodation here is in comfortable rooms (fan B400, a/c B600) in the garden of the family home. Very kind and welcoming owners.

ACCOMMODATION AND EATING

You have several options when it comes to **accommodation** in Khao Yai, either in the park, or on the road that leads up to it. Alternatively, you could stay in Pak Chong (see p.442), 37km from the park's centre. If you decide to do a tour, it's usual to stay in the lodgings run by your tour guide. But be wary of places not listed here; plenty of people have been ripped off by unscrupulous outfits, and we've even had reports of resorts offering to pick visitors up from the bus station and then adding huge transfer charges to the bill on departure. There are restaurants beside the Visitors' Centre and the lodges in the park, though they tend to close by 7pm, and plenty of options along the road to the park.

IN THE PARK

If you're intending to do several days' independent exploring in the park, the most obvious places to stay are the national park lodges, dorms and tents in the heart of Khao Yai. In high season, the lodges usually have to be booked in advance at the Royal Forestry Department office in Bangkok (☎02 562 0760) or at ⓦdnp.go.th/parkreserve. However, you could also contact the Khao Yai accommodation office direct (daily 8am–9pm; ☎086 092 6531), as accommodation is often available to walk-ins (Sun–Thurs). Advance booking is not usually necessary if camping, but is advisable at weekends.

Lodges Spread across the park, these sleep two to thirty people (the latter in dorms). If you book in advance, you'll need to bring the receipt to the accommodation office. On weekdays there's a thirty percent discount. **B800**

Camping Two-person tents can be rented at *Lam Takong* campsite, about 5km from the headquarters, and at *Pha Kluai Mai* campsite (aka *Orchid Camp*, very good for bird-spotting), about 4km east of the park headquarters, on the road to Haew Suwat falls. Equipment such as sleeping bags (B80) and pillows (B20) is available as well. You can pitch your own tent at either site for B30/ person. **B225**

THE PARK ROAD

The 23km road that runs from Pak Chong up to the park checkpoint is dotted with luxurious hotels and resorts; most guests arrive by car, but Pak Chong transfers are usually available and the Pak Chong songthaew will also bring you here. Addresses are determined by the nearest kilometre-stone on Thanon Thanarat.

Balios Khao Yai At kilometre-stone 17 ☎044 365 971–5, ⓦbalioskhaoyai.com. Offers good-value upmarket accommodation in its large a/c rooms and has a swimming pool, mountain-bike rental, and two restaurants. Includes breakfast. **B4800**

Green Leaf Guest House and Tour 12.5km from Pak Chong, at kilometre-stone 7.5 ☎044 365073, ⓦgreen leaftour.com. One of the cheapest places to stay on the park road, this friendly, family-run outfit has twenty en-suite fan rooms behind its good, cheap restaurant; it also does guided treks into the national park (see above). **B200**

Khao Yai Nature Life & Tours 15km from Pak Chong, turn west just beyond kilometre-stone 7.5 ☎081 827 8391, ⓦkhaoyainaturelifetours.com. Run by a switched-on couple, this smart resort has a good selection of a/c rooms and villas set around two excellent outdoor pools. The best rooms have wooden floors and bed covers made from fine Thai silk. There's also a good restaurant. Breakfast included. **B2500**

5

Pak Chong

Whether you decide to see Khao Yai National Park on your own or as part of a tour, your first port of call is likely to be the town of **PAK CHONG**, 37km north of Khao Yai's visitor centre and major trailheads, and served by trains and buses. One of the four recommended Khao Yai tour leaders (see p.441) operates from Pak Chong, and there are a couple of places to stay in town too. The obvious drawback to basing yourself here is that it's about an hour's journey from the Khao Yai trailheads, but if you make an early start you can make use of the cheap public songthaew service.

ARRIVAL AND DEPARTURE PAK CHONG

Thanon Tesaban cuts through central Pak Chong, and numerous small sois shoot off it: sois to the north are odd-numbered in ascending order from west to east (Soi 13–Soi 25) while those on the south side of the road have even numbers, from west to east (Soi 8–Soi 18). The heart of the town is on the north side, between the train station on Soi 15 and the footbridge a few hundred metres further east at Soi 21.

By train Pak Chong train station (☎044 311534) is on Soi 15, one short block north of Thanon Tesaban.
Destinations Ayutthaya (10 daily; 1hr 30min–2hr 30min); Bangkok (10 daily; 3hr 30min–4hr 45min); Khorat (11 daily; 1hr 15min–1hr 30min); Si Saket (8 daily; 4hr 20min–7hr 30min); Surin (10 daily; 3hr 10min–5hr 30min); Ubon Ratchathani (7 daily; 6hr 50min–8hr 40min); Udon Thani (2 daily; 6hr 30min–7hr 15min).
By bus and minibus The bus station is towards the west end of town, one block south off the main road between sois 8 and 10. Some long-distance buses also stop in the town centre, beside the footbridge, while a/c minibuses to Bangkok and Khorat leave from offices on opposite sides of the road near the Beautiful Optical shop on Thanon Tesaban, just west of Soi 18.
Destinations Bangkok (hourly; 2–3hr); Khorat (every 20min; 1hr).

ACCOMMODATION AND EATING

There's a **day market** selling fresh fruit and vegetables in the centre of town, between the train station on Soi 15 and the footbridge a few hundred metres further east at Soi 21. You'll find a **supermarket** near here on the south side of the main road.

★Ban Mai Chay Nam 21 Thanon Mittraphap ☎044 314 236, ⓦbanmaichaynam.com. Awesome old-style Thai restaurant stuffed with retro curios – from giant Spiderman figures to American gas pumps from the 1950s. It's often packed with Thai tourists, and the food is fresh and authentic. Dishes include a mean catfish salad. Most dishes B100–200. Daily 10am–10pm.
Night Market The cheapest and most popular place to eat after dark, the night market sets up along the main road between Tesaban sois 17 and 19. Daily 6–10/11pm.

Phubade Hotel 50m south of the train station down Tesaban Soi 15 ☎044 314964. Pak Chong's cheapest hotel with clean-ish, very basic rooms. A safe bet if you arrive late in the evening and need somewhere central to stay. Also offers a laundry service. Fan B350, a/c B500
Rim Tarn Inn 430 Thanon Mittraphap, 300m west of the bus station ☎044 313365-6, ⓦrimtarninn.com. Smarter and more appealing than Phubade, this tall multi-coloured building has large, comfortable a/c rooms, plus a pool and restaurant. B1000

DIRECTORY

ATMs There are several ATMs near the train station.
Hospital There's a branch of the Bangkok Hospital (☎044

316611) at 5/1 Thanon Mittraphap.
Post office On the corner of Soi 25 and Thanon Tesaban.

Khorat (Nakhon Ratchasima)

Beyond Pak Chong, Highway 2 and the rail line diverge to run either side of picturesque Lam Takong Reservoir, offering a last taste of undulating, forested terrain before reaching the largely barren Khorat plateau. They rejoin at **KHORAT** (officially known as **Nakhon Ratchasima**) – literally "Frontier Country" – which is considered the gateway to the northeast.

If this is your first stop in Isaan, it's not a pleasant introduction: Khorat is one of Thailand's most populous cities, its streets teem with traffic, and apart from the moat

KHORAT

0   250

meters

N

Airport, Surin & Dan Kwian

Khon Kaen

Tourist Police

Bus Terminal 2

Central Khorat (1.6km)

Banghok

Police

TAT

THANON MITTRAPHAP

Wat Mai Amphawan

THANON SUEBSIRI

THANON MUKKHAMONTRI

Maharat Hospital

Lam Takong

North Gate

THANON PRACHAK

Phimai Bus Stop

IT Plaza

THANON MITTRAPHAP

Bus Terminal 1

THANON TOMMARAT

THANON ASSADANG

THANON ASSADANG

Wat Narai

Iyara Hotel

THANON CHUMPHON

East Gate

Night Market

THANON CHAINARONG

Buses to Dan Kwian

City Pillar

South Gate

Police Station

THANON MANAT

Klang Plaza I

THANON CHUMPHON

THANON MAHATHAI

THANON KAMJENG SONGKHRAN

THANON SANPASIT

THANON RATCHANIKUN

THANON WATCHARASRIT

Thao Suranari Monument

Tourist Police

Currency Exchange

THANON CHUMPHON

THANON RATCHADAMNOEN

Market

Klang Plaza II

Wat Suthachinda & Maha Veeravong Museum

THANON BUARONG

THANON SURANARI

Night Market

THANON YOTA

THANON JOMSURANGYAT

THANON PHO KLANG

THANON SURANARI

SOI KASETR

SOI JANT

TROK SAMORAI

THANON MUKKHAMONTRI

Train Station

The Mall

Bangkok Hospital & budget Car Rental

See inset map

● RESTAURANTS & CAFÉS
C&C (Cabbages & Condoms)   1
Chez Andy   5
Check Inn   4
George & Dragon   3
Hansa   2
Suan Sin

● SHOPS
Basket shops   3
Big C Hypermarket Mall   1
Jiaranai Silk   2
Night bazaar   4/5

■ ACCOMMODATION
Sansabai House   2
Sima Thani   1
Siri Hotel   3

5

round the old city, there's nothing here you could call a genuine tourist attraction. On the plus side, Khorat is at the centre of a good transport network and is within striking distance of the **Khmer ruins** at Phimai, Phanom Rung and Muang Tam, as well as the archeological remains of **Ban Prasat** and the pottery village at **Dan Kwian**. Aside from serving Bangkok and all the main centres within Isaan, Khorat's bus network extends south along Highway 304 to the east coast, enabling you to travel directly to Pattaya, Rayong and Chanthaburi without going through the capital.

Thao Suranari Monument

Sights are thin on the ground in Khorat, but if you spend more than a couple of hours in the city you're bound to come across the landmark statue at the western gate of the old city walls. This is the much-revered **Thao Suranari Monument**, erected to commemorate the heroic actions of the wife of the deputy governor of Khorat, during an attack by the kingdom of Vientiane – capital of modern-day Laos – in 1826. Some chronicles say she organized a feast for the Lao army and enticed them into bed, where they were then slaughtered by the Thais; another tells how she and the other women of Khorat were carted off as prisoners to Vientiane, whereupon they attacked their guards with such ferocity that the Lao retreated out of fear that the whole Thai army had arrived. At any rate, Thao Suranari saved the day and is still feted by the citizens of Khorat, who lay flowers at her feet, light incense at her shrine and even dance around it. From March 23 to April 3, the town holds a week-long **festival** in her honour, with parades through the streets and the usual colourful trappings of Thai merry-making.

Maha Veeravong Museum

In the grounds of Wat Suthachinda, Thanon Ratchadamnoen • Wed–Sun 9am–4pm • B100

The **Maha Veeravong Museum** houses a small and unexceptional collection of predominantly Dvaravati- and Lopburi-style Buddha statues that belonged to a monk who was once the abbot of Wat Suthachinda (the grounds of which house the museum). The single-storey museum was built by Thailand's Fine Arts Department in 1954, and makes for a pleasant diversion from the chaos of the city.

Dan Kwian

15km south of Khorat on Route 224 • Local bus #1307 (destination Chok Chai; every 30min; 30min) from Bus Terminal 2, or at Khorat's South Gate; get off as soon as you see the roadside pottery stalls

Some of the most popular household pottery in Thailand is produced by the potters of **DAN KWIAN**, a tiny village 15km south of Khorat. The local clay, dug from the banks of the Mun River, has a high iron content, which when fired in wood-burning kilns combines with ash to create the unglazed metallic finish that is characteristic of Dan Kwian pottery. The geometrical latticework pattern is also typical, and is incorporated into everything from incense burners and ashtrays to vases and storage jars. Dan Kwian potters also produce ceramic tiles and large-scale religious and secular murals, a favourite in modern wats and city homes.

ARRIVAL AND DEPARTURE

BY TRAIN

The train station, on Thanon Mukkhamontri (☎ 044 242044), is served by city bus routes #2 and #3.

Destinations Ayutthaya (10 daily; 4hr); Bangkok (10 daily; 4hr 30min–6hr 40min); Khon Kaen (daily; 3hr 20min); Pak Chong (11 daily; 1–2hr); Si Saket (8 daily; 4hr–5hr 30min); Surin (10 daily; 2hr–3hr 20min); Ubon Ratchathani

(7 daily; 4hr–6hr 10min); Udon Thani (daily; 5hr).

BY BUS

Bus Terminal 2 (☎ 044 256006–9), the main terminal, is situated on the far northern edge of the city on Highway 2. It's the arrival and departure point for regular and a/c buses serving regional towns such as Pak Chong (for Khao Yai)

and Phimai, as well as long-distance destinations such as Bangkok, Ban Tako (for Phanom Rung), Chiang Mai, Khon Kaen, Nong Khai, Pattaya, Rayong (for Ko Samet) and Surin. Traffic is chaotic in the city, so avoid choking in a tuk-tuk and take a cheaper a/c taxi instead (B35 to train station or nearby hotels).

Bus Terminal 1 (☎ 044 268899) is more centrally located just off Thanon Suranari, and also operates both fan and a/c buses to Bangkok, via Pak Tong Chai and Pak Chong, though departures are less frequent.

Destinations Bangkok (every 40min; 3–4hr); Ban Tako (for Phanom Rung; every 30min; 2hr); Buriram (every 30min; 3hr); Chanthaburi (2 daily; 6–8hr); Chiang Mai (12 daily; 12–14hr); Chiang Rai (5 daily; 14–16hr); Dan Kwian (every 30min; 30min); Khon Kaen (at least every 40min; 2hr 30min–3hr); Lopburi (12 daily; 3hr 30min); Nakhon Phanom (2 daily; 8hr); Nong Khai (2 daily; 6–8hr); Pattaya (10 daily; 5hr); Phimai (every 30min; 1hr–1hr 30min); Phitsanulok (9 daily; 7–9hr); Rayong (for Ko Samet; at least 8 daily; 6–8hr); Si Racha (7 daily; 5hr); Surin (every 30min; 4–5hr); Ubon Ratchathani (every hour; 5–7hr); Udon Thani (at least hourly; 3hr 30min–5hr).

GETTING AROUND AND INFORMATION

By songthaew and city bus Flat-fare songthaews (B8) and city buses (B8) travel most main roads within town. Expect to pay up to B15 for longer journeys to the city limits. The most useful routes – served by both songthaews and buses – are #2, which runs between the main TAT office in the west, via the train station, along Thanon Suranari and Thanon Assadang to beyond the *lak muang* (city pillar) in the east, and #3, which also runs right across the city, via Mahathai and Jomsurangyat roads, past the train station, to the TAT office in the west.

By tuk-tuk Easily flagged down off the main routes around town. Expect to pay B60 for journeys of 1–2km (from the Thao Suranari Monument to the Big C hyper-market, for example).

By taxi Metered taxis cruise the streets but are not yet as ubiquitous as tuk-tuks. Expect to pay a minimum fee of B30.

Car rental Cars are available from Budget at 719/5 Thanon Mittraphap, outside Tesco Lotus (daily 8am–6pm; ☎ 044 341 654, ⊛ budget.co.th).

Tourist information The TAT office (daily 8.30am–4.30pm; ☎ 044 213666, ✉ tatsima@tat.or.th) is 1.6km west of the train station on Thanon Mittraphap. It's only really worth making the trip for one of their free maps of the city. To reach it from the city centre, take city bus #2 or #3.

ACCOMMODATION

Khorat has a few budget hotels that are reasonable value, but if you're planning to visit Phimai, consider staying there instead.

Sansabai House 335–337 Thanon Suranari ☎ 044 255 855, ✉ sansabaikorat@yahoo.com. Smart, good-value rooms in a central location. They have just a few fan rooms, but most are a/c and are often full. No breakfast included but there's a decent on-site café. Fan **B300**, a/c **B450**

Sima Thani 2112/2 Thanon Mittraphap, near the TAT office ☎ 044 213100, ⊛ simathani.com. One of the city's best hotels, with smart a/c rooms, a swimming pool, three restaurants and a babysitting service. There's a relaxed feel

to the place despite its popularity with businesspeople, and the rooms are good value. It's located beside Highway 2 (the Bangkok–Nong Khai road), and buses from Bangkok or Khao Yai can drop you at the door en route to Bus Terminal 2, but it's too far to walk from the hotel to the town centre. **B1500**

Siri Hotel 688–690 Thanon Pho Klang ☎ 044 242831, ⊛ sirihotelkorat.com. Less than a 10min walk from the train station, the *Siri* is ideal for budget travellers. Rooms are surprisingly quiet and spacious. **B450**

EATING AND DRINKING

The night bazaar on and around Thanon Manat includes a few hot-food stalls, but there's a bigger selection of **night-market**-style food stalls, with some streetside tables, about 800m further east near the *Iyara Hotel* on Thanon Chumphon. A smaller, more convenient grouping sets up about 400m east of *Siri Hotel* on the corner of Thanon Yota. Because of its sizeable contingent of expats, Khorat also offers the chance to satisfy foreign-food cravings. For big international-brand **restaurants**, head for the huge shopping mall that houses the Big C hypermarket. After dark, Westerners tend to head for the bars along Thanon Suranari, while young Thais head for those along Thanon Yommarat.

C&C (Cabbages & Condoms) 86/1 Thanon Suebsiri. Excellent Thai food at this cosy, mid-priced restaurant (most dishes B80–B120), managed along the same lines as its sister operation in Bangkok (see p.156), with all proceeds going to the Population and Community Development Association of Thailand (PDA). Daily 10am–10pm.

Check Inn 423–425 Thanon Suranari ☎ 086 254 5437. Popular among expats, this bar features a pool table, live music on weekend evenings, and a wide range of Thai (around B90) and Western (around B200) dishes. Mon–Sat 11am–midnight, Sun 4pm–midnight.

Chez Andy 5–7 Thanon Manat ☎ 044 289556, ⊛ chez

5

andy.com. This Swiss-run restaurant has a distinguished ambience and is famous for its Australian steaks (around B500–2200), but they also serve some Swiss and Thai dishes. Mon–Sat 11am–11pm.

George & Dragon 361 Thanon Suranari ☏085 076 9708. As you might guess from the name, this English-run pub offers a range of beers and comfort food, including a filling Full Monty breakfast (B200). There's also a pool table, friendly service and sports on TV. Daily 10am–midnight.

★**Hansa** 266 Thanon Yommarat ☏044 269 108. Excellent place serving a wide range of Thai and fusion dishes such as grilled salmon with red curry (B230), on a breezy terrace or in the a/c interior. Low-key live music in the evenings and a selection of imported beers add to the appeal. Daily 5pm–midnight.

Suan Sin 163 Thanon Watcharasrit. Simple place that's highly rated by locals for its tasty Isaan favourites, especially *laap* (spicy salad with minced meat) and *pla chon pao* (grilled fish). Most dishes B80–220. Daily 10am–10pm.

SHOPPING

Basket shops Thanon Chumphon. Along Thanon Chumphon is a cluster of authentic basketware shops whose sticky-rice baskets, fish traps and rice winnowers make attractive souvenirs. Daily 8am–5pm.

Big C Hypermarket Mall Just off Thanon Mittraphap. Your best bet for cheap music, DVDs and trainers. Daily 10am–10pm.

Jiaranai Silk 140/2 Thanon Pho Klang, on the corner with Thanon Buarong ☏044 243 819. Khorat is a good

place to buy silk, much of which is produced in nearby Pak Tong Chai. This city-centre place has the best and most exclusive selection, while the specialist shops along Thanon Chumphon sell lengths of silk at reasonable prices. Mon–Sat 9.30am–5pm.

Night bazaar Thanon Manat and Thanon Mahathai. This sets up at dusk every evening and deals mainly in bargain-priced fashions. Daily 6–10pm.

DIRECTORY

Hospitals Expats favour the private Bangkok Hospital (☏044 262000), 1308/9 Thanon Mittraphap (Highway 2), near Tesco Lotus; the government Maharat Hospital (☏044 254990) is on the northeast edge of town.

Tourist police For all emergencies, call the tourist police

(☏1155; free, 24hr), or contact them at one of their booths in town: their main office (☏044 341777–9) is opposite Bus Terminal 2 on Highway 2, and there's a more central booth beside the Thao Suranari Monument on Thanon Chumphon.

Ban Prasat

The quintessentially northeastern village of **BAN PRASAT**, north of Khorat, became a source of great interest to archeologists following the 1990s discovery of a series of **burial grounds** within its boundaries, some of which date back three thousand years. The skeletons and attendant artefacts have been well preserved in the mud, and many are now on display; the village has made extra efforts to entice tourists with low-key craft demonstrations and a homestay programme. It's also a pleasant village in its own right, a traditional community of stilt houses set beside the Tarn Prasat River.

There are currently three **excavation pits** open to the public, each clearly signed from the centre of the village and informatively labelled. From these pits, archeologists have surmised that Ban Prasat was first inhabited in around 1000 BC and that its resident rice farmers traded with coastal people. Each pit contains bones and objects from different eras, buried at different depths but also with the head pointing in different directions, suggesting a change in religious or superstitious precepts.

Signs in the village direct you to local family-run projects, such as the household of **silk-weavers**, where you should be able to see several stages of the sericulture process (see box, p.459) and buy some cloth. Other village crafts include the weaving of floor mats from locally grown bulrushes, and the making of household brooms.

ARRIVAL AND ACCOMMODATION

BAN PRASAT

By bus Ban Prasat is 2km off Highway 2, 46km north of Khorat and 17km southwest of Phimai. Any Khorat–Phimai bus (#1305 from Khorat's Bus Terminal 2; every 30min;

about 1hr from Khorat or 20min from Phimai) will drop you at the Highway 2 junction, from where motorbike taxis will ferry you to the village.

Accommodation There are no hotels or restaurants in the village, but there is a homestay programme (B400/person including two meals) giving visitors a chance to join in activities such as making baskets and farming; contact Khun Jarun at ☎ 081 725 0791.

Phimai

Hemmed in by its old city walls and encircled by tributaries of the Mun River, the small modern town of **PHIMAI**, 60km northeast of Khorat, is dominated by the charmingly restored Khmer temple complex of **Prasat Hin Phimai**. No one knows for sure when the prasat was built or for whom, but as a religious site it probably dates back to the reign of the Khmer king Suriyavarman I (1002–49), and parts of the complex are said to be older than Cambodia's Angkor Wat. The complex was connected by a direct road to Angkor and oriented southeast, towards the Khmer capital. Over the next couple of centuries Khmer rulers made substantial modifications, and by the end of Jayavarman VII's reign in 1220, Phimai had been officially dedicated to Mahayana Buddhism. Phimai's other claim to fame is **Sai Ngam** (Beautiful Banyan), reputedly the largest banyan tree in Thailand. Otherwise there's plenty to like about its peaceful, small-town feel. Most visitors arrive here on day-trips, but with an excellent guesthouse and plenty of opportunities for early-morning bike rides, it's worth staying overnight.

Prasat Hin Phimai

Ruins Daily 7.30am–6pm • B100 • **Visitors' centre** Daily 8.30am–4.30pm • Free

Built mainly of dusky pink and greyish white sandstone, **Prasat Hin Phimai** is a seductive sight from a distance; closer inspection reveals a mass of intricate carvings. Entering the complex from the main southeastern gate, it's worth checking out the visitors' centre on the right-hand side after the ticket office, which uses simple wall-hung exhibits to explain the history of the site.

Outer areas

Heading into the complex from the southeastern gate, a staircase ornamented with classic naga (serpent) balustrades leads to a gopura in the **outer walls**, which are punctuated on either side by false balustraded windows – a bit of sculptural sleight-of-hand to jazz up the solid stonework without piercing the defences. A raised pathway bridges the space between these walls and the inner gallery that protects the prangs of the **inner sanctuary**. The minor prang to the right, made of laterite, is attributed to the twelfth-century Buddhist king Jayavarman VII, who engaged in a massive temple-building campaign. His statue is enshrined within; it's a copy of the much more impressive original, now housed in the Phimai National Museum. The pink sandstone prang to the left, connected to a Brahmin shrine where seven stone linga were found, was probably built around the same time.

PHIMAI BOAT RACES

Phimai's biggest event of the year is its festival of **boat races**, held on the Mun's tributaries over a weekend in early November, in a tradition that's endured for over a century. In common with many other riverside towns, Phimai marks the end of the rainy season by holding fiercely competitive longboat competitions and putting on lavish parades of ornate barges done up to emulate the Royal Barges of Bangkok. During the festival, a **son et lumière** show is staged at the temple ruins for five nights in a row; check with the Khorat TAT office for details (☎ 044 213666, ✉ tatsima@tat.or.th).

PHIMAI CARVINGS

1 Exterior: The dance of Shiva.
   Interior: Buddha sheltered by a naga.

2 Exterior: Krishna lifting Mount Govadhana. Rama and his brother Lakshaman bound with serpentine ropes.

3 Exterior: Battle scene from the Ramayana; Rama and his monkeys build a bridge by hurling mountains into the sea.
   Interior: Buddha beneath trees; dancers and musicians embellish Buddha's sermons.

4 Exterior: Ramayana battle; Vishnu holding conch shell, lotus, club and chakri disc.
   Interior: Five Vajarasatvas, each with six hands and three faces.

5 Exterior: The God of Justice pronounces on the Rama/Ravana dispute; Rama kills the giant Viradha.
   Interior: Boddhisatva Trailokayavicha with his left foot suspended over Ignorance.

5

The main prang
After more than twenty years of archeological detective work and painstaking reassembly, the towering white-sandstone **main prang** was restored to its original cruciform groundplan and conical shape in the 1960s, complete with an almost full set of carved lintels, pediments and antefixes, and capped with a stone lotus bud. The impressively detailed **carvings** around the outside of the prang depict predominantly Hindu themes. Shiva the Destroyer dances above the main entrance to the southeast antechamber: his destruction dance heralds the end of the world and the creation of a new order, a supremely potent image that warranted this position over the most important doorway. Inside, sedate Buddhist scenes give evidence of the conversion from Hindu to Buddhist faith, and the prasat's most important image, the Buddha sheltered by a seven-headed naga, sits atop a base that once supported a Hindu Shiva lingam.

Phimai National Museum
Just northeast of Prasat Hin Phimai • Wed–Sun 9am–4pm • B100 • ⓦ nationalmuseums.finearts.go.th • Walking distance from the ruins, though the Khorat–Phimai bus will stop outside the museum if requested

Much of the ancient carved stonework discovered at Phimai but not fitted back into the renovated structure can be seen at the **Phimai National Museum**, where it's easier to appreciate, being at eye level, well labelled and put in context. The museum's *pièce de résistance* is the exceptionally fine sandstone statue of Jayavarman VII that was found in Phimai's laterite prang; seated and leaning slightly forward, he's lost his arms and part of his nose, but none of his grace and serenity. Elsewhere in the galleries, displays take you through the religious and cultural history of the Phimai region, featuring prehistoric items from Ban Prasat as well as some exquisite Buddha statues from more recent times.

Sai Ngam
2km northeast of the museum • Walk or rent a bicycle from one of the guesthouses (B80/day) – locals will be able to point you in the right direction if you get lost en route

Sai Ngam is a banyan tree so enormous that it's reputed to cover an area about half the size of a football pitch (approximately 2300 square metres). It might look like a grove of small banyans, but Sai Ngam is in fact a single *Ficus bengalensis* whose branches have dropped vertically into the ground, taken root and spawned other branches, so growing further and further out from its central trunk. Banyan trees are believed to harbour animist spirits, and you can make merit here by releasing fish or turtles into the artificial lake that surrounds Sai Ngam. The tree is a popular recreation spot, and several restaurants have sprung up alongside it.

ARRIVAL AND GETTING AROUND   PHIMAI

By bus Phimai's bus station is inconveniently located 1.5km southwest of the ruins, on the bypass, but nearly everybody gets on and off in the town centre, either by the clock tower in the night-market area or in front of the museum. Regular bus #1305 runs direct to Phimai from Khorat's Bus Terminal 2, with a pick-up point near the Thanon Mittraphap/Ratchadamnoen junction (every 15min until 5.30pm, then sporadically until 10pm; 1hr 30min); the last return bus departs for Khorat at 7pm. The bus passes the turn-off to Ban Prasat, so if you get up early you can combine the two places on a day-trip from Khorat. If travelling from Khon Kaen, Udon Thani or Nong Khai, take

any Khorat-bound bus along Highway 2 as far as the Phimai turn-off (Highway 206), then change onto the Khorat–Phimai service for the last 10km; the same strategy works in reverse.

By bicycle The best way to get around, although cycling isn't permitted inside the ruins. *Boonsiri Guest House* has bicycles for rent (B80/day). Aside from the ride out to Sai Ngam, the area just west of the ruins, beyond the post office, is especially atmospheric: many of the traditional wooden houses here double as workshops, and you'll often see householders weaving cane chairs in the shade beneath the buildings.

5

INFORMATION AND TOURS

Tourist information *Boonsiri Guest House* (see below) is an excellent source of local information.

Tours The *Moon River Resort* (see below) runs day-trips to Phanom Rung (B2800 for 2 people; see p.450) and Khao Yai

National Park (B3600 for 2 people; see p.437).

Services There's a post office just west of Prasat Hin Phimai on Thanon Wonprang.

ACCOMMODATION AND EATING

If you fancy a meal with a view, head out to the string of basic **restaurants** just across from Sai Ngam. The **night market** sets up at dusk on the eastern stretch of Thanon Anantajinda, just southeast of the ruins.

Bakery At the southeastern corner of the ruins. A nice shady place to cool off with a banana split or a cold frappe after wandering around the ruins; serves a few rice dishes (B50–70) at lunchtime, but don't expect to get any hearty evening meals. Daily 8am–8pm.

Boonsiri Guest House Above a duck restaurant on Thanon Chomsudasadet ☎044 471159, ⓦboonsiri .net. Central, family-run place offering clean dorms and en-suite rooms that are stylishly put together. The owners'

cheery and knowledgeable son speaks great English, and can provide a map and tips for getting around Phimai. Dorm B150, fan double B350, a/c double B500

Moon River Resort Ban Sai Ngam, Pattana Soi 2 ☎085 633 7097, ⓦmoon-river-resort-phimai.com. Located by the river and near the museum, this place offers traditional stilt houses in a rambling garden and a choice of fan or a/c rooms. The river is good for swimming here. Fan B400, a/c B600

Phanom Rung and around

East of Khorat the bleached plains roll on, broken only by the occasional small town and, if you're travelling along Highway 24, the odd tantalizing glimpse of the smoky Phanom Dangkrek mountain range above the southern horizon. That said, it's well worth jumping off the Surin-bound bus for a detour to the fine Khmer ruins of **Prasat Hin Khao Phanom Rung**, **Prasat Muang Tam** or **Wat Khao Angkhan**. Built during the same period as Phimai, and for the same purpose, Phanom Rung and Muang Tam form two more links in the chain that once connected the Khmer capital of Angkor with the limits of its empire. Sited dramatically atop an extinct volcano, Phanom Rung has been beautifully restored, and the more recently renovated Muang Tam lies on the plains below. Wat Khao Angkhan, also located on an extinct volcano, features some *sema* (boundary) stones that date back to the eighth or ninth century, though the temple itself is quite modern. Early morning or late afternoon are the best times to visit, when the sites are less crowded.

Prasat Hin Khao Phanom Rung

Main complex Daily 6am–6pm • B100, joint ticket with Muang Tam B150 • **Tourist Information Centre** Daily 9am–4.30pm

Prasat Hin Khao Phanom Rung is the finest example of Khmer architecture in Thailand, graced with innumerable exquisite carvings, its sandstone and laterite buildings designed to align with the sun at certain times of the year (see box below). As at most Khmer prasats, **building** here spanned several reigns, probably from the beginning of the tenth century to the early thirteenth. The heart of the temple was constructed in

> ### SPIRITUAL ALIGNMENT
>
> **Prasat Hin Khao Phanom Rung** is so perfectly built that on the morning of the fifteenth day of the waxing moon in the fifth month of the lunar calendar, you can stand at the westernmost gopura and see the sun rising through all fifteen doors. This day (in early April: check exact date with TAT in Surin ☎044 514 447) is celebrated with a day-long **festival** of huge parades all the way up the hill to the prasat – a tradition believed to go back eight hundred years.

the mid-twelfth century, in early Angkorian style, and is attributed to local ruler Narendraditya and his son Hiranya. Narendraditya was a follower of the Shivaite cult, a sect which practised yoga and fire worship and used alcohol and sex in its rituals; carved depictions of all these practices decorate the temple. There are cheap food stalls outside the Gate 1 entrance and in its car park area, where the museum-like tourist information centre provides an outstanding introduction to the temple's construction, iconography and restoration.

The approach

The **approach** to the temple is one of the most dramatic of its kind. Symbolic of the journey from earth to the heavenly palace of the gods, the ascent to the inner compound is imbued with metaphorical import: by following the 200m-long avenue, paved in laterite and sandstone and flanked with lotus-bud pillars, you are walking to the ends of the earth. Ahead, the main prang, representing Mount Meru, home of the gods, looms large above the gallery walls, and is accessible only via the first of three **naga bridges**, a raised cruciform structure with sixteen five-headed naga balustrades. Once across the bridge, you have traversed the abyss between earth and heaven. A series of stairways ascends to the eastern entrance of the celestial home, first passing four small ponds, thought to have been used for ritual purification.

A second naga bridge crosses to the **east gopura**, entrance to the inner sanctuary, which is topped by a lintel carved with Indra (god of the east) sitting on a lion throne. The gopura is the main gateway through the **gallery**, which runs right round the inner compound and has been restored in part, with arched stone roofs, small chambers inside and false windows; real windows wouldn't have been strong enough to support such a heavy stone roof, so false ones, which retained the delicate pilasters but backed them with stone blocks, were an aesthetically acceptable compromise.

The main prang

Phanom Rung is surprisingly compact, the east gopura leading almost directly into the **main prang**, separated from it only by a final naga bridge. A dancing Shiva, nine of his ten arms intact, and a lintel carved with a relief of a **reclining Vishnu** preside over the eastern entrance to the prang. This depicts a common Hindu creation myth, known as "Reclining Vishnu Asleep on the Milky Sea of Eternity", in which Vishnu dreams up a new universe, and Brahma (the four-faced god perched on the lotus blossom that springs from Vishnu's navel) puts the dream into practice. This lintel had been stolen, but was returned in 1988 from the Art Institute of Chicago, culminating seventeen years of restoration work on this outstanding example of Khmer architecture.

On the pediment above this famous relief is a lively carving of **Shiva Nataraja**, or Shiva's Dance of Destruction, which shows him dancing on Mount Kailash in front of several other gods, including Ganesh, Brahma and Vishnu. The dance brings about the total destruction of the world and replaces it with a new epoch. Of the other figures decorating the prang, one of the most important is the lion head of Kala, also known as Kirtimukha, symbolic of both the lunar and the solar eclipse and – because he's able to "swallow" the sun – considered far superior to other planetary gods. Inside the prang kneels an almost life-size statue of Shiva's vehicle, the bull Nandi, behind which stands the all-powerful **Shiva lingam**, for which the prang was originally built; the stone channel that runs off the lingam and out of the north side of the prang was designed to catch the lustral water with which the sacred stone was bathed.

Two rough-hewn laterite libraries stand alongside the main prang, in the northeast and southeast corners, and there are also remains of two early tenth-century brick prangs just northeast of the main prang. The unfinished **prang noi** ("Little Prang") in the southwest corner now contains a stone Buddha footprint, which has become the focus of the merit-making at the annual April festivities, neatly linking ancient and modern religious practices.

5

Prasat Muang Tam

8km southeast of Phanom Rung · **Main complex** Daily 6am–6pm · B100, joint ticket with Phanom Rung B150 · **Tourist Information Centre and Film** Daily 9am–4.30pm · Free

Down on the plains, and accessed via a scenic minor road that cuts through a swathe of rice fields, the small but elegant temple complex of **Prasat Muang Tam** is sited behind a huge kilometre-long *baray* (Khmer reservoir), which was probably constructed at the same time as the main part of the temple, in the early eleventh century. Like Phanom Rung, Muang Tam was probably built in stages between the tenth and thirteenth centuries, and is based on the classic Khmer design of a central prang flanked by minor prangs and encircled by a gallery and four gopura. The history of Muang Tam is presented in brief at the Tourist Information Centre in the temple car park.

The ruins

The approach to Muang Tam is nothing like as grand as at Phanom Rung but, once through the main, eastern, gopura in the outside wall, it's a pretty scene, with the central gallery encircled by four **L-shaped ponds** – such important features that they are referred to in a contemporary inscription that states "this sanctuary is preserved by sacred water". The shape of the ponds gives the impression that the prasat is set within a moat that's been severed by the four entrance pathways at the cardinal points. Each pond is lined with laterite brick steps designed to enable easy access for priests drawing sacred water, and possibly also for devotees to cleanse themselves before entering the central sanctuary. The rims are constructed from sandstone blocks that form naga, the sacred water serpents.

The rectangular central **gallery** was probably roofed with timber (long since rotted away) and so could be punctuated with real windows, rather than the more load-bearing false versions that had to be used at Phanom Rung. Inside, the **five red-brick towers** of the inner sanctuary are arranged on a laterite platform, with three prangs in the front (eastern) row, and two behind. The main, central, prang has collapsed, leaving only its base, but the four other towers are merely decapitated and some have carved **lintels** intact. The lintel above the doorway of the front right tower is particularly lively in its depiction of the popular scene known as Ume Mahesvara (Uma and her consort Shiva riding the bull Nandi). There are interesting details in the temple complex, including recurrent motifs of foliage designs and Kala lion-faces, and figures of ascetics carved into the base of the doorway pillars on the eastern gopura of the outer wall.

Wat Khao Angkhan

Approx 20km west of Phanom Rung · Daily dawn to dusk; admission free.

While **Wat Khao Angkhan** receives far fewer visitors than Phanom Rung and Muang Tam, it's worth heading to the top of the extinct volcano on which this temple sits, both to admire its unusual combination of ancient and modern features, and to soak up the tranquil atmosphere, as there's rarely anyone here apart from a few monks. The first sight on reaching the top of the hill is a giant reclining Buddha, before you reach the main temple buildings and some fine views over the surrounding countryside. The temple incorporates a set of ancient sema stones that date back to the Dvaravati era (eighth to ninth century), and are so worn that the bas-reliefs on them (of the Buddha, lotus and stupa) have almost disappeared. The stones are now surrounded by a low wall surmounted by a line of sitting Buddha images draped in saffron robes. The ubosot, which stands inside this wall, was built in 1977 in a modern Khmer style and its interior features some rather whimsical murals of the life of the Buddha, though they are already deteriorating due to damp weather.

FROM TOP PRASAT HIN PHIMAI (P.447); NIGHT MARKET, KHORAT (P.445) >

5

Many people check out the ruins of Phanom Rung and Muang Tam on a **day-trip** from Khorat, though recent improvements to lodging options in Nang Rong now make it possible to stay closer to the sights. There's public transport from Khorat or Nang Rong as far as the little town of **Ban Tako**, from where you'll need to take a motorbike taxi for the final few kilometres to the ruins. However, this works out quite expensive, so it makes more sense to arrange a tour through your hotel. There are three car parks and three entrances to the Phanom Rung complex: if you have your own transport, ignore the Gates 2 and 3 (west) entrances, signed off the access road, and carry on to the main, Gate 1 (east), entrance and car park – the drama of the site is lost if you explore it back-to-front; motorbike taxis should take you to the main entrance.

GETTING TO BAN TAKO

By bus Ban Tako is located on Highway 24 about 115km southeast of Khorat (about 2hr) and 83km southwest of Surin (about 1hr 30min). Frequent buses run from Khorat (via Nang Rong) and Surin; bus #274 travels between the two provincial capitals roughly every 30min.

BAN TAKO TO THE RUINS

By taxi or hitching From Ban Tako it's 12km south to Phanom Rung and another 8km southeast along a side road to Muang Tam. There's no public transport to the ruins, so most people take a motorbike taxi here (B400–500/person) for the round trip to Phanom Rung, Muang Tam and back to Ban Tako.

NANG RONG TO THE RUINS

By bus Nang Rong is 14km west of Ban Tako on Highway

24 and served by the #274 and #523 bus routes from Khorat or Surin. For transport to the ruins at Phanom Rung and Muang Tam, either take the #274 bus to Ban Tako, then a motorbike taxi (see above); hire a motorbike taxi all the way from Nang Rong (pricier than from Ban Tako), or rent a car or motorbike from *Phanomrung Puri Resort* or *P. Inter California Hostel*.

By rented car or motorbike If you want to visit Wat Khao Angkhan by yourself, visit Khun Wicha at *P. Inter California Hostel* (see below), who can provide a sketch map of the area; however, the route is not clearly signposted, so you might want to arrange a tour through your hotel.

By tour All hotels and guesthouses in Nang Rong and Khorat can arrange a day tour of Phanom Rung, Muang Tam and Wat Khao Angkhan; one-day tours of all three sites cost around B2500 per person for four people.

ACCOMMODATION

The nearest accommodation to Phanom Rung is in Nang Rong, 14km west of Ban Tako on Highway 24. There's little to see here, but there are few tourists and its quaint guesthouses are handy bases for a bit of temple exploring.

NANG RONG

★ Phanomrung Puri Resort 212 Thanon Prachanta-khet ☎044 632 222, ⓦphanomrungpuri.co.th. This comfortable resort constitutes Nang Rong's most luxurious place to stay and offers spacious, well-equipped rooms, along with a swimming pool and decent restaurant, in a quiet location just north of the town centre. **B1300**

P. Inter California Hostel 59/9 Thanon Sangkakrit, east

of the bus station (B50 by samlor or motorbike from the bus station to the hostel) ☎081 808 3347. The comfortable rooms at this family-owned guesthouse have views across the surrounding countryside, and range from simple fan rooms to bigger, better furnished a/c rooms, with rates up to B600. Breakfast costs a little extra. Owner Khun Wicha is a mine of local information, and they have motorbikes for rent at B250/day. Fan **B250**, a/c **B350**

Surin and around

Best known for its much-hyped annual elephant round-up, the provincial capital of **SURIN**, around 150km east of Khorat, is an otherwise typical northeastern town, a reasonably comfortable place to absorb the easy-going pace of Isaan life. There's a handful of good, mid-range hotels in the centre and, as a bonus, there are some fantastic Khmer ruins in the vicinty. Many visitors pass through the city on their way to the village of Ban Tha Sawang, 7km away, where Thailand's most exclusive silk is produced.

Surin's elephant tie-in comes from the local Suay people, whose prowess with pachyderms is well known and can be seen first-hand in the nearby village of **Ban Ta Klang**. Thais, Lao and Khmers make up the remainder of the population of Surin province; the Khmers have lived and worked in the region for over a thousand years, and their architectural legacy is still in evidence at the ruined temples of Ta Muean

SURIN ELEPHANT ROUND-UP

Surin's **elephant round-up**, held every year on the third weekend of November, draws some forty thousand spectators to watch four hundred elephants play football, engage in tugs of war and parade in full battle garb. These shows last about three hours and give both trainers and animals the chance to practise their skills, but if you arrive early (about 7.30am) you can watch the preliminary street processions when locals set out long trestle tables filled with pineapples, bananas and sugar cane so the elephants can munch their way into town. Note that however well controlled the elephants appear, you should always approach them with caution – in the past, frightened and taunted elephants have killed tourists. Tickets cost B500–1000 and can be booked through TAT, the provincial government website (⊕ surin .go.th), or Saren Travel (see p.458), who can also arrange accommodation and transport if you contact them three months ahead; alternatively, you could join one of the overnight packages organized by Bangkok travel agencies.

and Sikhoraphum. There's also **overland access between Thailand and Cambodia** via Surin province's Chong Chom checkpoint near Kap Choeng.

Ban Tha Sawang

10km northwest of Surin • Songthaews to Ban Tha Sawang leave regularly from near the clock tower on Thanon Krungsrinai

Some of Thailand's most exclusive silk is produced in the village of **BAN THA SAWANG**. Though it is possible to visit by yourself, there is no English information and going with a guide will offer some behind-the-scenes insight (see box, p.459); you can arrange a guide through *Pirom & Aree's House* or Saren Travel (see p.458) in Surin. The best months to visit are between November and June, when the women aren't required to work all day in the fields.

The **Tha Sawang fabric** is gold-brocade silk whose ancient designs are so intricate that it takes four weavers working simultaneously on a single loom a whole day to produce just 6cm. And while a standard everyday *mut mee* sarong might use five heddles (vertical frames of threads that determine the pattern) in its design, a Ban Tha Sawang sarong will use more than a thousand; not surprisingly, Ban Tha Sawang sarongs cost around B50,000 and must be ordered several months in advance. The Ban Tha Sawang Weaving Centre (daily 8.30am–5pm) houses around twenty looms, and visitors are welcome to observe the weavers at close quarters. There's a display area across the road where you can see some fine examples of brocade cloth. Several stalls in the village sell local silk, but not the Ban Tha Sawang brocades.

Ban Ta Klang

58km north of Surin • Local bus from Surin (hourly; 2hr); if driving, head north along Highway 214 for 36km, turn left at the village of Ban Nong Tad and continue for 22km • Centre for Elephant Studies daily 8.30am–4.30pm • Free • Elephant shows 10am & 2pm daily • B100

The quiet, ramshackle "elephant village" of **BAN TA KLANG** is the main settlement of the Suay people and the training centre for their elephants. One out of every two Ta Klang

SURIN VILLAGE TOURS

One of the best reasons for coming to Surin, other than November's elephant round-up (see box above), is to take one of the excellent **local tours** (from B1700/person for a group of four) organized from *Pirom & Aree's House*. Pirom is a highly informed former social worker whose trips give tourists an unusual chance to catch glimpses of rural northeastern life as it's really lived. His village tours feature visits to local silk-weavers and basket-makers, as well as to Ban Ta Klang elephant trainers' village, and it's also possible to do overnight village trips, as well as tours to Khao Phra Viharn (when open), Khong Chiam, Pha Taem and That Phanom.

5

families owns its own elephant, occasionally using it as a Western farmer would a tractor, but otherwise treating it as a much-loved pet (see box opposite).

Ban Ta Klang's busy time, elephant-wise, is November, when the creatures and their mahouts help with the rice harvest and to prepare for the annual elephant show in Surin. In addition, every year on the first weekend of November, the elephants compete in **swimming races**, held further up the Mun River in the town of Satuk, 30km west of Ta Klang. A more authentic local spectacle is the annual **monks' ordination ceremony**, which usually takes place in May in Ban Ta Klang as part of the preparations for the

SURIN

Roi Ét & Ban Ta Klang

Ban Tha Sawang

THANON THUNG PO
900m (not to scale)
200m (not to scale)
SOI ARUNEE

THANON THETSABARN 3

THANON THEP SURIN

Train Station

THANON NONGTOOM

SHOPS
Ake Anun — 1
Nong Ying — 2

Surin Plaza

THANON SANITNIKHOMRUT

A/C buses to Bangkok

THANON THETSABARN 1

Ruen Mai

Phetkasem Department Store

THANON JITBUMRUNG

Bus Terminal

The Strip & Thong Tarin

School

Clocktower

THANON KRUNGSRINAI

THANON THETSABARN 3

THANON TANNASARN

Night Bazaar

Wat Buraparam

THANON THETSABARN 1

TAT Office

Ruam Phet Hospital

THANON MULASAT

THANON PHO RANG

THANON LAK MUANG

Lak Muang Shrine

THANON PHROM THEP

THANON TANNASARN

Provincial Hall

Elephant Sculptures

THANON LAK MUANG

Police Station

Saren Travel

THANON THETSABARN 2

Surin Hospital

Buriram

THANON KRUNG SRINOK

THANON KRUNG SRINOK

Ubon Ratchathani; Elephant Stadium & PrasatSikhoraphum

ACCOMMODATION
Maneerote Hotel — 4
Pirom & Aree's House — 1
Sangthong Hotel — 3
Suring Majestic Hotel — 2

RESTAURANTS & CAFÉS
Big Bite — 2
Coca — 3
Kidteung Bakery & Café — 1

THANON THETSABARN 2
THANON THETSABARN 4

0 — 200
metres

Prasat, Surin National Museum, Rajamangala Institute, Khorat & Prasat Ta Muean

THE SUAY AND THE SURIN PROJECT

Traditionally regarded as the most expert hunters and trainers of elephants in Thailand, the **Suay tribe** (also known as the Kui people) migrated to Isaan from Central Asia before the rise of the Khmers in the ninth century. It was the Suay who masterminded the use of elephants in the construction of the great Khmer temples, and a Suay chief who in 1760 helped recapture a runaway white elephant belonging to the king of Ayutthaya, earning the hereditary title "Lord of Surin". Surin was governed by members of the Suay tribe until Rama V's administrative reforms of 1907.

Now that elephants have been replaced almost entirely by modern machinery in the agricultural and logging industries, there's little demand for the Suay mahouts' skills as captors and trainers of wild elephants, or their traditional pre-hunting rituals involving sacred ropes, magic clothing and the keeping of certain taboos.

There are currently around two hundred elephants registered as living in Ban Ta Klang, and their mahouts are given subsidies for keeping them there. This discourages them from taking the elephants to Bangkok, where curious urbanites would have been charged for the pleasure of feeding the elephants or even walking under their trunk or belly for good luck (pregnant women who do this are supposedly guaranteed an easy birth). The downside is that there's very little for the elephants to do at the study centre, and they spend much of their time shackled up.

In a bid to give Surin's elephants a better life, the not-for-profit Elephant Nature Foundation has set up the **Surin Project** (Ⓦ surinproject.org), which provides open spaces for elephants to roam in and teaches mahouts the benefits of ecotourism. At the time of writing, just twelve of the study centre's elephants were being cared for full-time at the project, with five more elephants at the centre on a part-time basis. It's possible to volunteer at the camp, and for B13,000 a week you can help to dig irrigation channels, build shelters and plant food for the animals. The rate includes food, accommodation and transport from Buriram, Bangkok or Chiang Mai (pick-ups every Mon).

beginning of Buddhist Lent, when young men ride to the temple on ceremonially clad elephants.

The traditions of mahouts are documented, along with other elephant-related subjects, at the rather desultory **Centre for Elephant Studies** in the southern part of Ban Ta Klang village. To satisfy tourist curiosity, the centre also puts on elephant shows to coincide with the arrival of tour groups.

Prasat Ta Muean

78km south of Surin on the Cambodian border • Daily 8am–4pm • Free • No public transport; follow H214 south to H24, turn west, then south on H2397 and west on H224. Finally, at Ban Ta Miang, turn south on H2407

Atmospheric **Prasat Ta Muean** – comprising three laterite ruins – is so remote and hemmed in by dense vegetation that you can't help but feel like an intrepid explorer when you finally reach the site. The first of the three sites is a simple, laterite sanctuary snuggled in a shady glade, while the second consists of a gopura, mondop and prang, also of laterite, surrounded by a wall and with an adjacent pond. The last and biggest site, a few hundred metres further south and known as Prasat Ta Muean Thom, is much larger, consisting of three prangs and several other structures, some of laterite and others of sandstone, though few carvings remain. Unusually, like Phimai, the temple is oriented to the south rather than to the east, and the steep stairway which leads directly to Cambodia is heavily guarded by Thai military. In fact, visitors need to exchange their passports for visitors' passes on entering the site and reclaim them on leaving. Though it's in Surin province, it makes a convenient final destination on a day's exploration of Khmer temples between Nang Rong and Surin, after visiting Wat Khao Angkhan, Phanom Rung and Muang Tam (see p.450).

5

Prasat Sikhoraphum

Sikhoraphum, 30km northeast of Surin, just north of the H226 • Daily 8.30am–6pm • B50 • Regular buses between Surin and Si Saket stop at Sikhoraphum

Easily accessible and carefully maintained, Prasat Sikhoraphum consists of five prangs set on a laterite base, surrounded by a U-shaped moat and trim lawns. Built by King Suryavarman in the twelfth century, it boasts one of the most beautiful lintels in Thailand, depicting Shiva, Brahma, Ganesha and Vishnu, above the eastern entrance to the main prang. The temple runs a light-and-sound show to coincide with the elephant round-up, and occasionally dancers practise a classical performance in the shade of an enormous bo tree at the entrance to the site.

ARRIVAL AND DEPARTURE

SURIN

By train The train station (☎044 511295) is on the northern edge of town.

Destinations Ayutthaya (10 daily; 5hr–7hr 30min); Bangkok (10 daily; 6hr 30min–9hr 30min); Buriram (10 daily; 40–50min); Khorat (10 daily; 1hr 50min–3hr 10min); Pak Chong (10 daily; 3hr 10min–5hr); Si Saket (8 daily; 1hr 15min–1hr 50min); Ubon Ratchathani (7 daily; 2hr 15min–3hr 20min).

By bus and minibus The bus terminal (☎044 511756) is off Thanon Jitbumrung. Minibuses from here run from Surin to Cambodia (see box below).

Destinations Bangkok (at least hourly; 7hr); Ban Ta Klang (hourly; 2hr); Buriram (hourly; 35–55min); Chiang Mai (5 daily; 15–18hr); Khorat (every 30min; 4–5hr); Khon Kaen (20 daily; 4hr–5hr 30min); Pattaya (12 daily; 8–10hr); Roi Et (hourly; 2–3hr); Si Saket (every 25min; 3hr–3hr 30min).

INFORMATION, TOURS AND GETTING AROUND

Tourist information There's a helpful TAT office (daily 8.30am–4.30pm; ☎044 514447–8, ✉tatsurin@tat.or.th) at 355/3-6 Thanon Thetsabarn 1, just east of the town centre, and the provincial government has a quite useful website (☎surin.go.th), which includes booking forms for the elephant round-up.

Travel agency Saren Travel, 202/1-4 Thanon Thetsabarn 2 (Mon–Sat 8am–6pm; ☎044 713828, ✉sarentour @hotmail.com; outside office hours ☎089 949 1185), sells air and train tickets and offers cars with/without driver (from B1800/day, excluding fuel). They can also arrange day-trips to Phanom Rung, Muang Tam and Ban Ta Klang (B2800 for four people sharing a car, excluding entry fees).

Transfers to Siem Reap (Cambodia) via Chong Chom and Chong Sa Ngam (around B1800 per person) are also available, as are elephant-show tickets. Elephant rides in Ban Ta Klang can be arranged too, from B200–400/person.

Village tours At Pirom & Aree's House, at the far end of Soi Arunee off Thanon Thung Po ☎044 515140. Great opportunities to explore the villages around Surin with a friendly and very knowledgeable guide (see box, p.455).

Hospitals Ruam Phet Hospital, on the eastern arm of Thanon Thetsabarn 1 (☎044 513638 & ☎044 513192); and the government-run Surin Hospital on Thanon Lak Muang (☎044 511006 & ☎044 511757).

ACCOMMODATION

Except during the elephant round-up – when room rates in Surin rocket and **accommodation** is booked out weeks in advance – you'll have no trouble finding a place to stay.

CROSSING THE CAMBODIAN BORDER VIA CHONG CHOM

There are a/c minivans (daily every 30min 6am–5.30pm; 2hr; B45) via Prasat to the **Chong Chom border pass**, 70km south of Surin. Cambodian visas are issued on arrival at the Chong Chom–O'Smach checkpoint (daily 7am–8pm; US$20, although if you don't have dollars, you may be asked for B1000), from where you can get transport to Anlong Veng and then on to Siem Reap, which is 150km from the border crossing (start negotiations for a taxi transfer to Siem Reap at B400/car, but expect to pay slightly more). There have been reports of people on visa runs being asked for more money by officials on the Cambodian side, especially if they try to return to Thailand on the same day.

Arriving **from Cambodia**, songthaews and motorbike taxis ferry travellers from the border checkpoint to the minibus stop for Prasat and Surin. For details on other overland routes into Cambodia, see p.27.

Maneerote Hotel 11/1 Soi Poytungko, Thanon Krungsrinai ☎044 539 477. It may be set a short way west of the centre, but rooms at the *Maneerote* are some of the best value in town. They are a good size and bright, with marble floors and bathrooms, and each has its own balcony. **B450**

★ **Pirom & Aree's House** At the far end of Soi Arunee, off Thanon Thung Po, 1.5km northwest of the train station ☎044 515140. Surin's famously long-running guesthouse occupies a tranquil spot overlooking rice fields. The super-clean rooms in this modern take on a traditional home are large and simply furnished with fans and shared bathrooms, plus there are garden seating areas. The owners are incredibly friendly and welcoming, and can tell you everything you need to know about the local area. Good rates for singles. **B200**

Sangthong Hotel 279–281 Thanon Tannasarn ☎044 512099. The best of the budget hotels, this place is friendly, good value and well run. All rooms are large and en suite, and some have a/c and TV. Fan **B150**, a/c **B400**

Surin Majestic Hotel 99 Thanon Jitbumrung, at the back of the bus station ☎044 713980, ⊛surinmajestic hotel.com. Still the nicest hotel in town, with smartly furnished rooms. All have a/c and TV plus a balcony overlooking the attractive, good-sized ground-floor swimming pool. **B1200**

SILK PRODUCTION

Most hand-woven **Thai silk** is produced by Isaan village women, some of whom oversee every aspect of sericulture, from the breeding of the silkworm to the dyeing of the fabric. Isaan's pre-eminence is partly due to its soils, which are particularly suitable for the growth of mulberry trees, the leaves of which are the **silkworms'** favoured diet. The cycle of production begins with the female silk-moth, which lives just a few days but lays around 300–500 microscopic eggs in that time. The eggs take about nine days to hatch into tiny silkworms, which are then kept in covered rattan trays and fed on mulberry leaves three or four times a day. The silkworms are such enthusiastic eaters that after three or four weeks they will have grown to about 6cm in length (around ten thousand times their original size), ready for the cocoon-building **pupal** stage.

The silkworm constructs its **cocoon** from a single white or yellow fibre that it secretes from its mouth at a rate of 12cm a minute, sealing the filaments with a gummy substance called sericin. The metamorphosis of the pupa into a moth can take anything from two to seven days, but the sericulturist must anticipate the moment when the new moth is about to break out in order to prevent the destruction of the precious fibre, which at this stage is often 900m long. At the crucial point the cocoon is dropped into boiling water, killing the moth (which is often eaten as a snack) and softening the sericin, so that the unbroken filament can be unravelled. The fibres from several cocoons are "reeled" into a single thread, and two or three threads are subsequently twisted or "thrown" into the yarn known as **raw silk** (broken threads from damaged cocoons are worked into a second-rate yarn called "spun silk"). In most cases, the next stage is the "de-gumming process", in which the raw silk is soaked to dissolve away the sericin, leaving it soft and semi-transparent. Extremely absorbent and finely textured, reeled silk is the perfect material for **dyeing**; most silk producers now use chemical dyes, though traditional vegetable dyes are making a bit of a comeback.

These days, it's not worth the bother for women who live near town to raise their own silkworms and spin their own thread as they can easily buy Japanese ready-to-weave silk in the market. **Japanese silk** is smoother than Thai silk but lasts only about seven years when woven into a sarong; hand-raised, raw Thai silk is rougher but lasts around forty years, and so is still favoured by women living in remote villages.

Once dyed (or bought), the silk is ready for **weaving**. This is generally done during slack agricultural periods, for example just after the rice is planted and again just after it's harvested. Looms are usually set up in the space under the house, in the sheltered area between the piles, and most are designed to produce a sarong of around 1m by 2m. Isaan weavers have many different weaving techniques and can create countless patterns, ranging from the simplest single-coloured plain weave for work shirts to exquisitely complex wedding sarongs that may take up to six weeks to complete. The most exclusive and intricate designs are those produced in Ban Tha Sawang (see p.455), costing tens of thousands of baht for a single sarong.

5

EATING AND DRINKING

Aside from a reasonable range of local **restaurants**, Surin boasts a good-sized **night bazaar**, which occupies the eastern end of Thanon Krungsrinai and offers a tasty selection of local food (including roasted crickets and barbecued locusts in season), as well as stalls selling fashions and toys. Surin also has a surprisingly wild **nightlife** for a provincial town, with a clutch of seedy bars and discos around the neon-lit "Strip" east of the centre at the northern end of Thanon Sirirath and along Soi Kola, just north of the *Thong Tharin Hotel*.

Big Bite 60 Thanon Sirirat, in front of the Thong Tarin Hotel. This welcoming, a/c restaurant serves a good range of Thai and Western dishes such as fish and chips (B280), as well as chilli dips and fresh fruit juices. Daily 10am–2am.
Coca 128 Thanon Thetsabarn 1 (no English sign but it's easy to spot opposite and just east of the Phetkasem Department Store). A good range of Chinese and Thai dishes such as crispy catfish salad with mango and stewed

duck feet with noodles (both B80), served in a clean and welcoming setting. Daily 10am–10pm.
Kidteung Bakery & Café 28 Thanon Sanitnikhomrut, close to the junction with Thanon Tannasarn. Breezy alfresco seating area draped in foliage and lined with pretty elephant statues. Serves delicious cakes and ice vanilla lattes (B55) to a mixed crowd, which includes local expats. Daily 7am–8pm.

SHOPPING

Surin is famous for the variety of **silk weaves** produced here: there are seven hundred designs in Surin province alone, many of them of Cambodian origin, including the locally popular rhomboid pattern. In high season, there are usually several women selling their cloth around the Tannasarn–Krungsrinai intersection, and you can also visit local silk-weaving villages (see p.455).

Ake Anun 122–124 Thanon Sanitnikhomrut ☎ 044 511 441. Sells ready-made *pha sin* (wrap-around skirts; B2500–3800), scarves, ties, jackets, and souvenirs such as silk elephants. Daily 8am–7.30pm.

Nong Ying 52 Thanon Jitbumrung ☎ 044 511 606. A superb selection of silks as well as ready-made silk jackets, bags and accessories and axe pillows. Daily 8am–8pm.

Khao Phra Viharn (Preah Vihear)

140km southwest of Ubon Ratchathani and 220km southeast of Surin • Closed at time of writing: when open, daily 8.30am–3.30pm • B605 (in a combination of entry fees)

Perched atop a 547m-high spur of the Dangkrek mountains right on the Thai–Cambodian border, the ninth-to-twelfth-century Khmer ruins of **KHAO PHRA VIHARN** (or **Preah Vihear** to Cambodians) surpass even the spectacularly set Phanom Rung (see p.450). A magnificent avenue over 500m long rises to the clifftop sanctuary, from where you get breathtaking views over the jungle-clad hills of Cambodia.

Unfortunately, the sanctuary has been closed on and off since 2008 due to a **territorial dispute** between Thailand and Cambodia over who owns the site. In July 2011, following a fresh series of skirmishes, the International Court of Justice ruled that both countries should remove their forces from the area, but the stalemate continued, and, at the time of writing, the complex remained closed.

In fact, the complex was not opened to visitors until 1998, following almost a century of squabbling between the two governments. During Cambodia's civil war, the Khmer Rouge laid mines around the temple, and while the ruins have been de-mined, there are skull-and-crossbones signs in the vicinity, which should be heeded if and when the temple reopens to visitors.

The ruins

The temple buildings themselves, built of grey and yellow sandstone, retain some fine original carvings and have been sufficiently restored to give a good idea of their original structure. Constructed over a three-hundred-year period, Khao Phra Viharn was dedicated to the Hindu god Shiva and is thought to have served both as a retreat for Hindu priests – hence the isolated site – and an object of pilgrimage, with the difficulty of getting there an extra challenge. The large complex would have also been inhabited by a big cast of supporting villagers who took care of the priests and the pilgrims, which explains the presence of several large reservoirs on the site.

The approach to the **temple complex** begins with a steep stairway and continues up the cliff face via a series of pillared causeways, small terraces with naga balustrades and four cruciform-shaped **gopura** (pavilions), each built with doorways at the cardinal points, and decorated with carved reliefs of tales from Hindu mythology. Beyond the first gopura, you'll see to the left (east) one of the temple's biggest **reservoirs**, a large stone-lined tank sunk into the cliff and guarded by statues of lions.

The Churning of the Sea of Milk

As you pass through the last, southernmost, doorway of the second gopura, look back at the door to admire the pediment carving, which depicts the Hindu creation myth, the **Churning of the Sea of Milk**, in which Vishnu appears in his tortoise incarnation and, along with a naga and a sacred mountain (here symbolized by the churning stick), helps stir the cosmic ocean and thereby create the universes, as well as the sacred nectar of immortality.

The central sanctuary

The ascent of the cliff face finally reaches its climax at the **central sanctuary**, built on the summit and enclosed within a courtyard whose impressive colonnaded galleries are punctuated by windows to the east and west. The pediment above the northern entrance to this shrine depicts the multi-armed **dancing Shiva**, whose ecstatic dance brings about the destruction of the existing world and the beginning of a new epoch. Climb through one of the gallery windows to walk across to the cliff edge, from where you get far-reaching views of Cambodia. A look back at the temple complex shows that though the sanctuary's southernmost wall is punctuated by a couple of beautifully carved false doors, there are no genuine south-facing doors or windows; experts assume that this was to stop priests being distracted by the clifftop panorama.

ARRIVAL AND ACCOMMODATION   **KHAO PHRA VIHARN**

Khao Phra Viharn is not served by **public transport**, so the easiest way of getting to the ruins is to join a **tour** or rent a vehicle from Ubon Ratchathani, Surin or Si Saket. Alternatively, you can take a combination of motorbike taxi and songthaew to the temple from the nearby town of **Kantharalak**. From the temple car park it's about 1km to the base of the temple steps.

From Kantharalak Buses run to Kantharalak, 36km north of the temple, from Ubon Ratchathani's Warincham-rab suburb (every 30min; 1hr 30min), and from Si Saket (hourly; 2hr); the bus station (☎045 661486) is on the main street, Thanon Sinpradit, 50m from the market. There is no songthaew service from Kantharalak to Khao Phra Viharn, but occasional songthaews do connect Kantharalak with Ban Phum Saron, the junction near the national park barrier 12km north of Khao Phra Viharn, from where you

can get a motorbike taxi to the temple; you can also get a motorbike taxi all the way from Kantharalak to Khao Phra Viharn (fare depends on current petrol prices).

Krachang Yai Guesthouse 53 Moo 2, Tambon Krachang (about 2km west of the town centre) ☎086 1645648, ⓦsiambaan.com. This cosy guesthouse features a small pool and disabled-friendly rooms, as well as a restaurant and tour service. All rooms have a/c and include hot-water bathrooms. Call for pick-up from the town centre. B500

Si Saket

The quiet provincial capital of **SI SAKET** has no attractions in the municipal area, though it has a reasonable choice of hotels, a good night market and decent transport connections. The only reason to stay here is to use it as a base for a visit to Khao Phra Viharn (when open), or to check out a couple of quirky temples near town (Wat Sa Kamphaeng Yai and Wat Laan Khuat). It's also near the Cambodian border crossing at Chong Sa Ngam, though there's no public transport there.

5

Wat Sa Kamphaeng Yai

30km west of Si Saket, just south of H226 before the road crosses the railway (no English sign) • Daily 5.30am–6.30pm • Free • Bus from Si Saket (every 20min; 30min) or Surin (every 20min; 1hr 30min)

The temple compound at **Wat Sa Kamphaeng Yai** combines modern temple buildings with Khmer ruins which have been rather insensitively restored, using new bricks to replace sandstone blocks on the main prang, while two adjacent prangs have been almost entirely rebuilt of brick. There is some excellent detail on some of the lintels, though others have worn away. The most striking aspect of this temple, however, is its "Garden of Hell", behind the Khmer buildings and near the car park. The statues of people with enlarged heads, hands, eyes and sexual organs serve as a warning to young children of the dangers of not following the Middle Way of Buddhism.

Wat Laan Khuat (Million Bottle Temple)

65km south of Si Saket • Daily dawn to dusk • Free • No public transport; follow H221 south from Si Saket, turn west on to H2111, cross H24 and the temple is on H2128 in Khun Han village

In the 1980s, the abbot at Wat Phra Maha Chedi Kaeo struck on the bright idea of decorating his temple with bottles to symbolize the clarity of purpose that all Buddhists seek. As a result, the buildings, pathways and balustrades here are now decorated with brown and green beer bottles and bottle tops – more than a million and a half of them. The result creates a striking sight, and has attracted a steady stream of visitors to see the temple, now known as **Wat Laan Khuat** – the million bottle temple.

ARRIVAL AND DEPARTURE   SI SAKET

By train Si Saket train station (☏ 045 611525) is in the centre of the town.

Destinations: Bangkok (8 daily; 8–11hr); Khorat (8 daily; 3–4hr 30min); Surin (8 daily; 1hr 10min–2hr); Ubon Ratchatani (7 daily; 50min–1hr 10min).

By bus The bus station (☏ 045 612500) is in the southern part of town and connects Si Saket with Ubon Ratchathani, Surin and Bangkok. There are no buses from here to Khao Phra Viharn, so you have to get the bus to Kantharalak (hourly; 2hr) and make onward arrangements from there.

You should also be able to get buses from here towards Chong Sa Ngam for access to the Cambodian border crossing to Choam (for Anlong Veng and Siem Reap). Buses don't run all the way, so you'll need to get dropped off on Highway 24 and flag down a songthaew for the rest of the journey to the border.

Destinations: Bangkok (3 daily; 7hr); Kantharalak (hourly; 2hr); Surin (hourly; 3hr–3hr 30min); Ubon Ratchathani (every 30min; 45min–1hr).

ACCOMMODATION AND EATING

The best place to eat in town is the lip-smackingly diverse **night market**, which sets up around a small plaza along the southern edge of the rail line. There are half-a-dozen small Thai–Chinese **restaurants** on Thanon Khukan, which runs north–south about 150m east of the railway station.

Boonsiri Boutique Hotel 1191/3 Thanon Vijitkakorn ☏ 045 622222, ⓦ boonsiriboutiquehotel.com. This newish place offers well-equipped rooms with cable TV, just a short walk from the station. The rate includes American breakfast. <u>B450</u>

Prompiman Hotel 849/1 Thanon Lak Muang ☏ 045 612677, ⓦ prompimanhotel.com. A better choice for its location near the train station (it's about 200m west of the station on the road that parallels the rail line to the south) than its rather characterless a/c rooms, which are big, clean and bright nevertheless. <u>B700</u>

Ubon Ratchathani

The sprawling provincial capital of **UBON RATCHATHANI** (almost always referred to simply as Ubon – not to be confused with Udon, aka Udon Thani, to the north) holds little in the way of attractions beyond a couple of wats and a decent museum. Still, it's more sedate than many northeastern cities, with plenty of opportunities for getting to grips with Isaan culture. The best bet is to visit at festival time (see box, p.464), but Ubon also makes a handy base for trips east to Khong Chiam and Sam Phan Bok, both beside the Mekong River, and the Lao border market at Chong Mek, or southwest to the Khmer ruins of Khao Phra Viharn (see p.460), astride the Cambodian border, when they are open.

● RESTAURANTS		■ ACCOMMODATION	
Boon Ni Yom Uthayaan		Outside Inn	1
Vegetarian Restaurant		Phadaeng Mansion	2
and Centre	6	Ratchathani	4
Chiokee	7	Sri Isan	5
Jumpa-Hom	4	Toh Sang Ubo Ratchathani	3
Outside Inn	3		
Pornthip Kai Yang	1	● SHOPS	
Pratheung Thong	5	Maybe	2
Sincere Restaurant	2	Punchard	1

5

UBON FESTIVALS

If you're near Ubon in early July, you should definitely consider coming into town for the local **Asanha Puja** festivities, an auspicious Buddhist holiday celebrated all over Thailand to mark the beginning of Khao Pansa, the annual three-month Buddhist retreat. Ubon's version is the most spectacular in the country, famous for the majestic orange beeswax sculptures created by each of its temples, which are mounted on floats around enormous candles and paraded through the town – hence the tourist name for the celebrations, the **Ubon Candle Festival**. The sculptures are judged and then returned to the temple, where the candle is usually kept burning throughout the retreat period. The end of the retreat, **Awk Pansa** (early to mid-Oct), is also exuberantly celebrated with a procession of illuminated boats, each representing one of the city's temples, along the Mun River between Wat Suphat and the night market, as well as beauty contests, parades and lots of fireworks throughout the city, and *likay* theatre shows in Thung Si Muang Park. Traditional longboat races are staged on the river in the days following Awk Pansa.

Thung Si Muang Park

Just south of Thanon Phalorangrit

Ubon's centrepiece is **Thung Si Muang Park** and its unmissable 22m-high **Candle Sculpture**, an enormous yellow-painted replica of the wax sculptures that star in the annual Candle Festival (see box above). This particular sculpture was inspired by a story written by the king and features a boat with an enormous garuda figurehead that's ploughing past various figures who are apparently being devoured by sea monsters.

In the northeast corner of the park stands a far more unassuming memorial in the shape of a 3m-high obelisk. Known as the **Monument of Merit**, it was erected by a group of Allied POWs who wanted to show their gratitude to the people of Ubon for their support during World War II. Despite the real threat of punishment by the Japanese occupiers, between 1941 and 1943 Ubon citizens secretly donated food and clothes to the POWs imprisoned in a nearby camp.

Ubon Ratchathani National Museum

Thanon Khuenthani • Wed–Sun 9am–4pm • B100

Ubon Ratchathani National Museum is airily designed around a central courtyard in a building constructed in 1918, which previously functioned as Ubon's City Hall. Re-opened as a national museum in 1989 by the Fine Arts Department, it offers a good overview of the history, geology and culture of southern Isaan, with well-labelled displays on everything from rock formations to folk crafts, such as the star-embroidered fabric that is a speciality of Ubon. There are also copies of the Pha Taem cliff paintings (see p.469) and a ninth-century representation of Ardhanarishvara, the union of Shiva and his consort Uma.

Wat Thung Si Muang

Entrance on Thanon Luang

Of the city's eight main wats, **Wat Thung Si Muang** is the most noteworthy, mainly for its unusually well-preserved teak library (*ho trai*) which is raised on stilts over a pond to keep book-devouring insects at bay. The murals in the bot, to the left of the library, have also survived remarkably well; their lively scenes of everyday life in the nineteenth century include local merit-making dances and musicians playing *khaen* pipes, as well as conventional portraits of city activities in Bangkok.

Wat Nong Bua

5

Thanon Thammawithi (west of Thanon Chayangkun, near the main bus terminal at the northern edge of town) • City songthaew #2 or #3 via Thanon Khuenthani

The modern **Wat Nong Bua** is modelled on the stupa at Bodh Gaya in India, scene of the Buddha's enlightenment; the white and gold replica is carved with scenes from the *Jataka* and contains a scaled-down version of the stupa covered in gold leaf. Also of interest, especially if you don't happen to be here during the Candle Festival, is the wax float behind the chedi.

ARRIVAL AND DEPARTURE

UBON RATCHATHANI

BY PLANE

The airport (☎045 245612-4) is just north of the town centre; a metered taxi to the town-centre hotels costs around B80 (☎045 265999; call to ask for a pick-up). Thai Airways (☏thaiairways.com) operates at least two flights a day between Ubon and Bangkok (1hr 5min), as does budget airline Air Asia (☏airasia.com). Also cheap is Nok Air (☏nokair.com), which operates seven flights a day between Bangkok and Ubon. Kan Air has daily flights to Chiang Mai.

BY TRAIN

Ubon's train station (☎045 321004) is in the suburb of Warinchamrab (Warin Chamrap), about 2km south across the Mun River from central Ubon. White city songthaew #2 meets all trains at Warinchamrab and takes passengers into central Ubon (B10), passing along Thanon Khuenthani, where several hotels and the TAT office are located.

Destinations Ayutthaya (7 daily; 7hr–10hr 40min); Bangkok (7 daily; 8hr 30min–12hr 15min); Buriram (7 daily; 2hr 30min–3hr 30min); Khorat (7 daily; 3hr 45min–6hr); Si Saket (7 daily; 40min–1hr); Surin (7 daily; 1hr 50min–2hr 40min).

BY BUS

Confusingly, several different companies run long-distance bus services in and out of Ubon, each with their own drop-off and pick-up points. Bus company depots are shown on our map (see p.463).

Main bus terminal Nearly all services pass through the main terminal (☎045 314 299) on Thanon Chayangkun, on

the northwest edge of town, which is served by city songthaews #2 and #3 from Warinchamrab via Thanon Khuenthani in central Ubon. The government Baw Khaw Saw bus company is based here and runs regular and a/c services to Bangkok, Buriram, Chiang Mai, Khorat, Si Saket, Surin and Yasothon, plus Pakse in Laos.

Nakhon Chai Air This nationwide private company (☎045 269777, ☏nca.co.th) runs a/c services from its terminal just south of the Mun River, on the road to Warinchamrab, served by city buses #1, #2, #3 and #6. There's a non-stop service to Bangkok as well as routes to and from Buriram, Chiang Mai, Khorat, Rayong, Si Saket and Surin.

Sahamit A/c services (☎045 285534) to Udon Thani run from the northwest of town, off Thanon Ratchathani.

Talat Warinchamrab Most local buses and songthaews to Phibun Mangsahan, as well as those to Si Saket, use this terminal near the marketplace in Warinchamrab, southeast of the river and served by city songthaews #1 (grey), #3 (pink) and #6 (pink) from Ubon. Minibuses to Khong Chiam (☎045 316 085) leave hourly until 3.30pm.

Destinations Bangkok (hourly; 10–12hr); Buriram (8 daily; 6–8hr); Chiang Mai (6 daily; 17–18hr); Chong Mek (17 daily; 1hr); Kantharalak (every 15min; 1hr 30min); Khon Kaen (19 daily; 4–6hr); Khong Chiam (hourly; 2–3hr); Khorat (hourly; 5–7hr); Mukdahan (every 30min; 2–3hr); Pakse (Laos; 2 daily; 2–3hr); Pattaya (10 daily; 12hr–13hr 30min); Phibun Mangsahan (every 25min; 1hr); Rayong (11 daily; 14hr); Si Saket (every 45min; 45min–1hr); Surin (at least 7 daily; 2hr 30min–3hr); Udon Thani (19 daily; 5–7hr); Yasothon (19 daily; 1hr 30min–2hr).

GETTING AROUND

By bike Try Ubon Cycle Rental, 115 Thanon Sri Narong, east of the post office (☎091 721 7461; B100/24hr).

By motorbike or car Motorbikes (B250–1000/day) and cars (B1500/day) can be rented from Chow Wattana (☎045 242202) at 269 Thanon Suriyat, opposite Nikko Massage, and at the airport (☎086 779 9322). Avis (☎02 251 1131, ☏avisthailand.com) and Budget (☎045 240507, ☏budget.co.th) car rental are also based at the airport.

By songthaew Numbered songthaews follow fixed

routes in central Ubon and run a regular service (every 10–15min). Those of most use to visitors are mentioned in the text. TAT provides a sketch map of routes.

By taxi Metered taxis (☎045 265 999) charge B30 flag fare and B20 per call.

By tourist bus A free tourist bus service operated by pink electric carts starts from Thung Si Muang Park (9am–4pm; leaves when full) and stops at nine temples around town, taking about three hours to complete the circuit.

5

BRUSH UP ON YOUR THAI IN UBON

If you find yourself in Ubon for more than a few days, and want to learn some **Thai**, check out English Center Ubon, where teacher Ooh offers a range of useful one-to-one courses.

English Center Ubon 100 Thanon Ratchabut ☎ 086 2460754, ✉ englishcenterubon@hotmail.com. Rates start at B300/hr, but it's possible to get a discount for longer courses – 10hr course for B2900 or a 50hr course costs B13,500. Daily 9am–7pm.

INFORMATION AND TOURS

Tourist information Staff at the TAT office (daily 8.30am–4.30pm; ☎ 045 243770, ✉ tatubon@tat.or.th) at 264/1 Thanon Khuenthani can provide a helpful map of the city with songthaew routes marked, and should be able to give information about the latest situation at Khao Phra Viharn.

Tours Sakda Travel World, 150/1 Thanon Kantaralak, Warinchamrab (☎ 045 323048, ⊕ sakdatour.com), offers guided tours around Isaan and into Laos, sells air tickets and offers car plus driver from B1800/day.

ACCOMMODATION

Ubon's choice of hotels is broad enough, but as there's not much of a travellers' scene in the city, there are none of the cosy, great-value guesthouses you'll find elsewhere in Thailand. Prices shoot up during the Candle Festival, when you'll need to book a room as far ahead as possible.

★**Outside Inn** 11 Thanon Suriyat ☎ 088 581 2069, ⊕ theoutsideinnubon.com. Located at the eastern end of Thanon Suriyat, this gem of a place offers great value, with just a handful of tastefully furnished rooms in a quiet location with a laidback vibe. Owners Brent and Tun go out of their way to guarantee guests a pleasant stay. They can advise and help out with travel arrangements, and also happen to run the best restaurant in town (see opposite). B650

Phadaeng Mansion 126 Thanon Pha Daeng, near Punchard crafts shop ☎ 045 254600, ✉ thephadaeng @gmail.com. Clean, good-sized rooms in a quiet part of town, all with TV and a/c. Some have their own private balconies – although don't expect a great view. There's a rather bizarre "fine art gallery" on the ground floor, featuring prints of works by the likes of Da Vinci and Michelangelo, but it gives a splash of colour to the place. B500

Ratchathani 297 Thanon Khuenthani ☎ 045 244388, ✉ theratchathani@gmail.com. This mid-range hotel has a great central location and rooms are equipped with attractive fixtures and fittings. However, rooms are smallish and some are dimly lit, so take a look before deciding. Avoid rooms out front as it can be noisy. B600

Sri Isan 62 Thanon Ratchabut ☎ 045 261011, ⊕ sriisan hotel.com. This small, quite classy hotel enjoys a good location in Ubon's old quarter, just across from the market and night market, and a mere 100m from the river. Its 33 small rooms (some with no window) are set around an open-roofed atrium and all have a/c and cable TV. Breakfast included. B450

Toh Sang Ubon Ratchathani 251 Thanon Phalochai ☎ 045 245531, ⊕ tohsang.com. The poshest hotel in town, with comfortable a/c rooms and gorgeous suites in a peaceful but rather inconvenient location 1km west of Thanon Chayangkun or about 2km from TAT. It also houses one of the city's smartest restaurants, the *Pratheung Thong* (see opposite). City songthaews #4 and #8 pass the door. Breakfast included. B2200

EATING

Ubon is a good place for sampling local Isaan specialities, either in a/c comfort at some of the **restaurants** listed below, or at one of the city's **night markets**: try the one on Thanon Ratchabut (north off Thanon Khuenthani) for chicken satay, *phat thai* and cheap fruit shakes, or the one to the east of Thanon Upparat for fiery Isaan dishes.

Boon Ni Yom Uthayaan Vegetarian Restaurant and Centre Thanon Sri Narong; no English sign but its barn-like, open-sided wooden structure is unmistakeable. Famous, canteen-style veggie place that's run by members of a Buddhist organization who grow, sell and cook their own produce. All sorts of meat substitutes and tasty veg and tofu dishes are on offer here at very cheap per-plate prices (B20–30). Tues–Sun 6am–2pm.

Chiokee 307–317 Thanon Khuenthani. Café-style place serving a large menu of Thai and Western staples (B40–120). Especially popular at breakfast time, when Westerners come for the ham and eggs, and local office workers for rice gruel. Daily 6am–6pm.

Jumpa-Hom 49/3 Thanon Pichitrangsan ☎ 045 260398. A classy restaurant with a choice of inside or outside dining, the latter on a shady wooden terrace. Specialities include marinated and oven-baked ribs (B175), and there's a good range of drinks as well. Daily 5pm–midnight.

★**Outside Inn** 11 Thanon Suriyat ☎088 581 2069, ⓦtheoutsideinnubon.com. Delicious American, Mexican and Thai dishes served up by Tun, who has a real flair for creating unique dishes using locally sourced ingredients. Try the signature burger (B200), the burritos or home-made tacos, and don't miss the lip-smacking spicy dips. Reservations recommended. Mon & Wed–Sun 11am–2.30pm & 5–9pm.

Pornthip Kai Yang 136 Thanon Sumpasit, just east of Wat Jaeng. This simple streetside restaurant, which also has an a/c dining room, is famous across town for its signature barbecued chicken (*kai yang*) and papaya salad (*som tam*), for B80–150. Daily 7am–8pm.

Pratheung Thong Toh Sang Hotel, 251 Thanon Phalochai ☎045 245531. With its starched tablecloths and wide-ranging menu of Thai and Chinese dishes (B100–260), this restaurant oozes sophistication, and a pianist serenades diners in the evening. Daily 6am–midnight.

Sincere Restaurant 126/1 Thanon Sumpasit ☎045 245061. High-quality American steaks (from B900) and baby clams (B200) served in an intimate little a/c restaurant just back from the main road by the police station. Mon–Sat 11am–10pm.

SHOPPING

Silk, cotton and silverware are all good buys in Ubon. Both shops listed here specialize in fine-quality regional goods, like triangular axe pillows (*mawn khwaan*) and lengths of silk. There's a walking street on Friday to Sunday evenings (5–11pm) along Thanon Ratchabut, beside the *Ratchathani Hotel*.

Maybe 124 Thanon Sri Narong ☎045 254932. This shop has a good selection of clothes made from the stripy rough cotton weaves peculiar to the Ubon area. Daily 8am–6pm.

★**Punchard** 156/1 Thanon Pha Daeng ☎045 265751, ⓦpunchard.net. *Punchard* is packed with stylish items such as cotton tableware and clothes made to local designs, as well as Ubon's best collection of northeastern crafts, and lots of home decor items upstairs. Daily 9am–6.30pm.

DIRECTORY

Hospitals Sappasit Prasong Hospital (☎045 240074), to the northeast of the town centre, has a 24hr emergency clinic.

Immigration office In the town of Phibun Mangsahan, 45km east of Ubon (Mon–Fri 8.30am–4.30pm; ☎045 441108). Phibun Mangsahan is best accessed by bus (see p.465).

Tourist police For all emergencies, call the tourist police on ☎1155 (free) or contact them at their office on Thanon Suriyat ☎045 245505.

Around Ubon

The area **around Ubon** is a good deal more interesting than the metropolitan hub, particularly if you venture eastwards towards the appealing Mekong riverside town of **Khong Chiam**, the prehistoric paintings at **Pha Taem** or the other-worldly landscape at **Sam Phan Bok**. There is also a crossing into Laos, and a border market, southeast of Ubon at **Chong Mek**.

Khong Chiam

The riverside village of **KHONG CHIAM** (pronounced Kong Jiem) is a popular destination for day-tripping Thais, who drive here from across Isaan to see the somewhat fancifully named "two-coloured river" for which the village is nationally renowned. Created by the merging of the muddy brown Mun with the muddy brown Mekong at the easternmost point of Thailand, the water is hardly an irresistible attraction (come in April to see the colour contrast at its most vivid), but the village itself has plenty of tranquil appeal. If you have your own transport, Khong Chiam combines well with visits to Chong Mek (just 27km away) and Kaeng Tana National Park.

Comprising little more than a collection of wooden houses and a few resorts, Khong Chiam feels like an island, with the Mun defining its southern limit and the Mekong its northern one. A concrete walkway runs along the banks of the Mekong, lined by predictable souvenir stalls and leading to the large *sala* that's built right over the confluence and affords uninterrupted views. Behind the *sala*, **Wat Khong Chiam** is a

5

TRIPS FROM KHONG CHIAM

Khong Chiam doesn't have many sights, but you can rent motorbikes (B200/day) or bicycles (B100/day) from *Apple Guest House* (opposite the post office) or *Ban Pak Mongkhon* (see below) and explore the quiet streets around the riverfront, or charter a **boat** for a trip to the "two-coloured river" (B400) or up the Mekong River to see the Pha Taem cliff paintings (B1500/boat; ask at your hotel). Otherwise you could charter a songthaew to **Pha Taem** from Khong Chiam (round trip about B700); ask at the bus station.

Even distant **Laos** is just a few hundred metres away from Khong Chiam, on the other bank of the Mekong, foreigners are not supposed to cross the border here, though you may be able to persuade boatmen to take you there and back for B350/boat, with a quick stop at the bankside village of Ban Mai; the official border crossing is further downstream at Chong Mek.

typically charming rural Thai temple and has an old wooden bell tower in its compound. Khong Chiam's other temple, the cliffside **Wat Tham Khu Ha Sawan**, located near the point where Route 2222 turns into Khong Chiam, is a striking white colour, with natural wood sculptures festooned with orchids in its grounds, and a huge Buddha image staring down on the villagers below.

ARRIVAL AND SERVICES   KHONG CHIAM

Khong Chiam is 30km northeast of **Phibun Mangsahan**, along Route 2222, and 75km from Ubon.

By minibus Minibuses terminate in front of the market at the west end of Thanon Kaewpradit, Khong Chiam's main drag. From Ubon, hourly minibuses (9.30am–3.30pm; 2hr 30min) run from Talat Warinchamrab terminal; the last bus back to Ubon leaves at 6pm. Two daily buses (departing Khong Chiam 7.30am and 4.30pm; 12hr) run between Khong Chiam and Bangkok (travelling via Yasothon).

Services There are a few banks and ATMs on Thanon Kaewpradit. The small pharmacy on Thanon Kaewpradit sells basic supplies.

ACCOMMODATION

Khong Chiam's **accommodation** options are relatively limited, and apart from a couple of exceptions, most places feel poor value compared to other parts of the northeast.

Ban Pak Mongkhon 595 Thanon Klaewpradit ☏ 045 351352. A good budget alternative, just a few steps from the bus stop, offering decent a/c bungalows on the north side of the road, and fan rooms in a house on the south side of the road. No wi-fi in the fan rooms as yet. Fan B250, a/c B350

Ban Rim Khong Resort 37 Thanon Kaewpradit ☏ 045 351101. Great-looking little resort with five timbered a/c chalets wreathed in bougainvillea and ranged round a lawn, plus three fabulous riverside ones (B1500, worth phoning ahead to reserve) with huge verandas overlooking the Mekong. The interiors are nothing special but all are spacious and have a/c, TVs and fridges, and there are discounts for stays of more than one night. B1000

Sibae Guest House 380 Moo 1 Ban Dankao, Thanon Radsadornbamroong; turn left off Thanon Klaewpradit just west of Tesco Lotus, then left again and it's on the left ☏ 045 351068, ✉ watasinsibae@hotmail.com. A beautiful wooden house that has very clean (but very plain) rooms, the most luxurious of which have a/c, bathtubs, TVs and fridges. Friendly owner. Fan B200, a/c B400

Toh Sang Khongjiam Resort On the south bank of the Mun, about 3km east of Khong Chiam ☏ 045 351174, ⊚ tohsang.com. Romantically located, upmarket resort where all rooms have balconies overlooking the river and are very comfortably, if a little kitschly, furnished. There's a swimming pool, table-tennis room, spa, bicycle and kayak rental, plus a couple of restaurants and boat trips to Pha Taem and other riverside sights. Check out their website for spa/resort package offers. With your own wheels, follow Highway 2134 south past Khong Chiam bus station, cross the river, take the first left and follow the signs. B4500

EATING

There's not much happening in Khong Chiam after dark, and restaurants tend to close early.

Araya On the Mekong in front of the district office. Two floating restaurants – *Araya* and nearby *Chonlada* – are the most popular places for Thai visitors to eat at lunch and dinner. Neither is signed in English, and there's little to choose between them; both serve fairly pricey menus of Thai–Chinese dishes (around B100 for basics) and, of course, plenty of fish. Daily 10am–8pm.

Rim Khong Next to the riverside bungalows at Ban Rim Khong Resort. Cheaper and less flashy than the other riverside restaurants (fried rice from B40), with better views, and friendly staff too. A good spot for a sunset beer.

Daily 8am–9pm.

Tuk Tik Tham Mua 100m east of the bus station on Thanon Kaewpradit (no English sign or menu), just east of Tesco Lotus. Good local dishes at good cheap prices: spicy *som tam* (B35) and *laap* (B50) served with individual baskets of sticky rice. Daily 8am–7pm.

Pha Taem National Park

18km north of Khong Chiam • Daily 5am–6pm • B400 • To get here, head north out of town on H2173, continue northwest on H2134, then turn north on to H2112 for about 5km, where the park entrance is signposted to the east

The main attraction in craggy **Pha Taem National Park**, which overlooks Laos and occupies an area of 340 square kilometres bordering the Mekong River, is the **Pha Taem cliff paintings**, though the park also features waterfalls, giant vines and weird rock formations. One of these clusters of odd-shaped rocks is at **Sao Chaliang**, which you pass just after entering the park. It's a group of mushroom-shaped sandstone rocks standing about 10m tall, which have been eroded by centuries of wind and rain and are well worth stopping to admire and photograph.

From Sao Chaliang the road continues to a car park, where there's a restaurant and visitor centre on top of the cliff by the Mekong River. To see the cliff paintings, follow the path from the car park to the left of the visitor centre, which runs down the cliff face and along a shelf in the rock. The bold, childlike paintings cover a 170m stretch of cliff face and are clear proof of the antiquity of the fertile Mekong valley, as they are believed to be between three thousand and four thousand years old – the work of rice-cultivating settlers who lived in huts rather than caves.

Protected from the elements by an overhang, the clearly discernible red-painted images (daubed from a mixture of soil, tree gum and fat) include alien-like forms, handprints and geometric designs as well as massive depictions of animals and enormous fish – possibly the prized catfish still occasionally caught in the Mekong. Try to avoid coming here on a weekend when the place gets swamped with tour buses, as the narrow path along the cliff gets very crowded. It's an especially popular spot at sunrise, this being the first place in Thailand to see the sun in the morning – a full eighteen minutes ahead of Phuket, the westernmost point.

If you continue along the path past the paintings, you'll eventually climb back up to the top of the cliff, via the viewpoint at Pha Mon, taking in fine views of the fertile Mekong valley floor and glimpses of hilly western Laos. It's just under 2km from Pha Mon back to the car park, along a signed trail across the rocky scrub.

ARRIVAL AND ACCOMMODATION
PHA TAEM NATIONAL PARK

By songthaew Aside from using your own wheels, the most practical way to reach the national park is by chartering a songthaew from Khong Chiam, 18km away (see opposite).
National park bungalows Sao Chaliang, book in advance through the Pha Taem office (☎ 045 252581,

e phataem_np@hotmail.com) or via w dnp.go.th /parkreserve. If you want to stay and catch the sunrise, you can rent bungalows and large two-person tents near the national park checkpoint at Sao Chaliang, about 2km before the car park. Tents B225, fan B1200, a/c B2000

Sam Phan Bok

120km northeast of Ubon and about 40km southeast of Khemmarat on H2112 • Nov–May only • No public transport; take H2050 northeast from Ubon, then go east on H2337, and finally south on H2112. Alternatively, head north on H2112 from Khong Chiam, but the road is in poor condition

Along 4350km between its source and the sea, the Mekong River creates some striking sights, such as whirlpools, rapids and temporary islands that disappear in the rainy season. One such sight is **Sam Phan Bok** (three thousand holes), an other-worldly

5

CROSSING THE LAO BORDER VIA CHONG MEK

It is possible to get a Lao **visa** on arrival at Chong Mek **border crossing**; you'll be charged US$30–42, depending on your nationality, and will receive a thirty-day visa; you'll also need two passport photos (expect to pay an extra dollar if you turn up without photos). If you get an advance visa from Khon Kaen or elsewhere, it must specify Chong Mek as the entry point (see p.28).

Whichever option you choose, once at Chong Mek you first need to get the **Thai exit stamp** from the immigration office on the Thai side (daily 6am–8pm); you then need to walk through an underground tunnel to the Lao immigration office (daily 6am–8pm). Most people travel on the direct bus from Ubon to Pakse, which waits for passengers to complete formalities, though there's also a songthaew service there from Vang Tao, on the Lao side of the border. In reverse, you simply pay the Lao stamping fee (usually around B30/US$1) and get your Thai visa on arrival for free.

---

landscape where erosion has created an area of thousands of circular pools that are exposed during the dry season when the level of the Mekong River drops by several metres. There's nothing to see during the wet season from June to October, but for the rest of the year you can wander across the bed of the receding river to marvel at the unique terrain that is caused by the erosive power of the rushing river on the soft sandstone. It makes a superb subject for abstract photographs, and the best light is early or late in the day. There's no accommodation here yet, but that may change as the place is becoming popular among Thai tourists.

Chong Mek and the Lao border

The village of **CHONG MEK**, 44km east of Phibun Mangsahan at the Thai–Lao border, hosts a busy Thai–Lao market and is one of the legal border crossings for foreigners, with onward transport to Pakse.

Even if you're not planning to cross into Laos, the **border market** is good for a browse, especially at weekends when it's at its liveliest. The market on the Thai side of the border is full of Bangkok fashions, jeans and sarongs, but you'll also find traditional herbalists selling dried leaves and roots, lots of basketware sellers and plenty of restaurant shacks serving Thai and Lao dishes.

ARRIVAL AND DEPARTURE
CHONG MEK

By bus There are five daily buses between Chong Mek and Bangkok (10hr). Buses run twice a day (9.30am & 3.30pm; 3hr; B200) from Ubon Ratchathani's main bus station to Pakse in Laos, the easiest way to do the trip. The bus station in Chong Mek is about 1km from the border, and motorbike taxis and tuk-tuks are on hand to take travellers there.

By songthaew Large pale-blue songthaews run to Chong Mek from Phibun Mangsahan bus station (approximately hourly 7am–3.30pm; 1hr 30min).

Yasothon and around

By the beginning of May, Isaan is desperate for rain; there may not have been a significant downpour for six months and the rice crops need to be planted. In northeastern folklore, rain is the fruit of sexual encounters between the gods, so at this time villagers all over Isaan hold the bawdy, merit-making **Bun Bang Fai rocket festival** to encourage the gods to get on with it. The largest and most public of these festivals takes place in the provincial capital of **YASOTHON**, 98km northwest of Ubon, on a weekend in mid-May (check with TAT for dates). Not only are the fireworks spectacular, but the rockets built to launch them are superbly crafted machines in themselves, beautifully decorated and carried proudly through the streets before blast-off. Up to 25kg of gunpowder may be packed into the 9m-long rockets and, in keeping with the fertility theme, performance is everything. Sexual innuendo, general flirtation and dirty jokes are essential components of Bun Bang Fai; rocket-builders compete to shoot their rockets the highest, and anyone whose missile fails to leave the ground gets coated in mud as a punishment.

At other times of the year, Yasothon has little to tempt tourists other than a handful of unremarkable wats and a few evocative old colonial-style shopfronts near **Wat Singh Tha** at the west end of Thanon Srisonthoon.

Ban Sri Than

21km east of Yasothon • Follow Route 202 northeast towards Amnat Charoen as far as kilometre-stone 18.5km, then turn south (right) off the highway for 3km; or take a songthaew (every 30min until noon) or bus (hourly throughout the day) to Ban Ni Khom on Route 202, then a motorbike taxi for the last 3km

The most interesting attraction in the surrounding area is the village of **BAN SRI THAN**, where nearly every household is employed in the making of the famous *mawn khwaan* triangular **axe pillows**. However, the scenes of sewing machines surrounded by heaps of cloth are not exactly photo contest winners, so it's really only worth a visit if you plan to buy the product. These pillows (*mawn*), so named because their shape supposedly resembles an axe-head (*khwaan*), have been used in traditional Thai homes for centuries, where it's normal to sit on the floor and lean against a densely stuffed *mawn khwaan*. It's possible to buy the cushions unstuffed so you can actually fit them in your luggage. The price depends on the number of triangular pods that make up the pillow and the number of attached cushions: in Ban Sri Than, a stand-alone ten-triangle pillow costs B160, or B470 with three attached cushions – about half of what it'll cost in Bangkok or Chiang Mai.

ARRIVAL AND DEPARTURE   YASOTHON

By plane The nearest airports are in Roi Et (85km northwest) and in Ubon Ratchathani (see p.462). Nok Air operates three flights a day and Air Asia has two flights a day to Roi Et from Bangkok. The travel agent inside the *JP Emerald* hotel sells domestic and international air tickets.

By bus Buses between Ubon and Khon Kaen stop at the bus station on Thanon Rattanakhet (21 daily; 3hr–3hr 30min from Khon Kaen, 1hr 30min–2hr from Ubon).

Services Thanon Chaeng Sanit is where you'll find all the main banks, with ATMs and currency exchange facilities. The post office is on Thanon Chaeng Sani, a couple of blocks west of the night bazaar.

ACCOMMODATION

If you want to stay here during festival time, book your **hotel** well in advance and be prepared to pay double the normal prices quoted here. The most lively place to **eat** is at the covered night bazaar, which runs east off the central section of Thanon Chaeng Sanit; some of the stalls here also open during the day.

Green Park Grand 209/12 Thanon Wareerachadet, just a block west of the bus station ☎045 714700–4, ⓦthegreenparkgrand.com. This newish place offers spacious rooms, helpful staff and a good restaurant, though the beds are rather hard. Breakfast included. **B800**

JP Emerald 36 Thanon Prapa ☎045 724848, ⓦjpemerald.com. The *JP Emerald* has large, attractive a/c rooms close to the provincial hall, though the place is a bit run-down and in need of a makeover. Breakfast costs an additional B150. **B550**

Khon Kaen

At Isaan's centre, **KHON KAEN** is the wealthiest and most sophisticated city in the northeast, seat of a highly respected university as well as the Channel 5 and Channel 11 television studios. There's a noticeably upbeat feel to the place, underlined by its apparently harmonious combination of traditional Isaan culture – huge markets and hordes of street vendors – with flashy shopping plazas and a world-class hotel. Its

5

location, 188km northeast of Khorat on the Bangkok–Nong Khai rail line and Highway 2, makes it a convenient resting point, even though a startling modern temple and the provincial museum are the only real sights in town. However, the wider province has some impressive prehistoric credentials, which you can get to grips with at Phuwiang's **dinosaur graveyard** (see p.477), within day-tripping distance of the city. Local silk is another draw; available year-round at outlets across the city, it gets special focus during the annual **Silk and Phuk Siao Festival** (usually Nov 29–Dec 10; check with TAT) when weavers from across the province congregate at the City Hall on Thanon Na Soon Rachakarn to display and sell their fabrics; this is also the chance to witness the moving *phuk siao* ceremony, a traditional friendship-deepening ritual involving the exchange of symbolic wrist strings. During the rest of the year, the foreigners staying in the city tend to be expat husbands of local women, businesspeople or university teachers rather than tourists, though an increasing number of travellers are stopping here for **Lao and Vietnamese visas**, now that both nations have consulates in Khon Kaen.

Wat Nongwang Muang Kao

Far southern end of Thanon Klang

Khon Kaen's most arresting sight is the enormous nine-tiered pagoda at **Wat Nongwang Muang Kao**. Unmissable in its glittering livery of red, white and gold, this breathtakingly grand structure was the brainchild of the temple's famously charismatic and well-travelled abbot, Phra Wisuttikittisan. The nine-tiered design is said to have been inspired by Myanmar's most sacred stupa, Shwedagon, but the gallery running around each tier is more Lao in style, and the crowning *that* (tower) is typically Thai. Nine is an auspicious number in Thailand, triply so in this case as the current king is Rama IX and the current abbot of the temple is the ninth since the wat's foundation in 1789. Inside the pagoda, the walls of the first tier are painted with modern murals that depict the founding of Khon Kaen. Each tier has its different purpose, with the first used for assemblies, the second for monks' residences, the third for a scripture library and so on. If you arrive before 4pm, you can climb the staircase all the way up to the ninth tier for views north across the city and east to the lake, Beung Kaen Nakhon.

Beung Kaen Nakhon

In the southeast of town, 500m from the Fairy Plaza • Bike rental B20/hr, pedalo rental B40/hr

A walk or cycle round the rippling waters of **Beung Kaen Nakhon** and its perimeter park is a pleasant way to spend an hour or two and it's very popular with locals in the morning and evening. You can rent bicycles at three different spots, close to each of the lakeside temples, there are table-tennis tables near the Wat Klang Muang Kao entrance, several kids' playparks, and food stalls all over, as well as restaurants. It's also possible to rent pedalos from the northern shore of the lake.

Hong Moon Mung Khon Kaen City Museum

On the eastern shore of Beung Kaen Nakhon, across from the ornate Chinese temple in the utilitarian building beneath the outdoor amphitheatre • Mon–Sat 9am–5pm • B90

The **Hong Moon Mung Khon Kaen City Museum**, sometimes referred to as the "treasure hall", presents the history of Khon Kaen province in a series of tableaux. It showcases the region's rich cultural heritage, from the first signs of settlement right up to the present day. The museum is organized into five chronological sections, making it easy to find your way around, and there's a fair amount of explanation in English. While not as engaging as the city's national museum, it's worth a visit if you're interested in Isaan history or culture.

Khon Kaen National Museum

North of the centre at Thanon Lung Soon Rachakarn • Wed–Sun 9am–4pm • B100

Khon Kaen National Museum presents a digestible introduction to the region through an assortment of locally found artefacts, some of which date back to the Bronze Age. The star **exhibit** on the ground floor of the museum is a ninth-century Dvaravati-era *sema* (boundary stone), carved with a sensuous depiction of Princess Bhimba wiping the Buddha's feet with her hair. Also on this floor is an interesting reconstruction of a local musical ensemble centred around the *pong lang*, a wooden xylophone that's particular to the region. The highlights of the upstairs gallery are some exquisite little Khmer-influenced Lopburi-style bronze Buddha images.

5

ARRIVAL AND DEPARTURE

By plane Khon Kaen airport (☎043 468170), 10km northwest of the city centre, is served by Thai Airways, Air Asia and Nok Air flights to and from Bangkok, while Kan Air operates a service to Chiang Mai. Hotel minibuses meet all flights – some hotels provide this service for free, others charge B80–100. Alternatively, pick up a metered taxi (around B80 to central hotels) from the road approaching the airport. The Thai Airways office (☎043 227701; Mon-Fri 8am–5pm) is inside the *Pullman Hotel* on Thanon Prachasamran.

Destinations Bangkok (10 daily; 55min); Chiang Mai (daily; 1hr 15min).

By train The train station (☎043 221112) is to the southwest of the city centre, a short walk from downtown hotels and bars.

Destinations Ayutthaya (4 daily; 7hr–8hr 30min); Bangkok (4 daily; 8hr 30min–9hr 45min); Khorat (daily; 3hr 20min); Nong Khai (3 daily; 2hr 25min–3hr 30min); Udon Thani (4 daily; 1hr 50min–2hr 30min).

By bus Khon Kaen has three bus terminals, which are numbered by location, north to south. Number one (☎043 237300) is on Thanon Prachasamoson, a 5min walk northwest of the Thanon Klang Muang hotels, and operates fan-cooled buses and a few a/c buses, but no VIP service. Number two (☎043 239910) is on Thanon Klang Muang in the town centre, and is used by minibuses to and from local destinations such as Udon Thani. Finally, number three (☎043 471563) is the newest and biggest, located south of the centre at the junction of Thanon Mittraphap with the ring road, which operates a/c and VIP services nationwide. Services to all destinations below leave from both terminals 1 and 3, apart from Pattaya and Rayong, which are only served by terminal 3.

Destinations Bangkok (every 30min; 6–7hr); Chiang Mai (12 daily; 10–12hr); Khorat (every 30min; 3hr); Loei (every 30min; 4hr); Nong Khai (5 daily; 3hr 30min); Pattaya (daily; 11hr); Phitsanulok (12 daily; 6–7hr); Rayong (6 daily; 10–12hr); Sukhothai (2 daily; 7hr); Surin (hourly; 5hr 30min); Ubon Ratchathani (21 daily; 4hr–4hr 30min); Udon Thani (every 30min; 2hr–2hr 30min).

GETTING AROUND

By songthaew Numbered and colour-coded songthaews ply the streets 6am–7pm, charging a fixed fare of B9–13. A useful map showing their routes is available at the bus station.

By tuk-tuk or samlor A short tuk-tuk ride within the city should cost you B50–60, while the minimum fare in a samlor is B40.

By taxi Taxis tend to congregate near the *Pullman Hotel*, or call ☎043 465777. Ask for the meter to be switched on; short journeys within the city should cost B40–50.

Car rental Avis (☎043 344313, ⓦavisthailand.com) and Budget (☎043 345460, ⓦbudget.co.th) both have desks at the airport. Cars with a driver (B1500/day, excluding fuel) are available at Top Car Rent (☎043 227448), just opposite the *Pullman Hotel* on Thanon Prachasamran. The service here is reliable, and the owners are able to plan customized trips around the northeast.

Motorbike rental Ask around at the bars near the *Pullman Hotel*, which can help arrange a daily rental for about B200/day.

INFORMATION AND TOURS

Tourist information The TAT office (daily 8.30am–4.30pm; ☎043 227714–5, ⓔtatkhkn@tat.or.th) is at 277/20-21 Thanon Klang Muang, at the northwest corner of Bueng Kaen Nakhon. For information about the city and attractions in the surrounding area, ⓦkhonkaen.com is a useful resource, but it's not especially up to date.

Tours and trips Kangwal Holiday (☎043 227777, ⓦkangwal.com), on the *Charoen Thani* approach road on Thanon Si Chan, can arrange trips across Thailand, as well as flights and organized tours to destinations across the region.

ACCOMMODATION

Khon Kaen has some of the best **accommodation** anywhere in the northeast, from all-out luxury to quirky and clean city hotels.

Glacier Hotel 141 Thanon Prachasamran ☎043 334999, ⓦglacier-hotel.com. A cool, crisply styled hotel that's vaguely themed around ice and snow (yes, there's a/c throughout). There are white pod chairs in the lobby, and the carpeted rooms have unusual touches like see-through glass walls separating the bathroom from the bedroom. B3000

Piman Garden Boutique Hotel 6/110 Thanon Klang Muang ☎043 334111. Though all rooms here are spacious and well equipped, it's worth paying a bit extra for the deluxe rooms (B1300), which are brighter than the superior rooms and also have balconies. Breakfast is included, staff are helpful and the location is very convenient. B1000

★**Pullman Khon Kaen Raja Orchid** 9/9 Thanon Prachasamran ☎043 322155, ⓦpullmanhotels.com. Quite simply the nicest hotel in the northeast, this gorgeously appointed, luxury high-rise hotel has extremely

5

comfortable rooms, a swimming pool and spa, and plenty of bars and restaurants. It's shaped in the form of a giant *khaen*, the bamboo panpipes played in northeastern folk music. Significant discounts are often available, which makes it well worth splashing out on. B2500

Roma 50/2 Thanon Klang Muang ☎043 334444. The best of several budget hotels in the city centre, the *Roma* is nothing to write home about, but rooms are good value, the place is efficiently run and it has a central location. A/c rooms have a few features lacking in fan rooms, such as fridge, bathtub and

padded headboards. Fan B230, a/c B500

★**Supanniga Home** 130/9 Thanon Potisarn ☎089 944 4880, ⓦsupannigahome.com. It's well worth heading a couple of kilometres east of Khon Kaen's centre to discover this gorgeous property – just three luxurious villas, all with different design and character, set in a delightfully landscaped garden. It's a wonderful place to relax and enjoy nature, and the restaurant seves excellent Thai cuisine (see below), though it's best for those with their own transport as no buses go near. B4800

EATING, DRINKING AND ENTERTAINMENT

Khon Kaen has a reputation for very **spicy food**, particularly sausages, *sai krog isaan*, which are occasionally available with cubes of raw ginger, onion, lime and plenty of chilli sauce at stalls along Thanon Klang Muang around the *Roma Hotel*. In high season, these and other local favourites – such as pigs' trotters, roast duck and shellfish – can also be sampled at the stalls along the northern edge of lake Bueng Kaen Nakhon. Food stalls pop up across town at dusk, with a particular concentration at the **night bazaar** on the eastern end of Thanon Ruen Rom. **Nightlife** is mainly focused along Thanon Prachasamran, behind the *Pullman Hotel*.

CAFÉS AND RESTAURANTS

D'lite 348/17 Thanon Prachasamran, the lane immediately east of the Pullman Hotel ☎043 321124. The place to come for stylishly presented Isaan dishes like long bean salad with crispy pork (B99). You can sit outside in the dimly lit garden, which has soothing water features, or in the small a/c area. Daily 6pm–late.

★**Krua Supanniga** 130/9 Thanon Potisarn ☎089 944 4880. The gourmet cuisine in this atmospheric restaurant, which is part of *Supanniga Home*, is beautifully prepared and presented, and makes a great place for a lazy lunch. It features some unusual dishes such as *mu cha muong* (slow steamed pork with sour leaves), and prices are very reasonable (B70–200). Reservations necessary as it is sometimes closed for private functions. Daily 11.30am–8.30pm.

Naem Nuang Lab Lae 61–67 Thanon Klang Muang ☎043 236296; also opposite on the west side of Thanon Klang Muang. With two locations on the main road just north of the *Roma*, this place can be confusing, but it's hugely popular with Thai visitors. The one on the west side of the road (daily 11am–2pm) serves Vietnamese buffet only, but the main restaurant is at the end of the lane on the opposite (east) side of Thanon Klang Muang, which serves both buffet (B169) and à la carte Vietnamese food plus some northeastern standards. Their eponymous speciality is *naem nuang*, Vietnamese spring rolls made with barbecued fermented pork sausage, which you assemble yourself from half a dozen or more ingredients of your choice, including lots of fresh coriander, mint, ginger,

lemon rind, thin noodles and beansprouts (B90–190). Daily 9am–8.30pm.

Pomodoro 348/16 Thanon Prachasamran ☎043 270464. Next to *D'lite* on the lane to the east of the *Pullman Hotel*. A popular expat hangout serving good Italian pizzas, pastas and meat dishes. Most dishes are around B200–250, but portions are generous. Eat on the terrace or in the a/c interior. Daily 5–11pm.

Turm Rom 4/5 Thanon Chetakhon ☎043 221752. This cool café a couple of blocks north of Bueng Kaen Nakhon is hugely popular with locals and is often packed. All dishes are well prepared, such as soft-shell crab (B149) and steamed curry seafood (B99). Acoustic musicians serenade diners in the garden. Daily 5pm–1am.

BARS AND ENTERTAINMENT

4am Bar Just east of the Pullman Hotel driveway, off Thanon Prachasamran. Popular little roadside hut serving strong drinks late into the night; one of several in the area. A large Sangsom and cola will set you back B80. Daily 7pm–4am.

Cinema Fairy Cineplex inside Fairy Plaza, between southern Thanon Nah Muang and Klang Muang. Tickets B80–120.

Rad 231/2 Thanon Prachasamran ☎043 225988. This one-stop entertainment complex has it all – restaurant and coffee shop, raucous rock and easy-listening live music venues, plus girls dancing on the bar. Coffees around B50, beers around B100. Daily 6pm–late.

SHOPPING

Khon Kaen's shops carry a wide range of regional **arts and crafts**, particularly high-quality Isaan **silk** of all designs and weaves. Vendors, who you'll sometimes see wandering the main streets with panniers stuffed full of silk and cotton lengths, also offer competitive prices. Usually they're gathered on Thanon Klang Muang around the *Roma Hotel*. On Friday and Saturday evenings from 5–11pm, there's a walking street along Thanon Soon Ratchakan, just north of the non a/c bus terminal, where vendors sell T-shirts, bags and other items, and musicians entertain.

Fairy Plaza Between Nah Muang and Klang Muang. A huge modern mall with all the usual clothes, accessories and mobile phone concessions, plus fast food and a cinema (see opposite). Mon–Fri 10.30am–9.30pm, Sat & Sun 10am–9.30pm.

Prathamakant Local Goods Centre 81 Thanon Ruen Rom. One of the best outlets in Khon Kaen, with a phenomenal selection of gorgeous *mut mee* cotton and silk weaves, as well as clothes, furnishings, triangular axe pillows (B400 for an unstuffed three-seater), *khaen* pipes and silver jewellery. It's much better than the disappointing government-sanctioned OTOP (One Tambon One Product)

shop beside the *Kosa Hotel* on Soi Kosa, and though it feels touristy, locals buy their home furnishings and dress fabrics here too. Mon–Sat 9am–8pm.

Rin Thai Silk 410–412 Thanon Nah Muang. Stocks a smaller range of Isaan silk, but will tailor clothes too. Mon–Sat 8am–6.30pm.

Suebsan Isaan Cooperative 21/2 Thanon Klang Muang. Another fair-trade outlet for local craftspeople, which sells textiles fabricated from bamboo fibre and water hyacinth, as well as more usual *mut mee* silks, cottons, basketware, herbal cosmetics and other traditional products. Mon–Sat 8am–5.30pm.

DIRECTORY

Consulates The Lao consulate (Mon–Fri 8am–noon & 1–4pm; ☎ 043 393 402) is located 8km north of the city centre at 512 Thanon Mittraphap, opposite Raja City. Thirty-day tourist visas for the trip over the border (see p.494) can be processed here on the spot; fees vary according to the applicant's nationality. There's also a Vietnamese consulate (Mon–Fri 8–11.30am & 1.30–4.30pm; ☎ 043 242190, ⓦ vietnamconsulate-khonkaen.org) at 65/6 Thanon Chataphadung, off Thanon Prachasamoson.

Hospitals Khon Kaen Ram Hospital (☎ 043 333800), on the far western end of Thanon Si Chan, is the main private hospital. The government Srinakarin Hospital (☎ 043 244701) is attached to Khon Kaen University, north of town on Highway 2.

Pharmacy Pharmakon, Thanon Nah Muang (Mon–Sat 8am–6.30pm, Sun 8am–1pm).

Tourist police For all emergencies, call the tourist police on ☎ 1155 (free; 24hr).

Around Khon Kaen

The outer reaches of Khon Kaen province hold a couple of places that are worth exploring on **day-trips**. Chonnabot is a good place to see silk weavers at work, while Phuwiang National Park is most famous for Dinosaurland, a paleontological attraction with nine dig sites and its own museum.

Chonnabot

54km southwest of Khon Kaen • Any ordinary Khorat-bound bus to Ban Phae (every 30min), then a songthaew for the final 10km

Khon Kaen makes a reasonable base from which to explore the local silk-weaving centre of **CHONNABOT**. Traditionally a cottage industry, this small town's **silk production** (see box, p.459) has become centralized over the last few years, and weavers now gather in small workshops in town, each specializing in just one aspect of the process. You can walk in and watch the women (it's still exclusively women's work) at their wheels, looms or dye vats, and then buy from the vendors in the street out front.

Dinosaurland at Phuwiang National Park

Nai Muang sub-district, Amphur Phuwiang • ☎ 043 358073, ⓦ dnp.go.Th/parkreserve • **Park** daily 8.30am–6pm • B200 • **Museum** Thurs–Tues 9am–5pm • Free

Khon Kaen hit the international headlines in 1996 when the oldest-ever fossil of a tyrannosaur **dinosaur** was unearthed in Phuwiang, about 90km northwest of Khon Kaen, which has since been made into a national park. Estimated to be 120 million years old, the fossil measures 6m from nose to tail and has been named *Siamotyrannus isanensis* – Siam for Thailand, and Isan after the northeastern region of Thailand. Before this find at Phuwiang, the oldest tyrannosaur fossils were the 65-million- to 80-million-year-old specimens from China, Mongolia and North America. These

5

younger fossils are twice the size of the *Siamotyrannus*; the latter's age and size have therefore established the *Siamotyrannus* as the ancestor of the *Tyrannosaurus rex*, and confirmed Asia as the place of origin of the tyrannosaur genus, which later evolved into various different species.

The fossil of this extraordinary dinosaur – together with eight moderately interesting paleontological finds – is on show to the public at Dinosaurland in **Phuwiang National Park**. The main attractions here, apart from waterfalls and nature trails, are nine dig sites and a **museum**, which is located just before the park entrance.

The *Siamotyrannus isanensis* is displayed at **Site 9**, which is accessible via the 1.5km track that starts across the road from the visitor centre; from the car park at the end of the track, it's a 500m climb to the quarry. The fossil is an impressive sight for paleontologists, with large sections of the rib cage almost completely intact, but many visitors will wonder what all the fuss is about. **Site 1**, 900m south along a track from Site 9, contains the cream of the other finds, including two previously undiscovered species. The theropod *Siamosaurus suteethorni* (named after the paleontologist Warawut Suteethorn) is set apart from the other, carnivorous, theropods by its teeth, which seem as if they are unable to tear flesh; the 15–20m-long *Phuwiangosaurus sirindhornae* (named in honour of Thailand's Princess Royal) is thought to be a new species of sauropod.

ARRIVAL AND DEPARTURE   DINOSAURLAND

By bus Non-a/c buses run from Khon Kaen to Phuwiang town (every 30min; about 1hr) – you then need to hire a motorbike taxi to Dinosaurland and back (about B250 return).

By car It's easier to rent your own wheels in Khon Kaen (see p.474) than to go by bus. To get to the park, head west out of Khon Kaen on Highway 12, following the signs for

Chumpae as far as kilometre-stone 48, marked by a dinosaur statue. Turn right off the main road here, and continue for another 38km along Highway 2038, passing through the small town of Phuwiang, and follow signs for the national park. About halfway between Phuwiang and the national park, there is a park to the left of the road containing life-size statues of many species of dinosaur.

ACCOMMODATION AND EATING

In addition to the options listed below, two-bedroom tents are also available to rent (B225; call ☎02 562 0760 or book online at ⓦdnp.go.th/parkreserve). There's a **food** and drink stall at the car park in front of Quarry #3, about 1km north of the visitor centre.

Bungalows ⓦdnp.go.th/parkreserve. There are two basic bungalows in the park, each sleeping six people

(fan and bedding included). B1200

Udon Thani

The capital of an arid sugar-cane and rice-growing province, 137km north of Khon Kaen, **UDON THANI** was given an economic boost during the Vietnam War with the siting of a huge American military base nearby, and despite the American withdrawal in 1976, the town has maintained its rapid industrial and commercial development. Seen as charmless but economically important for many years, Udon has now started to attract more casual visitors, with the city's entertainment plaza and the relaxing Nong Prajak park providing the main focus for a couple of days in the city. By night, the area known as UD Town springs into life, with tourists and locals thronging the pedestrianized streets to eat, chatter and watch local dance troupes. Apart from these places, and the excavated Bronze Age settlement of **Ban Chiang** (see p.480), 50km to the east, there aren't many tourist attractions in the area, though **Phu Phra Bat Historical Park** (see p.497) is as easy to get to from here as from Nong Khai.

Nong Prajak Park

Just west of the TAT office • Bike rental B30/hr

Away from the racket of Udon's busier streets is **Nong Prajak Park**, a surprisingly quiet space set around a tranquil, fish-filled lake. Approaching from Thanon Thesa, on the eastern shore of the lake, it's possible to walk across a bridge to the central island. An alternative to feeding the fish (local women sell bags of food) is cycling around the lake's perimeter; bikes can be rented from its northeastern edge.

ARRIVAL AND DEPARTURE

UDON THANI

By plane The airport is located 3km southwest of the centre; a/c minibuses meet incoming flights. Thai Airways, Thai Lion Air, Bangkok Airways and Air Asia operate several flights a day from Bangkok to Udon Thani, while Nok Air currently runs a daily service from Chiang Mai and Air Asia flies daily from Phuket. There are also direct a/c minibuses (B150–200) from the airport that head north to the Friendship Bridge and downtown Nong Khai.

Destinations Bangkok (26 daily; 1hr); Chiang Mai (daily; 1hr); Phuket (daily; 1hr 50min).

By train Udon's train station is on the east side of the centre, close to the night market.

Destinations Ayutthaya (4 daily; 7hr 30min–9hr 30min); Bangkok (4 daily; 10–12hr); Khon Kaen (6 daily; 1hr 35min–2hr 15min); Khorat (3 daily; 4hr 30min–5hr 30min); Nong Khai (4 daily; 40min–1hr).

By bus Buses pull in at a variety of locations, depending on where they've come from: Loei, Phitsanulok and Chiang

Mai services use the terminal on the town's western bypass; Nong Khai buses are stationed at Talat Rangsina (Rangsina market, also used by Ban Phu buses) on the north side of town; and Bangkok, Khorat, Khon Kaen, Nakhon Phanom and Ubon Ratchathani services use the other main terminal on Thanon Sai Uthit, which also has a service direct to Vientiane, across the border in Laos, for those who have arranged their visa in advance.

Destinations Bangkok (every 30min; 9hr); Chiang Mai (10 daily; 11–13hr); Chiang Rai (10 daily; 12–14hr); Khon Kaen (every 30min; 1hr 30min–2hr); Khorat (hourly; 3hr 30min–5hr); Loei (every 30min; 3–4hr); Mukdahan (7 daily; 4hr–4hr 30min); Nakhon Phanom (14 daily; 5hr); Nong Khai (every 30min; 1–2hr); Phitsanulok (4 daily; 7hr); Rayong (7 daily; 12hr); Sakon Nakhon (every 20min; 3hr); That Phanom (7 daily; 4–5hr); Ubon Ratchathani (9 daily; 6hr); Vientiane (Laos; 8 daily; 1hr 30min).

GETTING AROUND AND INFORMATION

By songthaew Numbered songthaews ply set routes around town for B10/person (a map is available from TAT); among the more useful routes, #7 connects the central bus

terminal with the western bus terminal on the western bypass, while #6 runs the length of Thanon Udon-Dussadi to Talat Rangsina (for buses to Nong Khai).

5

By tuk-tuk and samlor There are plenty of skylabs, Udon's version of tuk-tuks, for hire (about B70–100 for a medium-length journey). Samlors are cheaper still.

Car rental Avis (☎042 244770, ⓦavisthailand.com) has a desk at the airport.

Tourist information Udon's TAT office (daily 8.30am–4.30pm; ☎042 325406–7, ⓔtatudon@tat.or.th) is at 16/5 Thanon Mukmontri on the southeast side of Nong Prajak, to the northwest of the centre.

Services Wattana Hospital, 70/7–8 Thanon Supakitjunya (☎042 325999, ⓦwattanahospital.net), on the north shore of Nong Prajak towards the north of town, has international-standard facilities.

Shopping There's a walking street on Thanon Athibodi, just north of the TAT office, on Fridays and Saturday evenings from 5–11pm, but it's not as lively as similar markets in other towns.

ACCOMMODATION

Most budget travellers skip Udon Thani's **hotels** in favour of the guesthouse at Ban Chiang (see opposite), but for those with a little extra cash, there are some great mid-range choices in the city.

Much-che Manta 209-211 Thanon Makkeng ☎042 245222, ⓦmuch-chemanta.com. This slick, modern hotel features well-equipped rooms (rain showers, cable TV and minibar) with a range of prices. The cheapest ("Cozy") are a bit cramped, though the biggest ("Fabulous"; B1600) are a good size, with king-size beds and microwaves as well. **B900**

Pannarai 19/8 Thanon Sampantamit ☎042 344999, ⓦthepannaraihotel.com. Reliable, central hotel with helpful staff and a swimming pool. Rooms are big and well lit, with ceiling-to-floor windows. **B1480**

The One Residence 251/5 Thanon Prajak ☎042 244330, ⓦtheoneud.com. With bright, clean rooms in a central location, this newish place is very popular and often full. Go for a room out back to avoid street noise. **B600**

EATING, DRINKING AND ENTERTAINMENT

In Udon the main **night market**, on the west side of the train station, is the place to come for food and cut-price clothing. Just south of here is **UD Town**, a massive entertainment complex that is *the* commercial face of modern Udon Thani. After dark you'll find street entertainers, dance shows and stalls selling everything from indulgent perfumes to fruit shakes and spicy sausages. Thais and tourists pour into the restaurants, which range from Western fast-food joints to high-end noodle bars, giving the place a real buzz in the evenings. For cheaper eats, head to Thanon Thesa, where several simple bar-restaurants set out low-slung tables in the evening, alongside paint-your-own-pottery and massage stalls.

★**Good Everything** 254/24 Thanon Prajak ☎042 245544, ⓦgoodeverything.com. This place opposite one of the entrances to Nong Prajak Park is a great find, and is well named. The ambience is very agreeable, with a choice of seating in a flower-filled garden or in the sparkling white interior. A range of Thai and Western dishes such as spicy salads and pasta is on offer, and both preparation and presentation are very impressive. Prices seem a bit steep (B150–600) but the quality warrants it. Daily 8am–10pm.

Irish Clock 19/5–6 Thanon Sampantamit ☎042 247450. Located on the street known as "Farang Street" for its Western-oriented bars, the *Irish Clock* is the place to go for big Western breakfasts, imported beers and sports on TV. They also have some rooms to rent (B882 per night). Daily 8am–midnight.

Maeya 79-81 Thanon Rachapatsadu ☎042 223 889. On a quiet side street, covering three floors and frequented by a loyal clientele, *Maeya* is well worth tracking down. Its waiters are the best-dressed in town (starched shirts and bow ties), the menu covers a broad range of Thai and Western dishes, some with amusing names, such as pork babygue (read BBQ), and prices are very reasonable. Basic rice dishes from B60 and most main dishes around B120. Ice creams too. Daily 10am–10pm.

Ban Chiang

The excavated Bronze Age settlement of **BAN CHIANG**, 50km east of Udon Thani in sleepy farming country, was listed as a UNESCO World Heritage Site in 1992. It achieved worldwide fame in 1966, when a rich seam of archeological remains was accidentally discovered: clay pots, uncovered in human graves alongside sophisticated **bronze** objects, were eventually dated to around 2000 BC, implying the same date for the bronze pieces. Ban Chiang has been hailed as the Southeast Asian vanguard of the Bronze Age, about three hundred years after Mesopotamia's discovery of the metal.

The village of Ban Chiang is unremarkable nowadays, although its fertile setting is attractive and the villagers, who still weave (and sell) especially rich and intricate lengths of silk and cotton *mut mee*, are noticeably friendly to visitors. The museum here, which focuses on the Bronze Age finds, is one of the region's most interesting.

National Museum

Towards the north of the village • Tues–Sun 8.30am–4pm • B150

The village's fine **National Museum** has managed to retain some of the choicest Bronze Age finds, which it fleshes out with a fascinating and thoughtful rundown of Ban Chiang culture, including its agriculture, pathology and burial rites. It also houses the country's best collection of characteristic late-period Ban Chiang clay pots, with their red whorled patterns on a buff background, which were used as funeral offerings – although not of prime historical significance, these pots have become an attractive emblem of Ban Chiang, and are freely adapted by local souvenir producers.

Excavation Site

In the grounds of Wat Pho Si Nai, on the east side of the village • Daily 8.30am–6pm • Same ticket as the museum

In the grounds of Wat Pho Si Nai, on the east side of the village, part of an early dig has been covered over and opened to the public. A **large burial pit** has been left exposed to show how and where artefacts were found, providing an interesting insight into the work of archeologists here.

ARRIVAL AND GETTING AROUND
BAN CHIANG

By bus and samlor Catch a Sakon Nakhon-bound bus from the Thanon Sai Uthit terminal in Udon (1hr) to Ban Palu and then a motorized samlor (about B60) for the last 5km or so from the main road to the village.

Getting around Bicycles are available from shops near the museum (around B50/day) for exploring the surrounding countryside – there's a bird and animal sanctuary 6km away, and a couple of interesting forest wats closer to the village, all marked on a useful hand-drawn map of the area produced by *Lakeside Sunrise* guesthouse.

ACCOMMODATION

Lakeside Sunrise A few mins' walk from the museum ☎ 080 193 4300 or ☎ 042 208167. Guests at this excellent guesthouse sleep in clean first-floor rooms with fans and mosquito screens, some sharing hot showers (en-suite rooms are B500), and can relax on a huge balcony, equipped with a small library, and access the internet; the friendly owner, Tong, can help out with travel queries. Facing the museum, head left then turn right at the first intersection and look for a large Western-style wooden two-storey house overlooking an artificial lake. B400

Loei

Most visitors carry on from Udon Thani due north to Nong Khai, but making a detour via **LOEI**, 147km to the west, takes you within range of several towering national parks and sets you up for a lazy tour along the Mekong River. The capital of a province renowned for the unusual shapes of its stark, craggy mountains, Loei is also the crossroads of one of Thailand's least-tamed border regions, with all manner of illegal goods coming across from Laos. This trade may have been reined in – or perhaps

---

CROSSING THE LAO BORDER VIA THA LI

Now that improvements have been made to roads in Laos, it's possible to hop on a bus in Loei in the morning, exit the country at **Tha Li** by the Mekong River and hop off in **Luang Prabang** in the afternoon. Visa on arrival is available at the Thai–Lao Nam Heuang Friendship Bridge, and the immigration office is open from 8am to 6pm.

5

spurred on – by the opening in 2008 of a 3km-long bridge across the Heuang River at Ban Nakaseng in Tha Li district, 80km northwest of Loei, to Sainyabuli province in Laos. With improved roads in Laos, there's now a daily bus from Loei to Luang Prabang. Despite its frontier feel, the town, lying along the west bank of the small Loei River, is friendly and offers legitimate products of its own, such as sweet tamarind paste and pork sausages, which are for sale along Thanon Charoenrat, Loei's main street, and the adjacent Thanon Oua Aree. But Loei is really only useful as a transport hub and a base for the nearby national parks. The most popular are Phu Kradung National Park, which has some excellent walking trails, Nam Nao National Park, home to around a hundred different species of mammals, and Phu Reua National Park, which affords magnificent views over Laos.

ARRIVAL AND INFORMATION

By air Nok Air currently operates two flights a day to and from Don Muang airport, Bangkok. Loei's airport is about 5km south of town on H201; a tuk-tuk into town should cost around B120.

By bus The bus terminal (☎ 042 833586) is on Thanon Maliwan, the main through north–south road (Highway 201), about 2.5km south of the centre. The daily bus to Luang Prabang (☎ 042 811706) leaves at 8am every day, arrives at 5pm and costs B700. A tuk-tuk to the bus terminal costs around B60.

Destinations Bangkok (hourly; 10hr); Chiang Khan (every 20min; 1hr); Chiang Mai (3 daily; 9–11hr); Chiang Rai (3 daily; 9–12hr); Khon Kaen (every 30min; 4hr); Lom Sak (3 daily; 3hr); Luang Prabang (Laos; daily; 9hr); Nong Khai (daily via Pak Chom; 6–7hr); Phitsanulok (8 daily; 4hr); Sang Khom (daily; 3hr); Udon Thani (every 30min; 3–4hr).

Tourist information The TAT office (daily 8.30am–4.30pm; ☎ 042 812812, ✉ tatloei@tat.or.th), on Thanon Charoenrat, has information about the region's many national parks, including Phu Kradung and Phu Reua to the west.

Services The tourist police have an office on Thanon Maliwan (☎ 042 861164 or ☎ 1155).

Shopping On Friday and Saturday evenings from 5–11pm, Thanon Ruamjit is closed to traffic while the weekly walking street takes over.

PHI TA KON

One reason to make a special trip to Loei province is to attend the unique rainmaking **festival of Phi Ta Kon**, or Bun Phra Wet, held over three days either at the end of June or the beginning of July (check ⓦtourismthailand.org near the time for exact dates) in the small town of **Dan Sai**, 80km to the southwest of the provincial capital. In order to encourage the heavens to open, townsfolk dress up as spirits in colourful patchwork rags and fierce, brightly painted masks (made from coconut palm fronds and the baskets used for steaming sticky rice), then rowdily parade the town's most sacred Buddha image round the streets while making fun of as many onlookers as they can, waving wooden phalluses about and generally having themselves a whale of a time. Top folk and country musicians from around Isaan perform in the evenings during Phi Ta Kon; the afternoon of the second day of the festival sees the firing off of dozens of bamboo rockets, while the third day is a much more solemn affair, with Buddhist sermons and a purification ceremony at Wat Phon Chai. The carnival can be visited in a day from Loei (ask at Loei's TAT office for transport details), though rooms are hard to come by at this time. The town's main permanent attraction is the **Dan Sai Folk Museum** at Wat Phon Chai on Thanon Kaew Asa, the town's high street (daily 8am–5pm; free), which explains some of the traditions surrounding Phi Ta Kon, shows the steps in building the masks, and has an impressive collection of vivid costumes and masks.

ACCOMMODATION   DAN SAI

Phunacome Resort 461 Moo 3, Ban Doen, 2km east of Dan Sai ☎042 892005–6, ⓦphunacomeresort .com. This laidback resort has a water buffalo theme, with many statues and a few real ones on the grounds. Choose between bungalows on stilts and rooms in a two-storey block; all are sumptuously furnished and enjoy great views. It's also a "green" resort, so it's smoke-free and the restaurant uses organic ingredients. If you're looking for luxury accommodation as a base for visiting Loei's national parks, this is your spot. B4200

ACCOMMODATION AND EATING

Unless it's festival time, finding a decent place to stay in Loei shouldn't be a problem. During the evening your best bet for Isaan and Thai food is the pleasant **night market** on a broad, pedestrianized street off Thanon Chumsai, which wears its "Clean Food, Good Taste" signs with pride.

Loei Palace Hotel 167/4 Thanon Charoenrat ☎042 815668–73, ⓦmosaic-collection.com/loeipalace. A shining landmark in the landscaped city park on the southeast side of the centre, and the best hotel in Loei. The attractive, international-standard rooms are ranged around an echoing, full-height atrium. They all enjoy fine views, and there's a large swimming pool, a hot tub and a fitness centre. B1250

Sariya 1/41 Thanon Sathon Chiang Khan ☎042 861888. A smart little place at the front of the *Loei Orchid Hotel* serving Thai dishes (including the house speciality – Thai-style steak). There are tables inside and out. Most dishes B60–90. Daily 6–11pm.

★**Sugar Guest House** 4/1 Soi 2, Thanon Wisuttitep ☎042 812982. Set in a quiet residential area a 5min walk from the top of Thanon Charoenrat on the north side of the centre. The bright, colourful rooms with gleaming wood floors are either fan-cooled with shared hot-water bathrooms, or a/c with cable TV and en-suite hot-water bathrooms. Bicycles (B50) and motorbikes (B250) can be rented, and the owners can arrange day-trips in a car with driver to, for example, Phu Reua (B1600) or the relaxing Huay Krating (B600), where bamboo rafts are towed out onto the reservoir and you can eat lunch delivered to you by longtail boat. Good rates (B200) for singles. Fan B250, a/c B380

Sun Palace Hotel 191/5 Thanon Charoenrat ☎042 815714. This hotel south of the centre offers a/c, hot water, TVs and fridges throughout, and some of the rooms on the higher floors offer good mountain views. B350

Phu Kradung National Park

80km south of Loei · Oct–May dawn–dusk · B400 · ☎042 810833–4, ⓦdnp.go.th

The most accessible and popular of the parks in Loei province, **PHU KRADUNG NATIONAL PARK** protects a grassy 1300m plateau whose temperate climate supports a number of tree, flower and bird species not normally found in Thailand. Walking trails crisscross much of sixty-square-kilometre Phu Kradung (Bell Mountain), and you could spend three days here exploring them fully – you'll need one night as a minimum, as the

5

trip from Loei to the top of the plateau and back can't be done comfortably in a day. The park is at its busiest during weekends in December and January, when the main headquarters up on the plateau is surrounded by a sea of tents.

The attractions of the mountain come and go with the seasons. October is muddy after the rains, but the waterfalls that tumble off the northwestern edge of the plateau are in full cascade and the main trail is green and shady. December brings out the maple leaves; by February the waterfalls have disappeared and the vegetation on the lower slopes has been burnt away. April is good for rhododendrons and wild roses, which in Thailand are only found at such high altitudes as this.

Among the park's **wildlife**, mammals such as elephants, sambar deer and gibbons can be seen very occasionally, but they generally confine themselves to the evergreen forest on the northern part of the plateau, which is out of bounds to visitors. In the temperate pines, oaks and beeches that dot the rest of the plateau you're more likely to spot resident **birds** such as jays, sultan tits and snowy-browed flycatchers if you're out walking in the early morning and evening.

The trails

The challenging main **trail** leads from the Sri Taan visitor centre, at the base of the mountain, 5.5km up the eastern side of Phu Kradung, passing occasional refreshment stalls, and becoming steeper and rockier on the last 1km, with wooden steps over the most difficult parts; most people take at least three hours, including rest stops. It's a good idea to hire a porter (around B30/kg) to carry your gear so that you can enjoy the surroundings on the walk. The main trail is occasionally closed for maintenance, when a parallel 4.5km trail is opened up in its place. At the end of the actual climb, the unbelievable view as your head peeps over the rim more than rewards the effort: flat as a playing field, the broad plateau is dotted with odd clumps of pine trees thinned by periodic lightning fires, which give it the appearance of a country park.

Several feeder trails fan out from here, including a 9.5km path along the precipitous southern edge that offers sweeping views of Dong Phaya Yen, the untidy range of mountains to the southwest that forms the unofficial border between the northeast and the central plains. Another trailheads along the eastern rim for 2.5km to Pha Nok An – also reached by a 2km path east from the main visitor centre – which looks down on neat rice fields and matchbox-like houses in the valley below, an outlook that's especially breathtaking at sunrise.

ARRIVAL AND INFORMATION
PHU KRADUNG NATIONAL PARK

By public transport To get to the park, take any bus from Loei to Khon Kaen (every 30min; 1hr 30min) or Khon Kaen to Loei (every 30min; 2hr 30min) and get off at the village of Phu Kradung, then hop on a songthaew for the remaining 5km to the Sri Taan visitor centre.

Tourist information The well-organized Sri Taan visitor

centre (daily Oct–May 8.30am–4.30pm) at the base of the plateau has a trail map. You can leave your gear at the visitor centre, or hire a porter to carry it to the top for you. The main visitor centre, which also gives out maps, is up on the plateau at Wang Kwang, 8km from the Sri Taan visitor centre.

ACCOMMODATION AND EATING

It's best to avoid going up and back down the mountain in one day, so try to stay here if you can. Simple restaurants at Wang Kwang rustle up inexpensive, tasty food from limited ingredients, so there's no need to bring your own provisions.

Sri Taan There are four national park bungalows at Sri Taan, with the added bonus of hot water. Each sleeps four people. These tend to take the overflow when accommodation on the mountain itself is full. B1200

Wang Kwang Up on the plateau at the main visitor centre, 8km from the Sri Taan visitor centre ⓦ dnp

.go.th/parkreserve. There are over twenty bungalows and rooms (mattresses only, no beds) sleeping four to twelve people here, most with hot-water bathrooms; at busy times it's best to reserve in advance. There are also fully equipped tents for rent, sleeping two people. Tents B270, rooms B900, bungalows B2400

Nam Nao National Park

5

160km south of Loei by road · B200 · ☎ 056 810724 or ☎ 081 9626236, ⓦ dnp.go.th/parkreserve

With its tallest peak reaching 1271m, **Nam Nao National Park** is easily visible among the undulating sandstone hills of the Phetchabun range. However, it remains a seldom-visited place, at least as far as tourists go, with plenty of wildlife and some good, challenging hikes.

At just under a thousand square kilometres, Nam Nao is home to a healthy wildlife population: around a hundred mammal species, including large animals such as forest elephant and banteng and a handful of tigers, and more-often-seen barking deer, gibbons and leaf monkeys, as well as over two hundred bird species. These creatures thrive in habitats ranging from tropical bamboo and banana stands to the dominant features of dry evergreen forest, grasslands, open forest and pine stands that look almost European.

Though the park was established in 1972, it remained a stronghold for guerrillas of the Communist Party of Thailand until the early 1980s and was long regarded as unsafe for visitors. Still much less visited than Phu Kradung (see p.483), it can provide a sense of real solitude. The range of wildlife here also benefited from a physical isolation that stopped abruptly in 1975, when Highway 12 was cut through the park and poachers could gain access more easily. However, as the park adjoins the Phu Khieo Wildlife Sanctuary, there is beneficial movement by some species between the two areas.

The trails

A good network of clearly marked circular forest **trails** begins near the **park headquarters**, ranging from a 1km nature trail teeming with butterflies to a 6km track known for occasional elephant sightings; another 3.5km trail climbs through mixed deciduous forest to the Phu Kor outlook, with its sweeping views across to Phu Phajit.

Other trails can be accessed directly from **Highway 12**, most of them clearly signposted from the road: at kilometre-stone 39, a steep climb up 260 roughly hewn steps leads to the Tham Pha Hong viewpoint, a rocky outcrop offering stunning panoramas of the park; at kilometre-stone 49, there's a 4km nature trail taking in Suan Son Dang Bak viewpoint; and at kilometre-stone 67, a 700m trail leads to the beautiful Haew Sai waterfall, best seen during or immediately after the rainy season. Experienced hikers can reach the top of Phu Phajit along a rugged trail which begins from kilometre-stone 69; you need to hire a guide from the visitor centre (best booked in advance) for the steep six-hour climb.

ARRIVAL AND DEPARTURE

NAM NAO NATIONAL PARK

By bus Several buses a day run through the park at irregular times from the bus stations in Khon Kaen, Phitsanulok and Loei – all about 2–3hr journeys. The driver drops passengers off at the access road to the park headquarters.

By car The turn-off to the park headquarters is on Highway 12; look out for the sign at kilometre-stone 50, 147km west of Khon Kaen and 160km by road from Loei. The park entrance, where you'll be asked to pay, is 2km from the main road.

INFORMATION AND ACCOMMODATION

Tourist information Once you've paid the admission fee, walk or hitch the 2km down the potholed road past the park HQ to the visitor centre, where you can pick up an English-language brochure that contains a rough sketch map of the park.

Accommodation There are a dozen or so bungalows and a campsite near the visitor centre. Stalls near the headquarters sell simple meals. Camping per person B30, four-person unit B1000

5

Phu Reua National Park

50km west of Loei · B200 · ☎ 088 509 5299, ⓦ dnp.go.th

The 120-square-kilometre **PHU REUA NATIONAL PARK** gets the name "Boat Mountain" from its resemblance to an upturned sampan, with the sharp ridge of its hull running southeast to northwest. The highest point of the ridge, Yod Phu Reua (1365m), offers one of the most spectacular panoramas in Thailand: the land drops away sharply on the Laos side, allowing views over toy-town villages and the Heuang and Mekong rivers to countless green-ridged mountains spreading towards Luang Prabang. To the northwest rises Phu Soai Dao (2120m) on the Laos border; to the south are the Phetchabun mountains.

In the park itself, a day's worth of well-marked trails fans out over the mountain's meadows and pine and broad-leaved evergreen forests, taking in gardens of strange rock formations, orchids that flower year-round, the best sunrise viewpoint, Loan Noi, and, during and just after the rainy season, several waterfalls. The most spectacular **viewpoint**, Yod Phu Reua (Phu Reua Peak), is an easy 1km stroll or songthaew ride (B10) from the top of the summit road. The park's population of barking deer, wild pigs and pheasants has declined over recent years, but you may be lucky enough to spot one of 26 bird species, which include the crested serpent-eagle, green-billed malkoha, greater coucal, Asian fairy-bluebird, rufescent prinia and white-rumped munia, as well as several species of babbler, barbet, bulbul and drongo.

Warm clothes are essential on cool-season nights – the lowest temperature in Thailand (-4°C) was recorded here in 1981 – and even by day the mountain is usually cool and breezy.

ARRIVAL AND INFORMATION   PHU REUA NATIONAL PARK

The 9km paved road north from the village of Ban Phu Reua on Highway 203 to the summit means the park can get crowded at weekends, though during the week you'll probably have the place to yourself. The headquarters and Visitor Centre One are located 4km after the checkpoint on the summit road (where you'll pay the admission charge).

By bus and songthaew There's no organized public transport up the steep summit road – regular Lom Sak and Phitsanulok buses (3 daily; 1hr 30min) from Loei can drop you at the turn-off to the park on Highway 203, but then you'll have to walk/hitch or charter a songthaew (around B800, including waiting time).

By bike The easiest way of accessing Phu Reua is probably to rent a motorbike at the *Sugar Guest House* in Loei (see p.483).

Tourist information Visitor Centre One is 4km after the entrance checkpoint, and has a trail map and a simple restaurant. Visitor Centre Two (Phuson), a 3km walk or 5.5km drive further up the mountain near Hin Sam Chan waterfall, boasts several restaurants and is at the heart of the mountain's network of paths.

ACCOMMODATION AND EATING

You can sleep in government-owned **bungalows** inside the park, which offer easy access to the trails. There are also plenty of private accommodation options, both on Highway 203 around Ban Phu Reua and on the summit road itself. *Phunacome Resort* in Dan Sai (see p.483) is about 40km southwest of the park. There are several **restaurants** and coffee shops along the main road in town.

CHÂTEAU DE LOEI VINEYARD

If you happen to be driving yourself here from the west along Highway 203, it might be worth breaking your journey 10km from the Phu Reua turn-off at the **Château de Loei vineyard** (161 Moo 6, Highway 203, Rong Chik, Phu Reua; daily 8am–7pm; ☎ 042 809521, ⓦ chateaude loei.com), for the novelty value if nothing else: you can drive for 6km around the vast, incongruous fields of vines and taste a variety of wines and brandy, as well as getting something to eat at the simple restaurant and perusing a dizzying array of local foodstuffs in the attached shop. Bottles of wine cost around B600.

Chatchada Grand Resort At the eastern end of Ban Phu Reua, 1km towards Loei from the turn-off to the national park ☎ 042 899399 or ☎ 086 392 7601. Decent, spacious chalets that are set around a lawn, all with hot water; there's also a decent restaurant. Fan B900, a/c B1500

Phupet Hill Resort 369 Moo 7, 800m up the summit road ☎ 042 039853 or ☎ 081 320 2874. A small and friendly place with large, attractive rooms and chalets with hot water, a/c and TV. Fan B500, a/c B800

Visitor Centre One There are six four- to six-berth national park bungalows with hot showers at Visitor Centre One. B2000–3000

Chiang Khan

A road runs parallel to the Mekong for 630km, linking the fast-growing border town of Mukdahan with **CHIANG KHAN**, a friendly town 55km north of Loei, which happily hasn't been entirely converted to concrete yet. Rows of shuttered wooden shophouses stretch out in a 2km ribbon parallel to the river, which for much of the year runs red with what locals call "the blood of the trees": rampant deforestation on the Lao side causes the rust-coloured topsoil to erode into the river. The town has only two streets – the main through-route (Highway 211), also known as **Thanon Sri Chiang Khan**, and the quieter **Thanon Chai Khong** on the waterfront – with a line of sois connecting them, numbered from west to east. Both streets are bordered by wooden shophouses, giving the town an air of Old Siam. There's a cool vibe to the place, with entrepreneurial young Thais setting up quirky new gift shops and guesthouses all the time and there are a few interesting sights to see out of town. Arguably the most enjoyable thing you can do here is to join up with other travellers for a **boat trip** on the river.

Wat Tha Khaek

To get here, travel about 3km east of town along the main highway, then turn north towards the river

Wat Tha Khaek, a formerly ramshackle forest temple, has, on the back of millions of bahts' worth of donations from Thai tourists, embarked on an ambitious but slow-moving building programme in a bizarre mix of traditional and modern styles. The result is a temple that looks half finished, but if you grow weary of looking at the retro memorabilia that seems to clutter the main hotel street, it makes for a refreshing change.

5

Kaeng Kut Khu

East of town, about 2km along a side road from Wat Tha Khaek • Boats B400/30min

A couple of kilometres east of Wat Tha Khaek, the river runs over rocks at a wide bend to form the modest rapids of **Kaeng Kut Khu**. Set against the forested hillside of imaginatively named Phu Yai (Big Mountain), it's a pretty enough spot, with small restaurants and souvenir shops shaded by trees on the river bank. If you're feeling brave, try the local speciality *kung ten*, or "dancing shrimp" – fresh shrimp served live with a lime juice and chilli sauce. Boats can be rented here for a pootle around the rapids – you can also get a boat here from Chiang Khan (see box opposite).

Phu Thok

Daily 5am–6pm • Head east from Chiang Khan on Highway 211, then just beyond the turn-off to Wat Tha Khaek and Kaeng Kut Khu to the north, turn south along 3km of rough paved road, before parking up (B20) and hopping on a songthaew (B25) for the last 2km to the summit

With your own transport you could continue your explorations to **Phu Thok**, an isolated hill topped by a communications mast to the south of town. From there, you'll be rewarded with splendid views of Chiang Khan, the Mekong and the striking patchwork of fields in the broad valley to the south. It's especially popular at sunrise in the cool season, when crowds of Thais come to look out over a sea of mist.

ARRIVAL AND GETTING AROUND   CHIANG KHAN

By bus and songthaew Big, slow songthaews (roughly every 30min) and buses from Loei (roughly hourly) stop at the west end of town near the main junction of Highway 201 (the road from Loei) and Highway 211.
Destinations Bangkok (4 daily; 9–11hr); Khorat (hourly;

7hr); Loei (hourly, plus frequent songthaews; 45min–1hr).
By bicycle and motorbike Most of Chiang Khan's guesthouses rent out bicycles (B50–100/day) and motorbikes (B200–250/day).

ACCOMMODATION

Truly budget accommodation is not easy to find in Chiang Khan as wealthy Thais tend to holiday here, which pushes prices up. Most guesthouses and hotels and can arrange herbal steam baths and traditional massages, as well as boat trips and bus tickets.

Chiang Khan Guesthouse 282 Thanon Chai Khong, near Soi 19 ☎042 821691. Chiang Khan's best budget option, offering fan and a/c rooms, plus a dorm in a friendly, well-kept old wooden house with a riverside balcony upstairs. There are mosquito nets and some rooms share hot-water bathrooms. The owner, Mr Ong, knows a lot about the area. Dorm B150, fan B300, a/c B600
★**Mekong Villas** 96 Moo 6, Thanon Leab Mekong River, km 53, Ban Kok Pai, Pak Chom district (about 30km northeast of Chiang Khan and 15km west of Pak Chom) ☎089 810 0498, ⓦmekongvillas.com. This dreamlike

location with just three traditional Thai villas is part of the aptly named "Secret Retreats" group. Occupying a promontory with fabulous views of the Mekong, the villas are furnished with every luxury, including an infinity pool. The River House (B11,235) is the best of the three, with glorious views from its balcony. Ideal for a splurge such as a honeymoon. B3370
The Royal Chiang Khan 195 Thanon Chai Khong, between Soi 15 and 16 ☎089 900 9788, ⓦtheroyal chiangkhan.com. *The Royal* has to be given credit for its lavish styling, with exposed bricks and gleaming plastic panels all over the place. The a/c rooms here are individually

---

THE MAGNIFICENT MEKONG

The **Mekong** is one of the great rivers of the world and the third longest in Asia, after the Yangtse and the Yellow rivers. From its source 4920m up on the east Tibetan plateau it roars down through China's Yunnan province – where it's known as Lancang Jiang, the "Turbulent River" – before snaking its way a little more peaceably between Myanmar and Laos, and then, by way of the so-called "Golden Triangle", as the border between Thailand and Laos. After a brief shimmy into rural Laos via Luang Prabang, the river reappears in Isaan to form 750km of the border between Thailand and Laos. From Laos it crosses Cambodia and continues south to Vietnam, where it splinters into the many arms of the Mekong Delta before flowing into the South China Sea, 4350km from where its journey began.

BOAT TRIPS FROM CHIANG KHAN

Most guesthouses can arrange these tours, or variations of them, charging per boat.

Downstream The journey to Pak Chom and back takes you through some of the most beautiful scenery on the Thai Mekong: hills and cliffs of all shapes and sizes advance and recede around the winding flow, and outside the rainy season, the rapids are dramatic without being dangerous (best Dec–April), and the shores and islands are enlivened by neat grids of market gardens. B4000/boat, around 6hr.
Kaeng Kut Khu (See opposite). B1000/boat.
Sunset on the Mekong The most basic of the boat trips, giving you the chance to see Chiang Khan from the water when the sunlight is at its best. B800/boat,

lasts around 1hr.
Upstream Upstream trips head west towards the lofty mountains of Khao Laem and Khao Ngu on the Thai side and Phu Lane and Phu Hat Song in Laos, gliding round a long, slow bend in the Mekong to the mouth of the Heuang River tributary, 20km from Chiang Khan. Stops can be arranged to share the fine views with Phra Yai, a 20m-tall golden Buddha standing on a hilltop at the confluence, and at Hat Sai Kaew, a sandy beach for swimming, fishing and picnicking. Best undertaken in the afternoon, returning at sunset. B2000/boat, around 3hr.

themed and, as a general rule, the most expensive ones (B2500) are on the top floors, while the cheaper rooms share bathrooms; our pick are the en-suite rooms "Sunshine 2" and "Sunshine 4" (B2500). The roof terrace has magnificent views, though it's not on the riverfront. B1500
Tonkong Guesthouse 62/1 Thanon Chai Khong, between sois 3 & 4 ☏042 821879, ✉ben_jama @hotmail.com. A good variety of bright, clean and airy rooms (though mattresses are rather thin), including an en-suite family room that sleeps six (B2000) and three

simple rooms with fan and a shared bathroom. Owner Ben (female) runs a cooking course (B500) which includes a trip to the local market. Fan B400, a/c B500
The White House 112 Thanon Chai Khong, near Soi 5 ☏042 821269 or ☏086 221 8140. This spacious, colonial-style white mansion adorned with green shutters and hung with modern art has loads of character. Most of the lovely, airy, fan rooms share hot showers, though a few rooms are en-suite, and there's a large dorm for seven people, plus a pretty garden terrace overlooking the river. Dorm B200, doubles B800

EATING

Most visitors eat at their guesthouses or at the **night market**, which sets up along Thanon Chai Khong, between sois 17 and 18, every night, serving up everything from chicken on a stick to sweet, freshly made pancakes.

Rabiang Khong 299/4 Thanon Chai Khong, between sois 9 and 10, on the river side of Thanon Chai Khong (no English sign). Set in a large wooden building with an attractive riverside terrace, this place serves a wide range

of Thai dishes such as *tom yam koong* (spicy sour soup with shrimp, B150) and *kai phat met mamuang* (chicken with cashew nuts, B120). Daily 10.30am–10pm.

Sang Khom and around

The scenery downstream from Chiang Khan is still relatively wild, with just a couple of small towns dotted between the stretches of lush vegetation. Unfortunately there's no public transport along the river road between Chiang Khan and the otherwise forgettable town of Pak Chom, 41km downriver, so having your own wheels in this area is handy, if not vital. With the flexibility of a car or bike, a pleasant stopover on the much longer journey to Nong Khai is the peaceful town of **SANG KHOM**, about 60km east of Pak Chom, which has some basic amenities and a smile-inducing location by the water.

Than Tip Falls

3km south off Highway 211, just 14km west of Sang Khom

Than Tip Falls is well worth seeking out from May to November, though there's little water from December to April. The 10m-high waterfall splashes down into a rock pool overhung by jungle on three sides; from here, a steep stairway leads to a bigger waterfall that has a good pool for swimming, and if you can face the climb you can explore still higher levels.

5

Sang Khom

Staying in **SANG KHOM**, which straggles along the tree-shaded south bank of the Mekong about 60km east of Pak Chom, puts you in the heart of an especially lush stretch of the river within easy striking distance of several backroad villages and temples – a lovely guesthouse here offers bike rental and boat trips.

Wat Hin Maak Peng

19km east of Sang Khom on Route 211

Overlooking a narrow section of the Mekong, **Wat Hin Maak Peng** is a famous meditation temple, popular with Thai pilgrims and rich donors. The long white boundary wall, huge modern buildings and extensive riverside gardens are evidence of the temple's prosperity, but its reputation is in fact based on the asceticism of the monks of the Thammayut sect, who keep themselves in strict poverty and allow only one meal a day to interrupt their meditation. The flood of merit-makers, however, proved too distracting for the founder of the wat, Luang Phu Thet, who before his death in 1994 decamped to the peace and quiet of Wat Tham Kham near Sakon Nakhon. Further east, between Tha Bo and Ban Nong Song Hong, the main route to Nong Khai passes Wat Phra That Bang Phuan (see p.497).

ARRIVAL AND INFORMATION   **SANG KHOM AND AROUND**

By bus Buses run between Sang Khom and Bangkok (3 daily; 10hr), Loei (1 daily via Pak Chom; 3hr) and Nong Khai (daily; 3–4hr). There's no bus station in Sang Khom; buses pull up in the middle of town a short walk from the guesthouse listed below. Than Tip Falls are best visited by rented motorbike, and for Wat Hin Maak Peng, take a bus bound for Nong Khai and ask to be dropped at the temple.

By boat Trips up the Mekong (B250/person for groups of 2–4) can be booked with *Bouy Guest House* in Sang Khom.

By motorbike You can rent motorbikes (B200/day) at *Bouy Guest House* in Sang Khom.

Banks Sang Khom has two banks and several ATMs.

ACCOMMODATION

★**Bouy Guest House** 60/4 Moo 4 Sang Khom, by the river ☎042 441065, ✉toy_bgh@hotmail.com. The best of the accommodation in Sang Khom, enjoying a particularly choice location. The decent bamboo huts, some with fan and others a/c, have beautiful views out over the river and are set in a spacious, flower-strewn compound on a spit of land that's reached by a wooden bridge over a small tributary. The welcoming owners can arrange day-trips to Phu Phra Bat Historical Park (see p.497); if that sounds too strenuous, you can settle for a massage (B250) or just relax in the hammocks strung from the veranda of each hut. Wi-fi in restaurant area only. Good Thai and Western food is available on a deck overlooking the stream (most of it also in vegetarian versions). **B280**

Nong Khai

The major border town in Northern Isaan is **NONG KHAI**, an ethnically diverse town that's thrived since the construction of the **Thai-Australian Friendship Bridge** over the Mekong on the west side of town in 1994. Occupying a strategic position at the end of Highway 2 and the northeastern rail line, and just 24km from Vientiane, Nong Khai acts as a conduit for goods bought and sold by Thais and Lao, who are allowed to pass

> **BOAT TRIPS FROM NONG KHAI**
>
> To catch the best of life on the river, take a **boat trip** on the *Nagarina*, which sets out from the *Mut Mee Guest House* every evening at around 5pm (B100) and runs up and down the length of Nong Khai for an hour or so, sticking to the Thai side. Drinks are available and food (see p.495) can be ordered before the boat leaves. There's no stunning scenery, but there's plenty of activity to watch on both river banks as the sun sets behind the Friendship Bridge.

SALA KAEO KOU, NONG KHAI (P.496) >

▼ Tourist office, Udon Thani, Route 211 & Wat Phra That Bang Phuan

between the two cities freely for day-trips. Consequently, the covered souvenir market that sprawls to the east of the main pier, **Tha Sadet**, carries Lao silver, wood and cane items, as well as goods from as far afield as China, Korea and Russia, plus local basketware and silk.

As with most of the towns along this part of the Mekong, the thing to do in Nong Khai is just to take it easy, enjoying the **riverside atmosphere** and the peaceful settings of its guesthouses, which offer good value. Before you lapse into a relaxation-induced coma, though, try joining an evening **river tour**, or make a **day-trip** out to see the impressive sculptures and rock formations in the surrounding countryside (see p.496).

Thanon Meechai

Nong Khai is laid out for 4km along the south bank of the Mekong. Running from east to west, **Thanon Meechai** dominates activity; the main shops, banks and businesses are plumb in the middle around the post office. Although most of the old buildings have been replaced by concrete boxes, a few weather-beaten wooden houses remain, their attractive balconies, porticoes and slatted shutters showing the influence of colonial architecture, which was imported from across the river before the French were forced out of Laos in 1954.

Wat Pho Chai

Off the east end of Thanon Prajak

The main temple of the region is **Wat Pho Chai**. The cruciform viharn, with its complex and elegant array of Lao tiers, shelters a venerated golden image, the Phra Sai Buddha, which is paraded around town and blessed with water during Songkhran. Prince Chakri, the future Rama I, is said to have looted the image from Vientiane, along with the Emerald Buddha, but the boat which was bringing back the Phra Sai overturned and sank in the Mekong. Later, the statue miraculously rose to the surface and the grateful people of Nong Khai built this great hangar of a viharn to house it, decorating the walls with murals of its miraculous journey. It's worth a visit for the Buddha's stagy setting, in front of a steep, flame-covered altar, dazzlingly lit from above and below. The solid gold head is so highly polished that you have to peer carefully to make out the Sukhothai influence in its haughty expression and beaked nose.

The riverside

The most pleasant place for a stroll is the **riverside area**. There's a pedestrianized promenade in the centre to the east of Tha Sadet, while things become more rustic and leafy around the fringes, which are often busy with people bathing, washing their clothes and fishing, especially in the early morning and evening.

Phra That Nong Khai

At the far eastern end of town

If you're lucky, you might catch sight of a sunken chedi at the far eastern end of town. **Phra That Nong Khai** (also known as Phra That Klang Nam) slipped into the river during floods in 1847 and has since subsided so far that it's only visible in the dry season, though a replica, brightly illuminated at night, has been constructed on the adjacent bank.

Hat Jommani

2km west of the centre beyond the Friendship Bridge

If you're toiling around Nong Khai in the dog days of the hot season, you might want to cool off at **Hat Jommani**, the so-called "Pattaya of Isaan": this sunny riverine beach can stretch for up to 200m when the river is at its lowest in April.

ARRIVAL AND DEPARTURE   NONG KHAI

By plane A/c minibuses (B150–200) from Udon Thani airport (see p.479) meet incoming flights from Bangkok and drop passengers at the Friendship Bridge or at their downtown hotels.

By train The station is 3km southwest of the centre near the Friendship Bridge. From Bangkok, you'll most likely be coming to Nong Khai by night train, arriving just after dawn. Tuk-tuks and motorbike taxis are on hand to run passengers into town. Destinations Ayutthaya (3 daily; 9hr 30min–11hr); Bangkok (3 daily; 11–13hr); Khon Kaen (3 daily; 2hr 45min); Tha Naleng (for Vientiane, Laos; daily; 10min);

Udon Thani (3 daily; 1hr).

By bus Day buses from all points in Isaan and night buses from further afield pull in at the bus station on the east side of town off Thanon Prajak; Udon Thani buses make an extra stop at the corner of highways 2 and 212.

Destinations Bangkok (8 daily; 11hr); Bueng Kan (hourly; 2hr); Chiang Mai (daily; 12hr); Khon Kaen (8 daily; 3hr 30min); Khorat (8 daily; 6hr 30min); Loei (daily via Pak Chom; 7hr); Nakhon Phanom (2 daily; 6hr); Rayong (11 daily; 12hr); Sang Khom (daily; 3–4hr); Udon Thani (every 30min; 1hr); Vientiane (Laos; 6 daily; 1hr).

NAGA FIREBALLS

Nong Khai celebrates the generic Thai and Isaan **festivals** with due gusto, but in recent years a peculiarity of this stretch of the Mekong River has been attracting thousands of celebrants from Bangkok and beyond. Every year on the full-moon night in October, silent and vapourless **naga fireballs** appear from the river, small, pink spheres that float vertically up to heights of as much as 300m, then disappear; in some years, several thousand appear, in others, just a handful. A tentative scientific theory proposes that the balls are a combination of methane and nitrogen from decomposed matter on the bottom of the river, which reach a certain temperature at that time of the year and are released, combusting in the presence of oxygen when they break the water's surface; romantics will prefer the local belief that the nagas or naks (serpents) of the river breathe out the fireballs to call the Buddha to return to earth at the end of Buddhist Lent.

This strange occurrence has now been consolidated into the two-day festival of **Bang Fai Phaya Nak**, which coincides with Awk Phansa and the end of the longboat-racing season on the river. The fireballs have appeared as far afield as Sang Khom and Bueng Kan, but are generally most numerous around Phon Phisai, 40km east of Nong Khai; if you make the trek out there, take great care on the way back, when the road is thronged with drunk drivers. Since by going it alone you chance seeing nothing at all, it makes sense to sign up for the cruise on the *Nagarina* organized by *Mut Mee Guest House* (ⓦ mutmee.com; B2800). The boat leaves in the morning, heading east to Phon Phisai and Ban Nam Phe, and after watching the fireballs, returns to Nong Khai at around 3am; all meals included.

5

CROSSING THE LAO BORDER VIA NONG KHAI

The crossing at Nong Khai is popular with tourists and relatively easy to use. Thais and Laos can cross the border via the ferry at Tha Sadet, but everyone else must use Nong Khai's **Thai-Australian Friendship Bridge** (daily 6am–10pm, although the buses across the bridge stop at 9pm, and we've had reports of it sometimes closing as early as 6pm).

GETTING A VISA ON ARRIVAL

To get a **visa at the border**, take a tuk-tuk to the foot of the bridge (about B50 from the railway station), where you'll be stamped out of Thailand. You'll then need to take a bus (B20–30) across the span itself to the Laos immigration post, where you can get a thirty-day tourist visa for US$30–42 (depending on nationality; pay $1 extra if you arrive after 6pm), plus one photo. It's possible to pay in baht at the bridge, though it's over the odds at B1500 and upwards; *Mut Mee Guest House* sells dollars at a decent rate. From the Laos immigration post, you can catch a shared air-conditioned minibus (B100–150/person), tuk-tuk (about B300/vehicle) or infrequent bus (B30) to Vientiane, 24km away.

WITH A VISA

If you have already arranged a visa through a Lao embassy or consulate, you can head straight from Nong Khai into Laos. Six daily **buses** run all the way through to Vientiane from the bus station (B55, plus B5 to Thai immigration). **Trains** also run from Nong Khai to Tha Naleng in Laos (daily; B20–50), but as the tracks stop here (around 20km from downtown Vientiane) you'll need to charter a tuk-tuk, car or minibus for the rest of the journey. The border is also accessible from further afield – there are direct buses from Bangkok, Udon Thani and Khon Kaen to Vientiane.

GETTING AROUND

As everything in Nong Khai is so spread out, you might want to consider hopping on a **tuk-tuk** for getting around, or renting a bicycle or motorbike.

By tuk-tuk Around B50 for a short journey such as bus station to Tha Sadet, up to B80 for bus station to train station. The rates for these and other journeys are posted up in the bus station.

By bicycle and motorbike Nong Khai's flat terrain makes it ideal for exploring by bicycle. They are available at *Mut Mee*, *Ruan Thai* and *Sawasdee* guesthouses for around B50–100/day. Motorbikes (from B200/day) can be rented at Noui Motorcycle (☎081 975 4863) on Thanon Kaewworut in front of *Mut Mee Guesthouse*.

INFORMATION

Tourist office The TAT office, 1.5km south of the centre on the west side of Highway 2 (daily 8.30am–4.30pm; ☎042 421326, ✉tat_nongkhai@yahoo.com), has information about local homestays.

Massages Good, strong body and foot massages can be had at Suan Sukapab (Healthy Garden), 623 Thanon Banterngjit (☎042 423323).

Police The tourist police are based on Thanon Prajak (☎042 460186 or ☎1155).

ACCOMMODATION

Baan Sabai Rimkhong 168 Thanon Rimkhong ☎042 413545, ⊛baansabairimkhong.com. If you're looking for a room with a good view of the Mekong River, you won't find better than this. The cheapest rooms have no view, but others (priced from B690–2000) have sweeping views and some have big balconies too. All rooms are a/c, equipped with modern furnishings and spotlessly clean. B490

Grand Paradise Hotel 589 Moo 5, Nongkhai–Phonpisai road ☎042 420033, ⊛galahotels.com. On the southern bypass but handy for the centre, this mid-range hotel has high standards of service and a small swimming pool. There's also a rooftop terrace restaurant offering panoramic views over Nong Khai and Laos. Breakfast included. B2260

Janhom Apartment 479 Soi Srichumchuen, Thanon Prajak ☎042 460293. Located on a quiet soi, set against the wall of Wat Sri Chum Chuen and with a pleasant, shady sitting area at the front. Not really apartments, though they are available by the month, with substantial discounts, but large, clean, a/c rooms with armchairs, fridges, TVs and hot-water bathrooms. Some are rather dim so take a look first. B370

★**Mut Mee Guest House** 1111 Thanon Keawworut ☎042 460717, �🌐mutmee.com. A huge range of well-kept rooms sprawl around an attractive riverside restaurant at this magnet for travellers. Choose between ultra-basic single rooms (B200), clean twin rooms (some with shared bathrooms) or top-notch en-suite doubles with their own balconies and river views (B1650). With helpful, well-informed staff, it also offers yoga, meditation and massage sessions (high season only), as well as local information about bicycle tours and homestays. Julian, the English owner, has added loads of useful information about the area to the guesthouse's website. Fan B300, a/c B600

Pantawee Hotel 1049 Thanon Haisoke ☎042 411568, �🌐pantawee.com. A comfortable, efficiently run, mid-range choice, with its cheapest, dimly lit rooms on the opposite side of the road. The clean a/c rooms come with hot-water bathrooms, TVs, DVD players, fridges and computers. There's also a small jacuzzi pool, a spa and a 24hr restaurant. B700

Ruan Thai Guest House 1126/2 Thanon Rimkhong ☎042 412519. A variety of large and small wooden houses in a quiet compound with attractive, well-maintained rooms, which range from keenly priced singles with fan and shared hot-water bathrooms, through standard rooms with a/c and hot-water en suites to family rooms. Fan B300, a/c B400

Sawasdee Guest House 402 Thanon Meechai ☎042 412502, ⚁sawasdeeguesthouse.com. A grand old wooden shophouse set around a pleasant courtyard, with helpful and meticulous management, plus free luggage storage and showers available for those catching a night train or bus. Rooms are either fan-cooled (try to avoid those overlooking the noisy main road) with shared bathrooms and hot showers available, or a/c with en-suite hot-water bathrooms. Fan B200, a/c B400

EATING AND DRINKING

Nong Khai is a great place to sample Isaan cuisine, as well as Vietnamese at *Daeng Namnuang*, the town's most famous **restaurant**. If you're counting the baht, head for the night-time **stalls** on Thanon Prajak, near the corner of Soi Watnark.

★**Daeng Namnuang** 526-527 Thanon Rimkhong ☎042 411961. Delicious, inexpensive Vietnamese food at this immaculately clean and popular place, with an a/c room and a lovely riverside terrace, though most Thais come for the take-away service. Specialities include *nam nuang* (roll-your-own Vietnamese spring rolls with grilled pork) and deep-fried prawns on sugar-cane skewers (3 for B130). Daily 8am–8pm.

Dee Dee Pochana 1155/9 Thanon Prajak ☎042 411548. This no-frills place is a classic Thai restaurant, serving all the usual staples like beef in oyster sauce (B120), as well as several Chinese and seafood dishes. Probably the fastest service in town. Daily 11am–2am.

★**Mut Mee Guest House** 1111 Thanon Keawworut ☎042 460717. You're spoilt for choice at this traveller's favourite. The *Nagarina* floating restaurant specializes in seafood and Isaan dishes, though the menu changes regularly and there are daily specials. The cosy, attached *Gaia* bar hosts singer-songwriters on Sunday night. Under bamboo shelters back on dry land, the main guesthouse restaurant is a relaxing spot: good Thai and Isaan dishes (around B80–100), particularly vegetarian versions, vie with tasty Western efforts (B200–250) including home-made apple pie. Small beer B56. Daily 7am–10pm.

Nam Tok Rim Khong Thanon Rimkhong (no English sign). Simple but popular and cheap restaurant in an old wooden building with an attractive terrace overlooking the river, specializing in *nam tok* (spicy hot beef salad, B60), as well as other Isaan delicacies such as *som tam*, dried beef and sausages. Daily 8am–8.30pm.

Riverview Café 577 Thanon Rimkhong ☎042 423383. This large restaurant occupies a breezy terrace beside the Mekong and offers a fantastic range of Thai and Western dishes. Comfort food such as sausage and mash or fish and chips (B150) are on offer as well as ribeye steaks (B300), and the staff are very attentive. Daily 8am–1am.

SHOPPING

Woven handicrafts are the main attraction here, shopping-wise. The northeastern method **mut mee** (literally "tied strings") involves tie-dyeing bundles of cotton thread before hand-weaving, which produces geometrical patterns on a coloured base. Tha Sadet market (7am–6.30pm), also known as the Indochina Market, which occupies a huge area by the Mekong River, has a selection of ready-made clothes, wall hangings, bags and axe pillows. On Saturday evenings (5–10pm), Thanon Rimkhong is closed to traffic between the pier and market for the weekly walking street.

Hornbill Bookshop On the narrow lane leading down to Mut Mee Guest House. Stocks a reasonable selection of new and secondhand books in English. Mon–Sat 10am–7pm.

Village Weaver Crafts 1020 Thanon Prajak ☎042 422652–3. A superb selection of silk and cotton clothes, either off-the-peg or tailor-made. They also sell some lovely axe pillows, scarves and bags. Daily 8.30am–7.30pm.

5

Around Nong Khai

The most memorable sight around Nong Khai is **Sala Kaeo Kou**, also known as Wat Khaek, where you'll find dozens of curious stone sculptures. To the southwest of Nong Khai is **Wat Phra That Bang Phuan**, which offers some classic temple sightseeing, while the natural rock formations at **Phu Phra Bat Historical Park** and the spectacular temple **Wat Phu Tok** require much more effort and a full day out.

Sala Kaeo Kou (Wat Khaek)

5km east of Nong Khai • Daily 8am–6pm • B20 • About B150 return from Nong Khai in a tuk-tuk

By far the easiest and most popular day-trip out of Nong Khai is to **Sala Kaeo Kou**, a short hop to the east. The temple is best known for its bizarre sculpture garden, which looks like the work of a giant artist on acid. Also known as Wat Khaek, it was founded by the late **Luang Phu Boonlua Surirat**, an unconventional Thai holy man who studied under a Hindu guru in Vietnam and preached in Laos until he was thrown out by the Communists in the 1970s. His charisma – those who drank water offered by him would, it was rumoured, give up all they owned to the temple – and heavy emphasis on morality attracted many followers among the farmers of Nong Khai. Luang Phu's popularity suffered, however, after his eleven-month spell in prison for insulting King Bhumibol, a crime alleged by jealous neighbours and probably without foundation; he died aged 72 in August 1996, a year after his release.

If you're heading over to Laos, the **Xiang Khouan** sculpture garden – Sala Kaeo Kou's precursor, 25km from downtown Vientiane on the Mekong River – shouldn't be missed; Luang Phu spent twenty years working on the sculptures there before his expulsion.

The sculpture garden

Arrayed with pretty flowers and plants, the **sculpture garden** bristles with Buddhist, Hindu and secular figures, all executed in concrete with imaginative abandon by unskilled followers under Luang Phu's direction. The religious statues, in particular, are radically modern. Characteristics that marked the Buddha out as a supernatural being – tight curls and a bump on the crown of the head called the *ushnisha* – are here transformed into beehives, and the *rashmis* on top (flames depicting the Buddha's fiery intellect) are depicted as long, sharp spikes. The largest statue in the garden shows the familiar story of the kindly naga king, Muchalinda, sheltering the Buddha, who is lost in meditation, from the heavy rain and floods: here the Buddha has shrunk in significance and the seven-headed snake has grown to 25m, with fierce, gaping fangs and long tongues.

Many of the statues illustrate **Thai proverbs**. Near the entrance, an elephant surrounded by a pack of dogs symbolizes integrity, "as the elephant is indifferent to the barking dogs". The nearby serpent-tailed monster with the moon in his mouth – Rahoo, the cause of eclipses – serves as an injunction to oppose all obstacles, just as the people of Isaan and Laos used to ward off eclipses by banging drums and firing guns. In the corner furthest from the entrance, you enter the complex Circle of Life through a huge mouth representing the womb, inside which a hermit, a policeman, a monk, a rich man and a beggar, among others, represent different paths in life (for a detailed map of the Circle of Life sculpture, go to ⓦmutmee.com). A man with two wives is shown beating the older

---

CROSSING THE LAO BORDER VIA BUENG KAN

It's possible to cross from **Bueng Kan** to **Paksan** on the opposite side of the river in Laos (immigration office daily 8.30am–4.30pm), though there's no visa on arrival at this crossing. Take a tuk-tuk (around B60) to the ferry (B60), which leaves when it's got enough passengers, and then another tuk-tuk into Paksan. It's likely that another Thai-Lao Friendship Bridge will be built here within a few years. From Paksan there are buses west to Vientiane or south to Savannakhet.

one because he is ensnared by the wishes of the younger one, and an old couple who have made the mistake of not having children now find they have only each other for comfort.

The disturbingly vacant, smiling faces of the garden Buddhas bear more than a passing resemblance to Luang Phu himself, photos of whom adorn the **temple building**, a huge white edifice with mosque-like domes. On the second floor, his corpse is preserved in a domed palanquin, which is decorated with fairy lights and a virtual fish-tank.

Wat Phra That Bang Phuan

Ban Bang Phuan hamlet, around 22km southwest of Nong Khai on Highway 211 • Buses from Nong Khai to Pak Chom and Loei pass this way; depending on departure times it may be quicker to take an Udon-bound service 12km down Highway 2 to Ban Nong Song Hong, then change onto an Udon–Sri Chiangmai bus

More famous as the site of a now-concealed two-thousand-year-old Indian chedi than for its modern replacement, rural **Wat Phra That Bang Phuan** remains a highly revered place of pilgrimage.

The original **chedi** is supposed to have been built by disciples of the Buddha to hold 29 relics – pieces of breastbone – brought from India. A sixteenth-century king of Vientiane earned himself merit by building a tall Lao-style chedi over the top of the previous stupa; rain damage toppled this in 1970, but it was restored in 1977 to the fine, gleaming white edifice seen today. The unkempt compound also contains a small museum, crumbling brick chedis and some large open-air Buddhas.

Phu Phra Bat Historical Park

61km southwest of Nong Khai, near Ban Phu • Daily dawn–dusk • B100 **Information Centre** daily 8.30am–4.30pm

Deep in the countryside, the wooded slopes around the village of **BAN PHU** are dotted with strangely eroded sandstone formations, which have long exerted a mystical hold over people in the surrounding area. Local wisdom has it that the outcrops, many of which were converted into small temples from around the ninth century onwards, are either meteorites – believed to account for their burnt appearance – or, more likely, were caused by glacial erosion. Together with a stupa enshrining a Buddha footprint that is now an important pilgrimage site, especially during its annual festival in March, the rock formations have been linked up under the auspices of fifty-square-kilometre **Phu Phra Bat Historical Park**.

The **information centre** by the park entrance contains fairly interesting displays on the red prehistoric paintings of animals, humans, hands and geometric patterns that are found on the rock formations, and on the tale of Ussa and Barot. Around the information centre, a well-signposted network of **paths** has been cleared from the thin forest to connect 25 of the outcrops, each of which has a helpful English-language information board attached. It would take a good five hours to explore the whole park on foot, but there are electric carts available at B100, and the most popular circuit, covering all the sights listed below, can be completed in an ambling two hours.

The outcrops

Among the most interesting of the outcrops are **Tham Wua** and **Tham Khon**, two natural shelters whose paintings of oxen and human stick figures suggest that the area was first settled by hunter-gatherers two to three thousand years ago. A legend that's well known in this part of Thailand and Laos accounts for the name of nearby **Kok Ma Thao Barot** (Prince Barot's Stable), a broad platform overhung by a huge slab of sandstone. A certain Princess Ussa, banished by her father to these slopes to be educated by a hermit, sent out an SOS that was answered by a dashing prince, Barot. The two fell in love and were married against the wishes of Ussa's father, prompting the king to challenge Barot to a distinctly oriental sort of duel: each would build a temple, and the last to finish would be beheaded. The king lost. Kok Ma Thao Barot is celebrated as the place where Barot kept his horse when he visited Ussa.

5

The furthest point of the circuit is the viewpoint at **Pha Sadej**, where the cliff drops away to give a lovely view across the green fields and forests of the Mekong valley to the distant mountains. More spectacular is **Hor Nang Ussa** (Ussa's Tower), a mushroom formed by a flat slab capping a 5m-high rock pillar. Under the cap of the mushroom, a shelter has been carved out and walled in on two sides. The *sema* found scattered around the site, and the square holes in which others would have been embedded, indicate that this was a shrine, probably during the ninth to eleventh centuries in the Dvaravati period. Nearby, a huge rock on a flimsy pivot miraculously balances itself against a tree at **Wat Por Ta** (the Father-in-Law's Temple); the walls and floor have been evenly carved out to form a vaguely rectangular shrine, with Dvaravati Buddha images dotted around.

Wat Phra Bat Bua Bok

The left fork shortly before the park entrance leads to **Wat Phra Bat Bua Bok**: a crude *that* built in imitation of Wat Phra That Phanom (see p.501), it's decorated with naive bas-reliefs of divinities and boggle-eyed monsters, which add to the atmosphere of simple, rustic piety. In a gloomy chamber in the tower's base, the only visible markings on the sandstone **Buddha footprint** show the Wheel of Law. Legend has it that the Buddha made the footprint here for a serpent that had asked to be ordained as a monk, but had been refused because it was not human. Higher up the slope, a smaller *that* perches on a hanging rock that seems to defy gravity.

ARRIVAL AND DEPARTURE	PHU PHRA BAT HISTORICAL PARK

By bus From Nong Khai, take the 7.15am bus to Ban Phu; if you leave any later you won't have time to see the park properly, as the whole journey takes at least a couple of hours and the last bus back leaves at around 3.15pm. From Ban Phu, it's another 14km west to the historical park; take a songthaew for the first 10km to the Ban Tiu intersection; from here a motorbike taxi will bring you the final 4km up to the main park entrance. If you are coming from Udon Thani, catch a bus from Talat Rangsina towards either Nam Som or Na Yung, which will drop you off at Ban Tiu.

Wat Phu Tok

The most compelling destination in the area to the east of Nong Khai is the extraordinary hilltop retreat of **Wat Phu Tok**. One of two sandstone outcrops that jut steeply out of the plain 35km southeast of Bueng Kan, Phu Tok has been transformed into a meditation wat, its fifty or so monks building their scattered huts on perches high above breathtaking cliffs. The outcrop comes into sight long before you get there, its sheer red face sandwiched between green vegetation on the lower slopes and tufts of trees on the narrow plateau above. As you get closer, the horizontal white lines across

---

HOMESTAYS IN THE NORTHEAST

The lazy **villages** just downstream from Nong Khai and close to Mukdahan can be a welcome breath of fresh air after traipsing around Isaan's dusty cities. There's a good selection of welcoming **homestays** to bed down in, providing an opportunity to unwind and enjoy the slow pace of rural Isaan – and many rent out bikes and motorbikes for local exploration.

Homestay Ban Kham Pia Off Highway 212 between Bueng Kan and Nakhon Phanom, 7km southwest of Bung Khla, on the road running towards Phu Wua Wildlife Reserve ☏087 861 0601, ⓦbunloedhuts .jimdo.com. Close to a reserve that's packed with wildlife, this homestay offers simple wooden bungalows, some with shared bathroom. See website for directions. **B200**
Thai House Isaan Around 60km southwest of

Mukdahan, just off Highway 2042 ☏087 0654635, ⓦthaihouse-isaan.com. Set around an attractive northeastern-style building in a peaceful Phu Thai village, with a handful of a/c bungalows, a swimming pool and an apartment that has its own living room and karaoke machine. The owners can arrange tours lasting between a day and a week, ranging all over Isaan. Pick-ups available from Khon Kaen. **B750**

the cliffs reveal themselves to be painted wooden walkways, built to give the temple seven levels to represent the seven stages of enlightenment.

The ornamental garden
In an ornamental garden at the base, reflected in a small lake, an elegant, modern marble chedi commemorates **Phra Ajaan Juen**, the famous meditation master who founded the wat in 1968 and died in a plane crash ten years later while on his way to Bangkok to celebrate the queen's birthday. Within the chedi, the monk's books and other belongings, and diamond-like fragments of his bones, are preserved in a small shrine.

The ascent
The first part of the **ascent** of the outcrop takes you to the third level up a series of long, sometimes slippery, wooden staircases, so you'll need something more sturdy than flip-flops on your feet. A choice of two routes – the left fork is more interesting – leads to the fifth and most important level, where the **Sala Yai** houses the temple's main Buddha image in an airy, dimly lit cavern. The artificial ledges that cut across the northeast face are not for the faint-hearted, but they are one way of getting to the dramatic northwest tip here on level five: on the other side of a deep crevice spanned by a wooden bridge, the monks have built an open-sided Buddha viharn under a huge anvil rock. This spot affords stunning **views** over a broad sweep of countryside and across to the second, uninhabited, outcrop. The flat top of the hill forms the seventh level, where you can wander along overgrown paths through thick forest. At times on the walkways you are walking above thin air, so it's not advisable to go up if you suffer from vertigo.

ARRIVAL AND DEPARTURE

WAT PHU TOK

Getting to Wat Phu Tok isn't easy – the location was chosen for its isolation, after all – but the journey out gives you a slice of life in remote countryside. The attached village sports a collection of simple **restaurants** and food stalls.

By motorbike or hired car The best option is to rent a motorbike and get a sketch map from *Mut Mee Guesthouse* (see p.495) or charter a car and driver in Nong Khai (B1500–2000) – leave early to make it there and back in a day, allowing two hours to explore the temple.
By bus Going via public transport is a slog. Catch a bus

from Nong Khai to Bueng Kan (hourly; 2hr); once there, you might be lucky enough to coincide with one of the occasional songthaews to Phu Tok via Ban Siwilai, 25km south on Route 222; otherwise, take one of the hourly buses to Siwilai and charter a motorized samlor (around B300) for the last 20km east to Phu Tok.

Nakhon Phanom
Beyond Bueng Kan, the river road rounds the hilly northeastern tip of Thailand before heading south through remote country with very few communities of any size. The Mekong can only be glimpsed occasionally until you reach **NAKHON PHANOM** ("City of Mountains"), a clean and prosperous town which affords the finest view of the river in northern Isaan, framed against the giant ant hills of the Lao mountains opposite.

The town makes a pleasant place to hang out, its quiet, broad streets lined with some grand old public buildings, colonial-style houses and creaking wooden shophouses. But most importantly for those with their sights set on Laos, the town is home to the third Thai-Lao Friendship Bridge, which opened to much fanfare in November 2011.

BOAT TRIPS FROM NAKHON PHANOM
Even if you're not crossing the border, you can still appreciate the beautiful riverscape by joining one of the daily **boat trips** that depart from just south of the main pier at 5pm (B50; drinks available). Setting out as the sun begins to sink, they motor along between the banks nice and slowly, usually returning just before dark.

5

Walking around town, you'll see several lit-up boat shapes around the place, a reminder of Nakhon Phanom's best-known festival, the **illuminated boat procession**, which is held on the river every year at the end of the rainy season, usually in late October. Around fifty boats of up to 10m in length, adorned with elaborate lights and carrying offerings of food and flowers, are launched on the river in a spectacular display. The week-long celebrations – marking the end of the annual three-month Buddhist Rains Retreat – also feature colourful dragon-boat races along the Mekong, pitting Thai and Lao teams against each other.

Ho Chi Minh's House

5km southwest of Nakhon Phanom at Ban Na Chok (ask for directions at TAT) • **House** daily 8am–5pm • Free • **Museum** daily 8am–4pm • Free

The Vietnamese national hero, Ho Chi Minh, lived in Ban Na Chok in the late 1920s, when he was forced to go underground during the struggle for independence from France. His Vietnamese-style **wooden house** – terracotta roof tiles and no stilts – has been reconstructed, and there's a small museum nearby too, dedicated to the Vietnamese in Thailand. However, there's not much to see apart from some black-and-white photographs of Uncle Ho and a couple of trees he planted, so a visit here is really only recommended for Ho Chi Minh devotees; homestays in the village can be arranged through TAT (see below).

ARRIVAL AND INFORMATION

NAKHON PHANOM

By plane You can fly to Nakhon Phanom from Bangkok with Air Asia (daily; 1hr 15min) or Nok Air (2 daily; 1hr 15min); taxis from the airport 15km west of town cost B100 per person.

By bus The main bus station is about 1km west of the centre off the north side of Highway 22.

Destinations Bangkok (21 daily; 12hr); Khon Kaen (5 daily; 5hr 30min); Mukdahan (every 25min; 2hr); Nong Khai (1 daily; 6hr); Thakhek (Laos; 8 daily; 1hr 30min); That Phanom (every 25min; 1hr); Ubon Ratchathani (11 daily; 5hr); Udon Thani (18 daily; 5hr).

Tourist information TAT has an office in an impressive old mansion at 184/1 Thanon Suntorn Vichit, corner of Thanon Salaklang (daily 8.30am–4.30pm; ☎ 042 513490–1, ✉ tatphnom@tat.or.th), 500m north of the pier for Laos; they also cover Mukdahan province.

Services There's a tourist police office on the riverfront just north of the *Fortune River View Hotel* (☎ 1155). On Friday and Saturday evenings (5–9pm), Thanon Sunthorn Wijit (the riverside road) is closed to traffic for two blocks north of the clock tower, and vendors set up stalls for a walking street.

ACCOMMODATION AND EATING

Thanon Fueng Nakhon, which runs west from the clock tower just north of the pier, has a choice of several simple places to **eat** and is a lively spot at night.

Chez Simian 149/23 Thanon Aphiban Bancha ☎ 042 514535. Located opposite the hospital to the north of the town centre, this welcoming place serves a range of appealing Thai and Western dishes such as T-bone steaks and grilled salmon (B250–490). Most Thai dishes are around B90–140. Daily 10am–9pm.

Fortune River View On Highway 212 towards the southern edge of town ☎ 042 522333. A recent change of ownership and name, accompanied by a major refurbishment, makes this the best place in town, with an outdoor swimming pool and smart, tasteful riverside rooms that boast bathtubs. B1300

The River On Highway 212 about 2km south of the town centre ☎ 042 522999, ✆ therivernakhonphanom .com. This smart, newish hotel makes the most of Nakhon Phanom's expansive river views. Comfortable beds with thick mattresses, modern furnishings and rain showers make for a comfy stay, and each room has a small balcony.

CROSSING VIA THE THIRD THAI-LAO FRIENDSHIP BRIDGE

The third **Thai-Lao friendship bridge** opened in late 2011 at a site 8km north of Nakhon Phanom's town centre. If you're heading for Laos, take a bus from Nakhon Phanom to Thakhek (daily 8am–5pm; B75) and complete immigration formalities on the bridge; Lao **visas** are available on arrival for US$30–42. There's also a passenger ferry that crosses the river, but this is for Thais and Lao only.

South to Khao Takiab and Suan Son Pradiphat

Green songthaews run to Khao Takiab every 20min or so from central Thanon Sa Song

South of the *Centara Grand*, holiday homes and high-rise condos overshadow nearly the whole run of beach down to the promontory known as Khao Takiab (Chopstick Hill), but during the week it's fairly quiet along here, with just a few widely spaced food stalls along the broad, squeakily soft beach. **Khao Takiab** itself is a wooded outcrop surmounted by a temple and home to a troupe of monkeys, about 6km south of the town centre; the road to the top is guarded by a tall, golden, standing Buddha and affords good coastal views. Beyond Khao Takiab stretches another quiet beach, **Suan Son Pradiphat**, which is backed by casuarina trees and maintained by the nearby army camp.

6

ARRIVAL AND DEPARTURE   HUA HIN

BY PLANE
Only Kan Airlines (Ⓦkanairlines.com) currently uses Hua Hin Airport, 6km north of town by the Phetkasem Highway, flying down from Chiang Mai thrice weekly (1hr 45min). Green songthaews run to Thanon Sa Song in town from the main road by the airport every 20min, while a taxi to town will cost around B300–500.

BY TRAIN
All services between the south and Bangkok (mostly using Hualamphong, with a few stopping trains serving Thonburi station) stop at Hua Hin's photogenic 1920s station, a 10min walk west of the seafront.

Destinations Bangkok (14–15 daily; 3hr 30min–5hr); Butterworth (Malaysia; 1 daily; 17hr 30min); Chumphon (13 daily; 3hr 30min–5hr 20min); Nakhon Si Thammarat (2 daily; 12hr); Prachuap Khiri Khan (11 daily; 1hr 30min); Surat Thani (11 daily; 5hr 40min–8hr); Trang (2 daily; 12hr).

BY BUS
Baw Khaw Saw terminal Most government and private buses use the main Baw Khaw Saw terminal, which is well to the south of the centre, between Thanon Phetkasem sois 96 and 98, though some services will drop you off at the central clocktower (Wat Hua Hin) on their way in. Roong Reuang operate coaches between the terminal and Suvarnabhumi Airport (Ⓦairporthuahinbus.com).

Destinations Bangkok (Suvarnabhumi Airport; 6 daily; 4hr); Chiang Mai (3 daily; 12hr); Chumphon (hourly in the

morning, fewer in the afternoon; 3hr 30min–4hr 30min); Phuket (3 daily; 9–10hr); Prachuap Khiri Khan (roughly hourly; 1hr 30min–2hr); Pranburi (roughly hourly; 30min); Surat Thani (4 daily; 7hr).

From/to Bangkok A/c buses (every 1hr 30min; 3hr) to Bangkok's Southern Bus Terminal, stopping at Cha-am and Phetchaburi, leave from beside the *Siri Phetkasem* hotel on Thanon Sa Song (as do half-hourly a/c minibuses to Bangkok's Victory Monument).

Non-a/c Phetchaburi buses, via Cha-am From a spot north of TAT on Thanon Phetkasem opposite the Esso petrol station (roughly every 30min; 1hr 50min).

To the islands Lomprayah, with offices on Soi Kanjanomai (☎032 533739, Ⓦlomprayah.com) and on Thanon Phetkasem, south of Thanon Damnern Kasem (where the bus picks passengers up), runs a twice-daily bus and catamaran service (daily at 8.30am & 11.30pm) to Ko Tao (B1050), Ko Pha Ngan (B1300) and Ko Samui (B1400 including transport to your hotel), via Chumphon.

BY MINIBUS
Several private companies run a/c minibuses to and from Bangkok's Victory Monument, including Porn Piya Tour on Thanon Naebkehat, south of Thanon Chomsin (about every 45min; 2hr 30min; ☎081 571 0071; in Cha-am ☎082 249 2882; in Bangkok ☎084 464 6586), which has its base in Bangkok at Century Plaza, on the corner of Thanon Phrayathai and Thanon Rangnam, on the south side of the monument.

GETTING AROUND

By taxi service Hua Hin's taxi services include plentiful motorcycle taxis, samlors and pricy tuk-tuks.

By songthaew Shared songthaews of different colours operate several fixed routes in Hua Hin. Green ones run from the airport, 6km north of town, via Thanon Sa Song to Khao Takiab in the south. White songthaews head down Thanon Phetkasem from the railway station all the way to Soi 112 and Wat Huay Mongkol (daytime only). White ones with a red flash have a circular route that includes a stretch up Thanon Phetkasem from Soi 94, then up Thanon Naebkehat, while the orange ones also run up Thanon

Phetkasem from Soi 94, terminating on Thanon Sa Song by the market.

By car or motorbike Car rental outlets include Avis, on the north side of town at 15/112 Thanon Phetkasem, near Soi 29 (Ⓦavisthailand.com), while Mermaid Cruises (see opposite) rent out electric cars and tuk-tuks. Among the transport touts who rent out mopeds for B200/day on Thanon Damnern Kasem, try Khun Dennapa (☎081 942 5615, Ⓦden-carrental.com), who hangs out on the pavement in front of the *Sirin Hotel*, near 7-Eleven.

INFORMATION

Tourist information The TAT office is on Thanon Phetkasem, just north of Thanon Chomsin (daily 8.30am–4.30pm; ☎ 032 513885). There's also a helpful municipal tourist information office (Mon–Fri 8.30am–4.30pm, sometimes closing for lunch; ☎ 032 511047, ext 100) in the local government buildings on the corner of Thanon Damnern Kasem and Thanon Phetkasem, with a satellite office just up Phetkasem at the clocktower (Mon–Fri 8.30am–7pm, Sat & Sun 9am–5pm).

Publications and websites Among Hua Hin's many English-language publications and maps, the *Hua Hin Pocket Guide*, a free, monthly booklet, is worth keeping half an eye out for.

ACCOMMODATION

A night or two at the former *Railway Hotel* (now the *Centara Grand*) is reason in itself to visit Hua Hin, but there are plenty of other **places to stay**. The most unusual **guesthouses** are those built on the **squid piers** on Thanon Naretdamri, north of the pagoda, with rooms strung out along wooden jetties so you can hear, feel – and smell, especially at low tide – the sea beneath you, even if you can't afford a room with an actual sea view. Room rates at many places can drop significantly from Mondays to Thursdays, so don't be afraid to ask for a discount.

All Nations 10 Thanon Dechanuchit ☎ 032 512747, ⓦ allnationshuahin.com. A range of comfortable rooms in varying sizes, most with balconies, a few with distant sea views. Double rooms have a/c, hot showers, TVs and fridges and are priced according to size; there are also a couple of small, basic, fan-cooled single rooms with cold showers on the balconies and shared toilets (B400). **B700**

Amari 117/74 Thanon Takiab ☎ 032 616600, ⓦ amari .com. About 3km south of the centre on the road to Khao Takiab (with a free shuttle service to town), the *Amari* is set around a beautiful, 40m garden pool fed by fountains. The spacious rooms are elegantly contemporary with big walk-in showers, and there's a delightful spa, Breeze, offering innovative treatments to suit your mood. It's not on the strand itself, but has a beach club and restaurant a 5min walk (or a shuttle ride) away. **B4000**

Anantara 5km north of central Hua Hin on Thanon Phetkasem ☎ 032 520250, ⓦ anantara.com. Set in effusive, beautifully designed tropical gardens, this is a lovely resort-style idyll, just out of town (with a regular shuttle service). Accommodation is in eight-room Thai-style pavilions, whose stylishly appointed rooms use plenty of red wood. The hotel has very good Italian, Thai and grill restaurants, two pools, a gorgeous spa, a cooking school, two tennis courts and its own stretch of beach, with kayaks available. **B8100**

Baan Somboon 13/4 Thanon Damnern Kasem ☎ 032 511538, ⓔ baansomboon@gmail.com. Down a quiet but very central soi, this guesthouse divides between a lovely, old-fashioned house with polished teak floors, decorated with a melange of Thai antiques, woodcarvings and Western "old master" prints, and a small annexe. Spruce, homely rooms come with small, hot-water bathrooms, fridges, TVs and either fan or a/c, and there's a small garden crammed with plants, songbirds and a fish tank. Continental breakfast included. **B1000**

★**Centara Grand** 1 Thanon Damnern Kasem ☎ 032 512021–38, ⓦ centarahotelsresorts.com. The original Thai "destination hotel", the main building is a classic of colonial-style architecture, boasting high ceilings, polished wood panelling, period furniture, wide sea-view balconies and a huge, landscaped garden full of topiary animals. Across the road, lush gardens shelter gorgeous, all-white clapboard villas, most with their own small marble pools, some with large outdoor jacuzzis. With a total of four swimming pools, a lovely spa, tennis courts, a kids' club and a giant chessboard, you need never leave the grounds. You can even tuck into afternoon tea at *The Museum*, the original lobby, which now displays hotel memorabilia. **B8160**

Chomsin Hotel 130/4 Thanon Chomsin ☎ 032 515348–9, ⓦ chomsinhuahin.com. Handsome, sand-coloured, small hotel with a pleasant welcome, offering smart, bright, compact rooms in neutral colours with a few decorative touches and plenty of amenities: a/c, hot showers, cable TV, mini-bars and safes. **B1200**

SOI 67 GUESTHOUSES

About fifteen minutes' walk south down the beach from the *Centara Grand*, or 2km by road down Thanon Phetkasem, there's a little knot of accommodation on Soi 67. Here, facing each other across the short, narrow soi about 100m back from the beach, are a dozen little guesthouses, mainly Scandinavian–Thai run, which share a swimming pool; none comprises more than twenty rooms and most charge about B1000. They're very popular with older European couples, many of whom return for several months every winter, so booking is essential.

corner of Thanom Pitakpanomkhet, the main east–west street, and Thanon Samut Sakdarak, the main north–south street (B10–15/person).

Destinations Bangkok (20 daily; 11hr); Khon Kaen (every 30min; 4hr); Khorat (20 daily; 6hr); Nakhon Phanom (every 25min; 2hr); That Phanom (every 25min; 1hr 20min); Ubon Ratchathani (every 30min; 2–3hr); Udon Thani (5 daily; 4hr–4hr 30min).

By bicycle Good Mook café (see below) has mountain bikes for rent (B100/day).

ACCOMMODATION

Huanum 36 Thanon Samut Sakdarak at the corner of Thanon Song Nang Sathit, a block back from the pier ☎ 042 611137. There is a variety of rooms on offer at this budget hotel, which was undergoing extensive renovations at the time of this update. Fan rooms share cold-water bathrooms while a/c rooms have en-suite hot showers and TVs. Fan B200, a/c B350

Ploy Palace Hotel West of the centre at 40 Thanon Pitakpanomkhet ☎ 042 631111, ⓦ ploypalace.com. A grand pink edifice with a marbled lobby and tasteful

bedrooms, this is probably the best of Mukdahan's big business hotels, with good service, a rooftop restaurant with fine views and an outdoor swimming pool on the third floor. B1180

Riverfront 22 Thanon Samranchaikhong, opposite the Indochina Market ☎ 042 633348, ⓦ riverfrontmukdahan .com. The wood-fronted lobby of this place is right by the main river road. Superior rooms and suites (B1200–1800) have balconies that face Laos, and inside there are solid furnishings and cable TV. B800

EATING AND DRINKING

There's a lively, popular **night market** selling deep-fried insects and plenty of other Isaan specialities, four blocks back from the pier along Thanon Song Nang Sathit.

Good Mook 10 Thanon Song Nang Sathit ☎ 042 612091. Just a few steps west of the river, this classic travellers' café is a great find, with a laidback feel and cool sounds. They serve both Western and Thai dishes, such as phat thai and green curry, with prices ranging from B70–420. Tues–Sun 9am–10pm.

Wine Wild Why 11 Thanon Samranchaikhong ☎ 042 633122. This small restaurant, housed in a wooden building with a riverside terrace, has a short menu that includes Thai classics such as spicy soups, curries and spicy salads. Try the kaeng liang kung (B80), a peppery soup with lots of veggies and shrimp. Daily 11am–10pm.

Mukdahan National Park

15km southeast of town • B100 • ☎ 042 601753, ⓦ dnp.go.th/parkreserve

If you're tired of concrete Isaan towns, stretch your legs exploring the strange rock formations and beautiful waterfalls of **Mukdahan National Park** (aka Phu Pha Thoep or Phu Pha Turm). Just above the headquarters is a hillside of bizarre rocks, eroded into the shapes of toadstools, camels and crocodiles, which is great for scrambling around. The hillside also bears two remnants of the area's prehistory: the red finger-painting under one of the sandstone slabs is reckoned to be four thousand years old, while a small cage on the ground protects a 75-million-year-old fossil. Further up, the bare sandstone ridge seems to have been cut out of the surrounding forest by a giant lawnmower, but from October to December it's brought to life with a covering of grasses and wildflowers. A series of ladders leads up a cliff to the highest point, on a ridge at the western end of the park (a 2km walk from the headquarters), which affords a sweeping view over the rocks to the forests and paddies of Laos. Nearby, at least from July to November, is the park's most spectacular waterfall, Nam Tok Phu Tam Phra, a 30m drop through thick vegetation, and a cave in which villagers have enshrined scores of Buddha images.

ARRIVAL, ACCOMMODATION AND EATING   MUKDAHAN NATIONAL PARK

The simple **food stalls** near headquarters will keep you going with fried rice and noodles.

By songthaew Regular songthaews from Mukdahan's bus terminal to Don Tan pass the turning for the park 14km out of town, from where it's a 1km walk uphill to the park headquarters.

Bungalow Near the headquarters. The park has just one standard-issue bungalow, sleeping six. It's also possible to camp here, but you will need to bring your own gear. Camping B30, bungalow B1800

Southern Thailand: the Gulf coast

LIMBO DANCER, FULL MOON PARTY, KO PHA NGAN

Southern Thailand: the Gulf coast

Southern Thailand's gently undulating Gulf coast is famed above all for the Samui archipelago, three small, idyllic islands lying off the most prominent hump of the coastline. This is the country's most popular seaside venue for independent travellers, and a lazy stay in a beachfront bungalow is so seductive a prospect that most people overlook the attractions of the mainland, where the sheltered sandy beaches and warm clear water rival the top sunspots in most countries. Added to that you'll find scenery dominated by forested mountains that rise abruptly behind the coastal strip, and a sprinkling of fascinating historic sights.

The crumbling temples of ancient **Phetchaburi** are the first historic sight you'll meet heading south out of Bangkok and fully justify a break in your journey. Beyond, the stretch of coast around **Cha-am** and **Hua Hin** is popular with weekending Thais escaping the capital and is crammed with condos, high-rise hotels and bars, not to mention a large population of foreign tourists. Far quieter and preferable are the beaches further south: the sophisticated little resort of **Pak Nam Pran**; golden-sand **Hat Phu Noi**, which is also the best base for exploring the karsts and caves of **Khao Sam Roi Yot National Park**; the welcoming town of **Prachuap Khiri Khan**, fronted by a lovely bay and flanked by an equally appealing beach; and laidback, lightly developed **Ban Krud**.

Of the islands, **Ko Samui** is by far the most naturally beautiful, with its long white-sand beaches and arching fringes of palm trees. The island's beauty has not gone unnoticed by tourist developers of course, and its varied spread of accommodation these days draws as many package tourists and second-homers as backpackers. In recent years the next island out, **Ko Pha Ngan**, has drawn increasing numbers of independent travellers away from its neighbour: its accommodation is generally simpler and cheaper than Ko Samui's, and it offers a few stunning beaches with a more laidback atmosphere. The island's southeastern headland, **Hat Rin**, has no fewer than three white-sand beaches to choose from, but now provides all the amenities the demanding backpacker could want, not to mention its notorious full moon parties. The furthest inhabited island of the archipelago, **Ko Tao**, has taken off as a **scuba-diving** centre, but despite a growing nightlife and restaurant scene, still has the feel of a small, rugged and isolated outcrop.

Tucked away beneath the islands, **Nakhon Si Thammarat**, the cultural capital of the south, is well worth a short detour from the main routes through the centre of the peninsula – it's a sophisticated city of grand old temples, delicious cuisine and distinctive handicrafts. With its small but significant Muslim population, and machine-gun dialect, Nakhon begins the transition into Thailand's deep south.

Highlights

❶ **Phetchaburi** Charming historic town, boasting several fine old working temples, as well as delicious traditional desserts. **See p.509**

❷ **Pak Nam Pran** Chic, artfully designed boutique hotels on a long, sandy beach, a popular weekend escape for design-conscious Bangkokians. **See p.522**

❸ **Ang Thong National Marine Park** A dramatic, unspoilt group of over forty remote islands, accessible on boat trips from Ko Samui or Ko Pha Ngan. **See p.552**

❹ **Full moon at Hat Rin, Ko Pha Ngan** Party on, and on… **See p.560**

❺ **Ao Thong Nai Pan on Ko Pha Ngan** Beautiful, secluded bay with good accommodation. **See p.563**

❻ **A boat-trip round Ko Tao** Satisfying exploration and great snorkelling, especially off the unique causeway beaches of Ko Nang Yuan. **See p.570**

❼ **Nakhon Si Thammarat** Historic holy sites, intriguing shadow puppets, great-value accommodation and excellent cuisine. **See p.575**

❽ **Krung Ching waterfall** Walk past giant ferns and screeching monkeys to reach this spectacular drop. **See p.581**

HIGHLIGHTS ARE MARKED ON THE MAP ON P.508

The Gulf coast has a slightly different **climate** from the Andaman coast and much of the rest of Thailand, being hit heavily by the northeast monsoon's rains, especially in November, when it's best to avoid this part of the country altogether. Most times during the rest of the year should see pleasant, if changeable, weather, with some effects of the southwest monsoon felt between May and October. Late December to April is the driest period, and is therefore the region's high season, which also includes July and August.

ARRIVAL AND GETTING AROUND
THE GULF COAST 6

The main arteries through this region are highways 4 (also known as the Phetkasem Highway, or usually Thanon Phetkasem when passing through towns) and 41, served by plentiful buses.

By plane The main airports in this region are on Ko Samui, at Chumphon, Surat Thani and Nakhon Si Thammarat, the last three providing, in combination with buses and boats, cheaper but slower competition for getting to the islands.
By train The railway from Bangkok connects all the mainland towns, including a branch line to Nakhon; nearly all services depart from Hualamphong Station, but a few slow trains use Thonburi Station. You can also head south from Kanchanaburi by train, changing at Ban Pong or Nakhon Pathom.
By boat Daily boats run to all three main islands from two jumping-off points: Surat Thani, 650km from Bangkok, is close to Ko Samui and is generally more convenient for Ko Pha Ngan too, but if you're heading from Bangkok to Pha Ngan you might want to consider Chumphon, which is certainly the main port for Ko Tao.

Phetchaburi

Straddling the Phet River about 120km south of Bangkok, the provincial capital of **PHETCHABURI** (sometimes "Phetburi") has been settled ever since the eleventh century, when the Khmers ruled the region. It was an important producer of salt, gathered from the nearby coastal salt pans, and rose to greater prominence in the seventeenth century as a trading post between the Andaman Sea ports and Ayutthaya. Despite periodic incursions from the Burmese, the town gained a reputation as a cultural centre – as the ornamentation of its older temples testifies – and after the new capital was established in Bangkok it became a favourite country retreat of Rama IV, who had a hilltop palace, **Phra Nakhon Khiri**, built here in the 1850s. Modern Phetchaburi is known for its limes and rose apples, but its main claim to fame is as one of Thailand's finest sweet-making centres, the essential ingredient for its assortment of *khanom* being the sugar extracted from the sweet-sapped palms that cover the province. This being very much a cottage industry, today's downtown Phetchaburi has lost relatively little of the ambience that so attracted Rama IV: the central riverside area is hemmed in by historic wats in varying states of disrepair, along with plenty of traditional wooden shophouses. The town's top three temples, described below, can be seen on a leisurely two-hour circular walk beginning from Chomrut Bridge, while Phetchaburi's other significant sight, the palace-museum at Phra Nakhon Khiri, is on a hill about 1km west of the bridge.

Despite the attractions of its old quarter, Phetchaburi gets few overnight visitors as most people see it on a day-trip from Bangkok, Hua Hin or Cha-am. The town sees more overnighters during the **Phra Nakhon Khiri Fair**, spread over at least a week in March or April, which features parades in historic costumes, cooking demonstrations and traditional entertainments such as *likay* and *lakhon*.

Wat Yai Suwannaram

Thanon Phongsuriya, about 700m east of Chomrut Bridge

Of all Phetchaburi's temples, the most attractive is the still-functioning seventeenth-century **Wat Yai Suwannaram**. The temple's fine old teak **sala** has elaborately carved

6

doors, bearing a gash reputedly inflicted by the Burmese in 1760 as they plundered their way towards Ayutthaya. Across from the *sala* and hidden behind high, whitewashed walls stands the windowless Ayutthaya-style bot. The bot compound overlooks a pond, in the middle of which stands a small but well-preserved scripture library, or **ho trai**: such structures were built on stilts over water to prevent ants and other insects destroying the precious documents. Enter the walled compound from the south and make a clockwise tour of the cloisters filled with Buddha statues before entering the bot itself via the eastern doorway (if the door is locked, one of the monks will get the key for you). The **bot** is supported by intricately patterned red and gold pillars and contains a remarkable, if rather faded, set of murals, depicting Indra, Brahma and other lower-ranking divinities ranged in five rows of ascending importance. Once you've admired the interior, walk to the back of the bot, passing behind the central cluster of Buddha images, to find another Buddha image seated against the back wall: climb the steps in front of this statue to get a close-up of the left foot, which for some reason was cast with six toes.

Wat Kamphaeng Laeng

Thanon Phra Song, a 15min walk east and then south of Wat Yai

The five tumbledown prangs of **Wat Kamphaeng Laeng** mark out Phetchaburi as the likely southernmost outpost of the Khmer empire. Built probably in the thirteenth century to honour the Hindu deity Shiva and set out in a cruciform arrangement facing east, the laterite corncob-style prangs were later adapted for Buddhist use, as can be seen from the two that now house Buddha images. There has been some attempt to restore a few of the carvings and false balustraded windows, but these days worshippers congregate in the modern whitewashed wat behind these shrines, leaving the atmospheric and appealingly quaint collection of decaying prangs and casuarina topiary to chickens, stray dogs and the occasional tourist.

Wat Mahathat

Thanon Damnoen Kasem

Heading west along Thanon Phra Song from Wat Kamphaeng Laeng, across the river you can see the prangs of Phetchaburi's most fully restored and important temple, **Wat Mahathat**, long before you reach them. Boasting the "Mahathat" title only since 1954 – when the requisite Buddha relics were donated by the king – it was probably founded in the fourteenth century, but suffered badly at the hands of the Burmese. The five landmark prangs at its heart are adorned with stucco figures of mythical creatures, though these are nothing compared with those on the roofs of the main viharn and the bot. Instead of tapering off into the usual serpentine *chofa*, the gables are studded with miniature *thep* and *deva* figures (angels and gods), which add an almost mischievous vitality to the place. In a similar vein, a couple of gold-embossed crocodiles snarl above the entrance to the bot, and a caricature carving of a bespectacled man rubs shoulders with mythical giants in a relief around the base of the gold Buddha, housed in a separate mondop nearby.

6

Khao Wang

Dominating Phetchaburi's western outskirts stands Rama IV's palace, a stew of mid-nineteenth-century Thai and European styles scattered over the crest of the hill known as **Khao Wang** ("Palace Hill"). During his day, the royal entourage would struggle its way up the steep brick path to the summit, but now there's a **cable car** (daily 8.30am–4.30pm; B200 including admission to the palace) which starts from the western flank of the hill off Highway 4; there's also a path up the eastern flank, starting near Thanon Rajwithi. If you do walk up the hill, be warned that hundreds of quite aggressive monkeys hang out at its base and on the path to the top.

Up top, the wooded hill is littered with wats, prangs, chedis, whitewashed gazebos and lots more, in an ill-assorted combination of architectural idioms – the prang-topped viharn, washed all over in burnt sienna, is particularly ungainly. Whenever the king came on an excursion here, he stayed in the airy summer house, **Phra Nakhon Khiri** (daily 8.30am–4pm; B150), with its Mediterranean-style shutters and verandas. Now a museum, it houses a moderately interesting collection of ceramics, furniture and other artefacts given to the royal family by foreign friends. Besides being cool and breezy, Khao Wang also proved to be a good stargazing spot, so Rama IV, a keen astronomer (see p.526), had an open-sided, glass-domed observatory built close to his sleeping quarters.

ARRIVAL AND DEPARTURE
                                              PHETCHABURI

BY TRAIN

Phetchaburi station is on the north side of the town centre.
Destinations Bangkok (Hualamphong Station 11 daily, Thonburi Station 2 daily; 2hr 45min–3hr 45min); Chumphon (12 daily; 4hr–6hr 30min); Hua Hin (14 daily; 1hr); Nakhon Pathom (13 daily; 1hr 30min–2hr); Nakhon Si Thammarat (2 daily; 12–13hr); Prachuap Khiri Khan (10 daily; 2–3hr); Ratchaburi (13 daily; 40min–1hr); Surat Thani (9 daily; 6hr 45min–9hr); Trang (2 daily; 13hr).

BY BUS

Phetchaburi is served mostly by through-buses on their way to or from Bangkok – all services between the capital and southern Thailand have to pass through the town on Highway 4.
Through-buses There's a small Baw Khaw Saw terminal on the east side of Highway 4 (Thanon Phetkasem), which is where southbound through-buses will set you down or pick you up. Northbound through-buses on their way to

Bangkok stop on the opposite side of the highway: ask to get off at "Sii Yaek Phetcharat", the crossroads of Highway 4 and Thanon Bandai-It by Phetcharat Hospital – otherwise you might be put off at the Big C Department Store about 5km south of town. Songthaews and motorbike taxis run between Highway 4 and the town centre.

From/to Cha-am and Hua Hin Non-a/c buses from and to Cha-am and Hua Hin use the small terminal in the town centre, less than a 10min walk from Chomrut Bridge.

From/to Bangkok The terminal for the one dedicated Phetchaburi–Bangkok a/c bus per day is about a 10min walk from Chomrut Bridge, on Thanon Matayawong. Note that if you're coming here from Kanchanaburi, you can avoid Bangkok by heading for Ratchaburi, where you can catch a bus, a/c minibus or train to Phetchaburi.

Destinations Bangkok (1 daily; 2hr 15min); Cha-am (roughly every 30min; 1hr 20min); Hua Hin (roughly every 30min; 1hr 50min).

BY MINIBUS

Several companies offer licensed a/c minibuses to the Southern Bus Terminal and Victory Monument in Bangkok, including one southeast of the train station (marked on our map) that also covers Ratchaburi.

GETTING AROUND

By samlor or songthaew Shared songthaews circulate round the town, but to see the major temples in a day and have sufficient energy left for climbing Khao Wang, you might want to hire a samlor or a songthaew for a couple of hours, at about B100–200/hr, depending on distance.

By bicycle or motorbike You can rent bicycles (B100/day) and motorbikes (B250–350/day) from *Rabieng Rimnum Guest House*.

INFORMATION AND TOURS

Tourist information There's no TAT office in town, but *Rabieng Rimnum Guest House* is a good source of local information. It also organizes day-trips and multi-day visits to Kaeng Krachan National Park for bird-watching and hiking (two or three nights are good for trekking into the jungle), roughly from November to June or July.

ACCOMMODATION

Rabieng Rimnum (Rim Nam) Guest House 1 Thanon Chisa-in, on the southwest corner of Chomrut Bridge ☎ 032 425707 or ☎ 089 919 7446, ⊕ rabiengrimnum .com. Occupying a century-old house next to the Phet River and, less appealingly, a noisy main road, this popular, central guesthouse offers very simple rooms with shared, cold-water bathrooms, lots of local information and the best restaurant in town. Excellent rates for singles; en-suite bathrooms planned in some rooms. B240

Royal Diamond Soi Sam Chao Phet, in a grid of small streets just off the Phetkasem Highway ☎ 032 411061–70, ⊕ royaldiamondhotel.com. On the northwest side of Khao Wang, this welcoming place is Phetchaburi's best upmarket option. The large, comfortable a/c rooms with hot water, TVs and fridges are fairly well insulated from the noise of the highway (though not necessarily from the live bands in the hotel's own beer garden). Very modest breakfast included. B800

Sabai Dee Resort 65 Thanon Khong Kacheng ☎ 086 344 4418. Centrally placed and friendly budget option opposite *Rabieng Rimnum*. All sharing cold-water bathrooms, accommodation is either in very simple bamboo bungalows with mosquito nets in a small garden by the river; or in more expensive but better-value, large, white rooms (fan or a/c) with polished wooden floors in the bright, airy, mostly wooden main building, which has a ground-floor café. Fan B250, a/c B500

EATING

As well as for *khanom*, Phetchaburi is famous for savoury **khao chae**: originally a Mon dish designed to cool you down in the hot season, it consists of rice in chilled, flower-scented water served with delicate, fried side dishes, such as shredded Chinese radish and balls of shrimp paste, dried fish and palm sugar. It's available at the day market until sold out, usually around 3pm. There's a nice little **night market** on the small road parallel to and immediately west of Thanon Matayawong.

Rabieng Rimnum (Rim Nam) Guest House 1 Thanon Chisa-in, on the southwest corner of Chomrut Bridge ☎ 032 425707 or ☎ 089 919 7446, ⊕ rabiengrimnum .com. The town's best restaurant, an airy, wooden house with riverside tables attached to the guesthouse of the same name. It offers a long and interesting menu of inexpensive Thai dishes, from banana-blossom salad (B80) to the tasty Phetchaburi speciality, sugar-palm fruit curry with prawns (B80), and is deservedly popular with local diners. Daily 8am–midnight.

PHETCHABURI'S KHANOM

Almost half the shops in Phetchaburi stock the town's famous **khanom** (sweet snacks), as do many of the souvenir stalls crowding the base of Khao Wang and vendors at the day market on Thanon Matayawong. The most well-known local speciality is *maw kaeng* (best sampled from Raan Khanom Waan Mee Pin on the west side of Thanon Matayawong, just north of Phongsuriya), a baked sweet egg custard made with mung beans and coconut and sometimes flavoured with lotus seeds, durian or taro. Other Phetchaburi classics to look out for include *khanom taan*, small, steamed, saffron-coloured cakes made with local palm sugar, coconut and rice flour, and wrapped in banana-leaf cases; and *thong yot*, orange balls of palm sugar and baked egg yolk.

Cha-am and around

Forever in the shadow of its more famous neighbour, Hua Hin, 25km to the south, the resort of **CHA-AM** is nevertheless very popular with Thais on short breaks, and it sports one or two package-holiday high-rises and Western-style restaurants for Europeans, too. Mostly, though, it's weekending families and partying student groups from Bangkok who eat and drink at the rows of umbrella-shaded tables and deckchairs on the sand, or brave the sea on banana boats or rubber tyres, the women clad modestly in T-shirts and shorts rather than bikinis. The long, straight beach here is pleasantly shaded, though rather gritty and very narrow at high tide, and the water is perfectly swimmable, if not pristine. During the week the pace of life in Cha-am is slow, and it's easy to find a solitary spot under the thick canopy of casuarinas, particularly at the northerly end of the beach, but that's rarely possible at weekends, when prices shoot up and traffic thickens considerably.

Cha-am has a functional pocket of development around Thanon Phetkasem (Highway 4), close to the junction with Thanon Narathip, the main access road to the beach, 1km to the east. However, the 3km seaside promenade of Thanon Ruamchit is where you'll find most of the hotels, restaurants, a small police station (corner of Thanon Narathip) and a few other tourist-oriented businesses; Thanon Ruamchit's sois are numbered according to whether they're north or south of Thanon Narathip.

Phra Ratchaniwet Marukhathaiyawan

10km south of Cha-am, off the road to Hua Hin, Highway 4 • Daily except Wed 8/8.30am–4/4.30pm • Grounds B30, palace B30; English guidebook B80 • Dress politely (with shoulders and knees covered) as it's a former royal palace • Best accessed by private transport, but Cha-am–Hua Hin buses (roughly every 30min) stop within 2km of the palace at the sign for Rama VI Camp – just follow the road through the army compound

Set in beautiful grounds, the lustrous seaside palace of Rama VI, **Phra Ratchaniwet Marukhathaiyawan** (aka Mrigadayavan Palace), is rarely visited by foreigners, though it sees plenty of Thai visitors. Designed by an Italian architect, Ercole Manfredi, in a westernized Thai style, and completed in 1924, the entire, 400m-long complex of sixteen golden teak pavilions and connecting walkways is raised off the ground on over a thousand concrete columns, with a niche for water at the base of each to keep out ants. It's often referred to as "the palace of love and hope" as Rama VI first visited with his pregnant queen, who later miscarried (and was subsequently demoted to royal consort), but it was abandoned to the corrosive sea air after the king's death in 1925. Restoration work began in the 1970s, and today most of the structure looks as it once did, a stylish composition of verandas and latticework painted in shades of cream and light blue, with an emphasis on cool simplicity. The spacious open hall in the north wing, hung with chandeliers and encircled by a first-floor balcony, was used as a meeting room and as a theatre for the king to perform in his own plays. The king stayed in the central group of buildings, with the best sea view and a 50m-long elevated walkway to his private bathing pavilion, while the south wing contained the apartments of the royal consorts, with its own bathing pavilion connected by a walkway.

ARRIVAL AND DEPARTURE
CHA-AM

By train The station (called "Ban Cha-am" on the State Railways' website) is a few blocks west of the main Phetkasem–Narathip junction.

Destinations Bangkok (Hualamphong Station 2–3 daily, Thonburi Station 3 daily; 3hr 30min–4hr 30min); Chumphon (3 daily; 5–7hr); Hua Hin (5–6 daily; 30min); Prachuap Khiri Khan (4 daily; 2hr).

By bus Through-buses and local services from and to Hua Hin and Phetchaburi stop on Highway 4, close to the

junction with Thanon Narathip, the main road running east to the beach; Roong Reuang coaches between Hua Hin and Suvarnabhumi Airport will pick up passengers here if pre-booked (see p.517). Dedicated Bangkok–Cha-am a/c buses use the depot at the little plaza off the beachfront Thanon Ruamchit, just south of Thanon Narathip.

Destinations Bangkok (2–3 daily; 2hr 45min–3hr 15min); Hua Hin (roughly every 30min; 35min); Phetchaburi (roughly every 30min; 50min–1hr 20min).

By minibus If you're heading for Bangkok, you could catch one of the frequent Hua Hin–Victory Monument a/c minibuses (every 20min or so), operated by several companies: either go to one of the companies' pavement desks at the Phetchaburi–Narathip junction, or phone ahead to book (see p.517).

GETTING AROUND

By bicycle or motorbike A number of shops along the beachfront rent motorbikes as well as bicycles, tandems and even three- and four-person bikes.

INFORMATION

Tourist information The local TAT office (daily 8.30am–4.30pm; ☎032 471005–6, ✉tatphet @tat.or.th), which provides information about the whole of Phetchaburi province, is on Highway 4 (west side), about 1km south of Thanon Narathip.

ACCOMMODATION

There are no obvious backpacker-oriented places in Cha-am; instead you'll find mainly small, mid-range hotels and guesthouses, concentrated on Thanon Ruamchit and the adjoining sois, and upmarket, out-of-town resorts, many on the road down to Hua Hin (covered on p.518). Many Cha-am hotels put their prices up on Saturdays and over bank-holiday weekends.

Golden Beach Cha-am Hotel Just south of Soi Cha-am North 8 at 208/14 Thanon Ruamchit ☎032 433833, ⓦgoldenbeachchaam.com. Good-value twenty-storey hotel with a full-height atrium, a swimming pool and gym, set back from the promenade. The nicely appointed rooms have a/c, hot water, mini-bars and TVs, as well as balconies, most with sea views. B1690

Hôtel de la Paix 6km north of central Cha-am ☎032 709555, ⓦhoteldelapaixhh.com. Sleek designer hide-away featuring a triumphal, white-marble staircase up to the lobby and a huge reflective pool as its centrepiece. The accommodation blocks have a striking cubic look but are very comfortable for all that, while creative, Mediterranean-influenced food is served at the breezy restaurant, *Clouds Loft*. There are two swimming pools, an active pool by the beach and an adults-only chill pool (plus seven villas with private pools), and a luxurious spa. B5900

Nana House North of Soi Cha-am North 10 towards the canal ☎032 433632, ⓦnanahouse.net. Wide range of well-kept accommodation with a/c, hot water and fridges, including two-bedroom houses (B3500). The bright, pretty, tiled rooms in the purple building down the quieter side alley are better value than the swankier affairs in the main building on the front. Breakfast included in the room rate. B1500

Nirandorn 3 Just south of the Narathip junction on Thanon Ruamchit ☎032 470300. Clean, well-maintained hotel rooms and a few tightly packed, motel-style bungalows, decorated in crisp, modern whites and browns, with sofas, safes, a/c, TVs, fridges and hot water; all rooms in the hotel block are sea-facing, sporting balconies and deckchairs. There's also a small, attractive swimming pool. Room B700, bungalow B1000

EATING AND DRINKING

The choice of **restaurants** in Cha-am is not a patch on the range you get in Hua Hin, but there should be enough Thai-style seafood to keep you satisfied, including at the dozens of deckchair-and-umbrella places on the beach and at the night market near the train station.

Didine Golden Guesthouse, on the same soi as the Bangkok bus stop, just off Thanon Ruamchit to the south of Thanon Narathip ☎032 433316. One of the best places in Cha-am to get Western food, with a French chef and a long menu of tasty traditional favourites, such as beef bourguignon (B290), pizzas, pastas and plenty of fish and seafood. Daily 7am–11.45pm.

Krua Medsai North end of the beach, just after the canal ☎032 430196. A very Thai institution, this huge, open-sided, thatched pavilion sits on the beach, with *luk thung* on the sound system, views down to Hua Hin and nice breezes off the sea. People flock here for the very good seafood, simply grilled or in dishes such as delicious *hoy jor*, crabmeat, minced pork and water chestnuts wrapped in tofu skin (B120). Daily 10am–10pm.

O-Zone Thanon Ruamchit, north of Soi Cha-am North 7 ☎032 470897. Popular bar-restaurant whose attractions include mellow live folk music early evening, followed from about 9pm by bands playing Thai and Western pop, and a menu that encompasses a few Western dishes such as pizza and steak, one-plate Thai dishes and more complex offerings such as crispy fried catfish salad (B150). Mon–Thurs & Sun 4pm–midnight, Fri & Sat 4pm–1am.

Hua Hin

Thailand's oldest beach resort, **HUA HIN** used to be little more than an overgrown fishing village with one exceptionally grand hotel, but the arrival of mass tourism, high-rise hotels and farang-managed hostess bars has made a serious dent in its once idiosyncratic charm. With the far superior beaches of Ko Samui, Krabi and Ko Samet so close at hand, there's little to draw the dedicated sunseeker here. The town's most distinctive attractions are its squid-pier restaurants and guesthouses on Thanon Naretdamri, characterful spots to stay or enjoy fine seafood, while at the other end of the scale the former *Railway Hotel* (now the *Centara Grand*) provides all the atmosphere you can afford. In addition, the town makes a convenient base for day-trips to Khao Sam Roi Yot National Park to the south and Pala-u Falls in Kaeng Krachan National Park to the west.

Brief history

The **royal family** were Hua Hin's main visitors at the start of the twentieth century, but the place became more widely popular in the 1920s, when the opening of the Bangkok–Malaysia rail line made short excursions to the beach much more viable. The Victorian-style *Railway Hotel* was opened in 1922, originally as a necessary overnight stop on the three-day journey to Malaysia. At the same time Rama VI commissioned the nine-hole Royal Hua Hin Golf Course (now 18 holes; ☎032 512475) to the west of the station, and in 1926 Rama VII had his own summer palace, Klai Klangwon ("Far from Worries"), erected at the northern end of the beach. It was here, ironically, that Rama VII was staying in 1932 when the coup was launched in Bangkok against

the system of absolute monarchy. The current king also stays here as often as he can, which means that the navy is on constant guard duty in the resort and the police are also on their best behaviour; consequently both Thais and expats consider Hua Hin an especially safe place to live and do business – hence the number of farang-oriented real-estate agencies in the area.

The central shorefront

The prettiest part of Hua Hin's 5km-long **beach** is the patch in front of and to the south of the *Centara Grand*, where the sand is at its softest and whitest. North of here the shore is crowded with tables and chairs belonging to a string of small restaurant shacks, beyond which the beach ends at a Chinese temple atop a flight of steps running down to Thanon Naretdamri. The coast to the north of the pagoda is dominated by the jetties and terraces of the squid-pier guesthouses and seafood restaurants, the hub of the original fishing village, which dates back to the early nineteenth century.

EXCURSIONS AND ACTIVITIES AROUND HUA HIN

A popular day-trip from Hua Hin is 63km west to the fifteen-tiered **Pala-u Waterfall**, situated close to the Burmese border and within **Kaeng Krachan National Park** (B300; ⓦ dnp.go.th). Though the falls themselves are hardly exceptional, the route there takes you through lush, hilly landscape and past innumerable pineapple plantations. There's no public transport to the falls, but every tour operator features them in its programme. To get there under your own steam, follow the signs from the west end of Thanon Chomsin along Highway 3218. Once inside the park you'll see hundreds of butterflies and may also catch sight of monitor lizards and six species of hornbill. A slippery and occasionally steep path follows the river through the fairly dense jungle up to the falls, passing the (numbered) tiers en route to the remote fifteenth level, though most people opt to stop at the third level, which has the first pool of any decent depth (full of fish but not that clear) and is a half-hour walk from the car park.

Hua Hin also offers excursions to Khao Sam Roi Yot National Park, Phetchaburi, Amphawa floating market and Kanchanaburi, not to mention the old summer palace of Phra Ratchaniwet Marukhathaiyawan just to the north (see p.513). In addition, a number of **activities** are available, such as cycling and kiteboarding.

TOUR OPERATORS

Hua Hin Adventure Tour 69/7 Thanon Naebkehat ⓣ032 530314, ⓦ huahinadventuretour.com. A huge range of tours, including Pala-u Falls (from B1700/person), a boat trip in Kaeng Krachan National Park (from B2000), Khao Sam Roi Yot National Park (from B1700; including kayaking on Khao Daeng canal, from B2000) and elephant watching in Kui Buri National Park (from B1900), plus diving and Thai cooking classes.

Hua Hin Bike Tours 15/120 Thanon Phetkasem ⓣ081 173 4469, ⓦ huahinbiketours.com. A variety of guided half-day (B1500) and day rides (from B2500 including lunch), including transfers, as well as rental for B500/day and multi-day tours.

Kiteboarding Asia ⓣ081 591 4593, ⓦ kiteboardingasia.com. Kiteboarding courses and rental from three shops on the beach to the south of the *Centara Grand*, the first of which is between Soi 73 and Soi 71 (B4000 for a one-day course, B11,000 for three days; best conditions from Feb to mid-May); also offers stand-up paddleboarding.

Mermaid Cruises ⓣ032 632223 or ⓣ084 800 7400, ⓦ huahincruises.com. Eco-friendly trips on the Pran River to the south of Hua Hin (B1950/person, including lunch and transfers), using quiet electric-powered longtails that allow you to get close to the wildlife, including 3m-long monitor lizards, egrets, ospreys, wild peacocks and six species of kingfisher. Kayaking day-trips on the river are also offered (B1250, including lunch), as well as afternoon tours to Amphawa floating market, including a boat trip among the fireflies (B1950, including dinner). Among several sea cruises, Mermaid also run full-day trips on a big boat down to Khao Sam Roi Yot (B1950, including lunch and park admission fee).

Western Tours 11 Thanon Damnern Kasem ⓣ032 533303–4, ⓦ westerntourshuahin.com. Weekly roster of day-trips including Phetchaburi (B1500), Amphawa Floating Market (B2200) and a snorkelling tour (B2700).

ACCOMMODATION AND EATING

Kritsada Rimkhong 90 Moo 2, Thanon Rim Khong ☏ 042 540088. On the riverside road about 1km north of the centre, opposite the hotel of the same name. The breezy terrace of this restaurant, with expansive views across to Laos, is a good spot to enjoy a simple fried rice (B50) or a *tom yam koong* (spicy sour soup with shrimp; B150). Daily 8am–10pm.

That Phanom Riverview 258 Moo 2, Thanon Rim Khong ☏ 042 541555, ⓦ thatphanomriverviewhotel .com. This newish riverside hotel is the town's most comfortable place to stay, with good-sized, well-equipped rooms (work desks, cable TV) in an apartment-style complex, though few rooms actually have a view of the river. **B850**

Mukdahan

Fifty kilometres downriver of That Phanom, **MUKDAHAN** is the last stop on the Mekong trail before Highway 212 heads off inland to Ubon Ratchathani, 170km to the south. You may feel a long way from the comforts of Bangkok out here, but this is one of the fastest-developing Thai provinces, owing to increasing friendship between Laos and Thailand and the proximity of **Savannakhet**, the second-biggest Lao city, just across the water. Few farang visitors make it this far, though Mukdahan–Savannakhet is an officially sanctioned crossing to Laos, via the new bridge 7km north of town, and as the cranes dominating the skyline show, new hotels are springing up all the time.

Indochina Market

Daily 8am–6pm

The promenade overlooking Savannakhet is swamped by the daily **Indochina Market**, which is especially busy at weekends. On sale here are household goods and inexpensive ornaments, such as Vietnamese mother-of-pearl and Chinese ceramics, brought over from Laos; the market is also good for local fabrics like lengths of coarsely woven cotton in lovely muted colours, and expensive but very classy silks.

Mukdahan Tower

Thanon Samut Sakdarak • Daily 8am–6pm • B50

At the southern edge of town rises the 65m-high **Mukdahan Tower** (*Ho Kaeo Mukdahan*), a modern white edifice that looks somewhat out of place in the low-rise outskirts. Built in 1996 to commemorate the fiftieth anniversary of the king's accession to the throne, the tower houses an interesting array of historic artefacts from the Mukdahan area, including traditional Isaan costumes, pottery, coins, amulets, vicious-looking weaponry and fossils. The highlight, however, is the expansive view from the sixth floor – 50m high to reflect fifty years of Rama IX – over Mukdahan and the Mekong into Laos. On the smaller floor above is a much-revered, Sukhothai-style silver Buddha image, the Phra Phuttha Nawaming Mongkhon Mukdahan, fronted by the bone relics of famous monks in small glass containers.

ARRIVAL AND GETTING AROUND   MUKDAHAN

By bus Regular buses from That Phanom and Ubon Ratchathani stop at the bus terminal about 2km northwest of the centre on Highway 212. Songthaews shuttle between the bus station and Mukdahan Tower via the

---

CROSSING THE LAO BORDER VIA MUKDAHAN

Mukdahan–Savannakhet is an officially sanctioned **crossing** to Laos, via the second **Thai-Lao Friendship Bridge**, 7km north of town. Buses (12 daily 7.30am–7pm; B45–50) cross the bridge to **Savannakhet**, and it's possible to get a visa on arrival (US$30–42; see p.28 for further details). When being stamped out of the country, you may be charged B20 by the officials.

There are bicycles (B40/hr) and motorbikes (B250/day) for rent, and a shuttle bus to run guests into town. B790
Sri Thep Hotel 150m south of the main road (Highway 22), and one block west of the river ☏ 042 512395. By far the friendliest budget choice, this Chinese-style hotel has tiled floors and solid wooden furniture in its clean, airy rooms. Fan B300, a/c B400

That Phanom

THAT PHANOM, a riverside village of weather-beaten wooden buildings, sprawls around Isaan's most important shrine, **Wat Phra That Phanom**. This far-northeastern corner of Thailand may seem like a strange location for one of the country's holiest sites, but the wat was built to serve both Thais and Lao, as evidenced by the ample boat-landing in the village. Plenty of Lao still come across the river for the fascinating Monday and Thursday morning waterfront **market**, bringing for sale such items as wild animal skins, black pigs and herbal medicines, alongside the usual fruit and veg.

Wat Phra That Phanom

Just off Highway 212, five blocks west from the Mekong

Popularly held to be one of the four sacred pillars of Thai religion (the other three are Chiang Mai's Wat Phra That Doi Suthep, Wat Mahathat in Nakhon Si Thammarat, and Wat Phra Phutthabat near Lopburi), **Wat Phra That Phanom** is a fascinating place of pilgrimage, especially at the time of the ten-day Phra That Phanom festival, usually in February, when thousands of people come to pay homage and enjoy themselves in the traditional holiday between harvesting and sowing; pilgrims believe that they must make the trip seven times during a full moon before they die.

The temple reputedly dates back to the eighth year after the death of the Buddha, when five local princes built a simple brick chedi to house bits of his breastbone. It's been restored or rebuilt seven times, most recently after it collapsed during a rainstorm in 1975; the latest incarnation is in the form of a Lao *that*, 57m high, modelled on the That Luang in Vientiane. From the river pier, a short ceremonial way leads under a Disneyesque **victory arch** erected by the Lao, through the temple gates to the present chedi, which, as is the custom, faces water and the rising sun.

The chedi

A brick-and-plaster structure covered with white paint and gold floral decorations, the **chedi** looks like nothing so much as a giant, ornate table leg turned upside down. From each of the four sides, an eye forming part of the traditional flame pattern stares down, and the whole thing is surmounted by an umbrella made of 16kg of gold, with precious gems and gold rings embedded in each tier. The chedi sits on a gleaming white marble platform, on which pilgrims say their prayers and leave every imaginable kind of offering to the relics. Look out for the **brick reliefs** in the shape of four-leaf clovers above three of the doorways in the base: on the northern side, Vishnu mounted on a garuda; on the western side, the four guardians of the earth putting offerings in the Buddha's alms bowl; and above the south door, a carving of the Buddha entering nirvana. At the corners of the chedi, brick plaques, carved in the tenth century but now heavily restored, tell the stories of the wat's princely founders.

ARRIVAL AND INFORMATION   **THAT PHANOM**

By bus The bus station is out to the west of the town centre, but all services from Nakhon Phanom and Mukdahan also stop in front of the temple; the Nakhon Phanom route is also covered by frequent songthaews, which gather to the north of the wat.

Destinations Bangkok (4 daily; 12hr); Mukdahan (every 25min; 1hr 20min); Nakhon Phanom (every 25min; 1hr); Ubon Ratchathani (hourly; 3–4hr); Udon Thani (4 daily; 4–5hr).
Banks There are several banks with ATMs on Thanon Chayangkun, near the wat.

6

Dusit Resort Hua Hin 9km north of Hua Hin on Thanon Phetkasem ☎ 032 520009, ⓦ dusit.com. One of the most luxurious spots on this stretch of coast, with large, elegant rooms set around a tropical garden and lotus-filled lagoon. Facilities include four restaurants, a huge swimming pool with children's pool and a separate saltwater pool, a spa, fitness centre, watersports, a kids' club, tennis and squash courts and an Avis car rental desk. B6300

Fu-Lay Guest House and Hotel 110/1 Thanon Naretdamri, guesthouse ☎ 032 513145, ⓦ fulayhuahin .net; hotel ☎ 032 513670, ⓦ fulayhuahin.com. *Fu-Lay* is in two halves, with guesthouse rooms strung along a jetty and balconied, a/c hotel accommodation in a low-rise block across the street. The jetty guesthouse is the most stylish of its kind in Hua Hin, offering attractively appointed a/c rooms with nice hot-water bathrooms (B1050), plus some cheap en-suite fan rooms (some with hot water) and a breezy seating area set right over the water. Fan B550, a/c B950

Hilton Hua Hin 33 Thanon Naretdamri ☎ 032 538999, ⓦ huahin.hilton.com. Set bang in the centre of Hua Hin's beachfront, the *Hilton's* high-rise profile disfigures the local skyline, but the facilities are extensive and the views excellent. There's a large, inviting lagoon-like swimming pool right on the seafront, a spa, tennis courts, a kids' club, a panoramic rooftop Chinese restaurant and an impressive indoor-outdoor water garden in the lobby. All three hundred rooms are large and comfortable and have sea-view balconies. B6500

Mod 116 Thanon Naretdamri ☎ 032 512296. A friendly and well-maintained little jetty guesthouse, where rooms

are all shining white, with cable TV and small but attractive bathrooms, and come with either fan and cold water or a/c and hot. There's a nice, breezy, covered sea-view terrace at the end. Fan B600, a/c B900

Sirima Guest House 31/3 Thanon Naretdamri ☎ 032 511060. Plenty of pot plants enliven this otherwise typical jetty guesthouse, which offers mostly small rooms with shiny wood panelling and mosquito screens and a large communal deck. B450

Sunshine Hotel Soi 67, off Thanon Phetkasem ☎ 032 515309, ⓔ sunshine.guesthouse.beach@gmail.com. Typical Soi 67 guesthouse, with friendly staff and a wide variety of clean, well-maintained a/c rooms, most with small verandas, and all with hot water, TV and fridge. B1000

Tong Mee House 1 Soi Ruam Phow, Thanon Naebkehat ☎ 032 530725, ⓦ tongmeehousehuahin.com. In a modern, five-storey block on a quiet soi, this friendly guesthouse offers great value: six small but neat rooms with a/c, hot water, fridges, TVs and small balconies, and an attractive "penthouse" double with a large, shaded roof terrace. B600

Veranda Lodge Soi 67, Thanon Phetkasem ☎ 032 533678, ⓦ verandalodge.com. Chic boutique hotel set in its own beachfront garden. Deluxe rooms have a contemporary look, some with lime green, pink or china blue walls, and petite balconies; most of the various suites and bungalows have separate living rooms and small kitchen areas, and all have balconies. A/c, cable TV, DVD players and mini-bars throughout, and there's a small pool fed by a waterfall, and a seafront terrace restaurant. Breakfast included. B3200

EATING AND DRINKING

Hua Hin is renowned for its **seafood**, and some of the best places to enjoy the local catch are the seafront and squid-pier restaurants along Thanon Naretdamri. Fish also features heavily at the large and lively **night market**, which sets up at sunset along Soi 72 (the western end of Thanon Dechanuchit). The biggest concentration of **bars** is in the network of sois between the *Hilton Hotel* and Wat Hua Hin, particularly along Soi Bintabat, Soi Kanjanomai and Thanon Poonsuk; most of these places are so-called "bar-beers", with lots of seating round the bar and hostesses dispensing beer and flirtation through the night.

★ **Baan Itsara** 7 Thanon Naebkehat, near Soi 10, north of Thanon Damrongrat (Phetkasem Soi 51) ☎ 032 530574. Excellent seafood in a traditional lime-green wooden house with simple tables on a seaside terrace. The speciality here is sweet basil sauce – which comes out something like pesto – with, for example, squid (B220) or king prawns (B450), but the grilled mackerel and the seafood *laap* with land-lotus leaves are also very good. Daily 11am–10pm.

Chao Lay 15 Thanon Naretdamri. Hua Hin's most famous jetty restaurant is deservedly popular, serving up high-quality seafood from live tanks out front, including rock lobster, blue crab, scallops, cottonfish, mixed seafood hot plates and specialities such as "prawn curry mousse" (*haw mok*). Most main dishes cost B200–300. Daily 10am–10pm.

Cool Breeze 62 Thanon Naretdamri ☎ 032 531062. Either in the nice little garden at the back or amid the fresh, leafy decor inside, you can tuck into some very tasty tapas (including plenty of vegetarian options) at this bar-café, which imports many of its ingredients from Spain. You can get a set of seven tapas for B900, and they also do baguettes, paella and other seafood and meat mains. Lunch set menus cost B260, while happy hour till 7pm includes 3-for-2 tapas and 2-for-1 sangria. Daily 11am–11pm.

Hua Hin Brewing Company Thanon Naretdamri. Owned by the adjacent *Hilton*, this lively bar sports a nautical theme on its tiered streetside terraces and offers own-brewed lagers and wheat ale, as well as DJs, live bands and TV sports. Daily 6pm–2am.

Koti Thanon Dechanuchit, corner of Thanon Phetkasem. With pavement tables right on a prominent corner opposite the night market, this very simple Thai-Chinese restaurant rustles up justifiably famous *hoy jor* (deep-fried crab sausage; B120), which goes nicely with its tasty fried rice with salted fish. Daily noon–4pm & 6–10pm.

Pa Jeua Thanon Naretdamri, opposite the Hilton Hua Hin. Famous roadside stall that sells Thailand's favourite dessert, delicious *khao niaw mamuang* (fresh mango with sticky rice and coconut milk), for B80. Daily 9.30am– roughly 3pm.

Sara Jane's 28/1 Thanon Poonsuk ☎032 532990. This branch of an old Bangkok favourite provides authentic northeastern food, including *som tam* with raw salted crab, delicious central Thai dishes such as *yam plaa duk foo*, as well as pizzas, pastas and other Western mains, in a lovely big garden that's shaded by trees and almost carpeted with orchids. Daily 9.30am–2pm & 5–11pm.

Som Moo Joom (Jek Pia) 51/6 Thanon Dechanuchit (corner of Thanon Naebkehat); no English sign. Exceptionally good seafood at very cheap prices has made this bare-bones evening restaurant in an old wooden house extremely popular with Thai holiday-makers. The trademark dish, *moo joom*, is a clear soup in which you cook your own pork (or shrimp/squid), but the menu also covers the range of standard seafood dishes. From 6.30am to 1.20pm, several popular stalls take over the space, offering coffee and typical Thai morning food, such as *khao man kai* and noodle soup with seafood. Daily 5.30–7.30pm.

ENTERTAINMENT

Thai Boxing Garden Down a small soi off Thanon Poonsuk ☎032 515269, ⓦfacebook.com/thaiboxing garden. Tuesdays and Saturdays are fight nights at the *Thai Boxing Garden* with programmes starting at 9pm (B600–800); it's owned by local *muay thai* champion Khun Chop, who also runs Thai boxing classes every day (B400/hr for a one-to-one session).

SHOPPING

Bookazine Near the corner of Damnern Kasem and Naretdamri roads ☎032 516512. Small outlet in a supermarket for English books, magazines and newspapers. Daily 8am–midnight.

Cicada Market Suan Sri, Thanon Takiab (near the Hyatt Regency, about 4km south of the Centara Grand) ⓦcicadamarket.com. Modelled on Chiang Mai's walking streets, this weekend market features jewellery, cute accessories, lots of T-shirts and other clothes, art galleries and, of course, plenty of food, plus regular performances of all kinds in the amphitheatre. Fri & Sat 4–11pm, Sun 4–10pm.

Khomapastr 218 Thanon Phetkasem ☎032 511250, ⓦkhomapastrfabrics.com. Famous outlet for *pha kiaw* (or *pha khomapastr*), brightly coloured, hand-printed cotton with lovely, swirling *kannok* patterns, usually with strong elements of gold – Khomapastr's founder, himself a prince, was inspired to start the business when rummaging through trunks of nineteenth-century royal clothing at Bangkok's National Museum in the 1940s. You can buy the cloth by the piece or metre, or made up into skirts, shirts, cushion covers and bags. Mon–Sat 9am–7pm, Sun 9am–5pm.

Plearn Wan Thanon Phetkasem, between sois 38 and 40 ⓦplearnwan.com. Curious exercise in nostalgia and commercialism – the name "Enjoy the Past" says it all – that's been a raging success with Thais from all over the country. It's essentially a shopping mall, but in the vintage style of Thai-Chinese wooden shophouses, selling retro everything: *luk krung* CDs, old-fashioned toys, traditional coffee and desserts, ukuleles... Mon–Thurs & Sun 9am–9pm, Fri & Sat 8am–11pm.

DIRECTORY

Banks and exchange There are currency-exchange counters all over the resort, especially on Thanon Damnern Kasem and Thanon Naretdamri; most of the main bank branches with ATMs are on Thanon Phetkasem.

Hospital Bangkok Hospital, 888 Thanon Phetkasem, south of the centre near Soi 94 (☎032 616800, ⓦbangkok hospital.com).

Immigration office Soi 35, Thanon Phetkasem, on the beachfront just north of Klai Klangwon Palace (Mon–Fri 8.30am–4.30pm; ☎1178).

Meditation English-medium courses in sitting and walking meditation, either weekly or week-long, with talks on Buddhism, at Wat Khao Santi, just off Soi 91, Thanon Phetkasem (free, donations welcome; ⓦmeditationin huahin.org).

Pharmacy Several in the resort, including the helpful and well-stocked Medihouse (daily 9.30am–11pm), opposite the *Hilton* on Thanon Naretdamri.

Thai language Classes and private lessons at TLC, 83/14 Wongchomsin Building, Thanon Phetkasem (near Soi 63/1; ☎032 533428, ⓦthailanguagecentre.org).

Tourist police For all emergencies, call the tourist police on the free, 24hr phoneline (☎1155), or contact them at their office opposite the *Centara Grand* at the beachfront end of Thanon Damnern Kasem.

Travel agency Reliable Western Tours (see p.516) sells international and domestic air tickets, as well as taxi transfers to Bangkok's Suvarnabhumi Airport.

Pak Nam Pran

The stretch of coast between Hua Hin and Chumphon barely registers on most foreign tourists' radar, but many better-off Bangkokians have favourite beaches in this area, the nicest of which is sophisticated **PAK NAM PRAN** (aka Pranburi). Just 30km or so south of Hua Hin, Pak Nam Pran used to cater only for families who owned beach villas here, but in the past few years the shorefront homes have been joined by a growing number of enticing, if pricey, boutique hotels, and signs are there's more development to come. For now, facilities consist of just a few minimarkets, car-rental outlets and independent bars and restaurants, especially around the *Evason* hotel towards the northern end of the beach, plus the possibility of organizing day-trips to nearby Khao Sam Roi Yot National Park through hotel staff; there's also kiteboarding through Kiteboarding Asia, about 1km south of the *Evason* (☎089 743 5564, ⊛kiteboardingasia.com).

As along much of the Gulf coast, the **beach** itself, also known as Hat Naresuan, is not exceptional (it has hardly any shade and is suffering from erosion in parts), but it is long, with fine sand, and nearly always empty, and you're quite likely to see dolphins playing within sight of the shore. The strand stretches south from Pak Nam Pran town at the mouth of the Pran River – which is known for its colourful fishing boats, specializing in squid – for around 7km to the headland at Khao Kalok ("Skull Mountain") and the tiny Thao Kosa Forest Park.

ARRIVAL AND DEPARTURE

Easiest access is via the town of **Pranburi**, which straddles Highway 4 some 23km south of Hua Hin. There's no public transport from Pranburi to Pak Nam Pran beach, 10km or so away, but hotels can arrange transfers and any Pranburi songthaew driver will taxi you there. Because of this and because the hotels and restaurants are well spread out along the beach, it's best to have your own transport. Pranburi's main crossroads (Highway 4 and Thanon Ratbamrung) is 2km south of Tesco Lotus at Talat Chaikaew – if making your own way, the easiest route is to turn east off Highway 4 here and take minor road 3168 down to the sea, picking up the relevant sign for your hotel.

FROM/TO PRANBURI

By train Pranburi's quaint old station is 4km east of the Highway 4 crossroads (Talat Chaikaew) towards the beach, off the north side of Route 3168.

Destinations Bangkok (Hualamphong 1 daily, Thonburi 2 daily; 5hr–5hr 30min); Chumphon (2 daily; 4hr 30min); Prachuap Khiri Khan (3 daily; 1hr).

By bus As well as many through services to and from the south, Pranburi is served by a/c buses from Bangkok's Southern Bus Terminal and non-a/c buses from Thanon

Sa Song in Hua Hin, which drop passengers close by the main Highway 4 crossroads at Talat Chaikaew.

Destinations Bangkok (every 30min; 3–4hr); Hua Hin (roughly hourly; 30min).

By minibus A/c minibuses from Bangkok's Victory Monument generally stop at the Tesco Lotus supermarket on Highway 4 opposite Pranburi's City Hall, but you could ask the driver to take you to your beach hotel for a little extra money.

ACCOMMODATION

Pak Nam Pran's charming **accommodation** is its biggest draw: for once, "boutique" is the appropriate term, as many of the hotels here offer a dozen or fewer rooms. With influences ranging from Greece to the South Pacific, from Morocco to Scandinavia, the style tends to be more arty than five-star, though you will certainly be comfortable. Some hotels aren't suitable for kids owing to their multiple levels and unfenced flights of steps. Breakfast is generally included in the price of the room. During weekends in high season (Nov–May), hoteliers routinely put their prices up and you'll need to book ahead. The following are spread over a 2km stretch of the beachfront road, starting about 4km south of Pak Nam Pran town.

★**Aleenta** Central Pak Nam Pran beach ☎032 618333, ⊛aleenta.com. This stunningly designed, eco-friendly hotel, divided between the Main Wing and the Frangipani Wing, 500m down the beach, offers gorgeous circular, thatched bungalows and very tasteful villa-style rooms, most with uninterrupted sea views, decks and plunge pools. The feel is modernist chic, with elegantly understated local furnishings and huge windows, and

Khao Sam Roi Yot National Park

National park entry fee B200 • ☎ 032 821568, ⊛ dnp.go.th

With a name that translates as "The Mountain with Three Hundred Peaks", **KHAO SAM ROI YOT NATIONAL PARK**, with its northern entrance 28km south of Pak Nam Pran beach or 63km from Hua Hin, encompasses a small but varied, mosquito-ridden coastal zone of just 98 square kilometres. The dramatic limestone crags after which it is named are the dominant feature, looming 600m above the Gulf waters and the forested interior, but perhaps more significant are the mud flats and freshwater marsh which attract and provide a breeding ground for thousands of migratory birds. **Bird-watching** at Thung Khao Sam Roi Yot swamp is a major draw, but the famously photogenic Phraya Nakhon Khiri cave is the focus of most day-trips, while a few decent trails and a couple of secluded beaches provide added interest.

Orientation in the park is fairly straightforward. One main inland road runs roughly north–south through it from the R3168 (the road from Pranburi's main junction to Pak Nam Pran), passing, in order: the 2km side road to **Hat Phu Noi**, a quiet, golden-sand beach that offers several resort alternatives to the park's accommodation and the chance to see dolphins in the cool season; the northern park checkpoint, 4km further on; the turn-offs for Ban Bang Pu (the jumping-off point for Tham Phraya Nakhon), Ban Khung Tanot (for Tham Sai) and Hat Sam Phraya (all to the east); then going over Khao Daeng canal, before looping westwards around the main massif, past the **park headquarters** (where park

EATING

Krua Jaew On the edge of Pak Nam Pran town, about 2km north of the Evason ☎ 032 63302. The best of several neighbouring seafront restaurants, offering an enormous, mid-priced menu of 120 mostly fish and seafood dishes, including excellent crab curry, seafood curry soufflé (*haw mok thalay*, on the menu as "steamed seafood with spicy and coconut milk"; B150) and the local speciality, deep-fried dried squid (*pla meuk det diaw*; B150). Unsigned in English, but it's the first restaurant you'll come to heading up the beach road into Pak Nam Pran, with its kitchen and most of its tables on the

SLEEPING

Evason Northern Pak Nam Pran beach ☎ 032 632111, ⊛ sixsenses.com/evason. The biggest and best-known hotel in Pak Nam Pran, but as accommodation is screened by graceful gardens, the feel is quite private and small-scale. Rooms are attractively cool and contemporary, with big balconies; for extra privacy, you could check into a super-luxe private-pool villa, a favourite choice of Thai film stars. Facilities include a huge pool, a spa, three restaurants, tennis courts and a kids' club with its own pool. B7540

★ **Huaplee Lazy Beach** Central Pak Nam Pran beach ☎ 032 630554–5, ⊛ huapleelazybeach.com. This exceptionally cute collection of seven idiosyncratic white-cube beachfront rooms around a pretty lawn and iPods and wi-fi capability rather than TVs. There's a small rooftop pool and spa; yoga, t'ai chi and cooking classes are available, while the restaurant uses produce from its own organic farm. B9530

Pran Havana Central Pak Nam Pran beach ☎ 032 570077, ⊛ pranhavanabluemorpho.com. More white-cube architecture and aquamarine paint at this charming beachfront accommodation, where the warren of individually furnished rooms is accessed by a series of painted concrete steps, wooden walkways and sea-view terraces. Interiors are idiosyncratic seaside-chic, persona-lized with hand-crafted furnishings and artworks. The price depends on the view. B2200

two suites (one with its own pool) 200M away is the work of the architect-interior designer owners. It's a characterful place of whimsical, marine-themed interiors done out with white-painted wood floors, blue-and-white colour schemes and funky shell and driftwood decor. The rooms are airy and bright but all have a/c, fridges and TVs; some have fantastic sea-view terraces. B3500

Krua Sawatdikan Khao Kalok On the south side of Khao Kalok's rocky outcrop at the far southern end of Pak Nam Pran beach, about 1km from Baan Panali ☎ 086 701 8597. This simple shorefront restaurant has an extensive menu of very good seafood dishes (mostly B80–150) and great views of Khao Sam Roi Yot from its beach tables under the casuarinas; mosquitoes are a problem here though, so take repellent. Daily 11am–8pm, sometimes later.

left-hand side, and a few tables towards the beach on the right. Daily roughly 10am–8.30pm.

brochures and maps are available) and the southern checkpoint (14km from the northern checkpoint), to Highway 4 at kilometre-stone 286.5.

Tham Phraya Nakhon
B300 return per boat from Wat Bang Pu

Khao Sam Roi Yot's most visited attraction is the **Tham Phraya Nakhon** cave system, hidden high up on a cliffside above **Hat Laem Sala**, an unremarkable sandy bay with a national park visitor centre that's inaccessible to vehicles. The usual way to get to Hat Laem Sala is by a five-minute boat ride from the knot of food stalls behind Wat Bang Pu on the edge of **Ban Bang Pu** fishing village (6km from the northern checkpoint). It's also possible to walk over the headland from behind Wat Bang Pu to Hat Laem Sala, along a signed, but at times steep, 500m trail. From Hat Laem Sala, another taxing though shaded trail runs up the hillside to Tham Phraya Nakhon in around thirty minutes.

The huge twin **caves** are filled with stalactites and stalagmites and wreathed in lianas and gnarly trees, but their most dramatic features are the partially collapsed roofs, which allow the sunlight to stream in and illuminate the interiors, in particular beaming down on the famous royal pavilion, Phra Thi Nang Khua Kharunhad, which was built in the second cave in 1890 in honour of Rama V.

Tham Sai
A three-hour trek south from Tham Phraya Nakhon brings you to **Tham Sai**, a thoroughly dark and dank limestone cave, complete with stalactites, stalagmites and petrified waterfalls (lamps and torches are available to rent). The trek offers some fine coastal views, but a shorter alternative is the twenty-minute trail from **Ban Khung Tanot** village (accessible by road, 8km on from the Ban Bang Pu turn-off).

Khao Daeng and around
Canal cruise B500 for up to six people ☎ 089 903 1619

The next turning off the main road will take you down to **Hat Sam Phraya**, a quiet, kilometre-long beach with a national park visitor centre, while a little further on the road crosses mangrove-fringed **Khao Daeng canal**. From beside **Wat Khao Daeng**, on the west side of the main road here, you can charter a boat for a one-hour cruise that's best in the early morning or the late afternoon.

A couple of kilometres on, you can scramble up **Khao Daeng** itself, a 157m-high outcrop that offers good summit views over the coast, via a thirty-minute trail that begins near the park headquarters. The park's 45-minute **Mangrove Forest Nature Trail** also begins close to the headquarters leading through the swampy domiciles of monitor lizards and egrets, with the chance of encountering long-tailed (crab-eating) macaques.

Thung Khao Sam Roi Yot
Accessed not from the main park road, but by turning east off Highway 4, 200m north of kilometre-stone 276, and continuing for 9km

The park hosts up to three hundred species of **birds** and between September and November the mud flats are thick with migratory flocks from Siberia, China and northern Europe. To the west of Khao Sam Roi Yot lies Thailand's largest freshwater marsh, **Thung Khao Sam Roi Yot** (aka Beung Bua), near the village of Rong Jai (Rong Che). With boardwalks and open-sided shelters over the water, this is an excellent place for observing waders and songbirds, and is one of only two places in the country where the **purple heron** breeds.

ARRIVAL AND GETTING AROUND **KHAO SAM ROI YOT**

Like most of Thailand's national parks, Khao Sam Roi Yot is hard to explore without your own **transport**, and its sights are spread too far apart to walk between.

By bicycle, motorbike or car All three are available at *Dolphin Bay Resort*, while motorbikes can be rented in Hua Hin (which also has car rental) or Prachuap Khiri Khan.

With a tour The park can be visited on a one-day tour from Hua Hin, including cycling tours and cruises (see p.516), Pak Nam Pran or *Dolphin Bay Resort*.

ACCOMMODATION AND EATING

Given the limitations of the park accommodation, many people prefer to stay a few kilometres to the north at the long, pleasingly shaded beach of Hat Phu Noi.

IN THE PARK

National Park accommodation ☎032 821568, ⓦdnp.go.th. Accommodation is at headquarters, at Hat Sam Phraya, a beach between Khao Daeng canal and Ban Khung Tanot, at Hat Laem Sala and at Thung Khao Sam Roi Yot; all four sites have restaurants. At Hat Laem Sala it's a choice between camping, at B150–225 per tent, or staying in one of the national park bungalows with hot showers (for 6–9 people); at Sam Phraya and Thung Khao Sam Roi Yot it's camping only; and at the headquarters it's bungalows only (for 5–6 people, with hot showers). Bungalows must be booked ahead through the National Parks office in Bangkok (see p.37). Hat Laem Sala B1600, HQ B1200

HAT PHU NOI

Brassiere Cozy Beach Bottom end of Hat Phu Noi ☎032 630555, ⓦbrassierebeach.com. Under the same architect owners as *Huaplee* at Pak Nam Pran (see p.523), *Brassiere Cozy Beach* gets its name from the two conical Nom Sao ("Breast") islands offshore and the mainland spirit house where fishermen leave bras for good luck, and contains rooms with playful monikers like "La Perla". That may sound a bit naff to some, but the hotel itself is the height of quirky chic, airy and light-filled, with a mostly white-and-blue colour scheme. Some rooms have their own small jacuzzi and pool or an outdoor bathroom, and kayaks and bicycles are available, as well as sailing and stand-up paddleboarding. Breakfast included. B3740

Dolphin Bay Northern end of the beach ☎032 559333, ⓦdolphinbayresort.com. Eco-conscious, family-focused resort just across the quiet road from the beach, offering comfortable a/c rooms, bungalows, apartments and villas with fridges, hot water and TVs, large children's and adults' pools set in an attractive, palm-fringed lawn, plus a kids' playground. Pick-ups from Pranburi (B350) and Hua Hin (B700) can be arranged and there's plenty of things to do once you're here: half-day tours of the park (B800 for a car with driver), boat trips to Tham Phraya Nakhon and local islands, plus kayak, catamaran and stand-up paddleboard rental. B1690

Prachuap Khiri Khan and around

Despite lacking any must-see attractions, the tiny, unfrequented provincial capital of **PRACHUAP KHIRI KHAN**, 67km south of Pranburi, makes a pleasant place to break any journey up or down the coast. Apart from pineapples – the province is the biggest producer in Thailand, with truckloads for sale all along Highway 4 – its greatest asset is its setting: a huge, palm-fringed, half-moon bay, dotted with colourful fishing boats and tipped by a rocky outcrop at the north end and by a small group of jungly islands to the south – the waterfront promenade in the town centre is great for a seafood lunch with a view. There's a lovely **beach** in the next bay to the south, Ao Manao, and generally Prachuap is a fine spot to settle into small-town Thai life.

The town is contained in a small grid of streets that runs just 250m east to west, between the sea and the train station – with Highway 4 beyond the railway tracks – and around 1km north to south, from the Khao Chong Krajok hill at the northern end to the Wing 5 air-force base in the south. **Orientation** couldn't be simpler. The major central road across from the station to the pier is Thanon Kongkiat, while Highway 326, the main east–west access road to Highway 4, cuts across the north end of town, and there are four main north–south roads: Thanon Phitak Chat near the station, Thanon Salacheep, Thanon Susuek and the seafront road, Thanon Chai Thalay, which to the north of the pier becomes a **walking street** on Friday and Saturday evenings, selling food, clothes and handicrafts.

Khao Chong Krajok

The monkey-infested hill of **Khao Chong Krajok** is Prachuap's main sight: if you climb the 417 steps from Thanon Salacheep to the golden-spired chedi at the summit you get a great perspective on the scalloped coast below and west to the mountainous Burmese border, just 12km away.

Ao Manao

Inside Wing 5 air-force base (you usually need to sign in at the base checkpoint) · Head south down Thanon Salacheep (or down the promenade and turn right) to reach the checkpoint and continue for 2km through the base to the beach · Tuk-tuk to the beach around B60

At the far southern end of town, the long sandy beach at **Ao Manao** is the best place in the area for swimming and sunbathing. On weekdays you're likely to have the sand almost to yourself, but it's a very popular spot with Thai families on weekends when the stalls at the beachfront food centre do a roaring trade in the locally famous *som tam puu* (spicy papaya salad with fresh crab), which you can eat at the deckchairs and tables under the trees on the beach. You can walk to the north end of the bay to the base of an outcrop known as Khao Lommuak, where a memorial commemorates the skirmish that took place here between Thai and Japanese forces in World War II.

King Mongkut Memorial Park of Science and Technology

12km south of town, on the beach at Wa Ko (Waghor) · Daily 9am–4pm, fish-feeding at 11am & 2pm (subject to change) · Aquarium B30 · ☎ 032 661103, ⍟ waghor.go.th · To get there, turn east off Highway 4 at kilometre-stone 335, or go through Ao Manao air-force base, bearing left along the coast all the way

The main feature of the **King Mongkut Memorial Park of Science and Technology** (also signed as Phra Chomklao Science Park) is the extensive and well-stocked **Waghor Aquarium**. Highlights include an underwater tunnel, touch pools and fish-feeding, and there are display boards and labels for most of the fish in English. It's nothing like as slick as Siam Ocean World in Bangkok, but then again it's less than a tenth of the price. About 500m south along the beach road, the park also contains an astronomy museum that's decidedly low-tech but with enough labels in English to maintain interest.

The park is thought to mark the spot where **Rama IV**, known as the father of Thai science, came to observe a solar eclipse on August 18, 1868. Having predicted the eclipse's exact course, King Mongkut decided to publicize science among his subjects by mounting a large expedition, aiming specifically to quash their centuries-old fear that the sun was periodically swallowed by the dragon Rahoo, and more generally to rattle traditional notions of astrology and cosmology. To this end, he invited scientists all the way from France and the British governor of Singapore, and himself turned up with fifty elephants and all his court, including the astrologers – who, as the leader of the French expedition noted, "could hardly be blamed if they did not display much enthusiasm for the whole project". Unfortunately, both the king and his 15-year-old son contracted malaria at Waghor; Mongkut passed away in Bangkok on October 1, but Chulalongkorn survived to become Thailand's most venerated king, Rama V.

ARRIVAL AND DEPARTURE
PRACHUAP KHIRI KHAN

BY TRAIN

Most services on the Southern Line from Bangkok stop at the train station, which is just on the west side of the centre, at the western end of Thanon Kongkiat.

Destinations Bangkok (11 daily; 5–7hr); Chumphon (10 daily; 2hr–3hr 30min); Nakhon Si Thammarat (2 daily; 10hr 30min); Surat Thani (8 daily; 4hr 30min–6hr); Trang (1 daily; 11hr).

BY BUS OR MINIBUS

Prachuap's bus terminal is out on Highway 4, north of Highway 326, the main access road to town. The number of long-distance bus services to and from the town centre is dwindling fast, with many people either heading out to the terminal to catch a through-bus (for points south, best in the morning or around midnight), or taking an a/c minibus from the centre.

Buses from/to Bangkok Pudtan Tour, on Thanon Phitak Chat just south of Thanon Kongkiat, runs a "first-class" a/c service to Bangkok's Southern Terminal (7–8 daily; 4–5hr), which stops at Pranburi and Phetchaburi, but takes the Hua Hin bypass, Highway 37.

A/c minibuses Several companies in the town centre offer a/c minibuses to Bangkok, including one near the start of Highway 326, just west of the Provincial Hall and the tourist office, which serves Victory Monument and the Northern Bus Terminal, as well as Hua Hin. Around the corner, a short way down Thanon Phitak Chat, you'll find a/c minibuses to Bangkok's Southern Bus Terminal and to Ranong. A little further south again on Thanon Tessaban Bamrung (the road immediately north of Thanon Kongkiat), between Phitak Chat and Salacheep roads, you'll find services to Chumphon, which will stop on Highway 4 near Ban Krut.

6

INFORMATION AND GETTING AROUND

Tourist information There's a small but helpful tourist information office (daily 8.30am–4.30pm, closing noon–1pm for lunch; ☎032 611491), where town maps are available, at the far northern end of town in a compound of provincial offices; it's on the ground floor of a modern, white building facing the beachfront road.

Bicycle and motorbike rental Bicycles (B60/day) and motorbikes (B200/day) can be rented from *Maggie's Home-stay*.

Kayak rental You can rent a kayak on the seafront just south of *Plern Smud* restaurant and the *Hadthong Hotel*.

ACCOMMODATION

Faa Chom Khleun Ao Manao ☎032 661088–9, ⓦaomanao.com. If you don't mind cosying up to the Thai military, this spruce air-force hotel on the Wing 5 base puts you right on the beach. All rooms have sea-view balconies, a/c, hot water, TV and fridge, and there's a large swimming pool. No English sign. B1100

Hadthong Hotel 21 Thanon Susuek, but also with an entrance just south of the pier on the beachfront road ☎032 601050–5, ⓦhadthong.com. Well-run spot that's had an attractive recent makeover, with comfortable rooms, many sporting balconies and peerless sea views, all with fridges, a/c, hot water and TVs – plus a 15m swimming pool and snooker club. The cheapest rooms are in a windowless basement, so better to pay B1140 for a sea view if you can. Breakfast included. B640

House 73 73 Thanon Susuek, about 400m south of Thanon Kongkiat ☎086 046 3923, ⓦhomestayprachuap .blogspot.com. Striking modernist guesthouse with great views of the bay from its roof terrace and four a/c rooms which have been hand-painted in bold colours by the owners, taking inspiration from their favourite songs. B800

Maggie's Home-stay 5 Soi Tampramuk 4, between Salacheep and Susuek roads, just south of Thanon Kongkiat ☎032 604216 or ☎087 597 9720, ⓦmaggies prachuap.webs.com. Welcoming spot behind a pretty front garden, with hammocks and *salas* for chilling out under the trees. The diverse rooms share hot-water bathrooms and are either in a bright and airy, traditional wooden house with polished floors (formerly the provincial governor's residence) or, less attractively, in the outhouses at the back. Good rates for singles. They've recently opened a branch, *Maggie's Seaview*, in a green and white wooden house south of *Plern Smud* restaurant on Thanon Chai Thalay (fan B350, a/c B450). Fan B200, a/c B450

★**Sun Beach Guesthouse** 160 Thanon Chai Thalay, 500m or so down the promenade from the pier ☎032 604770, ⓦsunbeach-guesthouse.com. Run by a welcoming and helpful Thai–German couple, this palatial guesthouse is done out like a Mediterranean villa, with Corinthian columns and smart tiling everywhere. The bright, comfortable, sky-blue rooms come with a/c, hot water, fridges, TVs and balconies, with prices varying according to the quality of the sea view. There's a seductive pool and whirlpool. B800

EATING AND DRINKING

Prachuap's famously good seafood is most cheaply sampled at the town's lively and varied main **night market**, which sets up shop in the empty lot around the junction of Thanon Kongkiat and Thanon Phitak Chat.

Ma-prow 48 Thanon Chai Thalay, south of the Hadthong Hotel ☎032 551208. Mellow, rustic, airy restaurant (main courses around B150–200), which serves tasty squid with salted eggs and deep-fried sea bass fillet with tamarind and peanut sauce, as well as a few Western dishes such as fish'n'chips. Daily roughly 11am–10pm.

★**Plern Smud (Ploen Samut)** South of the pier at 44 Thanon Chai Thalay, alongside the Hadthong Hotel ☎032 611115. The town's best restaurant has a pleasant, spacious courtyard facing the sea, and serves delicious pan-fried oysters, tasty crab claws and excellent *kaeng pa pla say* (silver whiting fish in country curry; B120) on its seafood-dominated menu. Daily 9.30am–10pm.

Rap Lom About 1km north of the centre, beyond Khao Chong Krajok and the adjacent bridge. Another locals' favourite for seafood, including a very good version of the regional speciality, *plaa meuk det diaw* (sun-dried squid; B150), but also offering some wild-boar dishes. On the landward side of the beach road, with views of the sea. Daily 10am–9pm.

Rome Beer (MC Club House) Thanon Chai Thalay,

south of Plern Smud. Excellent spot for a waterside drink, hung with motorcycle memorabilia and home to some of the friendliest bikers you're ever likely to meet. Hours erratic but should be open daily from at least 6pm till late.

6 Ban Krud

Graced with a tranquil, 5km sweep of white sand, pale-blue sea and swaying casuarinas, **BAN KRUD**, 70km south of Prachuap, supports a dozen or so fairly upmarket bungalow outfits and seafood restaurants along the central stretch of its shorefront road. About 1km inland from the main T-junction at the beach, the small, traditional village, which now includes several ATMs, clusters around the train station. At the beach's northern end are a colourful fishing village and a panoramic headland, **Khao Thongchai**, that's dominated by the 14m-high Phra Phut Kitti Sirichai Buddha image and its sparkling modern temple, **Wat Phra Mahathat Phraphat**. Crowned with nine golden chedis, the temple displays an impressive fusion of traditional and contemporary features, including a series of charming modern stained-glass windows depicting Buddhist stories; reach it via a 1.5km-long road that spirals up from the beachfront. Other than a visit to the temple and possibly a snorkelling trip to Ko Thalu (from B350/person through, for example, *Sala Thai Resort*), the main pastime in Ban Krud is sitting under the trees and enjoying a long seafood lunch or dinner.

ARRIVAL AND DEPARTURE   BAN KRUD

By train A handful of services on the Southern Line from Bangkok stop at Ban Krud's tiny train station, where you should be able to find a motorbike taxi (with sidecar).
Destinations Bangkok (4 daily; 5hr 30min–7hr 30min); Chumphon (7 daily; 2hr); Nakhon Si Thammarat (1 daily; 10hr); Surat Thani (6 daily; 4hr–5hr 30min); Trang

(1 daily; 10hr).
By bus Most southbound buses drop passengers on Highway 4, from where motorbike-and-sidecar taxis cover the 8km down to the beach; just two Bangkok–Bang Saphan a/c buses a day stop at Ban Krud itself.

ACCOMMODATION

Bayview North of the headland, 4km from Sala Thai on Hat Tangsai ☎ 032 695566–7, ⊛ bayviewbeachresort .com. Very welcoming and relaxed spot on a long, quiet stretch of beach, with a swimming pool, a kids' pool and a lovely area for deckchairs under the beachside casuarinas. All the well-spaced, diverse bungalows boast a/c, fridges, TVs and hot water, and there's an excellent restaurant, free bicycles, and cars to rent. Prices rise a little at weekends. Breakfast included. **B1600**

Sala Thai About 1km north of the central beachfront T-junction ☎ 032 695181, ⊛ salathaibeachresort.com. Friendly resort, whose cutesy wooden bungalows with a/c, hot water, fridge and TV are spread around a spacious, pretty garden with lots of shady trees, just across the road from the beach; it also has a popular burger bar. Bikes and motorbikes for rent. Prices rise a little at weekends. Breakfast included. **B600**

Chumphon

South Thailand officially starts at **CHUMPHON**, where the main highway splits into west- and east-coast branches, and inevitably the provincial capital saddles itself with the title "gateway to the south". Most tourists take this tag literally and use the town as nothing more than a transport interchange between the Bangkok train and boats to **Ko Tao, Pha Ngan and Samui**, so the town is well equipped to serve these passers-through, offering clued-up travel agents and efficient transport links. In truth, there's little call for exploring the fairly average beaches, islands and reefs around town when the varied and attractive strands of Ko Tao are just a short hop away.

ARRIVAL AND DEPARTURE

CHUMPHON

BY PLANE

Nok Air flies to Chumphon from Bangkok's Don Muang Airport (3 daily; 1hr). It's possible to buy a combination ticket from Nok all the way through to Ko Tao, or you can take an a/c minibus from the airport, which is 40km to the north, to town (B150/person, bookable through *Salsa Hostel*, for example); a taxi will set you back around B800.

BY TRAIN

Chumphon train station is on the northwest edge of town, less than a 10min walk from most guesthouses and hotels. Destinations Bangkok (10 daily to Hualamphong, 2 to Thonburi; 7hr–9hr 30min); Butterworth (Malaysia; 1 daily; 14hr); Nakhon Si Thammarat (2 daily; 7hr); Surat Thani (11 daily; 2hr 5min–4hr); Trang (2 daily; 7hr).

BY BUS OR MINIBUS

Government bus station The government bus station is 11km south of town on Highway 4, connected to the centre by songthaews (B50/person) and motorbike taxis (B100 or more), though long-distance services will sometimes drop in town.

Private bus and minibus services There are several private a/c bus and minibus services that depart from various locations (see map above), including Suwanathee buses to Bangkok; and Chokeanan Tour buses to Bangkok and Rungkit buses to Phuket, via Ranong and Khao Lak,

which start from the same spot. Agents such as *Suda* and *Fame* (see p.530) can also fix you up with private a/c minibuses to Krabi, Ko Lanta and Khao Sok.

Destinations Bangkok (roughly hourly; 7–9hr); Hua Hin (hourly; 3hr 30min–4hr 30min); Khao Lak (4 daily; 5hr); Phuket (4 daily; 7hr); Prachuap Khiri Khan (hourly; 2–3hr); Ranong (10–14 daily; 2–3hr); Surat Thani (roughly hourly; 3hr 30min).

BY BOAT

There are several different boat services from Chumphon to Ko Tao, Pha Ngan and Samui, tickets for all of which are sold by travel agents and guesthouses in town. Of these, the Songserm Express and the midnight boat are the most likely to be cancelled if the weather is very bad.

GETTING TO THE PIER

Songserm tickets include transport to the pier from town, with pick-ups available even from guesthouses and from the station, including off the overnight train from Bangkok that arrives around 4am. Lomprayah offers a bus to its pier from the station for B50/person. The car ferries and the less comfortable midnight boat do pick-ups from town guesthouses at around 10pm (included in the prices given below); however, these boats (and their pick-ups) sometimes leave an hour or two early, because of tides and the weather.

6

BOATS AND SERVICES

Lomprayah Catamaran Office at the train station ☎077 558212–3, ⓦ lomprayah.com. Daily 7.30am & 1pm, from Ao Thung Makham Noi, 27km south of Chumphon; 1hr 30min to Ko Tao (B600); around 3hr 30min to Ko Pha Ngan (B1000); around 4hr to Maenam, Ko Samui (B1100).

Songserm Express ⓦ songserm-expressboat.com. Daily 7am, from Pak Nam, about 20km south of Chumphon; 2hr 30min to Ko Tao (B500); around 4hr 30min to Ko Pha Ngan (B900); around 5hr 30min to Na Thon, Ko Samui (B1000).

Car ferries to Ko Tao Various boats Mon–Sat 11pm, from Tha Yang, about 15km south of Chumphon; 6hr; B450, including beds, blankets and pillows in an a/c room.

Midnight boat to Ko Tao Daily midnight, from Tha Yang, about 15km south of Chumphon; 6hr; B300.

INFORMATION AND TOURS

TAT office Down a short soi at 111 Thanon Tawee Sinka (daily 8.30am–4.30pm; ☎077 501831, ⓔ tatchumphon @tat.or.th).

Suda Guest House Thanon Sala Daeng Soi 3 (aka Soi Bangkok Bank), 30m off Thanon Tha Tapao ☎080 144 2079 or ☎077 504366. The best source of information and fixer in town, offering a personal, unbiased service, is Suda at her eponymous guesthouse. As well as tickets to Ko Tao, Suda offers discounted dive packages; bus and minibus tickets; twice-daily visa runs via Ranong to Myanmar (from B650); motorbike (B200–300/day) rental; packages to Ko Chang (Ranong) and Ko Phayam; and jungle treks and rafting at Pha To near Ranong.

ACCOMMODATION

Fame 188/20–21 Thanon Sala Daeng ☎077 571077, ⓦ chumphon-kohtao.com. Above the restaurant and tour agency of the same name, this place has basic but good-sized and very clean rooms, with fans and hot water in either shared or en-suite bathrooms; the cheapest have mattresses on the floor. B150

Nanaburi Hotel 335/9 Thanon Pracha Uthit ☎077 503888, ⓦ nanaburihotel.com. Spread across two buildings in a quiet area set back from the main roads, the large rooms at this recently built hotel have a pleasant, simple decor of wood and white paint and are equipped with a/c, hot showers, cable TV and fridges. B2700

Novotel 15km southeast near Pak Nam ☎077 529529, ⓦ novotel-chumphon.com. This low-rise luxury hotel on Paradornpab beach, done out in an unobtrusive Thai contemporary style, features spacious rooms with balconies and lots of dark wood, two restaurants (inter-national and northeastern Thai), two swimming pools, a spa, fitness centre, golf course and kids' club. Breakfast included. B2235

Paradorn Hotel 180/12 Thanon Sala Daeng ☎077 511598, ⓦ chumphon-paradorn.com. Formerly grand provincial hotel in a shining, white block that's now showing its age, but good value for decent-sized rooms with a/c, hot water, fridge and TV. The espresso bar is woeful, however. B360

Salsa Hostel Thanon Kromluang ☎077 505005, ⓦ salsahostel.com. Welcoming hostel offering shining white, six- and seven-bed a/c dorms with modern bunk beds – with nice touches like individual reading lights – as well as large private rooms, a kitchen and rooftop terrace. Breakfast included. Dorm B300, twin B800

★**Suda Guest House** Thanon Sala Daeng Soi 3 (aka Soi Bangkok Bank), 30m off Thanon Tha Tapao ☎080 144 2079 or ☎077 504366. Chumphon's most welcoming homestay, offering clean, well-maintained rooms, some en suite but most with shared hot-water showers (two bedrooms to one bathroom), in the owner's modern house; the a/c can be switched on for an extra B100–150/room/night. Plenty of information available, B30 showers for passers-through and much more (see above). Phone for free transport from the train station. B250

EATING AND DRINKING

The cheapest place to eat is the **night market**, which sets up along both sides of Thanon Kromluang and is an enjoyable place to munch your way through a selection of fried noodles, barbecued chicken and sticky, coconut-laced sweets.

Aeki's Bar (The 3 Independent) Opposite the train station. Rustic, wood-furnished bar with a pool table, which is popular with young expat teachers and has occasional DJs. Daily roughly 3pm–2am.

Boom (The Bakery Café) Thanon Tha Tapao ☎077 511523. A bakery with a few pavement tables for watching the world go by, serving good espressos, tasty brownies and other Western and Thai cakes. Mon–Sat 8am–7pm.

Fame 188/20–21 Thanon Sala Daeng ☎077 571077.

Travellers' restaurant specializing in Italian food, including pizzas, as well as Indian dhal, loads of sandwiches using home-baked bread, espresso coffees and huge breakfasts (B100–150). Daily 5am–9.30pm.

Green Kitchen Off Thanon Suksumer ☎077 571731. Good, reasonably authentic Vietnamese cuisine such as fresh spring rolls (B70) and sugar cane wrapped in minced shrimp, plus Thai food and some European dishes. Daily 11am–9pm; closed every second Thurs.

Papa Across from the train station on Thanon Kromluang ☎ 077 504504. One of the liveliest places to eat dinner, this huge restaurant – mostly open-air, but with an a/c room – has an extensive menu of fresh seafood, Thai salads such as wingbean salad (B120) and Chinese dishes, plus a few Western standards. Also puts on live music every evening, and has an attached nightclub,

Papa 2000. Daily roughly 11am–3/4am.

Prikhorm Thanon Tha Tapao. A good chance to try southern Thai food such as tasty *nam phrik kung siap* (chilli dip with dried prawns; B95) and spicy *kaeng som*, in a comfortable, a/c restaurant decked out in pastel colours. Daily 11am–11pm, though it closes earlier if there are no customers.

Chaiya

About 140km south of Chumphon, **CHAIYA** is thought to have been the capital of southern Thailand under the Srivijayan civilization, which fanned out from Sumatra between the eighth and thirteenth centuries. Today there's little to mark the passing of Srivijaya, but this small, sleepy town has gained new fame as the site of **Wat Suan Mokkh**, a progressively minded temple whose meditation retreats account for the bulk of Chaiya's foreign visitors (most Thais only stop to buy the famous local salted eggs). Unless you're interested in one of the retreats, the town is best visited on a day-trip, either as a break in the journey south, or as an excursion from Surat Thani.

Wat Phra Boromathat

Western side of town, on the access road from Highway 41

The main sight in Chaiya is **Wat Phra Boromathat**, where the ninth-century chedi – one of very few surviving examples of Srivijayan architecture – is said to contain relics of the Buddha himself. Hidden away behind the viharn in a pretty, red-tiled cloister, the chedi looks like an oversized wedding cake surrounded by an ornamental moat. Its unusual square tiers are spiked with smaller chedis and decorated with gilt, in a style similar to the temples of central Java.

National Museum

On the eastern side of the temple • Wed–Sun 9am–4pm • B100 • ⓦ thailandmuseum.com

The **National Museum** is a bit of a disappointment. Although the Srivijaya period produced some of Thailand's finest sculpture, much of it discovered at Chaiya, the best pieces have been carted off to the National Museum in Bangkok. Replicas have been left in their stead, which are shown alongside fragments of some original statues, two intricately worked 2000-year-old bronze drums, found at Chaiya and Ko Samui, and various examples of Thai handicrafts. The best remaining pieces are a calm and elegant sixth- to seventh-century stone image of the Buddha meditating from Wat Phra Boromathat, and an equally serene head of a Buddha image, Ayutthayan-style in pink sandstone, from Wat Kaeo.

Wat Kaeo

On the south side of town

Heading towards the centre of Chaiya from Wat Phra Boromathat, you can reach this imposing ninth- or tenth-century brick chedi by taking the first paved road on the right, which brings you first to the restored base of the chedi at Wat Long, and then after 1km to **Wat Kaeo**, enclosed by a thick ring of trees. Here you can poke around the murky antechambers of the chedi, three of which house images of the Buddha subduing Mara.

6

MEDITATION RETREATS AT SUAN MOKKH

Meditation retreats are led by Western and Thai teachers over the first ten days of every month at the International Dharma Heritage (Ⓦ suanmokkh-idh.org), a purpose-built compound 1km from the main temple at Wat Suan Mokkh. Large numbers of foreign travellers, both novices and experienced meditators, turn up for the retreats, which are intended as a challenging exercise in mental development – it's not an opportunity to relax and live at low cost for a few days. Conditions imitate the rigorous lifestyle of a *bhikkhu* (monk) as far as possible, each day beginning before dawn with meditation according to the Anapanasati method, which aims to achieve mindfulness by focusing on the breathing process. Although talks are given on Dharma (the doctrines of the Buddha – as interpreted by Buddhadasa Bhikkhu) and meditation technique, most of each day is spent practising Anapanasati in solitude. To aid concentration, participants maintain a rule of silence, broken only by daily chanting sessions, although supervisors are sometimes available for individual interviews if there are any questions or problems. Men and women are segregated into separate dormitory blocks and, like monks, are expected to help out with chores.

PRACTICALITIES

Turn up at Wat Suan Mokkh as early as possible (by 3pm at the latest) on the last day of the month to register (you can stay in Suan Mokkh the night before registration for free). The busiest period for the retreats is December–April, especially February and March. The fee is B2000 per person, which includes two vegetarian meals a day and accommodation in simple cells. Participants are required to hand in their mobile phones and tablets and are not allowed to leave the premises during the retreat – bring any supplies you think you might need (though there is a small, basic shop on site).

Wat Suan Mokkh

6km south of Chaiya on Highway 41 • Ⓦ suanmokkh.org • All buses between Surat Thani and Chumphon stop near the wat

The forest temple of **Wat Suan Mokkh** (Garden of Liberation) was founded by the abbot of Wat Phra Boromathat, **Buddhadasa Bhikkhu**, southern Thailand's most revered monk until his death in 1993 at the age of 87. His radical, back-to-basics philosophy, encompassing Christian, Zen and Taoist influences, lives on and continues to draw Thais from all over the country to the temple, as well as hundreds of foreigners. It's not necessary to sign up for one of the wat's **retreats** to enjoy the temple – you can simply drop by for a stroll through the wooded grounds. However, it's currently not as tranquil as it should be: former politician Suthep Thaugsuban, who orchestrated the mass anti-government demonstrations that eventually led to the coup in 2014, has recently been ordained and has set up camp with his entourage here.

The unusual layout of the wat is centred on the Golden Hill: scrambling up between trees and monks' huts, past the cremation site of Buddhadasa Bhikkhu, you'll reach a hushed clearing on top of the hill, which is the temple's holiest meeting place, a simple open-air platform decorated with images of the Buddha and the Wheel of Law. At the base of the hill, the outer walls of the Spiritual Theatre are lined with bas-reliefs, replicas of originals in India, which depict scenes from the life of the Buddha. Inside, every centimetre is covered with colourful didactic painting, executed by resident monks and visitors in a jumble of realistic and surrealistic styles.

ARRIVAL AND DEPARTURE

CHAIYA

By train The town lies on the main Southern Rail Line, served by trains (mostly overnight) from and to Bangkok (8 daily; 8–11hr).

By bus Chaiya is 3km east of Highway 41, the main road down this section of the Gulf coast: buses running between Chumphon and Surat Thani will drop off (or pick up) on the

highway, from where you can catch a motorbike taxi or blue songthaew into town.

By songthaew From Surat Thani's Talat Kaset II bus station, frequent songthaews take around an hour to reach Chaiya town centre.

Surat Thani

Uninspiring **SURAT THANI** ("City of the Good People"), 60km south of Chaiya, is generally worth visiting only as a jumping-off point for the Samui archipelago. Strung along the south bank of the Tapi River, with a busy port for rubber and coconuts near the river mouth, the town is experiencing rapid economic growth and paralyzing traffic jams. It might be worth a stay, however, when the Chak Phra Festival (see box, p.534) is on, or as a base for seeing the nearby historic town of Chaiya.

6

ARRIVAL AND DEPARTURE

Be aware that there have been reports of thefts from bags left in the luggage compartments of long-distance buses from Surat (keep your valuables with you); and of overcharging and **scams** by unregistered agents and touts selling tickets for minibus and bus services out of Surat, especially involving any kind of combination ticket, including those heading for Khao Sok National Park, Phuket, Krabi and Malaysia. To avoid the latter, either go direct to the relevant a/c minibus office at Talat Kaset II bus station (local offices are generally on the west side of the station, long-distance ones on the east side, and they all have to be authorized by the provincial office), or buy a bus ticket direct from the station.

BY PLANE

Arriving by air from Bangkok (currently Air Asia 5 daily, Nok Air 5 daily and Lion Air 2 daily from Don Muang, and Thai Smile 2 daily from Suvarnabhumi; 1hr 15min) or Chiang Mai (Air Asia 1 daily; 2hr), you can take a B100 shuttle bus through Phantip (see p.534) for the 27km journey south from the airport into Surat Thani, while combination tickets through Lomprayah, for example, cost B600 to Ko Samui, B700 to Ko Pha Ngan and B850–950 to Ko Tao. Avis (☎02 251 1131–2, ⓦavisthailand.com) and Budget (☎077 441166, ⓦbudget.co.th) have outlets at the airport for car

rental. If you're flying out of Surat, you can most easily catch the airport shuttle bus from town at the Phantip office.

BY TRAIN

Arriving by train means arriving at Phunphin, 13km to the west, from where buses run into Surat Thani, via the Baw Khaw Saw bus terminal, between around 5.30am and 7pm (if there are enough passengers; more frequent in the early morning), while share-taxis (based in Surat at Talat Kaset II) charge around B150 to charter the whole car into town. It's also possible to buy through-tickets to Ko Samui, Ko Pha

SURAT THANI

ACCOMMODATION

Ban Don Hotel	1
My Place	2
Roi Koh (100 Islands)	4
Wangtai Hotel	3

RESTAURANTS & CAFÉS

Ban Don Restaurant	2
Milano	1
Vegetarian restaurant	3

0 ——— 200 metres

6

THE CHAK PHRA FESTIVAL

At the start of the eleventh lunar month (usually in October) the people of Surat Thani celebrate the end of Buddhist Lent with the **Chak Phra Festival** (Pulling the Buddha), which symbolizes the Buddha's return to earth after a monsoon season spent preaching to his mother in heaven. On the Tapi River, tugboats pull the town's principal Buddha image on a raft decorated with huge nagas, while on land sleigh-like floats bearing Buddha images and colourful flags and parasols are hauled across the countryside and through the streets. As the monks have been confined to their monasteries for three months, the end of Lent is also the time to give them generous offerings in the *kathin* ceremony, of which Surat Thani has its own version, called Thot Pha Pa, when the offerings are hung on tree branches planted in front of the houses before dawn. Longboat races, between teams from all over the south, are also held during the festival.

Ngan and Ko Tao from the train station, including a connecting bus to the relevant pier. Buses heading out of Surat to Phang Nga and Phuket make a stop at Phunphin train station. You can book train tickets in Surat at Phantip travel agency, in front of Talat Kaset I at 293/6–8 Thanon Taladmai (☏ 077 272230 or ☏ 077 272906).

Destinations Bangkok (10 daily; 9–12hr); Butterworth (Malaysia; 1 daily; 10hr 30min); Nakhon Si Thammarat (2 daily; 4hr 30min); Trang (2 daily; 4hr 30min).

BY BUS

Buses use three different locations, two of which are on Thanon Taladmai in the centre of town: Talat Kaset I on the north side of the road (Phunphin, Nakhon Si Thammarat, non-a/c Chumphon services and other local buses) and opposite at Talat Kaset II (most long-distance buses, including those for Krabi, Phuket, Hat Yai and Ranong). The Baw Khaw Saw terminal, 2km southwest of the centre on the road towards Phunphin, handles mostly Bangkok services.

Destinations Bangkok (Southern Terminal; 12 daily; 10–12hr); Chumphon (roughly hourly; 3hr 30min); Khao Sok (8 daily; 2hr 30min); Krabi (roughly hourly; 3–4hr); Nakhon Si Thammarat (every 30min; 2hr 30min); Phang Nga (5 daily; 3hr 30min); Phuket (8 daily; 5hr); Phunphin (irregular; 40min); Ranong (8 daily; 4–5hr).

BY MINIBUS OR SHARE-TAXI

A/c minibuses (to Chumphon, Ranong, Ratchabrapa Dam, Khao Sok, Phang Nga, Phuket, Krabi, Trang and Nakhon Si Thammarat) and a dwindling number of share-taxis

congregate around Talat Kaset II bus station, on the south side of Thanon Taladmai.

BOAT OPERATORS IN SURAT

Details of boats to Ko Samui, Ko Pha Ngan and Ko Tao, most of which leave from Don Sak pier, 68km east of Surat, are given in the account of each island – see p.537, p.555 & p.569. Phunphin and the bus stations are teeming with touts, with transport waiting to escort you to their employer's boat service to the islands – they're generally reliable, but make sure you don't get talked onto the wrong boat. If you manage to avoid getting hustled, you can buy tickets direct from the boat operators.

Lomprayah In the Caltex petrol station on Thanon Taladmai, near Theppamit School ☏ 077 200932–3, ⓦ lomprayah.com. Catamarans to Samui and Pha Ngan, with their own connecting buses to Don Sak and connections on to Ko Tao.

Phangan Tour Thanon Taladmai ☏ 077 205799. Handles buses to Don Sak for the Raja vehicle ferries to Ko Pha Ngan.

Samui Tour Thanon Taladmai ☏ 077 282352. Handles buses to Ko Samui and Ko Pha Ngan via the Raja vehicle ferries from Don Sak.

Seatran Thanon Taladmai ☏ 077 251555, ⓦ seatran ferry.com. Vehicle ferries to Samui (with their own connecting buses), from Don Sak.

Night boats The night boats to Samui, Pha Ngan and Tao, which are barely glorified cargo boats, line up during the day at Ban Don Pier in the centre of Surat; it's just a question of turning up and buying a ticket.

GETTING AROUND

By share-songthaew Small share-songthaews buzz around town, charging around B15–20/person for a

short journey.

INFORMATION

Tourist information TAT's office is at the western end of town at 5 Thanon Taladmai (daily 8.30am–4.30pm; ☏ 077 288817–9, ✉ tatsurat@tat.or.th).

Tourist police On the southern bypass near the junction with Thanon Srivichai, the westward continuation of Thanon Taladmai (☏ 1155 or ☏ 077 405575).

ACCOMMODATION

A lot of **accommodation** in Surat Thani is noisy, grotty and overpriced, but there are a few notable exceptions.

Ban Don Hotel Above a restaurant at 268/2 Thanon Namuang ☎077 272167. Most of the very clean rooms here, with en-suite bathrooms, TV and fans or a/c (some of the latter have hot showers), are set back from the noise of the main road. Fan B300, a/c B400

My Place 247/5 Thanon Namuang ☎077 272288, ⓦmyplacesurat.com. Recently renovated Thai-Chinese hotel in the town centre with some bright splashes of colour and attractive floral motifs; the cheapest rooms have shared facilities. Fan B199, a/c B490

Roi Koh (100 Islands) On the southern bypass near the tourist police and opposite Tesco Lotus ☎077

201150–8, ⓦroikoh.com. Though out of the centre, this place offers attractive, comfortable rooms with a/c, hot water, TVs and mini-bars, a small spa and a decent-sized pool set in a lush garden with a waterfall. Breakfast included. B900

Wangtai Hotel 1 Thanon Taladmai, on the western side of the centre by the TAT office ☎077 283020–5, ⓦwangtaisurat.net. Surat Thani's best upmarket option, and surprisingly good value, with over two hundred large, smart, recently refurbished rooms around a good-sized swimming pool. B970

EATING

Besides the restaurants listed below, there's a large **night market** between Thanon Namuang and Thanon Ban Don, which displays an eye-catching range of dishes; a smaller offshoot by Ban Don pier offers less choice but is handy if you're taking a night boat.

Ban Don Restaurant 268/2 Thanon Namuang. Basic, bustling restaurant with plain, marble-topped tables, which serves large portions of tasty, inexpensive Thai and Chinese food – mostly noodle and rice dishes (around B50), but also green curry and *tom yam*. Daily 6am–4/5pm.

Milano Near the night-boat piers on Thanon Ban Don ☎077 285633. This place has an authentic oven turning out very tasty and reasonably priced pizzas (from B190), though

its home-made pasta is not so successful. Also serves other Western main courses, Mexican dishes, sandwiches, breakfasts and espresso coffee. Daily 10am–11pm.

Vegetarian restaurant One block east of Talat Kaset II bus station on Thanon Tha Thong. Wide selection of cheap and delicious curries and other tray food for around B30. Look for the yellow and red flags outside and a sign saying "vegetarian food". Daily 6/7am till about 3pm.

Ko Samui

Over a million visitors a year, ranging from globetrotting backpackers to suitcase-toting fortnighters, come to southern Thailand just for the beautiful beaches of **KO SAMUI**, 80km from Surat. At 15km across and down, Samui is generally large enough to cope with this diversity – except during the rush at Christmas and New Year – and the paradisal sands and clear blue seas have to a surprising extent kept their good looks, enhanced by a thick fringe of palm trees that gives a harvest of more than two million coconuts each month. However, development behind the beaches – which has brought the islanders far greater prosperity than the crop could ever provide – speeds along in a messy, haphazard fashion with little concern for the environment. At least there's a local bylaw limiting new construction to the height of a coconut palm (usually about three storeys), though this has not deterred either the luxury hotel groups or the real-estate developers who have recently been throwing up estates of second homes for Thais and foreigners.

For most visitors, the days are spent indulging in a few watersports or just lying on the beach waiting for the next drinks-seller, hair-braider or masseur to come along. For something more active, you should not miss the almost supernatural beauty of the **Ang Thong National Marine Park** (see p.552), which comprises many of the eighty islands in the Samui archipelago. Otherwise, a day-trip by rented car or motorbike on the 50km round-island road will throw up plenty more fine beaches.

The island's most appealing strand, **Chaweng**, has seen the heaviest, most crowded development and is now the most expensive place to stay, though it does offer by far the best amenities and nightlife, ranging from tawdry bar-beers to hip nightclubs. Its slightly smaller neighbour, **Lamai**, lags a little behind in terms of looks and top-end development, but retains large pockets of backpacker bungalow resorts. The other favourite for backpackers is **Maenam**, which, though less attractive again, is markedly quiet, with plenty of room to breathe between the beach and the round-island road. Adjacent **Bophut** is similar in appearance, but generally more sophisticated, with a cluster of boutique resorts, fine restaurants and a distinct Mediterranean feel in its congenial beachfront village. **Choeng Mon**, set apart in Samui's northeast corner, offers something different again: the small, part-sandy, part-rocky bay is tranquil and pretty, the seafront between the handful of upmarket hotels is comparatively undeveloped, and Chaweng's nightlife is within easy striking distance.

No particular **season** is best for coming to Ko Samui (see also p.10). The northeast monsoon blows heaviest in November, but can bring rain at any time between October and January, and sometimes causes high waves and strong currents, especially on the east coast. January is often breezy, March and April are very hot, and between May and October the southwest monsoon blows onto Samui's west coast and causes some rain.

At the lower end of Samui's **accommodation** scale, there are very few bungalows left for under B500, while at the most upmarket places you can pay well over B5000 for the highest international standards. The prices listed are based on high-season rates, but out of season (roughly April–June, Oct & Nov) dramatic reductions are possible.

KO SAMUI ACTIVITIES

Samui has over a dozen scuba-diving companies, offering trips for divers and snorkellers and courses throughout the year, and there's a recompression chamber at Bangrak (☎077 427427, ⓦsssnetwork.com). Most trips for experienced divers, however, head for the waters around Ko Tao (see p.566); a day's outing costs around B4000–5500, but of course if you can make your own way to Ko Tao, you'll save money. Also on offer are plenty of spas, as well as meditation retreats, island tours, ziplines, kiteboarding and cooking classes.

6

DIVE OPERATORS

Easy Divers Head office opposite Sandsea Resort, Lamai ☎077 231190, ⓦeasydivers-thailand.com. PADI Five-Star dive centre, with branches on Chaweng and Bangrak.

Planet Scuba Next to the Seatran pier on Bangrak ☎077 413050, ⓦplanetscuba.net.

SPAS

Eranda Far north end of Chaweng ☎077 300323, ⓦerandaspa.com. Set on a waterfall- and flower-splashed hillside with a plunge pool, offering plenty of style (2hr Thai massage B2200).

Peace Tropical Spa On Route 4169 near the centre of Bophut beach ☎077 430199, ⓦpeacetropicalspa .com. Many types of massage, including a 1hr 30min Thai massage for B1500, as well as body and facial treatments.

The Spa Resort Lamai ☎077 230855, ⓦthespa resorts.net. Everything from Thai massage (B450/hr) for non-guests, to residential fasting programmes (from B9300 for four days). Also on offer are body wraps and yoga, meditation and raw-food preparation classes, as well as in-house accommodation, either on the beach or in the hills above Lamai.

Tamarind Springs Lamai ☎077 424221, ⓦtamarind springs.com. Set in a beautiful, secluded coconut grove just off the main road. A session in its herbal steam caves, set between boulders by waterfall-fed rock pools, and a 2hr 30min Thai massage, for example, costs B5500; it also offers villas, a spa café and yoga holidays.

OTHER ACTIVITIES

Canopy Adventures ☎077 300340, ⓦcanopy adventuresthailand.com. A series of ziplines between treehouses and past waterfalls in the hills 4km above Maenam (2–3hr; B1900, including transfers).

Kiteboarding Asia ☎083 643 1627, ⓦkiteboarding asia.com. Instruction in kiteboarding (B4000 for one day), either from the beach south of Ban Hua Thanon or from Nathon, depending on the time of year, as well as rentals and stand-up paddleboarding.

Mr Ung's Magical Safari Tours ☎077 230114, ⓦungsafari.com. Day-trips that traverse the rough tracks of the mountainous interior to some spectacular viewpoints, as well as taking in Hin Yay Hin Ta, the Big Buddha, waterfall-swimming and monkey and elephant shows (B1900 for a full day, including transfers and lunch).

Samui Institute of Thai Culinary Arts (SITCA) Soi Colibri, opposite Centara Grand Resort in Chaweng ☎077 413172, ⓦsitca.net. This highly recommended outfit runs 3hr cookery classes in the morning and afternoon (B2250), plus six- and twelve-day courses and fruit-carving classes. Closed Sun.

Wat Suan Mokkh meditation retreats ⓦdipa bhavan.org. Wat Suan Mokkh (see p.532) offers retreats from the 7th to the 10th and the 20th to the 27th of each month at Dipabhavan, a hermitage in the hills above Lamai (full details on the website); pick-ups are laid on from *Utopia Resort*, north of the central crossroads in Lamai.

ARRIVAL AND DEPARTURE   **KO SAMUI**

BY PLANE

Flights to Samui Airport, in the northeastern tip of the island, are among the most expensive in Thailand, so you might want to consider flying from Bangkok to Surat Thani (see p.533) or Nakhon Si Thammarat (see p.575), nearby on the mainland; Nok Air, for example, offers good-value through-tickets via either of these airports, including flight, bus and boat to Samui.

Airlines You can get to Ko Samui direct from Suvarnabhumi Airport with Thai Airways (2 daily), or with Bangkok Airways (about 20 daily), which also operates flights from Chiang Mai, Hong Kong, Krabi, Kuala Lumpur, Pattaya, Phuket and Singapore; Firefly also flies from KL.

Airport facilities As well as bars and restaurants, the terminals have currency-exchange facilities and ATMs, a post office with international telephones and several car rental outlets including Avis (ⓦavisthailand.com).

Minibus transfers A/c minibuses meet incoming flights (and connect with departures, bookable through your accommodation), charging B130 to Chaweng for example. Destinations Bangkok (20 daily; 1hr–1hr 30min); Chiang Mai (1 daily; 2hr); Hong Kong (2 daily; 3hr 30min); Krabi (1 daily; 55min); Kuala Lumpur, Malaysia (1–2 daily; 2hr); Pattaya (U-Tapao; 1 daily; 1hr); Phuket (4–5 daily; 50min); Singapore (1–2 daily; 2hr).

6

BY BOAT AND BUS

The most obvious route for getting to Ko Samui by boat (45min–1hr 30min) is from Don Sak, 68km east of Surat Thani; catching a boat from Chumphon is generally more expensive and leaves you a long time on the sometimes choppy sea. There are also boats from Ko Samui to Ko Pha Ngan (see p.555) and to Ko Tao (see p.569); all offer the same service in the return direction.

FROM SURAT THANI

Don Sak to Na Thon From Don Sak, hourly Seatran vehicle ferries (on Ko Samui ☎077 426000–2, ⓦseatran ferry.com) and thrice-daily Lomprayah catamarans (on Samui ☎077 950028 or ☎077 427765–6, ⓦlomprayah .com) run to the island capital, Na Thon, all with their own connecting buses from Surat.

Don Sak to Lipa Noi Raja vehicle ferries run hourly between Don Sak and Lipa Noi, 8km south of Na Thon (on Samui ☎077 415230–3, ⓦrajaferryport.com). Roughly every 2hr, Samui Tour (on Samui ☎077 421092) runs buses from downtown Surat via the ferry, and there are buses at Phunphin train station in the morning to meet overnight trains; from Lipa Noi, you can catch an a/c minibus direct to the beaches (B160 to Chaweng, for example).

Surat Thani to Na Thon The night boat leaves Ban Don pier in Surat Thani itself for Na Thon at 11pm every night, as long as it has enough cargo and passengers to make it worthwhile; tickets are sold at the pier on the day of departure.

Fares and journey times Samui Tour charges B280 to get to Samui from Surat or Phunphin train station, including a

connecting bus, while Seatran charges B240 from Surat; total journey time from Surat is around 3hr. Lomprayah charges B450 from downtown Surat, B500 from Phunphin (total journey time about 2hr 15min–2hr 30min), including a connecting bus. The night boat takes 6hr and costs B250.

LONG-DISTANCE SERVICES

Ko Samui's government bus terminal (Baw Khaw Saw) is on Thanon Taweeratpakdee towards the north end of Na Thon (☎077 421125 or ☎077 420765). It handles bus-and-boat services (via Don Sak and Lipa Noi), for example from Bangkok's Southern Terminal (9–10 daily; 13hr; mostly overnight, some also stopping at Mo Chit bus terminal), which cost from B600 on a basic a/c bus to B1060 on a VIP bus – these are far preferable to the cheap deals offered by dodgy travel agents on Thanon Khao San, as the vehicles used on the latter services are often substandard and many thefts have been reported. The Baw Khaw Saw also sells through-tickets to Nakhon Si Thammarat, which involve catching the ferry to Don Sak, then changing on to an a/c minibus. Lomprayah also offers through-tickets from Bangkok, costing B1450 (14hr 30min), including an overnight VIP bus from its office on Thanon Ram Bhuttri in Banglamphu (☎02 629 2569–70), via Hua Hin, and a catamaran from Chumphon via Ko Tao and Ko Pha Ngan.

BY BOAT AND TRAIN FROM BANGKOK

At Hualamphong Station, you can buy a convenient through-ticket to Samui with the State Railway – B1028–1048, for example, for a second-class a/c bunk, upper tier, to Phunphin station and your bus and ferry ticket to Samui from there.

GETTING AROUND

BY SONGTHAEW

Songthaews, which congregate at the car park near the southerly pier in Na Thon, cover a variety of set routes during the daytime, either heading off clockwise or anticlockwise on Route 4169, to serve all the beaches; destinations are marked in English and fares range from B50 to Maenam to B80–100 to Chaweng or Lamai. In the evening, they tend to operate more like taxis and you'll have to negotiate a fare to get them to take you exactly where you want to go.

BY TAXI

Ko Samui sports dozens of a/c taxis. Although they all have meters, you'd be wasting your breath trying to persuade

any driver to use his; instead, you're looking at a flat fare of around B300 from Na Thon to Maenam, B500 to Chaweng, for example.

BY MOTORBIKE OR CAR

You can rent a motorbike for around B200 in Na Thon and on the main beaches. Dozens are killed on Samui's roads each year, so proceed with great caution, and wear a helmet – apart from any other consideration you can be landed with an on-the-spot B500 fine by police for not wearing one. In addition, thieves have been snatching bags from the front baskets of moving motorbikes on Samui, so keep yours on your person – or think about upgrading to a four-wheel drive, from around B800/day.

INFORMATION

Tourist information TAT runs a small but helpful office (daily 8.30am–noon & 1–4.30pm; ☎077 420504, ⓔtatsamui@tat.or.th), tucked away on an unnamed side road in Na Thon (north of the pier and inland from the post office). Here, and at many other places around Samui, you

can pick up Siam Map Company's detailed map of the island.
Tourist police The tourist police are on the Route 4169 ring road between Bophut and Chaweng, north of Big C supermarket on the same side of the road (☎1155 or ☎077 430018).

ANG THONG NATIONAL MARINE PARK (P.552) >

Na Thon

The island capital, **NA THON**, at the top of the long western coast, is a frenetic small town which most travellers use only as a service station before hitting the sand: although all the main beaches now have currency-exchange facilities, ATMs, supermarkets, travel agents and clinics, and most of them have post offices, the tightest concentration of amenities is here. The town's layout is simple: the three piers come to land at the promenade, Thanon Chonvithi, which is paralleled first by narrow Thanon Ang Thong, then by Thanon Taweeratpakdee, aka Route 4169, the round-island road; the main cross-street is Thanon Na Amphoe, by the central pier. If you're driving yourself, note that there's a one-way system in the centre of town: south on Taweeratpakdee, north on Chonvithi.

ACCOMMODATION AND EATING   NA THON

Several stalls and small cafés purvey inexpensive Thai food around the market on Thanon Taweeratpakdee and on Thanon Chonvithi (including a lively night market by the piers).

Coffee Island Corner of Thanon Chonvithi and Thanon Na Amphoe, in front of the Lomprayah pier ☏ 077 420153. Inexpensive and popular for breakfast; also serves sandwiches (tuna B90), pastas and pizzas, as well as Thai food and a wide variety of coffees. Daily 6.30am–roughly 8pm.

Nathon Residence Thanon Taweeratpakdee next to Thanachart Bank ☏ 077 236081, bookable through ⓦ agoda.com. If you really need a place to stay in Na Thon, this is your best bet, a friendly, well-run establishment with plain but spotless tiled rooms with a/c, cable TV, fridges and en-suite, hot-water bathrooms – ask for a quiet room at the back. **B650**

DIRECTORY

Bookshop Nathon Book Store on Thanon Na Amphoe (daily 9.30am–7pm; ☏ 077 420332) is a good secondhand place, with some new titles.

Hospital The state hospital (☏ 077 421230–2) is 3km south of town off Route 4169.

Immigration office Located 2km south of town down Route 4169 (Mon–Fri 8.30am–4.30pm; ☏ 077 421069).

Post office Towards the northern end of the promenade, just north of the central pier (Mon–Fri 8.30am–4.30pm, Sat & Sun 9am–noon), with poste restante and packing services. International telephones upstairs (Mon–Fri 8.30am–4.30pm).

Maenam

MAENAM, 13km from Na Thon in the middle of the north coast, is Samui's most popular beach for budget travellers. Its exposed 4km-long bay is not the island's prettiest, being more of a broad dent in the coastline, and the sloping, white-sand beach is relatively narrow and slightly coarse by Samui's high standards. But Maenam features many of the cheapest bungalows on the island, unspoilt views of fishing boats and Ko Pha Ngan, and good swimming. Despite the recent opening of some upmarket developments on the shoreline and a golf course in the hills behind, this is still the quietest and most laidback of the major beaches. Though now heavily built up with multistorey concrete shophouses (including several banks) and rows of small bars, the main road is set back far from the sea, connected to the beachside bungalows by an intricate maze of minor roads through the trees. At the midpoint of the bay, **Ban Maenam** is centred on a low-key road down to the fishing pier, which is flanked by cafés, travel agents, dive shops, secondhand bookshops and small boutiques. On Thursday evenings this becomes a pleasant **walking street** (modelled on those in Chiang Mai), with performances of traditional music and dance. On offer are lots of cheap clothes and some souvenirs, everything from bras to ukeleles, but what's most tempting is the panoply of food, both savoury and sweet, that locals cook up to sell.

6

ACCOMMODATION   MAENAM

★ Four Seasons Resort About 5km west of Maenam near Laem Yai ☎ 077 243000, ⓦ fourseasons.com. The top hotel in the Maenam area, this ultra-luxury spot has its own small beach and enjoys lovely views of Ko Pha Ngan and the setting sun. Each of the large, beautiful villas, designed for indoor-outdoor living in a subtle, modern but natural style, using brown and marine colours, has its own infinity-edge swimming pool; the resort lays on a wide range of other activities, from spa treatments to *muay thai* and cooking classes. **B31,900**

The Hammock Just east of the village ☎ 077 247198–9, ⓦ hammocksamui.com. Stylish, new, flashpacker resort with a small, fountain-fed swimming pool surrounded by red beanbags and swings. Featuring beige- and white-painted concrete and lots of dark wood, the rooms offer a/c, small hot-water bathrooms, minibars, TVs and DVD players; though crammed together in one- and two-storey rows on a small plot, they all have a small balcony or patio. **B1700**

Harry's At the far western end, near Wat Na Phra Larn ☎ 077 447097, ⓦ harrys-samui.com. Popular, well-run place, set back about 100m from the beach amid a secluded and shady tropical garden. The public areas feature strong elements of traditional Thai architecture, less so in the bungalows, which are nevertheless clean and spacious, with

a/c, hot water, TV, fridge and safe. There's also a decent-sized, free-form swimming pool and jacuzzi. **B1200**

Lolita On the east side of Santiburi Resort ☎ 077 425134, ⓔ lolitabungalowsamui@gmail.com. Quiet, friendly and efficiently run resort in a beautiful, grassy garden on a long stretch of beach. A wide variety of large, wood and concrete bungalows, all with hot showers, cluster around a kitsch, circular bar-restaurant adorned with pink Corinthian columns, and come with fans (at the back), or with a/c and fridges on the beach. Fan **B800**, a/c **B1700**

Maenam Resort 500m west of the village, just beyond Santiburi Resort ☎ 077 247287, ⓦ maenamresort.com. A welcoming, tranquil resort (no TVs) in tidy, shady grounds, with an especially long stretch of beach. The large bungalows, with verandas, hot water, fridges and a/c, offer good-value comfort. **B1900**

Moonhut On the east side of the village ☎ 077 425247, ⓦ moonhutsamui.com. Welcoming English-run place on a large, sandy, shady plot, with a lively restaurant and beach bar, wi-fi and colourful, substantial and very clean bungalows; all have verandas, mosquito screens, wall fans and en-suite bathrooms, and some have hot water and a/c. Kayaking, waterskiing and wakeboarding available. Fan **B650**, a/c **B1300**

■ ACCOMMODATION		● RESTAURANTS & CAFÉS	
Four Seasons Resort	9	Angela's Bakery	3
The Hammock	6	Ko Seng	2
Harry's	1	Sunshine Gourmet	1
Lolita	5		
Maenam Resort	3		
Moonhut	7		
New Lapaz Villa	8		
Santiburi Resort	4		
Shangrilah	2		

BAN MAENAM

Police Station

Clinic

0   250
metres

Bophut

4169

New Lapaz Villa Down a 1km access road, east of the village centre but just west of the post office ☎077 425296, ⓦnewlapaz.com. Enjoying plenty of shade, the lush, spacious grounds here shelter a small swimming pool and fifty diverse bungalows on stilts, with verandas and hot showers, many in bright pastel colours – maintenance could be better but they're clean enough. Fan B600, a/c B1000

Santiburi Resort 500m west of the village ☎077 425031, ⓦsantiburi.com. German-run, top-end hotel in beautifully landscaped grounds spread around a huge freshwater swimming pool and stream. Accommodation is mostly in Thai-style villas, inspired by Rama IV's summer palace at Phetchaburi, each with a large bathroom and separate sitting area, furnished in luxurious traditional style; some also have a private outdoor plunge pool. Facilities include watersports on the private stretch of beach, tennis courts, squash court, gym and golf course, a kids' club and a spa. Breakfast included. B18,940

Shangrilah West of Maenam Resort, served by the same access road ☎077 425189. In this huge compound that sprawls onto the nicest, widest stretch of sand along Maenam, the main area of shoulder-to-shoulder bungalows sports beautiful flowers, trees and carefully tended topiary. All rooms are well maintained and en-suite, with verandas on stilts, ceiling fans and sturdy furniture; some fan rooms at the front boast hot showers, which are also provided in all of the large, a/c rooms. The restaurant serves good Thai food. Discounts for long stays. Fan B500, a/c B1300

EATING AND DRINKING

Angela's Bakery Almost opposite the police station on the main through-road, east of the pier ☎077 427396. American-style, a/c diner, offering great breakfasts (French toast B100) and a wide choice of sandwiches (chicken and avocado B150), salads, soups and Western main courses, as well as home-made cakes and apple pie (B100 with ice cream). Daily 8am–4pm.

Ko Seng On the road parallel to and just east of the pier road ☎077 425365. This locally famous seafood restaurant, simply decorated apart from the chunky wooden tables and chairs, has featured on national TV. Buy your fish and seafood according to weight, or plump for noodles (B80) or dishes such as *kaeng som plaa* (B200), a fish curry with tamarind paste, which can be spiced to order. Daily 10am–10pm.

Sunshine Gourmet At the west end of the bay, signposted on a lane that runs east from Wat Na Phra Larn. Popular, clean and friendly spot that does a bit of everything, from cappuccino, through own-baked pies (B150 for steak and kidney), sandwiches and cakes, to international, especially German, main courses, seafood and other Thai dishes. Daily noon–9pm.

Bophut

The next bay east is **BOPHUT**, which has a similar look to Maenam but shows a marked difference in atmosphere and facilities, with a noticeable Mediterranean influence. The quiet, 2km-long beach attracts a mix of young and old travellers, as well as families, and **Ban Bophut**, now tagged **"Fisherman's Village"**, at the east end of the bay, is well geared to meet their needs, with a sprinkling of boutique hotels and banks, ATMs, scuba-diving outlets, travel agents and minimarts. While through traffic sticks to Route 4171 towards the airport and Route 4169 to Chaweng, which is now lined with hypermarkets and multiplex cinemas, development of the village has been reasonably sensitive, preserving many of its old wooden shophouses on the two narrow, largely car-free streets that meet at a T-junction by the pier. At night, in sharp contrast to Chaweng's frenetic beach road, it's a fine place for a promenade, with a concentration of good upmarket restaurants and low-key farang-run bars; on Friday evenings, the village hosts a **walking street**, very similar to Maenam's Thursday affair (see p.541). The nicest part of the beach itself is at the west end of the bay, towards *Zazen* resort, but again the sand is slightly coarse by Samui's standards. Kayaks and windsurfing are available, for example, near the centre of the beach at *Bandara Resort*, next to *Anantara*.

ACCOMMODATION

BOPHUT

Most establishments here are well spaced out at regular intervals along the length of the beach, though a handful of small, comfortable, good-value operations cluster together in Ban Bophut itself, offering enough in the way of style and facilities to justify tagging them "boutique hotels".

Anantara West of the village on the main road ☎077 428300, ⓦanantara.com. Luxury hotel with attentive service in the style of an opulent oriental palace. Blocks of balconied rooms are arrayed round lush gardens, ponds, an attractive infinity-edge swimming pool on the beachfront and a central bar and restaurant, specializing in chargrills. There's also a very attractive spa, a kids' club and a huge range of activities, from yoga and Thai cooking classes to tennis and watersports. B8300

Cactus Access from the highway, west Bophut ☎077 245565, ✉cactusbung@hotmail.com. Ochre cottages with attractive bed platforms, large French windows and stylish, earth-tone bathrooms stand in two shady rows, running down to the inviting beachfront restaurant with a pool table. Fan B650, a/c B1200

Cocooning East of the village T-junction, opposite The Waterfront ☎085 781 4107, ⊛cocooninghotel.com. Small, good-value hotel with compact but well-equipped rooms (a/c, hot shower, fridge, safe, DVD player) in a bright and breezy contemporary style. Not on the beachfront, but it has a small plunge pool/jacuzzi; the English owner is a mine of local information. B1400

Free House West of the village ☎077 427517, ⊛freehousesamui.com. On a quiet plot that's shaded by a thick canopy of trees, running back from the popular beachfront bar-restaurant, the tasteful en-suite bungalows here are very well designed and maintained, with plenty of natural light. Made either of white-painted concrete or slatted dark wood, they feature mosquito nets, hammocks, hot showers and verandas. Fan B700, a/c B1800

Hansar At the west end of the village ☎077 245511, ⊛hansarsamui.com. You'll be surprised how spacious this hotel feels, with its long beachfront and just 74 low-rise rooms (all with huge shower areas and sea views from their big balconies), set around gardens and a pool. The stylish decor is a riot of geometry in brown and beige – unvarnished wood, bamboo, marble and granite – and there's a spa, gym and luxury restaurant, _H Bistro_, with ingredients flown in from around the world. Breakfast included. B8150

Juzz'a Pizza 2 East of the village T-junction ☎077 245663. Above a good restaurant (see below), four small but smart rooms, well equipped with comfy beds, a/c, hot showers, fridges, cable TV and DVD players. Two rooms have no view, while the other two have beachside terraces with great views. B1200

Khunthai Guesthouse West of the pier, 30m behind The Shack restaurant, Bophut village ☎077 245118 or ☎086 686 2960. Friendly spot set back from the beach in an orange, two-storey concrete house, offering basic, clean rooms with hot showers, TVs and fridges. Fan B500, a/c B800

The Lodge Towards the western end of the village ☎077 425337, ⊛lodgesamui.com. Small, two-storey, beachfront hotel with immaculately clean and tastefully decorated modern rooms, all with balconies looking over the water, and boasting a/c, ceiling fan, mini-bar, satellite TV, plus marble bathrooms with tubs to soak in. There's a seafront bar downstairs where you can get breakfast. B2690

The Waterfront East of the village T-junction ☎077 427165, ⊛thewaterfrontbophut.com. English-run boutique hotel, sociable and family-friendly, with a small swimming pool in a grassy garden. All of the tastefully decorated rooms and bungalows have a/c, hot water, mini-bars, safes, cable TV and views of the sea. Free pick-ups from the airport and bicycles for guests' use; breakfast included in the price. B3045

Zazen At the far west end of the beach ☎077 425085, ⊛samuizazen.com. Stylish bungalows and villas clustered round a cute pool and kids' pool, furnished with Thai and other Asian objets d'art, as well as satellite TV, DVD player, mini-bar and daybed; all sport a tropical-style open-air bathroom with rain shower. Other facilities at this eco-friendly resort include a spa, a fine restaurant that hosts Thai dancing (Thurs & Sun), cooking classes, kayaks and free bicycles. Breakfast included. B5950

EATING AND DRINKING

Café 69 On Highway 4169 west of the traffic lights, opposite The Wharf community mall ☎081 978 1945. This plush roadside restaurant conjures up creative fusion dishes that really work: the green curry roti pie with mango (B229) is a great combination and goes well with the spring rolls with soft-shelled crab _som tam_. Mon–Sat 1–10pm.

Enjoy West of the village T-junction ☎081 485 7112, ⊛enjoybeach-hotel-samui.com. At this very friendly, French-run hotel, the café-restaurant is a great spot for a breakfast of croissants and coffee on the lovely, breezy seafront terrace. Later in the day, it serves a few French specialities such as tournedos of charolais beef with pepper sauce (B490), lots of tempting Western desserts and a decent selection of wine and brandy. Daily 11am–10pm.

Happy Elephant West of the village T-junction ☎077 245347. This long-standing restaurant offers a good choice of mostly Thai food, including a few less mainstream dishes such as pork _nam tok_ (B240) and lots of seafood, which is displayed out front and priced by weight. Service is friendly and there's an attractive beachside terrace. Daily 11am–10.30pm.

Juzz'a Pizza 2 East of the village T-junction ☎077 245663. Friendly, small, elegant restaurant with a beach-side terrace, serving excellent, authentic pizzas (from B230), with vegetarian and seafood options, as well as pastas, sandwiches and Thai and Western main courses. Tues–Sun 4–11pm.

Ristorante alla Baia Just west of the village T-junction ☎077 245566. Run by an Italian who is passionate about his food and has come up with a well-designed menu of standard but authentic dishes, such as _scaloppine al vino bianco_ (pork or chicken fillets in white wine; B350). Also on offer are pizzas, home-made pasta and seafood, with the catch of the day displayed outside. With white tablecloths and plants, lots of wrought iron and a terrace on the beach, you could almost be overlooking the Adriatic. Daily 11am–10.30pm.

Satsuman Elysia Resort, Bophut village, 100m east of the pier ☎077 425029, ⓦ satsumansamui.com. Great Japanese food, good service and killer cocktails at this stylish, airy restaurant; the breaded chicken is tasty and hearty (B220), or treat yourself to a mixed sushi plate

(B390). Mon–Sat 5–11pm.

The Shack Grill West of the village T-junction ☎077 246041 or ☎087 264 6994, ⓦ theshackgrillsamui.com. Small, pricey spot, run by an ebullient New Yorker, and focused on the large, open grill at the front of the restaurant: here all manner of local seafood and imported meats priced by weight, such as Wagyu beef (B1095/100g) and New Zealand lamb, are cooked to your liking. Delicious apple pie and decent house wine. Daily 3–11pm.

Bangrak

Beyond the sharp headland with its sweep of coral reefs lies **BANGRAK**, sometimes called **Big Buddha Beach** after the colossus that gazes sternly down on the sun worshippers from its island in the bay. The beach is no great shakes, especially during the northeast monsoon, when the sea retreats and leaves a slippery mud flat, and generally it's hard to recommend staying here, as the resorts are squeezed together in a narrow, noisy strip between busy Route 4171 and the shore, underneath the airport flight path.

The **Big Buddha** (*Phra Yai*) is certainly big and works hard at being a tourist attraction, but is no beauty. A short causeway at the eastern end of the bay leads across to a messy clump of souvenir shops and food stalls in front of the temple, catering to day-tripping Thais as well as foreigners. Ceremonial dragon-steps then bring you up to the covered terrace around the Big Buddha, from where there's a fine view of the sweeping north coast. Look out for the B10 rice-dispensing machine, which allows you symbolically to give alms to the monks at any time of the day.

Choeng Mon

After Bangrak comes the high-kicking boot of Samui's **northeastern cape**, with its small, rocky coves overlooking Ko Pha Ngan and connected by sandy lanes. Songthaews run along Route 4171 to the largest and most beautiful bay, **Choeng Mon**, whose white sandy beach is lined with casuarina trees that provide shade for the bungalows and upmarket resorts. Choeng Mon is now popular enough to support small supermarkets, travel agents and banks, but on the whole it remains relatively uncommercialized and laidback.

ACCOMMODATION CHOENG MON

Boat House Hotel Central Choeng Mon ☎077 425041, ⓦ imperialhotels.com. Named after the two-storey rice barges that have been converted into suites in the grounds, the *Boat House* also offers good-value luxury rooms with balconies in more prosaic modern buildings, often filled by package tours. As well as a beachside boat-shaped pool, there's a garden pool, a spa, a fitness room, a kids' club, kayaks and table tennis. Breakfast included. **B4600**

Island View Tucked in on the east side of the Boat House Hotel ☎083 221 2450, ⓦ islandviewsamui.com. Smart, good-value rooms and chalets with a/c, hot water, TV and fridge, in a lively compound that crams in a supermarket and a beachfront bar-restaurant that specializes in southern Thai food, as well as a massage *sala* and jet-skis on the beach. **B1350**

Kirati Resort 100m east of Island View ☎081 881 2703, ⓦ kiratisamui.com. All the accommodation here has a/c, hot water, TV, a balcony and a fridge. Choose between a variety of spacious chalets with nice decorative touches in the jungly garden, and more expensive bright, new rooms in a hotel-style block, with granite-tiled floors, dark-wood sofas and smart, modern bathrooms. **B1500**

Ô Soleil West of the Boat House Hotel ☎077 425232, ⓦ osoleilbungalow.com. Lovely, orderly, Belgian-run place in a tranquil, pretty garden dotted with ponds. Among the well-built, clean bungalows, the cheapest are fan-cooled, with cold showers, at the back, while the elegant beachside restaurant has a nice shaded deck area and serves six hundred cocktails. Fan **B400**, a/c **B700**

★Tongsai Bay North side of Choeng Mon ☎077 245480, ⓦ tongsaibay.co.th. Easy-going, environmentally aware establishment with excellent service. The luxurious rooms, red-tiled cottages and palatial villas (some with their own pool) command beautiful views over the huge, picturesque grounds, the private beach and two swimming pools. In addition they nearly all sport second bathtubs on their secluded open-air terraces, and some also have outdoor, four-poster beds with mosquito nets if you want to sleep under the stars. There's also an array of very fine restaurants and a delightful spa. Breakfast included. B10,500

Chaweng

For looks alone, none of the other beaches can match **CHAWENG**, with its broad, gently sloping strip of white sand sandwiched between the limpid blue sea and a line of palm trees. Such beauty has not escaped attention of course, which means, on the plus side, that Chaweng can provide just about anything the active beach bum demands, from thumping nightlife to ubiquitous and diverse watersports. The negative angle is that the new developments are ever more cramped and expensive, while building work behind the palm trees and repairs to the over-commercialized main beach road are always in progress.

RESTAURANTS & CAFÉS

Coast	6
Eat Sense	5
Mit Samui	2
Ninja Crepes	4
Noori	3
Prego	1

ACCOMMODATION

Akwa	14
Amari Palm Reef	5
Anantara Lawana	1
Baan Kluaymai Guesthouse	12
Centara Grand	13
Chaweng Regent	6
Coral Bay Resort	2
The Jungle Club	15
Le Paradis	9
The Library	8
The Loft Samui	10
Long Beach Lodge	7
Muang Kulaypan	4
Tango Beach Resort	3
Tradewinds by Lawana	11

BARS & CLUBS

Ark Bar	7
Bar Solo	4
Cha Cha Moon Beach Club	6
Green Mango	3
Q Bar	1
Reggae Pub	2
Sound	5
Tropical Murphy's	8

CHAWENG

North Chaweng

The 6km bay is framed between the small island of Ko Matlang at the north end and the 300m-high headland above Coral Cove in the south. From **Ko Matlang**, where the waters provide some decent snorkelling, an often exposed coral reef slices southwest across to the mainland, marking out a shallow lagoon and **North Chaweng**. This S-shaped part of the beach is comparatively peaceful, though it has some ugly pockets of development; at low tide it becomes a wide, inviting playground, and from October to January the reef shelters it from the northeast winds.

Central Chaweng and Chaweng Noi

South of the reef, the idyllic shoreline of **Central Chaweng** stretches for 2km in a dead-straight line, the ugly, traffic-clogged and seemingly endless strip of amenities on the parallel main drag largely concealed behind the tree line and the resorts. Around a low promontory is **Chaweng Noi**, a little curving beach in a rocky bay, which is comparatively quiet in its northern part, away from the road. Well inland of Central Chaweng, the round-island road, Route 4169, passes through the original village of **Ban Chaweng**.

Coral Cove

South of Chaweng, the road climbs past **Coral Cove**, a tiny, isolated beach of coarse sand hemmed in by high rocks, with some good coral for snorkelling. It's well worth making the trip to *Vikasa Resort*'s restaurant, at the tip of the headland dividing Chaweng from Lamai, for a jaw-dropping view over Chaweng and Choeng Mon to the peaks of Ko Pha Ngan.

ACCOMMODATION   CHAWENG

Over fifty **bungalow resorts** and **hotels** at Chaweng are squeezed into thin strips running back from the beachfront at right angles. The cheapest digs here, however, are set back from the beach and are generally little more than functional.

NORTH CHAWENG

Amari Palm Reef North Chaweng ☏ 077 422015–8, ⓦ amari.com. Congenial, eco-friendly luxury hotel that's unpretentious and good value. Spacious accommodation, stretching back across the road from the beach and all with DVD players, includes family-friendly duplexes, and there are two elegant restaurants, including *Prego* (see p.548), a full-service spa, a gym, two free-form swimming pools and a kids' pool. Large-scale renovation is planned, which may change prices and facilities. B4200

Anantara Lawana North Chaweng ☏ 077 960333, ⓦ anantara.com. The design of this luxury hotel was inspired by Chinese merchants' houses in Thailand in the last century, which gives a pleasing retro feel to the rooms, most of which have outdoor bathrooms. Much of the accommodation is in two-storey houses, in which the ground-floor room has a plunge pool and the first-floor room a terrace; other villas either have their own pools or share semi-private ones. There's also a main, semicircular pool, of course, down by the beach, as well as an excellent spa, a good concierge service and fine restaurants, including *Tree Tops*, where you eat in romantic, open-sided treehouses. Breakfast included. B6830

Chaweng Regent At the bottom end of North Chaweng ☏ 077 230391–400, ⓦ chawengregent.com. Reliable, well-run, luxury place offering elegant bungalows and low-rise rooms with private terraces and all mod cons, around lotus ponds, two pools, a fitness centre and spa. B4800

★ **Coral Bay Resort** At the far north end of North Chaweng ☏ 077 234555, ⓦ coralbay.net. A charming, eco-friendly vision of how Chaweng might have developed – if only there'd been more space. In quiet, delightful, ten-acre gardens with over 500 species of plants, the huge, thatched villas have been thoughtfully and tastefully designed with local woods, bamboo and coconut; all have extensive verandas, waterfall showers, free broadband and DVD/CD/MP3 players (movies available from the library). There's an attractive pool, a spa and a good beachside bar-restaurant. Breakfast included. B6850

Muang Kulaypan North Chaweng ☏ 077 230849–50, ⓦ kulaypan.com. Chaweng's original boutique hotel is arrayed around a large, immaculate garden with a black-tiled swimming pool and an excellent beachside restaurant. Stylish rooms – each with their own private balcony or garden – combine contemporary design with traditional Thai-style comforts. Breakfast included. B4450

Tango Beach Resort North Chaweng ☏ 077 300451, ⓦ tangobeachsamui.com. This helpful and welcoming place has a modern Thai style that sets it apart from most of Samui's farang-oriented hotels: a variety of cutesy, colourful, well-equipped rooms are separated by a small, shady pool (and kids' pool) and a wooden boardwalk that runs down to the beach, where kayaks are available. B1500

CENTRAL CHAWENG

★**Akwa** Towards the south end of Central Chaweng ☎084 660 0551, ⓦakwaguesthouse.com. Cute, homely, brightly coloured rooms all decorated with cartoon murals and well equipped with a/c, hot water, mini-bars, TVs and DVD players (with DVDs to borrow). "Deluxe" are bigger than "Standard", though the latter have balconies, and there's a penthouse. Not on the beach but close to it, with direct access opposite. B950

Baan Kluaymai Guesthouse Soi Colibri, a small lane at the south end of Central Chaweng, opposite the landmark Centara Grand Beach Resort ☎077 413836, ⓦbaankluaymaiguesthouse.com. Good-value rooms in a brick building above a pleasant Chinese restaurant. All have large beds, hot shower, a/c and satellite TV. B700

Centara Grand Central Chaweng ☎077 230500, ⓦcentarahotelsresorts.com. Modelled on the first Thai "destination hotel", the *Railway Hotel* in Hua Hin (now also a *Centara Grand* – see p.518), this place has added a smart contemporary finish to its graceful, low-rise, colonial-style architecture. All the rooms and their broad balconies face the sea across the broad immaculate gardens of hedgerows, palm trees and lawns, which also shelter a huge, free-form pool. The hotel lays on varied daily programmes of activities for both adults and kids, not to mention plenty of watersports, and there's a lovely spa and a fine bar-restaurant, *Coast* (see below). B6570

Le Paradis Central Chaweng ☎077 239041–3, ⓦleparadisresort.com. Set in lush gardens, this place offers fourteen very stylish contemporary villas hung with large, colourful paintings and equipped with open-air bathrooms with large baths, large balconies, a/c, cable TV, DVD players and safes. Attractive beachside swimming pool and health spa. B2000

The Library Central Chaweng ☎077 422767–8, ⓦthelibrary.co.th. High-concept design hotel, based

around a shining white library of books, DVDs and CDs. The idea is continued in the rooms, which all sport iMacs and DVD players, and have a sleek, cubic theme; they're divided into suites (downstairs) and studios with balconies (upstairs). There's a blood-red swimming pool, a fitness centre and a beachfront terrace restaurant, *The Page*. Breakfast included. B12,460

The Loft Samui Central Chaweng ☎077 413420, ⓦtheloftsamui.com. Off-beach hotel with a raised wooden bar and restaurant area full of nooks and crannies; a great place to watch the world go by on the street below. Enhanced with a few stylish touches, the seventy rooms vary widely; all have hot showers and TVs. Breakfast included. Fan B790, a/c B890

Long Beach Lodge Towards the north end of Central Chaweng ☎077 422162, ⓦlongbeachsamui.com. An unusually spacious and shady, sandy compound. All the orderly, clean bungalows and rooms are a decent size and have hot water, fridge, TV and a/c. Service is friendly, and breakfast is included in the price. B1200

Tradewinds by Lawana Central Chaweng ☎077 414293–4, ⓦtradewindsbylawana.com. A cheerful, well-run place of characterful, colourfully painted bungalows and rooms (all with a/c, hot water, mini-bar, cable TV and balcony), with plenty of room to breathe in colourful tropical gardens that run down to a beachfront swimming pool. The resort specializes in sailing, with its own catamarans (instruction available). Breakfast included. B3625

CHAWENG NOI

★**The Jungle Club** 2km up a steep, partly paved road from Chaweng Noi ☎081 894 2327, ⓦjungleclub samui.com. Breezy, French–Thai antidote to Chaweng's commercial clutter: a huge, grassy, shady plot with a small pool on the edge of the slope to catch the towering views of Ko Pha Ngan and beyond. A chic bar-restaurant has been built into the rocks, while the accommodation – nearly all thatched, with mosquito nets and fans – includes wooden huts with cold showers and concrete bungalows with hot water and DVD players. Free pick-ups twice a day. B800

EATING

Chaweng offers all manner of foreign **cuisines**, from French to Russian, much of it of dubious quality. Among all this, it's quite hard to find good, reasonably priced Thai food – as well as the places recommended below, it's worth exploring the cheap and cheerful food stalls, popular with local workers, at either **Laem Din night market**, on the middle road between Central Chaweng and Highway 4169, or Pang Bua market (roughly 6am–midnight) on the Ban Chaweng road, which includes a famous stall for *khao niaw mamuang* (mango with sticky rice).

Coast Centara Grand Hotel, Central Chaweng ☎077 230500, ⓦcentarahotelsresorts.com. Cool, beachclub-like bar-restaurant with swing chairs, sunken booths in the sand and lots of beachfront to make the most of the sea views. The focus of the well-designed menu

is on excellent seafood and grills, but you'll also find pizzas (from B340), tapas-like "bites", and meat and cheese platters. A DJ entertains over Sunday brunch, while other days see fire-jugglers and live acoustic musicians. Daily noon–11pm.

6

Eat Sense Central Chaweng ☎ 077 414242, ⊕ eatsense samui.com. Spacious, relaxing, mostly open-air restaurant on the beachfront, serving expensive but delicious Thai and international food, using only organic vegetables – try the deep-fried prawns with cashew nuts and tamarind sauce. Daily 11am–midnight.

Mit Samui Ban Chaweng road ☎ 089 727 2034, ⊕ mit -samui-restaurant.com. Very popular with both locals and tourists, this large, bustling, simple restaurant specializes in pick-your-own seafood (priced by weight), but also serves tasty stir-fried squid with salted egg (B200), satay and fresh fruit juices. Daily 11am–2am.

Ninja Crepes Opposite Burirasa Resort in Central Chaweng. Popular, well-run, very basic and cheap restaurant, serving simple Thai favourites such as *tom yam*, *som tam* and *phat thai*, as well as crêpes, breakfasts and other Western food. Main dishes around B70. Daily noon–11pm.

Noori Opposite Chaweng Buri Resort towards the north end of Central Chaweng, just up from McDonald's ☎ 077 413108, ⊕ nooriindiasamui.com. Superior Indian food in relatively basic surroundings, including all the old favourites such as chicken tikka masala (B210), as well as plenty of seafood and vegetarian options. Also offers Indian cooking classes. Daily 11.30am–11.30pm.

★Prego Amari Palm Reef Hotel, North Chaweng ☎ 077 300317, ⊕ prego-samui.com. Excellent, chic, open-sided restaurant that would stand on its own two feet in Milan, the head chef's home town. The varied menu of contemporary Italian dishes includes good *antipasti*, pizzas, handmade pastas and top-notch risottos, and there's a very good selection of wines. Booking advised in high season. Daily 11.30am–midnight.

DRINKING AND NIGHTLIFE

Avoiding the raucous hostess bars and English theme pubs on the main through road, the best place to **drink** is on the beach: at night dozens of resorts and dedicated bars lay out candlelit tables with axe cushions for reclining on the sand, especially towards the north end of Central Chaweng and on North Chaweng.

Ark Bar North end of Central Chaweng ⊕ ark-bar.com. Hosts very popular beach parties, with international and Thai house DJs, live saxophone and percussion, a pool bar and fire shows. Daily 2pm–2am.

Bar Solo North end of Central Chaweng, on the main road just north of Green Mango ⊕ barsolosamui.com. One of the bars of the moment, whose black-and-white industrial look is matched by tech house on the sound system (DJs with percussion from 9pm). Diversions include a pool table, and there's a happy hour till 10pm. Daily 2pm–3am.

Cha Cha Moon Beach Club North end of Central Chaweng ⊕ facebook.com/chachamoonbeachclub. Stylish new beach bar with daybeds on the sand and Thai and international DJs spinning deep house and techno, especially for the weekly climax of full, black and half moon parties. Daily roughly 3pm–3am.

Green Mango North end of Central Chaweng ⊕ thegreenmangoclub.com. Long-standing dance venue, in a huge shed that combines an industrial look with that of a tropical greenhouse. Now with its own alley, Soi Green Mango, lined with other vibrant bars and clubs. Daily roughly 10pm–3am.

Q Bar North off the Ban Chaweng road ☎ 077 962420, ⊕ qbarsamui.com. Sleek, futuristic decor, great views over the lake from high on its north shore and cutting-edge music from local and international DJs, at this branch of the famous Bangkok bar-club. Daily 6pm–late.

Reggae Pub Inland from Central Chaweng across the lake ☎ 077 422331–3, ⊕ reggaepubkohsamui.com. Chaweng's oldest nightclub is a venerable Samui institution – with a memorabilia shop to prove it. It does time now as an unpretentious, good-time, party venue, with plenty of drinking games, pool tables, big-screen sports and live bands, mostly reggae, every night. Daily 6pm–2am.

Sound Next soi south of Green Mango ⊕ soundclub samui.com. With its smart front bar and large garden club at the back, this is where people stagger on to when other places close. Daily 11pm–6am.

Tropical Murphy's Opposite McDonald's in Central Chaweng ☎ 077 413614, ⊕ tropicalmurphys.com. One theme pub that is worth singling out: with draught Guinness, Magners, Kilkenny and Hoegaarden, a huge range of big-screen sports and decent food, *Murphy's* has turned itself into a popular landmark and meeting place. Daily 9am–2am.

DIRECTORY

Airlines Bangkok Airways, south end of Ban Chaweng on Route 4169 ☎ 077 601300.

Bookshops Bookazine, next to *Tropical Murphy's* on the beach road in Central Chaweng (daily 11am–10pm; ☎ 077 413616), sells English-language books, newspapers and magazines.

Hospital The private Samui International Hospital in North Chaweng (☎ 077 230781–2, ⊕ sih.co.th) provides 24hr ambulance and emergency services, house calls, a dental clinic and travel inoculations.

Pharmacy Boots has a convenient branch in the middle of Central Chaweng, just up the road from *Tropical Murphy's* pub (daily 10am–11pm).

Lamai

LAMAI is like a second city to Chaweng's capital, not quite as developed and much less frenetic, while lacking the latter's wide range of chic hotels, restaurants and nightclubs. Development is concentrated into a farang toytown of tawdry open-air hostess bars and Western restaurants that has grown up behind the centre of the beach, interspersed with supermarkets, clinics, banks, ATMs and travel agents; on Sunday evenings, the area to the east of the market hosts a **walking street** similar to the one in Maenam on Thursday. Running roughly north to south for 4km, the white, palm-fringed beach itself is still a picture, and generally quieter than Chaweng, with far less in the way of watersports – it's quite easy to get away from it all by staying at the peaceful extremities of the bay, where the backpackers' resorts are preferable to Chaweng's functional

6

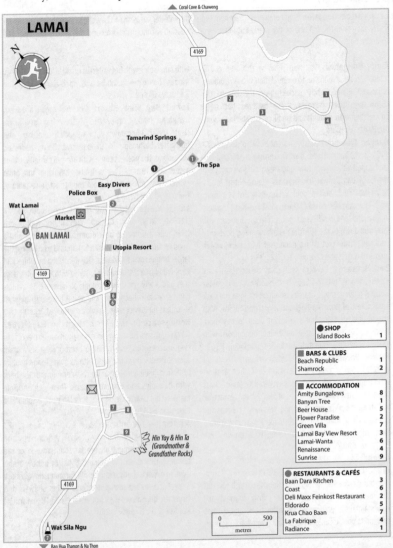

LAMAI

Coral Cove & Chaweng

4169

Tamarind Springs

The Spa

Easy Divers

Police Box

Wat Lamai

Market

BAN LAMAI

Utopia Resort

4169

Hin Yay & Hin Ta
(Grandmother &
Grandfather Rocks)

4169

Wat Sila Ngu

Ban Hua Thanon & Na Thon

0   500
metres

● **SHOP**
Island Books   1

■ **BARS & CLUBS**
Beach Republic   1
Shamrock   2

■ **ACCOMMODATION**
Amity Bungalows   8
Banyan Tree   1
Beer House   5
Flower Paradise   2
Green Villa   7
Lamai Bay View Resort   3
Lamai-Wanta   6
Renaissance   4
Sunrise   9

● **RESTAURANTS & CAFÉS**
Baan Dara Kitchen   3
Coast   6
Deli Maxx Feinkost Restaurant   2
Eldorado   5
Krua Chao Baan   7
La Fabrique   4
Radiance   1

6

guesthouses. At the northern end, the spur of land that hooks eastward into the sea is perhaps the prettiest spot and is beginning to attract some upmarket development: it has more rocks than sand, but the shallow sea behind the coral reef is protected from the high seas of November, December and January.

The original village of **Ban Lamai**, set well back on Route 4169, remains surprisingly aloof, and its wat contains a small museum of ceramics, agricultural tools and other everyday objects. Most visitors get more of a buzz from **Hin Yay** (Grandmother Rock) and **Hin Ta** (Grandfather Rock), small rock formations on the bay's southern promontory, which never fail to raise a giggle with their resemblance to the male and female sexual organs.

ACCOMMODATION

LAMAI

Lamai's **accommodation** is generally less cramped and slightly better value than Chaweng's, though it presents far fewer choices at the top end of the market. Budget accommodation is concentrated around the beach's northern and southern ends.

Amity Bungalows Southern end of the bay ☎ 077 424084. A huge range of accommodation in a welcoming, organized place. Tightly packed near the beach, the cheapest wooden bungalows are battered but clean enough, with fan, veranda and small, cold-water bathroom. Fan **B400**, a/c **B700**

Banyan Tree On the bay's northern headland ☎ 077 915333, ⊛ banyantree.com. Occupying a steep-sided, landscaped valley, with towering views of Chaweng from the lobby bar, *Banyan Tree* provides the height of luxury in its beautiful, stilted pool villas: lofty living rooms, walk-in wardrobes, possibly the biggest big-head showers in Thailand and landscaped pools. Electric buggies will ferry you down to the spa, the main swimming pool, kids' pool and private cove with a good stretch of beach, where plenty of watersports are on offer. **B23,330**

Beer House In the central section of the northern part of the beach ☎ 077 256591, ⊛ beerhousebungalow .com. A hidden, single-storey cement building at the back holds a row of down-at-heel but very cheap rooms, with shared cold showers, but you might want to pay more (from B500) for the more appealing bungalows with en-suite hot showers in its lush, shaded compound. **B300**

Flower Paradise On the bay's northern headland ☎ 077 270675, ⊛ samuiroestiland.com. Just a short walk from the beach, a friendly, well-run German–Swiss place in a small but beautiful garden. All the attractive, well-tended bungalows of varying sizes have verandas and hot water, and there's a good restaurant, *Röstiland* (closed Sun), specializing in the eponymous hash browns. Fan **B400**, a/c **B800**

Green Villa At the far southern end of the bay ☎ 077 424296 or ☎ 081 893 7227, ✉ greenvillasamui @hotmail.com. Though set back from the beach towards the main road, this resort enjoys a lush, spacious and well-maintained garden among palm trees, and a small swimming pool. Clean, simple, en-suite, wooden bungalows

with fans (some with hot water) or grand, a/c villas with TVs, fridges, hot-water bathtubs and open-air showers. Fan **B450**, a/c **B1600**

Lamai Bay View Resort On the bay's northern headland ☎ 077 458778–9, ⊛ bayviewsamui.com. Neat, stylish bungalows with verandas, mini-bars and hot-water bathrooms in an extensive, flower-bedecked compound; the poshest come with a/c and cable TV. Offers a friendly, German–Thai welcome, kayaking and great sunset views of the beach from the attractive restaurant. Fan **B1930**, a/c **B2050**

Lamai-Wanta East of the central crossroads ☎ 077 424550, ⊛ lamaiwanta.com. Welcoming, well-placed hotel with a seductive beachfront swimming pool and a good restaurant (see opposite). Set around trim lawns, the large, bright rooms and villas are decorated in white and dark wood in a restrained Thai style, with terracotta floor tiles and a few splashes of colour; all have a/c, TVs, mini-bars, safes and hot water, and some have DVD players. Discounts for longer stays. Breakfast included. **B2900**

Renaissance On the bay's northern headland ☎ 077 429300, ⊛ marriott.com. In a fine position with access to two beaches, this luxury Marriott resort presents a stark choice: long, lofty villas, each with its own plunge pool, in lush, frog-filled gardens, or far cheaper rooms at the back with balconies and outdoor jacuzzis. There's an enticing, many-tiered beachside pool, a 50m lap pool, a spa and a tapas bar. **B6880**

Sunrise On the Hin Yay Hin Ta access road ☎ 077 424433, ⊛ sunrisebungalow.com. Welcoming and clued-up establishment on the far southern end of the beach, with a decent restaurant, books to borrow and a gym. In a quiet, shady garden amid coconut palms, choose between clean fan rooms with cold or hot showers and larger a/c bungalows with hot water, cable TV and fridge. Fan **B600**, a/c **B1600**

EATING AND DRINKING

Besides the **restaurants** recommended below, there's a **market** of cheap takeaway food stalls and simple restaurants inland just off Highway 4169 (east of Tesco Lotus supermarket) that's popular with locals for lunch and dinner (closes around 8 or 9pm). Apart from a few bar-restaurants on the beach near *Lamai-Wanta*, Lamai's **nightlife** is all within spitting distance of the central crossroads.

Baan Dara Kitchen Highway 4169, Ban Lamai. A locals' favourite right beside the entrance to Wat Lamai, this basic restaurant serves cheap and very tasty noodle soup with pork, dim sum, *phat thai* and green curry. Daily 7am–4pm.

Beach Republic On the bay's northern headland ☎077 458100, ⓦbeachrepublic.com. Although it features accommodation and a spa, this chic beach club is best known for its restaurant and bar, arrayed around two pools and a jacuzzi, with plenty of loungers and day-beds and fine views of the bay. Among sandwiches, global tapas, pasta and pizza, the very good beer-battered fish and chips (B420) stand out. Weekly events include two DJ sets on weekend afternoons, "Soulful Saturdays" and "Sunday Sessions". Restaurant daily 7–10.30am & 11am–10.30pm.

Coast Lamai-Wanta, east of the central crossroads ☎077 424550. Hip, open-sided restaurant by the hotel pool and beach, minimalist but mellow, with a menu that's half Thai, including tasty *kaeng matsaman kai* (B180), and half international, with some touches of Asian fusion. Daily 7am–6pm.

Deli Maxx Feinkost Restaurant North of the central crossroads, near Highway 4169. At this popular little bar-restaurant with a free pool table, you can tuck into a wide selection of Western, mostly German, food, including plenty of sausages and good steaks and pizzas, and wash it all down with German beer. Tues–Sun 6pm–2am.

Eldorado Just west of the central crossroads. Highly recommended friendly, good-value Swedish restaurant,

serving a few Thai favourites, salads, steaks, pizzas and other international main courses. All-you-can-eat barbecue on Wednesday (B260). Daily 3–10.30pm.

Krua Chao Baan Highway 4169, about 1km south of Hin Yay Hin Ta ☎077 418589, ⓦkruachaobaansamui .com. With a cute little garden and scenic seafront terraces between the road and the sea, this well-regarded restaurant concentrates on seafood (mostly sold by weight) and serves a few southern Thai dishes such as *kaeng som kung* ("sour prawn curry"; B150). Daily 10am–10pm.

La Fabrique Route 4169, just south of the temple in Lamai village. Authentic French patisserie-café, a civilized retreat from the busy road. Superb custard cakes (B80), quiches (B60), omelettes, pizzas, salads and sandwiches. Daily 7am–8pm.

Radiance The Spa Resort, at the far north end of the beach. Excellent, casual beachside restaurant, serving a huge range of vegetarian Thai and international (including Mexican) dishes, plus raw and vegan food, as well as plenty of meat and marine offerings. The veggie "ginger nuts" stir-fry (B140) and *som tam* with spicy Thai sausage (B125) are excellent. A long menu of "longevity drinks" – juices, smoothies and shakes – includes a delicious lime juice with honey. Daily 7am–10pm.

Shamrock North of the central crossroads ⓦthesamui shamrock.com. Popular, friendly Irish bar with pool tables and TV sports, which hosts lively cover bands every evening and keeps Guinness and Kilkenny bitter on draught. Daily 9.30am–2am.

SHOPPING

Island Books On Highway 4169, opposite Beer House bungalows ☎077 961769, ⓦisland-books-samui.com. Samui's best secondhand bookshop, with its stock of

thousands of books detailed on the website (updated daily). Daily 8am–8pm.

The south and west coasts

Lacking the long, attractive beaches of the more famous resorts, the **south and west coasts** have much less to offer in the way of accommodation, though there are one or two interesting spots that are worth heading for on a round-island tour. If you happen to be here in November, the west coast's flat, unexceptional beaches might make a calm alternative when the northeast winds buffet the other side of the island.

Ko Taen and Ko Mad Sum

The two small islands of **Ko Taen** and **Ko Mad Sum**, a short way off the south coast, offer some of Samui's best snorkelling. TK Tour in Ban Thongkrut (☎077 334052–3, ⓦtktoursamui.com) covers both on a four- to five-hour boat trip, costing B1300 per person (B1500 with kayaking, or with a quick look at Ko Si Ko Ha, the heavily guarded islands to the west where sea gypsies gather swifts' nests for bird's-nest soup – see p.673), including pick-up from your accommodation, snorkelling equipment and lunch. Island Hoppers (☎081 361 5605, ☻islandhopperssamui.com) offers snorkelling and kayaking day-trips to Ko Taen (B1390, including pick-up from your accommodation, all equipment and lunch), as well as overnight camping and dolphin-watching trips and yoga and meditation retreats.

Na Muang Falls

About 5km inland of **Ban Hua Thanon**, near **Ban Thurian**, the **Na Muang Falls** make a popular outing as they're not far off the round-island road (each of the two main falls has its own signposted kilometre-long paved access road off Route 4169). The lower fall splashes and sprays down a 20m wall of rock into a large pool, while Na Muang 2, upstream, is a more spectacular, shaded cascade that requires a bit of foot-slogging from the car park (about 15min uphill).

Ang Thong National Marine Park

Closed Nov & early Dec • Park entry fee B300 • Park headquarters ☎ 077 280222 or ☎ 077 286025, ☻ dnp.go.th (look for "Mu Ko Ang Thong" – mu ko means "archipelago")

Even if you don't get your buns off the beach for the rest of your stay on Samui or Pha Ngan, it's worth taking at least a day out to visit the beautiful **Ang Thong National Marine Park**, a lush, dense group of 42 small islands strewn like dragons' teeth over the deep-blue Gulf of Thailand, 30km or so west of Samui. Once a haven for pirate junks, then a Royal Thai Navy training base, the islands and their white-sand beaches and virgin rainforest are now preserved under the aegis of the National Parks Department. Erosion of the soft limestone has dug caves and chiselled out fantastic shapes that are variously said to resemble seals, a rhinoceros, a Buddha image and even the temple complex at Angkor.

The surrounding waters are home to dolphins, wary of humans because local fishermen catch them for their meat, and *pla thu* (short-bodied mackerel), part of the national staple diet, which gather in huge numbers between February and April to spawn around the islands. On land, long-tailed macaques, leopard cats, wild pigs, sea otters, squirrels, monitor lizards and pythons are found, as well as dusky langurs, which, because they have no natural enemies here, are unusually friendly and easy to spot. Around forty bird species have had confirmed sightings, including the white-rumped shama, noted for its singing, the brahminy kite, black baza, little heron, Eurasian woodcock, several species of pigeon, kingfisher and wagtail, as well as common and hill mynah; in addition, island caves shelter swiftlets, whose homes are stolen for bird's-nest soup (see p.673).

Ko Wua Talab

The largest landmass in the group is **Ko Wua Talab** (Sleeping Cow Island), where the park headquarters shelter in a hollow behind the small beach. From there, you can climb to the island's peak to gawp at the panorama, which is especially fine at sunrise and sunset: in the distance, Ko Samui, Ko Pha Ngan and the mainland; nearer at hand, the jagged edges of the surrounding archipelago; and below the peak, a secret cove on the western side and an almost sheer drop to the clear blue sea to the east. It's a fairly tricky 500m trail, with some scrambling including a patch of sharp rocks at the summit (allow about 2hr return at a comfortable pace; bring walking sandals or shoes). Another climb from the beach (allow about 1hr return) leads to **Tham Buabok**, a cave set high in the cliff-face. Some of the stalactites and stalagmites are said to resemble lotuses, hence the cave's appellation, "Waving Lotus". If you're visiting in September, look out for the white, violet-dotted petals of **lady's slipper orchids**, which grow on the rocks and cliffs.

Ko Mae Ko

The park's name, Ang Thong ("Golden Bowl"), comes from a landlocked saltwater lake, 250m in diameter, on **Ko Mae Ko** to the north of Ko Wua Talab, which was the inspiration for the setting of the bestselling novel and film, *The Beach*. Steep steps (allow 30min return) lead from the beach to the rim of the cliff wall that encircles the lake, affording another stunning view of the archipelago and of the shallow, blue-green water below, which is connected to the sea by an impassable natural underground tunnel.

ARRIVAL AND DEPARTURE

ANG THONG 6

There are no scheduled boats to Ang Thong, only organized **day-trips**, which can be booked through your accommodation or a travel agent. If you do want to stay, you can go over on a boat-trip ticket – it's generally valid for a return on a later day.

FROM KO SAMUI

Blue Stars ☎077 300615 or ☎077 413231, ⓦbluestars .info. If you want to make the most of the park's beautiful scenery of strange rock formations and hidden caves, take a dedicated kayaking trip with Blue Stars. For a one-day trip, taking in the lake at Ko Mae Ko and kayaking and snorkelling at Ko Thai Plao in the northern part of the park, it charges B2500, including pick-up from your accommodation and boat from Na Thon over to the park, buffet lunch and snorkelling gear.

Highway ☎077 421290 or ☎081 843 1533, ⓦhighseatour.com. The main operator, whose big boats leave Na Thon every day at 8.30am, returning at 4.30–5pm. In between, there's a two-and-a-half-hour stop to explore Ko Wua Talab (just enough time to climb to the viewpoint and have a quick swim – and possibly visit the cave – so don't dally), lunch on the boat, some cruising through the archipelago, a visit to the viewpoint over the lake on Ko Mae Ko and some time for snorkelling. Tickets cost B1100/person (or B1650 with kayaking), including

pick-up from your accommodation.

Tours Koh Samui ☎077 961911, ⓦtourskohsamui .com. One of several companies in Maenam, Bangrak and Bophut offering speedboat day-trips to Ang Thong (B1800, including snorkelling and kayaking, but not Ko Wua Talab).

FROM KO PHA NGAN

Similar day-trips to those from Samui are available on Pha Ngan, and they include transfers from the main beaches, lunch and snorkelling.

Orion ☎081 894 5076, ⓦphanganboattrips.com. Recommended day-trips in a wooden cruiser, costing B1700, or B1900 with kayaking (including national park entrance fee, light breakfast, snacks, fruit and soft drinks).

Seaflower Bungalows (see p.565). Organizes occasional two-day, one-night boat treks into the park, which involve snorkelling, catching your own seafood, and sleeping in tents or hammocks on the beach (from B3500/person, including food and soft drinks).

GETTING AROUND

Boat rental For getting around the archipelago from Ko Wua Talab, it's possible to charter a motorboat or rent a kayak from marine park staff at headquarters, who also rent out snorkelling gear; the archipelago's waters are too shallow for really good coral, but the best of it is off Ko Thai Plao, in the north of the park.

ACCOMMODATION AND EATING

National park bungalows At park headquarters on Ko Wua Talab ☎077 280222 or ☎077 286025, ⓦdnp .go.th. Simple two- to eight-berth bungalows and a restaurant, in a sheltered grassy glade behind the main beach. B500

Camping At park headquarters on Ko Wua Talab and on Ko Samsao. Two-person tents can be rented for around B200 a night from headquarters.

Ko Pha Ngan

In recent years, backpackers have tended to move over to Ko Samui's fun-loving little sibling, **KO PHA NGAN**, 20km to the north, which still has a comparatively simple atmosphere, mostly because the poor road system is an impediment to the developers. With a dense jungle covering its inland mountains and rugged granite outcrops along the coast, Pha Ngan lacks the huge, gently sweeping beaches for which Samui is famous, but it does have plenty of coral to explore and some beautiful, sheltered bays. If you're seeking total isolation, trek out to **Hat Khuat** (**Bottle Beach**) on the north coast

6

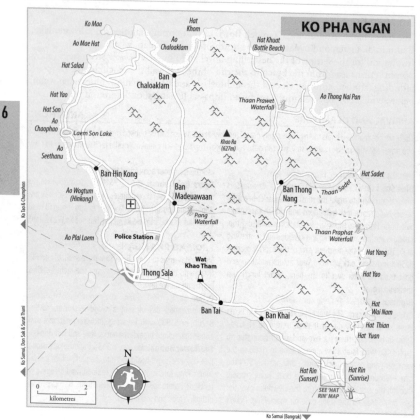

or the half-dozen pristine beaches on the east coast; **Thong Nai Pan**, at the top of the east coast, is not quite as remote, and offers a decent range of amenities and accommodation; while on the long neck of land at the southeast corner, **Hat Rin**, a pilgrimage site for ravers, is a thoroughly commercialized backpackers' resort in a gorgeous setting.

Much of Pha Ngan's development has plonked itself on the south and west sides along the only coastal roads on the island, which fan out from **Thong Sala**, the capital. The long, straight south coast is lined with bungalows, especially around **Ban Tai** and **Ban Khai**, to take the overspill from nearby Hat Rin, but it's hard to recommend staying here, as the beaches are mediocre by Thai standards, and the coral reef that hugs the length of the shoreline gets in the way of swimming. The west coast, however, offers several handsome sandy bays with great sunset views, notably **Hat Yao** and **Hat Salad**.

Pha Ngan's **bungalows** all now have running water and electricity, and plenty of places offer air conditioning, though there is only a handful of real luxury hotels. The three hundred-plus resorts generally have more space to spread out than on Ko Samui, and the cost of living is lower. The **prices** given on the following pages are standard for most of the year (though on Hat Rin they vary with the phases of the moon), but in slack periods you'll be offered discounts (possible, roughly, in May, June, Oct & Nov), and at the very busiest times (especially Dec & Jan) Pha Ngan's bungalow owners are canny enough to raise the stakes. **Nightlife** is concentrated at Hat Rin, climaxing every month in a wild **full moon party** on the beach; several smaller outdoor parties have now got in on the act, all at Ban Tai on the south coast: the **Half Moon Festival** (twice monthly, about a week before and after the full moon; ⓦhalfmoonfestival.com) and the monthly **Black Moon Culture** (ⓦblackmoon-culture.com) have now been joined by Sramanora Waterfall Party (two days before and one day after full moon) and Jungle Experience (one day and ten days before each full moon), which are both on Facebook.

ARRIVAL AND DEPARTURE

KO PHA NGAN

The most obvious way of getting to Ko Pha Ngan is on a boat from the **Surat Thani** area, but there are also boats from Chumphon (see p.528). Kan Airlines (ⓦkanairlines.com) are planning to build a small airport between Hat Sadet and Ao Thong Nai Pan.

FROM SURAT THANI OR DON SAK

Surat Thani to Thong Sala Boat services fluctuate according to demand, but the longest-established is the night boat from Ban Don pier in Surat Thani to Thong Sala, which leaves at 11pm every night (☎077 284928 or ☎081 326 8973; 7hr; B450); in the opposite direction, the night boat departs from Thong Sala at 10pm. Tickets are available from the pier on the day of departure, but note that sometimes these boats don't depart if they haven't got enough takers to make it worth their while, especially in the rainy season.

Don Sak to Thong Sala Out of five Raja vehicle ferries a day (on Pha Ngan ☎077 377452–3, ⓦrajaferryport.com), you can get connecting bus transport to the pier from Surat Thani three times a day, with a total journey time of around 4–5hr (B375). In addition, there are three Lomprayah

catamarans a day (on Pha Ngan ☎077 238411–2, ⓦlomprayah.com), charging B550 including bus transport to the pier, with a total journey time from Surat of about 3hr.

FROM BANGKOK

Bus and train packages From Bangkok bus and train packages similar to those for getting to Ko Samui are available (see p.537), notably government buses from the Southern Terminal (first-class a/c 1 daily B770; VIP 1 daily B1080; 13hr–14hr 30min). Leaving Pha Ngan, you can catch these buses from the Raja Ferry pier in Thong Sala (☎077 238507 or ☎077 238762). Lomprayah also offers through-tickets from Bangkok, costing B1350 (13hr 30min), including an overnight VIP bus from its office on Thanon Ram Bhuttri in Banglamphu (☎02 629 2569–70), via Hua Hin, and a catamaran from Chumphon via Ko Tao.

KO PHA NGAN ACTIVITIES

The most popular activities on Ko Pha Ngan are round-island **boat trips**, from Hat Rin and Hat Yao, for example (see the relevant accounts), and trips to Ang Thong National Marine Park (see p.552). The island isn't a great base for **scuba diving**: getting to the best sites around Ko Tao involves time-consuming and expensive voyages, and there aren't as many dive companies here as on Ko Samui or Ko Tao. Other **activities** include learning to cook Thai food, bicycle tours, yoga, meditation and kiteboarding.

Agama Yoga North of Thong Sala, with several bases around Ban Hin Kong ☎089 233 0217, ⓦagamayoga.com. Yoga classes.

Kiteboarding Asia Just west of Ban Tai ☎080 600 0573, ⓦkiteboardingasia.com. Kiteboarding, stand-up paddleboarding and wakeboarding.

Eco Nature Tour ☎077 377844–5, ⓦfacebook .com/eco-tourphanganthailand. A well-received programme of half- and one-day tours that might take in elephant trekking, snorkelling, ziplining, Thai boxing, archery, Pang Waterfall and boating to Bottle Beach; free pick-ups from most parts of the island.

Jungle Gym Near the pier in Hat Rin ☎077 375115. Gym offering Thai boxing classes and yoga.

Lotus Diving Dive resort on Ao Chaloaklam (plus an office at Backpackers Information Centre in Hat Rin) ☎077 374142, ⓦlotusdiving.com. PADI Five-Star

centre, which offers frequent courses and trips to Sail Rock (see p.569), halfway between Pha Ngan and Tao.

My Wok and Me Thong Sala ☎087 893 3804, ⓦfacebook.com/pages/My-Wok-and-Me /146999882047571. Cooking classes, including a bicycle trip to the market and free pick-ups in Hat Rin and around Thong Sala; vegetarian menu available.

Phangan Bicycle Tours Thong Sala ☎089 593 9732, ⓦphanganbicycletours.com. Danish-run half-day cycling tours on well-maintained bikes either for gentle sightseeing or for adventure riding.

Wat Khao Tham On a quiet hillside above Ban Tai ⓦnunamornpun-kohphangan.com. Week-long meditation retreats throughout the year, with registration in person on the 10th of each month (donations to cover costs). The website gives details of the schedule of retreats.

FROM KO SAMUI

To Thong Sala Three Lomprayah catamarans a day do the 30min trip from Na Thon on Ko Samui to Thong Sala (B300; at Na Thon ☎077 950028, on Ko Pha Ngan ☎077 238411–2). Three Seatran Discovery boats a day from the east end of Bangrak (B300; on Samui ☎077 246086–8, Pha Ngan ☎077 238679; ⓦseatrandiscovery.com) and two Lomprayah catamarans from Maenam (B300; at Maenam ☎077 427765–6) call in at Thong Sala after 30min, on their way to Ko Tao.

To Hat Rin and the east coast From the centre of Bangrak, the *Haad Rin Queen* crosses four times a day to Hat Rin in under an hour (times have remained constant over the years: from Bangrak 10.30am, 1pm, 4pm &

6.30pm, from Hat Rin 9.30am, 11.40am, 2.30pm & 5.30pm; B200; on Samui ☎077 484668, on Pha Ngan ☎077 375113). If there are enough takers and the weather's good enough – generally reliable between roughly mid-Jan and late Oct – one small boat a day crosses from the pier in Ban Maenam at noon to Hat Rin, before sailing up Ko Pha Ngan's east coast, via Hat Thian and Hat Sadet, to Thong Nai Pan; tickets to Hat Sadet, for example, cost B350.

FROM KO TAO

There are boats from Ko Tao to Ko Pha Ngan (see p.569); all offer the same service in the return direction.

INFORMATION

Tourist information There's no TAT office on Ko Pha Ngan, but a free, widely available booklet, *Phangan Info*, provides regularly updated information about the island, and has a website, ⓦphangan.info, on which you can book accommodation. Affiliated to this is the website of Hat Rin's

travel agency (see p.559), ⓦbackpackersthailand.com, which is also a good source of information.

Maps The best map for serious exploration of the island is Visid Hongsombud's *Guide Map of Koh Pha-ngan and Koh Tao* (B120), though it's hard to find.

Thong Sala

Like the capital of Samui, **THONG SALA** is a port of entrance and little more, where the incoming ferries, especially around noon, are met by touts sent to escort travellers to bungalows elsewhere on the island. Seatran and Lomprayah share a pier, while a short way to the north, the Raja Ferry pier gives onto the town's dusty main street, which is flanked by banks, supermarkets, travel agents, a day market and a night market. Branching off south is the old main street, which on Saturday evenings becomes a "Walking Street" weekly market, selling clothes, crafts and food. Songthaews, jeeps and air-conditioned minibuses to the rest of the island congregate by the pier heads.

GETTING AROUND

THONG SALA

By motorbike or jeep Motorbikes (B150–200/day) and jeeps (B800–1000/day) can be rented from many places

on the main road to the piers.

ACCOMMODATION AND EATING

Nira's South along the waterfront from the main street, opposite the Seatran pier. Very pleasant branch of the famous Hat Rin café (see p.562) offering "quick meals to catch the boat": all-day breakfasts, espressos, juices, shakes, bakery goods such as quiche lorraine and deli sandwiches. Daily 7am–7pm; closed on the 10th of every month.

Pha Ngan Chai Hotel By the piers, Thong Sala ☎077 238109. If you really need to stay in Thong Sala, head for this incongruous white high-rise overshadowing the piers, which makes a fair stab at international-standard features for visiting businesspeople and government officials, with a/c, hot water, TVs, fridges and, in some rooms, sea-view balconies, as well as a pool. Breakfast included. **B1000**

DIRECTORY

Hospital The island's basic main hospital (☎077 377034) lies 3km north of town, on the inland road towards Mae Hat. There's also a 24hr emergency rescue service, staffed by volunteers (☎077 377500).

Police The main station is 2km up the Ban Chaloaklam

road (☎077 377501), and there's a tourist police office at the main pier in Thong Sala (☎1155).

Post office About 500m southeast of the piers on the old main street (Mon–Fri 8.30am–noon & 1–4.30pm, Sat 9am–noon).

Pang (Phaeng) Waterfall

Than Sadet–Ko Pha Ngan National Park, 4km northeast of Thong Sala off the road to Chaloaklam • Free admission • Take a Chaloaklam-bound songthaew as far as Ban Madeuawaan, from where it's a 1km signposted walk east

From most places on the island, it's fairly easy to get to the grandiosely termed Than Sadet–Ko Pha Ngan National Park, which contains **Pang (Phaeng) Waterfall**, Pha Ngan's biggest drop. The park headquarters are northeast of Thong Sala off the main road to Chaloaklam. From here, the main fall – bouncing down in stages over the hard, grey stone – is a steep 250m walk up a forest path. The trail then continues for 300m to a stunning viewpoint overlooking the south and west of the island.

Hat Rin

HAT RIN is firmly established as the major party venue in Southeast Asia, especially in the peak seasons of August, December and January, but it's most famous for its

HAT RIN

ACCOMMODATION

Best Western Phanganburi Resort	3
Blue Marine	5
Coco Hut	9
Leela Beach Bungalows	11
Lighthouse Bungalows	10
Phangan Bayshore Resort	4
Rin Bay View	6
Same-Same Lodge	7
Sarikantang	12
Seaview Sunrise	1
Sun Cliff	8
Thai Dee Garden Resort	2

RESTAURANTS & CAFÉS

Bamboozle	4
Casa Nostra	2
Little Home	3
Nira's	1
Om Ganesh	5

BARS & CLUBS

Back Yard	8
Bom's Bar	5
Cactus Club	4
Mellow Mountain Bar	1
Outback Bar	6
Paradise	7
Sunrise	3
Tommy's	2

year-round **full moon parties** – something like *Apocalypse Now* without the war. Hat Rin's compact geography is ideally suited to an intense party town: it occupies the flat neck of Pha Ngan's southeast headland, which is so narrow that the resort comprises two back-to-back beaches, joined by transverse roads at the north and south ends.

The eastern beach, usually referred to as **Sunrise**, or Hat Rin Nok (Outer Hat Rin), is what originally drew visitors here, a classic curve of fine white sand between two rocky slopes; there's still some coral off the southern slope to explore, though the water is far from limpid these days. This beach is the centre of Hat Rin's action, with a solid line of bars, restaurants and bungalows tucked under the palm trees.

Sunset beach, or Hat Rin Nai (Inner Hat Rin), which for much of the year is littered with flotsam, looks ordinary by comparison but has plenty of quieter accommodation. Unfortunately, development between the beaches does no justice to the setting: it's ugly, cramped and chaotic, with new low-rise concrete shophouses thrown up at any old angle. Businesses here, concentrated around what's known as **Chicken Corner**, where the southern transverse road meets the road along the back of Sunrise, include supermarkets, overseas phone facilities, plenty of ATMs and bank currency-exchange booths, as well as outlets for more outré services such as bikini waxing and Playstation rental. Half-hearted attempts to tart up the large body of water in the middle of the headland with a few park benches and lights have been undermined by all-too-accurate signposts pointing to "Hat Rin Swamp".

ARRIVAL AND DEPARTURE   HAT RIN

By songthaew or minibus Songthaews and a/c minibuses run between Thong Sala and Hat Rin (B100 during the day, more at night); in Hat Rin, you can find them or their touts at the pier, Chicken Corner or near the police box.

By boat The easiest approach to Hat Rin, if you're coming from Ko Samui, or even Surat Thani, is on the boat from Bangrak on Samui's north coast (see p.556): four boats a day cross to the pier on Sunset beach in under an hour.

GETTING AROUND

By jeep or motorbike Plenty of places on Hat Rin rent jeeps (about B1000/day) and motorbikes (from B150/day). There have been lots of reports, however, of travellers being charged exorbitant amounts if they bring the vehicle back with even the most minor damage – at the very least, check the vehicle over very carefully before renting and ask

if you can leave cash instead of your passport as a deposit. *Sun Cliff* (see p.561), which has an office just off the southern transverse, is a reliable place for motorbikes, and won't try this scam. The section of road between Hat Rin and Ban Khai is paved but winding and precipitous – take care if you're driving yourself.

INFORMATION AND TOURS

★**Backpackers Information Centre** The excellent, English-Thai Backpackers Information Centre, based to the south of Chicken Corner (daily 11.30am–8.30pm, longer hours around full moon; ☏077 375535, ⓦbackpackers thailand.com), is a reliable, helpful and clued-up full-service travel agency, with a website that's very useful not just for Pha Ngan but for the whole of Thailand, including lots of advice and mini-package tours. Staff can book tours, full moon party accommodation packages and attractive

rental villas on Ko Pha Ngan and overland through-tickets to just about anywhere. They also act as agents for Ko Pha Ngan's Lotus Diving and Ko Tao's Crystal Diving (with discounted deals available for advance bookings).
Clinic Bandon International Hospital, a large private hospital on Ko Samui, runs several clinics in Hat Rin, including one on the southern transverse near the pier (☏077 375471–2).

HAT RIN BOAT TRIPS

Many places on Hat Rin, including the Backpackers Information Centre (see above), book one-day **boat trips** up the east coast and back, typically charging B850–950 (including simple lunch and snorkelling equipment, sometimes with the option of kayaking, too) and taking in Hat Salad, Mae Hat, Hat Khom, Bottle Beach or Thong Nai Pan, and Thaan Sadet.

FULL MOON PARTIES: A SURVIVOR'S GUIDE

Even if you're not the type to coat yourself in day-glo and dance till dawn, a **full moon party** at Hat Rin is certainly a sight to see, and the atmosphere created by thousands of folk mashing it up on a beautiful, moon-bathed beach, lit up by fireworks and fire-jugglers, is quite a buzz. If you're planning to get in on the action, first of all you'll need to check exactly when the party is: when the full moon coincides with an important **Buddhist festival**, the party is moved one night away to avoid a clash; check out ⓦfullmoon.phangan.info for details. There's also a big party at Hat Rin on Christmas Day, and a massive one on New Year's Eve. An **admission fee** to the parties of B100 is now charged. On the nights around the full moon, foam, pool and all sorts of other parties are organized.

On full moon night, *Paradise*, at the very southern end of Sunrise, styles itself as the main party **venue**, sometimes bringing in big-name international DJs. However, the mayhem spreads along most of Sunrise, fuelled by hastily erected drinks stalls and around a dozen major **sound systems** – listen out for reggae at *Bom's Bar* and funky house and drum'n'bass at *Sunrise* further up the beach. Next day, as the beach party winds down, *Back Yard* kicks off its afterparty at around seven in the morning, with the best of the previous night's DJs; it's up the hill behind the south end of Sunrise off the path to Leela Beach.

Drug-related horror stories are common currency in Hat Rin, and some of them are even true: dodgy MDMA, *ya baa* (Burmese-manufactured methamphetamines), Ice (crystal meth) and all manner of other concoctions put an average of two farangs a month into hospital for psychiatric treatment. The local authorities have started clamping down on the trade in earnest, setting up a permanent police box at Hat Rin (with a temporary tourist police office nearby for the full moon), instigating regular roadblocks and bungalow searches, paying dealers, bungalow and restaurant owners to inform on travellers to whom they've sold drugs, and drafting in scores of police (both uniformed and plain-clothes) on full moon nights. It doesn't seem to have dampened the fun, only made travellers a lot more circumspect.

Other **tips** for surviving the full moon are mostly common sense: leave your valuables in your resort's safe – it's a bad night for bungalow break-ins – and don't take a bag out with you; keep an eye on your drink to make sure it's not spiked; go easy on the buckets – the beach stalls often secretly substitute home-distilled Burmese hooch, of unknown strength and dubious quality, for the advertised name-brand spirits; watch out for broken bottles and anchors on the beach; and do not go swimming while under the influence – there have been several deaths by drowning at previous full moon parties. There have also been several reports of sexual assaults on women – don't walk or take a taxi home alone – of muggings and of unprovoked, violent attacks in Hat Rin, especially around full moon night.

ACCOMMODATION AND TRANSPORT

Hat Rin now has around five thousand **rooms** – some of them hastily converted into dorms at party time charging B500–1000 per person – but on full moon nights up to thirty thousand revellers may turn up. Unless you're prepared to forget about sleep altogether, you should book well in advance or arrive several days early to bag a room, as many resort owners specify a minimum stay of five nights (in some places up to ten nights, especially over the New Year's Eve party). Alternatively, hitch up with one of the many **party boats** (about B900 return per person) organized through guesthouses and restaurants on Ko Samui, especially at Bangrak and Bophut, which usually leave between 9pm and midnight and return around dawn, though they're sometimes dangerously overcrowded. There's also transport by boat or car from all the other beaches on Pha Ngan; at nearby Ban Tai, there are also dorms to take the overflow.

ACCOMMODATION

Staying on **Sunrise** is often expensive and noisy, though you should have more luck towards the north end of the beach. On **Sunset**, the twenty or more resorts are squeezed together in orderly rows, and are especially quiet and inexpensive between April and June and in October. Many visitors choose to stay on the **headland** to the south of the main beaches, especially at white-sand, palm-fringed **Leela Beach** on the west side of the promontory, which is a twenty-minute walk along a well-signposted route from Chicken Corner. At any of the places out here your bungalow is likely to have more peace and space and better views, leaving you a torchlit walk to the night-time action.

Best Western Phanganburi Resort Towards the north end of Sunset beach ☎077 375481, ⓦbest westernphanganburi.com. Welcoming, luxury complex that encompasses three hotel blocks, dozens of bungalows, a spa, a gym and two very attractive pools in its extensive, beachside grounds. Decorated in a simple but smart Thai style, all the rooms have a/c, hot water, fridge, safety box and satellite TV. Breakfast included. B2840

Blue Marine Sunset beach ☎077 375079–80, ⓦblue marinephangan.com. This friendly, sociable old-timer near the midpoint of Sunset offers a choice between large concrete bungalows around a well-tended lawn by the beach and more contemporary bungalows and rooms, decorated in earth tones, up the slope behind; all have a/c, hot shower, TV and minibar. B1200

Coco Hut Leela Beach ☎077 375369, ⓦcocohut.com. On a clean, quiet stretch of beach, this lively, efficiently run place is smart and attractive, with some traditional southern Thai elements in the architecture. On offer is a wide variety of upscale accommodation, from wooden bungalows with a/c, hot showers, fridges, TVs and DVDs, to beachfront villas with outdoor jacuzzis, as well as an attractive pool and an adobe-style spa. Free pick-up from Hat Rin's Sunset pier. Breakfast included. B3000

Leela Beach Bungalows Leela Beach ☎077 375368–9, ⓦleelabeachresort.com. A good, friendly and reliable budget choice, now owned by nearby *Coco Hut*, with plenty of space under the palm trees on a long stretch of white-sand beach. Many of the sturdy, well-built bungalows, with hammocks on their verandas and either cold or hot showers, are right on the sand. Fan B500, a/c B800

Lighthouse Bungalows On the far southwestern tip of the headland ☎077 375475 or ☎084 852 0029, ⓦlighthousebungalows.com. At this friendly haven, wooden and concrete en-suite bungalows, sturdily built to withstand the wind on a boulder-strewn slope and backed by trail-filled jungle, are priced according to size and comfort; all have good-sized balconies with hammocks. The restaurant food is varied and tasty. Phone for a pick-up from Sunset pier or Thong Sala, or do the 30min walk from Chicken Corner, the last section along a wooden walkway over the rocky shoreline. Fan B950, a/c B2000

Phangan Bayshore Resort In the middle of Sunrise ☎077 375224, ⓦphanganbayshore.com. Hat Rin's first upmarket resort, a well-ordered, slightly institutional place, boasting 80m of beachfront. There's a large, shamrock-shaped pool and a wide variety of close-knit bungalows and rooms with a/c, hot water, TV, DVD player and fridge, on a green lawn shaded with palms. Around the full moon, as well as a minimum stay of five nights, there's a big hike in prices. B1600

Rin Bay View Near the pier on Sunset ☎077 375188. A good-value, friendly option in a tightly squeezed central location, occupying a narrow strip of land by the beach, ornamented with flowers and trees. The a/c bungalows and rooms with mosquito screens, hot showers, TVs, fridges and balconies are a decent size and generally well maintained and clean. B1200

Same-Same Lodge Above Sunrise at the start of the road to Leela Beach ☎077 375200, ⓦsame-same.com. Sociable Danish-run spot set above a popular, often raucous, bar-restaurant that hosts lively full moon warm-up parties. The clean, colourful and decent-sized rooms come with fan and cold showers or a/c and hot water; there are also tightly packed a/c dorms. Dorm B500, double B550

Sarikantang Leela Beach ☎077 375055–6, ⓦsarikantang.com. Boutique resort with two swimming pools, a beachside spa and a good measure of style. Accommodation ranges from bungalows with a/c, TVs, fridges, verandas and hot-water bathrooms to villas with DVD players, separate living rooms and outdoor jacuzzis. Free kayaks and free pick-ups from Sunset pier and shuttles to downtown Hat Rin. Breakfast included. B2000

Seaview Sunrise Northern end of Sunrise ☎077 375160, ⓦseaviewsunrise.com. On a big plot of shady, flower-strewn land at the quieter end of the beach, this clean, friendly, orderly old-timer with a good restaurant offers over forty bungalows and rooms. Those on the beachfront are all fan-cooled, with cheaper versions available further back, with or without hot showers. The a/c offerings all have hot water, and most have TV and fridge. Kayaks for rent. Comparatively small price rise at full moon. Fan B500, a/c B900

Sun Cliff High up on the tree-lined slope above the south end of Sunset ☎077 375134 or ☎077 375463, ⓔrsvnsuncliff@hotmail.com. Friendly, spacious place with great views of the south coast and Ko Samui, especially from its heart-shaped pool by the restaurant. Among a wide range of bungalows that are a bit rough around the edges, you'll find some quirky architectural features such as rock-built bathrooms and fountains; some have huge decks for partying. A/c rooms all have hot showers, fridges and TVs. The cheapest options are rooms out on the road by the front office. Fan B300, a/c B600

Thai Dee Garden Resort Northern transverse ☎089 770 2290, ⓦthaideegarden.com. Pleasant staff and a range of smart concrete and white clapboard bungalows, on a broad, grassy slope strewn with trees and plants and set back from the road. Choose either fan and cold water or a/c and hot. A likely spot to have rooms free at full moon, although, as well as a minimum stay of five nights, there's a big hike in prices. Fan B450, a/c B650

6

EATING

Bamboozle Off the southern transverse, near Sunset pier ☎085 471 4211. Among a wide variety of tasty Mexican food here, the chicken fajitas with all the trimmings (B250) are especially good. Also offers pizzas and a short menu of tapas. Daily roughly 4pm–midnight.

★**Casa Nostra** On the southern transverse ☎086 267 8445. Excellent, tiny Italian café-restaurant which prepares great pastas – try the spaghetti bolognese (B200) – pizzas, espresso coffee, salads and plenty of other dishes for vegetarians, such as home-made ravioli with ricotta and spinach, and a chocolate mousse to die for. Daily 1–11pm.

Little Home On the southern transverse. This well-organized, basic restaurant is your best bet for cheap Thai food in Hat Rin, serving staples such as *phat thai* (B70), chicken and cashew nuts and green, red and yellow curries, plus Western breakfasts. Daily 11.30am–11pm.

Nira's Near Chicken Corner. Justly popular restaurant and bakery, offering great croissants – sweet and savoury – cakes, deli sandwiches, juices, shakes and espresso coffees. Daily 7am–7pm.

Om Ganesh On the southern transverse near the pier ☎086 063 2903. Relaxing Indian restaurant with good thalis (from B150), biryanis, plenty of veggie dishes and breads, Indian breakfasts and cheerful service. Free deliveries. Daily 9am–10.30pm.

NIGHTLIFE

Cactus Club South end of Sunrise. Open-air dance hall that pumps out mostly radio-friendly dance music onto low-slung candlelit tables and mats on the beach. Evenings till late.

Mellow Mountain Bar North end of Sunrise. Made for chilling, this trippy hangout occupies a great position up in the rocks, with peerless views of the beach. Evenings till late.

Outback Bar On the southern transverse. Lively, British-run meeting place that hosts open-deck nights, with a "no trance" music policy, free pool tables, big-screen sports, draught Guinness and cider and well-received steak pies and the like. Daily 10am–late.

Hat Yuan, Hat Thian and Hat Sadet

North of Hat Rin, there are no roads along the rocky, exposed east coast, which stretches as far as **Ao Thong Nai Pan**, the only substantial centre of development. First up are the adjoining small, sandy bays of **HAT YUAN** and **HAT THIAN**, which have established a reputation as a quieter alternative to Hat Rin. A rough track has recently been bulldozed from Ban Khai, and the bays now sport about a dozen bungalow outfits between them.

Steep, remote **HAT SADET**, about 8km as the crow flies from Hat Rin, has a handful of bungalow operations, sited here because of their proximity to **Thaan Sadet**, a boulder-strewn brook that runs out into the sea. The spot was popularized by various kings of Thailand – Rama V visited no fewer than fourteen times – who came here to walk, swim and vandalize the huge boulders by carving their initials on them; the river water is now considered sacred and is transported to Bangkok for important royal ceremonies. A rough track runs through the woods above and parallel to Thaan Sadet to connect with the road from Thong Sala to Ao Thong Nai Pan.

If you're feeling intrepid, you could try hiking along this stretch of coast, which in theory is paralleled by a steep, 15km trail (as marked on Visid Hongsombud's map – see p.556), though it's reported to be overgrown in many places. With decent navigational skills, the leg between Hat Rin, starting from near *Laluna Bungalows*, and Hat Yuan should certainly be manageable (about 2hr), aided by green dot and white arrow markers.

ARRIVAL AND DEPARTURE   HAT YUAN, HAT THIAN, HAT SADET

By boat A daily, seasonal boat runs via the east coast beaches from Hat Rin to Thong Nai Pan, having started its voyage across at Maenam on Ko Samui (see p.556). Otherwise there are ample longtails at Hat Rin that will take you up the coast – around B150/person to Hat Yuan, for example.

ACCOMMODATION

HAT YUAN

Barcelona ☎077 375113. Good, relaxing budget choice, with great views and decent accommodation, mostly in white, stilted bungalows running up the hillside from the beach, the best of them (B700) with large verandas and hot showers. <u>B350</u>

Pariya ☎ 081 737 3883, ⓦ pariyahaadyuan.com. The most luxurious resort in the vicinity of Hat Rin comprises forty spacious villas, some with their own private jacuzzi pool, all with rain showers, bathtubs and large verandas, set on a steep slope running down to the beach. There's a free-form pool and kids' pool and a spa, as well as plenty of watersports. Breakfast included. B8000

HAT THIAN

The Sanctuary ⓦ thesanctuarythailand.com. The main operation on Hat Thian hosts yoga, Pilates and meditation classes, open-mike and film nights, and provides two kinds of treatment: the spa does massage, facials and beauty treatments, while the wellness centre goes in for fasting and cleansing. It also offers a huge range of basic and luxury en-suite bungalows and family houses, as well as dorm accommodation (B220), and good vegetarian meals, seafood and home-made bread and cakes. B770

HAT SADET

Mai Pen Rai ☎ 095 934 8077, ⓦ thansadet.com. Best of the bungalows on Hat Sadet, this welcoming spot has a wide variety of attractive accommodation with airy bathrooms, fans and hammocks (some with big upstairs terraces), either on the beach at the stream mouth or scattered around the rocks for good views. A jeep taxi leaves Thong Sala pier for the resort every day at 1pm (B200). B580

6

Ao Thong Nai Pan

AO THONG NAI PAN is a beautiful, semicircular bay backed by steep, green hills, which looks as if it's been bitten out of the island's northeast corner by a gap-toothed giant, leaving a tall hump of land (occupied by *Panviman Resort*) dividing the bay into two parts: **Thong Nai Pan Noi** to the north, **Thong Nai Pan Yai** to the south. With lovely, fine, white sand, the longer, more indented Thong Nai Pan Yai has marginally the better beach, but both halves of the bay are sheltered and deep enough for swimming. A paved road winds its way for 13km over the steep mountains from Ban Tai on the south coast to Thong Nai Pan, but once you get here you'll find most of the basic amenities you'll need: travel agents, dive outfits, ATMs and a tiny post office (on Thong Nai Pan Yai).

ARRIVAL AND DEPARTURE

AO THONG NAI PAN

By jeep Jeeps connect with incoming and outgoing boats at Thong Sala every day (B300/person).

By boat One seasonal boat a day runs via the east coast beaches from Hat Rin to Thong Nai Pan, having started its voyage across at Maenam on Ko Samui (see p.556).

ACCOMMODATION AND EATING

★**Anantara Rasananda** Thong Nai Pan Noi ☎ 077 239555, ⓦ anantara.com. Congenial and chic luxury hideaway, with speedboat transfers from Samui. Accommodation is in sixty spacious, contemporary villas and suites, all with their own plunge pool, most with outdoor bathrooms. There's also a main, infinity-edge swimming pool, which forms the central hub of the resort, along with the sociable bar and excellent restaurant. The very good spa stretches up the hillside behind, with a steam room built into the rocks. Other activities include kayaking, cooking and yoga classes. B7510

Baan Panburi Village Southern end of Thong Nai Pan Yai ☎ 077 445075, ⓦ baanpanburivillage.com. Two rows of well-designed bungalows with verandas and deckchairs run down a slope dotted with wicker hammocks, either side of a small, artificial waterfall. Choose between old-style, thatched, wood-and-bamboo huts with mosquito nets, fans and cold showers, and large, wooden, a/c affairs with hot water and tiled floors. Free kayaks. Fan B600, a/c B1300

Longtail Beach Resort At the far southern end of Thong Nai Pan Yai ☎ 077 445018, ⓦ longtailbeach resort.com. In two quiet, leafy rows on either side of a long strip of lawn that runs down to the attractive beachfront restaurant, these thatched wooden en-suite bungalows are well designed and maintained; all have verandas and hammocks, most have hot showers. Fan B550, a/c B900

★**Siam House** About 100m from the beach towards the main road, behind Dreamland Resort, Thong Nai Pan Yai. Run by the former proprietors of Dolphin Resort, this good, mellow café-bar in a lovely, open-sided, two-storey house serves everything from Western breakfasts, great coffee and lemon cheesecake, to pastas, salads, sandwiches with home-made bread, tapas and Thai food (mains from around B100). Daily 9am–midnight.

The north coast

The largest indent on the **north coast**, Ao Chaloaklam, has long been a famous R&R spot for fishermen from all over the Gulf of Thailand, with sometimes as many as a hundred trawlers littering the broad and sheltered bay. As a tourist destination, it has little to recommend it – save that its village, **Ban Chaloaklam**, can easily be reached from Thong Sala, 10km away, by songthaew (B150) along a paved road – but the small, quiet beaches to the east, Hat Khom and Hat Khuat, have much more to offer.

Hat Khom

Dramatically tucked in under Ao Chaloaklam's eastern headland is the tiny cove of **HAT KHOM**. Linked to the outside world by a partly paved road, it offers a handful of simple bungalows, a secluded strip of white sand and good coral for snorkelling.

Hat Khuat (Bottle Beach)

If the sea is not too rough, longtail boats run several times a day for most of the year from Ban Chaloaklam (east of the fishing pier; B100/person or about B600/boat) to isolated **HAT KHUAT** (**BOTTLE BEACH**), the best of the beaches on the north coast, sitting between steep, jungle-clad hills in a perfect cup of a bay that's good for swimming. You could also walk there along a testing trail from Hat Khom in around ninety minutes.

ACCOMMODATION AND EATING   THE NORTH COAST

Caffè della Moca (Cucina Italiana) Ban Chaloaklam ☎ 086 470 4253. Run by a friendly, enthusiastic native of Rimini, this simple, authentic Italian restaurant towards the west end of the village offers tables on the sand and great pizzas (around B200), home-made gnocchi, lasagne and other pastas. 5pm–late; closed Wed.

Coral Bay Hat Khom ☎ 077 374245. Friendly, laidback outfit with plenty of space and great views on the grassy, flower-strewn promontory dividing Hat Khom from Ao Chaloaklam. The sturdy bungalows range from simple affairs with cold showers to large pads with a/c and hot showers, some with funky bathrooms built into the rock; snorkelling equipment can be rented to make the most of Hat Khom's reef. Phone ahead to ask about the daily transfers from Thong Sala. Fan B400, a/c B1200

Haad Khuad Resort Hat Khuat ☎ 077 445153–4, ⓦ haadkhuadresort.com. Well-organized spot in the middle of the bay, offering deluxe rooms in a two-storey hotel block with view-filled French windows, a/c, hot water, TV, DVD players, mini-bars and breakfast included. Also has a choice of wooden or concrete fan bungalows with cold showers on the beachfront and in the garden. Kayaks available. Four daily transfers from Thong Sala (B400/person). Fan B700, a/c B1800

Smile Resort Western end of Hat Khuat ☎ 085 429 4995, ⓦ smilebungalows.com. Set on a rocky slope strewn with flowers and trees on the western side of the beach, with fun owners and a sociable bar-restaurant area. The attractive, bamboo-clad bungalows come with wall fans and mosquito nets. B520

The west coast

Pha Ngan's **west coast** has attracted about the same amount of development as the forgettable south coast, but the landscape here is more attractive and varied, broken up into a series of long sandy inlets with good sunset views over the islands of the Ang Thong National Marine Park to the west. Most of the bays, however, are sheltered by reefs which can keep the sea too shallow for a decent swim, especially between May and October.

Laem Son Lake and Ao Chaophao

About halfway up the west coast from Thong Sala, there's a surprise in store in the shape of **Laem Son Lake**, a tranquil stretch of clear water cordoned by pines; however, you should avoid swimming here, as the lake, site of a former tin mine, is apparently considered toxic. Beyond, on the small, pretty bay of **AO CHAOPHAO**, there's good accommodation and food at *Seaflower*.

Hat Yao

North of Chaophao, the long, gently curved, fine-sand beach of **HAT YAO** is gradually and justifiably becoming busier and more popular, with several stand-alone bars, diving outfits, a 7-Eleven supermarket, a currency-exchange booth, ATMs and jeep and bike rental, as well as a nonstop line of bungalows. **Boat trips** from here to Hat Salad, Ao Mae Hat, Hat Khom, Bottle Beach and, if the sea's calm enough, Thong Nai Pan or Than Sadet waterfall (B850/person, including snorkels and lunch) can be arranged, for example, with Khun Tuan (☎086 279 0166).

Hat Salad

To the north of Hat Yao, **HAT SALAD** is another pretty bay, sheltered and sandy, with good snorkelling off the northern tip. On the access road behind the beach is a rather untidy service village of shops, travel agents, and bike and jeep rental outlets. Take your pick from a dozen or so bungalow outfits.

Ao Mae Hat

On the island's northwest corner, **AO MAE HAT** is good for swimming and snorkelling among the coral that lines the sandy causeway to the tiny islet of Ko Maa. The broad, coarse-sand bay supports several bungalow resorts.

ARRIVAL AND GETTING AROUND   THE WEST COAST

By motorbike or jeep There's a paved coastal road up as far as Hat Salad, where it loops inland to meet the main inland road from Thong Sala via the hospital to Ao Mae Hat.

By songthaew Songthaews from Thong Sala serve all of the beaches on the west coast, charging B200–300/person to go as far as Hat Yao, for example.

ACCOMMODATION

AO SEETHANU

Loy Fa ☎077 377319, ⍉loyfanaturalresort.com. Well-run, friendly, flower-strewn place that commands good views from its perch on the steep southern cape of otherwise nondescript Ao Seethanu. There's good snorkelling and swimming from its private beach below, as well as two saltwater pools. Smart bungalows are scattered around the hilltop and the slope down on the beach, and come with large verandas, a/c, hot water, mini-bar, TV and DVD player. B2200

AO CHAOPHAO

Seaflower ☎077 349090, ⍉seaflowerbungalows .com. Quiet spot, set in a lush garden, with good veggie and non-veggie food. En-suite bungalows with their own hot-water bathrooms vary in price according to their size and age: the newer ones – more like cottages – have marble open-air bathrooms and big balcony seating areas. Kayaks available for rent, as well as fishing and snorkelling day-trips and occasional overnighters to Ang Thong National Marine Park (see p.552). Free pick-ups from Thong Sala with 24hr notice. Minimum stay two nights. Fan B700, a/c B1100

HAT YAO

Long Bay Resort ☎077 349057, ⍉longbay-resort .com. Hat Yao's nicest upmarket spot boasts a long stretch of beach and spacious gardens towards the north end of the bay. Choose between small but smart bungalows ("Garden Huts") and a range of large cottages, all with verandas, a/c and hot water. There's an attractive, free-form swimming pool and kayaks and snorkels to rent. Transfer from Thong Sala and breakfast included. B1800

Shiralea ☎077 349217, ⍉shiralea.com. On a broad, grassy bank beneath coconut trees behind the north end of the beach, the spacious, very attractive thatched bungalows here all come with hot water and verandas with hammocks, and there's a seductive pool with a pool bar and a sociable atmosphere. Fan B600, a/c B1100

HAT SALAD

★**Salad Hut** ☎077 349246, ⍉saladhut.com. Among the dozen or so bungalow outfits here, this congenial, family-friendly and well-run old-timer stands out. Parallel to the beachfront behind a small, infinity-edge swimming pool, in a shady, colourful garden, are twelve stylish bungalows done out in dark woods, red and white, with day beds with axe cushions and large verandas. All come with hot water, mini-bar and TV, and a cooked breakfast at the chic bar-restaurant is included. Library and snorkel and kayak rental. Fan B2200, a/c B2500

AO MAE HAT

Wang Sai Resort ☎077 374238, ⍉wangsairesort kohma.com. Popular, friendly spot by a shady creek at the south end of the bay. On a huge plot of land, most of the en-suite bungalows are set back from the beach, with fans and cold showers – pay B150 extra for those that are up the slope, with great sunset views. The best and most expensive are across the creek on the beach, all with a/c, fridge and hot water, some with TV. On-site dive school and kayaks and snorkels for rent. Fan B850, a/c B1600

EATING AND DRINKING

Most people staying on the west coast eat and drink at their resort, but one bar here is worth a detour.

6

AO CHAOPHAO

Pirates Bar ☎ 084 728 6064. On its own tiny beach cove (reached by a short wooden walkway at the south end of Ao Chaophao), with a stonking sound system right on the sand, this is a great place for regular parties, especially its popular Moon Set parties, featuring top Thai and international DJs, three or four nights before and after the full moon. Evenings till late.

Ko Tao

KO TAO (Turtle Island) is so named because its outline resembles a turtle nose-diving towards Ko Pha Ngan, 40km to the south. The rugged shell of the turtle, to the east, is crenellated with secluded coves where one or two bungalows hide among the rocks. On the western side, the turtle's underbelly is a long curve of classic beach, **Hat Sai Ree**, facing **Ko Nang Yuan**, a beautiful Y-shaped group of islands offshore, also known as Ko Hang Tao (Turtle's Tail Island). The 21 square kilometres of granite in between are topped by dense forest on the higher slopes and dotted with huge boulders that look as if they await some Easter Island sculptor. It's fun to spend a couple of days exploring the network of rough trails, after which you'll probably know all 1700 of the island's inhabitants. Ko Tao is now best known as a venue for **scuba-diving courses**, with a wide variety of dive sites in close proximity.

The island is the last and most remote of the archipelago that continues the line of Surat Thani's mountains into the sea. It served as a jail for political prisoners from 1933 to 1947, then was settled by a family from Ko Pha Ngan. Now, there are around 150 sets of **bungalows** for visitors, just about enough to cope during the peak seasons of December to March and August, concentrated along the west and south sides; they include a rapidly growing number of upscale resorts with such luxuries as air conditioning, hot water and swimming pools. There's a limited government supply of electricity, so some of it still comes from private generators on the remotest beaches, usually evenings only.

ECO TAO

With so many divers and other visitors coming to this tiny island, the pressures on the environment, both above and below the waterline, are immense. To minimize your impact, look out for the work of a community group, **Save Koh Tao** (🅦 savekohtao.com or go to 🅦 ecokohtao.com), which has been formed among concerned locals and resident Westerners. Activities include monthly beach and dive-site clean-ups, monitoring programmes, installing and maintaining mooring buoys, coral nurseries and more than half a dozen artificial reefs around Ko Tao, which allow divers to practise their skills without damaging coral. Its main event of the year is a two-day **Underwater Festival** in June, which involves underwater and beach-cleaning, fundraising, live bands and turtle releasing.

Much of what visitors can do to help is common sense: avoiding littering, recycling where possible and turning down plastic bags when you're shopping. The island suffers from a scarcity of water, with occasional droughts during the hot season after a poor rainy season, so conserve water whenever possible. In the sea, the main rule is not to touch the coral, which may mean avoiding snorkelling when the water is low from April to September – if in doubt, ask locally for advice, be careful and go out at high tide. Don't take away dead shells, and don't buy coral or shell jewellery.

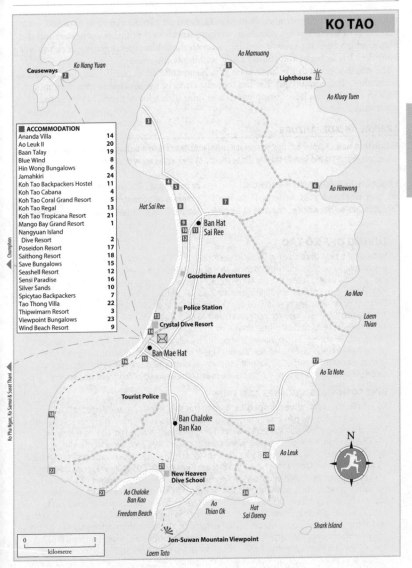

KO TAO

ACCOMMODATION

Ananda Villa	14
Ao Leuk II	20
Baan Talay	19
Blue Wind	8
Hin Wong Bungalows	6
Jamahkiri	24
Koh Tao Backpackers Hostel	11
Koh Tao Cabana	4
Koh Tao Coral Grand Resort	5
Koh Tao Regal	13
Koh Tao Tropicana Resort	21
Mango Bay Grand Resort	1
Nangyuan Island Dive Resort	2
Poseidon Resort	17
Saithong Resort	18
Save Bungalows	15
Seashell Resort	12
Sensi Paradise	16
Silver Sands	10
Spicytao Backpackers	7
Tao Thong Villa	22
Thipwimarn Resort	3
Viewpoint Bungalows	23
Wind Beach Resort	9

If you're just arriving and want to stay on one of the less accessible beaches, it might be a good idea to go with one of the touts who meet the ferries at **Mae Hat**, the island's main village, with pick-up or boat on hand, since at least you'll know their bungalows aren't full; otherwise call ahead, as even the remotest bungalows now have landlines or mobile phones and most owners come to market once a day (pick-ups are either free or B50–150/person). Some resorts with attached scuba-diving operations have been known to refuse guests who don't sign up for diving trips or courses; on the other hand, most of the dive companies now have their own lodgings, available free or at a discounted price to divers. With a year-round customer base of divers – and resident dive instructors – a growing number of sophisticated Western **restaurants** and **bars** are springing up all the time, notably in Mae Hat and on Hat Sai Ree. For nightlife, your best bet is to watch out for posters advertising weekly and monthly parties around the island, which keep the crowds rotating; women should be careful getting back to their bungalow late at night and should avoid walking home alone.

The **weather** is much the same as on Pha Ngan and Samui (see p.536), but being that bit further off the mainland, Ko Tao feels the effect of the southwest monsoon more: June to October can have strong winds and rain, with a lot of debris blown onto the windward coasts.

ARRIVAL AND DEPARTURE   KO TAO

All boats to Ko Tao dock at Mae Hat. Boat services and prices fluctuate according to demand, and in high season extra boats may appear. Voyages to and from Ko Tao may also be affected by the weather at any time between June and January.

FROM CHUMPHON AND BANGKOK

The main jumping-off point for boats to Ko Tao is Chumphon (see p.528), which is connected to Bangkok by train and bus. The two main Chumphon–Ko Tao boat companies both offer through-tickets from Bangkok; with Lomprayah (on Ko Tao ☎ 077 456176, ⓦ lomprayah.com),

---

DIVING OFF KO TAO

Some of the best **dive sites** in Thailand are found off Ko Tao, which is blessed with outstandingly clear (visibility up to 35m), safe and relatively deep water close in to shore. On top of that, there's a kaleidoscopic array of coral species and other marine life, and you may be lucky enough to encounter whale sharks, barracudas, leatherback turtles and pilot whales. Diving is possible at any time of year, with sheltered sites on one or other side of the island in any **season** – the changeover from southwest to northeast monsoon in November is the worst time, while **visibility** is best from April to July, in September (usually best of all) and October. Dive courses on Ko Tao are particularly heavily subscribed in the days after the full moon party on Ko Pha Ngan, when it would be worth booking in advance. Ko Tao supports several evacuation centres, clinics that specialize in diving medicine, while the nearest recompression chamber is on Ko Samui, ninety minutes away by speedboat (see p.537).

DIVE COMPANIES, COURSES AND TRIPS

Ko Tao has about fifty **dive companies**, making this the largest dive-training centre in Southeast Asia; they're particularly busy in the days after each full moon party on Ko Pha Ngan. Most of the companies are staffed by Westerners and based at Mae Hat, Hat Sai Ree or Ao Chaloke Ban Kao. You'll generally be offered discounted or free accommodation while you're diving, but ask exactly how long it's for (three or four nights for an Openwater course), where it is and what it's like. **Operators** on Ko Tao include Crystal (☎ 077 456106–7, ⓦ crystaldive.com), a large, lively, sociable PADI 5-Star Career Development Centre based on the north side of Mae Hat just beyond Ananda Villa, with two swimming pools, three big boats and a speedboat, offering courses in dozens of languages and the chance to buy videos of your dives plus a wide choice of good accommodation in two resorts on the north side of Mae Hat. At the other end of the scale are schools that are small, personal and laidback (though with no compromising on safety) such as New Heaven in the centre of Ao Chaloke Ban Kao (☎ 077 457045, ⓦ newheavendiveschool.com), which boasts of later starts and a maximum of four people per course or dive trip. Both of these companies have a strong commitment to marine conservation (also check out the website of Crystal's marine conservation department, ⓦ ecokohtao.com, which features internships and gap-year programmes) and run reef conservation and research programmes for qualified divers among many other activities. You'll find further advice on choosing a dive company in Basics (see p.52).

By far the most popular **course**, PADI's four-day "Openwater" for beginners, costs around B9800 in high season with a reputable dive centre. One-day introductions to diving are also available for B2000, as is the full menu of PADI courses, up to "Instructor".

For **qualified divers**, one dive typically costs B1000, a ten-dive package B7000, with ten- to fifteen-percent discounts if you bring your own gear. Among specialities, Crystal (see above) offers nitrox and underwater photography and videography courses.

for example, this costs B1100, including a VIP bus from its office on Thanon Ram Bhuttri (☎ 02 629 2569–70), via Hua Hin (see p.515). It's better to buy a Bangkok–Tao through-ticket direct from the boat company's office in the capital rather than from a travel agency, otherwise you're unlikely to get your money back if the boat turns out to be full, which is possible in high season, or is cancelled because of very bad weather.

FROM KO PHA NGAN AND KO SAMUI
Two main companies operate daily scheduled boats between Thong Sala on Ko Pha Ngan and Ko Tao: Lomprayah (see opposite; 2–3 daily; 1hr 30min; B500–600) and Seatran (on Ko Tao ☎ 077 456907–8, ⊕ seatran discovery.com; 3 daily; 1hr 45min; B430). The Lomprayah

catamaran originates at Maenam, Seatran at Bangrak, on Ko Samui (total journey time to Ko Tao on either about 2hr–2hr 30min; B600–700).

FROM SURAT THANI
With Lomprayah If you're coming from Surat Thani, you could take Lomprayah's Don Sak–Na Thon (Samui)–Thong Sala catamaran all the way to Ko Pha Ngan, then change onto its Maenam (Samui)–Thong Sala–Ko Tao service (2 daily; total journey time from Surat about 5hr; B700–800).
With the night boat There's a night boat/car ferry from Ban Don pier in Surat Thani town, departing at 10pm (8hr; B550); in the opposite direction, this leaves Ko Tao at 9pm; book at the piers.

6

MAIN DIVE SITES
Ko Nang Yuan Surrounded by a variety of sites, with assorted hard and soft corals and an abundance of fish: the Nang Yuan Pinnacle, a granite pinnacle with boulder swim-throughs, morays and reef sharks; Green Rock, a maze of boulder swim-throughs, caves and canyons, featuring stingrays and occasional reef sharks; Twins, two rock formations covered in corals and sponges, with a colourful coral garden as a backdrop; and the Japanese Gardens, on the east side of the sand causeway, which get their name from the hundreds of hard and soft coral formations here and are good for beginners and popular among snorkellers.

White Rock (Hin Khao) Between Hat Sai Ree and Ko Nang Yuan, where sarcophyton leather coral turns the granite boulders white when seen from the surface; also wire, antipatharian and colourful soft corals, and gorgonian sea fans. Plenty of fish, including titan triggerfish, butterfly fish, angelfish, clown fish and morays.

Shark Island Large granite boulders with acropora, wire and bushy antipatharian corals, sea whips, gorgonian sea fans and barrel sponges. Reef fish include angelfish, triggerfish and barracuda; there's a resident turtle, and leopard and reef sharks may be found as well as occasional whale sharks.

Hinwong Pinnacle At Ao Hinwong; generally for experienced divers, often with strong currents. Similar scenery to White Rock, over a larger area, with beautiful soft coral at 30m depth. A wide range of fish, including blue-spotted fantail stingrays, sweetlips pufferfish and boxfish, as well as hawksbill turtles.

Chumphon or **Northwest Pinnacle** A granite pinnacle for experienced divers, starting 14m underwater and dropping off to over 36m, its top covered in anemones; surrounded by several smaller formations and offering the possibility of exceptional visibility. Barrel sponges, tree and antipatharian corals at deeper levels; a wide variety of fish, in large numbers, attract local fishermen; barracudas, batfish, whale sharks (seasonal) and huge groupers.

Southwest Pinnacle One of the top sites in terms of visibility, scenery and marine life for experienced divers. A huge pyramid-like pinnacle rising to 6m below the surface, its upper part covered in anemones, with smaller pinnacles around; at lower levels, granite boulders, barrel sponges, sea whips, bushy antipatharian and tree corals. Big groupers, snappers and barracudas; occasionally, large rays, leopard and sand sharks, swordfish, finback whales and whale sharks.

Sail Rock (Hin Bai) Midway between Ko Tao and Ko Pha Ngan, emerging from the sand at a depth of 40m and rising 15m above the sea's surface. Visibility of up to 30m, and an amazing 10m underwater chimney (vertical swim-through). Antipatharian corals, both bushes and whips, and carpets of anemones. Large groupers, snappers and fusiliers, blue-ringed angelfish, batfish, kingfish, juvenile clown sweetlips and barracuda; a possible spot for sighting whale sharks and mantas.

6

BOAT TOURS AND SNORKELLING ON KO TAO

Some dive companies will take along **snorkellers**, usually on their afternoon trips, when they visit the shallower sites, but your best bet for snorkelling is probably a round-island **boat tour**. Available at Mae Hat or through your bungalow (from B650/person, including lunch and pick-ups, or around B2000 to hire your own longtail boat for the day), these take in snorkelling in the beautiful Japanese Gardens off Ko Nang Yuan, but you'll have to pay the B100 entrance fee if you set foot on the island to climb up to the viewpoint.

GETTING AROUND

You can **get around** easily enough on foot, but there are roads of sorts now to most of the resorts, though many are still very rough tracks, suitable for 4WD only.

By motorbike taxi or pick-up Motorbike taxis (about B150 to Chaloke Ban Kao, for example) and pick-ups (B100/person to Chaloke Ban Kao, for example, minimum three people; rates are higher at night, or for a 4WD to somewhere more remote) are available in Mae Hat.

By motorbike As on Ko Phangan, there have been lots of reports of travellers being charged exorbitant amounts if they bring their rented motorbike back with even the most minor damage – avoid the outfits immediately in front of the main pier in Mae Hat, and rent from your bungalow or someone reliable like Island Travel (see opposite) or

Lederhosen Bikes, at the corner of Mae Hat's high street and the road to Chaloke Ban Kao (☎077 456658, ⓦkohtao motorbikes.com; from B200/day). If you can, resist the temptation to rent a quad bike, or ATV – not only do they have a disproportionate number of accidents, but they're also very polluting.

By mountain bike Mountain bikes can be rented for B100/day from Jiggo Bicycle and Tattoo (☎098 485 5716), on the southern edge of Mae Hat on the Ao Chaloke Ban Kao road, just beyond and opposite the mini-golf (Koh Tao Leisure Centre).

INFORMATION

Koh Tao Info There isn't a TAT office on Ko Tao, but the regularly updated and widely available free booklet, *Koh*

Tao Info, is a useful source of information, along with its associated website, ⓦkohtaoonline.com.

Mae Hat and around

MAE HAT, a small, lively village and port in a pleasant, beachfront setting, boasts the lion's share of the island's amenities. A paved high street heads straight up the hill from the main pier, paralleled by another paved road just to the north heading up the hill from the Seatran pier, with a narrower front street running at right angles, parallel to the seafront. Three of the ferry companies each have their own pier, Lomprayah and Songserm to the south of the main one, Seatran to the north.

ACCOMMODATION
MAE HAT AND AROUND

Ananda Villa North end of the village, on the beach ☎077 456478, ⓦanandavilla.com. Cute, well-designed and maintained a/c rooms in a two-storey block, sporting French windows that give onto balconies with wooden balustrades. Inside, silks and other decorative touches set off the dark-wood furniture; facilities include large, hot-water bathrooms, TVs and fridges. Also has some fan and a/c wooden bungalows in the garden and fan rooms in a beachside single-storey block that are tiny but boast hot showers. Fan B500, a/c B1800

Koh Tao Regal Just north of the village, on the beach beyond the affiliated Crystal dive centre ☎077 456007, ⓦkohtaoregal.com. Set in a handy location, this hotel has

one of the best pools on the island, a long, three-tiered affair with a children's section. The spacious rooms, which occupy a three-storey building at right angles to the beach, have a/c, hot showers, minibars, TVs and French windows giving onto large balconies ("Ocean View" rooms at the beach end have lovely wraparound balconies); Thai-style wooden bungalows are planned. B2000

Saithong Resort Sai Nuan beach, 40min walk south of Mae Hat pier ☎077 456868, ⓦsaithongresort.info. An isolated, shady place, with soft sand on two small beaches, offering various types of en-suite bungalow either in gardens or perched on the rocks – the latter with stunning sea views. Kayaks and snorkels for rent. B825

Save Bungalows At the Save Shop supermarket on the east side of the front street, just south of the piers ☎077 456347. Clean, good-value, functional wood and concrete bungalows and rooms, with en-suite cold or hot showers, in a leafy, tightly packed garden. Fan **B500**, a/c **B1100**

Sensi Paradise On the lower slopes of the headland just south of the village ☎077 456244, �***w*** kohtao paradise.com. Charming resort in flower-covered grounds, offering a pretty beachside restaurant, an attractive free-form pool and some of the best upmarket accommodation on the island: well-designed Thai-style cottages, family houses and villas made of polished red wood with mini-bars and a/c, most with hot showers and some with large terraces and open-air bathrooms. Transfer from the pier and breakfast included. **B2900**

Tao Thong Villa 50min walk south of Mae Hat (about B150/person in a taxi-boat) ☎077 456078. Sturdy, en-suite, stilted bungalows with large verandas and hammocks dotted around a rocky outcrop and the slope behind, with a breezy restaurant on the tiny, grassy isthmus with two small beaches in between. Plenty of shady seclusion, great views and good snorkelling and swimming. Fan **B500**, a/c **B1300**

EATING AND DRINKING

Cappuccino 100m from the pier, up the high street on the left ☎077 456870. French-run café and bakery that does a mean pain au chocolat, plus gourmet sandwiches, crêpes and salads. Daily 6.30am–6pm.

The Castle Just out of town on the Ao Chaloke Ban Kao road �***w*** facebook.com/thecastlekohtao. The island's biggest night-time venue usually hosts three or four parties a month (often including full moon party warm-ups and afterparties), featuring mostly international DJs. Three or four nights a month 8/9pm till late.

Kakureya Up a small hill on the southeast side of the village, inland from the Songserm pier ☎086 059 0408, �***w*** facebook.com/kakureyatao. Small, relaxing and thoroughly authentic Japanese restaurant, serving some of the best food on the island, including salmon and tuna sashimi and home-smoked ham. Asahi beer on draught and a good choice of sake. Usually closed June and Nov, plus some other short periods – check on the Facebook page. Daily 4–10pm.

Moov On the southeast side of the village, inland from the Songserm pier ☎098 325 8274, �***w*** facebook.com /moovinn. Chilled-out, artsy bar-restaurant, with plenty of sofas to recline on in the house and on the big lawn at the back, serving fusion tapas and New Zealand steaks, as well as an all-you-can-eat barbecue (B200) on Sunday night, when there's a jam session and open mike. There's also live music (acoustic) on Tuesday, accompanied by wine and cheese, while other nights might feature techno, reggae or drum and bass DJs. Daily 8am–late.

★**Whitening** 200m south of the main pier down the front street ☎077 456199. Congenial, mellow and chic bar-restaurant with a great deck and relaxing beach tables and beanbags overlooking the bay. It dishes up some very tasty Thai food, such as green curries (B160), and more creative, pricier Western food, as well as good cocktails. Daily 11am–1am (kitchen closes 11pm).

Zest 100m from the pier up the high street ☎077 456178. This eco-conscious café serves very good coffees, pastries, salads, build-your-own-sandwiches, a few simple Western lunches and breakfasts such as eggs Benedict (B95). Daily 6am–6pm.

SHOPPING

Tui and Pump Bookshop Just off the high street on the south side, in front of the main pier. Sells secondhand books, postcards and souvenirs. Daily roughly 8am–8.30pm.

DIRECTORY

Banks Thanachat (Siam City Bank), up the high street on the left, with an ATM.

Emergencies Ko Tao now has a 24hr volunteer emergency response team, based at the corner of the high street and the Ao Chaloke Ban Kao road (☎087 979 0191/1669).

Health Mae Hat has a small government health centre (halfway up the high street, turn right), plus several private clinics and pharmacies.

Police The tourist police (☎1155) are based a short way out on the Ao Chaloke Ban Kao road, just beyond and opposite the mini-golf (Koh Tao Leisure Centre), while the main police station is a 5min walk north of Mat Hat, on the narrow road towards Hat Sai Ree (☎077 456631).

Post office At the top of the Seatran road (parallel to and north of the high street), near the start of the main paved road to Ban Hat Sai Ree (Mon–Fri 9am–noon & 1–5pm, Sat 9am–noon).

Travel agent Reliable, English-run Island Travel on the Seatran road (parallel to and north of the high street; ☎077 456769, �***w*** islandtravelkohtao.com) sells all kinds of transport tickets and rents out good motorbikes, as well as offering a London Underground-themed hostel and a sports bar-restaurant.

6

Hat Sai Ree

To the north of Mae Hat, beyond a small promontory, you'll find **Hat Sai Ree**, Ko Tao's only long beach. The strip of white sand stretches for 2km in a gentle curve, backed by a smattering of coconut palms and scores of bungalow resorts. Around the northerly end of the beach spreads **BAN HAT SAI REE**, a burgeoning village of supermarkets, clinics, pharmacies, travel agents, currency-exchange booths, ATMs, restaurants and bars. A narrow, mostly paved track runs along the back of the beach between Mae Hat and Ban Hat Sai Ree, paralleled by the main road further inland.

6

ACCOMMODATION   HAT SAI REE

★**Blue Wind** North end of Ban Hat Sai Ree ☎077 456116, ✉bluewindkohtao@hotmail.com. This popular old-timer offers a variety of well-kept, en-suite rooms and bungalows scattered about a shady compound, most of which have been recently reconstructed in an appealing southern Thai style, with clapboard walls and nice balcony furniture, some with four-poster beds and mosquito nets. It also has a good restaurant (see opposite). Fan B700, a/c B1200

Koh Tao Backpackers Hostel Ban Hat Sai Ree, inland from Silver Sands Resort ☎077 601828, ✇kohtao backpackers.com. Functional, eight-bed dorms with a/c and hot showers in a small, concrete building set back from the beach. Free use of Davy Jones' Locker's adjacent pool, which has its own bar-restaurant. Dorm B350

Koh Tao Cabana Far north end of beach ☎077 456504–5, ✇kohtaocabana.com. Welcoming, eco-friendly, rustic-chic luxury resort and spa on a long beach frontage, backed by pleasant lawns that are dotted with elegant day beds. All the thatched, a/c rooms feature open-air bathrooms with hot water: choose between round, adobe-style villas up the slope behind the beach and stilted cottages on the headland, some with fantastic views and some with private pools. Round-trip pier transfers and breakfast included. B4500

Koh Tao Coral Grand Resort North of Ban Hat Sai Ree ☎077 456432, ✇kohtaocoral.com. Welcoming luxury beachfront development with a dive school, where the sandstone-pink octagonal cottages with polished coconut-wood floors and large, attractive bathrooms gather – some a little tightly – around a pretty, Y-shaped pool; all have hot water, TV and a/c. Thai cooking classes offered. Round-trip pier transfers and breakfast included. B3300

Seashell Resort Near the midpoint of the beach, a 20min walk from Mae Hat ☎077 456299–300, ✇seashell-resort.com. In a spacious, tidy compound, a

friendly, well-run place with a dive school that's been very successfully upgraded. Facilities now include two pools, one with a jacuzzi, a spa (which offers massage training courses) and a popular seafood restaurant. Among the a/c, hot-water rooms, it's well worth paying a little extra for the "Deluxe Garden View" offerings (B2780), which have a very attractive, contemporary look with dark wood furniture; those on the first floor have nice big balconies. B2680

Silver Sands Ban Hat Sai Ree ☎077 456606, ✇silver -sands-resort.com. Clean, well-kept bungalows and rooms, nearly all of them with hot water, on a narrow but lush and shady plot. Among its bungalows, the cheapest are simple wooden affairs well off the beach, while the priciest are beachside, a/c and cottage-like. New, distressed-concrete rooms, however, in a two-storey hotel block at the back of the compound are more industrial than chic and probably not worth the money. Guests can use the adjacent pool at the affiliated dive company, Davy Jones' Locker. Snorkels to rent. Free pick-ups from the piers at Mae Hat. Fan B900, a/c B1500

Spicytao Backpackers Inland from Ban Hat Sai Ree ☎077 456606, ✇spicyhostels.com. A 5min walk east of the village (fork left off the Hin Wong road), this sociable hostel stands on a broad, grassy, rural plot dotted with trees. Bunk beds are packed tightly into the en-suite dorms – pay B50 extra for a/c. Simple breakfast included. Dorms B200

Thipwimarn Resort North of Hat Sai Ree, opposite Ko Nang Yuan ☎077 456409, ✇thipwimarnresort.com. Stylish, eco-friendly, upscale spot with a spa, which tumbles down a steep slope, past an elevated, infinity-edge swimming pool, to its own small beach. Dotted around the hillside, smart, thatched, whitewashed, a/c villas, most with hot water, enjoy a fair measure of seclusion, satellite TV, DVD players, mini-bars and fine sunset views. Breakfast included. B2790

HAT SAI REE ACTIVITIES

The main organizers of activities on Hat Sai Ree are the folk at Goodtime Adventures, towards the southern end of the beach (☎087 275 3604, ✇gtadventures.com), who specialize in **rock-climbing** and **bouldering**, including courses for beginners. They also propose **abseiling** and **watersports** such as wakeboarding. Drop-in **yoga** classes are held at Blue Wind Bungalows (see opposite; 1–2 daily; ☎084 440 6755, ✇shambhalayogakohtao.com).

Wind Beach Resort Ban Hat Sai Ree ☎077 456082. Welcoming resort lined with mature trees and boasting a large and attractive free-form pool. Most of the rooms are in low-rise, hotel-style buildings with a/c, hot showers, TVs, fridges and breakfast included; a little bit extra (B2400) buys you a lot more style in their "deluxe" rooms. `B1700`

EATING AND DRINKING

Blue Wind North end of Ban Hat Sai Ree ☎077 456116. Good beachside restaurant serving home-made breads, croissants and fruit shakes, as well as Indian, Israeli and Thai food (B75 for a green curry), pasta, pizzas and evening seafood barbecues. Daily 8am–9.30pm.

Choppers On the main transverse road down to the beach ☎077 456641, ⓦchoppers-kohtao.com. Popular, well-run, full-service Aussie bar, with good food, plenty of imported bottled and draught beers and no fewer than seventeen screens for TV sports. Plenty of offers on drink, including happy hours 5–8pm. Daily 9am–late.

Fizz On the beach at Silver Sands Resort ⓦfacebook .com/fizz.beachlounge. Chic bar-restaurant, where you can sink into the green beanbags and soak up some mellow sounds from the nightly DJs over a drink, or sit up for some very good food: there's a long menu of Thai dishes (most under B100) and Western food, including veggie options, pasta, salads and very tasty tuna with tomato and mango salsa (B320). Daily noon–2am, kitchen closes 11pm (sometimes closing for lunch in low season).

★**The Gallery** On the east side of central Ban Hat Sai Ree, 50m down the Ao Hin Wong/Ao Mao road on the right ☎077 456547, ⓦthegallerykohtao.com. Aiming to be a complete sensory experience, with an attached full-service spa and a photographic gallery, this restaurant and wine bar serves carefully sourced Thai wines and excellent food from inherited family recipes (main courses start at B140), including its signature dish, *haw mok thalay* (seafood curry soufflé), superb prawn cakes and Thai desserts. Worth making a reservation in high season. Daily 10am–midnight, restaurant closes 10pm.

Lotus Bar On the beach near New Heaven Café. Raucous, very popular late-night haunt for drinking and dancing, with fire shows. Happy hour 4–7pm. Evenings till very late.

New Heaven Café On the beach road on the south side of the village centre. Stylish, mostly organic spot offering great home-baked breads and cakes, as well as sandwiches, salads, pizzas (from B100), ice cream, espressos and juices. Daily 7.30am–7.30pm.

Ko Nang Yuan

One kilometre off the northwest of Ko Tao, **KO NANG YUAN**, a close-knit group of three tiny islands, provides the most spectacular beach scenery in these parts, thanks to the causeway of fine white sand that joins up the islands. You can easily swim off the east side of the causeway to snorkel over the Japanese Gardens, which feature hundreds of hard and soft coral formations.

ARRIVAL AND DEPARTURE KO NANG YUAN

By boat Boats from the Lomprayah pier in Mae Hat, just south of the main pier, run back and forth (departing 10.30am, returning at 1.30pm & 4.30pm; B200 return), and there are other, irregular services from Hat Sai Ree.

Note that rules to protect the environment here include banning all visitors from bringing cans, plastic bottles and fins with them, and day-trippers are charged B100 to land on the island.

ACCOMMODATION AND EATING

Nangyuan Island Dive Resort ☎086 312 7128, ⓦnangyuan.com. The decor at this resort is not much to write home about but it makes the most of its beautiful location, its bungalows, all with en-suite bathrooms, TVs and fridges, nearly all with a/c and most with hot water, spreading over all three islands. There's also a restaurant, a coffee shop and an on-site dive shop. Transfers from and to Mae Hat are free for guests. Breakfast included. Fan `B1500`, a/c `B2000`

The north and east coasts

Ao Mamuang (Mango Bay), the lone bay on the **north coast**, is a beautiful, tree-clad bowl, whose shallow reef is a popular stop on snorkelling day-trips and on dive trips, though there's little in the way of a beach. The attractive bar-restaurant of *Mango Bay Grand Resort* spreads its large deck over the rocks here.

The sheltered inlets of the **east coast**, most of them containing one or two sets of bungalows, can be reached by boat, pick-up or 4WD. The most northerly habitation here is at **Ao Hinwong**, a deeply recessed, limpid bay strewn with large boulders and great coral reefs, which has a particularly remote, almost desolate, air.

In the middle of the coast, the dramatic tiered promontory of Laem Thian shelters on its south side a tiny beach and a colourful reef, which stretches down towards the east coast's most developed bay, **Ao Ta Note**, with half a dozen resorts and a mostly paved road from Mae Hat. Ta Note's horseshoe inlet is sprinkled with boulders and plenty of coarse sand, with excellent snorkelling just north of the bay's mouth.

The last bay carved out of the turtle's shell, **Ao Leuk**, has a well-recessed beach and water that's deep enough for good swimming and snorkelling, featuring hard and soft coral gardens. Snorkels are available to rent at the beachfront bar.

ACCOMMODATION   THE NORTH AND EAST COASTS

AO MAMUANG
Mango Bay Grand Resort ☎ 077 456948–9, ⓦ kohtao mangobay.com. At this remote resort, the well-appointed, colourful, heavily varnished wooden bungalows on stilts all come with hot water, and some have a/c and TV. Snorkels and kayaks available for rent. Transfers from Mae Hat included. Fan B1500, a/c B2800

AO HINWONG
Hin Wong Bungalows ☎ 077 456006 or ☎ 081 229 4810. The most spacious of this bay's small handful of resorts is welcoming and provides good en-suite accommodation on a steep, grassy slope above the rocks, in wooden huts with mosquito nets and large, cold-water bathrooms. It has a nice waterside deck in front of its restaurant and rents out kayaks and snorkels. Discounts for longer stays. B500

AO TA NOTE
Poseidon Resort ☎ 077 456734–5, ⓦ poseidontao .atspace.com. At this friendly, mellow resort, the basic en-suite bungalows with balconies and hammocks are set

back a little from the sands on the flower-strewn, rocky slopes. The beachfront restaurant has a nice big deck and there are kayaks and snorkels for rent. B400

AO LEUK
Ao Leuk II ☎ 077 456779 or ☎ 081 077 9574, ⓦ aowleuk2.com. Large bungalows and family rooms, with big balconies, panoramic windows, fans and hot showers, on the bay's southern cape. Discounts for longer stays. If there happens to be no room here, don't worry – the same friendly family own two other resorts in the bay (including some cheaper, cold-shower bungalows), its taxis and the beachfront bar. B1000

★**Baan Talay** ☎ 077 457045, ⓦ baantalaykohtao .com. Sustainable, secluded retreat owned by New Heaven Dive School (see p.568), with great views from its hillside location that slopes down to the north side of the bay. Stylish bungalows on stilts sport big verandas, mosquito nets on the beds and hot showers; the cheaper "huts" have shaggy thatched roofs and indoor-outdoor bathrooms. Yoga courses and kayaks for rent. Fan B1200, a/c B2500

The south coast

The southeast corner of the island sticks out in a long, thin mole of land, which points towards Shark Island, a colourful diving and snorkelling site just offshore; the headland shelters the sandy beach of **Hat Sai Daeng** on one side if the wind's coming from the northeast, or the rocky cove on the other side if it's blowing from the southwest. Beyond quiet, sandy **Ao Thian Ok**, the next bay along on the south coast, the deep indent of **Ao Chaloke Ban Kao** is protected from the worst of both monsoons, and consequently has seen a fair amount of development, with several dive resorts taking advantage of the large, sheltered, shallow bay, which sometimes gets muddy at low tide. Behind the beach are clinics, ATMs, bike rental shops, bars and restaurants. At New Heaven dive school (see p.568), drop-in **yoga** classes are held daily at 11am and 5.30pm on a veranda overlooking the bay.

On the east side of Ao Chaloke Ban Kao, carved out of the Laem Tato headland, the idyllic white sand of **Freedom Beach** is a secluded palm-lined spot with a beach bar; it's reached by walking through *Taatoh Freedom Beach Bungalows*. A fifteen-minute walk above the bungalows, the last stretch up a steep hillside, will bring you to **Jon-Suwan Mountain Viewpoint**, which affords fantastic views, especially at sunset, over the neighbouring bays of Chaloke Ban Kao and Thian Ok and across to Ko Pha Ngan and Ko Samui.

ACCOMMODATION AND EATING   **THE SOUTH COAST**

HAT SAI DAENG AND AO THIAN OK

Jamahkiri ☎ 077 456400, ⒲ jamahkiri.com. The remote, rocky coastline between Sai Daeng and Thian Ok provides the spectacular location for this luxurious resort. There's a panoramic bar-restaurant, a full-service spa, a dive centre and a tiered swimming pool, as well as opulent, secluded rooms and bungalows, in a chic mix of Thai and Western design, with great sea views. Free, thrice-daily transfers to and from Mae Hat. Breakfast included. B7400

AO CHALOKE BAN KAO

Koh Tao Tropicana Resort On the main road near the centre of the beach ☎ 077 456167, ⒲ koh-tao -tropicana-resort.com. Friendly, eco-conscious resort in a well-tended, sandy, shady garden on the beachfront, offering smart bungalows and rooms in two-storey hotel-

style blocks, all with hot showers. Fan B500, a/c B1200

Koppee On the main road near the centre of the beach. Lovely little bakery-café with books and magazines to browse. It offers a wide choice of tasty teas and espresso coffees (from B40), gourmet sandwiches, all-day breakfasts, smoothies and home-baked cakes. Daily 7.30am–7pm.

Viewpoint Bungalows ☎ 077 456444, ⒲ kohtao viewpoint.com. Run by a friendly bunch, these distinctive bungalows sprawl along the western side of the bay and around the leafy headland beyond, with great sunset views; architect-designed in chic Balinese style, they boast rock bathrooms (some with open roofs), lovely polished hardwood floors, mosquito nets and attractive verandas. There are also half a dozen tasty a/c villas with their own infinity-edge pools (from B10,000). B2500

6

Nakhon Si Thammarat

NAKHON SI THAMMARAT, the south's second-largest town, occupies a blind spot in the eyes of most tourists, whose focus is fixed on Ko Samui, 100km to the north. Nakhon's neglect is unfortunate, for it's an absorbing place: the south's major pilgrimage site and home to a huge army base, it's relaxed, self-confident and sophisticated, well known for its excellent cuisine and traditional **handicrafts**. The stores on Thanon Thachang are especially good for local nielloware (*kruang tom*), household items and jewellery, elegantly patterned in gold or silver, often on black, and *yan lipao*, sturdy basketware made from intricately woven fern stems of different colours. Nakhon is also the best place in the country to see how Thai **shadow plays** work, at Suchart Subsin's workshop, and the main jumping-off point for towering **Khao Luang National Park** and its beautiful waterfall, **Krung Ching** (see p.581).

Orientation in Nakhon is simple, though the layout of the town is puzzling at first sight: it runs in a straight line for 7km from north to south and is rarely more than a few hundred metres wide; originally this was a long sand dune dotted with fresh-water wells and flanked by low, marshy ground. The modern centre for businesses and shops sits at the north end around the landmark **Tha Wang intersection**, where Thanon Neramit meets Thanon Ratchadamnoen. To the south, centred on the elegant,

---

FESTIVALS IN NAKHON

Known as *muang phra*, the "city of monks", Nakhon is still the religious capital of the south, and the main centre for **festivals**. The most important of these are the **Tamboon Deuan Sip**, held during the waning of the moon in the tenth lunar month (either Sept or Oct), and the **Hae Pha Kheun That**, which is held several times a year, but most importantly on Makha Puja, the full moon of the third lunar month, usually February, and on Visakha Puja, the full moon of the sixth lunar month, usually May (see p.46). The purpose of Tamboon Deuan Sip is to pay homage to dead relatives and friends; it is believed that during this fifteen-day period all *pret* – ancestors who have been damned to hell – are allowed out to visit the world, and so their relatives perform a merit-making ceremony in the temples, presenting offerings from the first harvest to ease their suffering. A huge ten-day fair takes place at Thung Talaat park on the north side of town at this time, as well as processions, shadow plays and other theatrical performances. The Hae Pha Khun That also attracts people from all over the south, to pay homage to the relics of the Buddha at Wat Mahathat. The centrepiece of this ceremony is the Pha Phra Bot, a strip of yellow cloth many hundreds of metres long, which is carried in a spectacular procession around the chedi.

NAKHON SI THAMMARAT

traditional mosque on Thanon Karom, lies the old Muslim quarter; south again is the start of the old city walls, of which few remains can be seen, and the historic centre, with the town's main places of interest now set in a leafy residential area.

Brief history

Nakhon Si Thammarat seems to have been part of the shadowy early kingdom of Tambralinga, and was well placed for trade with China and southern India (via an overland route from the port of Trang, on the Andaman Sea) from at least the early centuries AD. The first local event that can be dated with any reliability occurred in 1001 AD, when Tambralinga asserted its independence from the regional powers of Srivijaya and Angkor by sending its own tribute mission to China. From the twelfth century, Nakhon had significant contacts with Sri Lanka, including a major rebuilding of the prestigious Buddha-relic chedi at Wat Mahathat in the Lankan style; in the following century, Sri Lankan monks from Nakhon are said to have helped spread the Theravada form of Buddhism to Sukhothai, the major new Thai city-state to the north.

By the sixteenth century, Nakhon Si Thammarat had come under the control of Ayutthaya, which sent out governors to rule this rich and important region, in place of native princes. In the same century, trading links began with the Portuguese, who were followed by the Dutch, the English and the French; Nakhon – which was generally known to the Westerners by its Malay name, Ligor, to Thais as Lakhon – could offer local pepper, tin and hides. After the Burmese destruction of Ayutthaya and its treasures in 1767, the town played an important part in the cultural rebirth of the nation, sending its copy of the Tripitaka (the Buddhist scriptures) to King Taksin's new capital at Thonburi to be transcribed, as all the kingdom's copies had been lost.

Wat Mahathat

Main entrance faces Thanon Ratchadamnoen, about 2km south of the modern centre

Missing out **Wat Mahathat** would be like going to Rome and not visiting St Peter's, for the Buddha relics in the vast chedi make this the south's most important shrine. In the courtyard inside the temple cloisters, row upon row of smaller chedis, spiked like bayonets, surround the main chedi, the 60m-tall **Phra Boromathat**. This huge, stubby

■ ACCOMMODATION	
Grand Park Hotel	2
Nakorn Garden Hotel	3
Twin Lotus	1

● RESTAURANTS & CAFÉS	
Copee	2
Hao Coffee	4
Khanom Jiin Muangkorn	3
Krua Thale	5
Wang Derm	1

6

Sri Lankan bell supports a slender, ringed spire, which is in turn topped by a shiny pinnacle said to be covered in 600kg of gold. According to the chronicles, tooth relics of the Buddha were brought here from Sri Lanka over two thousand years ago by an Indian prince and princess and enshrined in a chedi. It's undergone plenty of face-lifts since then: two earlier Srivijayan versions, models of which stand outside the entrance to the cloisters, are encased in the present twelfth-century chedi. The most recent restoration work, funded by donations from all over Thailand, rescued it from collapse, although it still seems to be leaning dangerously to the southeast. Worshippers head for the north side's vast enclosed stairway, framed by lions and giants, which they liberally decorate with gold leaf to add to the shrine's radiance and gain some merit. At the base of the stairway, look out for two delicate gilded reliefs showing the "Great Retirement", as the Buddha leaves his palace and family on horseback to become an ascetic; and for the two magnificent, Ayutthaya-period doors depicting Vishnu and Brahma.

Viharn Phra Kien Museum
Extends north from the chedi · Hours irregular, but usually daily 9am–3.30pm · Free

An Aladdin's cave of bric-a-brac, the **Viharn Phra Kien Museum** is said to house fifty thousand artefacts donated by worshippers, ranging from ships made out of seashells to gold and silver models of the Bodhi Tree. At the entrance to the museum, you'll pass the Phra Puay, an image of the Buddha giving a gesture of reassurance. Women pray to the image when they want to have children, and the lucky ones return to give thanks and leave photos of their chubby progeny.

Viharn Luang
Outside the cloister to the south

Raised on elegant slanting columns, the eighteenth-century **Viharn Luang** (actually a bot, surrounded by eight *sema* stones) is a beautiful example of Ayutthayan architecture. Beyond the pediment, with its gilded figure of Vishnu on his traditional elephant mount Erawan, you'll find that the interior is austere at ground level, but the red coffered ceiling shines with carved and gilded stars and lotus blooms. In the spacious grounds around the viharn, cheerful, inexpensive stalls peddle local handicrafts such as shadow puppets, bronzeware and basketware.

The National Museum

Thanon Ratchadamnoen, a 10min walk south from Wat Mahathat • Wed–Sun 9am–noon & 1–4pm • B150

The **National Museum** houses a small but diverse collection, mostly of artefacts from southern Thailand. In the prehistory room **downstairs**, look out for the two impressive ceremonial bronze kettledrums dating from the fifth century BC; they were beaten in rainmaking rituals and one of them is topped with chunky frogs (the local frogs are said to be the biggest in Thailand and a prized delicacy). Also on the ground floor are some interesting Hindu finds, including several stone lingams from the seventh to ninth centuries AD and later bronze statues of Ganesh, the elephant-headed god of wisdom and the arts. Look out especially for a vivacious, well-preserved bronze of Shiva here, dancing within a ring of fire on the body of a dwarf demon, who holds a cobra symbolizing stupidity. Among the collections of ceramics **upstairs**, you can't miss the seat panel from Rama V's barge, a dazzling example of the nielloware for which Nakhon is famous – the delicate animals and landscapes have been etched onto a layer of gold which covers the silver base, and then picked out by inlaying a black alloy into the background. The nearby exhibition on local wisdom includes interesting displays on Buddhist ordinations and weddings, and on *manohra*, the southern Thai dramatic dance form.

The shadow puppet workshop

Ban Nang Thalung Suchart Subsin, 110/18 Soi 3, Thanon Si Thammasok, a 10min walk east of Wat Mahathat • Daily 7am–5pm • Free • ⓘ 075 346394, ⓦ bannangthalung.com

The best possible introduction to *nang thalung*, southern Thailand's **shadow puppet theatre** (see box below), is to head for the atmospheric compound of Suchart Subsin,

---

SHADOW PUPPETS

Found throughout southern Asia, **shadow puppets** are one of the oldest forms of theatre, featuring in Buddhist literature as early as 400 BC. The art form seems to have come from India, via Java, to Thailand, where it's called *nang*, meaning "hide": the puppets are made from the skins of water buffalo or cows, which are softened in water, then pounded until almost transparent, before being carved and painted to represent the characters of the play. The puppets are then manipulated on bamboo rods in front of a bright light, to project their image onto a large white screen, while the story is narrated to the audience.

The grander version of the art, **nang yai** – "big hide", so called because the figures are life-size – deals only with the *Ramayana* story (see p.88). It's known to have been part of the entertainment at official ceremonies in the Ayutthayan period, but has now almost died out. The more populist version, **nang thalung** – *thalung* is probably a shortening of the town name, Phatthalung (which is just down the road from Nakhon), where this version of the art form is said to have originated – is also in decline now: performances are generally limited to temple festivals, marriages, funerals and ordinations, lasting usually from 9pm to dawn. As well as working the 60cm-high *nang thalung* puppets, the puppet master narrates the story, impersonates the characters, chants and cracks jokes to the accompaniment of flutes, fiddles and percussion instruments. Not surprisingly, in view of this virtuoso semi-improvised display, puppet masters are esteemed as possessed geniuses by their public.

At big festivals, companies often perform the *Ramayana*, sometimes in competition with each other; at smaller events they put on more down-to-earth stories, with stock characters such as the jokers Yor Thong, an angry man with a pot belly and a sword, and Kaew Kop, a man with a frog's head. Yogi, a wizard and teacher, is thought to protect the puppet master and his company from evil spirits with his magic, so he is always the first puppet on at the beginning of every performance.

In an attempt to halt their decline as a form of popular entertainment, the puppet companies are now incorporating modern instruments and characters in modern dress into their shows, and are boosting the love element in their stories. They're fighting a battle they can't win against television and cinemas, although at least the debt owed to shadow puppets has been acknowledged – *nang* has become the Thai word for "movie".

a designated National Artist and one of the south's leading exponents of *nang thalung*. He and his sons have opened up their workshop to the public, including a small museum of puppets dating back as far as the eighteenth century, and, especially if you phone in advance, they'll usually be able to show you a few scenes from a shadow play in the small theatre (B50/person). You can also see the intricate process of making the leather puppets and can buy the finished products as souvenirs: puppets sold here are of much better quality and design than those usually found on southern Thailand's souvenir stalls.

The Phra Buddha Sihing shrine

In the provincial administration complex on Thanon Ratchadamnoen • Mon–Fri 8.30am–4.30pm • Free

Magically created in Sri Lanka in the second century, the **Phra Buddha Sihing** statue was, according to legend, sent by ship to the king of Sukhothai in the thirteenth century, but the vessel sank and the image miraculously floated on a plank to Nakhon. Two other images, one in the National Museum in Bangkok, one in Wat Phra Singh in Chiang Mai, claim to be the authentic Phra Buddha Sihing, but none of the three is in the Sri Lankan style, and all three may have originated as replacements for a lost original. Although similar to the other two in size and shape, the image in Nakhon, dated between the thirteenth and sixteenth centuries, has a style unique to this area, distinguished by the heavily pleated flap of its robe over the left shoulder, a beaky nose and harsh features, which sit uneasily on the short, corpulent body. The statue's plumpness has given the style the name *khanom tom*, after a kind of coconut and rice pudding. The much-revered image is sheltered by a delicate, golden five-tiered parasol, and housed in an attractive, 100-year-old, Ayutthaya-style shrine.

ARRIVAL AND DEPARTURE	**NAKHON SI THAMMARAT**

BY PLANE

The airport (☎ 075 369540–2), served daily by Nok Air and Air Asia from Bangkok (14 daily; 1hr 10min), is about 20km northwest of the city off the Surat Thani road. From here, taxis charge around B300 to take you into Nakhon (B1500 to Don Sak, for ferries to Ko Samui and Ko Pha Ngan) while big hotels such as the *Twin Lotus* offer airport shuttle buses. Nok Air and Air Asia offer flight-and-boat through-tickets to Ko Samui, Ko Pha Ngan and Ko Tao.

BY TRAIN

The train station is very central and sits at the end of a branch off the main southern line from Bangkok (2 daily; 15–16hr).

BY BUS AND A/C MINIBUS

All buses and a/c minibuses now use the terminal on the west side of the centre.

Destinations Bangkok (Southern Terminal; 20 daily; 13hr); Chumphon (every 2hr; 4hr); Don Sak (for ferries to Ko Samui and Ko Pha Ngan; hourly; 1hr–1hr 30min); Krabi (hourly; 3–4hr); Phuket (hourly; 5–6hr); Surat Thani (every 30min; 2hr–2hr 30min); Trang (hourly; 2hr).

GETTING AROUND AND INFORMATION

By share-songthaew Small blue share-songthaews ply up and down Thanon Ratchadamnoen for B10 a ride.

Tourist information TAT has an office in a restored 1920s government officers' club on Sanam Na Muang (daily 8.30am–4.30pm; ☎ 075 346515–6, ✉ tatnksri@tat.or.th).

ACCOMMODATION

Nakhon has no guesthouses or traveller-oriented accommodation, but the best of its hotels offer very good value in all price ranges.

Grand Park Hotel 1204/79 Thanon Pak Nakhon ☎ 075 317666–75, ⊛ grandparknakhon.com. If you're looking for an upmarket option in the centre of town, this place, set back a little from the busy road, is worth considering – it's large, smart and bright, with a/c, hot water, TV and mini-bar in every room, and cheery and attentive staff. **B700**

★ **Nakorn Garden Hotel** 1/4 Thanon Pak Nakhon ☎ 075 313333, ✉ 075 342926. A rustic but sophisticated haven in two three-storey, red-brick buildings overlooking a tree-shaded courtyard. The large, attractive rooms are looking a bit tired now but come with a/c, hot water, cable TV and mini-bar. **B445**

Twin Lotus About 3km southeast of the centre at 97/8 Thanon Patanakarn Kukwang ☎075 323777, ⬯twin lotushotel.net. Gets pride of place in Nakhon – though not for its location; sports five bars and restaurants, a beer garden, a small spa, a large, attractive outdoor swimming pool, a sauna and a fitness centre. Breakfast and round-trip airport transfers included. B1500

EATING AND DRINKING

Nakhon is a great place for inexpensive food, not least at the busy, colourful **night market** on Thanon Chamroenwithi.

Copee Thanon Nang Ngam (no English sign). This faithful and attractive re-creation of an old Chinese-style, southern Thai coffee shop, with marble-topped tables, wooden shutters and ceiling fans, is famous nationwide and serves sweet and savoury roti pancakes, washed down with traditional, cloth-filtered coffee. Daily 6am–4.30pm.

Hao Coffee In the Bovorn Bazaar, Thanon Ratchadamnoen. Popular place in a quiet courtyard, modelled on an old Chinese-style coffee shop and packed full of ageing lamps, clocks and other antiques. Offers a wide selection of inexpensive Thai dishes, a few Western breakfasts, teas, juices and coffees, including Thai filter coffee and delicious iced cappuccinos. Daily 7am–4.30pm.

Khanom Jiin Muangkorn Thanon Panyom, near Wat Mahathat. Justly famous, inexpensive outdoor restaurant dishing up one of the local specialities, *khanom jiin*, noodles topped with hot, sweet or fishy sauce served with *pak ruam*, a platter of crispy raw vegetables. Daily 8am–3pm.

★**Krua Thale** Thanon Pak Nakhon, opposite the Nakorn Garden Hotel. The town's best restaurant, renowned among locals for its excellent, varied and inexpensive seafood. Plain and very clean, with an open kitchen and the day's catch displayed out front, and relaxing patio tables and an a/c room at the back. Recommended dishes include a very good *yam plaa duk foo*, shredded and deep-fried catfish with a mango salad dip (B120), whole baked fish and king prawns (priced by weight and delicious with tamarind sauce), and *hoy maleang poo op mordin*, large green mussels in a delicious herb soup containing lemon grass, basil and mint. Daily 3–10pm.

Wang Derm Next to Copee on Thanon Nang Ngam (no English sign). A great place to sample southern food, buffet-style in a big, open-air pavilion in an interesting complex of coffee shops and bakeries, with good *khanom jiin* and other very cheap local dishes (from B120): *kaeng som*, a yellow curry; *kaeng tai plaa*, fish stomach curry; *khao yam*, a delicious southern salad of rice and vegetables; and various *khanom wan* (desserts). Daily 6am–4pm.

Khao Luang National Park

Headquarters to the south of the summit near Karom Waterfall • National park admission fee B200 • ☎075 391240 or ☎075 391218, ⬯dnp.go.th

Rising to the west of Nakhon Si Thammarat and temptingly visible from all over town is 1835m-high **Khao Luang**, southern Thailand's highest mountain. A huge **national park** encompasses Khao Luang's jagged green peaks, beautiful streams with numerous waterfalls, tropical rainforest and fruit orchards. The mountain is also the source of the Tapi River, one of the peninsula's main waterways, which flows into the Gulf of Thailand at Surat Thani. **Fauna** here include macaques, musk deer, civets and binturongs, as well as more difficult-to-see Malayan tapirs, serows, tigers, panthers and clouded leopards, plus over two hundred bird species. There's an astonishing diversity of **flora** too, notably rhododendrons and begonias, dense mosses, ferns and lichens, plus more than three hundred species of both ground-growing and epiphytic orchids, some of which are unique to the park.

The best **time to visit** is after the rainy season, from January onwards, when there should still be a decent flow in the waterfalls, but the trails will be dry and the leeches not so bad. However, the park's most distinguishing feature for visitors is probably its difficulty of **access**: main roads run around the 570-square-kilometre park with spurs into some of the waterfalls, but there are no roads across the park and very sparse public transport along the spur roads. The Ban Khiriwong Visitor Service Centre (☎075 533113 or ☎075 533370) can arrange **treks** to the peak between January and June, beginning at Ban Khiriwong on the southeast side of the park and including two nights camping on the mountain, meals and guides, as well as homestays in the village. Otherwise only **Krung Ching Waterfall**, one of Thailand's most spectacular, really justifies the hassle of getting to the park.

Krung Ching Waterfall

A trip to **Krung Ching**, a nine-tier waterfall on the north side of the park, makes for a highly satisfying day out with a **nature trail** taking you through dense, steamy jungle to the most beautiful, third, tier. Starting at the Krung Ching park office, which lies 13km south of Ban Huai Phan, this shady, mostly paved, 4km trail is very steep in parts, so you should allow four hours at least there and back. On the way you'll pass giant ferns, including a variety known as *maha sadam*, the largest fern in the world, gnarled banyan trees, forests of mangosteen and beautiful, thick stands of bamboo. You're bound to see colourful birds and insects, but you may well only hear macaques and other mammals. At the end, a long, stepped descent brings you to a perfectly positioned wooden platform with fantastic views of the 40m fall, which used to appear on the back of thousand-baht notes; here you can see how, shrouded in thick spray, it earns its Thai name, Fon Saen Ha, meaning "hundreds of thousands of rainfalls".

6

ARRIVAL AND DEPARTURE KHAO LUANG

By songthaew Irregular songthaews on the main roads around the park and to Ban Khiriwong congregate on Thanon Klong Tha in Nakhon. None of them is scheduled to go to Krung Ching — you'd have to catch one to Ban Huai Phan (about 1hr) and then do a deal with the driver to take you the extra 13km to the Krung Ching park office.

By car Rental cars are available from Avis (☎02 251 1131–2, ⌨avisthailand.com), who are based at the

airport but will deliver anywhere in Nakhon. The easiest way to get to Krung Ching from Nakhon with your own transport is to head north on Highway 401 towards Surat Thani, turning west at Tha Sala on to Highway 4140, then north again at Ban Nopphitam on to Highway 4186, before heading south from Ban Huai Phan on Highway 4188, the spur road to the Krung Ching park office, a total journey of about 70km.

ACCOMMODATION AND EATING

National park accommodation ☎075 460463, ⌨dnp.go.th. Two- to twenty-person bungalows, most with hot water and fridges, are available at the Krung

Ching park office. There's also a campsite. Bungalows **B600**
National park canteen There's a basic canteen near the park office, where food needs to be ordered in advance.

Southern Thailand: the Andaman coast

AO MAYA, KO PHI PHI

Southern Thailand: the Andaman coast

As Highway 4 switches from the east flank of the Thailand peninsula to the Andaman coast it enters a markedly different country: nourished by rain nearly all the year round, the vegetation down here is lushly tropical, with forests reaching up to 80m in height, and massive rubber, palm-oil and coconut plantations replacing the rice and sugar-cane fields of central Thailand. Sheer limestone crags spike every horizon and the translucent Andaman Sea laps the most dazzlingly beautiful islands in the country, not to mention its finest coral reefs. This is of course the same sea whose terrifyingly powerful tsunami waves battered the coastline in December 2004, killing thousands and changing countless lives and communities forever. The legacies of that horrific day are widespread (see p.610), but all the affected holiday resorts have been rebuilt, with the tourist dollar now arguably more crucial to the region's well-being than ever before.

The **cultural mix** along the Andaman coast is also different from central Thailand. Many southern Thais are Muslim, with a heritage that connects them to Malaysia and beyond. This is also the traditional province of nomadic *chao ley*, or sea gypsies, many of whom have now settled but still work as boat captains and fishermen. The commercial fishing industry, on the other hand, is mostly staffed by immigrants – legal and not – from neighbouring Myanmar, just a few kilometres away along the northern Andaman coast.

The attractions of the northern Andaman coast are often ignored in the race down to the high-profile honeypots around Phuket and Krabi, but there are many quiet gems up

Highlights

❶ Island idylls Tranquillity rules on the uncommercial islands of Ko Phayam, Ko Ra, Ko Yao Noi and Ko Jum. **See p.595, p.599, p.643 & p.676**

❷ Khao Sok National Park Sleep in a jungle treehouse or on a lake amid spectacular karst scenery, and wake to the sound of hooting gibbons. **See p.604**

❸ Ko Similan Remote island chain offering the finest snorkelling and diving, and easily accessible on day-trips and live-aboards. **See p.614**

❹ Sea-canoeing in Ao Phang Nga The perfect way to explore the limestone karsts

and hidden lagoons of this spectacular bay. **See p.618**

❺ Phuket Town Handsome Sino-Portuguese architecture and some of the most interesting sleeping, eating and drinking options on the island. **See p.621**

❻ Rock-climbing Even novices can get a bird's-eye view of the Railay peninsula's fabulous coastal scenery. **See p.663**

❼ Ko Lanta Yai The "island of long beaches", with an atmospheric old town, offers an appealing choice of relaxing mid-range facilities. **See p.680**

HIGHLIGHTS ARE MARKED ON THE MAP ON P.586

THE KRA ISTHMUS

Thailand's Andaman coast begins at **Kraburi**, where, at kilometre-stone 545 (the distance from Bangkok), a signpost welcomes you to the **Kra Isthmus**, the narrowest part of peninsular Thailand. Just 44km separates the Gulf of Thailand from the Andaman Sea's Chan River estuary, and Burmese border, here. Though a seemingly obvious short cut for shipping traffic between the Indian Ocean and the South China Sea, avoiding the 1500km detour via the Strait of Malacca, the much-discussed **Kra Canal** project has yet to be realized, despite being on the table for over three hundred years.

---

here, beginning with the low-key little sister islands of **Ko Chang** (quite different from its larger, more famous east-coast namesake) and **Ko Phayam**, where the hammocks and paraffin lamps offer an old-style travellers' vibe that's harder to find further south. Snorkellers and divers are drawn in their hundreds to the reefs of the remote National Park island chains of **Ko Surin** and **Ko Similan**, with many choosing to base themselves at the mainland beach resort of **Khao Lak**, though homestay programmes around **Khuraburi** offer an interesting alternative. Inland, it's all about the jungle – with twenty-first-century amenities – at the enjoyable **Khao Sok National Park**, where accommodation is on rafts on the lake and in treehouses beneath the limestone crags.

Phuket, Thailand's largest island, is the region's major resort destination for families, package tourists and novice divers; its dining, shopping and entertainment facilities are second to none, but the high-rises and hectic consumerism dilute the Thai-ness of the experience. There's Thai life in spades across on the quiet rural island of **Ko Yao Noi**, scenically located within the spectacular bay of **Ao Phang Nga**, whose scattered karst islets are one of the country's top natural wonders, best appreciated from a sea-canoe. The Andaman coast's second hub is **Krabi** province, rightly famous for its turquoise seas and dramatic islands. Flashiest of these is the flawed but still handsome **Ko Phi Phi**, with its great diving, gorgeous beaches and high-octane nightlife. Mainland and mainstream **Ao Nang** can't really compete, but is at least close to the majestic cliffs and superb rock-climbing of the **Railay** peninsula at **Laem Phra Nang**. Offshore again, there's horizon-gazing aplenty at mellow, barely developed **Ko Jum** and the choice of half a dozen luxuriously long beaches, and plentiful resort facilities, at **Ko Lanta Yai**.

Unlike the Gulf coast, the Andaman coast is hit by the **southwest monsoon**, which usually generally lasts from the end of May until at least the middle of October. During this period, heavy rain and high seas render some of the outer islands inaccessible, but conditions aren't usually severe enough to ruin a holiday on the other islands, or on the mainland, and you'll get tempting discounts on accommodation. Some bungalows at the smaller resorts shut down entirely during low season (highlighted in the text), but most beaches keep at least one place open, and some dive shops lead expeditions year-round.

ARRIVAL AND DEPARTURE   **THE ANDAMAN COAST**

There is no rail line down the Andaman coast, but many travellers take the **train** from Bangkok to the Gulf coast and then nip across by bus; most direct **buses** from the capital travel south overnight. The fastest option is to arrive by plane: both Phuket and Krabi have international **airports**, and there's a domestic airport at Trang, not far from Ko Lanta in the deep south.

Ranong

Despite being the soggiest town in the country, with over 5000mm of rain a year, **RANONG** has a pleasing buzz about it, fuelled by the mix of Burmese, Thai, Chinese and Malay inhabitants. It's a prosperous town, the lucrative nineteenth-century tin-mining concessions now replaced by a thriving fishing industry centred on the port of Saphan Pla, 5km southwest of town, and its scores of fishing boats and fish-processing factories staffed mainly by notoriously poorly treated Burmese workers. As with most border

RANONG

ACCOMMODATION
Kiwi Orchard Guesthouse	4
Luang Poj	2
Suta House Bungalows	1
Tinidee Hotel & Inn	3

RESTAURANTS & CAFÉS
Pon's Place	2
Sophon's Hideaway	1

areas, there's also said to be a flourishing illegal trade in amphetamines, guns and labour, not to mention the inevitable tensions over international fishing rights, which sometimes end in shoot-outs, though the closest encounter you're likely to have will be in the pages of the *Bangkok Post*. Thai tourists have been coming here for years, to savour the health-giving properties of the local spring water, but foreign travellers have only quite recently discovered it as a useful departure point for the alluring nearby little islands of **Ko Chang** and **Ko Phayam**. The other reason to stop off in Ranong is to make a visa run to the Burmese town of **Kaw Thaung**.

A stroll along the town centre's main road, **Thanon Ruangrat**, brings its history and geography to mind. The handsome, if faded, shopfront architecture bears many of the hallmarks of nineteenth-century Sino-Portuguese design (see p.622), with its arched "five-foot" walkways shading pedestrians, pastel paintwork and shuttered windows. Chinese goods fill many of the shops – this is a good place to stock up on cheap clothes too – and many signs are written in the town's three main languages: Thai, Chinese and curly Burmese script.

First Governor's House

West off Thanon Ruangrat on the northern edge of town • Daily 9am–4.30pm • Free

Ranong's history is closely associated with its most famous son, Khaw Soo Cheang, a poor Hokkien Chinese emigrant turned tin baron who became the first governor of

Ranong province in 1854; he is still so esteemed that politicians continue to pay public homage at his grave, and his descendants bear the respected aristocratic surname "na Ranong" ("of Ranong"). Little now remains of Khaw Soo Cheang's house, but in its grounds stands a Khaw clan house and small museum, the **First Governor's House** (Nai Khai Ranong), containing interesting photos of the governor.

The geothermal springs

Raksawarin Park, about 3km east of the Thanon Ruangrat market · **Raksawarin Hot Springs** daily 7am–9pm · free; Tinidee pools B40, or B60 including transfer from Tinidee Hotel (see p.591) · **Siam Hot Spa Ranong** daily noon–9pm · treatments from B200 ☎ 077 813551–4, ⓦ siamhotsparanong.com · Accessible on red songthaew #2 from the market or by motorbike taxi

It can be fun to follow the crowds of domestic tourists who flock to Ranong's famously pure **geothermal springs** for its stress-relieving and supposed medicinal properties. The springs are the focus of forested Raksawarin Park, which is set in a narrow, lush river valley, surrounded by restaurants and souvenir shops. At the park's Raksawarin Hot Springs, you can bathe or paddle in either the open-access, public mineral spa pools or the better-appointed and deeper, jacuzzi-type spa pools, which are run by the *Tinidee Hotel*. Alternatively, you can opt for a more leisurely soak at the indoor Siam Hot Spa Ranong across the road, which offers public and private jacuzzi pools, private bathrooms and inexpensive massage and steam treatments.

ARRIVAL AND DEPARTURE

RANONG

By plane Budget airline Nok Air (ⓦ nokair.com) flies from Bangkok's Don Mueang airport (2 daily; 1hr 30min) to Ranong airport, 20km south of town on Highway 4. *Pon's Place* (☎ 081 597 4549, ⓦ ponplace-ranong.com) has a tours booth at the airport and can also arrange a transfer into town or the Saphan Pla pier for B200–300/person. You can also wait on the highway outside of the terminal for a songthaew (B25) into town.

By bus or minibus Most Andaman-coast buses travelling between Bangkok or Chumphon and Khuraburi, Takua Pa or Phuket stop briefly at Ranong's bus station on Highway 4 (Thanon Phetkasem), 1km southeast of the central market. If coming from Khao Sok or Surat Thani, you'll usually need to change buses at Takua Pa, though there is also an a/c minibus service from and to Surat Thani (hourly 6am–5pm; 3hr). There are direct buses operated by Rungkit from Chumphon (4 daily; 2–3hr), as well as faster a/c minibuses (hourly 6am–5pm; 2hr; B150), so from Bangkok it's often more comfortable to take a night train to Chumphon and then change on to a bus or minibus. Alternatively, Chokeanan and New Mittour run VIP buses from opposite Wat Bowoniwes and the Siam Commercial

Bank in Banglamphu, via the Southern Bus Terminal, to Chumphon's Thanon Tha Muang. Rungkit buses to Chumphon and Phuket and the a/c minibuses operate out of Ranong Bus Station.

Destinations: Bangkok (15 daily; 9hr); Chumphon (4 daily; 2–3hr); Khao Lak (7 daily; 3hr 45min); Khuraburi (7 daily; 2hr); Krabi (1–2 daily; 5hr); Phang Nga (1–2 daily; 4hr); Phuket (via Khao Lak; 7 daily; 5–7hr); Surat Thani (10 daily; 4–5hr); Takua Pa (7 daily; 3hr).

By boat to the islands via Saphan Pla Boats to Ko Chang (see p.591) and Ko Phayam (see p.595) leave from Ranong's port at Saphan Pla, 5km southwest of the town centre and served by songthaews (see below) or by share-taxi from *Pon's Place* (B50). Songthaews drop passengers on the main road through Saphan Pla, from where it's a 500m walk south to the Islands Pier, while share-taxis take you to the pier itself; phone *Pon's Place* if you want to arrange a pick-up from the pier on your return from the islands.

Destinations: Ko Chang (1–5 daily; 1hr–1hr 30min); Ko Phayam (1–5 daily; 45min–2hr).

GETTING AROUND AND INFORMATION

By songthaew Songthaews shuttle across and around Ranong, starting from the Thanon Ruangrat market, close to the town-centre hotels. Many have their destinations written in English on the side, and most charge around B15 per ride. Several songthaews pass Ranong bus station, including the #2 (red), which runs to the Thanon Ruangrat hotels and day market, and the #6 (blue), which starts at the day market and heads on to the port area at Saphan Pla,

5km to the southwest (for boats to Ko Chang, Ko Phayam and Kaw Thaung); red #3 songthaew runs direct from the market on Thanon Ruangrat to the Saphan Pla port area.

Car and bike rental *Pon's Place*, 129 Thanon Ruangrat (daily 7.30am–9pm; ☎ 081 597 4549, ⓦ ponplace-ranong .com), rents bicycles, motorbikes and cars.

Tourist information The best source of tourist information in town is the ever helpful Pon at *Pon's Place*

7

INTO MYANMAR: KAWTHAUNG (KO SONG)

The southernmost tip of Myanmar – known as **Kawthaung** in Burmese, Ko Song in Thai, and Victoria Point when it was a British colony – lies just a few kilometres west of Ranong across the gaping Chan River estuary, and is easily reached by longtail boat from Saphan Pla fishing port just outside Ranong town centre when the crossing is open (daily 8am–6pm). Kawthuang can be used as an entry point for travelling in Myanmar (you'll need to arrange a visa in advance), though its position in the far south doesn't make it the most convenient option; most people, however, choose to use this crossing for a visa run (see p.63).

You can either try the visa run independently, as described below, or you can make use of one of the all-inclusive **"visa run" services** advertised all over town, including at *Pon's Place* (B850 including visa; see p.589). Most visa-run operators use the Saphan Pla route, but they can also book you on the faster, more luxurious **Andaman Club boat** (6 daily 7am–4pm, later boats available for those staying overnight; 20min each way; B1000 including visa), which departs from the Andaman Club pier 5km north of Ranong's town centre and travels to and from the swanky *Andaman Club* hotel (wandamanclub.com), casino and duty-free complex, located on a tiny island in Burmese waters just south of Kawthaung.

Boats to Kawthaung leave from the so-called Burmese Pier (go through the PTT petrol station on the main road) in the port of Saphan Pla, 5km southwest of town and served by songthaews from Ranong market (B15) – the blue #6 goes via the bus station but the red #3 is more direct. Thai exit formalities are done at the pier (daily 8am–6pm), after which longtail boats take you to Kawthaung (B300–400 return per boat, or B50 one-way on shared boat – pay at the end; 30min each way) and **Burmese immigration**. Don't get off the boat at the mid-way checkpoint hut. Here you pay US$10 (or B500) for a pass that should entitle you to stay in Kawthaung for a week but forbids travel further than 8km inland. Note that Myanmar time is thirty minutes behind Thailand time, and that to get back into Thailand you'll have to be at the immigration office in Saphan Pla before it closes at 6pm. The photocopy shop at the pier in Saphan Pla often keeps US dollars, and you should be able to haggle them down to B400 for a US$10 bill. Thai money is perfectly acceptable in Kawthaung.

There's nothing much to do in **Kawthaung** itself, but it has quite a different vibe to Thai towns. As you arrive at the quay, the market, immigration office and tiny town centre lie before you, while over to your right, about twenty minutes' walk away, you can't miss the hilltop **Pyi Taw Aye Pagoda**, surmounted by a huge reclining Buddha and a ring of smaller ones. Once you've explored the covered market behind the quay and picked your way through the piles of tin trunks and sacks of rice that crowd the surrounding streets, all that remains is to take a coffee break in one of the quayside pastry shops.

restaurant and tour agency, 129 Thanon Ruangrat (daily 7.30am–9pm; ☏081 597 4549, wponplace-ranong.com; also a booth at Ranong airport), where you can also organize a visa run to Myanmar and back, arrange tours of the local area, book accommodation on Ko Chang and Ko Phayam, and buy air, bus and minibus tickets, as well as train tickets from Chumphon or Surat Thani. There's a branch of A-One Diving (see p.597) at 256 Thanon Ruangrat (☏077 832984).

ACCOMMODATION

Kiwi Orchid Guesthouse 96/19-20 Moo 1, off Thanon Phetkasem ☏077 832812, ✉kiwiorchid@hotmail .com. A run-down place right next to the bus terminal, but the fan rooms are surprisingly quiet and comfortable. Shared bathrooms are a little grimy, but the hostel makes a handy transit to plan your next move with other budget travellers over a beer in the restaurant, which serves good vegetarian dishes. **B300**

Luang Poj 225 Thanon Ruangrat ☏077 833377, ✉luangpoj@gmail.com. Appealing conversion of a Sino-Portuguese shophouse, maintaining its polished wooden floors, which styles itself as a "boutique hostel" though there are no dorms. The smart, modern bedrooms come with attractive murals: heavy sleepers who like to be in the thick of the action will like the two fan rooms with wooden shutters facing the street; others may prefer to opt for the same priced, windowless a/c options. Hot showers are shared and there's a restaurant upstairs. **B500**

Suta House Bungalows Thanon Ruangrat ☏077 832707–8. Set back 50m from the road, this is a tranquil, unusual find in a city, with its row of small but well-maintained a/c bungalows, all of them with clean tiled

floors, hot showers, fridges and cable TV, though the beds have seen better days. They're set round a small yard, with car parking, a little bar-coffee shop and a restaurant. **B420**
TCDF Eco-Logic Pak Song, near Pha To, 45km southeast of Ranong ⓦtcdf-ecologic.jimdo.com. Thai–Dutch ecotourism guesthouse on a farm in the mountains (and on the Ranong–Surat Thani bus route), with artistically decorated en-suite rooms and bungalows set in lovely grounds, some with garden bathrooms. Lots of activities for adults and kids, including bamboo rafting, hiking and Thai cooking classes. Proceeds go towards the Thai Child Development Foundation (see p.58). Wi-fi only in the restaurant. Dorms **B200**, doubles **B750**

★**Tinidee Hotel** 41/144 Thanon Tha Muang ⓣ077 835240, ⓦtinideeranong.com. The top digs in town are at this welcoming, good-value high-rise hotel, a 10min walk from the market, which fully lives up to its name ("It's good here"). The large, bright a/c rooms are tastefully furnished and all come with mini-bars, TVs and bathtubs fed by the local mineral water; there's also a spa and an attractive swimming pool and jacuzzi. **B1560**
Tinidee Inn 41/144 Thanon Tha Muang ⓣ077 834112, ⓦtinideeranong.com. A wing of the *Tinidee Hotel* has been converted into this low-cost inn, offering less style and smaller rooms, but all with a/c, hot showers, TV and fridge. Guests get access to the hotel's pool and jacuzzi. **B550**

EATING AND DRINKING

Ranong's ethnic diversity ensures a tasty range of eating options, and a stroll up Thanon Ruangrat takes you past Muslim food stalls and Chinese pastry shops as well as a small but typically Thai night market. A bigger night market convenes at dusk just east of the CAT phone office off Thanon Phoem Phon. The stretch of Thanon Ruangrat between the Thanon Luwang junction and *Sophon's Hideaway* is also abuzz after dark, especially at weekends, with urbane little local bars that keep reinventing themselves.

Pon's Place 129 Thanon Ruangrat ⓣ081 597 4549. This nice little restaurant hung with orchids is the obvious place for farang-style breakfast (French toast B55) with traditional Thai coffee, free wi-fi and as much local information as you care to gather. It also offers sandwiches and standard Thai dishes, including plenty of seafood and some veggie options. Daily 7.30am–9pm.
Sophon's Hideaway Thanon Ruangrat ⓣ077 832730.

Lively, enjoyable bar and rustic-style restaurant, where Thai families and expats congregate for the wide-ranging menu, which includes curried seafood with young coconut (B115), steak with pepper sauce (B165), pizzas (from B200), pasta, ice cream and breakfast. The cheapish beer and friendly staff are a plus and there's international sports on the TV, a free pool table and free wi-fi. Daily 10am–11pm.

Ko Chang

Not to be confused with the much larger Ko Chang off Thailand's east coast (see p.409), Ranong's **KO CHANG** is a forested little island about 5km offshore, whose car-free, ATM-free, ultra laidback, roll-your-own vibe more than compensates for the less than perfect beaches. The pace of life here is very slow, encouraging long stays, and for the relatively small number of tourists who make it to the island the emphasis is strongly on kicking back and chilling out – bring your own hammock and you'll fit right in. Those in search of (slightly) livelier scenes head across the water to sister-island Ko Phayam (see p.595). Most islanders make their living from fishing and from the rubber, palm and cashew nut plantations that dominate the flatter patches of the interior. The beaches are connected by tracks through the trees and there are only sporadic, self-generated supplies of electricity for a few hours each evening.

The best of Ko Chang's beaches are on the west coast, and of these the longest, nicest and most popular is **Ao Yai**. The tiny bays to the north and south mostly hold just one set of bungalows each and are good for getting away from it all, though access to Ao Yai is easy enough if you don't mind the hike. About halfway between the west and east coasts, a crossroads bisects Ko Chang's only **village**, a tiny settlement that is home to most of the islanders and holds just a few shops, restaurants and a clinic.

Nearly all the bungalows on Ko Chang **close** down from about late April or early May until mid- or late October, when the island is subjected to very heavy rain, the beaches fill with flotsam, paths become dangerously slippery and food supplies dwindle with no ice available to keep things fresh. Many bungalow staff relocate to the mainland for this period, so you should phone ahead to check first if you're thinking of heading out here.

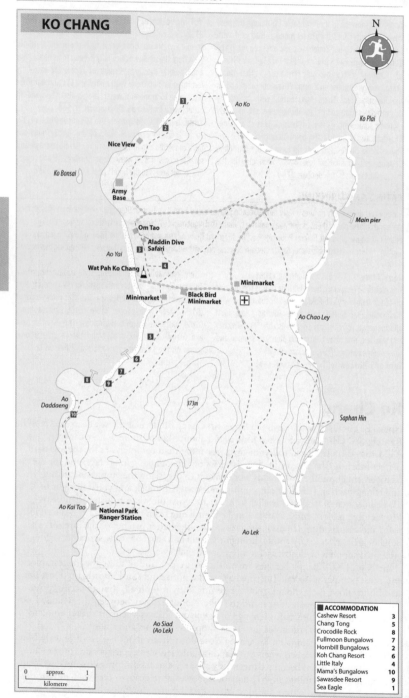

KO CHANG

N

7

Ao Ko

Ko Plai

Nice View

Ko Bonsai

Army Base

Om Tao

Aladdin Dive Safari

Ao Yai

Wat Pah Ko Chang

Main pier

Minimarket

Minimarket

Black Bird Minimarket

Ao Chao Ley

Chang Tong

Koh Chang Resort

Fullmoon Bungalows

Crocodile Rock

Sawasdee Resort

Ao Daddaeng

Mama's Bungalows

373m

Saphan Hin

Ao Kai Tao

National Park Ranger Station

Ao Lek

Ao Siad (Ao Lek)

0	approx.	1
kilometre		

■ ACCOMMODATION	
Cashew Resort	3
Chang Tong	5
Crocodile Rock	8
Fullmoon Bungalows	7
Hornbill Bungalows	2
Koh Chang Resort	6
Little Italy	4
Mama's Bungalows	10
Sawasdee Resort	9
Sea Eagle	1

Ao Yai (Long Beach) and Ao Daddaeng

Effectively divided in two by a khlong (canal) and the stumps of a long wooden pier, **Ao Yai**, or **Long Beach**, enjoys a fine view of the brooding silhouette of Myanmar's St Matthew's Island, which dominates the western horizon. The 800m-long stretch of Ao Yai that runs north from the khlong is the most attractive on the island, nice and wide even at high tide, and especially good for kids. South of the khlong, the beach is very narrow at high tide, but when the water goes out you have to walk a longish distance to find any depth. Further south still, around a rocky headland, tiny secluded gold-sand **Ao Daddaeng** (Tadang) is sandwiched between massive boulders and holds just a few bungalows: reach it via a five-minute footpath from behind *Tadang Bay Bungalows*.

A narrow concrete road connects central Ao Yai with the mangrove-filled little harbour on the east coast, a distance of around 1700m that can be walked in under half an hour. The western end of the road begins beside the island's only temple, **Wat Pah Ko Chang**, whose bot and monks' quarters are partially hidden among the trees beside the beach, with a sign that asks tourists to dress modestly when in the area and not to swim or sunbathe in front of it.

Northern Ko Chang

North of Ao Yai, the crenellated coast reveals a series of tiny bays occupied by just one set of bungalows apiece. The gritty gold-sand beaches are secluded and feel quite remote, accessible only via a track through forest and rubber plantations. Even if you don't want to base yourself up here, you can do an enjoyable **loop** around the northern bays in well under three hours from Ao Yai. Alternatively, you could make use of the Ranong boats, which charge about B50 for any hop up or down the west coast.

Following **the track** inland from just north of Om Tao, a ten-minute walk north brings you to the top of the first of several hills and the barbed-wire perimeters of a military camp, established here to monitor activity along the (maritime) Thai–Myanmar border. Ten minutes further on, *Nice View* restaurant and bungalows are aptly named: perched atop an outcrop with glorious panoramas over the unfolding little bays and islets beyond, it's a perfect spot to break for lunch or a drink. It's another twenty minutes to *Sea Eagle* (you need to go via the beach at *Hornbill* before returning inland), the last of the northern bay bungalows, beyond which a ten-minute walk up and over the next hill takes you to the edge of the northeast-facing fishing village, an unprepossessing place complete with incongruous Christian church. This is **Ao Ko**, which is linked by road to the east coast's rainy-season pier, and also to Ao Yai.

7

ACTIVITIES ON KO CHANG

Going for walks (and not minding getting lost) is the most popular activity on this large, traffic-free island, but several resorts, including *Koh Chang Resort*, run **fishing, snorkelling and camping trips** to Ko Kham, which is famed for its beautiful beaches and reefs, and to Ko Phayam. For **divers**, Ko Chang is particularly well placed for the sites in the Mergui Archipelago across the border in Myanmar, while the top local dive sites in Thailand are Ko Surin, Ko Bon, Ko Tachai, Ko Similan and Richelieu Rock.

Aladdin Dive Safari Cashew Resort, Ao Yai, and at the Islands Pier in Saphan Pla ☎ 087 278 6908, ⓦ aladdindivesafari.com. This German–Dutch-run dive shop teaches PADI diving courses and runs a huge selection of live-aboards that take in all the local dive sites (from B14,900 for three days excluding equipment and national park fees).

Om Tao North of Cashew Resort, Ao Yai ☎ 090 167 5384, ⓦ omtao.net. Morning yoga classes and t'ai chi in season.

Southern Ko Chang

Ao Siad, at the southern end of the island, is even more isolated than the north coast and makes a good focus for a day-walk. It's sometimes known as **Ao Lek**, though the real **Ao Lek** is the mangrove-lined bay fifteen minutes' walk to the northeast, on the other coast. From Ao Daddaeng, a clear path takes you south, in about an hour, to **Ao Kai Tao**, a pretty beach and site of the national park ranger station. From here, the route then follows an indistinct path across the saddle between two hills and along a creek bed to reach east-coast Ao Lek (this takes another hour), after which it's fifteen minutes south to Ao Siad. Retracing your steps to Ao Lek to start with, it's then about 5km (2hr) to the crossroads in the village.

ARRIVAL AND INFORMATION

Cashew Resort (see below) can arrange bus tickets.

BY BOAT

To/from Ranong The island's main link with the outside world is the daily boat service from the Islands Pier in Saphan Pla (see p.589) to the pier on the east coast (2pm; 1hr; B150; sometimes cancelled in the rainy season). You should be able to arrange some kind of pick-up from the pier through your resort; otherwise it's a 3km walk to Ao Yai. From about early November to late April, there are also daily boat departures to Ko Chang's west coast, stopping at most resorts, from Saphan Pla's Islands Pier (9.30am, noon & 2pm; 1hr 30min; B150); ask your resort or at *Pon's Place* in Ranong (see p.589) for the latest schedules.

To/from Ko Phayam The easiest and cheapest option for getting to or from Ko Phayam is to use the day-trippers' boat run by *Koh Chang Resort* (high season Mon–Fri daily 10am, returning to Ko Chang 4pm; B150); a charter between the two islands costs about B1500 per boat.

Tourist information For general information on the island see ⓦ kohchang-ranong.com.

ACCOMMODATION AND EATING

Most of the bungalows on Ko Chang are simple, old-school wooden-plank or woven bamboo constructions with mosquito nets on the beds; you shouldn't necessarily expect flush toilets (buckets and dippers are provided), curtains or a door on your bathroom. Though the bungalow resorts nearly all have their own generators (which usually only operate in the evenings), some stick to candles and paraffin lamps in the bungalows so it's best to bring a torch; very few bungalows have fans. There are no stand-alone restaurants, and as the distances between resorts are long and there's no transport, most visitors dine at their own resort's restaurant.

AO YAI (LONG BEACH)

Cashew Resort ☏ 077 820226 or ☏ 084 538 5385, ⓔ cashew_resort@hotmail.com. The longest-running accommodation on the island, and also the largest, *Cashew* feels like a tiny village, with its forty en-suite bungalows spread among the cashew trees along 700m of prime beachfront, and returnees personalizing their bungalows like mini homes. All the wood or brick bungalows enjoy both a sea view and some privacy, and some have big glass windows. The resort offers the most facilities on the island, including internet access, foreign exchange, Visa and MasterCard capability, an overseas phone service, transport bookings, massage and books to borrow. Its restaurant bakes bread and serves Thai and a few German dishes. No wi-fi. **B300**

Chang Tong ☏ 080 526 8422 or ☏ 089 875 3353, ⓔ aoy_changthong@hotmail.com. The cheapest wood and bamboo bungalows at this friendly spot are very basic, though they're all en suite and are well spaced beneath the shoreside trees; pay a bit more for newer, better appointed ones on the beachfront. No wi-fi. **B300**

★ **Crocodile Rock** ☏ 081 370 1434 or ☏ 087 040 8087, ⓦ kohchangandaman.webs.com. In a shady, secluded, elevated position at the start of Ao Yai's southern headland, with great views of the whole bay, on which the friendly owners have capitalized, with attractive decks at the restaurant and picture windows in some of the bathrooms. Bungalows have a touch more style than the Ko Chang average, though only the larger ones and the restaurant have electricity at night. The restaurant bakes its own bread, cookies and banana muffins, and serves fresh juices and espresso coffee. Computer-based internet access. **B300**

Fullmoon Bungalows ☏ 084 850 3809, ⓦ fullmoon bungalows.com. Though simple, the attractive wooden en-suite bungalows here are well designed and a cut above many others on Ao Yai. The cheaper ones are prettily painted, with cute stencil work in the bathrooms, and there are larger, pastel-painted, clapboard versions with big decks, but all have sea views. Beach bar and massage *sala*. No wi-fi. **B300**

Koh Chang Resort ☏ 081 896 1839, ⓦ kohchang andaman.net. Occupying a fabulous spot high on the rocks right over the water, the best of the en-suite wooden bungalows here have fine sea views from their balconies;

as described in Erich Krauss's *Wave of Destruction* (see p.778). Built by the Thai army, it's an evocative installation: you walk down a path between a curling, 4m-high, concrete "wave" and a grassy bank, representing the land, on which plaques commemorate individual victims. Through a window in the concrete wave, a fishing boat looms over you – this "miracle boat" was swept inland but stopped just short of devastating a house and its occupants.

While you're out here, it's worth popping in on the **Saori weaving factory and shop** (Mon–Sat), on the left about 1km further up Highway 4 from the Ban Nam Khem turn-off, towards the northern end of Ban Bang Muang village. It's a regeneration and occupational therapy project, where you can watch the women weaving and buy some lovely scarves.

ARRIVAL AND DEPARTURE KHAO LAK

By plane Khao Lak is just 70km north of Phuket airport (1hr; B1700–2200 by taxi; see p.619).

By bus and minibus All buses running from Phuket to Takua Pa and Ranong (and vice versa) pass through Khao Lak and can drop you anywhere along Highway 4; coming from Krabi or Phang Nga, you'll generally need to change buses in Khokkloi, from Khao Sok, in Takua Pa. On departure, you can flag down most buses on the main road, but the Bangkok services use a bus station at the far north end of Bang Niang. There are also a/c tourist minibuses that run at least daily to Surat Thani (via Khokkloi, not Khao Sok; 4hr), Krabi/Ao Nang (3hr/3hr

30min) and Trang (change in Krabi; 5hr 30min). Bus and a/c minibus tickets can be booked through a number of travel agents, including Khao Lak Land Discovery in Nang Thong (☎076 485411, ⬤khaolaklanddiscovery.com), who also offer transfers to and from Phuket Airport (B600/person or B1500/minibus).

Destinations: Bangkok (3 daily; 12hr); Phuket (20 daily; 2hr 30min); Ranong (8 daily; 2hr 30min–3hr); Takua Pa (18 daily; 30min).

By boat Boats to the Similans depart from the pier at Thap Lamu, which is 6km south of Nang Thong, then 5km west off Highway 4 (see p.616).

DIVING AND SNORKELLING AROUND KHAO LAK

Khao Lak is the closest and most convenient departure point for **diving and snorkelling trips** to the awesome national park islands of **Ko Similan** (see p.614), which can be reached in three to four hours on a live-aboard or other large boat or in two hours in a much less comfortable speedboat. The islands are currently only open from approximately October to May and all divers have to pay a one-off national park fee of B400 plus a B200-a-day diving fee, usually on top of dive-trip prices. **Local Khao Lak dives** are generally possible year-round, especially the highly rated **wreck** of a tin-mining boat near Bang Sak, which is especially rich in marine life such as ghost pipefish, moray eels, scorpion fish, nudibranchs and yellow-tail barracuda. All Khao Lak dive shops also teach PADI **dive courses**, with the last two days of the Openwater course often done on location in the Similans; for advice on choosing a dive shop see "Basics" (see p.52).

IQ Dive Nang Thong, opposite McDonald's ☎076 485614, ⬤iq-dive.com. Swiss–Thai-run PADI Five-Star Centre that specializes in one-day dive trips to the Similans, on a big dive boat (B4700 plus equipment; B2800 for snorkellers). Their Openwater courses cost B17,000 with two days spent diving the Similans.

Sea Dragon Dive Center Nang Thong ☎076 485420, ⬤seadragondivecenter.com. Highly recommended PADI Five-Star Instructor Development Centre which has three live-aboard boats – including budget and deluxe options – running frequent three-day trips to the Similans and Ko Bon (from B11,900 including equipment), and four-day trips to the Similans, Surin islands, Ko Bon, Ko Tachai and Richelieu Rock (from B19,600).

No national park fees are included here. Snorkellers get about one-third off. Also offers local wreck and other dives (starting from B2000, not including equipment, for a two-tank dive) and PADI dive courses: the four-day Openwater is B10,500, or B16,100 with two day-trips diving the Similans.

Similan Tour At Poseidon Bungalows, 7km south of central Nang Thong, in Khao Lak ☎076 443258, ⬤similantour.com. Highly recommended three-day live-aboard snorkelling trips to the Similans (B8900, includes fees). Current departures are twice weekly on Tuesdays and Fridays, from roughly the end of October to May.

7

GETTING AROUND

By songthaew A few public songthaews shuttle between Nang Thong and Bang Niang (where they have a base in front of the market), mostly by day, charging B20–50, but largely they act as private taxis instead and charge more than B100.

Motorbike and car rental Many hotels can rent motorbikes, and rental cars are available through tour operators; Budget also has an agent on the soi down to *Nang Thong Bay Resort* (☎076 443454, ⓦ budget.co.th).

ACCOMMODATION

LAEM PAKARANG

★**The Sarojin** 12km north of Khao Lak ☎076 427905, ⓦ thesarojin.com. With a staff-to-guest ratio of two to one and a style and attitude that exudes understated, unpretentious class, this is the top place to stay around Khao Lak. The 56 sleek, tastefully simple rooms are discreetly sited around the wide beachfront garden and stunning square turquoise swimming pool. It's an obvious honeymoon choice, with a policy of no under-10s, a range of excursions designed for two, and private candlelit tables for dinner on the beach or at a nearby waterfall. There are complimentary non-motorized watersports and mountain bikes, and a spa. All-day breakfast with sparkling wine included. Special promotions often available. B12,870

BANG NIANG

Amsterdam Resort Soi 3 ☎081 857 5881, ⓦ amsterdamresortkhaolak.com. Just 200m inland from the beach, this helpful little Dutch-run complex offers some of the cheapest accommodation in Bang Niang and serves good food. The rooms and red-brick bungalows of varying size have either fans or a/c; most have hot water. Also has cycle and motorbike rental and a tour desk. Fan B650, a/c B1000

Ayara Villas ☎076 486478–9, ⓦ ayara-villas.com. An attractive upper-mid-range option, spread over three different compounds with two swimming pools. At the top end are beachfront villas right on the sand; many others are terraced bungalows just a few metres from the sea, and the rest are in a three-storey building, with ground-floor rooms enjoying direct pool access. The a/c interiors are nicely furnished with dark wood in contemporary style and all have kitchenettes. Breakfast included. B5000

Fair House ☎089 473 7985. One of the cheapest places to stay in Bang Niang, with its handful of large, neat, fan-cooled concrete bungalows and rooms with fridges and hot showers, widely spaced around a pretty little garden set back about 50m from the highway, about 1km walk from the beach. B600

Sanuk Bungalows ☎081 979 0308, ⓦ sanukresort .com. Dinky little Swiss-managed group of five comfortable and spacious brick bungalows in a small garden with a heart-shaped whirlpool, just 100m from the beach. Bungalows come with a/c, hot showers, fridges and kitchenettes. B1400

NANG THONG

Jai ☎076 485390, ⓔ jai_bungalow@hotmail.com. A busy, family-run place that offers some of the cheapest accommodation in Khao Lak. The good-quality, decent-sized, en-suite concrete bungalows are set around a lawn dotted with trees behind the popular restaurant, quite close to the highway and about 600m from the beach; a/c options have hot showers and fridges. Fan B450, a/c B650

Khao Lak Banana Soi Bang La On ☎076 485889, ⓦ khaolakbanana.com. Dozens of thoughtfully designed fan and a/c bungalows packed into a garden of banana trees and tropical flowers. All have a safety box, hot shower and fridge and there's a tiny swimming pool. Fan B700, a/c B1000

★**Khao Lak Green Beach** ☎076 485845, ⓦ green beach.de. The attractive design and shorefront location of the bungalows here make this a good-value option, and the staff are great too. Arrayed around a pond, the cream-painted chalet-style bungalows have a/c, hot showers, polished wood floors, pretty furnishings and nice bathrooms, and most have a fridge. Price mainly depends on location: some are right on the shore and none is more than a few metres away. Discounts for singles. B1400

Khao Lak Seafood Family House Soi Noen Thong ☎076 485318, ⓦ khaolakseafood.com. The large, good-quality bungalows here are set well back from the road in a garden behind the eponymous restaurant. The fan ones are especially good value for Khao Lak: roomy and nicely designed with good, hot-water bathrooms; a/c rooms in a couple of two-storey blocks are also available. It's a family business and very popular with returning guests and long stayers. Fan B600, a/c B1200

Nang Thong Bay Resort ☎076 485088–9, ⓦ nang thong.com. Well priced considering its on-the-beach location, this popular, long-established place offers smartly maintained a/c bungalows that are well spaced around the shorefront garden and mostly enjoy sea views, plus some hotel-style rooms. There's a sea-view swimming pool, restaurant and a shuttle-bus service into town as well. B2000

★**Phu Khao Lak Resort** ☎076 485141, ⓦ phukhao lak.com. There is a luxurious amount of space at this well-run place, where the thirty large, spotlessly clean bungalows sit prettily amid a grassy park-style coconut plantation. Fan rooms have tiled floors and most have hot-water bathrooms; a/c ones have picture windows and quite stylish interiors. There's a swimming pool and a good restaurant. About 500m walk from the beach. Fan B600, a/c B1800

KHAO LAK DAY-TRIPS AND OTHER ACTIVITIES

Aside from diving and snorkelling trips (see p.611), there are several other attractions within day-tripping distance of Khao Lak, including a number of local **waterfalls**. Of these, Sai Rung (Rainbow Falls), about 16km north of Nang Thong in Bang Sak, is the most satisfying. Others include Tong Pling, across from the *Merlin* resort in Khao Lak; Nam Tok Lumphi, about 20km south of Khao Lak; and Chong Fah Falls, located less than 5km east of Bang Niang, but subject to a B200 entry fee because it's part of Khao Lak–Lam Ru National Park (w dnp.go.th). The national park's headquarters is on the headland between Nang Thong and Khao Lak beaches, and about 1km south of it, you can easily walk down to a quiet, pretty sandy cove – look for a sign saying "small sandy beach" on the west side of the main road, opposite a layby.

Everyday 2 Restaurant South end of Nang Thong ☎ 085 299 0410. Morning Thai cooking courses for B1200, including pick-ups.

The Green Biking Club Bang Niang ☎ 076 443211, w greenbikingclub.com. Runs interesting guided mountain-bike trips around rural and coastal Khao Lak (from B1850 for half a day).

Khao Lak Land Discovery Nang Thong ☎ 076 485411, w khaolaklanddiscovery.com. One of the best and most reputable, though not the cheapest, local tour operators, whose day-trips include elephant-riding (from B1600), kayaking around Ao Phang Nga (B3200), and trekking, canoeing and elephant-riding in Khao Sok National Park (B2800).

The Yoga Studio Khao Lak Community Appeal Foundation, Bang Niang ☎ 089 710 5770, w yoga khaolak.com. High-season yoga classes (B500 for one class) – call for the schedule.

7

KHAO LAK

Poseidon Bungalows 7km south of central Nang Thong ☎ 076 443258, w similantour.com. Surrounded by rubber plantations and set above a sandy shore of wave-smoothed rocks just north of the Thai navy's private beach, this Swedish–Thai-run guesthouse is both a quiet place to hang out for a few days and a long-established organizer of snorkelling expeditions to the Similan islands (see p.611). All fifteen bungalows are en suite and fan cooled, with generous amounts of space, hot showers and balconies, some enjoying sea views; there's also motorbike rental available. Get off the bus at the *Poseidon* sign between kilometre-stones 53 and 54, then phone for a pick-up or walk 1km. **B950**

EATING AND DRINKING

BANG NIANG

The Candle ☎ 076 486123. White-tablecloth bistro, with an a/c room and outdoor tables, serving tasty Thai traditional and fusion dishes, such as green curry with deep-fried crispy chicken and sweet peppers (B215), and Thai desserts. Daily 11.30am–10.30pm.

Degree Bar With its wooden tables, water-buffalo skulls and folksy, Thai-country vibe, this cheap, welcoming and enjoyably local bar-restaurant is a fun place to listen to live bands, from 10pm every night, playing Thai and Western pop, *luk thung* and "Songs for Life". Daily 9pm–2am.

Khao Niau w khao-niau.com. Rustic, open-sided restaurant dishing up very good northeastern Thai food, including loads of salads such as *som tam* (from B70), *laap* and *nam tok*. Daily 1–10pm; closed 9th and 23rd of each month.

Pinocchio ☎ 076 443079, w pinocchio-italian -restaurant.com. Home-made pasta, decent pizza made in a wood-fired oven (around B300), a few Italian meat main courses and lots of seafood, topped off with tiramisu and other home-made desserts. Look for the white picket fence and fairy lights. Daily 1–11pm.

Takieang Wooden roadside restaurant that's gone slightly upmarket, offering authentic Thai food, including good *tom yum kung* (B150), banana-flower salad (B120) and exceptional seafood hotplates (B270). Daily noon–10pm.

NANG THONG

Bussaba Welcoming bistro with a long menu of Thai food, including seafood and fish priced by weight and some slightly more unusual dishes such as shrimp green curry with roti bread (B189). Also does sandwiches and a few other Western choices, and good espressos. Daily 1.30–11pm.

★Dive In Khao Lak Banana resort, Soi Bang La On. Owner and chef Sunny cooks up a storm here and is a favourite with expats, locals and returning tourists. Highlights include a deliciously aromatic *matsaman* curry (B90), *khanom jiin* Phuket-style noodles with fish and red curry, and deep-fried fish topped with mango. The Western menu runs to home-made cakes and bread, breakfasts and espressos. Free wi-fi. Daily 6.30am–11pm.

Happy Snapper w facebook.com/HappySnapperBar. Khao Lak's most famous dive-staff hangout is chilled and pleasant, with a folksy lounge ambience and a drinks menu that runs to over a hundred cocktails. There's live music, including punk, Mon–Sat from around 10.30pm, and a chill-out DJ on Sun – plus the occasional open-mike session. Daily 8.30pm–1am.

Jai This lofty, open-sided, roadside restaurant is deservedly popular for its hearty, often fiery curries in good-sized portions (B80), including *kaeng phanaeng* and *matsaman*, seafood and *tom yam kung*. Also does a few Thai desserts and Western breakfasts. Daily 8.30am–10pm.

O Rendezvous ☎ 076 485108, 🌐 restaurant-khaolak .com. Thatched, indoor-outdoor, French–Thai bar-restaurant, very popular with local expats, where you can feast on duck in orange and wine sauce (B420) or Thai specialities like shrimp and banana-flower salad, as well as cheaper standard dishes such as chicken *matsaman* curry (B140). Daily 4–11pm.

Phu Khao Lak 🌐 phukhaolak.com. Well-known and good-value restaurant attached to the bungalows of the same name serving exceptionally good Thai food from a picture menu that stretches to over a hundred dishes.

Everything from red, yellow and green curries (B140–170) to seafood platters. Daily 7am–10pm.

Stempfer Café Genteel, German-style café serving good breakfasts, espresso coffees, hot chocolate and all kinds of teas, lots of bread and cakes including apple tart (B120), plus salads and sandwiches. Free wi-fi. Daily 8.30am–9.30pm.

THAP LAMU

Navy Club Restaurant On the right by the pier, 11km southwest of Nang Thong ☎ 081 648 8656. It's worth the trip out here for some authentic Thai food and the freshest seafood, at prices lower than in Khao Lak itself. Specialities include soft-shell crab, white snapper, pomfret (B35/100g), king prawns and squid, and there are dozens of Thai salads (B80). The restaurant is unprepossessing, but you could phone ahead to book a table on the terrace overlooking the harbour. Daily 10am–10pm.

SHOPPING

Nang Thong offers plenty of shopping, mainly for clothes, souvenirs and handicrafts, with countless tailors and opticians too.

Book Tree Far north end of Nang Thong. New and secondhand books plus magazines, newspapers and art cards, and also serves coffee. Daily 9am–9pm.

Community Crafts Khao Lak Community Appeal Foundation, on the east side of the main road in Bang

Niang. Non-profit shop selling bead jewellery, batiks, bags and lanterns, made by Thai, Moken and immigrant Burmese groups. Mon–Sat 1–6pm, sometimes open Mon–Fri mornings.

Ko Similan

Mu Ko Similan National Park • B400, valid for 5 days if staying within the national park • Closed May to Oct

Rated as one of the world's best spots for both above-water and underwater beauty, the eleven islands at the heart of the **Mu Ko Similan National Park** are among the most exciting **diving** destinations in Thailand. Massive granite boulders set magnificently against turquoise waters give the islands their distinctive character, but it's the 30m visibility that draws the divers. The 5000-year-old reefs are said to be the oldest in Thailand, so there's an enormous diversity of species, and the underwater scenery is nothing short of overwhelming: the reefs teem with coral fish, and you'll also see turtles, manta rays, moray eels, jacks, reef sharks, sea snakes, red grouper and quite possibly white-tip sharks, barracuda, giant lobster and enormous tuna.

The **islands** lie 64km off the mainland and include the eponymous Ko Similan chain of nine islands as well as two more northerly islands, Ko Bon and Ko Tachai, which are both favoured haunts of manta rays and whale sharks and are halfway between the Similan chain and the islands of Ko Surin. The Similans are numbered north–south from nine to one and are often referred to by number: Ko Ba Ngu (9), Ko Similan (8), Ko Payoo (7), Ko Hin Posar (aka Ko Hok; 6), Ko Ha (5), Ko Miang (4), Ko Pahyan (3), Ko Pahyang (2) and Ko Hu Yong (1). The national park headquarters and accommodation is on Ko Miang and there's also a campsite and restaurant on Ko Similan. Ko Similan is the largest island in the chain, blessed with a beautiful, fine white-sand bay and impressive boulders and traversed by two nature trails; Ko Miang has two pretty beaches, twenty minutes' walk apart, and three nature trails; Ko Hu

KHAO SOK TREEHOUSE (P.607) >

Yong has an exceptionally long white-sand bay but access is restricted by the Thai navy as **turtles** lay their eggs there from November to February.

Such beauty has not gone unnoticed and the islands are extremely popular with day-trippers from Phuket and Khao Lak, as well as with divers and snorkellers on longer live-aboard trips. This has caused inevitable congestion and environmental problems and the Similan reefs have been damaged in places by anchors and by the local practice of using dynamite in fishing. National parks authorities have responded by banning fishermen and enforcing strict regulations for tourist boats, including **closing the islands** during the monsoon season, from May to October.

ARRIVAL AND GETTING AROUND   KO SIMILAN

Independent travellers wanting to stay on the island for a few days can usually use the snorkelling tour boats for transfers. There are also plenty of live-aboard diving or snorkelling trips to the islands, the best and cheapest of which run out of Khao Lak (see p.611).

Snorkelling tours Most travel agents in Khao Lak, Phuket and Phang Nga sell snorkelling packages to Ko Similan, usually as day-trips featuring at least four island stops (from B3500 including national park fees); two-day, one-night (B5800 staying in tents), and three-day, two-night (B7200) packages, staying on Ko Miang, are also available. The majority of these trips carry quite large groups and use fast boats that depart from Thap Lamu pier, about 11km southwest of Khao Lak's Nang Thong, 90km north of Phuket town, at about 8.30am and get to the islands in under two hours. They depart the islands at

around 3pm. Companies offering this service, all of which offer pick-ups in Khao Lak and Phuket, include Medsye Travel and Tours, who also do pick-ups in Krabi (☎076 443276, �татmedsyetour.com), and Jack Similan (☎081 648 8656, ⍟jacksimilan.com), both of which have offices at the Thap Lamu pier; and Khao Lak Land Discovery in Nang Thong (☎076 485411, ⍟khaolaklanddiscovery.com).

Getting around If travelling independently, you'll need to use Ko Similan longtail boats to travel between the islands and to explore different reefs: prices are fixed and cost around B200 per person one-way.

ACCOMMODATION AND EATING

Limited accommodation is available on **Ko Miang**, in the shape of national park rooms and bungalows (fan B1000, a/c B2000) and tents (B450), and there's a campsite on **Ko Similan** too; both islands also have a restaurant. Accommodation should be booked ahead, either at the national parks office 500m east of Thap Lamu pier (☎076 453272) or online (⍟dnp .go.th or ⍟thaiforestbooking.com), as facilities can get crowded with tour groups, especially on weekends and holidays.

Phuket

Thailand's largest island and a province in its own right, **PHUKET** (pronounced "Poo-ket") has been a prosperous region since the nineteenth century, when Chinese merchants got in on its tin-mining and sea-borne trade, before turning to the rubber industry. It remains the wealthiest province in Thailand, with the highest per-capita income, but what mints the money nowadays is **tourism**: with an annual influx of visitors that tops five million, Phuket ranks second in popularity only to Pattaya, and the package-tour traffic has wrought its usual transformations. Thoughtless tourist developments have scarred much of the island, and the trend is upmarket, with very few budget possibilities (expect to shell out up to twice what you'd pay on the mainland for accommodation and food, and sometimes more than double for transport, which is a particular headache on Phuket). However, many of the beaches are still strikingly handsome, resort facilities are second to none, and the offshore snorkelling and diving are exceptional. Away from the tourist hubs, many inland neighbourhoods are clustered round the local mosque – 35 percent of Phuketians are **Muslim**, and there are said to be more mosques on the island than Buddhist temples; though the atmosphere is generally as easy-going as elsewhere in Thailand, it's especially important to dress with some modesty outside the main resorts, and not to sunbathe topless on any of the beaches.

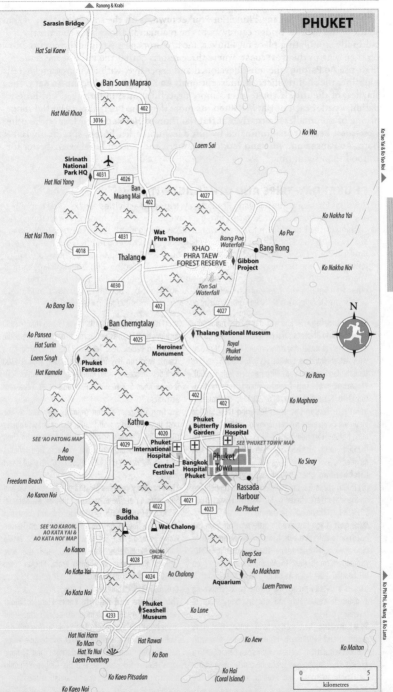

PHUKET

Ranong & Krabi

Sarasin Bridge

Hat Sai Kaew

Ban Soun Maprao

Hat Mai Khao

402

3016

Laem Sai

Ko Wa

Sirinath
National
Park HQ

4031

4026

Hat Nai Yang

Ban
Muang Mai

402

4027

Ko 'Yao 'Yai & Ko 'Yao Noi

Hat Nai Thon

4031

4018

Wat
Phra Thong

Thalang

KHAO
PHRA TAEW
FOREST RESERVE

Bang Pae
Waterfall

Gibbon
Project

Bang Rong

Ko Nakha Yai

Ao Por

Ko Nakha Noi

4030

Ton Sai
Waterfall

402

4027

Ao Bang Tao

Ban Cherngtalay

Thalang National Museum

Ao Pansea
Hat Surin

4025

Heroines'
Monument

Royal
Phuket
Marina

Laem Singh

Phuket
Fantasea

Hat Kamala

Ko Rang

Ko Maphrao

402

402

Kathu

Phuket
Butterfly
Garden

Mission
Hospital

SEE 'AO PATONG MAP'

4020

4029

Phuket
International
Hospital

Central
Festival

Bangkok
Hospital
Phuket

SEE 'PHUKET TOWN' MAP

Phuket
Town

Ao
Patong

Freedom Beach

Ao Karon Noi

Rassada
Harbour

Ko Siray

4022

4021

4023

Ao Phuket

Big
Buddha

SEE 'AO KARON,
AO KATA YAI &
AO KATA NOI' MAP

Wat Chalong

Ao Katon

4028

CHALONG
CIRCLE

Deep Sea
Port

Ao Kata Yai

4024

Ao Chalong

Aquarium

Ao Makham

Laem Panwa

Ao Kata Noi

Phuket
Seashell
Museum

Ko Lone

Hat Nai Harn
Ko Man
Hat Ya Nui
Laem Promthep

4233

Hat Rawai

Ko Aew

Ko Maiton

Ko Bon

Ko Kaeo Pitsadan

Ko Hai
(Coral Island)

Ko Kaeo Noi

Ko Phi Phi, Ao Nang & Ko Lanta

N

7

0   5
kilometres

Phuket's capital, Muang Phuket or **Phuket town**, is on the southeast coast, 42km south of the Sarasin Bridge causeway to the mainland. Though it's the most culturally stimulating place on Phuket, most visitors pass straight through the town on their way to the **west coast**, where three resorts corner the bulk of the trade: high-rise **Ao Patong**, the most developed and expensive, with an increasingly seedy nightlife; the slightly nicer, if unexceptional, **Ao Karon**; and adjacent **Ao Kata**, the smallest of the trio. If you're after a more peaceful spot, aim for the 17km-long national park beach of **Hat Mai Khao**, its more developed neighbour **Hat Nai Yang**, or one of the smaller alternatives at **Hat Nai Thon** or **Hat Kamala**. Most of the other west-coast beaches are dominated by just a few upmarket hotels, specifically **Hat Nai Harn**, **Ao Pansea** and **Ao Bang Tao**; the southern and eastern beaches are better for seafood than swimming.

PHUKET DAY-TRIPS AND OTHER ACTIVITIES

Bookings for most of the following **Phuket day-trips and activities** can be made through any tour agent and should include return transport from your hotel (though not for the cooking classes). In addition to the trips listed below, diving is also available (see p.636). Other **sights** worth checking out, especially for kids, include the Phuket Butterfly Garden and Insect World in Phuket town (see p.623), the Aquarium on Laem Panwa (p.640), the Shell Museum in Rawai (p.639), the Big Buddha near Chalong (p.640) and the Gibbon Rehabilitation Project near Thalang (p.642). Avoid any tour that features Ko Siray (Ko Sireh), the island across the narrow channel from Phuket town, which merely encourages tour-bus passengers to gawp at Phuket's largest and longest-established indigenous *chao ley* community (see p.602).

Bicycle touring Full- and half-day guided mountain-bike rides into Phuket's rural hinterlands and to Ko Yao Noi, as well as multi-day rides around Phang Nga Bay, with Action Holidays Phuket (☎076 263575, ⚅bike toursthailand.com; full day with transfers from B2600).

Elephant trekking Award-winning, conservation-conscious Siam Safari (☎076 280116, ⚅siamsafari .com) runs Four-in-One tours featuring their hillside elephant camp plus rubber tapping, making coconut milk, buffalo-cart riding and sailing on a Burmese junk (B2550); tours to Khao Sok National Park are also on offer.

Kiteboarding One- (B4000) and three-day courses (B11,000) at Hat Nai Yang and Ao Chalong (depending on the season) are offered by Kiteboarding Asia (☎081 591 4594, ⚅kiteboardingasia.com).

Mini-golf If you just need a little time off from the beach or to entertain kids, head for the eighteen-hole Dino Park mini-golf (daily 10am–midnight; B240; ⚅dinopark.com), next to *Marina Phuket Resort* on the headland between Ao Karon and Ao Kata, which is part of a pseudo-prehistoric theme park comprising a dinosaur restaurant and an erupting "volcano" (evenings only).

Sea-canoeing There are dozens of companies offering canoeing and kayaking in Phuket, but the two with the best reputations are John Gray's Sea Canoe (☎076 254505–7, ⚅johngray-seacanoe.com), who offer "Starlight" afternoon and evening trips around the

spectacular limestone karsts of Ao Phang Nga (B3950 includes transfers), as well as multi-day and self-paddle trips; and Paddle Asia (☎076 241519, ⚅paddleasia .com), who run day-trips to Ao Phang Nga (B4300 includes transfers) and multi-day trips, which can include Khao Sok National Park and other adventure activities.

Surfing The rainy season (roughly May–Oct) is the best time for surfing off Phuket's west coast; courses (B1500 for a 90min private lesson, discount on their website) and board rental are available from Phuket Surf on Ao Kata Yai (☎087 889 7308, ⚅phuketsurf .com).

Thai cookery courses Most famously, every Sat and Sun morning at *The Boathouse* hotel on Ao Kata Yai (B2200; ☎076 330015, ⚅boathousephuket.com); but also at the *Holiday Inn Phuket*, 86/11 Thanon Thavee Wong, Patong (Wed, Sat & Sun 10am; B2575; ☎076 340608, ⚅phuket.holiday-inn.com); and the *Blue Elephant Restaurant*, 96 Thanon Krabi, Phuket town (B3300 for a half-day class; daily 8.30am & 1.30pm; ☎076 354355, ⚅blueelephant.com).

Thai culture and wildlife tours Plan to Phuket (☎081 691 1955, ⚅plantophuket.com/culture-tour -page.htm) run a number of tours, including full-day "Culture Tours" that include market and temple visits, batik-making and rubber production; and "Jungle Tours" to Ton Sai waterfall and the Gibbon Rehabilitation project (see p.642); or a combination of both.

As with the rest of the Andaman coast, the sea around Phuket is at its least inviting during the **monsoon**, from June to October, when the west-coast beaches in particular become quite rough and windswept. At any time of year, beware the strong **undertow** and heed any red warning flags; there are dozens of fatalities in the water each year, but there is currently no official lifeguard service on the island. Some stretches of Phuket's coast were very badly damaged by the December 2004 **tsunami** (see box, p.610), which caused significant loss of life and destroyed a lot of property. Reconstruction was swift, however, and a first-time visitor to the island is now unlikely to notice any major post-tsunami effect.

ARRIVAL AND DEPARTURE
PHUKET

BY PLANE

Phuket International Airport (☎076 327230–79) is near the northern tip of the island, between Hat Mai Khao and Hat Nai Yang, 32km northwest of Phuket town. It has ATMs, currency exchange, a post office, a Bangkok Hospital clinic, hotel booking and travel agency counters plus a left-luggage service (daily 6am–10pm; B80 per item per day). There are scores of international flights into Phuket, including several direct services from Australia. Between them, Thai Airways, Air Asia, Bangkok Airways, Orient Thai, Thai Lion Air and Nok Air run around thirty domestic flights a day between Bangkok and Phuket, while Bangkok Airways and Air Asia fly from Chiang Mai, Air Asia flies from Udon Thani and Bangkok Airways connects Phuket with Pattaya and Ko Samui.

Onward transport The orange airport bus (☎076 232371, ⓦairportbusphuket.com; B90; 1hr 20min) runs every 90min to/from the bus station in Phuket town, via Thalang, with an inconvenient 2hr 30min wait after the 4pm bus from the airport and after the 8am bus from the bus station; as it doesn't serve the beaches, you'll need to change on to the songthaews in town to reach those. Travel agents in and outside the arrivals hall run a/c minibuses that seat ten, but is it up to passengers to rustle up other people if they wish to share the costs to Phuket town (B1100), Rassada Harbour pier (B1400), Patong (B1400) and Kata (B1600). Outside the arrivals hall at the south end of the building, you'll find booths for set-rate taxis to Phuket town (B450), Patong (B650) and Kata (B750), which includes a B100 airport charge. On departure from the beaches, most people use taxis organized by their hotel – about B500 for the hour's ride from Patong or Karon. If you're landing at the airport and want to catch a bus north, you can save going into Phuket town by getting a taxi or the airport bus to Ban Muang Mai, about 6km southeast of the airport on Highway 402, where you can pick up your northbound bus.

Destinations: Bangkok (30 daily; 1hr 20min); Chiang Mai (3 daily; 2hr); Ko Samui (2–5 daily; 50min); Pattaya/U-Tapao (daily; 1hr 35min); Udon Thani (1 daily; 2hr).

BY BUS AND MINIBUS

A pink songthaew from bay 12 of Bus Station 2 shuttles to/from Bus Station 1 (B10; every 30min until 7pm; 30min).

Bus Station 1 The "old" Baw Khaw Saw bus station, Bus Station 1, is off the eastern end of Thanon Phang Nga in Phuket town. It's a 10min walk or a short tuk-tuk ride to the town's central hotel area. On the west side of the bus station, licensed private companies offer a/c minibuses to Krabi, Ko Lanta, Surat Thani, Nakhon Si Thammarat, Trang and Hat Yai. Songthaews to the beaches depart from here and continue to the market area, so are another option for getting to the Old Town.

Destinations: Khao Lak (20 daily; 2hr 30min); Khao Sok (4 daily; 3–4hr); Takua Pa (20 daily; 2hr 30min–3hr); Phang Nga (at least hourly; 2hr 30min).

Bus Station 2 The "new" Phuket Bus Station 2, 4km north of Phuket town, is now the main station for long-distance destinations, and also has minibuses. Most a/c buses from Bangkok's Southern Bus Terminal to Phuket make the journey overnight, departing from mid-afternoon onwards. There's no train service to Phuket, but you could book an overnight sleeper train to Surat Thani, about 290km east of Phuket, and take one of the regular buses from there to Phuket Bus Station 2 (about 5hr).

Destinations: Bangkok (21 daily; 12hr); Chumphon (4 daily; 5hr); Hat Yai (43 daily; 6hr); Khuraburi (hourly; 3hr); Ko Samui (daily; 6hr); Krabi (at least hourly; 4hr); Nakhon Si Thammarat (17 daily; 6hr); Ranong (3 daily; 4hr); Satun (8 daily; 6hr); Surat Thani (17 daily; 4hr); Trang (17 daily; 5hr30min).

BY BOAT

If you're coming to/from Phuket from Ko Lanta or Ao Nang in Krabi province, the quickest and most scenic option is to take the boat. Most hotels can arrange trips that include minivan transfers to the harbour. Infrequent songthaews run between Phuket town's Thanon Ranong market and the pier at Bang Rong, via the Heroines' Monument (about 1hr; B50). A taxi to Bang Rong from town or the main beaches costs about B500, from Phuket airport B450, or about B260 if you can cajole the driver into turning his meter on; the taxi service at Bang Rong pier charges B500 to the airport, B800 to Patong.

To/from Ko Phi Phi During peak season, up to three ferries a day, plus a speedboat or two, make the trip to and from Ko Phi Phi, docking at Rassada Harbour on Phuket's

7

east coast; during low season, there's at least one ferry a day in both directions.

To/from Ko Yao Noi Boats from Ko Yao Noi and the high-season speedboat service from Ao Nang via Ko Yao Noi terminate at Bang Rong on Phuket's northeast coast.

To/from Ko Lanta Travellers from Sala Dan on Ko Lanta (Nov–May only) may have to change boats at Ao Nang or Ko Phi Phi to get to Phuket's Rassada Harbour.

To/from Ao Nang Ferries go to Rassada Harbour; the speedboat service from Ao Nang via Ko Yao Noi terminates at Bang Rong.

Onward transport from Rassada Harbour Shared a/c minibuses meet the ferries at Rassada Harbour and charge

B50 per person for transfers to Phuket town hotels, B150 to Patong and B200 to the airport; taxis charge B500–600 per car to the major west-coast beaches or the airport (leave plenty of extra time if you have a flight to catch as boats are notoriously tardy).

Onward transport from Bang Rong Infrequent songthaews shuttle between Bang Rong and Phuket town (about 1hr; B40), while taxis charge B500–800 to the airport or the west-coast beaches.

Destinations: Ao Nang (Nov–May 2 daily; 2hr); Ko Lanta Yai (Nov–May 2 daily; 4hr 30min); Ko Phi Phi Don (1–3 daily; 2hr); Ko Yao Noi (roughly hourly; 40min–1hr 10min).

GETTING AROUND

Getting around the island is a nightmare: on the one hand, tuk-tuks and taxis know that they have a captive audience and charge through the nose; on the other, Phuket has probably the worst, most dangerous drivers in Thailand, driving on roads that are often steep and winding, with quite a few hairpin bends – which all discourages renting a vehicle. If you do decide to drive yourself, stay alert and be defensive. There is a system of public songthaews (supplemented by buses) radiating out from Phuket town, but to get from one beach to another by this method you nearly always have to go back into town. For transport within resorts, the cheapest option is to make use of the public songthaews where possible, or to hail a motorbike taxi where available (B30–100).

By songthaew Songthaews run regularly throughout the day (when they have a full complement of passengers) from Thanon Ranong at the market in the centre of Phuket town to the coast and beaches and cost B25–45.

By tuk-tuk or taxi Tuk-tuks and taxis do travel directly between major beaches, but are notoriously overpriced (there are almost no metered taxis on the island), charging at least B100 from Kata to Karon or B250 between Patong and Karon and often doubling their prices after dark – they have been known to ask for B1000 to go from Patong to Karon at night. Phuket TAT (see p.624) issues a list of price guidelines but you'll have to bargain hard to get near the quoted prices.

Motorbike rental Many tourists rent their own motorbike or moped, which are widely available (from B250/day), but be warned that there is a very sobering average of ten thousand motorbike injuries a year on Phuket, and about a hundred fatalities; it makes sense to obey the compulsory helmet law, which is anyway strictly enforced in most areas of Phuket, with flouters subject to a B500 fine.

Car rental At the airport, there are offices of Avis (☎076 351244, ⓦavisthailand.com) and Budget (☎076 327744, ⓦbudget.co.th), who also have a branch on Patong (see p.629); both charge from around B1200/day.

INFORMATION

On the web There's a wide-ranging website about Phuket, ⓦphuket.com, which is particularly good for discounted accommodation.

Guidebooks For a detailed historical and cultural guide to the island, it's hard to better Oliver Hargreave's impressive

Exploring Phuket & Phi Phi (Within Books).

Tourist office Phuket's TAT office is in Phuket Town (see p.624), and has a small number of displays with photos on the history of Phuket Town but little else.

DIRECTORY

Dentists At Phuket International Hospital and Bangkok Hospital Phuket (see below).

Hospitals Phuket International Hospital (☎076 249400, emergencies ☎076 210935, ⓦphuketinternationalhospital .com), north of Central Festival shopping centre on Highway 402, just west of Phuket town, is considered to have Phuket's best facilities, including an emergency department and an ambulance service. Reputable alternatives include Bangkok Hospital Phuket, on the northwestern edge of Phuket town just off Thanon Yaowarat at 2/1 Thanon

Hongyok Uthis (☎076 254425, ⓦphukethospital.com), and the Mission Hospital (aka Phuket Adventist Hospital), on the northern outskirts at 4/1 Thanon Thepkasatri (☎076 237220–6, emergencies ☎076 237227, ⓦmissionhospital phuket.com).

Immigration office At the southern end of Thanon Phuket, in the suburb of Saphan Hin, Phuket town (☎076 221905, ⓦphuketimmigration.go.th; Mon–Fri 8.30am-noon & 1–4.30pm), plus an information centre in Patong (see p.629).

Tourist police For all emergencies, contact the tourist police, either on the free, 24hr phone line (☎1155), at their main office at 327 Thanon Yaowarat in Phuket town (☎076 223891, ⍵phukettouristpolice.go.th), or at their branch in Patong (see p.629).

Phuket town

Though it has plenty of hotels and restaurants, **PHUKET TOWN** (Muang Phuket) stands distinct from the tailor-made tourist settlements along the beaches as a place of tangible history and culture. Most visitors hang about just long enough to jump on a beach-bound songthaew, but you may find yourself returning for a welcome dose of real life; there's plenty to engage you in a stroll through the small but atmospherically restored heart of the Old Town, along with many idiosyncratic cafés and art shops, several notable restaurants and some good handicraft shops. The town works well as an overnight transit point between the islands and the bus stations or airport, but is also worth considering as a base for exploring the island, with more interesting and

7

PHUKET TOWN

ACCOMMODATION
Baan Suwantawe	3
Chinotel	7
Crystal Inn Hotel	8
The Memory at On On	6
Rommanee Classic	4
Sino House	2
Sunny Hostel	1
Thalang 37 Guest House	5

BARS
| Sanaeha | 1 |
| Soi Romanee | 2/3 |

RESTAURANTS & CAFÉS
Bo(ok)hemian Arthouse	1
China Inn Café	3
Ka Jok See	6
Kopitiam	2
Natural Restaurant (Thammachat)	5
On On Café	4

affordable accommodation, eating and drinking options than the beaches, but linked to them by regular songthaews.

The Old Town

Between Thanon Dibuk and Thanon Rat Sada ⓦ lestariheritage.net/phuket

Phuket town's most interesting features are clustered together in the **Old Town** conservation zone, a grid of streets between Thanon Dibuk and Thanon Rat Sada whose colonial-style **Sino-Portuguese shophouses** (see below) date back to the nineteenth century, the former homes of emigrant Chinese merchants from Penang, Singapore and Melaka. Modern-day residents have put a lot of effort into restoring these handsome old neighbourhoods and there's an engagingly bohemian style to a number of the businesses here. The Phuket Old Town Foundation helps to publish the excellent free **Phuket Town Treasure Map**, available all over the Old Town, and also stages the **Old Town Festival** just before Chinese New Year (sometime between Jan & March).

Some of the Old Town's most elegant buildings line the western arm of **Thanon Thalang**, where a dozen signboards – including at *Thalang Guest House* at no. 37 (see p.624) and outside the *China Inn Café* at no. 20 (see p.625) – highlight the special features worth an upward or sideways glance: pastel-coloured doors and shutters, elaborate stucco mouldings, ornate wooden doors, and the distinctively arched "five-foot walkways" that link them. Further east along Thanon Thalang there's more of an Islamic emphasis, with many old-style shops selling fabric and dressmaking accessories, including lots of good-value sarongs from Malaysia and Indonesia. The road's former red-light alley, **Soi Romanee**, has also been given a major multicoloured face-lift and these days buzzes come sundown with arty little bars and red lanterns, while on nearby **Thanon Dibuk** the doors and window shutters of *Dibuk Restaurant* at no. 69 display intricate wooden and gold-leaf fretwork. You'll find other renovated

---

PHUKET TOWN SINO-PORTUGUESE ARCHITECTURE

As Chinese immigrant merchants got rich on tin-mining profits they started building homes. Though the very richest commissioned enormous mansions, a number of which survive in Phuket town today, the vast majority bought themselves eminently practical terraced **shophouses** at the heart of the merchant district. Phuket's Old Town retains south Thailand's finest examples, some of which are open to the public, but there are also intact, if less well-conserved, shophouse neighbourhoods in many other southern cities, including Ranong and Takua Pa.

Shophouse design followed a standard prototype favoured by the mixed-race Chinese–Malay ("Baba", or "Straits Chinese") immigrants from Melaka and other parts of the Malay Peninsula. It's a style now widely dubbed **Sino-Portuguese** because Melakan architecture of the time was itself strongly influenced by the territory's Portuguese former colonists, though it also incorporates traits from Dutch and Anglo-Indian colonial architecture. Although some features have evolved with changing fashions the basic look is still recognizably mid-nineteenth century.

Because streetside space was at a premium, shophouses were always long and thin, with narrow frontages, recessed entrances and connecting porches that linked up all the way down the block to make shady, arched colonnades known as **five-foot walkways**, ideal for pedestrians and shoppers. The front room was (and often still is) the business premises, leaving the rest of the two- or three-storey building for living. A light well behind the front room encouraged natural ventilation and sometimes fed a small courtyard garden at its base, and the household shrine would always occupy a prominent and auspicious position. Outside, the hallmark features that make the neighbourhoods so striking today include pastel-painted **louvred windows** that might be arched or rectangular and perhaps topped by a pretty glass fantail, lacquered and inlaid wooden doors, fancy gold-leaf fretwork, detailed **stucco mouldings** and perhaps Neoclassical pilasters.

NGAN KIN JEH: THE VEGETARIAN FESTIVAL

For nine days, usually in October or November, at the start of the ninth lunar month (see
ⓦ phuketvegetarian.com for exact dates), the celebrations for **Ngan Kin Jeh** – the Vegetarian
Festival – set the streets of Phuket town buzzing with processions, theatre shows and food
stalls, culminating in the unnerving spectacle of men and women parading about with steel
rods through their cheeks and tongues. The festival marks the beginning of **Taoist Lent**, a
month-long period of purification observed by devout Chinese all over the world, but
celebrated most ostentatiously in Phuket, by devotees of the island's five Chinese temples.
After six days' abstention from meat (hence the festival's name), alcohol and sex, the white-clad
worshippers flock to their local temple, where drum rhythms help induce a trance state in
which they become possessed by spirits. As proof of their new-found transcendence of the
physical world they skewer themselves with any available sharp instrument – fishing rods and
car wing-mirrors have done service in the past – before walking over red-hot coals or up
ladders of swords as further testament to their otherworldliness. In the meantime there's
singing and dancing and almost continuous firework displays, with the grandest festivities
held at Wat Jui Tui on Thanon Ranong in Phuket town.

The ceremony dates back to the mid-nineteenth century, when a travelling Chinese opera
company turned up on the island to entertain emigrant Chinese working in the tin mines.
They had been there almost a year when suddenly the whole troupe – together with a
number of the miners – came down with a life-endangering fever. Realizing that they'd
neglected their gods, the actors performed elaborate rites and kept to a vegetarian diet, and
most were soon cured. The festival has been held ever since, though the self-mortification rites
are a later modification, possibly of Hindu origin.

Sino-Portuguese buildings on **Thanon Yaowarat**, and on **Thanon Ranong** (where the
Thai Airways office occupies a fine old mansion), **Thanon Phang Nga** (especially the
On On Hotel) and **Thanon Damrong**, whose town hall, just east of the Provincial Court,
stood in for Phnom Penh's US embassy in the film *The Killing Fields*.

Phuket Thaihua Museum

28 Thanon Krabi • Daily 9am–5pm • B200 • ⓦ phuket.com/attractions/phuket-thai-hua-museum.htm

The **Phuket Thaihua Museum** is housed in a 1930s Neoclassical former school –
complete with grand columns, stucco decoration, shuttered windows and central light
well. Some of the old school desks are still *in situ*, but the focus of the museum's
excellent displays, videos and historic photos is on the role and traditions of Phuket's
main immigrant groups, namely the Chinese and mixed-race Baba (Malay–Chinese)
communities who arrived to work in the island's burgeoning tin-mining industry.

San Jao Saeng Tham (Shrine of Serene Light)

Accessed via a soi through the narrow archway next to South Wind Books on Thanon Phang Nga • Daily 8.30am–noon & 1.30–5.30pm

The spiritual heritage of Phuket's Chinese immigrants is kept very much alive by
their descendants, notably in the extraordinary spectacle of the annual Vegetarian
Festival (see box above). They also maintain many shrines around town, including
San Jao Saeng Tham, the tiny **Shrine of Serene Light**, whose roof is decorated with
intensely coloured ceramic figurines of dragons, carp and sages in bright blues, greens
and reds.

Phuket Butterfly Garden and Insect World

2km beyond the northern end of Thanon Yaowarat at 71/6 Soi Paneang in Ban Sam Kong • Daily 9am–5pm • B300 • ☏ 076 210861,
ⓦ phuketbutterfly.com • A tuk-tuk from the town centre should cost around B150 return

Kids usually enjoy the **Phuket Butterfly Garden and Insect World**, whose thousands of
butterflies of some twenty indigenous species flit around the prettily landscaped
grounds; there's also a silk museum documenting the amazingly industrious short life
of the silkworm, plus scorpions, tarantulas and other notorious creepy-crawlies.

ARRIVAL AND INFORMATION

By songthaew Songthaews (supplemented by buses) run regularly throughout the day from the market on Thanon Ranong in the town centre to all the main beaches and cost B25–45. Return songthaews can finish as early as 4pm so check before you go.

Tourist information The TAT office is at 63 Thanon Thalang (daily 8.30am–4.30pm; ☎076 212213, @ tatphket@tat.or.th), and has a small number of displays with photos on the history of Phuket Town and unique souvenirs but little else.

Travel agent The travel desk in the lobby of *The Memory at On On Hotel* on Thanon Phang Nga (☎076 216161), is a helpful agent, good for all kinds of transport bookings, including cheap boat tickets, as well as activities and day-trips.

ACCOMMODATION

★**Baan Suwantawe** 1/10 Thanon Dibuk ☎076 212879, @ baansuwantawe.com. Offering four-star rooms at two-star prices, this apartment-style hotel is designed with long-stay residents in mind but is also exceptionally comfortable for tourists. The huge, pleasantly decorated a/c rooms all have a balcony overlooking the small swimming pool and come with TV, fridge and kettle. There's no restaurant but the front desk is helpful and the location very handy for the Old Town. B1820

Chinotel 133–135 Thanon Ranong ☎076 214455, @ chinotelphuket.com. Outside is the sometimes noisy fresh food market but inside it's calm in this business hotel with Chinese flourishes in the decor. All of the en-suite rooms come with a/c and flatscreen TVs; pay a little more to get away from the traffic noise. The entrance is on a side street opposite the night market and songthaews to the beaches. B950

Crystal Inn Hotel 2/1–10 Soi Surin, Thanon Montri ☎076 256789, @ phuketcrystalinn.com. Surprisingly stylish and contemporary cream- and dark-wood decor makes this small, 54-room downtown hotel an inviting and good-value option. All rooms have a/c and there's internet downstairs. Breakfast included. B950

The Memory at On On Hotel 19 Thanon Phang Nga ☎076 216161, @ thememoryhotel.com. This stunningly renovated, colonial-style 1920s building is a long-running travellers' favourite, mainly because the plentiful four- and six-bed dorms make an inexpensive way to experience the town's old-world charm without feeling budget. They have clean shared bathrooms and a/c, plus there's a tour agent on site. Dorms B400, doubles B1700

Rommanee Classic 4–6 Thanon Krabi ☎089 7289871, @ therommanee.com. Artistic flourishes abound in the seven rooms, which feel more luxurious than their great-value price tag. Rustic mirrors, designer furniture, high ceilings and plush bedding make a comfortable stay in the renovated 80-year-old building that matches the dressed-up Old Town just outside. All come with en suite, a/c and simple breakfast. Choose inner rooms to avoid street noise. B1000

Sino House 1 Thanon Montri ☎076 232494–5, @ sino housephuket.com. Beautifully styled with Chinoiserie artefacts and elegant flourishes, the apartment-style rooms in this striking Art Deco building are huge and light and all come with a/c, fridge, DVD player, coffee-making facilities and Continental breakfast. There's a restaurant and the Raintree Spa on site, plus some tour services, but no pool. B2300

Sunny Hostel Dibuk ☎076 355031. Well located in the Old Town with beautiful, if rumbling, dark-wood floorboards and spacious bathrooms with tasteful antique features and comfortable showers. The charming shutters in the compact rooms don't block out much street noise so light sleepers should opt for the inner rooms. Tours can be arranged and all rooms have carry-on sized lockers, using your own lock. Fan dorm B200, a/c dorm B300, a/c double B780

Thalang 37 Guest House 37 Thanon Thalang ☎076 214225, @ thalangguesthouse.com. Housed in a 1940s, Sino-Portuguese, wood-floored shophouse in one of the Old Town's most attractive streets, this place is fairly simple but full of character, traveller-friendly and good value. The twelve fan and a/c rooms are large and en suite – the best of them are up on the rooftop, affording unusual panoramic views. It's very popular, so it's best to book ahead; rates include a simple breakfast. Fan B400, a/c B500

EATING AND DRINKING

Phuket town has the largest concentration of good Thai food on the island, well worth making the trip here for. Unlike Thais in most other parts of the country, Phuketians like to breakfast on noodles rather than rice; spindly white *khanom jiin* noodles, made with rice-flour and ladled over with one of several different fiery, soupy curry sauces, are a local speciality and served at some of the restaurants listed below. You can try snacks such as fresh hot tofu and sticky rice at the night market, which starts by the beach songthaews on Thanon Ranong. Over half a dozen simple Thai vegetarian restaurants display tasty look-and-pick mock-meat curries and cold veg dishes with rice for B30–60 on Thanon Ranong and Soi Puthorn, west of Wat Jui Tui. They are open from the early morning till nearly midnight.

Bo(ok)hemian Arthouse 61 Thanon Thalang. Artsy little bookstore and hangout for cappuccinos (B60), free wi-fi, DVD rental and occasional film screenings. Mon–Fri 9am–7pm, Sat & Sun 9am–8.30pm.

China Inn Café 20 Thanon Thalang ☎ 076 356239. This beautifully renovated heritage house and courtyard garden would be reason enough to stop by for a meal, but the menu is also enticing, proffering Thai dishes such as *phat thai* (B210) and spicy salads like the inspired pomelo, coconut and prawn (B290), as well as a few Western, mostly Italian, dishes. Streetside, the gallery shop displays Asian antiques, textiles and lacquerware. Nov–April Mon–Wed 11am–6pm, Thurs–Sat 11am–10pm; May–Oct Mon–Sat 11am–6pm.

Ka Jok See 26 Thanon Takuapa ☎ 076 217903. A Phuket institution, housed in a charmingly restored traditional shophouse (unsigned), this place serves fabulous Thai food on a pricey set menu (B1500) and fosters a fun, sociable atmosphere. Mains are sophisticated and beautifully presented – their *goong sarong*, individual shrimps bound in a crisp-noodle wrap, is famous island-wide. Reservations are essential. Tues–Sun 7.30–10.30pm.

Kopitiam 14 & 18 Thanon Thalang ☎ 83 6069776. Eating at the dark-wood tables while surrounded by vintage Chinese scrolls and typewriters can transport you into the rustic world of old Phuket Town. The extensive Thai menu includes Phuket-style grilled pork with Chinese

herbs (B100); be sure to try the delicious passionfruit juice (B50). Mon–Sat 11am–10pm.

★**Natural Restaurant (Thammachat)** 62/5 Soi Putorn ☎ 076 214037. There are plenty of reasons to linger over a casual dinner at this rambling, hugely popular restaurant, not least the two hundred different choices on the menu, and the affordable prices (main dishes around B150). Highlights include fried sea bass with chilli paste, fried chicken with Muslim herbs, soft-shelled crab with garlic and pepper, and spicy Phuket bean salad. Daily 10.30am–11.30pm.

On On Café Thanon Phang Nga. Sociable spot for cheap, mostly Thai–Chinese meals, as well as breakfasts, including fry-ups (B200 for an "American" set breakfast) and espresso coffee. Mon–Sat 7am–7pm, Sun 7am–noon.

Sanaeha Thanon Yaowarat. Lively, hip bar in an old mansion, all done out in blue and white with chandeliers and mirror balls, with live bands playing jazz and other stuff on the central stage from 9pm. Daily 6/7pm–midnight.

Soi Romanee This artfully restored, plant-strewn soi connecting Dibuk and Thalang roads shows off its handsome pastel paintwork and stuccoed Old Town facades with half a dozen little café-bars whose seating spills out on to the pavement for ultimate architectural appreciation. Most places serve classic Thai dishes and beers and get going 6–10pm, staying open slightly later Nov–April.

ENTERTAINMENT

Siam Niramit Phuket North of town off Thanon Chalerm Prakiat ☎ 076 335000, ⌨ siamniramit.com. An offshoot of the Siam Niramit Bangkok extravaganza, this 70min show presents a tourist-oriented rendering of

traditional Thai theatre, in a high-tech spectacular of fantastic costumes and huge chorus numbers, enlivened by acrobatics and flashy special effects. Tickets from B1300. Mon & Wed–Sun 8.30pm.

SHOPPING

The two most fruitful shopping roads for handicrafts and antiques are Thanon Yaowarat and Thanon Rat Sada, while the shops on eastern Thanon Thalang keep a phenomenal range of well-priced sarongs, mostly of Burmese, Malaysian and Indonesian designs. *Art and Culture South*, a useful, free, quarterly booklet that's available at TAT and other outlets, details shops and galleries in the town and around. For retro enamelware and gifts, visit the shop attached to the *Rommanee Classic* hotel.

The Books Thanon Phuket. Decent selection of new English-language books and magazines, with a coffee corner and internet access. Daily 10am–9pm.

South Wind Books Thanon Phang Nga. Big, sprawling range of secondhand books. Mon–Sat 9am–5pm, Sun 10am–3pm.

Hat Mai Khao

Phuket's longest and quietest beach, the 17km **HAT MAI KHAO**, unfurls along the island's upper northwest coast, beginning some 3km south of the Sarasin Bridge causeway and ending just north of the airport (34km from Phuket town). It's a beautiful piece of casuarina- and palm-shaded coastline, minimally developed and protected in part as **Sirinath National Park** because of the few giant marine turtles that lay their eggs here between October and February.

7

It's possible to get here on foot via the adjacent beaches; otherwise, the beach is reachable with your own transport or a taxi, which is the most practical way.

ACCOMMODATION

Accommodation on Hat Mai Khao is predominantly five-star: an enclave of half a dozen luxury hotels is elegantly spaced behind the sloping shoreline towards the north end of the beach, accessed by an all-but-private road that is not served by any public transport. Most of the resorts have a swimming pool as the undertow here can be fierce and unpredictable.

★**Anantara Phuket Villas** ☎076 336100–9, ⓦphuket.anantara.com. Set amid stylishly landscaped grounds and lagoons, all the secluded villas here have their own plunge pool, outdoor bath and garden *sala*, while the luxurious interiors feature antique furniture, lots of dark wood, dressing rooms and espresso machines. There's an impressive selection of free activities, including sailing and yoga, a kids' club, a beautiful spa and excellent seafood at the stylish restaurant, *Sea Fire Salt*. Rates are sometimes reduced by more than half in low season. B18,000

Mai Khao Beach Bungalows Next door to the Holiday Inn ☎081 895 1233, ⓦmaikhaobeach.wordpress.com. Six simple en-suite bungalows sit in spacious, grassy grounds just behind the shore beneath coconut palms hung with hammocks. There's a restaurant and motorbike rental here too, but not much else. Easiest access to *Mai Khao Beach Bungalows* is by bus to or from Phuket town: ask to be dropped at Thachatchai police box, 4km away on Highway 402, from where you can phone the bungalows for a pick-up. Closed Aug, sometimes longer, during the rainy season; you have to pay more for hot water. Fan B1000, a/c B1500

Sala Phuket ☎076 338888, ⓦsalaresorts.com. The sharp, Sino-modern architecture of the villa compounds here – all done out in cool creams and silver, with colour-coordinated planting and the occasional lacquered screen – attract mainly couples, especially honeymooners, who enjoy the style and privacy, especially of the pool villas. There's an enticing open-air seafront lounging area here too, with deliciously squishy sofas, plus a rooftop terrace, a spa and three swimming pools. Breakfast included. B11,880

Hat Nai Yang

The long curved sweep of **HAT NAI YANG**, 5km south of Hat Mai Khao and 30km north of Phuket town, is partly under the protection of Sirinath National Park and has only fairly low-key development. In the plentiful shade cast by the feathery casuarinas and cajeput trees that run most of the length of the bay stand more than a dozen small seafood restaurants, and a small, low-rise tourist village of travel agents, a few accommodation options, ATMs, a massage pavilion, internet and dive shops. The beach is clean and good for swimming at the southern end, and there's a reasonable, shallow **reef** about 1km offshore (10min by longtail boat) from the Sirinath National Park headquarters, which is a fifteen-minute walk north of the tourist village (if you're driving yourself to Hat Nai Yang, when the main access road hits the beach, turn left for the tourist village, right for the national park).

By taxi Hat Nai Yang is just 2km south of the airport, about B150 by taxi.

By songthaew An infrequent songthaew service (B40; 1hr 45min) runs between Phuket town and Hat Nai Yang.

ACCOMMODATION AND EATING

The tourist village in Nai Yang is locally famous for its small shorefront restaurants that serve mostly barbecued seafood (and the odd wood-fired pizza), on mats under the trees and at tables on the sand, which are candlelit and exceptionally tranquil at night.

The Beach Club One of several little beach bars in the tourist village, a cool, relaxed place for a drink in its low-slung track-side chairs or on one of its day beds with triangular cushions on the beach. Happy hour 3–5pm & 10–11pm. Daily noon–1am.

Black Ginger Indigo Pearl ☎076 327006. For a really top-notch romantic dinner, you can't top the intimate, black-painted *sala* here. Highlights from the very classy menu (from B300) include the Phuket lobster with red coconut curry, fresh Vietnamese-style rice-flour pancakes stuffed with shrimps, coriander and herbs, and local *kaeng leuang*, yellow curry with fish fillet (B750). Reservations advisable. Daily 6.30–11pm.

Indigo Pearl ☎076 327006, ⓦindigo-pearl.com. Luxurious rooms and villas look onto attractively landscaped plantation-style gardens that run down to the southern end of the beachfront road; facilities include a meandering lagoon-like saltwater swimming pool, a dive shop, an inventively programmed activities centre, a spa and a kids' club. Interiors are designed to evoke Phuket's

tin-mining history, with metallic colour schemes, polished cement floors and a penchant for industrial art, but the look is softened by very comfortable furniture, generous balconies and plenty of greenery. **B5210**

Nai Yang Beach Resort ☎076 328300, ⓦnaiyang beachresort.com. Good upper-mid-range option at the south end of the beach, its cosy, modern, whitewashed a/c rooms fitted with attractive dark-wood furniture and ranged in two- and three-storey wings around pretty tropical gardens; there are three swimming pools, a dive centre and breakfast is included. **B1870**

Hat Nai Thon

The next bay south down the coast from Hat Nai Yang is the small but perfectly formed 500m-long gold-sand **HAT NAI THON**, with good snorkelling at reefs a brief longtail ride offshore. Shops, hotels and restaurants line the inland side of its narrow little shorefront road, but there's still a low-key, village-like atmosphere here.

ARRIVAL AND ACCOMMODATION   HAT NAI THON

Most visitors rent their own transport as songthaews don't make the detour from the highway and taxis are thin on the ground.

Andaman White Beach Resort ☎076 316300, ⓦandamanwhitebeach.com. About 2km south of Hat Nai Thon over the southern headland, occupying secluded cliffside land that runs down to a gorgeous little private bay of white sand and turquoise water (sometimes known as Hat Nai Thon Noia), this resort offers luxurious rooms and villas with unsurpassed views, including some

designed for families, plus a 40m swimming pool and a spa. **B7200**

Naithonburi Beach Resort ☎076 318700, ⓦnaithonburi.com. Huge resort, with over two hundred posh a/c rooms in a U-shaped complex enclosing an enormous pool, some of them with direct pool access, though it doesn't dominate the bay. **B2800**

Ao Bang Tao

Re-landscaped from a former tin-mining concession to encompass lagoons, parkland and Phuket's best eighteen-hole golf course, **AO BANG TAO** is dominated by the vast, upscale *Laguna Phuket*, a gated "integrated resort" of seven luxury hotels on an impressive 8km shorefront. It's a world away from the thrust and hustle of Patong and a popular choice for families, with no need to leave the *Laguna* village, though beware of the undertow off the coast here, which confines many guests to the hotel pools. There's free transport between the seven hotels, which between them offer a huge range of leisure and sports facilities, as well as a shopping centre.

ARRIVAL AND ACCOMMODATION   AO BANG TAO

Half-hourly **songthaews** (B25; 1hr 15min) cover the 24km from Phuket town to Ao Bang Tao during the day, or there are resort shuttle **buses** and on-site car rental.

Laguna Phuket ☎076 362300, ⓦlagunaphuket.com. The main website sometimes has discounted rates at *Laguna's* seven hotels, while the family-oriented *Best Western Allamanda Laguna* (☎076 362700, ⓦallamanda .com), comprising 150 apartment-style suites with kitchenette and separate living area, has the cheapest

rates in the complex. Haunt of high society and sports stars, the exclusive *Banyan Tree Phuket* (☎076 324374, ⓦbanyantree.com) offers lavish villas in private gardens, many with private pools, and the gloriously indulgent, award-winning, Banyan Tree spa. Best Western **B3400**, Banyan Tree **B22,555**

7

Hat Surin and Ao Pansea

South around Laem Son headland from Ao Bang Tao, handsome little **HAT SURIN** is a favourite weekend getaway for sophisticated Phuketians and a big draw for expats, who inhabit the ever-expanding forest of condo developments inland from the small, pretty beach. The shorefront gets very crowded, however, packed with sunloungers and beach restaurants, so it can be hard to appreciate the setting. Eating and shopping facilities cater to the upmarket clientele, and beachfront dining and drinking is the main pastime. Things are much quieter on Hat Surin's northern bay, **AO PANSEA**, which is divided from the main beach by a rocky promontory.

ARRIVAL AND DEPARTURE   HAT SURIN AND AO PANSEA

By songthaew Songthaews travel the 24km between Phuket town and Hat Surin approximately every half-hour during the day and cost B35.

ACCOMMODATION AND EATING

Benyada Lodge 103 Thanon Hat Surin ☏ 076 271261, ⊛ benyadalodge-phuket.com. Just across the small park from the beach, this thirty-room lodge with high standards of service is well maintained in a crisp, bright contemporary style, with the addition of a rooftop pool and bar-restaurant. The spacious a/c rooms all have hot showers, TV and fridge. Breakfast included. B2800

Surin Bay Inn 106 Thanon Hat Surin ☏ 076 271601, ⊛ surinbayinn.com. Large, attractive rooms above a restaurant and bar near *Benyada Lodge*, with in-room a/c, hot showers, TV and fridge. Breakfast included. B1800

Taste ☏ 076 270090, ⊛ tastesurinbeach.com. This sophisticated seafront restaurant and art gallery is especially known for its great seafood, such as steamed red snapper fillet with a lemon and butter sauce (B420) and wild ginger and green pepper shrimp (B420). Tues–Sun 2pm–midnight.

Twin Brothers ☏ 089 7231874. The eponymous local twins pair a spectacular location under the palm trees on the sand with down-to-earth prices for their Thai seafood dishes (white snapper B100/100g) and Western food. Daily 8am–10pm.

Hat Kamala and Laem Singh

With its cheerfully painted houses and absence of high-rises, the small, village-like tourist development at **HAT KAMALA** is low-key and mid-market, sandwiched between the beach and the predominantly Muslim town of Ban Kamala, about 300m west of the main Patong–Surin road, 6km north of Patong and 26km northwest of Phuket town. Accommodation, shops, restaurants and other tourist services are mostly clustered either side of shoreside Thanon Rim Had (also spelt Rim Hat) which, despite its limited choice, is a much pleasanter place to browse than the big resorts. The beach gets prettier and quieter the further north you go, away from Thanon Rim Had, with restaurant shacks renting sunloungers along most of its course. A stretch of this area is backed by the Muslim cemetery, so it's particularly important to respect local sensibilities and avoid going topless.

Kamala was very badly hit by the 2004 **tsunami**, which killed many residents and wiped out the beachfront school, the temple and countless homes and businesses. Though extensive rebuilding has extinguished most of the physical scars, a copper sculpture in the park opposite *Print Kamala* bears witness to the devastation, and a volunteer English-teaching programme at the school, Phuket Has Been Good to Us (see p.69), aims to continue rebuilding some of the young lives affected.

About 1km northeast of Hat Kamala, a couple of steep paths lead west off the main Patong–Surin road down to **Laem Singh** cape, a pretty little sandy cove whose picturesque combination of turquoise water and smooth granite boulders makes it one of Phuket's finest. It's good for swimming and very secluded, plus there's a decent patch of shade throughout the day.

ARRIVAL AND DEPARTURE   HAT KAMALA AND LAEM SINGH

By songthaew The cheapest way to get to Hat Kamala is by songthaew from Phuket town (about every 30min during the day, 1hr 15min; B40).

ACCOMMODATION

Hat Kamala is popular with long-stay tourists, and several hotels offer rooms with kitchenettes; there's also a preponderance of small-scale places.

Benjamin Resort 83 Thanon Rim Had, opposite the school at the southerly end of the beachfront road ☎076 385146–7, ⓦphuketdir.com/benjaminresort. Set right on the beach and about the best and friendliest deal in Kamala, this block of 37 a/c rooms lacks character but couldn't be closer to the sea. Although views are obstructed from all but the most expensive rooms, the spacious interiors are almost identical and all have a balcony, fridge, TV and hot water, use of sunloungers out front, and breakfast is included. B500

Coconut Garden Soi Police Station ☎081 477 3331, ⓦcoconutgarden.se. The best thing about the dozen good-sized but unexceptional concrete a/c bungalows, two- and three-bedroom houses here is their location on the nicer northerly stretch of the central beach; all have a/c, hot shower, fridge, TV and DVD. B2100

Kamala Dreams 74/1 Thanon Rim Had ☎076 279131, ⓦkamaladreams.net. Epitomizing all the best things about Kamala, this is a really nice, small hotel set right on the shore, in the middle of the tourist village. Its eighteen rooms are large and furnished in contemporary style, and all have a/c, TVs, a kitchenette and a large balcony overlooking the pool and the sea. B2600

Malinee House 75/4 Thanon Rim Had ☎081 691 7879, ⓦmalineehouse.com. Very friendly, traveller-oriented guesthouse in the middle of the tourist village, with the Jackie Lee travel agency downstairs, and large, comfortably furnished and cheerfully painted a/c rooms upstairs, all of them with balconies, hot showers and fridges. B1000

Print Kamala Resort 74/8 Thanon Kamala ☎076 385396–8, ⓦprintkamalaresort.net. The best accommodation here is in a village-like complex of very generously sized bungalows, connected via stilted walkways around a tropical Bali-style garden. The bungalows all have prettily furnished a/c bedrooms plus separate living rooms, and capacious, shaded decks. The hotel also has some less interesting, but more expensive, rooms in a hotel wing, and a large pool. Breakfast included. B3700

EATING, DRINKING AND ENTERTAINMENT

Most people eat and drink on the beach, especially at the restaurant shacks and bars that pretty much line the shore all the way north from opposite *Print Kamala*; seafood is the big seller here, and you can bury your feet in the sand.

Duck Spicy Thanon Kamala near corner with Thanon Rim Had. Spicy really means spicy here, so be careful what you ask for from the extensive, authentic Thai menu. The place itself is not fancy, but it makes a welcome dose of reality to eat dishes such as duck and mint salad (B90) with the locals, away from the resorts. Daily 8am–10pm.

Phuket FantaSea About 1km northeast of Hat Kamala off the main Patong–Surin road ☎076 385111, ⓦphuket-fantasea.com. The enjoyable, hi-tech mega-spectacular, "Fantasy of a Kingdom, Cultural Illusion Show", is staged at the enormous FantaSea entertainments complex, featuring seventy minutes of high-wire trapeze acts, acrobatics, pyrotechnics, illusionists, comedy and traditional dance – plus a depressing baby elephant circus. B1800 or B2200 including the unexciting pre-show dinner. Mon–Wed & Fri–Sun 9pm.

Ao Patong

The busiest and most popular of all Phuket's beaches, **AO PATONG** – 5km south of Ao Kamala and 15km west of Phuket town – is vastly overdeveloped and hard to recommend. A congestion of high-rise hotels, tour agents and souvenir shops disfigures the beachfront road, tireless and tiresome touts are everywhere, and hostess bars and strip joints dominate the nightlife, attracting an increasing number of single Western men to the most active scene between Bangkok and Hat Yai. On the plus side, the broad, 3km-long beach offers good sand and plenty of shade beneath the parasols and there are hundreds of shops and bars plus a surprising number of good restaurants to keep you busy after dark.

ARRIVAL AND GETTING AROUND   AO PATONG

By songthaew Songthaews from Phuket town (approx every 15min, 6am–6pm; 30min; B30) approach Patong from the northeast, driving south along one-way Thanon Raja Uthit Song Roi Phi (Thanon Raja Uthit 200 Phi) then

7

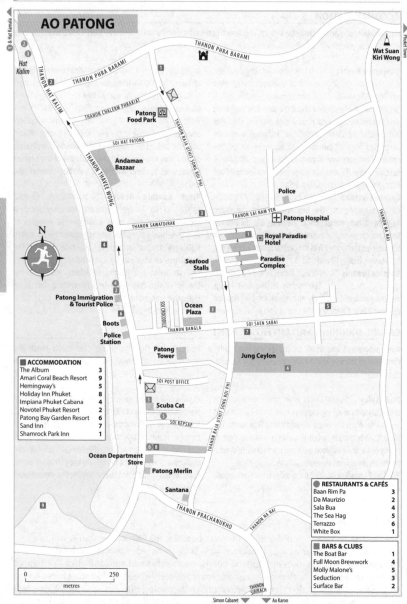

AO PATONG

Hat Kalim

Wat Suan Kiri Wong

Patong Food Park

Andaman Bazaar

Police

Patong Hospital

Royal Paradise Hotel

Seafood Stalls

Paradise Complex

Patong Immigration & Tourist Police

Boots

Police Station

Ocean Plaza

Patong Tower

Jung Ceylon

Scuba Cat

Ocean Department Store

Patong Merlin

Santana

THANON PHRA BARAMI

THANON HAT KALIM

THANON CHALERM PHRAKIAT

SOI HAT PATONG

THANON THAVEE WONG

THANON RAJA UTHIT SONG ROI PHI

THANON SAWATDIRAK

THANON SAI NAM YEN

THANON MA NAI

SOI CROCODILE

THANON BANGLA

SOI SAEN SABAI

SOI POST OFFICE

SOI KEPSAP

THANON RAJA UTHIT SONG ROI PHI

THANON PRACHANUKHO

THANON MA NAI

THANON SIRIRACH

N

■ ACCOMMODATION	
The Album	3
Amari Coral Beach Resort	9
Hemingway's	5
Holiday Inn Phuket	8
Impiana Phuket Cabana	4
Novotel Phuket Resort	2
Patong Bay Garden Resort	6
Sand Inn	7
Shamrock Park Inn	1

● RESTAURANTS & CAFÉS	
Baan Rim Pa	3
Da Maurizio	2
Sala Bua	4
The Sea Hag	5
Terrazzo	6
White Box	1

■ BARS & CLUBS	
The Boat Bar	1
Full Moon Brewwork	4
Molly Malone's	3
Seduction	3
Surface Bar	2

0 _____ 250
metres

Simon Cabaret ▼   ▼ Ao Karon

circling back north along beachfront Thanon Thavee Wong (also one-way) via the *Patong Merlin*, where they wait to pick up passengers for the return trip.

Vehicle rental National car rental (☏076 340608, ⓦnationalcarthailand.com) has a desk inside the *Holiday Inn*, the local Budget agent is at the nearby *Patong Merlin* (☏076 292389, ⓦbudget.co.th); beware of renting jeeps

and motorbikes from transport touts on Thanon Thavee Wong as scams abound.

Tours and activities Most of the tour agents have offices on the southern stretch of Thanon Thavee Wong, offering a number of day-trips and activities (see box, p.618); this is also where you'll find many of the dive operators (see box, pp.636–637).

ACCOMMODATION

It's hard to find much accommodation under B900 in Patong, and there are no backpacker places, but upper-end hotels are reasonable value and all have excellent facilities.

The Album 29 Thanon Sawatdirak ☎076 297023, ⓦthealbumhotel.com. Tiny urban-chic boutique inn, where the 22 carefully designed a/c rooms all have a flat-screen TV, DVD player and a petite balcony. There's a small jacuzzi pool on the fourth-floor roof terrace and rates include Continental breakfast and high tea. Online discounts of up to fifty percent. B4000

Amari Coral Beach Resort 104 Thanon Traitrang ☎076 340106, ⓦamari.com. Occupying its own secluded little beach on a headland at the southernmost end of the bay, this upmarket Thai chain hotel offers contemporary-chic rooms with generous sea-view balconies, plus two swimming pools, romantic spa facilities, tennis courts and several restaurants. The views are exceptional and the location peaceful but convenient; as it's ranged up a slope it's not ideal for guests with mobility problems. B6520

Hemingway's 179/95–8 Soi Saen Sabai ☎076 343264–5, ⓦpatonghemingways.com. Smart, modern, a/c rooms done out in dark wood, black and red, with small, hot-water bathrooms, TVs and fridges. Wicker chairs and old-fashioned ceiling fans downstairs are all that conjure up the ghost of Papa Hemingway, but the big plus-point of this place is the small rooftop pool, jacuzzi and bar with views of the surrounding hills. B1880

★**Holiday Inn Phuket** 86/11 Thanon Thavee Wong ☎076 340608, ⓦphuket.holiday-inn.com. Well-run, innovative, upmarket chain hotel that offers smart, contemporary rooms just across the road from the beach, and fosters an informal, unpretentious atmosphere. The poshest Busakorn villa rooms have their own inter-connected pools and there are several restaurants and an interesting programme of daily activities. The hotel makes a big effort to be family-friendly, with special "kid suites" for children, an all-day kids' club and a teens' club and two children's pools. Also offers wheelchair-accessible rooms. Breakfast included. B6070

Impiana Phuket Cabana 41 Thanon Thavee Wong ☎076 340138, ⓦimpiana.com. Located right on the beach and in the heart of the resort, the very tastefully designed a/c cabanas here are set around a garden and smallish swimming pool; also has a kids' pool and a spa. B8000

Novotel Phuket Resort Thanon Phra Barami/Thanon Hat Kalim ☎076 342777, ⓦnovotelphuket.com. Luxurious and relaxing chain hotel built on the hillside above Kalim Bay, the quieter, northern end of the resort, a 10min walk or a free shuttle ride to Patong's main beach and shops, but very close to some of the best restaurants. Occupying sloping landscaped tropical gardens and offering exceptional high-level sea views, it's especially popular with families as it offers heaps of activities plus a multi-level swimming pool. Large discounts online. B4500

Patong Bay Garden Resort 33/1 Thanon Thavee Wong ☎076 340297–8, ⓦpatongbaygarden.com. Lively 71-room hotel set right on the beach, with the top "studio" rooms having uninterrupted sea views, quite unusual in central Patong. Other rooms look out on the small shorefront pool or have no view at all. Rooms are quite elegantly furnished and all have a/c and TV. Breakfast included. B4100

Sand Inn 171 Soi Saen Sabai ☎076 340275, ⓦsandinn phuket.com. Thirty well-appointed a/c rooms, a little on the compact side, but maintained to a good standard and in the ideal location for nightlife, just east off bar-packed Thanon Bangla. There's TV, hot showers and fridges in all rooms, a *Euro Deli* restaurant downstairs, and use of a small swimming pool just a few metres up the soi. B1900

Shamrock Park Inn Above The Deli supermarket, 31 Thanon Raja Uthit Song Roi Phi ☎076 340991. Friendly, good-value three-storey hotel at the northern end of the resort with large, pleasant, well-maintained and cheerily painted a/c rooms, all with TVs, fridges and safety boxes. Ask for a room on the north side of the building: they're cooler, have balconies and are away from the noise of the adjacent Irish bar. B800

EATING

Much of the food on Patong is dire, but in among the disastrous little cafés advertising everything from Hungarian to Swedish "home cooking" you'll find a few genuinely reputable, long-running, upmarket favourites; reservations are recommended at all the places listed here. For well-priced Thai fast food, there are the regional speciality stalls at the *Food Haven* food centre in Jung Ceylon, the *Patong Food Park* night market that sets up around 5pm towards the northern end of Thanon Raja Uthit Song Roi Phi, and the row of seafood stall-restaurants further south, opposite the *Royal Paradise Hotel* complex.

★**Baan Rim Pa** Across from the Novotel on Thanon Hat Kalim ☎076 340789, ⓦbaanrimpa.com. One of Phuket's most famous fine-dining restaurants, this is an elegant spot that's beautifully set in a teak building on a clifftop overlooking the bay, with tables also on its sea-view terrace. Known for its classic "Royal Thai" cuisine (mains from about B350), including banana blossom salad, creamy duck curry and fried tiger prawns with tamarind sauce, as well as for its wine cellar. Live jazz every night in the *Piano Bar*. Daily noon–midnight.

7

Da Maurizio Across from the Novotel on Thanon Hat Kalim ☎ 076 344079, ⓦ damaurizio.com. Superior Italian restaurant in a stunning location set over the rocks beside the sea. Serves authentic antipasti and home-made pasta such as pappardelle with scallops and crab in a spicy tomato sauce, Phuket lobsters and other great seafood, and a good wine list. Main dishes from B450. Daily noon–midnight.

Sala Bua 41 Thanon Thavee Wong ☎ 076 340138, ⓦ sala-bua.com. Fabulously stylish, breezy, beach-view restaurant attached to the *Impiana Phuket Cabana* hotel. The innovative, pricey, Pacific Rim and Thai menus include Cajun-style red snapper with fermented black bean sauce (B485) and desserts such as sticky-rice sushi rolls with green mango shake (B250). Daily 6am–midnight.

★**The Sea Hag** Soi Dr Wattana (Soi Permpong 3) ☎ 076 341111, ⓦ kenyaphuket.com. The same chef has been cooking great seafood here for two decades and this is where expat hoteliers come for a good Patong feed. Fish

and seafood cooked any number of Thai-style ways for B200–400. Daily noon–4pm & 6pm–midnight.

Terrazzo Holiday Inn Phuket, 86/11 Thanon Thavee Wong ☎ 076 340608, ⓦ phuket.holiday-inn.com. Good, crispy, thin pizzas (B310/495) and tasty pastas including home-made ravioli and gnocchi, in a very pleasant, open-plan garden setting, with a popular oval bar, on the main beachfront drag. Daily 6–11pm.

White Box Thanon Hat Kalim, 1.5km north of the Novotel ☎ 076 346271, ⓦ whitebox.co.th. This chic, sophisticated waterside restaurant and bar, strikingly designed as a modernist cube with panoramic picture windows, is a magnet for visiting celebs and style-conscious expats. The very expensive menu (mains from B420) mixes Thai and Mediterranean flavours – grilled Phuket lobster with mint and ginger, pan-fried salmon with papaya (B550), red curry with roasted duck – and the rooftop sofas are ideal for a pre- or post-dinner drink. Daily 11am–11.30pm.

NIGHTLIFE AND ENTERTAINMENT

After dark, everyone heads to pedestrianized Thanon Bangla for their own taste of Patong's notorious **nightlife** and the road teems with a cross section of Phuket tourists, from elderly couples and young parents with strollers, to glammed-up girlfriends and groups of lads. The big draw for the more innocent onlookers is Thanon Bangla's Soi Crocodile, better known as Soi Katoey, or "Trannie Alley", where pouting, barely clad transsexuals jiggle their implants on podiums at the mouth of the soi and charge for photos with giggling tourists. But the real action happens further down the many bar-filled sois shooting off Thanon Bangla, where open-air bar-beers and neon-lit go-go clubs packed with strippers and goggle-eyed punters pulsate through the night. The pick-up trade pervades most bars in Patong, and though many of these joints are welcoming enough to couples and female tourists, there are a few alternatives, listed below, for anyone not in that kind of mood. The **gay** entertainment district is concentrated around the Paradise Complex, a network of small sois and dozens of bar-beers in front of *Royal Paradise Hotel* on Thanon Raja Uthit Song Roi Phi: see ⓦ gaypatong.com for events listings, including dates for the annual Gay Pride festival, which has recently been held in late April. If you're looking for something else to do with yourself (or your kids) in the evening, check out the katoey (transsexual) Simon Cabaret, or the spectacular show at nearby Phuket FantaSea (see p.629). The Jung Ceylon shopping centre has a seven-screen **cinema**, SF Cinema City.

The Boat Bar Soi 5, Paradise Complex, off Thanon Raja Uthit Song Roi Phi ⓦ boatbar.com. Long-running, very popular gay bar and disco, with two cabaret shows nightly, at around midnight and 1.30am. Daily 9pm–late.

Full Moon Brewwork Port Zone (next to the replica junk), Jung Ceylon shopping centre, Thanon Raja Uthit Song Roi Phi ⓦ fullmoonbrewwork.com. The best of this microbrewery's offerings is their dark ale, a decent bitter that might appease homesick Brits, and there's good food, too, including *tom yam kung* (B145) and bangers and mash. Live music upstairs (Mon, Wed & Fri–Sat 7.30–10pm). Daily 11am–midnight.

Molly Malone's 94/1 Thanon Thavee Wong ⓦ mollymalonesphuket.com. Genial Thai–Irish pub chain next to *McDonald's* that serves draught Guinness and Kilkenny, shows international sports TV, stages live bands playing pub rock from 9.30pm and has pool tables, a small beer garden and no overt hostess presence. Daily 10am–2am.

Seduction Soi Happy, off Thanon Bangla ⓦ seduction

disco.com. A favourite dance venue for partying couples and others not looking for freelance company, this three-storey bar and club has fairly classy lounge areas, hi-tech lighting and Euro dance, and occasionally brings in big-name international DJs. Free until midnight, B300–500 thereafter. Touts outside give useful discount vouchers but avoid the short-lived, diluted-drinks package on the door. Daily 10pm–4am.

Simon Cabaret 8 Thanon Sirirach, south end of Patong ☎ 076 342011–5, ⓦ phuket-simoncabaret.com. Famously flamboyant extravaganza starring a troupe of *katoey* (transsexuals). It's all very Hollywood – a little bit risqué but not at all sleazy – and popular with tour groups and families. B700. Daily 6pm, 7.45pm & 9.30pm.

Surface Bar Top floor, La Flora Resort Patong, 39 Thanon Thavee Wong ☎ 076 344241. The perfect place for a sophisticated sundowner, enjoyed from the comfort of enormous sofas on the hotel's wide rooftop terrace. Expansive ocean views and a sea breeze as well. Daily 5pm–midnight.

DIRECTORY

Immigration The tiny Patong branch (information only) of Phuket's immigration office is next to *Surface Bar* on Thanon Thavee Wong (☎076 340477; Mon–Fri 10am–noon & 1–3pm).

Post office Thanon Thavee Wong (daily 9am–7pm).

Shopping Though you can't move for shops in downtown Patong, by far the best, and least hectic, place to browse is Jung Ceylon on Thanon Raja Uthit Song Roi Phi (daily 11am–10pm; �◉jungceylon.com), an enormous shopping centre, whose refreshingly tasteful and spacious design includes fountains and plaza seating plus countless shops and restaurants. There are branches of Robinsons Department Store and, on the ground floor at the front end, Boots the Chemist and Asia Books (for English-language books, magazines and newspapers), plus the That's Siam Thai handicrafts emporium in the basement.

Tourist police In front of the immigration office on Thanon Thavee Wong (☎076 340244 or ☎1155).

Ao Karon

AO KARON, Phuket's second resort, after Patong, is very much a middle-of-the-road destination. Far less lively, or congested, than Patong, but more commercial and less individual than the smaller beaches, it's the domain of affordable guesthouses and package-tour hotels and appeals chiefly to mid-budget tourists, many of them from Scandinavia. The 2.5km-long **beach** is graced with squeaky soft golden sand and is completely free of developments, though there's very little natural shade; an embankment screens most of the southern half of the beach from the road running alongside, but north of the *Hilton* the road is more often in view and parts of the shore back on to lagoons and wasteland. Karon's main **shopping and eating areas**, with all the usual resort facilities, are grouped around the *Centara Karon Resort* on the northern curve of Thanon Patak; along and around Thanon Luang Pho Chuain, location of the Karon Plaza enclave of accommodation, restaurants and bars; and along Thanon Taina (sometimes referred to as Kata Centre).

The **undertow** off Ao Karon is treacherously strong during the monsoon season from June to October, so you should heed the warning signs and flags and ask for local advice – fatalities are not uncommon. The tiny bay just north of Ao Karon – known as **Karon Noi** or Relax Bay – is almost exclusively patronized by guests of the *Le Meridien* hotel, but non-guests are quite welcome to swim and sunbathe here.

ARRIVAL AND DEPARTURE   AO KARON

By songthaew Ao Karon is 5km south of Patong and 20km southwest of Phuket town. Most songthaews from Phuket town (approx every 20min; 30min; B40) arrive in Karon via Thanon Patak, hitting the beach at the northern end of Ao Karon and then driving south along beachfront Thanon Karon, continuing over the headland as far as *Kata Beach Resort* on Ao Kata Yai. To catch a songthaew back into town, just stand on the other side of the road and flag one down. Transport touts throughout the resort rent motorbikes and jeeps.

ACCOMMODATION

★**Casa Brazil** 9 Soi 1, Thanon Luang Pho Chuain ☎076 396317, ⊚phukethomestay.com. Appealingly arty little hotel, designed in Santa Fe style, with adobe-look walls, earth-toned paintwork, and funky decor and furnishings. The 21 rooms are comfortable, with hot showers, fridges and TVs, and nearly all have a/c. Choose rooms at the back for a rare green and peaceful view of Karon's hilly backdrop, best enjoyed from the French windows and private balconies. Rates include breakfast. Fan **B1200**, a/c **B1400**

Centara Grand Beach Resort 683 Thanon Patak ☎076 201234, ⊚centarahotelsresorts.com. Huge, low-rise, beachfront luxury hotel, which very loosely echoes Phuket's Sino-Portuguese architecture, all in different shades of pink. It's particularly good for children, with two kids' clubs, a kids' pool, a free-form main pool and a "Lazy River", an artificial river that runs under bridges and under tunnels for exploration on inner tubes. There's an adults-only pool too, and grown-ups can also enjoy kayaking, windsurfing, tennis, the spa and a long menu of other activities. Large discounts on their website. **B10,500**

Jum Guesthouse Off Thanon Kata, about 100m from the beach, directly behind and accessible through Andaman Seaview Hotel ☎076 396570. Friendly place in a lush, shady garden with just five large, concrete bungalows, all with fridges, TVs and a few decorative touches; the big, well-equipped bathrooms have hot showers. Fan **B1000**, a/c **B1200**

7

7

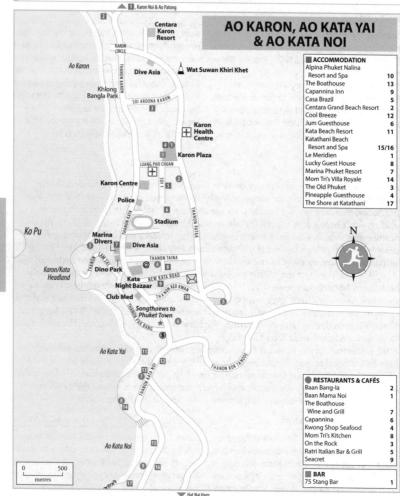

Le Meridien Ao Karon Noi (also known as Relax Bay), north of Ao Karon ☎076 370100, ⓦlemeridien.com. This huge hotel complex has the tiny bay all to itself and boasts an amazing breadth of facilities, including ten restaurants and bars, two lagoon-style swimming pools (with islands), a spa, squash and tennis courts, free non-motorized watersports and private woods. It's a good choice for kids, with reliable babysitting services and a kids' club. Breakfast included. **B8500**

Lucky Guest House 110/44–45 Thanon Taina, Kata Centre ☎076 330572, ⓔluckyguesthousekata@hotmail .com. Good-value place offering unusually large, bright en-suite rooms in a low-rise block (the best have balconies) and some rather plain but very clean semi-detached bungalows on land further back; set back a bit down a small

soi, this guesthouse has a refreshing sense of space that's at a premium on this road packed with shops, bars and restaurants. Fan **B600**, a/c **B900**

Marina Phuket Resort 47 Thanon Karon, far southern end of Ao Karon, on the Karon/Kata headland ☎076 330625, ⓦmarinaphuket.com. Enjoying both a very central location, backing on to the beach, just steps from restaurants and shops, and a luxuriously spacious and secluded tropical garden in a former coconut plantation, this is a good upper-end choice. Garden View cottages are old-fashioned and plain, but Jungle View versions are very appealing – and there's a pool and the prettily located *On the Rock* restaurant. Breakfast included; book through their website for free dinner and airport transfer. **B7290**

accommodation, at its most acute around the Ton Sai–Loh Dalum hub. There's always more building work going on, while thousands of visitors from all corners of the world fight for space in the narrow maze of pedestrianized alleys in Ton Sai village, sometimes generating an unusually aggressive atmosphere for Thailand. The noise pollution from the untrammelled outdoor bars and clubs is an additional turn-off for some – though it is a fun place to party, and there are enough more remote escapes for a peaceful stay too.

All boats dock in **Ao Ton Sai**, from where it's a short walk to the main accommodation centres – in **Ton Sai village**, at **Laem Hin**, the next little stretch of sand to the east, and on **Ao Loh Dalum**, the still attractive, deeply curved bay across the isthmus. **Hat Yao**,

PHI PHI ACTIVITIES

SNORKELLING

There's some great **snorkelling** around Phi Phi's shallow fringing reefs, most rewardingly at strikingly beautiful **Ko Mai Pai (Bamboo Island)**, off Phi Phi Don's northeast coast, where much of the reef lies close to the surface, and at nearby **Ko Yung (Mosquito Island)**, with its spectacular, steep-sided drop. Phi Phi Don has its own worthwhile reefs too, including at west-coast **Ao Yongkasem**, within kayaking distance of Loh Dalum, but **Ao Maya** on Phi Phi Leh is more famous, and a lot more crowded (see p.672).

Outings are easily arranged as part of an **organized tour** (B500–800 including equipment) or by **hiring your own longtail** boatman (B1500/3000 per boat per half/full day), the latter far preferable to the largest tourist boats, whose groups of forty-plus trippers inundate the reefs. **Overnight camping trips** to Ao Maya are a neat way of avoiding the crowds, offering late-afternoon snorkelling, and possibly kayaking, rounded off with a beach barbecue.

DIVING

Offering visibility touching 30m, a great diversity of healthy hard and soft corals, and potential encounters with white-tip sharks, moray eels and stingrays, the diving around Ko Phi Phi is the best in the area and the usual destination of dive boats from Ao Nang and Phuket. Highlights include the gorgonian sea fans, barracudas, manta rays and even whale sharks at **Ko Bidah Nok** and **Ko Bidah Nai**, the mass of leopard sharks at **Hin Bidah**, and the *King Cruiser* **wreck** (see p.637).

There are at least twenty dive shops on Phi Phi, the majority of them in Ton Sai; seven of them have formed the Phi Phi Diving Association (Ⓦphiphidivingassociation.com) to promote eco-friendly, responsible and safe diving practices (see p.52). Note that it's considered risky for a novice diver with fewer than twenty dives to dive at Hin Daeng and Hin Muang (see p.637), due to the depth and the current; reputable dive shops will only take Advanced Divers there. There are also small dive centres on Hat Yao, Ao Loh Bakao and Laem Tong.

Prices for **day-trips** including two tanks, equipment and lunch start at B2500, while the four-day PADI Openwater **course** costs B13,800. Check that your dive operator is insured to use one of the recompression chambers on Phuket (see p.636).

ROCK-CLIMBING

The main **rock-climbing** area is just to the west of Ao Ton Sai, and includes the Ton Sai Tower and the Drinking Wall, with thirty routes from grades 5 to 7a. A newer attraction is **deep-water soloing**, unaided climbing on cliffs and outcrops over the sea.

OPERATORS

Maya Bay Camping East of Ao Ton Sai pier, Ko Phi Phi Don, on the fourth north–south alley Ⓦmaya baycamping.com. Overnight camping on Phi Phi Leh for B2500.

Phi Phi Adventure Club East of Ao Ton Sai pier, Ko Phi Phi Don, on the fourth north–south alley Ⓣ081 895 1334, Ⓦphi-phi-adventures.com. Responsible, small-group dive trips, courses and snorkelling trips ("with sharks guaranteed"; 3hr; B800).

Spidermonkey Near The Rock on the route to the east end of Loh Dalum Ⓣ075 819384, Ⓦspidermonkey climbing.com. Climbing instruction (from B1000 for half a day), guide service and equipment rental. Also runs snorkelling (on Phi Phi Leh) and climbing day-trips (B1600).

Viking Divers East of the pier, on the fourth north–south alley Ⓦvikingdiversthailand.com. Phi Phi Diving Association member.

7

another fine beach just a short boat ride away, is also very popular. To escape the crowds you need to aim for one of the smaller bays further north: **Ao Toh Ko**, **Ao Rantee** and **Hat Pak Nam** are all good for moderately priced breakaways, while **Ao Loh Bakao** and **Laem Tong** are pricier and more luxurious.

Ton Sai village, Ao Loh Dalum and Laem Hin

Ton Sai village is a hectic warren of a place, both strangely old-fashioned with its alley traffic of bicycles and pushcarts, its fresh market tucked away in the middle and its squalid shanty town and stinky sewers hidden along the edges, and bang up to date, the narrow lanes bursting with state-of-the-art dive companies, shops advertising DVD players for rent and trendy boutiques.

West of the pier, **Ao Ton Sai** beach is an attractive little retreat under the limestone karsts, though it gets busy for a couple of hours around lunchtime and you're not far from the longtail moorings. Most people simply head for **Ao Loh Dalum** instead, less than 300m north across the narrow isthmus, which looks astonishingly pretty at high tide, with its glorious curve of powder-white sand beautifully set off by pale blue water; it's a different story at low water, however, as the tide goes out for many kilometres. There's a tiny Tsunami Memorial Park of carefully tended shrubs, epitaphs and photos at the eastern end, near *Sunflower Bar*.

East along the coast from the Ton Sai pier, about ten minutes' walk along the main alley, is the promontory known as **Laem Hin**, beyond which lies a small beach and bungalows that enjoy a little more space. Inland, there are island homes and a mosque.

The viewpoint

B30

The **viewpoint** that overlooks eastern Ao Loh Dalum affords a magnificent panorama over the twin bays and every evening a stream of people make the steep fifteen-minute climb up the steps for sunset shots; early morning is also photogenic, and the shop at the "Topview" summit, set within a pretty tropical garden, serves coffee as well as cold drinks. There are good, free views just metres before the viewpoint entrance and from the restaurant patio halfway up. From the viewpoint, you can descend the rocky and at times almost sheer paths to the trio of little east-coast bays at Ao Toh Ko, Ao Rantee (Lanti) and Hat Pak Nam, each of which takes about thirty minutes.

Hat Yao (Long Beach)

With its fine white sand and large reefs packed with polychromatic marine life just 20m offshore, **HAT YAO** (Long Beach) is considered the best of Phi Phi's main beaches, but it's lined with hotels so gets very busy. UK-run Long Beach Divers (ⓦlongbeachdivers.com) here runs all the same **dive** trips and courses as shops in the village and offers discounted stays at *Long Beach Bungalows* (see p.674) for dive students.

Longtail **boats** do the ten-minute shuttle between Hat Yao and Ao Ton Sai (B100/person, or B150 after dark), but at low tide it's also possible to **walk** between the two in half an hour, via the coast in front of *Bay View Resort* on Laem Hin and then via *Viking*. The island's single **road** follows an inland route to *The Beach Resort* from *The Rock* junction in the village, passing the post-tsunami housing project and Water Hill reservoir en route; it's a hot, hilly and unshaded forty-minute walk.

Ao Toh Ko, Hat Rantee and Hat Pak Nam

Travellers wanting to escape the crowds around Ton Sai and Hat Yao without spending a fortune head for the trio of little bays midway along the east coast: **AO TOH KO** and

adjacent **AO RANTEE** (Lanti) and **HAT PAK NAM**. You can reach the bays inland, via steep forest trails that run from the Viewpoint above Ao Loh Dalum (see p.670) in half an hour, while you can walk from Ao Toh Ko to Ao Rantee in five minutes at low tide. Rantee is probably the pick of the three, a palm- and casuarina-fringed white-sand bay, with great snorkelling at the reef right off the beach.

Ao Loh Bakao and Laem Tong

Far removed from the hustle of Ao Ton Sai and its environs, the beautiful, secluded northern beaches at Ao Loh Bakao and Laem Tong are the domain of just a few upscale resorts. *Phi Phi Island Village Beach Resort and Spa* (see p.675) has the gorgeous 800m-long white-sand beach and turquoise waters of **AO LOH BAKAO** all to itself. If you tire of these sands, and the hotel's four restaurants, there's a cluster of reasonably priced local restaurants behind the resort, and you can walk to the long, semicircular beach at **Ao Loh Lanaa**, across on the west coast, in ten minutes, or to Laem Tong in half an hour.

Almost right at Phi Phi's northernmost tip, **LAEM TONG** is busier and more commercial than Loh Bakao, with several upmarket resorts and stand-alone restaurants along its white-sand shores, and views across to nearby Bamboo and Mosquito islands. The beach is home to a group of Urak Lawoy *chao ley* "sea gypsies" (see box, p.602), whose village is next to the *Holiday Inn*; all longtail boat tours and transfers are run by Laem Tong's *chao ley* cooperative.

Ko Phi Phi Leh

B200

More rugged than its twin, Ko Phi Phi Don, and a quarter the size, **KO PHI PHI LEH** is the number one day-tripping destination from Phi Phi Don, twenty minutes north, and a feature of snorkelling tours out of Phuket and Ao Nang (the national park admission fee is only levied if you set foot on the island, but not if you only snorkel offshore). It is very scenic indeed, and world famous, following its starring role in the film *The Beach*, so expect huge crowds, a plethora of discarded polystyrene lunch boxes, and a fair bit of damage to the reefs from the carelessly dropped anchors of tourist and fishing boats. The best way to appreciate the island is probably on one of the overnight camping and snorkelling trips from Phi Phi Don (see p.669).

Most idyllic of all the island's bays, and the most famous backdrop of the film *The Beach*, is **Ao Maya** (or Maya Bay) on the southwest coast, where the water is still and very clear and the coral extremely varied; **Ao Phi Leh**, an almost completely enclosed east-coast lagoon of breathtakingly turquoise water, is also beautiful. Nearby, the **Viking Cave** gets its misleading name from the scratchy wall paintings of Chinese junks inside, but more interesting than this 400-year-old graffiti is the **bird's-nesting** that goes on here (see p.673): rickety bamboo scaffolding extends hundreds of metres up to the roof of the cave, where intrepid *chao ley* harvesters spend the day scraping the unfeasibly valuable nests made by tiny sea swifts off the rockface, for export to specialist Chinese restaurants all over the world.

ARRIVAL AND DEPARTURE	**KO PHI PHI DON**

Tour agents in Phuket, Ao Nang, Krabi town and Ko Lanta all organize snorkelling day-trips to Phi Phi Don and Phi Phi Leh. Touts and bungalow staff always meet the ferries at the pier in Ton Sai; if you've pre-booked accommodation your luggage will usually be transported in a handcart. There are also boat transfers to Ko Jum (see p.679), which can be arranged, at the pier or through travel agents on the main alley running east of the pier in Ton Sai village. There is a waste management fee of B20 in cash on arrival; and a left-luggage booth (B50/piece).

To/from Phuket Several companies run large, crowded ferries from Rassada Harbour (see p.619) in Phuket to Ko Phi Phi Don twice daily in high season (currently 8.30am & 1.30pm; 2hr), and there's at least one boat a day out of season. From travel agents in Phuket town, prices can start as low as B300 single, B550 return, including transfer from

BIRD'S-NESTING

Prized for its aphrodisiac and energizing qualities, **bird's-nest soup** is such a delicacy in Taiwan, Singapore and Hong Kong that ludicrous sums of money change hands for a dish whose basic ingredients are tiny twigs glued together with bird's spit. Collecting these nests is a lucrative but life-endangering business: sea swifts (known as edible-nest swiftlets) build their nests in rock crevices hundreds of metres above sea level, often on sheer cliff-faces or in cavernous hollowed-out karst. **Nest-building** begins in January and the harvesting season usually lasts from February to May, during which time the female swiftlet builds three nests on the same spot, none of them more than 12cm across, by secreting an unbroken thread of saliva, which she winds round as if making a coil pot. **Gatherers** will only steal the first two nests made by each bird, prising them off the cave walls with special metal forks. This in theory allows the bird to build a final nest and raise her chicks in peace. Gathering the nests demands faultless agility and balance, skills that seem to come naturally to the *chao ley* (see p.602), whose six-man teams bring about four hundred nests down the perilous bamboo scaffolds each day, weighing about 4kg in total. At a market rate of up to $2000 per kilo, so much money is at stake that a government franchise must be granted before any collecting commences, and armed guards often protect the sites at night. The *chao ley* seek spiritual protection from the dangers of the job by making offerings to the spirits of the cliff or cave at the beginning of the season; in the Viking Cave, they place buffalo flesh, horns and tails at the foot of one of the stalagmites.

In recent years, entrepreneurs in Ban Laem, near Phetchaburi, across on south Thailand's Gulf coast, have started competing with the *chao ley* – by constructing **sea swift condominiums** and trying to attract the swiftlets that frequent the attic of the nearby temple. The theory is that by constructing windowless concrete towers that mimic the Andaman Sea caves – complete with cool dark interiors and dropping-smeared walls, plus swiftlet soundtracks on continuous replay – they can entice the birds in to build their nests and harvest them with ease. To date, the main beneficiary seems to have been the construction company that builds these ugly towers, as the local swiftlet population suddenly has an awful lot of new accommodation to choose from.

7

Phuket town. Andaman Wave Master's boats call in at Ao Ton Sai, but continue up the west coast to Laem Tong (B500 single), where the resorts send out longtail boats to pick up guests from the ship. There are also deals such as Phuket–Ko Lanta, breaking the journey on Phi Phi, for B700; Phuket–Phi Phi–Krabi for B700; and Phuket–Phi Phi–Ao Nang/Railay for B850. A daily speedboat also runs from Rassada to Phi Phi (which continues to Ko Lanta), but it costs B1500 for the 50min journey.

To/from Krabi From Krabi Passenger Port, there are boats to Phi Phi daily year-round, with at least four a day in high season (2hr; B350–400). You can also reach Phi Phi by once-daily ferries from Ao Nang, via West Railay (2hr 30min; B450), which are year-round in theory though they sometimes don't run in the monsoon season.

To/from Ko Lanta Yai From Ban Sala Dan on Ko Lanta Yai, there are two daily departures to Ko Phi Phi in high season (1hr 30min; B400).

GETTING AROUND

It's possible to **walk** along the paths across the steep and at times rugged interior. There are only a few short motorbike tracks and one road, from the back of Ton Sai village to *The Beach Resort* on Long Beach, which takes around forty minutes on foot.

By boat From Ao Ton Sai, east of the main pier, you can catch a longtail to any of the other beaches, which range in price from B100 per person (minimum two people) to Hat Yao, to B1000 per boat to Laem Tong; prices often double after dark. The Andaman Wave Master ferry (see above) and a smaller shuttle boat each run twice a day between Ton Sai and the east-coast bays as far as Laem Tong (both B200). You could also get about by kayak (B700 per day from in front of *Slinky Bar* on Ao Loh Dalum), which is the perfect way to explore the limestone cliffs and secluded bays, without the roar of an accompanying longtail or cruise ship.

ACCOMMODATION

As demand for accommodation frequently outstrips supply on Phi Phi, if you haven't made a reservation, it's worth using the agents' booking service at the pier head, where pictures and – genuine – room prices for hotels in all categories are posted for easy browsing; staff then call ahead to secure your room, and might even carry your bag there. Be warned though that rooms are very expensive on Phi Phi, and often poorly maintained. We've quoted rates for high season, which runs from November to April, but most places slap on a thirty- to fifty-percent surcharge during Christmas and New Year and, conversely, will discount up to fifty percent in quiet periods between May and October.

TON SAI VILLAGE AND AO LOH DALUM

Ton Sai hotels are the least good value on the island and almost none, however expensive, is out of earshot of the thumping all-night beats cranked up by the various bars and clubs; bring some heavy-duty earplugs if you're not planning to party every night.

★**Chunut House** Turn right at The Rock and walk for about 5min back towards Laem Hin ☎075 601227, ⓦchunuthouse.com. Very welcoming, relaxing place in a leafy, sloping garden, in a relatively quiet location. Big, stylish, thatched cottages come with a/c, flat-screen TVs, mini-bars and spacious, attractive, hot-water bathrooms. Breakfast included. B2600

Phi Phi Inn Straight ahead from the pier next to the landmark Phi Phi Hotel ☎081 797 2088, ⓔphiphi _inn@hotmail.com. Small, sparklingly clean hotel in a white clapboard house, where all fifteen rooms have a/c, TVs, hot showers, mini-bars, safety boxes and balconies, though only the upstairs ones have the chance of a view and also enjoy more privacy. B1650

Phi Phi Island Cabana Hotel West of the pier on Ton Sai ☎075 601170–7, ⓦppislandcabana.com. The views from the contemporary a/c rooms at this large, imposing hotel are breathtakingly lovely. Most look out across the scoop of Ao Loh Dalum and its framing cliffs, and ground-floor ones have direct access to the sand. There's a huge pool too. On the minus side, the hotel lacks atmosphere, has a cavernous restaurant and some rooms are affected by late-night club noise. B5500

The Rock ☎081 607 3897 or ☎075 601021. Traveller-oriented hangout behind a landmark bar-restaurant, offering the cheapest beds on the island, in large mixed-sex dorms; up to seventeen bunk beds are crammed in each, but there are fans and lockers. Also has a few singles (B400) and doubles with shared, cold-water bathrooms. Dorms B300, doubles B800

Tropical Garden Beyond the turn-off for the path to the viewpoint ☎081 968 1436, ⓦthailandphiphitravel .com. Here you'll find a wide variety of rooms and good-sized rough-timber bungalows, which are mostly built on stilts up the side of an outcrop. The better ones have a breezy veranda (though not much of a view) and there's a refreshing amount of greenery around, plus a small pool, despite being surrounded by other accommodation. Book exchange and crafts shop on site. Fan B1100, a/c B1400

Viewpoint Bungalows ☎075 601200, ⓦphiphi viewpoint.com. Strung out across and up the cliffside at the far eastern end of Ao Loh Dalum, the a/c rooms and bungalows here enjoy great views over the bay, though interiors are nothing to write home about and the all-night

bars are too near to ignore. Facilities include a scenically sited restaurant, a tour desk and a small, idyllically situated, infinity-edged bayview pool. Breakfast included. B2500

LAEM HIN

Bay View Resort ☎075 601127, ⓦphiphibayview.com. The draw at the seventy large, a/c bungalows here is their prime location: they're set high on the cliffside at the far eastern end of Laem Hin beach, strung out along the ridge almost as far as Hat Yao. All have massive windows and decks to enjoy the great views and there's a pool here too. Be prepared for lots of steps though. Breakfast included. B3780

Gypsy Village About 150m down the track between the mosque and Phi Phi Andaman Legacy ☎075 601045. The thirty plain and pretty shabby pink-painted concrete bungalows here are relatively cheap, but they're all en suite and fan-cooled, and are set round a big dry lawn. B1400

Phi Phi Andaman Legacy ☎075 601106, ⓦppandaman legacy.com. Set in a secluded enclosure just a few metres back from the beach, the rather old-fashioned bungalows here are arranged in a square around a large lawn and small central swimming pool, while the 36 more modern rooms occupy a three-storey hotel building at the back. All rooms are a/c and come with TVs, hot water, fridges and safety boxes. Breakfast included. B2090

Phi Phi Villa Resort ☎075 601100, ⓦphiphivilla resort.com. The best of the many options at this outfit are the huge a/c family cottages occupying the front section of the prettily landscaped garden, near the pool. Also available are smaller bungalows and stylish newer rooms in an annexe set back from the beach, all with a/c, hot water, fridge and TV. Breakfast included. B3100

LONG BEACH (HAT YAO)

The Beach Resort ☎075 819206, ⓦphiphithebeach .com. Currently the poshest option on Hat Yao, this place has a throng of large, timber-clad chalets built on stilts up the hillside, with the tallest, most deluxe ones enjoying commanding views of Phi Phi Leh. Interiors are fairly upscale, with a/c and liberal use of wood for flooring and wall panels. There's also a small beachfront pool. B4300

Long Beach Bungalows ☎086 470 8984, ⓔlongbeach@gmail.com. The first choice of most budget travellers, this relatively cheap, well-located and long-running option has dozens of tightly packed huts for rent, ranging from simple, clean bamboo huts with fans, mosquito nets and cold-water bathrooms, to smart beach-front cottages with hot water. The room price includes a B100 food and drinks voucher for the restaurant, and there are discounts for divers (see p.670). B1000

7

the cheaper bamboo ones are set further back beside the path. Interiors are very rudimentary but the decks are huge, and there's also a large, more luxurious family bungalow, and two concrete bungalows with fans (all B1000). You can swim below the rocks at low tide, or the more reliable beach is just a couple of minutes' scramble to south or north. They offer fishing boat tours, and there's the very chilled, fairy-lit *Air Bar*. **B500**

Little Italy ☎ 084 851 2760, ✉ daniel060863@yahoo .it. This tiny Italian–Thai-run outfit has just two attractive bungalows set in a shady, secluded garden of paperbark trees 100m inland from *Cashew Resort*. The two-storey bungalows have exceptionally clean, smartly tiled papaya-coloured bathrooms downstairs and Thai-style bamboo-walled sleeping quarters upstairs, with varnished wood floors and big decks. The garden restaurant serves deliciously authentic pastas. **B350**

Sawasdee Resort ☎ 084 846 5828, 🌐 sawasdee kohchang.com. This welcoming place by a khlong at the far southern end of Ao Yai is a little pricier than many but more style-conscious too and tends to attract slightly older, less hammock-bound guests, and doesn't accept children under 7. The eleven thoughtfully designed wooden bungalows have big decks and good bathrooms, and a couple of them, by the beach, are especially large and well equipped, including fans (B800). There's a good, attractive restaurant, serving a wide variety of Thai dishes and plenty of vegetarian options, with decks and terraces under the shady trees. No wi-fi. **B350**

AO DADDAENG

★**Mama's Bungalows** 5min walk south over the headland from Ao Yai, on Ao Daddaeng ☎ 077 820180

or ☎ 088 476 7144, ✉ mamas-bungalows@hotmail .com. The fourteen attractive, well-maintained wooden and bamboo bungalows at this congenial spot have colourfully decorated bathrooms and come in several sizes, some of them with big decks. They're built in a pretty flower garden staggered up the hillside; several are on the beach and the uppermost ones overlook the bay from the edge of a rubber plantation. The restaurant serves espresso coffee and generous portions of carefully prepared food, including tasty tzatziki and many German specialities. Very popular, so book ahead. No wi-fi. **B250**

NORTHERN BAYS

Hornbill Bungalows North around two headlands from Ao Yai, about a 35min walk ☎ 077 870240, ✉ 66_hornbill@hotmail.com. Set among the trees fronting their own little gold-sand bay, the unobtrusive en-suite bungalows here are constructed to different designs, some of them extremely comfortable, and all enjoy sea views. The food here has a good reputation and the owner is very welcoming. It lives up to its name, as majestic black-and-white hornbills are a common sight. Internet access, kayaks and boat trips on offer. No wi-fi. **B250**

Sea Eagle About 40min walk from Ao Yai ☎ 082 289 0683, 🌐 seaeaglebangkalow.com. The sole occupants of the longest and widest of the northern bays, which is graced by an attractive band of gold sand, the en-suite bamboo and wooden bungalows here are set among trees just back from the shore. They have comfy deck furniture for soaking up the sea views and there are kayaks and windsurfers for rent and a beach volleyball net. The restaurant serves Thai and European food and has internet access. **B300**

Ko Phayam

The diminutive kangaroo-shaped island of **KO PHAYAM** offers fine white-sand beaches and coral reefs and is home to around five hundred people, most of whom either make their living from prawn, squid and crab fishing, or from growing cashew nuts, *sator* beans, coconut palms and rubber trees. Most islanders live in Ko Phayam's only **village**, behind the pier on the northeast coast, which connects to other corners of the island by a network of concrete roads and rutted tracks. The bays either side of the village have a couple of nice places to stay, but the main beaches and accommodation centres are on the west coast, at **Ao Yai** and **Ao Kao Kwai**. A motorbike taxi service covers all routes, but no journey is very long as the island measures just five by eight kilometres at its widest points.

Ko Phayam has a livelier, younger and slightly more developed feel than neighbouring Ko Chang (see p.591), underlined by a low-key beach-bar scene – all hand-painted signs and driftwood sculptures – and the presence of a significant number of foreigners who choose to spend six or more months here every year. Some expats even take up the **rainy-season** challenge, staying on through the downpours and rough seas that lash the island from June to October, but a number of bungalows close down during this time and staff take refuge in Ranong. As the island gets more popular, residents and expats are beginning to try and forestall the inevitable negative impact on the island's **environment**.

7

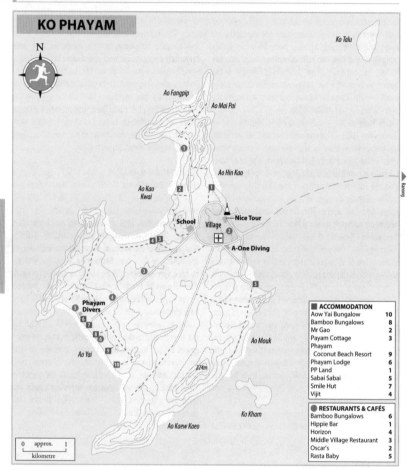

In particular, they are urging visitors not to accept plastic bags from the few shops on the island, to take non-degradable rubbish such as batteries and plastic items back to the mainland, and to minimize plastic water-bottle usage by buying the biggest possible bottles and refilling them from the water coolers that all bungalow resorts have.

The village and around

The tiny cluster of homes and shops that constitute Ko Phayam's only **village** is within a few minutes' walk of the pier. There are a few little general stores here, plus several restaurants and a **clinic**. A little way north up the shoreline stands the island **temple**, with its circular viharn resting on a huge concrete lotus flower at the end of its own pier.

Ao Yai

Ko Phayam's main beach is the 3km-long **AO YAI** on the southwest coast, a wide and handsome sweep of powdery white sand backed by an unbroken line of casuarina trees, which curves quite deeply at its northern and southern ends into rocky outcrops that offer some snorkelling possibilities. The shore is pounded by decent waves that are fun for boogie-boarding and pretty safe; the sunsets are quite spectacular too. For the moment Ao Yai's bungalow operations are mostly widely spaced along the shoreline, and much of the forest behind the beach is still intact. You're more than likely to see – and hear – some of the resident black-and-white hornbills at dawn and dusk, along with many white-bellied sea eagles, and sightings of crab-eating macaques are also common.

Ao Kao Kwai and around

The northwest coast is scalloped into **AO KAO KWAI**, a name that's pronounced locally as **Ao Kao Fai** and translates as **Buffalo Horn Bay**; from the cliffside midway along the bay you can see how the two halves of the beach curve out into buffalo-like horns. The southern half of Ao Kao Kwai is subject to both very low and very high tides, which makes it unreliable for swimming, but the northern stretch, from *Mr Gao* bungalows onwards, is exceptionally pretty, secluded between outcrops with decent swimming at any tide, and none of the big waves that characterize Ao Yai.

From the northern end of Ao Kao Kwai, a thirty-minute walk brings you to the pretty little sandy beach at **Ao Fangpip** (also spelt Ao Kwang Pib), which is the best spot on the island for snorkelling. There's also some snorkellable reef at **Ao Hin Kao** on the northeast coast.

ARRIVAL AND DEPARTURE

KO PHAYAM

Nice Tour and Travel, north of the pier-head in the village (☎ 089 651 5177, ✉ nicetour40@hotmail.com), sells bus, train, airline and boat tickets. Nearby *Oscar's* (☎ 084 842 5070; see p.599) also sells transport tickets and charters speedboats to other islands. Most bungalows sell boat tickets, and some sell bus tickets, too.

BY BOAT
Motorbikes meet incoming boats at the main pier on the northwest coast.

To/from Ranong From November to May there are two daily slow boats to Ko Phayam from the Islands Pier in Saphan Pla (see p.589), 5km south of Ranong town centre (9.30am & 2pm, returning from the island at 8am & 2pm; 2hr; B200), as well as up to three speedboat services

(45min; B350). During the rainy season only the 2pm slow boat runs, returning from the island at 8am; *Pon's Place* in Ranong (see p.589) keeps the latest timetables.

To/from Ko Chang The easiest and cheapest way of travelling between Ko Phayam and Ko Chang is on the day-trippers' boat organized by *Koh Chang Resort* several times a week in high season (see p.594).

GETTING AROUND

Many travellers heading into the village from one of the beaches opt to walk at least one way: from Ao Yai's *Smile Hut* it's an enjoyable 7km stroll along the narrow concrete road that cuts through the cashew plantations, with the possibility of stopping for a breather at the aptly named *Middle Village Restaurant*. It takes less than an hour to walk from southern Ao Kao Kwai to the village.

ACTIVITIES ON KO PHAYAM

Most bungalows can arrange **fishing** and **snorkelling** day-trips, while *Oscar's* in the village takes people **wakeboarding** in the bay. The **dive companies** teach PADI courses and run live-aboards to Ko Surin, Richelieu Rock, Ko Tachai, Ko Bon and Ko Similan (from about B16,000 for three days, plus B600 per day for equipment rental).

A-One Diving In the village ☎ 081 891 5510, ⓦ a-one-diving.com. Also does live-aboards to Burma Banks and the Mergui archipelago across the Burmese border.

Mr Gao Ao Kao Kwai ☎ 077 870222, ⓦ mr-trip -phayam.com. Runs occasional two-day snorkelling

trips to Ko Surin at B4000 per person, including accommodation in national park tents.

Phayam Divers Phayam Lodge, Ao Yai ☎ 086 995 2598, ⓦ phayamlodge.com. One-day trips to Ko Surin or Richelieu Rock for B4900 (plus equipment rental and national park fee).

Motorbike taxis Motorbike taxis can be booked through any bungalow; a ride between the village and the beaches costs about B80 (there are no cars on the island).

Motorbike rental You can rent your own motorbike for about B200 through resorts on the beaches and outlets in the village next to the pier, including *Oscar's* and Nice Tour and Travel.

Bike rental Nice Tour and Travel in the village.

INFORMATION

Nice Tour and Travel In the village ☎089 651 5177. Changes money and does Visa cash advances as there are no ATMs on the island. Can arrange boat hire and fishing tours, has a book exchange, and offers internet access and an international phone service.

Oscar's Bar In the village ☎084 842 5070. A good source of island information and tickets; also changes money at good rates.

ACCOMMODATION

Most bungalows only provide electricity from around 6 to 11pm and the cheapest rooms often don't have a fan. Unless otherwise stated, all bungalows open year-round.

THE VILLAGE AREA

Most people choose to stay at the west-coast beach centres, but there are a couple of nice little hideaways within easy reach of the village and its facilities.

PP Land ☎081 678 4310, ⓦppland-heavenbeach .com. Fronting a small beach about a 10min walk north from the village, this Belgian–Thai place with an organic garden is a cut above many places to stay on the island. Its tasteful, green-painted shaggy thatched bungalows line the beach and boast pretty furnishings, polished wood floors inside and out, nice bathrooms, and big comfy decks. They don't accept children under 15 so as to maintain the quiet atmosphere. There's an attractive swimming pool, plus 24-hour electricity. B900

Sabai Sabai ☎087 895 4653, ⓦsabai-bungalows .com. On their own secluded little beach, a 5min walk south of the pier, are these seven sea-breeze-catching wooden bungalows, some with 24hr electricity and all but one en suite. Tents are also available, and there's a shisha lounge and movie- and live-music nights. Motorbikes, bicycles, kayaks and snorkels available. B200

AO YAI

Aow Yai Bungalow ☎083 389 8688 or ☎084 061 3283, ⓦaowyai.com. Established by a French–Thai couple, this was the first set of bungalows on the island and remains one of the most popular, especially with return guests. The 26 good-quality en-suite bungalows are dotted around an extensive garden of flowers, fruit trees and palms and come in various styles: the cheapest wooden or thatched bamboo affairs come with mosquito nets but no fans, while the most expensive are built with concrete and have hot showers. Snorkels and kayaks available to rent. B300

Bamboo Bungalows ☎077 820012, ⓦbamboo -bungalows.com. Ao Yai's liveliest accommodation is Israeli–Thai managed and very traveller-savvy, offering snorkels, kayaks, surf- and boogie-boards, currency exchange and overseas phone services. Its en-suite bungalows are set under the trees in a well-tended flower garden and range from luxuriously large chalets with pretty furnishings to shell-studded concrete bungalows and a choice of bamboo and wood huts with mosquito nets, all with fan. Electricity is 24hr in high season, but with more limited hours in low season. B550

Phayam Coconut Beach Resort ☎089 920 8145 or ☎083 389 6408, ⓦkoh-phayam.com. Occupying a great spot in the centre of the bay and run by a Ko Phayam family, the 27 good-value bungalows here are of a high standard, each set in its own tiny garden. Accommodation ranges from small bamboo en-suite huts through larger wood or bamboo versions to big concrete or clapboard bungalows at the top end (up to B1200). Closed during the worst of the rainy season. B300

Phayam Lodge ☎086 995 2598, ⓦphayamlodge .com. This welcoming place is probably a sign of things to come on Ko Phayam: rows of large, smart concrete villas with attractive teak fittings, luxuriously comfortable beds, a/c, proper bathrooms with hot showers and 24hr electricity, a rarity on the island. B2900

Smile Hut ☎077 820335 or ☎081 515 0856, ⓦsmile hutthai.com. Like *Bamboo*, this is a very popular choice with travellers. The 35 split-bamboo and wooden huts with mosquito nets are simple but en suite and are spread among the shorefront trees, with the slightly cheaper versions set one row behind. Has internet access (no wi-fi) and kayaks. B400

AO KAO KWAI

Ao Kao Kwai is particularly popular both with long-stay guests and returnees, so you might want to book your accommodation in advance.

★Mr Gao ☎077 870222, ⓦmr-gao-phayam.com. Located on the best stretch of the beach, this well-established operation is one of the most famous and popular spots on the island. There are just nine well-designed bungalows here, in assorted sizes and luxury, set in a spacious, lovingly tended garden of shrubs and bamboos. All have good bathrooms and generous decks and most have polished wood floors, screened windows and thoughtfully furnished interiors. There's a good, large restaurant, and wi-fi is available in the evenings when there is electricity. B900

Payam Cottage ☎ 085 222 1847, ⓦ payamcottage .com. More resort-like in style and facilities than others on Ko Phayam, with 24hr electricity, the option of a/c, a kids'

play area and a good-sized swimming pool. Bungalows are tastefully furnished and built in angled rows across a central garden to give each one some sort of sea view. B1600

Vijit ☎ 077 834082, ⓦ kohpayam-vijit.com. This long-running outfit in a lush garden is very popular. Some of the en-suite, clapboard bungalows are designed for families and they're all reasonably spacious and have fans. B400

EATING AND DRINKING

Several laidback little beach-bars, including the long-running *Rasta Baby* on Ao Yai and *Hippie Bar* on Ao Kao Khwai, put on fireshows and occasional parties.

THE VILLAGE

★**Oscar's** Just north of the pier-head ☎ 084 842 5070. Offers breakfasts, including home-baked bread, Thai standards such as *tom yam kung* (B90), pizzas, Indian curries, shepherd's pie (B190) and other English favourites, but is most famous for its partially open-air bar, which is a fun, relaxed focal point of the expat social scene. Daily 7am–late.

AO YAI

Bamboo Bungalows Tasty spaghetti with pesto (B170), schnitzels, sandwiches and Western breakfasts at this

beachfront restaurant, as well as lots of Thai standards, including seafood priced by weight. Also does wine by the glass and Middle Eastern coffee. Daily 7.45am–10pm.

Horizon Just inland on the Ao Yai road. Congenial outdoor restaurant for very tasty Thai food, all of it offered vegetarian, with the option of adding meat: a toothsome *matsaman* curry with carrot, pumpkin and potatoes costs B70, and you can add chicken for B20. Also does a few Western main courses, sandwiches, a wide choice of breakfasts, Thai desserts, and all kinds of teas, juices and lassis. Nov–May daily 7/8am–8/9pm; June–Oct daily 7/8am–sunset (closed when it rains).

Khuraburi and around

The small town of **KHURABURI**, 110km south of Ranong on Highway 4, is the main departure point for the magnificent national park island chain of Ko Surin. Much closer to Khuraburi are the islands of **Ko Ra** and **Ko Phra Thong**, which offer empty beaches and decent snorkelling and bird-watching, or there's the chance to participate in typical village life at **homestays** in mainland coastal communities.

Khuraburi's commercial heart is a 500m strip of shops and businesses either side of Highway 4. Most travellers use the town just as a staging post en route to or from the Surin islands: the main pier for boats to the islands is just 7.5km away, and Khuraburi's tour agents sell boat tickets and offer transport to the pier. Though lacking in famous attractions, the local area is nonetheless scenic, both offshore and inland: with an afternoon or more to spare, you could either rent a motorbike, mountain bike or kayak to explore it independently, or charter a motorbike taxi or longtail boat.

Ko Ra

Hilly, forested **Ko Ra** (measuring about 10km north to south and 3km across) sits just off Khuraburi pier's mangrove-lined estuary and is graced with intact rainforest full of towering trees, hornbills and wild, empty beaches. The island is home to some two dozen *chao ley* people (see p.602), plus just one place to stay, the rather special American–Thai *Ko Ra Ecolodge*. On offer by the ecolodge are half-day guided tours to the nearby Moken village on Ko Ra; kayak rental and sea-kayaking trips; snorkelling to nearby Ko Surin (B2900/person, all-inclusive) and the little-visited islands of Laem Son National Park; and diving to the Surin islands (B6900 for two dives, not including national park fee and equipment rental). The ecolodge also offers hikes, bird-watching and yoga.

7

ANDAMAN DISCOVERIES HOMESTAY PROGRAMME

Khuraburi is the headquarters of the community-based tourism initiative Andaman Discoveries (☎087 917 7165, ⊛andamandiscoveries.com), which runs a recommended **day-trip and homestay programme** in several local villages, as well as interesting trips to Ko Surin (see p.603). It was established after the tsunami to help the area's many devastated fishing communities get back on their feet and has since developed a range of stimulating one- to five-day packages (from B1600 per person per day) featuring all sorts of village jobs and activities, from soap-making and batik design to cashew nut-farming and roof-thatching. The office is just east off the highway (south of the bus station), up the soi beside the police box, across from the post office.

Ko Phra Thong

Immediately to the south of Ko Ra, just 1km or so off the Khuraburi coast, **Ko Phra Thong** (Golden Buddha Island) also has some lovely beaches, the nicest of which, on the west coast, is 10km long and blessed with fine gold sand. This is the site of the *Horizon Beach Bungalows* and of the British-run Blue Guru Dive Centre (☎080 144 0551, ⊛blue-guru.org). The resort offers kayaking, trekking and yoga, while Blue Guru runs all manner of snorkelling tours, PADI courses, dive trips and live-aboards to Ko Tachai, Ko Surin, Richelieu Rock and into Myanmar. Blue Guru's owners also organize longtail tours of the island's mangroves and maintain a website to promote the island, ⊛kohphrathong.com, which includes information about homestays and budget bungalows.

ARRIVAL AND DEPARTURE   KHURABURI AND AROUND

KHURABURI
By bus The bus station is just off the east side of Highway 4 in the centre of town, but some long-distance through buses stop only on the highway.
Destinations: Bangkok (5 daily; 11hr); Khao Lak (12 daily; 1hr 45min); Phuket (12 daily via Khao Lak; 3hr 30min); Ranong (13 daily; 3hr); Takua Pa (12 daily; 1hr).

KO RA
By boat A longtail transfer to the *Ecolodge* from the pier at Khuraburi costs B600 (on demamd; 20min).

KO PHRA THONG
By boat A longtail transfer to your resort from the pier at Khuraburi (the only way to get to Ko Phra Thong) costs B1800 (90min) and B1700 (90min; must be pre-booked with Blue Guru Dive Centre).

GETTING AROUND

KHURABURI
Bike and motorbike rental Tom & Am Tour, who have their office on the west side of the main road in the town centre and maintain a desk in the bus station in high season (☎086 272 0588, ✉tom_am01@hotmail.com), rent bicycles, motorbikes and cars. *Boon Piya Resort* (see below) also rent motorbikes.

ACCOMMODATION

KHURABURI
Boon Piya Resort 100m north of the bus station, on the same side of the main road ☎081 752 5457. Well-appointed, if rather tightly packed, motel-style concrete bungalows in a tree-strewn courtyard set just back off the road. All have a/c and powerful hot showers; they're the usual choice of sales reps and NGOs. B750

Mr Tom's Bungalows On the north bank of the river, east of the bridge ☎086 272 0588, ✉tom_am01 @hotmail.com. Decent bungalows in a pleasant setting on the north bank of the river, with breakfast included, and kayaks for rent; call in at Tom & Am Tour (see above) first. B350

Tararin On the south bank of the river towards the northern end of town, about 200m north of the bus station ☎076 491789. This cute, rustic-style place has just a handful of simple but appealing en-suite wooden and concrete bungalows, some of them on stilts with balconies right over the water, plus an attractive riverside restaurant and eating deck. All rooms have TVs but no wi-fi; a/c ones have hot showers while those with fans have shared bathrooms. Fan B400, a/c B500

KO RA

★ **Ko Ra Ecolodge** ✆ 089 867 5288, ⊛ kohraecolodge .com. This ecotourism venture fronts a curve of bronze sand on the north coast of Ko Ra, with magnificent views to the Khuraburi hills, but its star feature is its wild, forty-acre forest garden. Filled with screw palms, red-barked *samet daeng* trees, dipterocarps and over seventeen epiphytic orchids, the private forest is crossed by trails and home both to a rich bird life, especially sunbirds and oriental pied hornbills, and to monitor lizards, crab-eating macaques and dusky langurs. Accommodation is in eighteen plain but spacious rooms in split-bamboo longhouses just back from the shore, communal meals are taken in the beach-side *sala* (B750 for three meals daily) and there's a genuine focus on community and environmental projects (volunteer placements and internships are offered). Closed May–Oct. B1100

KO PHRA THONG

Golden Buddha Beach Resort ✆ 081 892 2208, ⊛ goldenbuddharesort.com. Tasteful complex of 25 individually decorated wooden Thai-style homes, sleeping two to six, with a spa and clubhouse. It feels like you have the island and beach to yourself here, and this tranquillity is why most choose Ko Phra Thong over other islands. B4000

EATING AND DRINKING

KHURABURI

At night, many people eat at the night market south of the bus station, where the roti stall is a particular favourite, flipping out a constant pile of sizzling *roti mataba* (chicken) and *roti kluay* (banana). The morning market (daily from 5am) across from *Boon Piya* is the place to stock up on food for the Surin islands.

Tararin Bungalows On the south bank of the river towards the northern end of town, about 200m north of the bus station. Popular with visiting Thais, this riverside deck restaurant hits the spot with specialities such as *nam phrik kapii*, a southern relish made with shrimp paste, and *kaeng liang*, peppery vegetable soup, as well as loads of salads, fish and seafood. Mon–Sat 10am–9pm.

Ko Surin

Mu Ko Surin National Park, about 60km offshore • Nov–April • B400 entry fee, valid for 5 days • ⊛ dnp.go.th

Unusually shallow reefs, a palette of awesomely clear turquoise waters and dazzling white sands, and dense forests of lofty dipterocarps combine to make the islands of **Ko Surin** one of the most popular destinations in south Thailand. However, Ko Surin's most famous feature, its spectacular and diverse coral lying in fields just below the surface at the perfect depth for snorkelling, was severely bleached by a sudden rise in sea temperature in early 2010. Four of the most popular reefs are still closed to visitors, though half a dozen other sites that were less severely affected by the bleaching remain open; the national park is still a good spot for snorkellers, with plenty of fish to see, but it will take many years for the reefs to recover.

Ko Surin is very much an outdoors experience, with the bulk of accommodation in national park tents, no commerce on the islands at all, and twice-daily snorkelling the main activity. Several tour operators run snorkelling day-trips from Khuraburi, and there are diving trips too, most of which also take in nearby Richelieu Rock, considered to be Thailand's top dive site (see p.637), but independent travel is also recommended. Because the islands are so far out at sea, Ko Surin is closed to visitors from roughly May to October, when monsoon weather renders the 60km trip a potentially suicidal undertaking.

Surin Nua and Surin Tai

The most easily explored of the reefs are those off the two main islands in the group, Ko Surin Nua (north) and Ko Surin Tai (south), which are separated only by a narrow channel. **Surin Nua**, slightly the larger at about 5km across, holds the national park headquarters, visitor centre and park accommodation.

Across the channel, **Surin Tai** is the long-established home of a community of **Moken** *chao ley* (see box, p.602), who are no longer allowed to fish in national park

THE CHAO LEY: MOKEN AND URAK LAWOY

Sometimes called sea gypsies, the **chao ley** or *chao nam* ("people of the sea" or "water people") have been living off the seas around the west coast of the Malay peninsula for hundreds of years. Some still pursue a traditional nomadic existence, living in self-contained houseboats known as **kabang**, but many have now made permanent homes in Andaman coast settlements in Thailand, Myanmar and Malaysia. Dark-skinned and sometimes with an auburn tinge to their hair, the *chao ley* of the Andaman Sea are thought to number around five thousand, divided into five groups, with distinct lifestyles and dialects.

Of the different groups, the **Urak Lawoy**, who have settled on the islands of Ko Lanta, Ko Jum, Ko Phi Phi, Phuket and Ko Lipe, are the most integrated into Thai society. They came north to Thailand from Malaysia around two hundred years ago (having possibly migrated from the Nicobar Islands in the Indian Ocean some two centuries prior) and are known as *Thai Mai*, or "New Thai". Thailand's Urak Lawoy have been recognized as Thai citizens since the 1960s, when the late Queen Mother granted them five family names, thereby enabling them to possess ID cards and go to school. Many work on coconut plantations or as fishermen, while others continue in the more traditional *chao ley* **occupations** of hunting for pearls and seashells on the ocean floor, attaching stones to their waists to dive to depths of 60m with only an air-hose connecting them to the surface; sometimes they fish in this way too, taking down enormous nets into which they herd the fish as they walk along the sea bed. Their agility and courage make them good bird's-nesters as well (see box, p.673).

The **Moken** of Thailand's Ko Surin islands and Myanmar's Mergui archipelago probably came originally from Myanmar and are the most traditional of the *chao ley* communities. Some still lead remote, itinerant lives, and most are unregistered as Thai citizens, owning no land or property, but dependent on fresh water and beaches to collect shells and sea slugs to sell to Thai traders. They have extensive knowledge of the plants that grow in the remaining jungles on Thailand's west-coast islands, using eighty different species for food alone, and thirty for medicinal purposes.

The *chao ley* are **animists**, with a strong connection both to the natural spirits of island and sea and to their own ancestral spirits. On some beaches they set up totem poles as a contact point between the spirits, their ancestors and their shaman. The sea gypsies have a rich **musical heritage** too. The Moken do not use any instruments as such, making do with found objects for percussion; the Urak Lawoy, on the other hand, due to their closer proximity to the Thai and Malay cultures, are excellent violin- and drum-players. During community entertainments, such as the Urak Lawoy's twice-yearly full moon **festivals** on Ko Lanta (see p.680), the male musicians form a semicircle around the old women, who dance and sing about the sea, the jungle and their families.

Building a new boat is the ultimate expression of what it is to be a *chao ley*, and tradition holds that every newly married couple has a *kabang* built for them. But the complex art of constructing a seaworthy home from a single tree trunk, and the way of life it represents, is disappearing. In Thailand, where **assimilation** is actively promoted by the government, the truly nomadic flotillas have become increasingly marginalized, and the number of undeveloped islands they can visit unhindered gets smaller year by year. The 2004 tsunami further threatened their cultural integrity: when the waves destroyed the Moken's boats and homes on Ko Surin, they were obliged to take refuge on the mainland, where some were encouraged by missionaries to convert from their animist religion. Though the Moken have since returned to the Surin islands, inappropriate donations and the merging of two villages have exacerbated family rivalries and caused divisions that may prove lethal to their traditional way of life.

waters but make their living mostly as longtail boatmen for snorkellers staying on Surin Nua. Their recent history has been an unhappy one: not only were their settlements destroyed in the 2004 tsunami, but the aid and outside intervention that followed has changed the community forever, amalgamating two villages, building new homes too close together and introducing various modern-day vices; on top of that, tourist numbers are down since the coral bleaching in 2010. In **Ao Bon** village is a visitor centre built by Bangkok's Chulalongkorn University with English display boards, where you can hire a Moken guide to lead you on a nature trail around the village; don't go just in your swimwear, but take a sarong for modesty's sake. You can also make a positive contribution by buying one of the woven pandanus-leaf souvenirs or wooden model boats the villagers make; donations of toothpaste and clothes would also be appreciated. One of the Moken traditions that does persist is the new year celebration that's held every April, during Songkhran, when *chao ley* from nearby islands (including those in Burmese waters) congregate here and, among other rites, release several hundred turtles into the sea, a symbol of longevity.

ARRIVAL AND GETTING AROUND   KO SURIN

By boat There are no public boats to Ko Surin, but if you want to stay on the islands, it's perfectly possible to come over on one of the tour boats from Khuraburi and return on another day.

By longtail Once on the islands, there's an efficient system of boat hire: Moken longtails depart twice a day from the national park campsites to the different reefs and Ao Bon village and charge B100/person for about two hours (snorkel sets cost B80/day). You can also charter your own longtail for B1500/B2500 per half-day/day.

TOURS

Most visitors either do **snorkelling day-trips** to the islands from Khuraburi or opt for **dive trips** or live-aboards out of Ko Ra, Ko Phra Thong, Khao Lak, Phuket, Ranong, Ko Chang or Ko Phayam. For snorkellers, there are also day-trips from Ko Ra and Ko Phra Thong, and two-day trips run by *Mr Gao* on Ko Phayam (see p.597). During the season, speedboat snorkelling trips to Ko Surin depart most days from Khuraburi pier, 7.5km northwest of Khuraburi town; big, slow, wooden boats (2–3hr; B1300 return) only run at weekends and on national holidays for large groups of Thai tourists.

Andaman Discoveries Khuraburi (see p.600), ⓦandamandiscoveries.com. Four-day trips, with two nights on Ko Surin, focusing on learning about Moken life, including guided forest, village and snorkelling tours and cooking classes (B14,500).

Blue Guru Dive Centre Ko Phra Thong (see p.600). Upmarket day-trips on a dive cruiser or speedboat, including "gourmet lunch", for snorkelling (from B3900, plus B200 equipment) or diving (two dives; from B4900, plus B700 equipment); transfers from Khuraburi hotels included. Also offers multi-day trips to Surin; and transfers from Khao Lak.

Boon Piya Resort Khuraburi (see p.600). Sells boat tickets and packages, including discounts on national park bungalows on weekdays.

Tom & Am Tour Office on the west side of the main road in Khuraburi town centre, but they also maintain a desk in the bus station in high season ☎086 272 0588, ✉tom_am01@yahoo.co.th. Speedboats to Ko Surin (1hr 15min–2hr), departing the pier at 8.30am, leaving the islands at about 2pm; B1650 return including transfers. They also rent tents (B50–100/day), bedding sets (B20/day), snorkel sets (B50/day) and fins (B50/day) for Ko Surin (all cheaper than national park prices).

ACCOMMODATION

All island accommodation is on Surin Nua and is provided by the national park. Both campsites have bathrooms, lockers (B100/day) and dining rooms where meals are served at fixed times three times a day (B100–250; many people take their own supplies from Khuraburi instead. Bungalows need to be booked in advance either through the national parks websites (ⓦdnp.go.th or ⓦthaiforestbooking.com) or at the Khuraburi pier office (☎076 472145–6), but tents should be available on spec except during public holidays and long weekends.

Ao Chong Khad On the beach here, near the park headquarters and pier, you have the choice between en-suite national park bungalows (for two people) and either renting a national park tent or pitching your own (available for rent in Khuraburi); bedding sets cost B60/day. No wi-fi. Camping pitches B80, tents B300, bungalows B2000

Ao Mai Ngam Home to the nicer campsite, with tents (B300–450/day) and pitches (B80/day) but no bungalows, and reached via a 2km trail from headquarters or by longtail. No wi-fi. Pitches B80, tents B300

7

Khao Sok National Park

🕿 077 395154, 🌐 khaosok.com • B200, payable at the checkpoint at headquarters and valid for 24hr; you'll have to pay again at Cheow Lan Lake if you arrive more than 24hr later

Most of the Andaman coast's highlights are, unsurprisingly, along the shoreline, but the stunning jungle-clad karsts of **KHAO SOK NATIONAL PARK** are well worth heading inland for. Located about halfway between the southern peninsula's two coasts and easily accessible from Khao Lak, Phuket and Surat Thani, the park has become a popular stop on the travellers' route, offering a number of easy trails, a bit of amateur spelunking and some scenic rafthouse accommodation on Cheow Lan Lake. Much of the park, which protects the watershed of the Sok River and rises to a peak of nearly

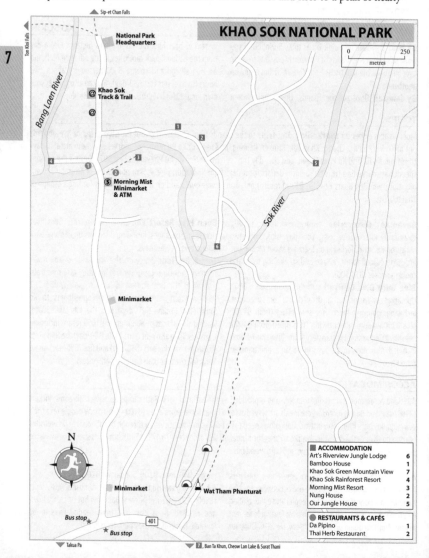

■ ACCOMMODATION

Art's Riverview Jungle Lodge	6
Bamboo House	1
Khao Sok Green Mountain View	7
Khao Sok Rainforest Resort	4
Morning Mist Resort	3
Nung House	2
Our Jungle House	5

● RESTAURANTS & CAFÉS

Da Pipino	1
Thai Herb Restaurant	2

GUIDED TREKS AND TOURS OF KHAO SOK

PARK TREKS AND NIGHT SAFARIS

The vast majority of visitors choose to join a **guided trek** at some point during their stay in the park. Though the trails are waymarked and easy to navigate alone, the guided experience alerts you to details you'd certainly miss on your own – the claw marks left by a sun-bear scaling a tree in search of honey, for example, or the medicinal plants used for malarial fevers and stomach upsets – and is both fun and inexpensive; prices are fixed but exclude the national park entrance fee.

The usual **day trek** (B700–900) goes to Ton Kloi waterfall, and from about December to March there's also a special route that takes in the blooming of the world's second-biggest flower, the **rafflesia kerrii meier**, a rather unprepossessing brown, cabbage-like plant whose enormous russet-coloured petals unfurl to a diameter of up to 80cm; it's also known as "stinking corpse lily" because it gives off a smell like rotting flesh.

After-dinner **night safaris** along the main park trails (B600–800 for 2–4hr) are also popular, not least because they're good for spotting civets, mouse deer and slow loris and, if you're exceptionally lucky, elephants and clouded leopards as well – more likely on darker nights away from the full moon.

You get to stay out in the jungle on the **overnight camping trips** (about B2200), usually around Tan Sawan falls.

Reputable and long-serving **guides** include those booked through *Bamboo House*, *Nung House* and *Khao Sok Rainforest Resort* and at Khao Sok Track & Trail (☎081 958 0629, ⓦkhaosoktrackandtrail.com).

Any guesthouse can also arrange **elephant rides** (B800–900) and fix you up with equipment and transfers for **tubing** and **canoeing** trips along the Sok River (from B500/800).

CHEOW LAN LAKE TOURS

The Australian–Thai-run Limestone Lake Rainforest Tours (☎087 268 8017, limestonelaketours .com) offers a big range of **lake-based tours**, including a two-hour trip (B1800/boat) and a full-day trip with optional overnight in a rafthouse (from B2500/3700 per person for up to three people, including park entry fee, or cheaper with larger groups).

Khao Sok guesthouses charge B1500 for a day-trip to the lake and around B2500 for two-day, one-night trips. It's also possible to simply turn up at the dam and hire a boat for around B2000.

7

1000m, is carpeted in impenetrable rainforest, home to gaurs, leopard cats and tigers among others – and up to 155 species of bird. The limestone crags that dominate almost every vista both on and away from the lake are breathtaking, never more so than in the early morning: waking up to the sound of hooting gibbons and the sight of thick white mist curling around the karst formations is an experience not quickly forgotten.

The park has two centres: the **tourist village** that has grown up around the park headquarters and trailheads, which offers all essential services, including an **ATM** at Morning Mist Minimarket and currency exchange and overseas phone services at Khao Sok Track & Trail; and the dam, 65km further east, at the head of **Cheow Lan Lake**. Most visitors stay in the tourist village and organize their lake trips from there, but it's also feasible to do one or more nights at the lake first. Take plenty of water when hiking as Khao Sok is notoriously humid.

The trails

Seven of the park's nine attractions (waterfalls, pools, gorges and viewpoints) branch off the clearly signed main **trail** that runs west of the park headquarters and visitor centre, along the Sok River. The first 3.5km constitute the **interpretative trail** described in *Waterfalls and Gibbon Calls* (see p.607), an unexceptional ninety-minute one-way trail along a broad, road-like track. Most people continue along the river to **Ton Kloi waterfall**, 7km from headquarters (allow 3hr each way), which flows year-round and tumbles into a pool that's good for swimming. En route, signs point to **Bang Liap Nam waterfall** (4.5km from headquarters), which is a straightforward hike; and **Tan Sawan waterfall** (6km from headquarters), which involves wading along a river bed for the final kilometre and should not be attempted during the rainy season. The trail to the rather spectacular eleven-tiered **Sip-et Chan waterfall**, which shoots off north from the park headquarters and follows the course of the Bang Laen River, is no longer much used and can be quite indistinct. Though the falls are only 4km from headquarters, there's a fair bit of climbing on the way, plus half a dozen river crossings, so you should allow three hours each way.

Cheow Lan Lake

65km from national park headquarters

Dubbed Thailand's Guilin because of its photogenic karst islands, forested inlets and mist-clad mountains encircling jade-coloured waters, the vast 28km-long **Cheow Lan Lake** (also known as **Ratchabrapa Dam** reservoir) is Khao Sok's most famous feature and the most popular destination for guided tours. It was created in the 1980s when the Khlong Saeng River was dammed to power a new hydroelectricity plant, and its forested shores and hundred-plus islands now harbour abundant bird life, as well as some primates, most easily spotted in the very early morning. Tours generally combine a trip on the lake with a wade through the nearby flooded cave system and a night on a floating rafthouse. The lake can only be explored by longtail boat tour, arranged either from Khao Sok or from Ratchabrapa Dam.

For many people, the highlight of their lake excursion is the adventurous three-hour trek to and through the 800m-long horseshoe-shaped **Nam Talu cave**, a five-minute boat ride from the national park rafthouses, or about an hour's boat ride from the dam. The **trek** is not for everyone, however, as the cave section entails an hour-long wade through the river that hollowed out this tunnel: it's slippery underfoot and pitch black and there will be at least one 20m section where you have to swim. When the river level is high there will be longer swims. Never attempt the cave without an authorized park guide and heed any closure signs posted because of high water levels and strong currents; in October 2007 a flash flood caused nine fatalities here and the park authorities are now stricter. Wear sandals with decent grip and request (or take) your own torch.

Part of the appeal of a night in a rafthouse on Cheow Lan Lake is the **dawn safari** the next morning, when you've a good chance of seeing langurs, macaques and gibbons on the lakeshore; some tours include this option, or you can usually borrow a kayak from your accommodation and paddle around the shore yourself.

ARRIVAL AND DEPARTURE   **KHAO SOK NATIONAL PARK**

Khao Sok National Park headquarters, its tourist village and Cheow Lan Lake are all north off Highway 401, which is served by frequent **buses**: all services between the junction town of **Takua Pa**, 40km south of Khuraburi, and Surat Thani come this way, including some Surat Thani services to and from Khao Lak and Phuket. Coming from Bangkok, Hua Hin or Chumphon, take a Surat Thani-bound bus as far as the Highway 401 junction, about 20km before Surat Thani, and change onto one for Takua Pa.

PARK HEADQUARTERS

The access road to the tourist village and trailheads is at kilometre-stone 109 on Highway 401, where guesthouse staff meet bus passengers and offer free lifts to their accommodation, the furthest of which is about 3km from the main road.

Khao Sok Track & Trail in the tourist village (☎ 081 958 0629, ✆ khaosoktrackandtrail.com) sells bus (including a

VIP bus to Bangkok, via Surat Thani), boat, plane and train tickets, as well as tickets for a/c minibuses to destinations that include Krabi (2hr), Surat Thani's Talat Kaset II via the train station at Phunphin (1hr 45min), Ko Samui (3hr) and Trang (4hr 30min).

Bus destinations: Bangkok (via Surat Thani; daily; 11hr); Khao Lak (9 daily; 1hr 30min); Surat Thani (hourly; 1–2hr); Takua Pa (9 daily; 50min).

CHEOW LAN LAKE

Access to the lake is via the town of Ban Ta Khun, 50km east of Khao Sok on Route 401, from where it's 12km north to the dam. Many travellers book their tour of the lake from their Khao Sok accommodation, in which case all transport is included, but if coming from Surat Thani or Phang Nga,

you could do the lake first. There's a regular minibus service from Talat Kaset II in Surat Thani, via Phunphin train station, to Cheow Lan Lake (about every 2hr; 1hr), or you could take a Surat Thani–Takua Pa bus, alight at Ban Ta Khun and get a motorbike taxi to the dam.

INFORMATION

Map The checkpoint office at headquarters supplies a small sketch map of the park and trails.

Guidebooks The best introduction to Khao Sok is the

guidebook *Waterfalls and Gibbon Calls* by Thom Henley, which is available at some Khao Sok minimarkets and bungalows.

ACCOMMODATION

PARK HEADQUARTERS

The bulk of the budget accommodation is scenically sited beneath the karsts near the park headquarters, but despite the edge-of-the-rainforest location, it can get noisy of an evening, with the sound systems at some backpacker bars pitched against the chattering of the cicadas. Some guesthouses (not listed here) can make life difficult for guests who choose not to book park trips through them. "Treehouses" round here means bungalows built on very tall stilts among the trees, rather than actually in the trees.

★ **Art's Riverview Jungle Lodge** ⓘ 086 479 3234 or ⓘ 087 885 6185. Popular place nicely located away from the main fray next to a good swimming hole, surrounded by jungle and enjoying pretty river views from its terrace restaurant (though the food's no great shakes). The cheaper bungalows are spacious, tastefully designed wooden affairs, with shutters and a deck, while the deluxe versions are bigger still and attractively furnished, some with red-brick outdoor bathrooms and waterfall-style showers; there are also treehouse-style bungalows and family cottages. All rooms have fans and mosquito nets. **B650**

Bamboo House ⓘ 081 787 7484, ⓦ krabidir.com /bamboohouse/index.htm. Set in a grassy orchard, this was one of the first guesthouses in the park and is run by welcoming members of the park warden's family. The simple, stilted, en-suite wooden huts with mosquito nets here are the cheapest in this part of the park and there are also pebble-dashed concrete versions, a couple of treehouse-style bungalows and large, wooden affairs with hot showers and balconies on stilts right over the river (B800). **B200**

Khao Sok Green Mountain View 1500m north up a mostly paved road from Highway 401, just east of the km 106 marker ⓘ 087 263 2481, ⓦ khaosok-greenmountain view.com. This is a great budget option if you want a remote location, situated as it is in a very quiet spot far from almost everyone else. The seven good-quality bamboo and wood bungalows of varying sizes are all en suite and have some nice touches, with pretty open-roofed bathrooms, fans, mosquito nets, decks and hammocks. They sit on the edge of a rubber plantation on the other side of the karsts from the main accommodation area. There's free transport to the park village

or you can walk to *Our Jungle House* across the river in 15min and on to the park headquarters in another 25. **B350**

Khao Sok Rainforest Resort ⓘ 077 395135, ⓦ khaosokrainforest.com. This welcoming place has some spectacularly sited "mountain view" bungalows – set high on a jungle slope and affording unsurpassed karst views – plus a/c treehouses and fan or a/c riverside bungalows. The a/c options have hot showers, TVs and mini-bars, and include breakfast in the price. Interiors are decent enough though lacking style. Fan **B500**, a/c **B1650**

★ **Morning Mist Resort** ⓘ 089 971 8794, ⓦ khaosok morningmistresort.com. Built within a profuse riverside garden that's filled with carefully tended tropical blooms and a big herb garden that supplies the excellent restaurant, this well-run place offers large, immaculate rooms in variously styled wooden and concrete bungalows, all with hot water and either river, mountain or garden view. It's nicely set up for families, with some rooms sleeping up to four, plus lots of space for kids to play in and a small swimming pool. Good rates for singles (B550). **B1300**

Nung House ⓘ 077 395147, ⓦ nunghouse.com. Friendly place run by the park warden's son and his family, with eighteen very good huts set around an attractive grassy garden full of rambutan trees. Choose between simple but sturdy bamboo and wood constructions with en-suite facilities, brick and concrete bungalows, and treehouses; some have hot showers and large verandas. **B300**

Our Jungle House ⓘ 081 417 0546, ⓦ khaosok accommodation.com. Peaceful riverside option, a 20min walk from park headquarters, secluded in lush rainforest where you might spot hornbills and several species of monkey. Choose between airy, well-designed, wood and bamboo bungalows and treehouses (B1300); all have fans and mosquito nets and most are on the river bank, which has a small beach. **B800**

CHEOW LAN LAKE

On overnight tours to the lake (see p.605), accommodation is either in tents in the jungle or at rafthouses on the lake. There are both private and national park rafthouses moored at various scenic spots around the lake shore,

7

mostly around an hour's boat ride from the dam. All rafthouse huts are rudimentary bamboo structures with nets and mattresses, offering fabulous lake views from your pillow. If you've arranged your own boat transport, you can fix accommodation at any of the lake's rafthouses for B600 per person including three meals. Accommodation packages that include boat transfers from the dam and a cave tour are about B1500 with *Sai Chol Raft House* (☎081 891 6052, ✐saicholsouthernthailand.com). Jungle Yoga runs yoga, meditation and massage retreats at the remote *Praiwan* rafthouses from December to April (✐jungleyoga .com).

EATING AND DRINKING

There are just a couple of places that might tempt you away from your guesthouse restaurant in the tourist village near park headquarters.

PARK HEADQUARTERS

Da Pipino Homely, rustic, not to say scruffy, Italian restaurant, strewn with lovely plants in a scenic spot by the river. The menu runs to seafood antipasti, decent fettuccine bolognese (B195), a few Italian main courses and a wide range of tasty handmade pizzas. Daily noon–10pm.

Thai Herb Restaurant Morning Mist Resort. Exceptionally tasty and inventive spicy *yam* salads (B90) and other Thai classics, plus a wide choice for vegetarians and breakfast; staff grow much of their own produce. Also does Thai desserts and lassis, shakes and herb juices such as roselle. Daily 8am–9pm.

Khao Lak

Handily located just an hour north of Phuket International Airport, and some 30km south of Takua Pa, **KHAO LAK** has established itself as a thriving, mid-market beach resort with plentiful opportunities for diving and snorkelling, easy access to the supreme national park reefs of Ko Similan, and a style that is determinedly unseedy. It lacks sophistication, and is mostly a bit pricey for backpackers, but is ideal for families and extremely popular with northern European tourists. High season here runs from November to April, when the weather and the swimming are at their best and the Similan Islands are open to the public; during the rest of the year, Khao Lak quietens down a lot – and becomes much cheaper too.

The area usually referred to as Khao Lak is in fact a string of beaches west off Highway 4. **Khao Lak** proper is the southernmost and least developed, 5km from the most commercial part of the resort, **Nang Thong** (aka Bang La On), which throngs with shops, restaurants, dive centres and countless places to stay, both on the beachfront and inland from Highway 4. North again about 3km (5min by taxi or a 45min walk up the beach) is lower-key, slightly more youthful **Bang Niang**, a lovely long stretch of golden sand that's backed by a developing tourist village whose network of sois is away from the highway and feels more enticing than its neighbour. Removed from all this commerce, **Laem Pakarang**, 12km further up the coast, a headland and popular sunset-watching spot that gives onto 11km Hat Pakweeb (Hat Bang Sak), is where you find the area's most exclusive accommodation.

There is, thankfully, little obvious evidence these days of the area's devastating experience during the December 2004 **tsunami**, when the undersea earthquake off Sumatra sent a series of murderous waves on to Khao Lak's shores (and the rest of the Andaman coast), vaporizing almost every shorefront home and hotel here and killing thousands. Nang Thong quickly became the centre of a huge reconstruction effort, with thousands of volunteers arriving to help, and rebuilding was mostly completed within a couple of years, though for many survivors recovery will probably take a lifetime.

Police Boat Memorial

Bang Niang

Inland from the highway – and accessible from it across a field and a bridge – a **beached police boat** has become a memorial to the extraordinary power of the tsunami

KHAO LAK, NANG THONG & BANG NIANG

N

Laem Pakarang, Hat Bang Sak, Ban Nam Khem, Takua Pa & Surat Thani

Bus Station

CHAI HAT BANG NIANG

Bang Niang

Bang Niang River

SEE INSET BELOW LEFT

SEE INSET BELOW RIGHT

Chong Fah Falls

Nang Thong

THANON NANG THONG

7

Khao Lak-Lam Ru National Park Headquarters

Police

Tong Pling Falls

Khao Lak

0   1
kilometre

4

Thap Lamu, Phang Nga, Phuket & Krabi

■ ACCOMMODATION
Amsterdam Resort	7
Ayara Villas	4, 5, 8
Fair House	6
Jai	10
Khao Lak Banana	13
Khao Lak Green Beach	11
Khao Lak Seafood Family House	9
Nang Thong Bay Resort	12
Phu Khao Lak Resort	14
Poseidon Bungalows	2
Sanuk Bungalows	3
The Sarojin	1

● RESTAURANTS & CAFÉS
Bussaba	9
The Candle	2
Dive In	10
Jai	7
Khao Niau	5
Navy Club Restaurant	1
O Rendezvous	6
Phu Khao Lak	11
Pinocchio	3
Stempfer Café	8
Takieang	4

■ BARS
Degree Bar	1
Happy Snapper	2

● SHOPS
Book Tree	1
Community Crafts	2

BANG NIANG

Bang Niang Beach

CHAI HAT BANG NIANG

Green Biking Club

Police Boat Memorial

Bang Niang Market

Tsunami Museum

Khao Lak Community Appeal Foundation

Bang Niang River

0   500
metres

NANG THONG

Sea Dragon Dive Centre

Khao Lak Inter Clinic

Khao Lak Land Discovery

Nang Thong Supermarket

Police Box

Budget Car Rental

THANON NANG THONG

Nang Thong

IQ Dive

SOI BANG LA ON

Everyday 2

0   500
metres

AFTER THE TSUNAMI

The **Boxing Day tsunami** hit Thailand's Andaman coast just after 9.30am on December 26, 2004. The first place to suffer significant damage was Phuket, and the next two hours saw village after resort get battered or decimated by the towering waves thundering in from the Sumatra fault line, 1000km away. The entire coastline from Ranong to Satun was affected, but not all of it with the same intensity: the worst-hit province was Phang Nga, where 4200 people were recorded dead or missing, many of them in the resort of Khao Lak; over 2000 suffered a similar fate on Ko Phi Phi; and more than 900 died on the beaches of Phuket, especially on Patong and Kamala. There were 8212 fatalities in all, a third of them holidaymakers. Another 6000 people were made homeless and some 150,000 lost their jobs, mostly in the tourism and fishing industries. By the end of that day, nearly a quarter of a million people in a dozen countries around the Indian Ocean had lost their lives in the worst natural disaster in recorded history.

Many homes, shops and hotels were quite swiftly rebuilt, but the emotional and social **legacy** of the tsunami endures and most residents along the Andaman coast have a story of terror and bereavement to tell. It's no surprise that many survivors are now afraid of the sea: fearing ghosts, some longtail boatmen won't motor solo past where villages once stood, and hundreds of hotel staff have since sought new jobs in the northern city of Chiang Mai, as far from the sea as they could go.

Immediately after the tsunami, many were surprised when then prime minister Thaksin Shinawatra declined offers of **aid** from foreign governments. But help poured in instead from the Thai government and from royal foundations and local and foreign NGOs and individuals. Of the many **projects** established to help support and rebuild affected communities, the majority have now completed their task; others have evolved into longer-term NGO ventures, including an English-teaching programme in Khao Lak (see p.69), and the community-based tourism company Andaman Discoveries in Khuraburi (see p.600).

Generosity and altruism were not the only responses to the disaster, however. Almost every tsunami-affected community talks of **dishonourable practice** and **corruption**, experiences which have caused bitterness and rifts. Many allegations concern donated money and goods being held back by the local leaders charged with distributing them, and in some cases big business interests muscled in on land deemed "ownerless" because the paperwork had been lost to the waves. Most small businesses had no insurance, and government **compensation** was inconsistently awarded and invariably lacking. In a country where most family enterprises scrape by season to season, it's sobering to contemplate the number of tsunami victims who simply picked up and started over.

Determined not to be caught unawares again, in the unlikely event of Thailand being struck by a second tsunami, the government has created a **tsunami early-warning system** that relays public announcements from towers all the way down the Andaman coast. They have also mapped out evacuation routes, flagged by innumerable "Tsunami Hazard Zone" signs in all the big resorts. For their part, Phuket authorities have remodelled stretches of Ao Patong's beachfront as a building-free zone, creating a park that doubles as a tsunami **memorial**. Krabi officials now require all new buildings to be constructed at least 30m inland from a high-tide boundary, and they even forbid the use of sunloungers below that point. In Khao Lak, a beached police boat (see p.608) has become an eloquent memorial: it rests where it was hurtled by the wave, 2km inland, on the other side of the highway.

waves. It was propelled up here, 2km inland, while patrolling the waters in front of *La Flora* resort, where Princess Ubolrat and her children, one of whom perished in the disaster, were staying.

Ban Nam Khem Memorial

13km north of Laem Pakarang up Highway 4, then left for a signposted 3km

The main local tsunami memorial is on the beach at **Ban Nam Khem**, the worst-hit village in Thailand, where half of the four thousand inhabitants died in the waves,

The Old Phuket Soi Aroona Karon, 192/36 Thanon Karon ☎076 396353–6, ⓦtheoldphuket.com. The Sino Wing at this attractive, peacefully secluded, heritage-conscious hotel is designed to evoke Sino-Portuguese shophouse architecture. Its rooms are both pretty and modern, with coloured glass window panels and East Indies-style wooden doors. Furnishings in the more expensive Serene Wing are much more contemporary and minimalist and many of its rooms have direct access to the lagoon-like pool. B8200

Pineapple Guesthouse Karon Plaza, off Patak and Luang Pho Chuain rds ☎076 396223, ⓦpineapple phuket.com. Good-value British–Thai guesthouse offering 21 sprucely kept, tiled-floor rooms, all with fridges, TV and hot water, most with a/c, plus a ten-bed mixed dorm, with lockers and several fans. The downstairs restaurant serves full English breakfasts and the guesthouse is surrounded by other expat bars and restaurants in the enclave known as Karon Plaza (not to be confused with the Karon Plaza market stalls at the north end of Karon beachfront). Dorm B280, fan double B500, a/c double B1050

EATING AND DRINKING

Karon's choice of restaurants is underwhelming, lacking either the big-name restaurants of Patong or Kata, or the authenticity of Phuket town. Though go-go bars haven't arrived yet, clusters of outdoor bar-beers with hostess service are popping up at a depressing rate.

75 Stang Bar Karon Plaza, up a lane off Thanon Luang Pho Chuain, near Thanon Patak. In among the sports bars and rooms for rent in Karon Plaza are a couple of "art bars" run by cool local creative types, including this invitingly bohemian little outdoor place. It's a mess of driftwood and found objects, where the only things that seem to have been designed are the red, gold and green stools, which match the wall-to-wall reggae on the sound system. Drinks aren't quite 75 *satang*, but they're certainly cheap. Daily 6pm–2am.

Baan Bang-la 6 Soi Patak, off Thanon Patak ☎81 968 5878. The seafood here has a good reputation and there are also pasta dishes and pizzas – made in a brick oven by an Italian *pizzaiolo* – on the menu too. Dining is mostly alfresco in Thai *salas* set around a pretty little garden. Mains B180–300. Daily 6pm–late.

Baan Mama Noi Karon Plaza, next door but one to Pineapple Guesthouse on a lane off Thanon Patak.

Expats, dive staff and Italian tourists fill this place at lunch and dinnertime, savouring the home-from-home taste of the excellent, mid-priced, Italian food, such as spaghetti bolognese (B150). Daily 7am–10pm.

Kwong Shop Seafood 114 Thanon Taina. Unassuming but very popular, friendly family-run institution sporting gingham tablecloths that's famous for its well-priced fresh fish (all B40/100g) and seafood cooked to order. Daily 8am–midnight.

On the Rock In the grounds of Marina Phuket Resort, Kata/Karon headland ☎076 330625, ⓦmarinaphuket .com. Occupying a fine spot above the rocks at the southern end of Ao Karon, this open-air restaurant serves especially good baskets of grilled and deep-fried seafood, such as lobster gratin (B1350), baked mussels and mixed seafood satay. Especially romantic at night. Main dishes from B350. Daily 11am–10.30pm.

Ao Kata Yai and Ao Kata Noi

Broad, curving **AO KATA YAI** (Big Kata Bay) is only a few minutes' drive around the headland from Karon (17km from Phuket town), but both prettier and safer for swimming, thanks to the protective rocky promontories at either end. It's also a good distance from the main road. The northern stretch of Kata Yai is overlooked by the unobtrusive buildings of the *Club Med* resort, and the southern by *Kata Beach Resort*: in between, the soft sand is busy with sunloungers and the occasional drink and fruit stall. The rest of the accommodation, and the bulk of the tourist village, with its restaurants, bars, tour operators and many shops, fans out eastwards from the walled *Club Med* compound, up to the main road, Thanon Patak.

Beyond the southern headland, **AO KATA NOI**'s (Little Kata Bay) smaller white-sand bay feels secluded, being at the end of a no-through road, but is very popular and filled with loungers and parasols. Kata Noi has its own low-key but rather charmless cluster of businesses, including an ATM and minimarket, though it's dominated by the various sections of the enormous *Katathani* hotel; public access to the beach is down to the right just beyond the hotel's Thani wing.

7

DIVING AND SNORKELLING OFF PHUKET

The reefs and islands within sailing distance of Phuket rate among the most spectacular in the world, and **diving and snorkelling** trips are both good value and hugely popular. Many trips operate year-round, though some of the more remote islands and reefs become too dangerous to reach during part or all of the monsoon season, roughly June to October.

DIVE SHOPS AND TRIPS

All the dive **shops** listed below are established and accredited PADI Five-Star Instructor or Career Development Centres; they teach courses, organize dive trips and rent equipment. Advice on choosing a dive shop and other general diving information can be found in "Basics" (see p.52). Expect to pay around B5150 for a one-day introductory **diving course**, and B16,050 for the four-day Openwater course, including equipment. **Day-trips** to the closest of the dive sites listed below, including at least two dives, cost around B4900, while multi-day **live-aboard** cruises to the more distant top-rated reefs of Ko Similan and Ko Surin, Hin Daeng and Hin Muang, and the Mergui archipelago can cost as much as B33,000 for four days, including sixteen dives and full board but excluding equipment and national park fees.

There are **recompression chambers** at Phuket International Hospital in Phuket town (see p.620), and at Vachira Hospital, Soi Wachira, Thanon Yaowarat, Phuket town (☎076 211114, ⓦvachiraphuket.go.th).

Dive Asia 24 Thanon Karon, Kata/Karon headland, Ao Karon, and 623 Thanon Patak, Karon Circle, Ao Karon ☎076 330598, ⓦdiveasia.com.

Marina Divers Next to *Marina Phuket Resort* at 45 Thanon Karon, Ao Karon ☎076 330272, ⓦmarinadivers.com.

Santana 240 Thanon Raja Uthit Song Roi Phi, Ao Patong ☎076 294220, ⓦsantanaphuket.com.

Scuba Cat 94 Thanon Thavee Wong, Ao Patong ☎076 293120, ⓦscubacat.com.

SNORKELLING TRIPS

The most popular snorkelling destination from Phuket is **Ko Phi Phi** (see p.667). All travel agents sell mass-market day-trips there, on huge ferries with capacities of a hundred plus; prices average B1700 and include snorkelling stops at Phi Phi Leh and Phi Phi Don, snorkel rental and a seafood lunch. Smaller speedboat trips to Ko Phi Phi are usually worth the extra money to avoid the big groups; those run by Offspray Leisure (B3500; ☎076 281375, ⓦoffsprayleisure.com) get good reviews, and they also run speedboat snorkel trips to **Ko Racha Yai** (B3500). Day-trip packages to the remote but beautiful **Ko Similan** islands start

ARRIVAL AND DEPARTURE

AO KATA YAI AND AO KATA NOI

By songthaew Most songthaews from Phuket go first to Karon, then drive south past *Club Med* and terminate beside *Kata Beach Resort* on the headland between Kata Yai and Kata Noi (B30; returning songthaews depart approx every 20min 5am–4.30pm). To get to Kata Noi, continue walking over the hill (around 20min), or take a tuk-tuk for about B200.

ACCOMMODATION

Alpina Phuket Nalina Resort and Spa 7/1 Thanon Ked Kwan, Kata Yai ☎076 370999, ⓦphuketnalina .com. Very pleasant hotel with comfortable, tastefully Thai-style rooms and a surprisingly quiet location that's close to shops and restaurants and about a 10min walk from the beach. A free shuttle also runs guests to the hotel's private beach club in front of *Club Med*. Rooms have generous balconies overlooking the free-form pool and the hills beyond, with some enjoying direct pool access; suites and private pool villas are enormous. Also has a spa and several restaurants. Breakfast included. **B6150**

The Boathouse Thanon Kok Tanode, Kata Yai ☎076 330015–7, ⓦboathousephuket.com. Exclusive beachfront boutique hotel in a graceful, contemporary style, with just 38 elegantly furnished seafront rooms, a reputation for classy service, and a famously top-notch restaurant. There's a pool, a spa and weekend cooking classes (see box, p.618). Advance booking essential. **B10,450**

Capannina Inn The Beach Centre, "New Kata Road", Kata Yai ☎076 284450, ⓦphuket-capannina-inn.com. Smart, modern, large bedrooms and well-equipped bathrooms, with a/c, cable TV, hot water, fridges and espresso machines. Guests have the use of an attractive, shared, garden pool in front. It's set in a newer development of shops and hotels, a 5min walk from the beach –there's a free tuk-tuk to the beach and the restaurant (see p.638). Continental breakfast included. **B2400**

from B3500 (see p.614). Many of the dive companies listed welcome snorkellers on board their day-trips, and sometimes on the live-aboards too, for a discount of about thirty percent.

ANDAMAN COAST DIVE AND SNORKEL SITES

Anemone Reef About 22km east of Phuket. Submerged reef of soft coral and sea anemones starting about 5m deep. Lots of fish, including leopard sharks, tuna and barracuda. Usually combined with a dive at nearby Shark Point. Unsuitable for snorkellers.

Burma Banks About 250km northwest of Phuket; only accessible on live-aboards. A series of submerged "banks", well away from any landmass and very close to the Burmese border. Only worth the trip for its sharks. Visibility up to 25m.

Hin Daeng and **Hin Muang** 56km southwest of Ko Lanta. Hin Daeng is an exceptional reef wall, named after the red soft corals that cover the rocks, with visibility up to 30m. One hundred metres away, Hin Muang also drops to 50m and is good for stingrays, manta rays, whale sharks and silvertip sharks. Visibility up to 50m. Because of the depth and the current, both places are considered too risky for novice divers who have logged fewer than twenty dives. Unsuitable for snorkellers.

King Cruiser Near Shark Point, between Phuket and Ko Phi Phi. Dubbed the *Thai Tanic*, this became a wreck dive in May 1997, when a tourist ferry sank on its way to Ko Phi Phi. Visibility up to 20m, but hopeless for snorkellers because of the depth, and collapsed sections make it dangerous for any but the most experienced divers.

Ko Phi Phi 48km east of Phuket's Ao Chalong (see p.667). Visibility up to 30m. The most popular destination

for Phuket divers and snorkellers. Spectacular drop-offs; good chance of seeing whale sharks.

Ko Racha Noi and **Ko Racha Yai** About 33km and 28km south of Phuket's Ao Chalong respectively. Visibility up to 40m. Racha Yai (aka Raya Yai) is good for beginners and for snorkellers; at the more challenging Racha Noi there's a good chance of seeing manta rays, eagle rays and whale sharks.

Ko Rok Nok and **Ko Rok Nai** 100km southeast of Phuket, south of Ko Lanta (see box, p.684). Visibility up to 18m. Shallow reefs that are excellent for snorkelling.

Ko Similan 96km northwest of Phuket; easiest access from Khao Lak (see p.614). One of the world's top diving spots. Visibility up to 30m. Leopard sharks, whale sharks and manta rays, plus caves and gorges.

Ko Surin 174km northwest of Phuket; easiest access from Khuraburi (see p.601). Shallow reefs of soft and hard corals that are good for snorkelling.

Richelieu Rock Just east of Ko Surin, close to Burmese waters. A sunken pinnacle that's famous for its whale sharks. Considered by many to be Thailand's top dive spot.

Shark Point (Hin Mu Sang) 24km east of Phuket's Laem Panwa. Protected as a marine sanctuary. Visibility up to 10m. Notable for soft corals, sea fans and leopard sharks. Often combined with the *King Cruiser* dive and/or Anemone Reef; unrewarding for snorkellers.

7

Cool Breeze 225 Thanon Kok Tanode, Kata Yai ☎076 330484 or ☎085 900 3681, ⓦphuketindex.com /coolbreezebungalows. Though one of the cheapest places in Kata, for your money you get a spacious private bungalow, plus a view of sorts from the terrace (either of the distant sea or of the hilltop Big Buddha in profile), the bungalows being ranged steeply up the hillside in a grassy palm- and shrub-filled garden. Wi-fi is only in public areas and interiors are nothing fancy but good value, with hot shower (in most), TV and fridge, and are sufficiently far above the narrow, noisy road. Fan B1000, a/c B1500

Kata Beach Resort Thanon Kata, Kata Yai ☎076 330530–4, ⓦkatagroup.com. This huge 275-room, four-storey hotel occupies a great spot right on the edge of the southern end of Kata Yai's white-sand beach. It has a shorefront restaurant and two swimming pools, a palm-shaded seaside garden, a spa and a dive shop. Some of the attractive, balconied, wooden-floored rooms have direct pool access, and some have sea views. B10,400

Katathani Beach Resort and Spa 14 Thanon Kata Noi, Kata Noi ☎076 330124–6, ⓦkatathani.com. The various wings and offshoots of the enormous and luxurious *Katathani* now occupy almost the entire shoreline of small, secluded Kata Noi. The beachfront all-suite Thani wing has the prime position, with the narrow lawn dropping seamlessly onto the white sand; all rooms here have seaview balconies. Across the effectively private, no-through road, the cheaper, garden-view Bhuri wing has a distinctively contemporary, pastel-coloured look and its rooms too are very deluxe. There's daily shuttle service to town and to Patong. The hotel has six restaurants, six swimming pools and a spa, plus an arm-long menu of activities and a kids' club. Breakfast included. B8750

Mom Tri's Villa Royale 12 Thanon Kata Noi, Kata Noi ☎076 333569, ⓦvillaroyalephuket.com. Luxurious suites, richly decorated with fine textiles and teak, a renowned restaurant (see p.638), an excellent spa and two saltwater and one freshwater pools, all set in landscaped tropical gardens with fine views above Kata Noi. B18,100

7

EATING AND DRINKING

The Boathouse Wine and Grill Thanon Kok Tanode, Kata Yai ☎076 330015–7, ⓦboathousephuket.com. One of the best-known restaurants on Phuket – not least for its famously extensive, award-winning wine list – where the skills of the French chef are best sampled on four-course Thai or French tasting menus (just over B1800, or B3300 with paired wines). The beachside terrace and dining room, decorated with nautical touches and attached to the boutique hotel of the same name, enjoy fine sunset views, and there are cooking classes here every weekend (see box, p.618). Reservations recommended. Daily 11am–11pm.

Capannina Down a short alley of shops off Kata Road, Kata Yai ☎076 284318, ⓦcapannina-phuket.com. Done out in cool red and black, this Italian-run, open-sided restaurant (with an a/c room) prepares good, home-made pastas (tagliatelle bolognese B250), pizzas from a wood-fired oven and a wide range of seafood and meat main courses; finish off with your choice of grappas and an Illy espresso. Daily 11am–late.

Mom Tri's Kitchen Mom Tri's Villa Royale, 12 Thanon Kata Noi, Kata Noi ☎076 333569, ⓦvillaroyalephuket .com. Highly regarded luxury restaurant, offering Thai and

European fine dining, in dishes such as veal parmigiana and jumbo prawns in red curry. Mains from B590. Reservations recommended. Daily 6.30am–11.30pm.

Ratri Italian Bar & Grill Reached by a vertiginous but short climb (or by road) east off Thanon Patak ☎076 333538, ⓦratrijazztaurant.com. This rather sophisticated eyrie makes a panoramic spot for cocktails at sundown, with high-level views across Kata, plenty of squishy sofas to sink into and a good if pricey menu of Thai food (B220–850), including *matsaman* and Indian–Thai curries. The enthusiastic in-house jazz band plays from about 8.30pm late into the night and is worth lingering for. Daily 3pm–late.

★**Seacret** Katathani Beach Resort and Spa, 14 Thanon Kata Noi, Kata Noi ☎076 330124–6, ⓦkatathani.com. Excellent Phuket and southern Thai cuisine, such as the classic dried-shrimp relish, *nam prik kung siap*, *pla thawt khamin* (deep-fried fish with turmeric and pineapple relish; B290) and *muu hong* (stewed pork belly with cinnamon). All this and an attractive, open-air setting by the swimming pool, with the best tables on a deck under fairy-lit trees by the beach. Daily 11am–5pm & 6–10.30pm.

Hat Nai Harn

The favourite beach of the many expats who live in nearby Rawai, **HAT NAI HARN**, 18km southwest of Phuket town, is an exceptionally beautiful curved bay of white sand backed by a stand of casuarinas and plenty of food stalls but only minimal development. It does get crowded with parasols and loungers, however, and during the monsoon the waves here are huge.

ARRIVAL AND DEPARTURE
HAT NAI HARN

By songthaew Songthaews from Phuket town (approx every 30min; 45min; B40) go to Nai Harn, via Rawai, with   the last one returning at an early 4pm.

ACCOMMODATION AND EATING

All Seasons Naiharn Phuket ☎076 289327, ⓦallseasons-naiharn-phuket.com. Run by the French Accor group, this well-sited hotel offers contemporary-styled rooms with ocean or garden view, five restaurants and bars, a spa, a kids' club and a decent-sized pool. It's just over the narrow road from the shore, next door to *Royal Phuket Yacht Club* (under lengthy renovations). B2950

★**Trattoria del Buongustaio** ☎087 467 2554, ⓦtrattoriabuongustaio.ilmiosito.net. This Italian-run restaurant offers gorgeous views of the bay from a lovely

balcony above the rocks on the northern headland; reach it via the paved road through *The Royal Phuket Yacht Club* (the road may appear to be private and is currently tricky to manoeuvre, but persevere). The full menu covers a wide choice of starters and meat and especially seafood main courses, plus risottos and pastas such as delicious seafood ravioli with sage and butter (B370). Daily noon–12.30am; the kitchen closes at 11pm, while the downstairs lounge bar closes at 2am.

Hat Ya Nui and Laem Promthep

Follow the coastal road 2km south around the lumpy headland from Hat Nai Harn and you reach the tiny roadside beach of **Hat Ya Nui**, which gets a surprising number of visitors despite being so small and right next to the admittedly quiet road. There are coral reefs very close to shore, though the currents are strong, and kayaks and sunloungers for rent.

The rugged, wind-blasted, grassy flanked headland of **Laem Promthep**, 1km beyond Hat Ya Nui, marks Phuket's southernmost tip, jutting dramatically – and photogenically – into the deep blue of the Andaman Sea. The cape is one of the island's top beauty spots, and at sunset busloads of tour groups get shipped in to admire the spectacle; Thais pay their respects at the Hindu shrine here, offering elephant figurines in honour of the enshrined four-headed god Brahma and his elephant mount, Erawan. You can escape the crowds by following the trail along the ridge and down to the rocks just above the water.

ARRIVAL AND ACCOMMODATION HAT YA NUI AND LAEM PROMTHEP

Songthaews to and from Nai Harn pass through Rawai, so to explore both places, you could catch a songthaew from Phuket town to Nai Harn (approx every 30min; 45min; B40), then walk up and around the promontory in a couple of hours, to pick up another songthaew back to town from Rawai (see below).

Nai Ya Beach Bungalow ☎ 076 238179, ⓦ naiyabeach bungalow.com. Two hundred metres uphill from Ya Nui beach towards the cape, this friendly and very pleasant place has attractive, sturdy, thatch-roofed bamboo bungalows with fans, en-suite cold showers and verandas. They're set in a flowery garden that's nicely shaded by cashew nut trees and bougainvillaea and enjoys high-level sea views. Closed May–Oct. **B990**

Hat Rawai

Phuket's southernmost beach, **HAT RAWAI**, was the first to be exploited for tourist purposes, but, half a century on, the hoteliers have moved to the far more appealing sands of Kata and Karon, leaving Rawai to its former inhabitants, the Urak Lawoy *chao ley* (see p.602), and to an expanding expat population. Most visitors are here for the many alfresco **seafood restaurants** along Thanon Viset's beachside promenade.

Phuket Seashell Museum

1500m north of the beach on Highway 4024 • Daily 8am–5.30pm • B200

Aside from its seafront restaurants, Rawai's chief attraction is the **Phuket Seashell Museum**, which displays some two thousand species of shell, including 380-million-year-old fossils, giant clams and a 140-carat gold pearl.

ARRIVAL AND EATING HAT RAWAI

By songthaew Songthaews from Phuket town pass through Rawai (approx every 30min, 35min; B30) on their way to and from Nai Harn.

Nikita's Towards the northern end of the promenade ☎ 076 288703, ⓦ nikitas-phuket.com. A standout among the many expat-favoured bar-restaurants in the area, not least for the horizon-gazing potential from its peaceful tables on the sand (candlelit at night). Pizzas from a wood-fired oven (from B240) feature on its Thai and Western menu, alongside well-priced cocktails, wines by the glass and espresso coffees. Daily 10am–2am at the latest, kitchen closes 11pm.

Salaloy Opposite Nikita's, towards the northern end of the promenade ☎ 076 613740. The best and most famous of Rawai's restaurants, whose highlights include *pla thawt khamin* (fried fish with turmeric) and omelette topped with baby oysters (B110); it has some lovely outdoor tables right on the shorefront under the casuarinas. Daily 10am–9.30pm.

Ao Chalong, Laem Panwa and around

North of Rawai, the sizeable offshore island of Ko Lone protects the broad sweep of **AO CHALONG**, where many a Chinese fortune was made from the huge quantities of tin mined in the bay. These days, Ao Chalong is the main departure point for dive excursions and snorkelling and fishing trips, which mostly leave from Chalong Pier, east of the bottle-neck roundabout known as Chalong Circle, or Chalong Ha Yaek.

7

Wat Chalong

8km southwest of Phuket town, on Thanon Chao Fa Nok, aka Route 4022 • Phuket–Karon songthaews pass the entrance

For islanders, Chalong is important as the site of **Wat Chalong**, Phuket's loveliest and most famous temple, which enshrines the statue of revered monk Luang Pho Saem, who helped resolve a violent rebellion by migrant Chinese tin miners in 1876. Elsewhere in the temple compound, the Phra Mahathat chedi is believed to contain a relic of the Buddha.

Big Buddha of Phuket

Access is via the very steep and winding 6km Soi Jao Fa 51, signed west off Thanon Chao Fa Nok (Route 422), 2km south of Wat Chalong, or 1km north of Chalong Circle • ⓦ mingmongkolphuket.com

With your own transport, a visit to Wat Chalong combines well with a pilgrimage to the modern-day **Big Buddha of Phuket** (officially Phra Phuttha Mingmongkol Eaknakakeeree), a towering 45m statue atop the aptly named Khao Nakkerd hill, which dominates many island vistas, including from Kata Yai to the southwest, and is easily spotted from aeroplane windows. Made of concrete but faced with glistening white-marble tiles, the eastward-looking Buddha boasts enormous proportions: sitting on a lotus flower that's nearly 25m across with individual hair curls measuring almost 1m each. Views from the base of the statue extend east over Ao Chalong to hilly Ko Lone beyond, while western panoramas take in Kata Noi; it's a popular sunset-viewing spot.

Phuket Aquarium

Laem Panwa, 10km south of Phuket town • Daily 8.30am–4.30pm, feeding show Sat & Sun 11am • B100 • ⓦ phuketaquarium.org • Songthaews leave from the market in Phuket town (B30), the last one returning at about 3.30pm

Ao Chalong tapers off eastwards into **Laem Panwa**, at the tip of which you'll find the **Phuket Aquarium**. Run by the island's Marine Biological Centre, it's not a bad primer for what you might see on a reef and has walk-through tunnels, a sea-turtle pool and a shark-feeding show.

ARRIVAL, ACCOMMODATION AND EATING   AO CHALONG

By songthaew Songthaews to Ao Chalong from Phuket town charge B30.

Kan Eang @ Pier Ao Chalong ☎076 381212, ⓦkaneang-pier.com. Classy, long-running restaurant, which is handily, and scenically, sited on a 200m frontage at the mouth of Chalong Pier. The big draw here is the seafood, the best of it barbecued old-style on burning coconut husks (from B1200/kg); deep-fried seaweed with shrimps and chilli sauce is also good, and the *haw mok* (fish curry steamed in a banana leaf) is exceptional. Sister restaurant *Kan Eang Seafood*, north up the beach (☎076 381323, ⓦphuket-seafood.com), enjoys a similarly good reputation and offers free pick-ups. Daily 10.30am–11pm.

Shanti Lodge Soi Bangrae, 1500m south down Thanon Chao Fa Nok from Wat Chalong (the Phuket–Karon songthaew can drop you close by) ☎076 280233, ⓦshantilodge.com. Though there's no special reason to stay in this part of the island, you might make an exception for this alternative, traveller-oriented place. It's set in a relaxing garden, with saltwater swimming pool, book exchange and predominantly vegetarian restaurant, and has fan and a/c doubles with or without private hot-water bathrooms, some of them wheelchair accessible, and family rooms. Long-termers get discounts. Fan **B750**, a/c **B850**

Thalang and around

There's not a great deal for tourists in the northeast of Phuket island around the district town of **THALANG**, but you're quite likely to pass the landmark **Heroines' Monument**, which stands in the centre of the Tha Rua junction, 12km north of Phuket town on Highway 402. The monument commemorates the repulse of the Burmese army by the widow of the governor of Phuket and her sister in 1785; together they rallied the island's womenfolk who, legend has it, frightened the Burmese away by cutting their hair short and rolling up banana leaves to look like musket barrels – a victory that's celebrated every March 13 to 15 with a monks' ordination ceremony and processions.

CLOCKWISE FROM TOP LEFT PHUKET SEAFOOD; MONK BOARDING A BUS IN AO PATONG (P.629); SINO-PORTUGUESE ARCHITECTURE IN PHUKET OLD TOWN (P.621) >

Thalang National Museum

On Route 4027, 200m east of the Heroines' Monument • Wed–Sun 9am–4pm • B30 • All mainland-bound traffic and all songthaews between Phuket and Hat Surin and Hat Nai Yang pass the monument

As the only official introduction to Phuket's rich and intriguing history, **Thalang National Museum** doesn't really match up to the task, but taken in conjunction with the privately funded Thaihua Museum in Phuket town (see p.623), the picture starts to flesh out. Displays include some interesting exhibits on the local tin and rubber industries, accounts of some of the more colourful folkloric traditions and photos of the masochistic feats of the Vegetarian Festival (see box, p.623).

Wat Phra Thong

Just beyond the crossroads in Thalang town, 8km north of the Heroines' Monument

Wat Phra Thong is one of Phuket's most revered temples on account of the power of the Buddha statue it enshrines. The solid gold image is half-buried and no one dares dig it up for fear of a curse that has struck down excavators in the past. After the wat was built around the statue, the image was encased in plaster to deter would-be robbers.

Khao Phra Taew Forest Reserve

Visitor centre 3km east of the crossroads in Thalang town • B200

Several paths cross the small hilly enclave of **Khao Phra Taew Forest Reserve**, leading you through the forest habitat of macaques and wild boar, but the most popular features of the park are the Gibbon Rehabilitation Project and the Ton Sai and Bang Pae waterfalls, which combine well as a day-trip or on a tour (see p.618). You can get drinks and snacks at the food stall next to the Rehabilitation Centre, and the route to the waterfalls is signed from here.

The Gibbon Rehabilitation Project

10km northeast of the Heroines' Monument, off Route 4027 • Daily 9am–3.30pm • ⓦ gibbonproject.org • Songthaews from Phuket town, more frequent in the morning, will take you most of the way: ask to be dropped off at Bang Pae (a 40min drive from town) and then follow the signed track for about 1km to get to the project centre

Phuket's forests used to resound with the whooping calls of indigenous white-handed lar gibbons (see p.755), but they make such charismatic pets that they were poached to extinction on the island by the mid-1980s. The lar is now an endangered species, and in 1992 it became illegal in Thailand to keep them as pets, to sell them or to kill them. Despite this, you'll come across a depressing number of pet gibbons on Phuket, kept in chains by bar and hotel owners as entertainment for their customers. The **Gibbon Rehabilitation Centre** aims to reverse this by rescuing pet gibbons and then re-socializing and re-educating them for the wild before finally releasing them back into the forests. It is not unusual for gibbons to be severely traumatized by their experience as pets: not only will they have been taken forcibly from their mothers, but they may also have been abused by their owners.

Visitors are welcome at the project, which is centred in the forests of Khao Phra Taew Forest Reserve, protected as a "non-hunting area", close to Bang Pae waterfall, but because the whole point of the rehab project is to minimize the gibbons' contact with humans, you can only admire the creatures from afar. There's a small exhibition here on the aims of the project, and the well-informed volunteer guides will fill you in on the details of each case and on the idiosyncratic habits of the lar gibbon. The website has details on how you can become a **project volunteer**, adopt a gibbon, or make a donation.

Bang Pae and Ton Sai waterfalls

If you follow the track along the river from the Gibbon Project, you'll soon arrive at **Bang Pae Falls**, a popular picnic and bathing spot, ten to fifteen minutes' walk away. Continue on the track south for another 2.8km (about 1hr 30min on foot) and you should reach **Ton Sai Falls**: though not a difficult climb, the route is unsigned and indistinct, is steep in places and rough underfoot. There are plenty of opportunities for cool dips in the river en route. Once at Ton Sai you can either walk back down to the access road to the Khao Phra Taew Forest Reserve visitor centre and try to hitch a ride back home, or return the way you came.

Ko Yao Noi

Located in an idyllic spot in Phang Nga bay, almost equidistant from Phuket, Phang Nga and Krabi, the island of **KO YAO NOI** enjoys magnificent maritime views from almost every angle and makes a refreshingly tranquil getaway. Measuring about 12km at its longest point, it's home to some four thousand islanders, the vast majority of them Muslim, who earn their living from rubber and coconut plantations, fishing and shrimp-farming. Tourism here is low-key, not least because the beaches lack the wow factor of more sparkling nearby sands, and visitors are drawn instead by the rural ambience and lack of commercial pressures. Nonetheless, there's decent swimming off the east coast at high tide, and at low tide too in a few places, and plenty of potential for kayaking, rock-climbing and other activities.

Most tourists stay on the east side, which has the bulk of the accommodation, at **Hat Tha Khao**, **Hat Khlong Jaak** (**Long Beach**), **Hat Pasai** and **Laem Sai**. Exploring the interior is a particular pleasure, either via the barely trafficked round-island road as it runs through tiny villages and the island's diminutive town, **Ban Tha Khai**, or via the trails that crisscross the forested interior, where you've a good chance of encountering monkeys as well as cobras and even pythons, not to mention plenty of birds, including majestic oriental pied hornbills.

Hat Tha Kao and Hat Sai Taew

The most northerly of the main eastern beaches is **HAT THA KAO**, site of a small village, **BAN THA KAO**, with a couple of shops and restaurants, the pier for boats to and from Krabi, and the cheapest and most backpacker-oriented bungalows on the island. It's not an attractive beach itself, barely swimmable, but is the closest point to Ko Yao's nicest beach, so-called **Temple Beach** or **Hat Sai Taew**, 2km away, whose pretty, gold-sand shore is great for swimming at any tide. However, it's backed by private land that belongs to the Dhammakaya Foundation, a populist Buddhist sect, and is unsigned and a bit tricky to find. From Tha Kao pier, head inland and take the first right behind the shops, walk alongside the khlong and its sheltered marina, over the bridge, then via the faint trail over the hill to the beach. Alternatively, you can kayak there from the pier.

Hat Khlong Jaak (Long Beach)

A couple of kilometres south of Hat Tha Kao, **HAT KHLONG JAAK**, more commonly referred to as **Long Beach**, is the site of the longest-running and best-known tourist accommodation and the liveliest places to eat and drink. The beach is indeed long, around 1500m from the northern end to *Sabai Corner* on the southern headland. Much of it is rocky and all but unswimmable at low tide, except in front of *Koyao Island Resort*, the smoothest stretch. The seaward views are glorious from every angle, however, taking in the many lovely islets of eastern Ao Phang Nga.

Hat Pasai and Laem Sai

A minute's walk south from *Sabai Corner* on Hat Khlong Jaak and you're on **HAT PASAI**, a rather pretty little beach, with some shade, several resorts and a few simple beach restaurants with tables under the casuarinas at the south end.

7

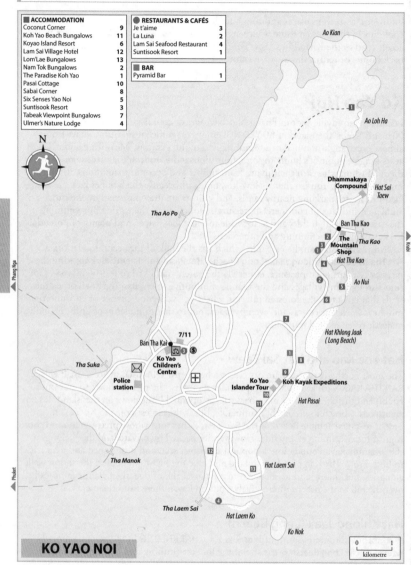

KO YAO NOI

ACCOMMODATION	
Coconut Corner	9
Koh Yao Beach Bungalows	11
Koyao Island Resort	6
Lam Sai Village Hotel	12
Lom'Lae Bungalows	13
Nam Tok Bungalows	2
The Paradise Koh Yao	1
Pasai Cottage	10
Sabai Corner	8
Six Senses Yao Noi	5
Suntisook Resort	3
Tabeak Viewpoint Bungalows	7
Ulmer's Nature Lodge	4

● RESTAURANTS & CAFÉS	
Je t'aime	3
La Luna	2
Lam Sai Seafood Restaurant	4
Suntisook Resort	1

■ BAR	
Pyramid Bar	1

Beyond Hat Pasai, tiny **HAT LAEM SAI** is often known simply as **Hat Lom'Lae**, after the appealing Thai–Canadian *Lom'Lae Bungalows*, which sits on the shore (see p.647).

A few hundred metres west from the *Lom'Lae* turn-off, about 3km from Tha Kai, another side-road takes you down towards **Tha Laem Sai** (Laem Sai pier), along a coast that has no real beach but is scenically dotted with houses on stilts, fishing platforms, dozens of longtails and some inviting views of Ko Yao Noi's larger twin, Ko Yao Yai, just across the channel. At the tip of the peninsula stands a good seafood restaurant (see p.647), and there's a nice little beach 300m east further around the rocks.

Ban Tha Kai and north

The island's commercial and administrative centre is **BAN THA KAI**, inland from the main piers on the southwest coast. This is where you'll find the post office, banks, hospital, police station, obligatory 7-Eleven shop with ATM, as well as several internet centres, the main market and several roti stalls.

Visitors are very much encouraged to drop by the **Ko Yao Children's Community Centre** (☎087 929 4320, ⓦkoyao-ccc.com), at the western end of town, an NGO that aims to help improve the English-language, arts, handicraft and computer skills of island children and adults, as well as organizing regular beach clean-ups.

The road running **north from Tha Kai**'s 7-Eleven is particularly scenic, taking you through several hamlets with their mosques and latex-pressing mangles, and past rice fields and their resident buffaloes, framed by mangroves in the middle distance, sea eagles hovering overhead, and the rounded hills of nearby islands in the background. At a junction about 3km from Tha Khai, the northbound road soon turns into a rough track leading to the beautiful beach at **AO LOH HA**, while veering right will take you over the hill and down to Tha Kao on the east coast, about 4km away.

7

KO YAO NOI ACTIVITIES

KAYAKING AND SNORKELLING

Kayaking around the coast is a very enjoyable pastime, and the dozens of tiny islands visible from eastern shorelines make enticing destinations for experienced paddlers; kayaks can be rented through Ko Yao Noi hotels for about B300 per day. Just about every hotel and travel agent sells kayaking and snorkelling trips to Ko Hong and other islands in Ao Phang Nga.

Koh Kayak Expeditions Just south of Coconut Corner on Hat Pasai ☎087 929 4320. Good-quality kayaks, fully equipped for self-guided overnight expeditions that can last anything from 24hr to a month, for rent (B1500 per single or B2000 per tandem per 24hr, including camping equipment plus an itinerary and maps).

Ko Yao Islander Tour Next to Pasai Cottage on Hat Pasai ☎084 744 3686. Friendly place offering local snorkelling trips from B650 per person (minimum 4 people) or B1800 per boat, and kayaking and snorkelling day-trips in Phang Nga bay from B1500 per person (minimum 4 people).

DIVING

Koh Yao Diver Lom'Lae Resort, Laem Sai ☎076 597406, ⓦkohyaodiver.com. Diving trips and courses on the island are the speciality of Koh Yao Diver, where

two local dives cost B4000, two dives at the reefs around Phi Phi in a longtail B6600, and the Openwater course is B16,700.

ROCK-CLIMBING

Ko Yao Noi is fast becoming a respected destination for **rock-climbers**, who appreciate the fresh sites and uncrowded routes compared to the hectic scene at nearby Ton Sai and Railay. There are over 150 bolted routes on the island, from beginner level to advanced (5 to 8A), established by the American and Thai climbers who run The Mountain Shop in Ban Tha Kao. Many routes are over water and accessible only by boat, or at the least via a hike off the dirt track to *Paradise* hotel.

The Mountain Shop At Sea Gypsy Restaurant in Ban Tha Kao ☎083 969 2023, ⓦthemountainshop .org. For beginners, prices start from B2500 for a

half-day's course, with multi-day courses also available; there are guides and rental gear for experienced climbers.

OTHER CLASSES AND ACTIVITIES

Lam Sai Hotel Laem Sai ⓦphuket-krabi-muaythai .com. B300 for a two-hour Thai boxing class or B2500 for a week of classes.

Tappi Thai Cookery School Ban Tha Kai ☎087 887 3161, ✉karin@pailins.com. Three-hour classes,

morning or afternoon, for B1600, including transfers.

Ulmer's Nature Lodge Hat Tha Kao ☎084 690 3731, ⓦthailandyogaretreats.com. Daily drop-in yoga classes (B400), plus diverse workshops and retreats.

ARRIVAL AND DEPARTURE

There are three mainland departure points for **boats** to Ko Yao Noi – from Phuket, Krabi's Ao Thalen, and Phang Nga – plus services from Ao Nang. On Ko Yao Noi, shared songthaew **taxis** meet all arriving boats and charge up to B100 per person (depending on distance) for transfers to accommodation, or B150 if chartered for a single traveller.

To/from Phuket The most common route is from Bang Rong on Phuket's northeast coast to Tha Manok on Ko Yao Noi's southwest coast, which is covered by seven longtail boats a day (1hr 10min; B120) and two speedboats a day (40min; B200), with the last service at around 5pm. Returning to Bang Rong, boats depart Tha Manok every hour or so until 4pm.

To/from Ao Thalen Most of the Krabi province boats leave from Ao Thalen, 33km northwest of Krabi town, and arrive at the Tha Kao pier on Ko Yao Noi's northeast coast: two longtail boats a day (1hr; B120) and four speedboats (30min; B200), with the last service at 5pm.

To/from Ao Nang In high season, the Green Planet speedboat service connects Ao Nang's Hat Nopparat Thara with Ko Yao Noi once a day (30min; B700, including pick-ups in the Krabi area) at the Tha Kao and then Tha Manok piers, and continues to Bang Rong in Phuket; there's also a daily big boat from Ao Nang (about 1hr; B350).

To/from Phang Nga The most scenic journey to Ko Yao Noi is the daily (Mon–Sat) service from Phang Nga, which takes you through the heart of Ao Phang Nga, passing close by the stilt-house island of Ko Panyi (see p.648). It departs the Phang Nga bay pier at Tha Dan, 9km south of Phang Nga town, at 1pm and returns from Tha Suka on Ko Yao Noi at 7.30am (90min; B200); songthaews connect Phang Nga town with the pier.

GETTING AROUND AND INFORMATION

Getting around Songthaew taxis are easily arranged and many hotels can organize motorbike (B250–350/day) and bicycle (B200) rental.

Tourist information A good, free, regularly updated map of the island and its tourist businesses, produced by Pakorn Photo Classic, is available on the island. There's an ATM at the 7-Eleven in Ban Tha Kai and in front of *Six Senses* on Hat Khlong Jaak.

ACCOMMODATION

HAT THA KAO

Nam Tok Bungalows ☎ 087 292 1102. Set back from the beach around a khlong, a 5min walk south from the Tha Kao ferry pier, this ultra laidback set of bungalows is one of the cheapest places to stay on the island. The budget options are comfortable bamboo and wood huts, with cute bathrooms and hammocks on the deck, encircling a small garden full of flowers and a fish pond; the more luxurious ones have hot water. *Nam Tok*'s manager, Danny, occasionally takes guests on camping trips to Ko Pak Bia (from B4000 per boat). Fan B550, a/c B1700

★**Suntisook Resort** ☎ 089 781 6456, ⓦ kohyaotravel .com/suntisook. Genial, well-organized place where the bungalows are nicely spaced around a garden and come with TVs, fridges and good, hot-water bathrooms. They're all a bit different but each has a deck and a hammock and some have a/c and three beds. Motorbikes, mountain bikes and kayaks for rent. Fan B1200, a/c B2500

Ulmer's Nature Lodge ☎ 084 848 5112, ⓔ almar_k @hotmail.com. Occupying a peaceful spot by a mangrove swamp, down a track at the far southern end of the bay, *Ulmer's Nature Lodge* is establishing itself as a centre for yoga, though of course anyone is welcome to stay at its en-suite shoreside bungalows, which are either small and thatched or large and smart, with lots of polished wood. Fan B600, a/c B1500

HAT KHLONG JAAK (LONG BEACH)

★**Koyao Island Resort** ☎ 076 597474, ⓦ koyao.com. This lovely, stylish resort occupies the best part of the beach and comprises just eighteen chic, thatched, mostly fan-cooled cottage compounds, all of them with separate living areas, huge bathrooms with open-air showers, and sliding doors that give access to the spacious garden and its fine bay views. There's a swimming pool and spa, and if you book directly on their website, free use of mountain bikes and kayaks. Breakfast included. B6150

Sabai Corner ☎ 081 892 1827, ⓦ sabaicornerbungalows .com. Occupying Long Beach's rocky southern headland, this long-established, laidback little Italian–Thai outfit has eleven thoughtfully designed wooden bungalows, all with fans, nets and rustic bathrooms, plus decks and hammocks. They're dotted along a rise between the road and the beach, under cashew and jackfruit trees. There's a good restaurant, serving home-made bread and yoghurt, plus Italian and Thai food, and kayak hire on site. B1000

Tabeak Viewpoint Bungalows ☎ 089 590 4182, ⓦ kohyaotravel.com/hotel.htm. Two hundred metres inland, on a cross-island track, this Japanese–Thai place has large, well-outfitted, fan-cooled, wood and bamboo bungalows, all with hot showers, polished wood floors and French windows and balconies that give commanding views of the islands. The Thai owner is a community policeman and enthusiastic fisherman, and an excellent source of island information. B900

HAT PASAI

Coconut Corner ☎076 454221, ⓦkohyaotravel.com
/hotel.htm. Offering some of the cheapest and most
traveller-friendly accommodation on the island, in simple
en-suite bungalows set around a small garden just across
the road from the northern end of Hat Pasai beach. It's just
a few minutes' walk from *Pyramid Bar* on Long Beach and
has bicycle and motorbike rental. B500

Koh Yao Beach Bungalows ☎076 454213, ⓦkohyao
travel.com/hotel.htm. Clean, well-kept bungalows around
a pretty, well-tended lawn, across the main road from the
south end of the beach. The fan bungalows are thatched,
with mosquito nets, cold-water bathrooms and TVs; a/c
options are big and smart with hot showers. Fan B900,
a/c B1500

Pasai Cottage ☎076 454235, ⓦkohyaotravel.com
/hotel.htm. The ten bamboo cottages here, just across
from Pasai's beach but set back from the road, have
unexpectedly tasteful interiors, folding glass doors and
prettily tiled bathrooms. B1200

LAEM SAI

Lam Sai Village Hotel ☎082 289 4276, ⓦlamsai
villagehotel.com. British-run hotel and *muay thai* training

camp on the less appealing western side of the peninsula,
with a two-storey block of good-quality tiled rooms and a
few bungalows, all with TVs, hot showers and balconies,
plus use of the small swimming pool. Kayaks and motorbikes for rent, free bicycles. Fan B1000, a/c B2500

★**Lom'Lae Bungalows** ☎076 597486, ⓦlomlae
.com. Beautiful, secluded haven, backed by rice fields and
rubber plantations and enjoying stunning bay views from
its palm-fringed beach and grassy garden. The attractive,
airy, wooden, fan-cooled bungalows are thatched and
widely spaced, and have sliding doors, decks and
hammocks to capitalize on the vistas. Some have additional
upstairs loft beds, and there are two-bedroom family
houses as well. Kayaks, bikes and motorbikes are available
for rent and there's a dive shop. Twenty percent discount for
stays of five nights or more. B3000

AO LOH HA

The Paradise Koh Yao ☎076 584450, ⓦtheparadise
.biz. Set on a lovely but isolated beach, these large, deluxe,
thatched, a/c rooms and villas all have plenty of outdoor
space and semi-outdoor bathrooms, some with private
jacuzzis. There's a huge pool, a spa, kayaks and yoga classes.
Breakfast included. B10,000

EATING AND DRINKING

HAT THA KAO

Suntisook Resort Charming restaurant serving a long
menu of Thai food, including fish (according to market
price) and a good, generous chicken *matsaman* curry, as
well as spaghetti, mashed potato and Western breakfasts.
Daily 7.30am–9pm.

HAT KHLONG JAAK (LONG BEACH)

★**La Luna** ☎084 629 1550, ⓦlalunakohyao.com.
Congenial, Italian-owned bar-restaurant in a garden
setting with hammocks. On offer are home-made pastas,
including very tasty tagliatelle with cream and prosciutto
(B230), proper pizzas (around B250), Italian desserts and
lots of cocktails. Call for free delivery to your resort. Daily
roughly 2pm till late (kitchen closes 9.30/10pm).

Pyramid Bar Famous island meeting place, with a pool
table, sports TV and extensive menu of cocktails, wine and
Thai and Western food, including sandwiches (from B120),
breakfasts and seafood; it's at its liveliest on Friday nights

when half the island turns up for the very enjoyable weekly
sets by island musicians. Daily 9/10am till late (kitchen
closes 10pm).

LAEM SAI

Lam Sai Seafood Restaurant About 1.5km further
down the road from the Lam Sai Village Hotel, just
beyond where the paving stops ☎081 446 0689. This is a
great place for Thai-style seafood, which is pulled up fresh
from nets off a pontoon according to your order (priced
according to weight). Tables are set on a deck over the water
with good views across to Ko Yao Yai. Daily 10am–10pm.

BAN THA KAI

Je T'aime ☎076 597495. At the T-junction at the heart
of the village, this welcoming French- and Danish-owned
restaurant is especially good for locally caught fish and
seafood – Thai-style spaghetti with lobster B650 – and
French wine, but also Western breakfasts. Daily 9am–10pm.

Ao Phang Nga

National Park admission B200 • ⓦ dnp.go.th

Protected from the ravages of the Andaman Sea by Phuket, **AO PHANG NGA** has a
seascape both bizarre and beautiful. Covering some four hundred square kilometres of
coast between Phuket and Krabi, the mangrove-edged bay is spiked with limestone
karst formations up to 300m in height, jungle-clad and craggily profiled. This is

7

THE HONGS

Hongs are the *pièce de résistance* of Ao Phang Nga: invisible to any passing vessel, these secret tidal lagoons are enclosed within the core of seemingly impenetrable limestone outcrops, accessible via murky tunnels that can only be navigated at certain tides in kayaks small enough to slip beneath and between low-lying rocky overhangs. Like the karsts themselves, the *hongs* have taken millions of years to form, with the softer limestone hollowed out from above by the wind and the rain, and from the side by the pounding waves. Eventually, when the two hollows met, the heart of the karst was able to fill with water via the wave-eroded passageway at sea level, creating a lagoon. The world inside these roofless hollows is an extraordinary one, protected from the open bay by a ring of cliff faces hung with vertiginous prehistoric-looking gardens of upside-down cycads, twisted bonsai palms and tangled ferns. And as the tide withdraws, the *hong's* resident creatures emerge to forage on the muddy floor, among them fiddler crabs, mudskippers, dusky langurs and crab-eating macaques, with white-bellied sea eagles often hovering overhead.

Thailand's own version of Vietnam's world-famous Ha Long Bay, reminiscent too of Guilin's scenery in China, and much of it is now preserved as **national park**. The bay is thought to have been formed about twelve thousand years ago when a dramatic rise in sea level flooded the summits of mountain ranges, which over millions of years had been eroded by an acidic mixture of atmospheric carbon dioxide and rainwater. Some of these karst islands have been further eroded in such a way that they are now hollow, hiding secret lagoons or *hongs* that can only be accessed at certain tides and only by kayak. The main *hong* islands are in the **western** and **eastern** bay areas – to the west or east of Ko Yao Noi, which sits roughly midway between Phuket and Krabi. But the most famous scenery is in the **central bay** area, which boasts the biggest concentration of karst islands, and the weirdest rock formations.

The central bay

On tours of the **central bay**, the standard itinerary follows a circular or figure-of-eight route, passing extraordinary karst silhouettes that change character with the shifting light – in the eerie glow of an early morning mist it can be a breathtaking experience. Some of the formations have nicknames suggested by their weird outlines – like **Khao Machu (Marju)**, which translates as "Pekinese Rock". Others have titles derived from other attributes – **Tham Nak** (or Nark, meaning Naga Cave) gets its name from the serpentine stalagmites inside; **Ko Thalu** (Pierced Cave) has a tunnel through it; and a close inspection of **Khao Kien** (Painting Rock) reveals a cliff wall decorated with paintings of elephants, monkeys, fish, crabs and hunting weapons, believed to be between three thousand and five thousand years old.

Ao Phang Nga's most celebrated features, however, earned their tag from a movie: the cleft **Khao Ping Gan** (Leaning Rock) and its tapered outcrop **Khao Tapu** (Nail Rock) are better known as **James Bond Island**, having starred as Scaramanga's hideaway in *The Man with the Golden Gun*. Every boat stops off here so tourists can pose in front of the iconic rock – whose narrowing base is a good example of how wave action is shaping the bay – and the island crawls with seashell and trinket vendors.

The central bay's other major attraction is **Ko Panyi**, a Muslim village built almost entirely on stilts around the rock that supports the mosque. Nearly all boat tours stop here for lunch, so you're best off avoiding the pricey seafood restaurants around the jetty, and heading instead towards the islanders' food stalls near the mosque. You can enjoy a more tranquil Ko Panyi experience by joining one of the overnight tours from Phang Nga town (see p.650), which include an evening meal and guesthouse accommodation on the island – and the chance to watch the sun set and rise over the bay; you can also rent a kayak from the jetty and go exploring yourself.

At some point on your central-bay tour you should pass several small brick **kilns** on the edge of a mangrove swamp, which were once used for producing charcoal from mangrove wood. You'll also be ferried beneath **Tham Lod**, a photogenic archway roofed with stalactites that opens onto spectacular limestone and mangrove vistas.

The western bay: Ko Panak and Ko Hong

The main attraction of **the western bay** is **Ko Panak**, whose limestone cliffs hide secret tunnels to no fewer than five different **hongs** within its hollowed heart. These are probably Ao Phang Nga's most spectacular hidden worlds, the pitch-black tunnel approaches infested by bats and the bright, roofless *hongs* an entire other world, draped in hanging gardens of lianas and miniature screw pines and busy with cicadas and the occasional family of crab-eating macaques. Western-bay tours also usually take in nearby **Ko Hong** (different from the Ko Hong in the eastern bay), whose exterior walls are coated with red, yellow and orange encrusting sponges, oyster shells and chitons (560-million-year-old slipper-shaped shells), which all make good camouflage for the scuttling red, blue and black crabs. Ko Hong's interior passageways light up with bioluminescent plankton in the dark and lead to a series of cave-lagoons.

The eastern bay: Ko Hong, Ao Thalen and Ao Luk

The principal *hong* island in the **eastern bay**, known both as **Ko Hong** and **Ko Lao Bileh**, lies about midway between Krabi's Hat Klong Muang beach and the southeast coast of Ko Yao Noi. The island is fringed by white-sand beaches and exceptionally clear aquamarine waters that make it a popular snorkelling destination. The island's actual *hong* lacks the drama of Ao Phang Nga's best *hongs* because it's not fully enclosed or accessed via dark tunnels as at Ko Panak, but it is pretty, full of starfish, and tidal, so can only be explored at certain times.

The eastern bay's other big attractions are the mangrove-fringed inlets along the mainland coast between Krabi and Phang Nga, particularly around **Ao Luk** and **Ao Thalen** (sometimes Ao Talin or Talane), though the latter can get very crowded with tour groups. Trips around here take you through complex networks of channels that weave through the mangrove swamps, between fissures in the limestone cliffs, beneath karst outcrops and into the occasional cave. Many of these passageways are *hongs*, isolated havens that might be up to 2km long, all but cut off from the main bay and accessible only at certain tides. The **Ban Bor Tor** (or Ban Bho Tho) area of Ao Luk bay is especially known for **Tham Lod**, a long tunnel hung with stalactites whose entrance is obscured by vines, and for nearby **Tham Phi Hua Toe**, whose walls display around a hundred prehistoric cave paintings, as well as some interestingly twisted stalactite formations.

TOURS OF THE BAY	**AO PHANG NGA**

By sea canoe The most rewarding, and generally the most expensive, option for exploring Ao Phang Nga is to join a sea-canoeing trip (either guided or self-paddle), which enables you both to explore inside the *hongs* and to see at close quarters the extraordinary ecosystems around and inside the karst islands. Most sea-canoeing tours use large support boats carrying groups of up to thirty people. They can be arranged from any resort in Phuket, or through the specialist operators John Gray's Sea Canoe and Paddle Asia (see p.618); at Khao Lak, for example through Khao Lak Land Discovery (see p.608); at all Krabi beaches and islands and in Krabi town

(see p.651), and on Ko Yao Noi (see p.643). The itinerary is usually determined by your departure point, with Phuket trips focusing on the western bay and Krabi tours concentrating on the eastern half.

By tour boat Most tours of the central bay are either in large tour boats booked out of Phuket or Krabi, which generally feature snorkelling and beach stops rather than kayaking, or in inexpensive, small-group longtail boats that depart from Phang Nga town (see p.650), as well as from Phuket and Ko Yao Noi. All the main areas of the bay are extremely popular so don't expect a solitary experience.

Phang Nga town

Friendly if unexciting little **PHANG NGA TOWN**, beautifully located under looming limestone cliffs edged with palm groves midway between Phuket and Krabi, serves mainly as a point from which to organize budget longtail trips around the spectacular karst islands of Ao Phang Nga (see p.647). But there are also several caves and waterfalls nearby, accessible on cheap tours run by Phang Nga tour operators.

ARRIVAL AND INFORMATION   PHANG NGA TOWN

Tour operators inside the bus station compound sell bus and boat tickets and will store your baggage for a few hours.

By bus Phang Nga has good bus connections: during the day, all services between Krabi and Phuket detour off Highway 415 to make a stop at the bus station (☏076 412014) on Thanon Phetkasem, located towards the northern end of this long, thin town; evening services don't make the detour, but Mr Kean (see box below) will give you a free lift to the junction of Highway 415 and Highway 4, 4km west of town, if you buy your bus ticket from him. If you're heading to Khao Sok National Park headquarters (see p.604), it's usually fastest to take a Surat Thani bus and change in Phanom. Some of the services to Bangkok's Southern Bus Terminal continue to Mo Chit station on the north side of the city.

Destinations: Bangkok (5 daily; 13hr); Ko Samui (daily; 6hr); Krabi (hourly; 1hr 30min–2hr); Phuket (at least hourly; 1hr 30min–2hr 30min); Ranong (5 daily; 3hr); Satun (3 daily; 8hr); Surat Thani (every 2hr; 4hr); Takua Pa (hourly; 1hr); Trang (every 1hr; 6hr).

By boat The pier for boats around Ao Phang Nga, and to Ko Yao Noi (daily; 90min), is at Tha Dan, 9km south of town and served by songthaews that pass the bus station (B25).

Tourist information The TAT information office for Phang Nga is inconveniently located 2km south of the town on Highway 4 (daily 8.30am–4.30pm; ☏076 411586). You may find the tour operators inside the bus station compound (see below) more helpful.

TOURS FROM PHANG NGA TOWN

AO PHANG NGA

The most popular budget tours of Ao Phang Nga (see p.647) are the **longtail-boat trips** run by tour operators based inside Phang Nga bus station. Competition between these outfits is fierce and the itineraries they offer are almost identical, so it's best to get recommendations from other tourists fresh from a bay trip, especially as reputations fluctuate with every change of staff. To date, the one that's remained most constant is Mr Kean Tour (☏076 430619 or ☏089 871 6092); next door but one is Sayan Tour (☏076 430348, ☒sayantour.com). Both offer half-day tours of the bay (daily at about 8.30am & 2pm; 3–4hr) costing B500 per person (including national park fee; minimum four people), as well as full-day trips, which cost B1250, including lunch and national park fee; take the 8.30am tour to avoid seeing the bay at its most crowded. All tours include a chance to swim in the bay, and most offer the option of an hour's canoeing around Ko Thalu as well, for an extra B350.

All tour operators also offer the chance to **stay** overnight at their own guesthouse on **Ko Panyi**. This can be tacked onto the half- or full-day tour for an extra B250–300; dinner, accommodation and breakfast are included in the price. Mr Kean can also sometimes offer (dependent on the tides) an interesting alternative overnight programme on his home island of **Ban Mai Phai**, a much less commercial version of Ko Panyi, with the chance to trek, cycle and kayak.

LOCAL SIGHTS AROUND PHANG NGA TOWN

Mr Kean can arrange trips (B600) to **Tham Phung Chang**, or **Elephant Belly Cave**, a natural 1200m-long tunnel through the massive 800m-high wooded cliff that towers over the Provincial Hall, about 4km west of the town centre. With a bit of imagination, the cliff's outline resembles a kneeling elephant, and the hollow interior is, of course, its belly. You can travel through the elephant's belly to the other side of the cliff and back on a two-hour excursion that involves wading, rafting and canoeing along the freshwater stream, Khlong Tham, that has eroded the channel.

Mr Kean also offers tours (B500) that take in several other local caves, plus **Sa Nang Manora Forest Park**, which has hiking trails through thick, impressive rainforest and several waterfalls with swimmable pools, 9km north of the town centre.

ACCOMMODATION

Phang Nga's best hotels are all within 250m of the bus station, heading northeast (right) up Thanon Phetkasem (Highway 4).

Baan Phang Nga 100/2 Thanon Phetkasem (on the left-hand side) ☎076 413276, ⓦfacebook.com /BaanPhangnga. Friendly, upmarket guesthouse and bakery above a café, offering a/c rooms with TVs, small, hot-water bathrooms and a few touches of kitsch contemporary decor. **B650**

Phang Nga Guest House 99/1 Thanon Phetkasem (next to Krung Thai Bank) ☎076 411358. The public areas are decorated with some colourful touches, but the clean and comfortable rooms with small, mostly cold-water, en-suite bathrooms and TVs remain much the same; few have anything but a brick-wall view. Fan **B380**, a/c **B480**

Thawisuk Hotel 77 Thanon Phetkasem (near Krung Thai Bank) ☎076 412100. The choice of local civil servants, this is an old-style, well-maintained hotel with very clean and bright fan rooms, a couple of huge a/c options, and a rooftop terrace. Fan **B380**, a/c **B680**

EATING

Duang Thanon Phetkasem, a couple of doors away from Baan Phang Nga Guesthouse (a tiny sticker shows the name in English). Locals rate this simple but friendly restaurant with a few outdoor tables as the best in town; it's been going 30 years and serves a good squid salad (*yam pla meuk*; B200), as well as rice and noodle dishes for about B80. Daily 10.30am–10pm.

Kafeh Thanon Phetkasem (no English sign). For a great Thai breakfast, go left down Phetkasem about 100m from the bus station to find this hugely popular dessert shop on the left. Fill your tray with assorted Thai *khanom* – banana-leaf parcels of sticky rice laced with sweet coconut milk and stuffed with banana, mango or other delights – at about B5 apiece, then order from the selection of hot and cold coffees and watch Thai breakfast TV with everyone else. Daily 6am–6pm.

Krabi town

The estuarine town of **KRABI** is both provincial capital and major hub for onward travel to some of the region's most popular islands and beaches, including Ko Phi Phi, Ko Lanta, Ao Nang, Klong Muang and Laem Phra Nang (Railay). So efficient are the transport links that you don't really need to stop here, but it also makes an appealing base, strung out along the west bank of the Krabi estuary, with mangrove-lined shorelines to the east, craggy limestone outcrops on every horizon, and plenty of guesthouses. The beaches of **Ao Nang** (see p.657) and **Railay** (see p.663) are both within 45 minutes of town, and other nearby attractions include the **mangrove swamps** and villagey **Ko Klang** peninsula across the estuary, the dramatically sited Tiger Cave Temple at **Wat Tham Seua** and **Khao Phanom Bencha National Park**. A number of organized **day-trips in the Krabi area**, including snorkelling and kayaking excursions, are available (see box, p.660).

Krabi town has no unmissable sights, but is small enough for a pleasant stroll around its main landmarks by day and excellent street food markets by night. Its chief attraction is its setting, and a good way to appreciate this is to follow the paved

> ## MANGROVE TOURS
>
> A boat trip through the eerily scenic **mangrove**-lined channels of the Krabi estuary is a fun way to gain a different perspective on the area. As well as a close-up view of the weird creatures that inhabit the swamps (see box, p.653), you'll get to visit a riverside cave or two. **Tours** are best organized directly with the longtail boatmen who hang around Krabi's two piers and the surrounding streets (B300–500/boat/hr), but can also be arranged through most tour agents.
>
> The estuary's most famous features are the twin limestone outcrops known as **Khao Kanab Nam**, which rise a hundred metres above the water from opposite sides of the Krabi River near the *Maritime Park and Spa Resort* and are so distinctive that they've become the symbol of Krabi. One of the twin karsts hides caves, which can be explored – many skeletons have been found here over the centuries, thought to be those of immigrants who got stranded by a flood before reaching the mainland. You can also choose to visit the Muslim island of Ko Klang (see p.653).

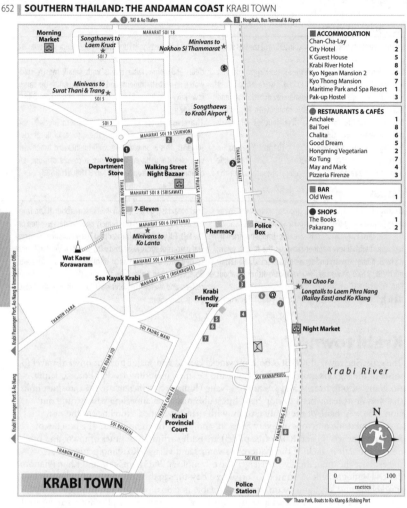

▲ ❶ TAT & Ao Thalen ▲ ❶ Hospitals, Bus Terminal & Airport

KRABI TOWN

Morning Market

Songthaews to Laem Kruat

SOI 7

MAHARAT SOI 18

Minivans to Nakhon Si Thammarat ★

Minivans to Surat Thani & Trang ★

SOI 5

⑤

Songthaews to Krabi Airport ★

SOI 3

MAHARAT SOI 10 (SUKHON)

❶

Vogue Department Store

Walking Street Night Bazaar

MAHARAT SOI 8 (SRISAWAT)

7-Eleven

MAHARAT SOI 6 (PATTANA)

Minivans to Ko Lanta ★

Pharmacy

Police Box

Wat Kaew Korawaram

MAHARAT SOI 4 (PRACHACHUEN)

Sea Kayak Krabi

MAHARAT SOI 2 (RUENRUDEE)

Krabi Friendly Tour

❸

Tha Chao Fa
Longtails to Laem Phra Nang (Railay East) and Ko Klang ★

⑥ @

Night Market

SOI PAUNG MANI

SOI VANNAPRUEG

Krabi River

SOI RUAM JID

THANON ISARA

Krabi Passenger Port, Ao Nang & Immigration Office ◀

Krabi Passenger Port & Ao Nang ◀

THANON CHAO FA

Krabi Provincial Court

SOI RUAMJAI

THANON KRABI

THANON RONG KA

SOI VIJIT

SOI 8

N

0   100
metres

Police Station

▼ Thara Park, Boats to Ko Klang & Fishing Port

THANON MAHARAT

THANON PRUKSA UTHIT

THANON UTHAKIT

■ ACCOMMODATION	
Chan-Cha-Lay	4
City Hotel	2
K Guest House	5
Krabi River Hotel	8
Kyo Ngean Mansion 2	6
Kyo Thong Mansion	7
Maritime Park and Spa Resort	1
Pak-up Hostel	3

● RESTAURANTS & CAFÉS	
Anchalee	1
Bai Toei	8
Chalita	6
Good Dream	5
Hongming Vegetarian	2
Ko Tung	7
May and Mark	4
Pizzeria Firenze	3

■ BAR	
Old West	1

● SHOPS	
The Books	1
Pakarang	2

riverside walkway down to the fishing port, about 800m south of Tha Chao Fa; several hotels capitalize on the views here, across to mangrove-ringed Ko Klang, and towards the southern end the walkway borders the municipal Thara Park.

Inland, in the centre of town, you can't fail to notice the bizarre sculptures of hulking **anthropoid apes** clutching two sets of traffic lights apiece at the Thanon Maharat/Soi 10 crossroads. They are meant to represent Krabi's most famous ancestors, the tailless _Siamopithecus oceanus_, whose forty-million-year-old remains were found in a lignite mine in the south of the province and are believed by scientists to be among the earliest examples worldwide of the ape-to-human evolutionary process.

Wat Kaew Korawaram

West off Thanon Maharat • Free

It's hard to miss the striking white walls of the minimalist modern bot at the town-centre temple, **Wat Kaew Korawaram** (Grovaram), approached via a grand naga staircase. The interior murals depict traditional scenes, including _Jataka_ episodes from the lives of the Buddha, but are spiced up with some modern twists – including warring hairy foreigners on either side of the door.

Ko Klang

Across the river from Krabi town • Frequent shared longtails from Tha Chao Fa (B20; 10min) and Tha Thara Park (B20; 3min; bicycles carried); longtail charter also possible (B60–100)

Most of Krabi's longtail boatmen come from **Ko Klang**, the mangrove-encircled peninsula just across the channel from Tha Chao Fa and Tha Thara Park. On a two-hour mangrove tour you can choose to stop off on the peninsula for a visit, or you can go there yourself, on one of the public longtail **boats** that shuttle across from Krabi town throughout the day. You can also stay in Ban Ko Klang as part of a **homestay** programme, which can be booked locally through Krabi Friendly Tour (see p.655) or in advance as part of a package with Tell Tale Travel (ⓦ telltaletravel.co.uk).

The predominantly Muslim peninsula is home to three small **villages** housing a total of around four thousand people, most of whom earn their living from tourism and fishing. Seafood restaurants have sprung up at the pier and can give free mini tours of their fish farms. The island is no great beauty but therein lies its charm, offering the chance to experience a little of typical southern Thai life, which is a highlight of staying in Krabi Town. You can swim off Ko Klang's long, wild southwestern **beach**, from where you also get an excellent view of the distinctive profiles of all the famous local **islands** – Laem Phra Nang (30min boat ride away), Ko Poda (45min), Bamboo Island, Ko Phi Phi (2hr) and Ko Jum; any Ko Klang boatman will take you to the beach for the same price as from Krabi town. Wandering around the village on foot is equally fascinating.

Wat Tham Seua

10km northeast of Krabi town, about 2km north of Highway 4 • Red songthaews from Krabi town, heading for the Tesco Lotus supermarket (about B20), pass the T-junction on Highway 4, from where you could take a motorbike taxi (about B30); you might be able to persuade the songthaew driver to detour to the temple for an extra fee (about B50) or you could walk the last 2km

Spectacularly situated amid limestone cliffs within a tropical forest, **Wat Tham Seua** (Tiger Cave Temple) is a famous meditation temple of caves, wooded trails and panoramic viewpoints. As it's a working monastery, visitors are required to wear respectable dress (no shorts or sleeveless tops for men or women).

LIFE IN A MANGROVE SWAMP

Mangrove swamps are at their creepiest at low tide, when their aerial roots are fully exposed to form gnarled and knotted archways above the muddy banks. Not only are these roots essential parts of the tree's breathing apparatus, they also reclaim land for future mangroves, trapping and accumulating water-borne debris into which the metre-long mangrove seedlings can fall. In this way, mangrove swamps also fulfil a vital ecological function: stabilizing shifting mud and protecting coastlines from erosion and the impact of tropical storms.

Mangrove swamp mud harbours some interesting creatures too, like the instantly recognizable **fiddler crab**, named after the male's single outsized reddish claw, which it brandishes for communication and defence purposes; the claw is so powerful it could open a can of baked beans. If you keep your eyes peeled you should be able to make out a few **mudskippers**. These specially adapted fish can absorb atmospheric oxygen through their skins as long as they keep their outsides damp, which is why they spend so much time slithering around in the sludge; they move in tiny hops by flicking their tails, aided by their extra-strong pectoral fins. You might well also come across **kingfishers** and white-bellied **sea eagles**, or even a **crab-eating macaque**.

Though the Krabi mangroves have not escaped the **environmentally damaging** attentions of invasive industry, or the cutting down of the bigger trees to make commercial charcoal, around fifteen percent of the Andaman coastline is still fringed with mangrove forest, the healthiest concentration of this rich, complex ecosystem in Thailand.

7

Wat Tham Seua's abbot is a renowned teacher of Vipassana meditation, and some of his educational tools are displayed in the main **bot**, on the left under the cliff overhang, in the main temple compound. Though these close-up photos of human entrails and internal organs may seem shockingly unorthodox, they are there as reminders of the impermanence of the body, a fundamental tenet of Buddhist philosophy; the human skulls and skeletons dotted around the rest of the compound serve the same purpose. Beyond the bot, follow the path past the nuns' quarters to reach the pair of steep **staircases** that scale the 600m-high cliffside. The first staircase is long (1272 steps) and very steep, and takes about an hour to climb, but the vista from the summit is quite spectacular, affording fabulous views over the limestone outcrops and out to the islands beyond. There's a large seated Buddha image and chedi at the top, and a few monks' cells hidden among the trees. The second staircase, next to the large statue of the Chinese Goddess of Mercy, Kuan Im, takes you on a less arduous route down into a deep dell encircled by high limestone walls. Here the monks have built themselves self-sufficient meditation cells (*kuti*) in and around the rocky crannies, linked by paths through the lush ravine: if you continue along the main path you'll eventually find yourself back where you began, at the foot of the staircase. The valley is home to squirrels and monkeys as well as a pair of remarkable trees with overground **buttress roots** over 10m high.

ARRIVAL AND DEPARTURE   KRABI TOWN

You can buy bus, a/c minibus, boat, train and air tickets, including combination bus and train tickets, to Bangkok via Surat Thani and through-tickets to Ko Samui and Ko Pha Ngan, from clued-up, helpful Krabi Friendly Tour & Travel, 9/3 Thanon Chao Fa (☎ 075 612558).

BY PLANE

Krabi airport (☎ 075 636541–2, ⓦ krabiairport.org) is just off Highway 4, 18km east of Krabi town, 35km from Ao Nang. It's served by many international flights and by domestic flights from Bangkok with Thai Airways, Bangkok Airways, Nok Air, Thai Lion Air and Air Asia, from Chiang Mai with Air Asia and from Ko Samui with Bangkok Airways. An airport shuttle bus (hourly; B150 per person) runs to Krabi town, stopping at Krabi Provincial Court, or

there are fixed-price taxis at B350 per car to Krabi town and port. Frequent songthaews (20min; B40) from the airport depart on the main road 400m from the terminal and drop passengers anywhere along Thanon Utrakit; but to the airport drop you off at departures, leaving from north Thanon Utrakit in Krabi Town. Car rental is also available (see opposite).

Destinations: Bangkok (up to 15 daily; 1hr 20min); Chiang Mai (2 daily; 2hr); Ko Samui (1 daily; 50min).

BY BUS

Numerous long-distance buses run to Krabi's bus terminal, which is 5km north of the town centre in the suburb of Talat Kao, beside Highway 4. Frequent red songthaews (B20) shuttle between the town centre (where they do a little circuit to pick up passengers, starting from the 7-Eleven on Thanon Maharat or *Pak-up Hostel* on Thanon Utrakit) and the bus station. White songthaews from Ao Nang marked "Bus Station" terminate at Krabi bus terminal.

To/from Bangkok A/c and VIP buses between Bangkok's Southern Bus Terminal and Krabi depart mainly in the late afternoon or evening, arriving at the other end in the early morning. Think twice before taking a private bus direct from Thanon Khao San (see p.136).

By a/c minibus Private a/c minibus services (all roughly hourly) run from Krabi to Surat Thani, Nakhon Si Thammarat, Trang and Ko Lanta (see map, p.652). Aimed specifically at tourists, in competition with the boats, the Lanta service will pick up from hotels in Krabi and charges B250–350, depending on which beach you want to be dropped off at on Ko Lanta Yai. From the Talat Kao bus terminal, you can also catch an a/c minibus that originates on Lanta to Phuket airport/town (roughly every 2hr; 2–3hr; B400/350 bookable through Krabi hotels and travel agents).

Bus destinations: Bangkok (12 daily; 12hr); Hat Yai (13 daily; 4–5hr); Nakhon Si Thammarat (at least hourly; 3hr); Phang Nga (every 30min; 2hr); Phuket Town Bus Station 2 (at least hourly; 3hr); Ranong (2 daily; 5hr); Satun (4 daily; 5hr); Surat Thani (at least hourly; 2hr); Takua Pa (4 daily; 3hr 30min–4hr 30min); Trang (at least hourly; 2–3hr).

BY TRAIN AND BUS

A more comfortable alternative to taking a bus from Bangkok is to catch an overnight train from the capital to Surat Thani and then change on to one of the frequent a/c buses or minibuses to Krabi (hourly; 2hr).

BY BOAT

Ferries to Ko Phi Phi, Ko Lanta and Ko Jum leave from Krabi Passenger Port (sometimes referred to as Tha Khlong Jilad; ☎ 075 620052), a couple of kilometres southwest of Krabi town centre. Ferry tickets bought from tour operators in town should include a free transfer to Krabi Passenger Port, but there are also red songthaews that do a circuit of the town centre before heading out to the port. Songthaews from Krabi town connect with most boats, leaving about an hour before from the morning market on Maharat Soi 7, passing the 7-Eleven on Thanon Maharat and Talat Kao bus terminal.

Ko Phi Phi Ferries to Ko Phi Phi from Krabi Passenger Port depart four times daily in high season and at least twice daily in low season (2hr; B350–400).

Ko Lanta Yai Going by a/c minibus to Ko Lanta (see above) is more popular these days, but there's still one ferry a day from Krabi Passenger Port, via Ko Jum (B350; 2hr), in peak season (roughly mid-Nov to mid-April 11.30am; 2hr 30min; B400).

Laem Phra Nang (East Railay) Longtail boats for East Railay on Laem Phra Nang (45min; B1500/boat or B150/ person if there are 8–10 passengers) leave on demand from the town-centre pier at Tha Chao Fa on Thanon Kong Ka.

Ko Yao Noi As well as boats from Ao Nang, there are services from the pier at Ao Thalen, 33km northwest of Krabi town, to Ko Yao Noi (see p.643).

Destinations: Ko Jum (roughly mid-Nov to mid-April daily; 1hr 30min–2hr); Ko Lanta Yai (roughly mid-Nov to mid-April daily; 2hr 30min); Ko Phi Phi Don (2–4 daily; 2hr); Ko Yao Noi (from Ao Thalen; 6–7 daily; 1hr).

GETTING AROUND

By songthaew Most of the public songthaew services to local beaches, towns and attractions circulate around town before heading out, making stops outside the 7-Eleven just south of the Soi 8 intersection on Thanon Maharat and along Thanon Utrakit; most run at least twice an hour from dawn till noon, and then less frequently until dusk. For getting around town, the most useful are probably the red songthaews that run between Tesco Lotus, out on Highway 4 beyond the Wat Tham Seua turn-off, and Krabi Passenger Port. White songthaews start at Talat Kao bus terminal and do a spin around town before heading out to Ao Nang (B50 daytime, B60 after 6pm).

By car or motorbike Budget (☎ 075 636171, ⊛ budget .co.th) and Avis (☎ 089 969 8676, ⊛ avisthailand.com) have desks at the airport, or try Krabi Friendly Tour in town at 9/3 Thanon Chao Fa (☎ 075 612558).

By bicycle *Pak-up Hostel* (see p.656) rents mountain bikes for B150/day.

INFORMATION AND TOURS

Tourist information Krabi's unhelpful TAT office (daily 8.30am–4.30pm; ☎ 075 612812, ⊛ tatkrabi@tat.or.th) is inconveniently located 2km north of the centre on Thanon Maharat.

Books If you're spending some time in this region, it's worth buying a copy of *Krabi: Caught in the Spell – A Guide to Thailand's Enchanted Province*, expat environmentalist Thom Henley's lively and opinionated book about Krabi people, islands and traditions (see p.781).

Tour agents Any of the town's numerous tour agents will fill you in on the many organized day-trip options (see p.660), and fix you up with a room on one of the beaches – a service that's worth considering for your first night or two, particularly during the notoriously oversubscribed Christmas–New Year period. Recommended agents include Krabi Friendly Tour & Travel, 9/3 Thanon Chao Fa (☎ 075 612558).

ACCOMMODATION

★**Chan-Cha-Lay** 55 Thanon Utrakit ☎075 620952, ⓦchanchalay.com. With its stylish blue-and-white theme throughout, funky bathrooms, white-painted wooden furniture and blue shutters, this is the most charming and arty place to stay in Krabi. The en suites in the garden come with fan or a/c and are by far the nicest option, further from the street; quieter rooms in the main building share bathrooms and some don't have windows. Fan <u>B350</u>, a/c <u>B450</u>

City Hotel 15/2–4 Soi 10, Thanon Maharat ☎075 611961, ⓦcitykrabi.com. Comfortable, friendly, modern hotel where most of the rooms are set well back from the road; choose between fan with cold shower and a/c with hot shower (all come with TVs). Fan <u>B450</u>, a/c <u>B950</u>

K Guest House 15–25 Thanon Chao Fa ☎075 623166, ⓔkguesthouse@yahoo.com. Deservedly popular and well run, in a peaceful but central spot, this long, timber-clad row house has bedrooms with wooden floors, panelled walls, streetside balconies and hot showers – ask for a more attractive upstairs room. Also offers some cheaper shabby rooms with windows onto the hall and shared bathroom downstairs and at the back. Fan <u>B200</u>, a/c <u>B500</u>

Krabi River Hotel 73/1 Thanon Kong Ka, a few minutes' walk south of Tha Chao Fa pier ☎075 612321, ⓦkrabiriverhotel.com. Occupying a scenic spot beside the estuary on the southern edge of Krabi town, this place offers high-standard a/c rooms, the best of which have big river-view balconies (B1200); the smaller, cheaper ones look onto the wall of the adjacent hotel. There's a riverside eating area too. <u>B800</u>

Kyo Ngean (Ngoen) Mansion 2 25/1 Thanon Chao Fa ☎075 621111, ⓔkyo-ngean@hotmail.com. Good-value little hotel in a modern block, popular with long-stay guests, with very clean and well-appointed rooms, all of them with a/c, TV, fridge, hot water and balconies; some on the upper floors have long-range river views. Staff are friendly but don't speak much English. <u>B600</u>

Kyo Thong Mansion 31 Thanon Chao Fa ☎075 613001, ⓔbaankyothong@hotmail.com. Very similar setup to *Kyo Ngean*, three doors away, with large, well-appointed, modern rooms with small, hot-water bathrooms, a/c, TV, fridge and balconies. <u>B600</u>

Maritime Park and Spa Resort 2km north of town off Thanon Utrakit ☎075 620028–35, ⓦmaritimeparkandspa.com. Beautifully located upper-end hotel, set beside the limestone karsts and mangroves of the Krabi River. Rooms are a little old-fashioned but large and comfortable, and have fine views over the extensive landscaped grounds and lake. There's a big pool and a spa, and shuttles into Krabi town and Ao Nang. Good-value packages sometimes available on their website. Breakfast included. <u>B2600</u>

Pak-up Hostel 87 Thanon Utrakit ☎075 611955, ⓦfacebook.com/pakuphostel. Colourful, modern hostel in a short tower block on probably Krabi's busiest corner, with smart ten-bed a/c dorms and two private doubles. Lots of tours available; there are plenty of guesthouses in town with cheaper private rooms for groups of two or more, but this is the place to come to be sociable, with lots of common areas, a rooftop bar and an adjacent garden bar. Dorm <u>B350</u>, double <u>B750</u>

EATING AND DRINKING

Krabi offers plenty of traveller-oriented restaurants – and Krabi Friendly Tour has a good juice bar – but there's also inexpensive local-style dining at the night markets on riverside Thanon Kong Ka and on Maharat Soi 10. The Walking Street **night bazaar** on Soi 8 (Fri, Sat & Sun 5–10pm) also brims with excellent food stalls, as well as an entertainment stage and trinket and craft stalls.

Anchalee About 2km north of the town centre at 315/5 Thanon Maharat. Popular with locals and well regarded, this inviting, artfully planted garden restaurant is well worth making the effort to get to. Among the many highlights of its mostly Thai menu (B60–180), standouts include the perfectly spiced *tom yam kung* with satisfyingly large prawns, juicy deep-fried ribs, and fried butterfish with tamarind and ginger. Daily 11am–9pm.

Chalita Thanon Chao Fa. Congenial Italian–Thai restaurant that serves mostly Thai food, but also steaks, burgers, pastas and one or two fusion dishes such as spaghetti with chicken green curry (B150), which works surprisingly well. Daily 4–10.30pm.

Good Dream 83 Thanon Utrakit ☎075 622993. A great, farang-run place for breakfast – very good French toast (B75), full-English fry-ups (B180), Continental sets, muesli

and fruit, all served with fresh coffee – plus plenty more Western and Thai dishes and cocktails later in the day. There's free wi-fi, internet access and movie nights for customers too. Daily 8am–11pm.

Hongming Vegetarian 83 Thanon Pruksa Uthit ☎075 621273. A relaxed local spot to get a mix of Thai greens in one dish, even if you aren't vegetarian. The bain-maries are loaded with soy-meat and veg dishes such as *matsaman* curry and aubergine tofu bake. Two choices on rice is a thrifty B35. Mon–Sat 7am–5pm.

★**Ko Tung** 36 Thanon Kong Ka ☎075 611522. Though it looks nothing much, this little Thai restaurant is always packed with locals savouring the excellent, good-value, southern-style seafood. Special highlights include the sweet mussels (*hawy wan*), baked crab, and mushroom, long bean and shrimp *yam* salads. Most dishes B80–100.

Mon–Sat 11am–10pm.

May and Mark Soi 2, Thanon Maharat. Early hours, home-baked bread (like real sourdough), fresh coffee and full-English fry-ups make this a popular spot for breakfast. Also does tacos, sandwiches, cheese and tuna melts (B180), pizzas and Thai, German and vegetarian food. Daily 6.30am–9pm.

Old West Thanon Utrakit. All bare wood and Wild West photos, with racks of imported spirits behind the long bar that get mixed into some serious cocktails. The top-notch sound system churns out wall-to-wall rock and there are a couple of pool tables. Daily 4pm–4am.

Pizzeria Firenze Thanon Kong Ka. Authentic Italian dishes, including twenty different thin-crust pizzas (from B180), home-made pasta, ice cream, tiramisu, espresso coffee and Italian wines. Daily 10am–9.30pm.

SHOPPING

Bookshops The Books, next to Vogue Department Store on Thanon Maharat (daily 8am–9.30pm), has a decent selection of new English-language books, and the well-stocked Pakarang on Thanon Utrakit (daily 8am–9pm) buys and sells secondhand books, as well as selling handicrafts and espresso coffees.

DIRECTORY

Hospitals Krabi Hospital is about 1km north of the town centre at 325 Thanon Utrakit (☎ 075 611202) and also has dental facilities, but the better hospital is considered to be the private Muslim hospital, Jariyatham Ruam Phet Hospital (☎ 075 611223), which is about 3km north of town at 514 Thanon Utrakit and has English-speaking staff.

Immigration office In the compound of government offices on the way to Krabi Passenger Port (Mon–Fri 8.30am–4.30pm; ☎ 075 611097).

Police For all emergencies, call the tourist police on the free, 24hr phone line ☎ 1155, or contact the local branch of the tourist police in Ao Nang on ☎ 075 637208.

Ao Nang

AO NANG (sometimes confusingly signed as Ao Phra Nang), 22km west of Krabi town, is a busy, continually expanding, rather faceless mainland resort that mainly caters for mid-budget and package-holiday tourists. Although it lacks the fine beaches of the nearby Railay peninsula (an easy 10min boat ride away), it is less claustrophobic, and has a much greater choice of restaurants and bars, masses of shopping (mostly beachwear, DVDs and souvenirs), plus a wealth of dive shops, day-tripping and snorkelling possibilities and other typical resort facilities. Adjacent **Hat Nopparat Thara**, part of which comes under the protection of a national marine park, is prettier, and divided into two separate beaches by a khlong. The uncrowded, 2km-long **eastern beach** is effectively linked to Ao Nang by a conurbation of accommodation and shops, but the **western beach**, sometimes known as

---

DIVING FROM AO NANG

Ao Nang is Krabi's main centre for **dive shops**, with a dozen or more outlets, the most reputable of which include Kon-Tiki (☎ 075 637826, �🌐 kontiki-thailand.com) and Poseidon (☎ 075 637263, 🌐 poseidon-diving.com); they have a price agreement for PADI courses, but Poseidon is cheaper for dive trips. Diving with Ao Nang operators is possible year-round, with some dive staff claiming that off-season diving is more rewarding, not least because the sites are much less crowded.

Most one-day **dive trips** head for the area round Ko Phi Phi (from B4500 including two tanks; B1700 for snorkellers with Poseidon) and often include dives at Shark Point and the "King Cruiser" wreck dive (see p.637); the Ko Ha island group, near Ko Lanta, is also popular but more expensive (see p.684).

Two dives in the Ao Nang area – at Ko Poda and Ko Yawasam – cost B2700–3200 (B1900 for snorkellers), much less if you go in a longtail with Poseidon. PADI dive courses cost B5500 for the introductory Discover Scuba day, or B14,900 for the Openwater.

The nearest recompression chambers are on Phuket (see p.636); check to see that your dive operator is insured to use one of them. General information on diving in Thailand can be found in Basics (see p.52).

Hat Ton Son, across the khlong, is an altogether quieter and more beautiful little enclave, accessible only via longtail or a circuitous back road. Fifteen kilometres' drive west of Ao Nang, **Hat Klong Muang** is no great shakes as a beach but does have some attractive four- and five-star accommodation.

Central Ao Nang and Ao Phai Plong

Ao Nang's central beach is unexceptional and busy with longtail traffic, though it's backed by a pleasantly landscaped promenade. The nicer stretch is east beyond *Ao Nang Villa Resort*, accessed by the pavement that takes you all the way along the shore to the appropriately named *Last Café*, a very pleasant spot for a shady drink. Follow the wooden walkway from beyond *The Last Café* and scale the steps up and over the headland to reach, in about ten minutes, the beach at diminutive **Ao Phai Plong**, which is the sole province of the luxurious *Centara Grand* hotel.

Hat Nopparat Thara east

Immediately west of Ao Nang, beyond the headland occupied by *Krabi Resort* but reached by simply following the road (on foot or in one of the frequent Krabi-bound songthaews), **Hat Nopparat Thara east** is long and pretty, with the road running along a landscaped promenade behind it. Its eastern hinterland is developing fast with hotels and restaurants, but the other end, close to the T-junction with Route 4202, is the site of the Hat Nopparat Thara–Mu Ko Phi Phi **national park headquarters** and accommodation. Here too is the **tsunami memorial**, *Hold Me Close* by Louise Bourgeois (2005), a roofless, wood-slatted corncob structure in disrepair enclosing two pairs of hands, joined, prayer like and pleading, extending from a lumpy sea.

At low tide it's almost impossible to swim on this beach, but the sands come alive with thousands of starfish and hermit crabs, and the view out towards the islands is glorious; you can walk to the nearest outcrop at low water.

The **national park visitor centre** is at the end of the beach, beside the khlong and its sheltered marina and jetty, Tha Nopparat Thara, which is the departure point for Ao Nang ferry services to Phuket, Phi Phi and Ko Lanta, as well as for longtails to the western beach. The visitor centre's car park is famous for its **seafood restaurants**, and Krabi residents also like to picnic under the shorefront casuarina trees here.

■ ACCOMMODATION	
Ao Nang Orchid Resort	6
Ao Nang Villa Resort	9
Cashew Nut	5
Centara Anda Dhevi Resort	2
Centara Grand Beach Resort	11
Ibis Styles Krabi Ao Nang	1
Jinda Guesthouse	8
Laughing Gecko	3
National Park Bungalows	10
PK Mansion, Top View and J Mansion	7
Somkietburi Resort	4

■ BAR	
Sally O'Malley's	1

● RESTAURANTS & CAFÉS	
Chanaya Thai-Dutch	2
Krua Thara (After Tsunami)	4
The Last Café	6
The Last Fisherman Bar	5
Longtail Boat	7
Sala Bua and Lo Spuntino	8
Ton Sai	1
Wang Sai	3

Hat Nopparat Thara west

Hat Nopparat Thara west has a quite different atmosphere from its eastern counterpart: just a handful of small bungalow hotels and a few private residences share its long swathe of peaceful casuarina- and palm-shaded shoreline, making it a great place to escape the crowds and commerce of other Krabi beaches. The views of the karst islands are magnificent, though swimming here is also tide-dependent. Without your own transport you can only get here by longtail across the narrow but deep khlong beside the national park visitor's centre, but with a car or bike you can arrive via the very quiet back road that snakes through the mangroves from the Klong Muang road to the edge of the bungalow properties.

ARRIVAL AND DEPARTURE
AO NANG

Ao Nang has no proper transport terminals of its own so most long-distance journeys entail going **via Krabi town** (see p.655), though tour services on every corner of Ao Nang can arrange direct a/c minivans to the same destinations with convenient hotel transfers, such as to Phuket town (B300). Taxis from Krabi to Ao Nang charge about B500. From the **airport** (see p.654), a shuttle bus runs to Ao Nang for B200, while taxis charge B600–900 to Ao Nang and Klong Muang.

By songthaew The cheapest onward connection from Krabi to Ao Nang is by white songthaew, which run regularly throughout the day from Krabi town centre and bus station (generally every 10min; 45min; B50 daytime, B60 after dark) and pass Hat Nopparat Thara east en route. Alight at the Nopparat Thara national park T-Junction and car park for longtails across the narrow khlong to the western beach (B100) or, with your own transport, follow the Klong Muang road until signs direct you off it. There's also a songthaew service from Krabi town to Hat Klong Muang.

By boat In addition to the ferries listed below, longtails to Laem Phra Nang (see p.663) and boats to Ko Yao Noi (see p.643) are also available; the latter include a daily, high-season Green Planet speedboat (book through any tour agent) that continues to Bang Rong in Phuket (B1200 from Ao Nang). There are once-daily ferry services from Tha Nopparat Thara west, near the national park visitors' centre, to Ko Phi Phi Don (2hr 30min; B400) and to Phuket (3hr; B650–700), both year-round in theory though they sometimes don't run in the monsoon season; and to Ko Lanta (2hr 30min; B550) from roughly November to May. Transfers from Ao Nang hotels are included in the ticket price.

GETTING AROUND AND SERVICES

Getting around The Krabi songthaews (see above) are useful for nipping between Ao Nang, Hat Nopparat Thara and town, and motorcycle taxis with sidecars buzz around Ao Nang and Hat Nopparat Thara. Motorbikes and jeeps are available for rent throughout the resort; and there are kayaks on the beach in front of *The Last Café* at the far eastern end of Ao Nang (B100–150/hr), from where, in calm seas, it's an easy 15min paddle to Ao Phai Plong or about 45min to Ao Ton Sai and West Railay.

Tourist police On the main road between Ao Nang and Hat Nopparat Thara (☎ 075 637208).

ACTIVITIES AROUND KRABI, AO NANG AND LAEM PHRA NANG

Any tour agent in Krabi town, Ao Nang, Klong Muang or Railay can set you up on these **snorkelling day-trips** and other **activities**; prices usually include transport from your accommodation. Diving (see p.657) and rock-climbing (see p.664) are also available.

SNORKELLING DAY-TRIPS

By far the most popular organized outings from Krabi, Ao Nang and Laem Phra Nang are the **snorkelling trips** to nearby islands. The main **islands** in question are Ko Poda, Ko Tub and Chicken Island, all of them less than half an hour's longtail ride from Ao Nang or Railay. There are various permutations, offered by numerous companies, including the number of islands you visit (usually three, four or five) and whether you go in a longtail boat, a larger wooden boat or speedboat; prices start as low as B450 for a longtail trip to three islands, including packed lunch and snorkel set. In all cases you should be prepared to share the experience with dozens, even hundreds, of others, because pretty much everyone congregates at the same spots. It's a lot more fun than it sounds though – so long as you're not expecting a solitary experience.

It's also possible to organize your own boat trip with the **longtail boatmen** on Ao Nang waterfront. Their prices are fixed, but don't include snorkelling equipment or lunch: for the return trip to either Ko Poda, Ko Tub or Chicken Island (8am–4pm), they charge B300 per person, minimum six people; for Ko Hong (see p.649) it's B2500 per boat per full day, for Bamboo Island, near Ko Phi Phi (see p.667), B3800 per boat per full day. Krabi town is quite a bit further away so its boatmen charge B1800–2300 for the three main islands.

From some angles, one of the pinnacles on **Chicken Island** does indeed look like the scrawny neck and beaky head of a chicken. There's decent snorkelling off its coast, with a fair range of reef fish and quite a lot of giant clams, though most of the reef is either bleached or dead. Its dazzlingly white-sand northeastern shore, which has a food stall, toilets and kayak rental, is connected to the islets of **Ko Tup** by a sandbank, which is walkable at low tide – quite a striking sight as you arrive to see other visitors seemingly walking on water. Nearby **Ko Poda**, which sits directly in front of the Ao Nang beachfront, is encircled by lovely white-sand beaches and clear turquoise water. There's a restaurant here and plenty of shade under the casuarina trees, so this is the typical lunch stop; sandwich-selling boats dock here too. Though you might get three hundred people lunching on the shore here at any one time, it's big enough to cope. Some itineraries also feature **Ao Phra Nang** and its cave, on the Laem Phra Nang (Railay) peninsula (see p.664), and this is the one to avoid unless you enjoy scrambling for your metre of sand on this overrun little bay.

OTHER ACTIVITIES

Cycle rides Half- and full-day rides into the Krabi countryside, or to Ko Klang, Khao Phanom Bencha falls or Khlong Tom's Emerald Pool, with Krabi Eco Cycle, based about 2km inland from the Hat Nopparat Thara National Park visitors' centre on Route 4202 (from B800; ☎ 081 607 4162, ⓦ www.krabiecocycle.com).

Elephant trekking Nosey Parker's Elephant Trekking (☎ 075 612258, ⓦ krabidir.com/noseyparkers), 7km north of Ao Nang, has a good reputation. From B800 for an hour's trek along the river and elephant bathing.

Sea canoeing Guided and self-paddle trips take place around the spectacular karst islands and secret lagoons of Ao Phang Nga, usually focusing on Ao Luk, Ao Thalen and Ko Hong in the eastern bay (see p.649). Dozens of companies offer this, including Sea Kayak Krabi, Soi 2, Thanon Maharat, Krabi town (☎ 075 630270, ⓦ seakayak-krabi.com), who offer a multitude of day and multi-day trips, charging B1500 for a full-day trip to Ao Thalen, for example.

Thai cookery lessons Ya's Thai Cookery School, about 4km inland of Ao Nang off Route 4203, runs morning and afternoon courses (Mon–Sat 9am–1pm & 2–6pm; from B1000 including transport; ☎ 081 979 0677, ⓦ thaicookeryschool.net).

Phi Phi Paradise Pearl Resort ☎075 601246, ⓦphiphiparadisepearl.com. The 35 bungalows and rooms at this efficiently run place are fairly well spaced along the western half of the beach, with none more than a few steps from the shore. Interiors are unremarkable but perfectly comfortable and all have a/c, hot water and verandas. There's a tour counter here, and free longtail pick-ups from the pier are offered. Breakfast included. **B3000**

Viking Nature Resort ☎075 819399, ⓦvikingnatureresort.com. Tucked away on and above two private little coves just west of Hat Yao, with easy access via a rocky path, this is a very stylish take on classic Thai beach-bungalow architecture. It's nearly all wood and bamboo here, with no a/c, but interiors are styled with Asian boho-chic artefacts. The most glamorous accommodation is in the enormous, high-level, one- to four-bedroom "Makmai" tree houses, with their massive living-room decks overlooking the bay. There's a stylish lounge and dining area on the beach; kayaks and snorkels are available. **B1500**

AO TOH KO

★**Ao Toh Ko Beach Resort** ☎081 537 0528, ⓦwww.tohkobeachresort.com. The exceptionally welcoming family who run this place keep people staying and returning – and they're great cooks too. The comfortable accommodation varies from attractive, breezy, en-suite, bamboo huts with mossie nets, some sitting right over the sea on the rocks, to smart, bright, concrete bungalows with a/c, hot water, fridge and TV. Kayaks and snorkels for rent. Fan **B2500**, a/c **B2800**

HAT RANTEE

Rantee Beach Resort ☎089 725 4411, ⓦkrabidir.com/ranteeresort. At this shady resort, you can choose between en-suite, thatched, bamboo huts and spacious, arched, Bali-style villas with a/c, hot showers and TV. Kayaks and internet access are available, while transfers from the pier cost B200 per person. Breakfast included. Fan **B1800**, a/c **B2500**

HAT PAK NAM

Phi Phi Relax Beach Resort ☎089 725 4411, ⓦphiphirelaxbeach.com. Rustic but comfortable and very welcoming accommodation, in 51 attractive, en-suite wood and bamboo bungalows, set in rows in among the beachfront trees. Kayaks available and there's pick-ups from the pier twice a day (B150 per person). **B2100**

AO LOH BAKAO

Phi Phi Island Village Beach Resort and Spa ☎075 628999, ⓦphiphiislandvillage.com. This plush, a/c resort on a lovely beach is a popular honeymoon spot, and a great location for anyone looking for a quiet, comfortable break. The thatched, split-bamboo bungalows and pool villas are mostly designed in traditional Thai style and furnished with character and elegance. There's a large pool and a spa in the prettily landscaped tropical gardens, as well as a dive centre. **B8900**

LAEM TONG

Holiday Inn Resort Phi Phi Island ☎075 627300, ⓦphiphi.holidayinn.com. The *Holiday Inn* enjoys nearly a kilometre of beachfront at the southern end of the bay, but its 120 deluxe a/c bungalows and spacious, balconied, sea-view rooms are nicely hidden by the shoreline trees and sit in graceful gardens of tidy lawns and flowering shrubs. There's a popular sunset bar at the top of the ridge, two swimming pools, a dive centre, a massage pavilion and tennis courts, plus cooking classes, free kayaks and snorkelling equipment are available. **B7000**

Phi Phi Natural Resort ☎075 819030–1, ⓦphiphinatural.com. Up at the northern end of the bay, the a/c rooms, wooden chalets and pool villas here are scattered around an extensive tropical shorefront garden, with pool, that stretches along the coast to the next tiny uninhabited bay. All come with a/c, TV, mini-bar, hot water, free breakfast and fairly traditional Thai-style decor. **B3600**

EATING

Ton Sai is the best place to eat on the island; elsewhere, visitors tend to eat at their resort's restaurant.

TON SAI VILLAGE

Cosmic East of the pier, on the fourth north–south alley, heading north from the yellow Phi Phi Divers shop. Popular for its well-priced pasta, which includes home-made ravioli and gnocchi (B100), and pizzas (B150). Daily 8am–10.30pm.

Le Grand Bleu Just east of the pier on the main east–west alley. Classy place serving a French-inspired menu that includes lots of fresh seafood, including risotto with calamari (B180), sirloin steak and changing dishes of the day. Daily 6.30–10.30pm.

Lemongrass East of the pier, on the first north–south alley. Friendly, basic restaurant with an open kitchen, serving very tasty Thai standards, starting with chicken fried rice for B100. Daily 10/10.30am–10.30/11pm.

Madame Restaurant East of the pier, off the fourth north–south alley, on the main route heading towards The Rock. Deservedly popular for its curries – *phanaeng*, *matsaman*, green and red – mostly B80. Also offers thin-crust pizzas and a decent vegetarian selection, as well as Western breakfasts and espresso coffees. Daily 8am–11pm.

Papaya East of the pier, just off the fourth north–south alley. One of the best of several village-style kitchens whose authentic and reasonably cheap Thai standards, including noodle soups, *phat thai*, fried rice dishes and fiery curries (B150), make it very popular with locals and dive staff. Daily 9am–10pm.

Patcharee Bakery On the main alley running east from the pier. This place and *Phi Phi Bakery* square up to each other across the narrow alley, vying for the breakfast trade. Croissants – plain, chocolate (B30), almond or savoury – are the thing here, washed down with espresso coffees. Daily 7am–8pm.

Phi Phi Bakery On the main alley running east from the pier, opposite Patcharee Bakery. Good choice for breakfast or lunch, with espresso coffees, set breakfasts (from B145), sandwiches and piles of home-made breads, cakes and cookies. Daily 7am–5pm.

Pluto On the main alley running east from the pier. A/c café serving delicious Italian ice cream made in Phuket (from B80 for one scoop) and excellent Illy espressos. Daily 10am–10pm.

Pum East of the pier, on the fourth north–south alley ☎081 521 8904, ⊛pumthaifoodchain.com. Small, comfy, contemporary chain restaurant, serving basic Thai dishes, such as noodles (B99), fried rice and curries, in some strange combinations that sometimes work. They also offer cooking classes at their school on the next alley west for B1500 for 3hr. Daily 11am–9pm.

NIGHTLIFE AND ENTERTAINMENT

TON SAI VILLAGE AND AO LOH DALUM

Concentrated on the beach at Loh Dalum, Ton Sai nightlife is young and drunken, involving endless buckets of SangSom Thai rum and Red Bull, dance music played until dawn, and fire-juggling shows on the beach. Most of the bars offer a pretty similar formula, so it's often the one-off events and happy hours that make the difference.

Reggae Bar East of the pier, off the fourth north–south alley, on the main route heading towards The Rock. A Phi Phi institution in the heart of the village that's been running for years in various incarnations. These days it arranges regular amateur *muay thai* bouts in its boxing ring at around 9pm – "beat up your friend and win free buckets" – and has pool tables and a bar around the sides. There's even reggae karaoke. Daily roughly 10am–1am.

Slinky Towards the east end of Loh Dalum, where the left fork just before The Rock hits the beach. The messy, throbbing heart of Phi Phi nightlife, with a booming sound system, fire shows, and buckets and buckets of booze. Daily 6pm–late.

Stones Bar On the beach at the east end of Loh Dalum. One of the bars of the moment, with dozens of red, gold and green axe cushions scattered on the beach and on platforms under the trees, and a DJ station in a treehouse. Claims to be open 24hr.

Sunflower Bar On the beach at the east end of Loh Dalum. Timber-built chillout spot with tables, axe cushions and plants strewn around the garden, plus great views, good music, free wi-fi and a pool table. Happy hour daily 5.30–8.30pm. Daily roughly 10am–2pm.

DIRECTORY

ATMs and exchange Plenty of machines in Ton Sai village, including next to the Siam Commercial Bank exchange counter (daily 9am–8.30pm), on the main alley running east of the pier.

Hospital Phi Phi Hospital (☎075 622151 or ☎081 270 4481), at the western end of Ao Ton Sai.

Police As well as a police station (☎075 611177), next to *Carlito's Bar* on the main alley running east of the Ao Ton Sai pier, out towards Laem Hin, there's a tourist policeman on Phi Phi (☎1155).

Ko Jum

Situated halfway between Krabi and Ko Lanta Yai, **KO JUM** (whose northern half is known as **Ko Pu**) is the sort of laidback spot that people come to for a couple of days, then can't bring themselves to leave. Though there's plenty of accommodation on the island, there's nothing more than a handful of beach bars for evening entertainment, and little to do during the day except try out the half-dozen west-coast beaches. The beaches may not be pristine, and are in some places unswimmably rocky at low tide, but they're mostly long and wild, and all but empty of people. Nights are also low-key: it's paraffin lamps and starlight after about 11pm (or earlier) at those places that are off the main grid, and many don't even provide fans as island breezes are sufficiently cooling.

The island is home to around three thousand people, the majority of them Muslim, though there are also communities of *chao ley* sea gypsies on Ko Jum (see p.602), as well as Buddhists. The main village is **Ban Ko Jum**, on the island's southeastern tip, comprising a few local shops and small restaurants, one of the island's three piers for boats to and from

ACCOMMODATION

Because demand is so high, from November to March it's often hard to get a room on spec on West or East Railay, though you should have more luck on Ao Ton Sai. Mains electricity hasn't yet reached Ton Sai: very few of the bungalows have electricity during daylight hours, and in the cheapest places you'll just get a few hours' worth out of the generator in the evening.

WEST RAILAY

Railay Bay Resort and Spa ☎ 075 819407, ⓦ railay bayresort.com. There's a huge range of rooms and bungalows here, in a shady coconut grove that runs down to both East and West Railay, plus two swimming pools and a spa. The pick of the bunch are the very large beachfront suites, which have marble bathrooms with jacuzzi tubs and great sea views from their verandas. B3900

Railay Village ☎ 075 819412–3, ⓦ railayvillagekrabi .com. Occupying very pretty gardens in between the two beaches, with nowhere more than 300m from the West Railay shore, the style here is elegant tropical, in white-washed jacuzzi villas and pool-access hotel rooms, all roofed in low-impact wooden tiles, with wooden floors and Thai furnishings completing the look. There are two pools and a spa. Breakfast included. B5250

Railei Beach Club ☎ 086 685 9359, ⓦ raileibeachclub .com. Unusual compound of charming, mostly fan-cooled private houses, built of wood in idiosyncratic Thai style and rented out by their owners. One- to four-bed houses are available, all well-spaced, and there are a couple of cheaper private rooms; most have kitchen. The compound is only minimally screened from the beach, so seafront houses get good views but may lack privacy and bear the brunt of the noisy longtail traffic. Minimum stays of three nights, rising to seven from mid-Dec to mid-Jan. B3000

AO PHRA NANG

Rayavadee ☎ 075 620740, ⓦ rayavadee.com. The supremely elegant two-storey spiral-shaped pavilions here, some set in enclosed gardens, some with whirlpools, are set in a beautifully landscaped, eco-friendly compound with lotus ponds that borders all three beaches. Facilities include a pool with a kids' pool, a spa, a squash court and tennis courts, a gym and two restaurants. B17,550

EAST RAILAY

Railay Cabana ☎ 084 057 7167. In a spacious, grassy, tree-filled amphitheatre of majestic karst cliffs, a 5min walk from the beach on the track to Ton Sai, this friendly family-run place offers simple bamboo bungalows with thick mattresses, mosquito nets, fans and bathrooms. It's a lovely quiet spot, away from the East Railay crassness, though without wi-fi. Staff can help transport luggage from the pier. B500

★**Railay Garden View Resort** ☎ 085 888 5143, ⓦ railaygardenview.com. This place really stands out for its simple rustic-chic style, great high-level views over the mangroves and sea beyond, and green surrounds in a garden of jackfruit, banana and papaya trees. The fan-cooled

bungalows, built from good-quality split bamboo, are widely spaced and on stilts, with colour-washed cold-water bathrooms, wooden-floored bedrooms and decks, and plenty of triangular cushions for lounging. The drawback is that it's up a steep stairway beyond the far north end of East Railay, accessed via a short walkway beyond *The Last Bar*, about 15min walk from West Railay. Breakfast included. B1450

Rapala Rock Wood Resort ☎ 075 622586, ⓔ rapala @loxinfo.co.th. Climb a steep flight of stairs to reach the thirty rough-hewn, fan-cooled timber and brick huts here, which are among the cheapest on Railay, set around a scruffy, breezy garden high above the beach, with some enjoying dramatic karst views from their verandas. There's also a nice communal deck among the treetops, and a friendly restaurant that serves Indian food and bakes its own tasty biscuits and bread. Walk-ins only and no wi-fi. B400

★**Sunrise Tropical Resort** ☎ 075 819418–20, ⓦ sunrisetropical.com. The most stylish of the affordable hotels on the cape offers just forty rooms, most in elegantly designed a/c bungalows, and some in a couple of two-storey buildings, all with Thai furnishings and generously spacious living areas, set around a landscaped tropical garden with a pool and spa. Doubles B3000, villas B4500

Ya Ya Bungalows (Railay Princess Budget) ☎ 075 622998, ⓦ railaybayresort.com/hotel/yaya. This idiosyncratic place is built almost entirely of wood, with most rooms contained in a series of sturdy, quite well-designed, three-storey buildings. They all have verandas and en-suite bathrooms and many have hot showers, but soundproofing is not great and most rooms are quite dark. B3400

AO TON SAI

Country Side Resort ☎ 084 848 0146. Solar-powered eco-resort offering airy and attractive wooden bungalows on stilts, some with stunning views of the karsts, some with hot showers – including the a/c rooms, which have iPod docks and can sleep three people. Fan B850, a/c B1380

Dream Valley Resort ☎ 075 819810–2, ⓦ dreamvalley krabi.com. The ninety bungalows here are ranged discreetly among the trees, running far back towards the cliff-face, offering a range of good-quality accommodation in various categories, from wooden bungalows with fans, mosquito screens and bathrooms through to a/c villas with hot showers, the best of which are the premier accommodation on Ao Ton Sai. Breakfast included. B2500

Pasook Resort ☎ 089 645 3013. Friendly, welcoming spot, set on sloping lawns amid flowers and small trees, offering en-suite, fan-cooled concrete rooms and clapboard bungalows – best value are the larger concrete rooms with sellers and crowds of day-trippers who are deposited here in their hundreds, by boats that pollute the coastal waters. Better to visit before 10am or after 4pm if you can.

The walkway from East Railay winds between the super-lux *Rayavadee* hotel and the lip of a massive karst before emerging at the beach beside **Tham Phra Nang**, or **Princess Cave**. The beach and cave, and indeed the peninsula, are named for this princess (*phra nang* means "revered lady"): according to legend, a boat carrying an Indian princess sank in a storm here and the royal spirit took up residence in the cave. Local fisherfolk believe she controls the fertility of the sea and, to encourage large catches, leave red-tipped wooden phalluses as offerings to her at the cave entrance. Buried deep inside the same cliff is **Sa Phra Nang** (**Princess Lagoon**), which is accessible only via a steep 45-minute descent that starts halfway along the walkway. You'll need proper shoes for it, as slippery descents and sharp rocks make it hard in flip-flops or bare feet. After an initial ten-minute clamber, negotiated with the help of ropes, the path forks: go left for a panoramic view over East and West Railay, or right for the lagoon. (For the strong-armed, there's the third option of hauling yourself up ropes to the top of the cliff for a bird's-eye view.) Taking the right-hand fork, you'll pass through the tropical dell dubbed "big tree valley" before eventually descending to the murky lagoon.

Ao Ton Sai

The beach at **AO TON SAI**, north across the oyster rocks from West Railay, is not the prettiest, prone to murk and littered with rocks that make it impossible to swim at low tide. But its orange-and-ochre-striped cliffs are magnificently scenic, dripping with curlicues and turrets that tower over a central tree-filled bowl and host scores of challenging rock climbs. Most of the accommodation here is aimed at climbers and travellers, and is well hidden several hundred metres back from the shore, scattered within the remains of a forest and along the shady path that, beyond *Sai Tong*, takes you to East Railay in about twenty minutes. The vibe here is green and comradely, with climbers doing their thing during the day and partying at the several chilled bars after dark. At low tide you can pick your way over the razor-sharp rocks from West Railay, while at high tide you either need to swim or get a longtail, or walk over the hill from East Railay.

ARRIVAL AND DEPARTURE   LAEM PHRA NANG

Laem Phra Nang is only accessible by **boat**.

To/from Krabi town Longtail boats to Laem Phra Nang depart from the Krabi riverfront (45min; B150/person, minimum eight people, or around B1500 when chartered), leaving throughout the day as soon as they fill up. Depending on the tide, all Krabi boats land on or off East Railay, so you may have to wade; they do run during the rainy season, but the waves make it a nerve-wracking experience, so you're advised to go via Ao Nang instead. Coming back, contact a travel agent or your guesthouse on Laem Phra Nang about the half a dozen timed departures a day.

To/from Ao Nang and beyond Ao Nang is much closer than Krabi town to Laem Phra Nang, and shared longtails run from the beachfront here to West Railay, Ao Phra Nang and Ao Ton Sai when full (10min; B100; B150 after dark; minimum eight people; return tickets are open, allowing return from any of the three beaches). There are several longtail boat stations with ticket booths, including one at the Hat Nopparat Thara national park visitor centre, all charging the same price; the one at the eastern end of the beachfront road is the most popular, so you'll probably have the shortest wait for the boat to fill up here. Expect to get your legs wet wading out to the songthaew. During high season there should also be daily ferries from Ao Nang via West Railay to Ko Phi Phi (2hr 30min), Ko Lanta (2hr 30min) and Phuket (3hr); if not, you'll need to travel via Ao Nang.

GETTING AROUND AND SERVICES

Getting around Shared longtail boats between Ao Ton Sai and West Railay cost B50 per person (minimum four people).

ATM Several in the resort, including nearly opposite *Flame Tree* restaurant.

Chaibancha, Thailand's greatest-ever film star. He played the handsome hero in 265 films, in many of them performing opposite former beauty queen **Petchara Chaowarat**. Of the 165 movies they made together, their most famous was *Mon Rak Luk Thung* (*Enchanting Countryside*, 1969), a folk-musical about life and love in the countryside that played continuously in Bangkok for six months and later spawned a bestselling soundtrack album. Every Thai adult of a certain age can recall the days when Mitr co-starred with Petchara, and when Mitr fell to a dramatic death in 1970 – during a stunt involving a rope ladder suspended from a helicopter – it caused nationwide mourning. He was cremated at Wat Theparin in Bangkok (off Thanon Luang in Chinatown), where photos of the cremation ceremony and the crowds of fans who attended are still on display. Though non-Thai speakers are denied the pleasure of seeing Mitr and Petchara in action, you can get a good idea of the general tone of their films from the 2000 hit *Tears of the Black Tiger* (see p.776), which affectionately parodies the films of this period.

The 1970s and 1980s

For many years after Mitr's death, Thai cinema continued to be dominated by action melodramas, though a notable exception was *Khao Chua Karn* (*His Name is Karn*), the first Thai film to tackle corruption in the civil service – it was released in 1973, not long before mass student demonstrations led to the ousting of the military government, and was made by Chatri Chalerm Yukol, who went on to direct the 2001 epic *The Legend of Suriyothai* (see p.776). The other standout film of the 1970s is *Phae Khao* (*The Old Scar*, 1977), in which director Cherd Songsri uses traditional rural Thailand as a potent setting for a tragic romance that ends with the heroine's death.

With competition from television and large numbers of imported Hollywood films, Thai film production dwindled during the 1980s, but in 1984 the **Thai National Film Archive** was set up to preserve not only Thai films but also many of the wonderful posters used to promote them. A rare gem from the 1980s is Yuttana Mukdasanit's coming-of-age drama *Butterflies and Flowers* (*Pee Sua Lae Dok Mai*, 1986), which is set in a Muslim community in southern Thailand and looks at the pressures on a poor teenager who ends up smuggling rice across the nearby Malaysian border. The film won an award at the Hawaii International Film Festival.

By the 1990s, the Thai film industry was in a rather sorry state and the few films still produced were mainly trite melodramas aimed at an undiscerning teenage audience. But everything started to change for the better in 1997.

Modern Thai cinema

The rebirth of the Thai film industry started in 1997 with the release of Pen-Ek Ratanaruang's *Fun Bar Karaoke* and Nonzee Nimibutr's *Daeng Birley and the Young Gangsters*. Fuelled by a **new wave** of talented directors and writers, including Nonzee and Pen-Ek, this resurgence has seen Thai films benefiting from larger budgets and achieving international acclaim. The new breed of Thai film-makers has moved away from traditional action melodramas and soap operas to create films that are more imaginative and stylish. With a new emphasis on production values, they also look very good, yet it is the fresh, distinctly Thai flavour that most charms Western audiences, a style summed up by one Thai film commentator as "neo-unrealist", and by another as being influenced by the popular *likay* genre of bawdy, over-the-top Thai street-theatre, where actors use song and dance as well as speech to tell their story.

Directors of the new wave

Daeng Birely and the Young Gangsters (*2499 Antaphan Krong Muang*) was the surprise hit of 1997; **Nonzee Nimibutr** showed in this story of 1950s gangsters that he was able to appeal to the international festival circuit as well as local cinema-goers. He followed it up with the even more successful *Nang Nak* in 1999, giving the big-budget treatment to a traditional nineteenth-century Thai ghost story about a woman who dies while in labour, along with her unborn child. In *Jan Dara* (2001), the 1930s story of a young man who despises his womanizing stepfather, yet eventually becomes just such a person, Nonzee pushed the envelope of what was acceptable in Thai cinema by including scenes of rape and lesbianism that would not have been permitted a decade earlier. *Queens of Langkasuka* (*Puen Yai Jom Salad*, 2008) saw him turning to the more conservative genre of historical action fantasy, complete with sumptuous costumes, pirates, sea gypsies and sorcerers, while his latest, *Distortion* (2012), is a psycho-thriller, full of stylized gore.

In a wry tale of messages received from beyond the grave, **Pen-Ek Ratanaruang**'s first film *Fun Bar Karaoke* (1997) looked at how the lives of modern middle-class Thais are still affected by traditional superstitions. His next film *Sixtynine* (*Ruang Talok 69*, 1999) was a fast-paced thriller set during the Asian financial crisis, with a down-on-her-luck woman stumbling upon a hoard of money. Pen-Ek followed this with *Mon Rak Transistor: A Transistor Love Story* (2003), a bitter-sweet love story about a naïve boy from the country with ambitions to be a *luk thung* singer. It's full of charm and the popular soundtrack is available on CD (see p.768). Pen-Ek's *Last Life in the Universe* (2003) is a much darker, more melancholy affair, following two very different personalities – a suicidal Japanese man and a Thai girl – who are brought together in grief. In *Ploy* (2007), a jet-lagged night in a Bangkok hotel sees the marriage of an expat Thai couple unravel, with sex scenes deemed too explicit by Thai censors. Pen-Ek's latest fiction, *Headshot* (*Fon Tok Kheun Faa*, literally "Rain Falling up to the Sky"; 2011), which tells of a hitman who wakes up from a coma seeing the world upside down, is a noirish thriller with a satirical political edge. He followed this up with a controversial documentary on Thailand's recent political history, *Paradoxocracy* (*Prachathipathai*; 2013).

The scriptwriter on Nonzee's *Daeng Birely* and *Nang Nak* was Wisit Sasanatieng, who, in 2000, directed *Tears of the Black Tiger* (*Fah Talai Jone*). This gentle send-up of the old Thai action films of the 1960s and 1970s uses exaggerated acting styles and irresistible comic-book colours to tell the story of handsome bandit Dum and his love for upper-class Rumpoey. Writer-director Wisit grew up watching the spaghetti westerns of Sergio Leone and includes more than a few passing references to those films. His *Citizen Dog* (*Mah Nakorn*, 2004) is an even more surreal colour-saturated satire, both comic and pointed, about a country boy looking for work and romance in Bangkok.

Blockbusters at home and abroad

Among other high-profile international successes, the warm and off-beat comedy *Iron Ladies* (*Satri Lek*, 2000) charts the often hilarious true-life adventures of a Lampang volleyball team made up of transsexuals and transvestites. *Beautiful Boxer* (2003) fashions a sensitive, insightful biopic out of a similar subject – the true story of transvestite *muay thai* champion Nong Toom who fights in order to win money for sex-change surgery. *Bangkok Dangerous* (*Krung Thep Antharai*, 2000) is a riveting John Woo-style thriller directed by brothers Oxide and Danny Pang; both a brutal tale about a deaf hitman and the story of his love affair with a girl innocent of his occupation, it features several scenes shot in the streets of Bangkok.

The visually stunning historical blockbuster *The Legend of Suriyothai* (2001) tells the true story of a sixteenth-century queen of the Ayutthayan court who gave her life defending her husband during a Burmese invasion. Keen to give international appeal to

★**Wang Sai** Beside the bridge at the eastern end of Thanon Nopparat Thara ☎075 638128. Good sunset views from its beachfront tables, an enormous range of seafood and lots of southern Thai specialities. The hearty *haw mok thalay* (on the menu as "steam seafood curry sauce"; B180) is excellent, stuffed with all kinds of fish and seafood, or you can get seafood fried rice for just B80. Daily 10.30am–10pm.

Laem Phra Nang: Railay and Ton Sai

Seen from the close quarters of a longtail boat, the combination of sheer limestone cliffs, pure white sand and emerald waters around the **LAEM PHRA NANG** peninsula is spectacular – and would be even more so without the hundreds of other admirers gathered on its four beaches. The peninsula (often known simply as **Railay**) is effectively a tiny island, embraced by impenetrable limestone massifs that make road access impossible – but do offer excellent, world-famous **rock-climbing**; transport is by boat only, from Krabi town or, most commonly, from nearby Ao Nang. It has four beaches within ten minutes' walk of each other: **Ao Phra Nang** (walkable via East Railay) graces the southwestern edge, and is flanked by **East and West Railay**, just 500m apart; **Ao Ton Sai** is beyond West Railay, on the other side of a rocky promontory. Almost every patch of buildable land fronting East and West Railay

7

▪ ACCOMMODATION	
Country Side Resort	3
Dream Valley Resort	5
Paasook Resort	4
Railay Bay Resort and Spa	12
Railay Cabana	2
Railay Garden View Resort	7
Railay Village	10
Railei Beach Club	9
Rapala Rock Wood Resort	8
Rayavadee	14
Sai Tong Resort	1
Sunrise Tropical Resort	13
Tonsai Bay Resort	6
Ya Ya Bungalows	11

● RESTAURANTS & CAFÉS	
Flame Tree	3
Phutawan Resort	1
Pyramid Bar	2

LAEM PHRA NANG: RAILAY & TON SAI

ROCK-CLIMBING AND KAYAKING ON LAEM PHRA NANG

Ton Sai and Railay are Thailand's biggest **rock-climbing** centres, attracting thousands of experienced and novice climbers every year to the peninsula's seven hundred bolted routes, which range in difficulty from 5a to 8c (see ⓦ railay.com for a full rundown). Of the many climbing **schools** that rent out equipment and lead guided climbs, the most established include King Climbers on Walking Street on West Railay (☎075 662096, ⓦ railay.com/railay /climbing/climbing_king_climbers.shtml) and Basecamp Tonsai on Ton Sai (☎081 149 9745, ⓦ basecamptonsai.com). A typical half-day introduction costs B1000, a full day B1800, while B6000 will get you a three-day course, learning all rope skills; equipment can be rented for about B2200 per day for two people from Railay Rock Climbing Shop (☎081 7972517) on West Railay's Walking Street. If you don't need instruction, the locally published and regularly updated guidebooks, Basecamp Tonsai's *Rock Climbing in Thailand and Laos* and King Climbers' *Thailand Route Guide Book*, will give you all the route information you need. Unaided over-water climbing on cliffs and outcrops out at sea, known as **deep-water soloing**, with no ropes, bolts or partner, is also becoming a big thing around here and can be arranged through most climbing schools for about B1000.

Kayaking around this area is also very rewarding – you can get to Ao Nang in less than an hour; kayaks cost B200 per hour to rent, for example on the beach in front of *Flame Tree* restaurant on West Railay. There are plenty of other activities in the Krabi area that you could hook up with from Laem Phra Nang (see p.660).

---

has been taken over by bungalow resorts, and development is creeping up the cliffsides and into the forest behind. But at least high-rises don't feature, and much of the construction is hidden among trees or set amid prettily landscaped gardens. Accommodation is at a premium and not cheap, so the scene on West and East Railay, and Ao Phra Nang, is predominantly holidaymakers on short breaks rather than backpackers. The opposite is true on adjacent Ao Ton Sai, Krabi's main travellers' hub and the heart of the rock-climbing scene.

West Railay

The loveliest and most popular beach on the cape is **WEST RAILAY**, with its gorgeous white sand, crystal-clear water and impressive karst scenery at every turn. The best of the peninsula's bungalow hotels front this shoreline, and longtail boats from Ao Nang pull in here too, so it gets crowded.

East Railay

Follow any of the paved tracks inland, through the resort developments, and within a few minutes you reach **EAST RAILAY** on the other coast, lined with mangrove swamps and a muddy shore that make it unsuitable for swimming; boats from Krabi town dock here. Accommodation on this side is a bit cheaper, and there's more variety in price too, though – aside from a couple of gems – it's mostly an uncomfortable mix of uninspired, low-grade developments and unsubtle bars with names like *Skunk* and *Stone*. Depressingly, much of East Railay's hinterland is despoiled by trash and building rubble, but inland it's another story, with a majestic amphitheatre of forested karst turrets just ten minutes' walk away, on the back route to Ao Ton Sai.

Ao Phra Nang

Head to the far south end of East Railay's shoreline to pick up the path to the diminutive, cliff-bound beach at **AO PHRA NANG** (also called **Hat Tham Phra Nang**). Though exceptionally pretty, the bay can be hard to appreciate beneath the trinket nice bathrooms (B450). Prices change frequently, according to demand. Doubles B400, bungalows B700

Sai Tong Resort 400m along the track to East Railway ☎081 079 6583. This friendly, good-value little place offers cheap, woven-bamboo huts with nets, fans and bathrooms, and bigger, more comfy, cute-looking split-bamboo ones, also en suite and with nets, fans and proper beds. B300

Tonsai Bay Resort ☎075 695599, ⓦtonsaibaykrabi .com. With its large, widely spaced and plain but comfortable bungalows, this is one of the top places to stay on Ao Ton Sai. The detached and semi-detached bungalows boast huge glass windows and big decks from which to soak up the pretty location in a grove of trees set back from the shore, and all have a/c, hot shower, satellite TV, fridge and safety box. Breakfast included. B2500

EATING AND DRINKING

There's no shortage of traveller-style bars on Laem Phra Nang, especially at the north end of East Railway and on the beach at Ton Sai, with their fire-juggling, driftwood furniture, chillums and occasional parties.

WEST RAILWAY

Flame Tree On the seafront. This sprawling, laidback, semi-outdoor place has a more varied menu than most of the restaurants on Laem Phra Nang, including cashew nut salad (B175), some southern Thai dishes, mushroom sauce steak (B395), pasta, sandwiches, a variety of breakfasts and espresso coffees. Daily 6.30am–10.30pm.

EAST RAILWAY

Phutawan Resort Quietly located in the middle of the spectacular cliff-lined basin on the track to Ton Sai, a 10min

walk from both East and West Railay, the restaurant here offers fine views and good food, mostly seafood and Thai curries, and largely in the reasonable B120–150 range. Daily 7.30am–10pm.

AO TON SAI

Pyramid Bar Busy day and night with climbers scoffing Thai food, the fresh coffees, tuna and cheese melts (B100) and ciabatta sandwiches on home-made bread. There's a lot of chatter but it's casual and relaxing, especially in a hammock. High season only, hours variable.

Ko Phi Phi Don

About 40km south of Krabi, the island of **KO PHI PHI DON** looks breathtakingly handsome as you approach from the sea, its classic arcs of pure white sand framed by dramatic cliffs and lapped by water that's a mouthwatering shade of turquoise. A flat sandy isthmus connects the hilly east and west halves of the island, scalloped into the much photographed symmetrical double bays of Ao Ton Sai and Ao Loh Dalum. The vast majority of the tourist accommodation is squashed in here, as is the island's wild nightlife, with just a few alternatives scattered along eastern coasts. Phi Phi's few indigenous islanders mostly live in the northeast.

Such beauty, however, belies the island's turbulent recent history. By the early 1990s, Phi Phi's reputation as a tropical idyll was bringing unfeasibly huge crowds of backpackers to its shores, and the problem worsened after uninhabited little sister island **Ko Phi Phi Leh** – under national marine park protection on account of its lucrative bird's-nest business (see box, p.673) – gained worldwide attention as the location for the movie *The Beach* in 1999, adding day-trippers, package tourists and big hotels to the mix on Phi Phi Don. Then, in December 2004, the **tsunami** struck (see p.610). As a 5m-high wave crashed in from the north, over the sunbathers on Ao Loh Dalum, a 3m-high wave from the south hurtled in across the ferry dock and tourist village at Ao Ton Sai. The waves met in the middle, obliterating seventy percent of all buildings on the sandy flats and killing two thousand. The rest of the island was barely affected.

Volunteers and donations poured in to help the island back on its feet, and though the rebuild was dogged by much political wrangling, the Phi Phi of today thrives much as it ever did, firmly re-established as the destination to be ticked off on almost any itinerary in southern Thailand. Unfortunately, few of the pre-tsunami **problems** have been properly resolved – in part because tsunami survivors were desperate to make a new start as fast as they could. The island is now once again floundering under unregulated, unsightly and unsustainable development, with inadequate rubbish disposal and a plague of overpriced

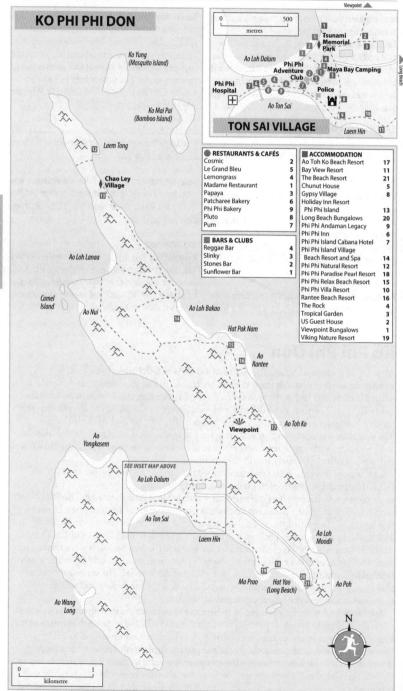

KO PHI PHI DON

TON SAI VILLAGE

Ko Yung
(Mosquito Island)

Ko Mai Pai
(Bamboo Island)

Laem Tong

Chao Ley Village

Ao Loh Lanaa

Camel Island

Ao Nui

Ao Loh Bakao

Hat Pak Nam

Ao Rantee

Ao Yongkasem

Viewpoint

Ao Toh Ko

SEE INSET MAP ABOVE

Ao Loh Dalum

Ao Ton Sai

Laem Hin

Ao Loh Moodii

Ao Wang Long

Ma Prao

Hat Yao
(Long Beach)

Ao Poh

Viewpoint

Tsunami Memorial Park

Ao Loh Dalum

Phi Phi Adventure Club

Maya Bay Camping

Phi Phi Hospital

Police

Ao Ton Sai

Laem Hin

Long Beach

Ko Phi Phi Leh

● RESTAURANTS & CAFÉS

Cosmic	2
Le Grand Bleu	5
Lemongrass	4
Madame Restaurant	1
Papaya	3
Patcharee Bakery	6
Phi Phi Bakery	9
Pluto	8
Pum	7

■ BARS & CLUBS

Reggae Bar	4
Slinky	3
Stones Bar	2
Sunflower Bar	1

■ ACCOMMODATION

Ao Toh Ko Beach Resort	17
Bay View Resort	11
The Beach Resort	21
Chunut House	5
Gypsy Village	8
Holiday Inn Resort Phi Phi Island	13
Long Beach Bungalows	20
Phi Phi Andaman Legacy	9
Phi Phi Inn	6
Phi Phi Island Cabana Hotel	7
Phi Phi Island Village Beach Resort and Spa	14
Phi Phi Natural Resort	12
Phi Phi Paradise Pearl Resort	18
Phi Phi Relax Beach Resort	15
Phi Phi Villa Resort	10
Rantee Beach Resort	16
The Rock	4
Tropical Garden	3
US Guest House	2
Viewpoint Bungalows	1
Viking Nature Resort	19

bungalows, 2km from Ao Nang's main facilities but just across the (quite busy) road from a nice stretch of beach and a 5min walk from the seafood restaurants near the visitors' centre. **B1000**.

HAT NOPPARAT THARA WEST

Long Beach Villa 600m west from the khlong ☎ 087 465 6680, ⊛ longbeachvilla.com; map p.654. Set round a grassy, tree-strewn lawn next to a secluded beach, the main offerings at this place are attractive wood-and-bamboo bungalows with fans, mosquito nets and an en-suite bathrooms; it also has large, concrete eight-person family bungalows with two bathrooms and four bunk beds, with fan (B4500). Electricity at night only and wi-fi only in restaurant. Informal cooking classes, snorkelling trips reasonably priced pick-ups. **B2490**

PAN Beach At the westermost end of the beach, about 700m walk from the khlong ☎ 089 866 4373, ⊛ panbeachkrabi.com; map p.654. Sturdy, simply furnished wooden bungalows in two sizes and styles, each with screened windows, fans and bathrooms, set just back from the shore around a lawn. Also has motorbikes and cars for rent, and organizes local boat trips. Electricity at night only. Free pick-ups in the morning from Ao Nang. **B1200**

HAT KLONG MUANG

Sheraton Krabi Beach Resort ☎ 075 628000, ⊛ sheraton.com/krabi; map p.654. Unusually for a top-notch beach-front hotel, the *Sheraton Krabi* does not boast of its sea views because the entire low-rise resort has been built among the mangroves and alongside a khlong; the result is refreshingly green and cool — and full of birdsong. The sandy shore — the nicest in Klong Muang — is anyway just a few steps away, accessed via a series of wooden walkways, and there's a seafront lawn for lounging. Rooms are large, sleek and very comfortable; there's a big pool, a spa, a tennis court, a watersports centre and bicycle rental. Breakfast included. **B7230**

EATING AND DRINKING

Eating and drinking options in Ao Nang are not sophisticated and there are few places that stand out from the crowd. At weekends, locals flock to the **seafood restaurants** in the national park visitors' centre car park on Hat Nopparat Thara, or buy fried chicken from nearby stalls and picnic on mats under the shorefront trees. In central Ao Nang, there are cheap **hot-food stalls** on the road outside *Krabi Resort*, opposite Kontiki Diving, and handcarts selling Muslim roti pancakes (filled with milk, banana or chocolate) pitch up all over the resort. The bar scene is mainly focused around Center Point Walking Street, a U-shaped passageway behind the beachfront shops that's packed with rock, reggae and all-sorts bars, including krabi's first pole-dancing club. There's also a small knot of makeshift little bars on the beach next to the *Wang Sai Restaurant* on Thanon Nopparat Thara.

CENTRAL AO NANG

Chanaya Thai-Dutch Thanon Ao Nang. With its fairy lights, trailing plants and wooden tables, this place always gets a good crowd. The menu is mostly European – T-bone steaks done various ways, ostrich steaks, asparagus, ham and cheese bake – and there are tempting set dinners rounded off with Dutch apple pie and cream. Mains from B280; sets from B350. Daily 8am–2am.

The Last Fishermen Bar Soi Ao Nang 17. On the sand at the far eastern end of the beach, serving simple Thai food and a huge range of sandwiches for lunch, but most famous for its evening barbecues (from B500), which come with baked potatoes, corn-on-the-cob, salads and desserts. Daily 11.30am–4.30pm & 6pm–midnight.

Longtail Boat Soi Seafood ☎ 075 638093. All the Thai standards, including plenty of fish and seafood, which is displayed on ice and in tanks at the entrance, but especially good for thick, toothsome *matsaman* curries served with roti pancakes (B350). Daily 2–10.30pm.

Sala Bua and Lo Spuntino Soi Seafood, a pedestrianized alley of upmarket restaurants running off the promenade ☎ 075 637110, ⊛ salabua-lospuntino.com. does the Thai dishes under *Sala Bua*, including excellent *phanaeng* curries (B280) and seafood, while the other cooks authentic Italian off a wide-ranging menu – lots of appetizers and home-made pastas, pizzas, and imported Australian meats for the main courses – for *Lo Spuntino*. Daily 11am–10pm.

Sally O'Malley's Up a small soi off the promenade. Friendly, Scottish-run, Irish theme pub with a long bar, Kilkenny bitter, Guinness and cider on draught, regular live guitar music and a pool table. Daily 11am–1/2am.

Ton Sai 150m north of McDonald's on Thanon Ao Nang. Home-style Thai cooking is the calling card at this bamboo-shack family-run restaurant. The curries are delicious, there's plenty of seafood and you can get almost any dish cooked to order. Most mains B80–100. Daily 8.30am–10pm.

HAT NOPPARAT THARA EAST

Krua Thara (After Tsunami) National park visitors' centre car park. Hugely popular with locals, expats and visiting Thais for its reasonably priced fresh seafood (mostly sold by weight), but also serves northeastern salads, rice and noodle dishes (around B80) and excellent espresso coffees. Daily 11am–10pm.

ACCOMMODATION

During high season, it's almost impossible to get a double room for under B600 in Ao Nang, though there is one exceptional traveller's place, *Laughing Gecko*, on contiguous Hat Nopparat Thara east. For a simpler beach bungalow on the beach you need to go to Hat Nopparat Thara west. Mid- and upper-end accommodation is plentiful throughout and of a high standard; you can usually get decent discounts through online booking agents. Prices across the board drop by up to fifty percent during the rainy season (May–Oct).

Jinda Guesthouse Off Thanon Ao Nang 📞 075 695068. There are fewer cheaper places in Ao Nang so close to the beach, which makes Jinda a good choice if you're just looking for somewhere to sleep and can handle some street noise. The unattractive but clean rooms have en suites with hot showers, plus a TV and mini-bar. Quieter rooms face inside. Fan **B800**, a/c **B1000**

PK Mansion, Top View and J Mansion Off Thanon Ao Nang 📞 075 637431 or 075 695128, 🌐 krabidir.com /pkmansion or jmansionaonang.com. Three adjacent budget hotels with the same owners and one reception at *PK Mansion*, the cheapest and shabbiest, where there are cheaper windowless room options. *Top View* and *J Mansion* (the newest, with panoramic rooftop views), the slightly pricier siblings, have a range of mostly very good-quality rooms, with hot-water bathrooms, fan or a/c, balconies (many with partial sea views), TVs and fridges, even if the location isn't very tranquil. Reservations advisable. *PK Mansion* **B800**. *Top View* and *J Mansion* fan **B1100**, a/c **B1300**

Somkietbut Resort Thanon Ao Nang 📞 075 637990–1, 🌐 somkietbut.com. Guests here enjoy one of the most delightful settings in Ao Nang, with the 26 rooms and swimming pools surrounded by a feral, jungle-style garden that's full of hanging vines and lotus ponds. Rooms are perfectly pleasant but nothing special; all have a/c and TV, and there's a spa. Breakfast included. **B3000**

HAT NOPPARAT THARA EAST

Cashew Nut Soi Hat Nopparat Thara 13 📞 075 637560, 🌐 cashewnutbungalows.com. Good, sturdy en-suite brick and concrete bungalows with fan or a/c and hot showers ranged around a peaceful garden full of cashew trees, just 5min walk from Hat Nopparat Thara east. Family-run, welcoming and peaceful. Fan **B500**, a/c **B1000**

★ **Laughing Gecko** Soi Hat Nopparat Thara 13 📞 081 270 5028, 🌐 laughinggeckobungalows.com. Perhaps the last of the old-style bungalows left in the Ao Nang area, this is an easy-going and exceptionally traveller-friendly haven run by a Thai–Canadian couple. Choose from a range of simple, thatched, fan-cooled, en-suite bamboo huts set around a garden dotted with cashew trees, including four-person dorms. Also has nightly all-you-can-eat Thai buffets (B150–200). Dorms **B180**, doubles **B500**

National park bungalows Beside the national park headquarters on Thanon Nopparat Thara east 📞 075 637200, 🌐 dnp.go.th. Standard-issue, fan-cooled, en-suite

AO PHAI PLONG

Centara Grand Beach Resort Ao Phai Plong, east end of Ao Nang 📞 075 637789, 🌐 centarahotelsresorts .com. Ao Nang's top hotel has the secluded sandy bay of Ao Phai Plong all to itself, and is connected by longtail boat to the shops and restaurants of Ao Nang or free speedboat shuttle to Hat Nopparat Thara east. Designed to sit almost seamlessly against the forested crags behind, there's a lovely green feel here and seaward vistas are also beautiful. Nearly all rooms in the four-storey hotel buildings and detached villas have sea views. Interiors are modern and generous with sun-balconies and shaded outdoor daybeds. There's a big pool, a diving and watersports centre, kids' club, gym and spa. **B11,280**

CENTRAL AO NANG

Ao Nang Orchid Resort 141 Thanon Ao Nang 📞 075 638426–8, 🌐 aonangorchid-resort.com. This medium-sized but well-appointed hotel is good value for Ao Nang. Choose from rooms in the hotel wing, where the nicest overlook the pool and karst mountains beyond (rather than those with "city" views), or go for stand-alone villas with direct access to the lagoon pool. Interiors are chic and attractive, and the rooms and bungalows all have wood decks. **B3850**

Ao Nang Villa Resort 113 Thanon Ao Nang 📞 075 637270, 🌐 aonangvilla.com. A very popular hotel and spa whose grounds run down to the beachfront walkway. The upscale, a/c rooms are contained within several low-rise wings, a few of them enjoying a sea view, but most overlooking the garden or the bigger of the resort's two pools. Breakfast included. **B4500**

Centara Anda Dhevi Resort Ao Nang Soi 8 📞 075 626222, 🌐 centarahotelsresorts.com. Modern luxury hotel that cleverly squeezes in 130 spacious, contemporary-style rooms around an attractive 43m pool, which features a waterslide and a swim-up bar; ground-floor rooms have direct pool access, others have balconies. There's also a very good food and kids' club. **B4500**

Ibis Styles Krabi Ao Nang 725 Moo 2, Thanon Ao Nang, opposite a mosque 📞 026 592888, 🌐 ibis.com. Being further away from the beach has its benefits with the karst cliffs and wild trees shielding the pool and kids playground here, offering an oasis of good-value rooms. Rooms are comfortable and a/c, with TV and large safes. The beach is just a 20min walk away past the Ao Nang shops and good street food, or there's a shuttle bus. Breakfast included. **B2200**

Film

Until recently, Thai cinema was almost impenetrable to the outside world. But the West began to take notice in 2000, when films such as *Iron Ladies*, *Tears of the Black Tiger* and later *The Legend of Suriyothai* showed that Thai directors had the style and wit to entertain non-Thai-speaking audiences. Many larger-budget Thai films are now released outside Thailand and with English subtitles.

A brief history

Thailand's first **cinema** was built in 1905 in Bangkok, behind Wat Tuk on Thanon Charoen Krung, and for a couple of decades screened only short, silent films from America, Europe and Japan. Though nothing remains of the earliest film-theatres, the renovated Art Deco Sala Chalermkrung, which was built in 1933 in Bangkok's Chinatown, is still in use today as a venue for live theatre and the occasional screening.

The **first home-grown film**, *Chok Sawng Chan* (*Double Luck*), made by the Wasuwat brothers of the Bangkok Film Company, didn't emerge until 1927, and it was another five years before *Long Thang* (*Going Astray*), the first Thai film with sound, followed.

During the 1920s, a few foreign film companies came to Thailand to film the local culture and wildlife. One early classic from this period is *Chang* (1927; available on video), which tells the simple story, in documentary style, of a family who live on the edge of the forest in Nan province. *Chang*'s American directors Merian Cooper and Ernest B. Schoedsack later drew on their experiences in the Thai jungle for their 1933 classic, *King Kong*.

Though Thai film-making continued throughout the 1930s and 1940s, it was virtually suspended during World War II, before re-emerging with a flourish in the 1950s. The 1950s, 1960s and 1970s were golden years for the production of large numbers of hastily made but hugely popular low-budget escapist films, mainly action melodramas featuring stereotypical characters, gangsters and corny love interest. Many of these films starred **Mitr**

POSTERS AND BILLBOARDS

Until the 1990s, domestic and foreign films were always promoted in Thailand with **original Thai artwork**, especially commissioned to hang as billboards and to be reproduced on posters. The artists who produced them really poured their hearts into these images, interpreting the film in their own style and always including an extraordinary amount of detail, usually as montage. Unlike the films themselves, Thai film posters were rarely subject to any censorship and as a result they were often far more eye-catchingly graphic and explicit than Western artwork for the same films. Posters for horror films (always very big in Thailand) depicted particularly gruesome, blood-drenched images, while ads for the (illegal) screenings of soft-porn movies often displayed a surprising amount of naked flesh.

Locally produced posters are still used to advertise films in Thailand, but for over a decade now they have featured photographic images instead of original artwork. However, there's still a chance to admire the exuberant creativity of Thai cinema art because many provincial cinemas continue to employ local artists to produce their own **billboard** paintings every week. Look for these giant works of art above cinema doors, at key locations around town, and on the sides of the megaphone trucks that circulate around town screeching out the times and plot lines of the next show. Within seven days they will have been dismantled, reduced to a pile of planks and painted over with the artwork for next week's film.

to have a written language, and a codified religion based on medieval Chinese Taoism, although in recent years there have been many Mien converts to Christianity and Buddhism. In general, the Mien strike a balance between integration into Thai life and maintenance of their separate cultural base. Many earn extra cash by selling exquisite embroidery and religious scrolls, painted in bold Chinese style.

Mien villages are not especially distinctive: their houses are usually built of wooden planks on a dirt floor, with a guest platform of bamboo in the communal living area. The **clothes** of the women, however, are instantly recognizable: long black jackets with glamorous-looking stole-like lapels of bright scarlet wool, heavily embroidered loose trousers in intricate designs which can take up to two years to complete, and a similarly embroidered black turban. The caps of babies are also very beautiful, richly embroidered with red or pink pom-poms. On special occasions, like weddings, women and children wear silver neck-rings, with silver chains decorated with silver ornaments extending down the back, and even their turbans are crossed with lengths of silver. A Mien woman's wedding headdress is quite extraordinary, a carefully constructed platform with arched supports that are covered with red fabric and heirlooms of embroidered cloth. Two burgundy-coloured fringes create side curtains obscuring her face, and the only concession to modernity is the black insulating tape that holds the structure to her head.

Lisu

The **Lisu** (Lisaw in Thai), who originated in eastern Tibet, first arrived in Thailand in 1921 and are found mostly in the west, particularly between Chiang Mai and Mae Hong Son, but also in western Chiang Rai, Chiang Mai and Phayao provinces, with a population of around 30,000. Whereas the other hill tribes are led by the village headman or shaman, the Lisu are organized into patriarchal clans which have authority over many villages, and their strong sense of clan rivalry often results in public violence.

The Lisu live in extended families at moderate to high altitudes, in houses built on the ground, with dirt floors and bamboo walls. Both men and women dress colourfully; the women wear a blue or green parti-coloured knee-length tunic, split up the sides to the waist, with a wide black belt and blue or green pants. At New Year, the women don dazzling outfits, including waistcoats and belts of intricately fashioned silver and turbans with multicoloured pom-poms and streamers; traditionally, the men wear green, pink or yellow baggy trousers and a blue jacket.

Lawa

The history of the **Lawa** people (Lua in Thai) is poorly understood, but it seems very likely that they have inhabited Thailand since at least the eighth century; they were certainly here when the Thais arrived around eight hundred years ago. The Lawa people are found only in Thailand; they believe that they migrated from Cambodia and linguistically they are certainly closely related to Mon-Khmer, but some archeologists think that their origins lie in Micronesia, which they left perhaps two thousand years back.

This lengthy cohabitation with the Thais has produced large-scale integration, so that most Lawa villages are indistinguishable from Thai settlements and most Lawa speak Thai as their first language. However, in an area of about 500 square kilometres between Hot, Mae Sariang and Mae Hong Son, the Lawa still live a largely traditional life, although even here the majority have adopted Buddhism and Thai-style houses. The basis of their economy is subsistence agriculture, with rice grown on terraces according to a sophisticated rotation system. Those identified as Lawa number just over ten thousand.

Unmarried Lawa women wear distinctive strings of orange and yellow beads, loose white blouses edged with pink, and tight skirts in parallel bands of blue, black, yellow and pink. After marriage, these brightly coloured clothes are replaced with a long fawn dress, but the beads are still worn. All the women wear their hair tied in a turban, and the men wear light-coloured baggy pants and tunics or, more commonly, Western clothes.

Burmese word for "hunter" – by the Thais, because many of the first Lahu to reach northern Thailand were professional hunters. With a population of about 80,000, they are the third-largest hill-tribe group: most of their settlements are concentrated close to the Burmese border, in Chiang Rai, northern Chiang Mai and Mae Hong Son provinces, but families and villages change locations frequently. The Lahu language has become a *lingua franca* among the hill tribes, since the Lahu often hire out their labour. About one-third of Lahu have been converted to Christianity (through exposure in colonial Burma), and many have abandoned their traditional way of life as a result. The remaining animist Lahu believe in a village guardian spirit, who is often worshipped at a central temple that is surrounded by banners and streamers of white and yellow flags. Village houses are built on high stilts with walls of bamboo or wooden planks, thatched with grass. While subsistence farming is still common, sustainable agriculture – plantations of orchards, tea or coffee – is becoming more prevalent, and cash crops such as corn and cotton have taken the place of opium.

Some Lahu women wear a distinctive black cloak with diagonal white stripes, decorated in bold red and yellow at the top of the sleeve, but traditional costume has been supplanted by the Thai shirt and sarong among many Lahu groups. The tribe is famous for its richly embroidered **yaam** (shoulder bags), which are widely available in Chiang Mai.

Akha

The poorest of the hill tribes, the **Akha** (Kaw or Eekaw in Thai) migrated from Tibet over two thousand years ago to Yunnan in China, where at some stage they had an organized state and kept written chronicles of their history – these chronicles, like the Akha written language, are now lost. From the 1910s the tribe began to settle in Thailand and is found in four provinces – Chiang Rai, Chiang Mai, Lampang and Phrae – with a population of nearly 50,000 in about 250 villages. A large Akha population still lives in Yunnan and there are communities in neighbouring Laos as well as in Myanmar.

The Akha are less open to change than the other hill tribes, and have maintained their old agricultural methods of **shifting cultivation**. The Akha's form of animism – *Akhazang*, "the way of life of the Akha" – has also survived in uncompromised form. As well as spirits in the natural world, *Akhazang* encompasses the worship of ancestor spirits: some Akha can recite the names of over sixty generations of forebears.

Every Akha village is entered through ceremonial **gates** decorated with carvings depicting human activities and attributes – even cars and aeroplanes – to indicate to the spirit world that beyond here only humans should pass. To touch any of these carvings, or to show any lack of respect to them, is punishable by fines or sacrifices. The gates are rebuilt every year, so many villages have a series of gates, the older ones in a state of disintegration. Another characteristic of Akha villages is a giant **swing** (also replaced each year), and used every August or early September in a swinging festival.

Akha **houses** are recognizable by their low stilts and steeply pitched roofs, though some may use higher stilts to reflect higher status. Even more distinctive is the elaborate **headgear** which women wear all day; it frames the entire face and usually features white beads interspersed with silver coins, topped with plumes of red taffeta and framed by dangling, hollow silver balls and other jewellery or strings of beads. The rest of their heavy costume is made up of decorated tube-shaped ankle-to-knee leggings, an above-the-knee black skirt with a white beaded centrepiece, and a loose-fitting black jacket with heavily embroidered cuffs and lapels.

Mien

The **Mien** (called Yao in Thai) consider themselves the aristocrats of the hill tribes. Originating in central China, they began migrating southward more than two thousand years ago to southern China, Vietnam, Laos and Thailand. In Thailand today the Mien are widely scattered throughout the north, with concentrations around Nan, Phayao and Chiang Rai, and a population of about 40,000. They are the only hill tribe

Karen

The **Karen** (called Kaliang or Yang in Thai) form by far the largest hill-tribe group in Thailand with a population of 500,000, and are the second oldest after the Lawa, having begun to arrive here from Burma and China in the seventeenth century. The Thai Karen, many of them refugees from Burma (see box, p.261), mostly live in a broad tract of land west of Chiang Mai, which stretches along the border from Mae Hong Son province all the way down to Kanchanaburi, with scattered pockets in Chiang Mai, Chiang Rai and Phayao provinces.

The Karen traditionally practise a system of **rotating cultivation** – ecologically far more sensitive than slash-and-burn – in the valleys of this region and on low hills. Their houses, very similar to those of lowland Thais, are small (they do not live in extended family groups), built on stilts and made of bamboo or teak; they're often surrounded by fruit gardens and neat fences. As well as farming their own land, the Karen often hire out their labour to Thais and other hill tribes, and keep a variety of livestock including elephants, which used to be employed in the teak trade but are now often found giving rides to trekking parties.

Unmarried Karen women wear loose white or undyed V-necked shift dresses, often decorated with grass seeds at the seams. Some subgroups decorate them more elaborately, Sgaw girls with a woven red or pink band above the waist, and Pwo girls with woven red patterns in the lower half of the shift. Married women wear blouses and skirts in bold colours, predominantly red or blue. Men generally wear blue, baggy trousers with red or blue shirts, a simplified version of the women's blouse.

Hmong

Called the Meo ("barbarians") by the Thais, the **Hmong** ("free people") originated in central China or Mongolia and are now found widely in northern Thailand. There are two subgroups: the **Blue Hmong**, who live around and to the west of Chiang Mai; and the **White Hmong**, who are found to the east. Their overall population in Thailand is about 110,000, making them the second-largest hill-tribe group.

Of all the hill tribes, the Hmong have been the quickest to move away from subsistence farming. In the past, Hmong people were more involved in opium production than most other tribes in Thailand, though now many have eagerly embraced the newer cash crops. Hmong clothing has become much in demand in Thailand, and Hmong women will often be seen at markets throughout the country selling their handicrafts. The women, in fact, are expected to do most of the work on the land and in the home.

Hmong **villages** are usually built at high altitudes, below the crest of a protecting hill. Although wealthier families sometimes build the more comfortable Thai-style houses, most stick to the traditional house, with its dirt floor and a roof descending almost to ground level. They live together in extended families, with two or more bedrooms and a large guest platform.

The Blue Hmong dress in especially striking **clothes**. The women wear intricately embroidered pleated skirts decorated with parallel horizontal bands of red, pink, blue and white; their jackets are of black satin, with wide orange and yellow embroidered cuffs and lapels. White Hmong women wear black baggy trousers and simple jackets with blue cuffs. Men of both groups generally wear baggy black trousers with colourful sashes round the waist, and embroidered jackets closing over the chest with a button at the left shoulder. All the Hmong are famous for their chunky **silver jewellery**, which the women wear every day, the men only on special occasions: they believe silver binds a person's spirits together, and wear a heavy neck-ring to keep the spirits weighed down in the body.

Lahu

The **Lahu**, who originated in the Tibetan highlands, migrated to southern China, Burma and Laos centuries ago; only since the end of the nineteenth century did they begin to come into Thailand from northern Burma. They're called Muser – from the

animists. In this belief system, all natural objects are inhabited by spirits which, along with the tribe's ancestor spirits and the supreme divine spirit, must be propitiated to prevent harm to the family or village. Most villages have one or more religious leaders, which may include a priest who looks after the ritual life of the community, and at least one shaman who has the power to mediate with the spirits and prescribe what has to be done to keep them happy. If a member of the community is sick, for example, the shaman will be consulted to determine what action has insulted which spirit, and will then carry out the correct sacrifice.

The most important festival, celebrated by all the tribes, is at **New Year**, when whole communities take part in dancing, music and rituals particular to each tribe: Hmong boys and girls, for instance, take part in a courting ritual at this time, while playing catch with a ball. The New Year festivals are not held on fixed dates, but at various times during the cool-season slack period in the agricultural cycle from January to March.

Costumes and handicrafts

The most conspicuous characteristics of the hill tribes are their exquisitely crafted **costumes** and adornments, the styles and colours of which are particular to each group. Although many men and children now adopt Western clothes for everyday wear, with boys in particular more often running around in long shorts and T-shirts with logos, many women and girls still wear the traditional attire. It's the women who make the clothes too – some still spin their own cotton, though many Hmong, Lisu and Mien women are prosperous enough to buy materials from itinerant traders. Other distinctive hill-tribe artefacts – tools, jewellery, weapons and musical instruments – are the domain of the men, and specialist **blacksmiths** and **silversmiths** have such high status that some attract business from villages many kilometres away. Jewellery, the chief outward proof of a family's wealth, is displayed most obviously by Lisu women at the New Year festivals, and is commonly made from silver melted down from Indian and Burmese coins, though brass, copper and aluminium are also used.

Clothing and **handicrafts** were not regarded as marketable products until the early 1980s, when cooperatives were set up to manufacture and market these goods, which are now big business in the shops of Thailand. The hill tribes' deep-dyed coarse cloth, embroidered with simple geometric patterns in bright colours, has become popular among middle-class Thais as well as farang visitors. Mien material, dyed indigo or black with bright snowflake embroidery, is on sale in many shops, as is the simple but very distinctive Akha work – coarse black cotton, with triangular patterns of stitching and small fabric patches in rainbow colours, usually made up into bags and hats. The Hmong's much more sophisticated **embroidery** and **appliqué**, added to jacket lapels and cuffs and skirt hems, is also widely seen.

Besides clothing, the hill tribes' other handicrafts, such as knives and wooden or bamboo musical pipes, have found a market among farangs, the most saleable product being the intricate engraving work of their silversmiths, especially in the form of chunky bracelets. For a sizeable minority of villages, handicrafts now provide the security of a steady income to supplement what they make from farming.

The main tribes

Within the small geographical area of northern Thailand there are at least ten different hill tribes, many of them divided into distinct subgroups – the following are the main seven, listed in order of population and under their own names, rather than the sometimes derogatory names used by Thais. Beyond the broad similarities outlined above, this section sketches their differences in terms of history, economy and religion, and describes elements of dress by which they can be distinguished.

The hill tribes

Originating in various parts of China and Southeast Asia, the hill tribes are sometimes termed Fourth World people, in that they are migrants who continue to migrate without regard for established national boundaries. Most arrived in Thailand during the last century, and many of the hill peoples are still found in other parts of Southeast Asia – in Vietnam, for example, where the French used the *montagnards* ("mountain dwellers") in their fight against communism. Since 1975, a large percentage of the one million refugees that Thailand has accepted from Myanmar, Laos and Cambodia has been hill-tribe people. Some, however, have been around for much longer, like the Lawa, who are thought to have been the first settlers in northern Thailand, though these days they have largely been assimilated into mainstream Thai culture.

Called **chao khao** (mountain people) by the Thais, the tribes are mostly pre-literate societies, whose sophisticated systems of customs, laws and beliefs have developed to harmonize relationships between individuals and their environment. In recent years their ancient culture has come under threat, faced with the effects of rapid population growth and the ensuing competition for land, discrimination and exploitation by lowland Thais, and tourism. However, the integrity of their way of life is as yet largely undamaged, and what follows is the briefest of introductions to an immensely complex subject. If you want to learn more, visit the Hill Tribe Museum and Handicrafts Shop in Chiang Rai (see p.354) before setting out on a trek.

Agriculture

Although the hill tribes keep some livestock, such as pigs, poultry and elephants, the base of their economy is **swidden agriculture** (slash-and-burn), a crude form of shifting cultivation also practised by many Thai lowland farmers. At the beginning of the season an area of jungle is cleared and burned, producing ash to fertilize rice, corn, chillies and other vegetables, which are replanted in succeeding years until the soil's nutrients are exhausted. This system is sustainable with a low population density, which allows the jungle time to recover before it is used again. However, with the increase in population over recent decades, ever greater areas are being exhausted, and the decreasing forest cover is leading to erosion and microclimatic change.

As a result, many villages took up the large-scale production of **opium** to supplement the traditional subsistence crops, though the Thai government has now largely eradicated opium production in the north. However, the cash crops which have been introduced in its place have often led to further environmental damage, as these low-profit crops require larger areas of cultivation, and thus greater deforestation. Furthermore, the water supplies have become polluted with chemical pesticides, and although more environmentally sensitive agricultural techniques are being introduced, they have yet to achieve widespread acceptance.

Religion and festivals

Although some tribes have taken up Buddhism and others – especially among the Karen, Mien and Lahu – have been converted by Christian missionaries bringing the incentives of education and modern medicine, the hill tribes are predominantly

LUK THUNG

If you can't find any of the albums below, go for a compilation of past albums, usually under a title like *Ruam Hits* (*Mixed Hits*).

"Got" Chakrapand Arbkornburi *12 Years of Grammy Gold*. Packed with slow ballads, this is one for the ladies from *luk thung*'s heartthrob.

Pumpuang Duangjan In Thailand, the best of many albums to go for is *Pumpuang Lai Por Sor* ("Pumpuang's Many Eras"). Her early spine-tingling hits can be found on several CD compilations from Bangkok Cassette, some recorded when she was known as Nampung Petsupan (Honey Diamond from Suphanburi).

Sayan Sanya *Sayan Tao Thong* ("Sayan Golden Star"). Classic 1970s *luk thung* featuring the "honey-voiced" master. As Yodrak said, "Women cry when he [Sayan]

sings."

Suraphon Sombatjalern *Ruam Phleng* ("Mixed Songs") Vols 1–4. Greatest hits by the king of *luk thung*. Great voice, great songs, great backing – Siamese soul.

Various *Mon Rak Transistor* ("A Transistor Love Story"). From the hit movie about a young country boy who tries to make it in the big city as a *luk thung* singer. Includes Suraphon's wonderful theme song, *Mai Leum* ("Don't Forget").

Various *The Rough Guide to the Music of Thailand*. Good review of some recent *mor lam* and *luk thung*, despite confusing liner notes, elephants, and the odd pop group.

MOR LAM/NORTHEASTERN MUSIC

Chalard Songserm *Rhythms of I-Sarn Vols 1 & 2*. Top-quality album from National Artist Chalard, *khaen* maestro Sombat Simlao and a band of great musicians, covering many styles of Lao music in the region. Sombat's train-sounding *khaen* solo is a standout.

Isan Slété *Songs and Music from North East Thailand*. Excellent selection of traditional *mor lam*. Vocal and instrumental numbers, played by a band of master musicians.

Jintara Poonlarp *Ruam Hit 19 Pii Tawng Chut*. Nineteen years at the top on two killer volumes. Vol. 1 features

haunting *mor lam*.

Various *Instrumental Music of Northeast Thailand*. Wonderful Japanese collection of *pong lang* and related instrumental northeastern styles. Lively and fun.

Various, featuring Chaweewan Damnoen *Mor Lam Singing of Northeast Thailand*. Female *mor lam* National Artist, Chaweewan, headlines this fine Japanese collection of many *lam* styles. Most *mor lam klawn* narrative and dance styles, even spirit-possession rituals, are included.

KANTRUM

Darkie *Darkie, Rock II: Buk Jah*. The first-ever *kantrum* crossover album achieved nationwide stardom for the King of Kantrum. Darkie's booming voice moves from rap-like delivery to moans and wails, shadowed closely by the

fiddle and some funky riddims. Unmissable.

Songsaeng Lungluangchai *Songsaeng Kantrum Rock: Chut Ta Don Duay*. Keyboardless, rootsy sound. Look out for his tribute album to Darkie, *Kantrum Rock*.

John Clewley (Adapted from *The Rough Guide to World Music*)

Discography

In Bangkok, ask the vendors at the day and night markets about **CDs**, or the stores on Thanon Charoen Krung (New Road) or at Sunday's Klong Thom market (in the small sois behind Thanon Charoen Krung, between Plaplachai and Mahachak intersections). Most major *luk thung* or *mor lam* artists release an album every three months, which is often given an artist's series number. Old-style recordings of Suraphon Sombatjalern and the like can be found on the ground floor of the Mah Boon Krong Shopping Centre at Mae Mai Phleng Thai, while DJ Siam, nearby on Soi 11, Siam Square, is good for Thai indie and pop. Look out for the intriguingly diverse output of Zudrangma Records (ⓦzudrangmarecords.com): they've released compilations of old *luk thung* and *mor lam* on their own label, and it's well worth browsing their record store, next door to *WTF* (see p.162), just off Soi 51, Thanon Sukhumvit; they have also opened a nearby bar, Studio Lam, and run awesome club nights in the capital, where you might find *mor lam* mixed with Jamaican dancehall.

In addition, several **DVDs** are well worth seeking out: Jeremy Marre's episode on music in Thailand, *Two Faces of Thailand: A Musical Portrait* (Shanachie, US), from his award-winning *Beats of the Heart* music-TV documentary series; *Homrong* (see p.761); and *Mon Rak Transistor* (see p.776).

CLASSICAL

Fong Naam *The Hang Hong Suite*. A good introduction to the vivacious and glittering sound of classical Thai music, this CD includes some upbeat funeral music and parodies of the musical languages of neighbouring cultures. *The Sleeping Angel* is also a splendid recording.

Lai Muang Ensemble *The Spirit of Lanna: Music from the North of Thailand*. Top-quality recording, featuring multi-instrumentalist Somboon Kawichai on the *peejum*

(bamboo pipes) and the eerie-sounding *pin pia*, a chest-resonated oboe.

The Prasit Thawon Ensemble *Thai Classical Music*. Brilliant playing (and outstanding recording quality) from some of Thailand's best performers, mainly of *piphat* style. Includes the overture *Homrong Sornthong* and, on *Cherd Chin*, some scintillating dialogues between different instruments.

FOLK MUSIC

David Fanshawe *Music From Thailand and Laos: Southeast Asia Recordings*. Excellent range of folk music from different regions of both countries.

Various *Sea Gypsies of the Andaman Sea*. The traditional music of nomadic Moken (*chao ley*) fisherfolk in southern Thailand, mostly recorded in the Surin islands.

Various *Thailand: Musiques et Chants des Peuples du Triangle d'Or*. Recordings of the traditional music of Thailand's main hill-tribe groups by the French label, Globe Music: Hmong, Lisu, Lahu, Yao, Akha and Karen, as well as Shan (Thai Yai).

THAI SAKON

Euah Sunthornsanan *Chabab Derm* ("Old Songs") Vols 1–5, 6–10. Modern Thai music was popularized by the late master Euah. Some of the most popular Thai songs ever

were performed by the Suntharaporn band and a bevy of singers.

STRING AND SONGS FOR LIFE

Carabao *Made in Thailand* and *Ameri-koi*. Two classic albums from the Songs for Life giants. *Made in Thailand* was right in tune with the times and targeted social problems like consumerism, the sex trade and a failing education system. *Ameri-koi* (*Greedy America*) is even more nationalistic than the previous one, but it also hits out at Thai migrant workers exploited by labour brokers.

Futon *Never Mind the Botox*. Electro-clash with a punk attitude from the kingdom's favourite underground band.

Excellent cover of Iggy Pop's *I Wanna Be Your Dog*.

Loso/Sek Loso The best compilation of Loso's music is the 2001 release *The Red* album, while the solo work of Sek Loso is best captured on the same year's *Black & White* and live on *10 Years Rock Volumes 1 & 2*.

Modern Dog *Modern Dog*. This album of alternative rock marked an important change of direction for the Thai rock scene. Also see albums *Love Me Love My Life*, *That Song* and their most recent, *Ting Nong Noy*.

The style came to national prominence more than twenty years ago, when a female *mor lam* singer, **Banyen Rakgan**, appeared on national TV. In the early 1980s the music was heard not only in Isaan but also in the growing slums of Bangkok, as rural migrants poured into the capital in search of work. By the end of the decade, stars like **Jintara Poonlarp** (with her hit song *Isaan Woman Far From Home*) and **Pornsak Songsaeng** could command the same sell-out concerts as their *luk thung* counterparts. Jintara remains one of the biggest stars, and her shows mix both *luk thung* and *lam*; for a big raucous show, **Nok Noi Ulaiporn** and Pong-Lang Sa-Orn (see p.762) are probably the hottest acts. **Siriporn Ampaiporn**, whose strong vocals burst upon the *lam* scene with the monster-selling *Bor Rak Si Dam* album, mainly records *luk thung* these days.

The format of a *mor lam* **performance** is similar to that of *luk thung* shows – lots of dancers in wild costumes, comedy skits and a large backing orchestra – as is the subject matter. The music is definitely hot, especially if you see it live, when bands will often play through the night, never missing the groove for a minute, driven on by the relentless *phin* and *khaen* playing. To some people, the fast plucking style of the *phin* gives a West African or Celtic tinge; the *khaen* has a rich sound – over a bass drone players improvise around the melody, while at the same time vamping the basic rhythm. Male and female singers rotate or duet humorous love songs, which often start with one of the *mor khaen* setting up the beat. They sing about topical issues, bits of news, crack lewd jokes or make fun of the audience – all very tongue-in-cheek.

Musically, however, *mor lam* and *luk thung* are very different; *mor lam* has a much faster, relentless rhythm and the vocal delivery is rapid-fire, rather like a rap. You'll immediately recognize a *mor lam* song with its introductory wailing moan "*Oh la naw*", meaning "fortune". *Mor lam* artists, brought up bilingually, can easily switch from *luk thung* to *mor lam*, but *luk thung* artists, who often only speak the national central Thai dialect, cannot branch out so easily.

In the 1990s, *mor lam* musicians headed off the challenge of increasingly popular *string* bands by creating **mor lam sing**, a turbo-charged modern version of *mor lam klawn* played by small electric combos. The number of large touring *luk thung* or *mor lam* shows has declined in recent years, owing to high overheads, TV entertainment and the popularity of *string* bands, so *mor lam sing* satisfies the need for local music with a modern edge.

Mor lam sing was followed quickly by a more rock-oriented *mor lam* sound (this is a little similar to Grand X in the 1980s, which played a mix of rock and *luk thung*), led by funky little combos like **Rocksadert** and **Rock Saleang**, actually much better live than on recordings, although the latter had a hilarious hit in 2006 with *Motorcy Hoy*.

Kantrum: Thai–Cambodian pop

"Isaan *neua* (north) has *mor lam*, Isaan *tai* (south) has *kantrum*," sings **Darkie**, the first star of **kantrum**, Thai–Cambodian pop, in his song *Isaan Tai Samakkhi* (Southern Isaan Unity). His music is a very specific offshoot, from the southern part of Isaan, where Thai–Cambodians mix with ethnic Lao and Thais. So far *kantrum* is only popular in Isaan in Thailand but it has spread over the border to nearby Cambodian towns like Siem Reap where the style is known as Khmer Ler or Khmer Surin.

Modern *kantrum* has developed from Cambodian folk and classical music, played in a small group consisting of fiddle, small hand-drums and *khrab* (pieces of hardwood bashed together rather like claves). This traditional style is now quite hard to find in Thailand; twenty years ago, musicians started to electrify the music, using both traditional and Western instruments. Shunning the synthesizer preferred by his competitors such as **Khong Khoi**, Oh-Yot and Samanchai, Darkie added the wailing fiddle centre-stage and cranked up the rhythms (*kantrum* has a harder beat than even *mor lam*). In 1997, he broke new ground with *Darkie Rock II: Buk Jah*, the first *kantrum* crossover album to have success in the mainstream pop market. Sadly, in 2001, Darkie died aged 35, but a new generation of *kantrum* stars is now emerging, led by **Songsaeng Lungluangchai**, who has recorded several excellent albums of Darkie covers.

always the lyrics that carry the sexual charge of the song (and if lyrics are deemed too risqué by the authorities the song will be subject to strict censorship) but rather the vocal style and the stage presentation, which can be very bawdy indeed.

With the advent of TV and the rise in popularity of *string*, the number of large upcountry *luk thung* shows has declined. It's not easy, said Pumpuang, to tour with over a hundred staff, including the dancers in the *hang kruang* (chorus). "We play for over four hours, but *string* bands, with only a few staff members, play a paltry two hours!" Her response to the advent of *string* and the increasing importance of promotional videos was to develop a dance-floor-oriented sound – **electronic luk thung** (Grand X had already experimented with *luk thung* and disco a few years earlier). Few *luk thung* singers are capable of this, but Pumpuang had the vocal range to tackle both ballad forms and the up-tempo dance numbers. Her musical diversification increased her popularity enormously, and when she died in 1992, aged only 31, up to 200,000 people, ranging from royalty to the rural poor, made their way to her funeral in her home town of Suphanburi (look out for the major biopic, *Pumpuang*, made in 2011).

Pumpuang's death pushed ongoing political problems (the 1992 coup) off the front pages of newspapers, a situation that was repeated in 2008 when **Yodrak Salakjai** died. Yodrak was the most recorded *luk thung* star of all time, with some three thousand songs and five hundred albums to his credit.

After Pumpuang's death, the top *luk thung* slot was occupied by "**Got**" **Chakrapand Arbkornburi**, whose switch from pop to full-time *luk thung* brought many younger listeners to the style, while the reigning female singer was **Sunaree Ratchasima**, but she has been superseded by the perkier **Arpaporn Nakornsawan** and, more recently, by Ying Lee and Tai Orathai. **Mike Piromporn**, originally a *mor lam* man, became Got's main challenger, but both now have to give way to Phai Phongsathon. Bangkok's first 24-hour *luk thung* radio station, Luk Thung FM (at 90 FM), was launched in 1997, and it's even cool for the middle class to like *luk thung* these days. There is some truth, however, in the criticism that some new *luk thung* stars are being artificially manufactured just like their pop and rock counterparts, and there's a tendency to rate a pretty face over vocal expertise.

For many years, *luk thung* was sung by performers from the Suphanburi area in the central plains, but more regional voices are being heard in the genre now, with northeasterners now outnumbering these singers. A slightly faster rhythm, *luk thung Isaan*, has been developed, initially by "**Khru**" (**Teacher**) **Saleh Kunavudh** in the 1980s. The south, too, has its own *luk thung* star, in the enormously popular **Ekachai Srivichai**.

As well as at temple fairs, fairs at district offices in provincial capitals, national holiday events at Bangkok's Sanam Luang by companies like Waitee Thai and New Year celebrations are the best places to catch *luk thung* shows.

Mor lam

Mor lam is the folk style from the poor, dry northeastern region of Isaan, an area famed for droughts, spicy food, good boxers and great music. Over the past 25 years, the modern pop form of this style has risen dramatically. Traditionally, a *mor lam* is a master of the *lam* singing style (sung in the Isaan dialect, which is actually Lao), and is accompanied by the *khaen* (bamboo mouth organ), the *phin* (two- to four-string guitar) and *ching* (small temple cymbals). Modern **mor lam** developed from *mor lam klawn*, a narrative form where all-night singing jousts are held between male and female singers, and from *mor lam soeng*, the group-dance form. Both still play an important part in many social events like weddings, births and deaths, festivals and temple fairs. A *mor lam* may sing intricate fixed-metre Lao epic poems or may relate current affairs in a spontaneous rap. In the large groups, Western instruments like guitar (replacing the *phin*) and synthesizer (for the *khaen*) are used.

years has generally been replaced by more individual and personal themes. The current top act is fresh-faced singer-songwriter **Pongsit Kamphee**, whose earnest approach and rise through the ranks (he was reportedly once a stagehand for Caravan) have garnered him a sizeable following.

Musically, the genre has developed little over the years, remaining strongly rooted in Western folk-rock styles. Recently, however, this has begun to change as musicians have belatedly discovered that **reggae** riddims work well with Songs for Life vocals; perhaps they were inspired by **T-Bone**, for so long the only reggae band in the kingdom. Best of this new sub-genre is Southerner **Job** of the **Job 2 Do** band, while the best classic Marley-style reggae band is the **Srirajah Rockers**. There's a weekend reggae festival held in the north in Pai every winter (ⓦfacebook.com/paireggaefestival).

Songs for Life fans should check out CD stalls at Bangkok's Chatuchak Weekend Market, several of which specialize in this genre.

Luk thung

Go to one of the huge **luk thung** shows held in a temple or local stadium on the outskirts of Bangkok, or to any temple fair in the countryside, and you'll hear one of the great undiscovered popular musics of Asia. The shows, amid the bright lights, food stalls and fairground games, last several hours and involve dozens of dancers and costume changes. In contrast with *luk krung*, *luk thung* (literally, "child of the field") has always been associated with the rural and urban poor, and because of this has gained nationwide popularity over the past forty years.

According to *luk thung* DJ Jenpope Jobkrabuanwan, the term was first coined by Jamnong Rangsitkhun in 1964, but the first song in the style was *Oh Jao Sao Chao Rai* (Oh, the Vegetable Grower's Bride), recorded in 1937, and the genre's first big singer, **Kamrot Samboonanon**, emerged in the mid-1940s. Originally called *phleng talat* (market songs) or *phleng chiwit* (songs of life), the style blended together folk songs, central Thai classical music and Thai folk dances. Malay strings and fiddles were added in the 1950s, as were Latin brass and rhythms like the cha-cha-cha and mambo (Asian tours by Xavier Cugat influenced many Asian pop styles during the 1950s), as well as elements from Hollywood movie music and "yodelling" country and western vocal styles from the likes of Gene Autry and Hank Williams. In 1952, a new singer, **Suraphon Sombatjalern**, made his debut with a song entitled *Nam Ta Lao Wiang* (Tears of the Vientiane Girl) and became the undisputed king of the style until his untimely murder (for serious womanizing, rumour has it) in 1967. Suraphon helped develop the music into a mature form, and was known as the "King" of the genre, along with his Queen, sweet-voiced Pongsri Woranut.

Today, *luk thung* is a mix of Thai folk music and traditional entertainment forms like *likay* (travelling popular theatre), as well as a range of Western styles. There are certainly some strong musical affinities with other regional pop styles like Indonesian *dangdut* and Japanese *enka*, but what is distinctly Thai – quite apart from the spectacular live shows – are the singing styles and the content of the lyrics. Vocal styles are full of heavy ornamentation (*luk khor*) and sustained notes (*auen* or "note-bending"). A singer must have a wide vocal range, as the late *luk thung* megastar **Pumpuang Duangjan** explained: "Making the *luk thung* sound is difficult, you must handle the high and low notes well. And because the emotional content is stronger than in *luk krung*, you must also be able to create a strongly charged atmosphere."

Pumpuang had the kind of voice that turns the spine to jelly. She rose to prominence during the late 1970s, joining **Sayan Sanya** as the biggest male and female names in the business. Like Suraphon Sombatjalern, both came from the rural peasantry, making identification with themes and stories that related directly to the audience much easier. Songs narrate mini-novellas, based around typical characters like the lorry driver, peasant lad or girl, poor farmer, prostitute or maid; and the themes are those of going away to the big city, infidelity, grief, tragedy and sexual pleasure. Interestingly, it is not

Megastars such as veteran **Thongchai "Bird" Macintyre** generally record on either of the two major labels, GMM Grammy and RS. Grammy, which controls more than half the market, has an umbrella of labels that release everything from popster **Bie The Star** to *luk thung* star "Got" Chakrapand Arbkornburi. Their most famous Thai rock act of recent years, though, the talented brothers **Asanee and Wasan (Chotikul)**, have now set up their own label, Music Union, to produce a new generation.

The Thai alternative rock scene developed in the mid-1990s with the emergence, on the then-indie Bakery label (now part of Sony BMG), of **Modern Dog**, whose last album *Ting Nong Noy* (2008) swept various Thai rock awards. Bakery helped kick-start indie rock and rap with the mercurial **Joey Boy** (the hip only buy his profane and savage MP3 underground songs). **Loso** developed into the most popular rock band, with leader **Sek Loso** enjoying a serious solo career and iconic status, but over the last few years his main starring role has been on the gossip pages because of his rehab and marital problems.

Recently, more Western and Asian musicians have joined their Thai counterparts – as with electro-clash band **Futon** (Thai–Japanese–Western). And no list of current Thai pop stars and rockers would be complete without mentioning **Ebola** (metal plus rap), **Bodyslam** (heavy rock), **Thaitanium** (hip-hop from US-raised Thais), **Tattoo Colour** (indie rock), **Cocktail** (soft rock) and singer-songwriters **Palmy** and **Stamp**.

Thailand, and in particular Bangkok, is developing its own musical identity, partly as a result of many high-profile **festivals**, such as the Pattaya Music Festival in March, which showcases Asian bands, and partly because of the explosion of new genres and the emergence of a busy underground and **live scene**. You'll find Thai, foreign and mixed bands and DJs playing in Bangkok's many clubs and bars, and dynamic scenes in Chiang Mai, Khorat and Ko Samui.

Campuses such as Ramkhamhaeng University are good places to get information on upcoming **events**, as are radio stations (especially Fat Radio FM). Bangkok is the best place to catch gigs – check out ⓦbk.asia-city.com for listings.

Songs for Life and reggae

Another important genre is **phleng pheua chiwit**, or "**Songs for Life**", which started as a kind of progressive rock in the early 1970s, with bands like **Caravan** (no relation to the British songsters) blending *phleng pheun bahn* (folk songs) with Western folk and rock. Caravan were at the forefront of the left-wing campaign for democracy with songs like *Khon Kap Khwai* (*Human with Buffaloes*):

> *Greed eats our labour and divides people into classes*
> *The rice farmers fall to the bottom*
> *Insulted as backward and ignorant brutes*
> *With one important and sure thing: death.*

Although an elected government survived from 1973 to 1976, the military returned soon after, and Caravan, like many of the student activists, went into hiding in the jungle. There they performed to villagers and hill-tribe people and gave the occasional concert. When the government offered an amnesty in 1979, most of the students, and Caravan too, disillusioned with the Communist Party's support for the Khmer Rouge in Cambodia, returned to normal life.

In the 1980s a new group emerged to carry on Caravan's work, **Carabao**. The band split up in 1988 but has had many reunions and reincarnations since; their influence is still strong, with leader Ad Carabao still in the limelight but now more as a businessman hawking his "energy" drink, Carabao Daeng, via the band's gigs and nasty nationalistic TV ad campaigns. However, despite the bloody street riots of 1992 (in protest at the then military-installed government) once again bringing Songs for Life artists out to support the pro-democracy protests, since the 1980s the strong social activism of Caravan's early

Folk music

Thailand's folk music is called **phleng pheun bahn**, and different styles are found in the country's four distinct regions (central, north, northeast and south). Despite Thailand's rush to modernity, numerous folk styles are still enthusiastically played, from the hill-tribe New Year dances in the far north to the *saw* (a kind of three-stringed violin) and *fon lep* (fingernail dance) of Chiang Mai, from the all-night singing jousts of northeastern *lam klawn*, to the haunting Muslim vocals of *likay huuluu* in the deep south.

Most Thais are familiar with the exciting central folk styles like *lam tad*, *phleng choi* and *phleng I-saw*, which often feature raunchy verbal jousting between male and female singers. Styles like these and the ever-popular *mor lam* from the northeast (see p.765) are incorporated into modern popular styles such as *luk thung* (see p.764).

One notable folk style to have grown in popularity in recent years is the up-tempo and danceable northeastern instrumental style known as **pong lang** (a wooden xylophone that is attached vertically to a tree and was originally used to keep birds off crops). *Pong lang* is ancient, predating Indian–Thai culture, and was updated by National Artist Pleung Chairaasamee in the 1970s. A few years ago, **Pong-Lang Sa-Orn** emerged with an action-packed comedy show that propelled the band to national fame, million-selling albums and movies.

The best place to see *pong lang* is upcountry, especially in Kalasin province in central Isaan in the dry season between November and March. Folk music also features prominently at the major festivals (see p.46) held in the northeastern cities of Khon Kaen, Ubon Ratchathani and Udon Thani, particularly during Songkhran (April), the Bun Bang Fai rocket festival (May), and the Asanha Puja candle festival (July). Generally, any national holiday or religious festival is a good time to look out for folk music, in any region.

Popular styles

Thailand is the second-biggest Southeast Asian music market after Indonesia, and Bangkok is a major and increasingly important regional hub for pop music and popular culture.

Western orchestration for Thai melodies was introduced in the 1920s and 1930s and this led to the development of *phleng Thai sakon*, or "international Thai music", in the form of big band and swing, country and western, Hollywood film music, rock'n'roll, and so on. In the early days, two distinctive Thai genres developed: *phleng luk krung*, a romantic ballad form, popularized by Thailand's most beloved composer and bandleader Euah Sunthornsanan and his Suntharaporn band; and *phleng luk thung* (country music). **Luk krung**, with its clearly enunciated singing style and romantic fantasies, was long associated with the rich strata of Bangkok society (*krung* comes from Krung Thep, the Thai name for the capital); it's the kind of music that is played by state organs such as Radio Thailand. However, it was largely transformed during the 1960s by the popularity of Western stars like Cliff Richard; as musicians started to mimic the new Western music, a new term was coined, *wong shadow* (*wong* meaning group, *shadow* from the British group The Shadows).

String

The term **string** came into use as Thai-language pop music rapidly developed in the economic boom times of the 1980s. *String* encompasses ballads, rock and alternative, indie, disco, techno/house, J-Pop and K-Pop (Japan and Korea), heavy metal, reggae, ska, rap and underground; whatever trend is popular internationally is picked up and put into the Thai cultural blender. Currently popular are all things Korean – boy bands, girl bands, fashion styles and haircuts, teen TV shows, soap operas, food and comics.

Music

Music is an important part of Thai culture, whether related to Buddhist activities in the local temple (still a focal point for many communities), animist rituals, Brahmanic ceremonies or the wide range of popular song styles. While local forms of Thai popular music such as *luk thung* and *mor lam* remain very popular and distinctively Thai in character, a lively, ever-changing rock, indie, DJ/clubbing and underground scene is also fast developing.

The classical tradition

Thai classical dance and music can be traced back to stone engravings from the Sukhothai period (thirteenth to fifteenth centuries), which show ensembles of musicians playing traditional instruments, called **piphat**. The *piphat* ensembles include many percussion instruments, rather like Indonesian gamelan – gong circles, xylophones and drums – plus a raucous oboe called the *pinai*. The music was developed to accompany classical dance-drama (*khon* or *lakhon*) or shadow-puppet theatre (*nang*): a shadow-puppet show is depicted in the magnificent *Ramayana* murals at Wat Phra Kaeo in Bangkok's Grand Palace complex.

Piphat music sounds strange to Western ears as the seven equal notes of the Thai scale fall between the cracks of the piano keyboard. But heard in the right environment – in a temple, at a dance performance or at a Thai boxing match – it can be entrancing. As there is no notation, everything is memorized. And, as in all Thai music, elements have been assimilated over the years from diverse sources, and synthesized into something new. Check out any of the international albums by the Prasit Thawon Ensemble (Prasit was a National Artist).

Despite the country's rapid westernization, Thai classical music has been undergoing something of a revival in the past few years, partly as a result of royal patronage. There have been recent experiments, too, at blending Thai classical and Western styles – often jazz or rock – led by groups like **Kangsadan** and **Fong Naam**. **Boy Thai** followed their lead, albeit with a more pop-oriented sound, and had some mainstream success with two albums. The two *ranat* (xylophone) playing brothers from Boy Thai, Chaiyoot and Narongrit Tosa-nga, have their own bands now: Chaiyoot with his huge **Bangkok Xylophone Orchestra** and Narongrit as **Khun-In and Off-Beat Siam**. The 2004 biopic *Homrong* (*The Overture*) features a character called Khun-In (played by Narongrit) who duels on the *ranat* against Thailand's greatest classical musician Luang Pradit Phairoh.

There are dance and classical music **performances** in Bangkok at the Sala Chalermkrung Theatre, the National Theatre and the Thailand Cultural Centre (see p.164), and you may also come across some more lacklustre examples at the Erawan Shrine on Thanon Rama I and the *lak muang* shrine in front of the Grand Palace, where people give thanks to deities by paying for the temple musicians and dancers to go through a routine. A number of Bangkok restaurants also feature music and dance shows for tourists, including regular shows by Bruce Gaston of Fong Naam at the *Tawandang German Brewery* (see p.163), and **Duriyapraneet**, the latter being the country's longest-established classical band.

There is also increasing concern about the **ethics of elephant trekking**, a fast-growing and lucrative arm of the tourist industry that some consider has got out of hand. What began as a canny way for elephants to earn their (very expensive) keep, after the 1989 ban on logging rendered most working elephants unemployed, is now endangering Southeast Asia's dwindling population of wild elephants as more and more are captured for the trekking trade (see p.316). Burmese elephants are particularly vulnerable and reportedly get smuggled across the border in significant numbers. In addition, welfare standards at these elephant trekking centres vary enormously. On the positive front, there's an increasing number of **animal sanctuaries** working to look after abused and endangered animals, especially elephants and gibbons (see box, p.759), which operate both as safe havens and as educational visitor attractions.

The wildlife trade
Though Thailand signed the Convention on the International Trade in Endangered Species – **CITES** – in 1983, and hosted the annual CITES conference in 2004, the trading of threatened animals and animal products continues.

Most of the trade in **endangered species** is focused along the borders with Cambodia and Myanmar, where Thai middle-merchants can apparently easily acquire any number of creatures. Some will be sold as pets and to zoos, while others are destined for dining tables and medicine cabinets. **Tiger** body-parts are especially lucrative and mostly end up on the black markets of China, Korea, Taiwan and Hong Kong, where bones, skin, teeth, whiskers and penis are prized for their "medicinal" properties; it's thought that much of Thailand's dwindling tiger population ends up this way. **Bear** paws and gall bladders are considered to have similar potency and are a star feature, along with other endangered species, at certain clandestine restaurants in Thailand catering to "gourmet" tourists from China and Korea; the traditional custom of slicing paws off a living bear and enhancing gall-bladder flavour by taking it from an animal that is literally scared to death make this practice particularly vile. The Burmese border market at Thachilek near Mae Sai is a notorious outlet for tiger and bear body-parts, while Chatuchak Weekend Market in Bangkok has long had a thriving trade in live animals – everything from hornbills to slow loris – despite occasional crackdowns.

National parks

Although Thailand has since the 1970s been protecting some of its natural resources within **national parks**, these have long been caught between commercial and conservationist aims, an issue which the government addressed in 2002 by establishing a new National Park, Wildlife and Plant Conservation Department (DNP; ⓦdnp .go.th/parkreserve), separate from the Royal Forestry Department and its parent Ministry of Agriculture.

With 140 national parks and marine parks across the country, as well as various other protected zones, over thirteen percent of the country is now, in theory at least, protected from encroachment and hunting (a high proportion compared to other nations, such as Japan at 6.5 percent, and the US at 10.5 percent).

However, the **touristification** of certain national parks endures; Ko Phi Phi and Ko Samet in particular have both suffered irreversible environmental damage as a direct result of the number of overnight visitors they receive. While most people understand that the role of the national parks is to conserve vulnerable and precious resources, the dramatic hike in entrance fees payable by foreign visitors to national parks – from B20 up to B200 in 2000 and up again to B400 or B500 for a few special parks – was greeted with cynicism and anger, not least because there is often little sign of anything tangible being done on site with the money.

Elephant trekking and the wildlife trade

Despite the efforts of local and international conservation and wildlife-protection organizations, **animal rights** issues often meet with a confused response in Thailand. The muddled thinking behind the launch of the Chiang Mai Night Safari park was typical: not only was this commercial animal park erected on land appropriated from a national park, but early publicity trumpeted the fact that meat from many of the exotic animals kept in the park – including tigers, lions and elephants – would be available in the park's restaurant. Negative comment soon quashed that, but exotic meats from endangered animals are served, albeit clandestinely, all over Thailand.

Some of Thailand's many **zoos**, such as those in Bangkok and Chiang Mai, are legitimate, reasonably decent places, but a number of the country's other private wildlife theme parks and zoos – particularly those specializing in tigers and crocodiles – have more dubious purposes and some have been targeted by international animal welfare organizations such as Born Free.

WILDLIFE CHARITIES AND VOLUNTEER PROJECTS

The Golden Triangle Asian Elephant Foundation *Anantara Resort*, Sop Ruak, Chiang Rai ⓦhelpingelephants.org. Elephant welfare is the primary concern at this well-regarded elephant camp, which offers elephant treks and mahout courses. Profits support the foundation's elephant rescue centre. See p.369.

Elephant Nature Park Near Chiang Mai ⓦelephantnaturefoundation.org. Famous conservation-education centre and sanctuary for elephants that's open to pre-booked visitors, overnight guests and volunteers. See p.351.

Gibbon Rehabilitation Project Phuket ⓦgibbonproject.org. Resocializes abused pet gibbons before releasing them back into the forests. Visitors and volunteers welcome. See p.642.

Highland Farm Gibbon Sanctuary Near Mae Sot ⓦgibbonathighlandfarm.org. Day-trippers and homestay guests are welcome at this haven caring for injured and abandoned gibbons. One-month placements are also possible. See p.260.

Wild Animal Rescue Foundation of Thailand (WAR) ⓦwarthai.org. A campaigning organization that runs animal rescue sanctuaries, hospitals and research centres in various locations across Thailand and is open to unskilled paying volunteers.

Some reef fish, among them the ubiquitous turquoise and purple **parrot fish**, eat coral. With the help of a bird-like beak, which is in fact several teeth fused together, the parrot fish scrapes away at the coral and then grinds the fragments down with another set of back teeth – a practice reputedly responsible for the erosion of a great deal of Thailand's reef. The magnificent mauve and burgundy **crown-of-thorns starfish**, named for its "arms" covered in highly venomous spines, also feeds on coral, laying waste to as much as fifty square centimetres of stony coral in a 24-hour period.

Larger, less frequent visitors to Thailand's offshore reefs include the **moray eel**, whose elongated jaws of viciously pointed teeth make it a deadly predator, and the similarly equipped **barracuda**, the world's fastest-swimming fish. **Sharks** are quite common off the reefs, where it's also sometimes possible to swim with a **manta ray**, whose extraordinary flatness, strange wing-like fins and massive size – up to 6m across and weighing some 1600kg – make it an astonishing presence. **Turtles** sometimes paddle around reef waters, too, but all four local species – leatherback, Olive Ridley, green and hawksbill – are fast becoming endangered in Thailand.

Environmental issues

Thailand's rapid economic growth has had a significant effect on its environment. Huge new infrastructure projects, an explosion in real-estate developments and the constantly expanding tourist industry have all played a part, and the effects of the subsequent **deforestation** and pollution have been felt nationwide. Such was the devastation caused by floods and mud slides in Surat Thani in 1988 that the government banned commercial logging the following year, though land continues to be denuded for other purposes. There is also the endemic problem of "influence" so that when a big shot wants to clear a previously pristine area for a new property development, for example, it is virtually impossible for a lowly provincial civil servant to reject their plan, or money.

Flooding has always been a feature of the Thai environment, crucial to the fertility of its soil, and its worst effects are obviated by the stilted design of the traditional Thai house. However, there is now an almost annual inundation in certain riverside town centres, and of roads and railways, particularly along the Gulf coast; 2011 saw especially severe floods, when towns in the Central Plains, including the World Heritage Site of Ayutthaya and many suburbs of Bangkok, were under metres of water for weeks on end. And in recent times, far more dangerous **flash floods** have recurred with depressing frequency, most dramatically around the northern town of Pai in 2005, where many homes and guesthouses were washed away. The link between deforestation and floods is disputed, though encroaching cement and tarmac on Thai flood plains surely play a part, as does the clogging of exit channels by garbage and other pollutants, and of course climate change.

Reefs and shorelines

A number of Thailand's **coral reefs** – some of which are thought to be around 450 million years old – are being destroyed by factors attributable to tourism, most significantly the pollution generated by coastal hotels with inadequate sewage systems. Longtail boats that anchor on reefs, souvenirs made from coral, and the use of harpoon guns by irresponsible dive leaders all have a cumulative effect, dwarfed however by the local practice of using dynamite to gather fish, including reef fish for sale to aquariums.

The 2004 **tsunami** also caused significant damage to coastal and marine environments the length of the Andaman coast. Reefs close to shore were crushed by debris (furniture, machinery, even cars) and buried under displaced soil; the sea was temporarily polluted by extensive damage to sewage systems; and tracts of shorefront farmland were rendered unusable by salt water. In 2010, a mass **coral bleaching** event occurred in all of the world's oceans, damaging especially shallow-water reefs in Thailand, such as Ko Surin's; the event was caused by sudden, steep rises in sea temperatures, and has been interpreted as dramatic evidence of the effects of climate change.

Snakes

Thailand is home to around 175 different species and subspecies of **snake**, 56 of them dangerously venomous. Death by snakebite is not common, however, but all hospitals should keep a stock of serum, produced at the Snake Farm in Bangkok (see p.124).

Found everywhere and highly venomous, the 2m, nocturnal, yellow-and-black-striped **banded krait** is one to avoid, as is the shorter but equally venomous **Thai** or **monocled cobra**, which lurks in low-lying humid areas and close to human habitation and sports a distinctive "eye" mark on its hood. The other most widespread venomous snake is the 60cm **Malayan pit viper**, which has an unnerving ability to camouflage its pinky-brown and black-marked body. Non-venomous, but typically measuring an amazing 7.5m (maximum 10m) and with a top weight of 140kg, the **reticulated python** frequents human habitation all over Thailand and feeds on rats, pigs, cats and dogs, strangling them to death; it will do the same to humans if provoked.

Marine species

The Indian Ocean (Andaman Sea) and the South China Sea (Gulf of Thailand) together play host to over 850 species of open-water fish, more than one hundred species of reef fish and some 250 species of hard coral. Forty percent of Thailand's coral reef is protected within **national marine parks**, and these offer the best snorkelling and diving, particularly around Ko Similan, Ko Surin and Ko Tarutao (see p.52).

Coral

Coral reefs are living organisms composed of a huge variety of marine life forms, but the foundation of every reef is its ostensibly inanimate **stony coral** – hard constructions such as boulder, mushroom, bushy staghorn and brain coral. Stony coral is composed of colonies of polyps – minuscule invertebrates which feed on plankton, depend on algae and direct sunlight for photosynthesis, and extract calcium carbonate (limestone) from sea water in order to reproduce. The polyps use this calcium carbonate to build new skeletons outside their bodies (an asexual reproductive process known as budding), and this is how a reef is formed. It's an extraordinarily slow process, with colony growth averaging somewhere between 5mm and 30mm a year.

The fleshy plant-like **soft coral**, such as dead man's fingers and elephant's ear, generally establishes itself on and around these banks of stony coral, swaying with the currents and using tentacles to trap microorganisms. Soft coral is also composed of polyps, but a variety with flaccid internal skeletons built from protein rather than calcium. **Horny coral**, like sea whips and intricate sea fans, looks like a cross between the stony and the soft varieties, while **sea anemones** have the most obvious, and venomous, tentacles of any member of the coral family, using them to trap fish and other large prey.

Fish and turtles

The algae and plankton that accumulate around coral colonies attract a huge variety of **reef fish**. Most are small, with vibrant colours that serve as camouflage against the coral, and flattened bodies and broad tails for easy manoeuvring around the reef.

Among the most easily recognizable is the **emperor angel fish**, which boasts spectacular horizontal stripes in bright blue and orange, and an orange tail. The bizarrely shaped **moorish idol** trails a pennant fin from its dorsal fin and has a pronounced snout and dramatic black, yellow and white bands of colour; the ovoid **powder-blue surgeon fish** has a light blue body, a bright yellow dorsal fin and a white "chinstrap". The commonly spotted **long-nosed butterfly fish** is named for the butterfly-like movements of its yellow-banded silver body as it darts in and out of crevices looking for food. The bright orange **clown fish**, whose thick white stripes make it resemble a clown's ruff, is more properly known as the anemone fish because of its mutually protective relationship with the sea anemone, near which it can usually be sighted.

THE GECKO

Whether you're staying on a beach, in a national park or in a town, chances are you'll be sharing your room with a few **geckos**. These pale green tropical lizards, which are harmless to humans and usually measure a cute four to ten centimetres in length, mostly appear at night, high up on walls and ceilings, where they feed on insects. Because the undersides of their flat toes are covered with hundreds of microscopic hairs that catch at the tiniest of irregularities, geckos are able to scale almost any surface, including glass, which is why you usually see them in strange, gravity-defying positions. The largest and most vociferous gecko is known as the **tokay** in Thai, named after the disconcertingly loud sound it makes. *Tokays* can grow to an alarming 35cm, but are welcomed by most householders, as they devour insects and mice; Thais also consider it auspicious if a baby is born within earshot of a crowing *tokay*.

many of the same birds that inhabit India, Myanmar and Indochina, while the mountains of the north share species with the Himalayas and Tibet, and the peninsular forests are home to birds found also in Malaysia and Indonesia. Khao Yai and Khao Nor Chuchi are prime year-round sites for bird-spotting, and, during the dry season, Doi Inthanon is a good place for flycatchers and warblers, while Khao Sam Roi Yot and Thale Noi Waterbird Park are rewarding areas to see migrant waders and waterfowl. For exhaustive information on specific **bird-watching** locations throughout Thailand see ⓦthaibirding.com; for guided birding tours contact Thailand Bird Watching (ⓦthailandbirdwatching.com); bird-watching guidebooks are listed in Books (see p.778).

There are twelve species of **hornbill** in Thailand, all majestic with massive, powerful wings (the flapping of which can be heard over long distances) and huge beaks surmounted by bizarre horny casques. Khao Yai is one of the easiest places to spot the plain black-and-white **oriental pied hornbill** and the flashier **great hornbill**, whose monochromic body and head are broken up with jaunty splashes of yellow; the little islands of Ko Phayam and Ko Chang in Ranong province also have many resident oriental pied hornbills.

The shyness of the gorgeous **pitta** makes a sighting all the more rewarding. Usually seen hopping around on the floor of evergreen forests, especially in Doi Inthanon, Doi Suthep and Khao Yai, these plump little birds – varieties of which include the **rusty-naped**, the **blue** and the **eared** – have dazzling markings in iridescent reds, yellows, blues and blacks. The one pitta you might see outside a rainforest is the **blue-winged** pitta, which occasionally migrates to drier bamboo forests. Thailand is also home to the extremely rare **Gurney's pitta**, found only in Khlong Thom National Park, in Krabi province.

Members of the pheasant family can be just as shy as the pittas, and are similarly striking. The black-and-white-chevron-marked **silver pheasant** and the **green peafowl** are particularly fine birds, and the commonly seen **red jungle fowl** is the ancestor to all domestic chickens.

Thailand's **rice fields** attract a host of different birds including the various species of **munia**, a chubby relative of the finch, whose chunky, conical beak is ideally suited to cracking unripened rice seeds. **Egrets** and **herons** also frequent the fields, wading through the waterlogged furrows or perching on the backs of water buffaloes and pecking at cattle insects, while from November to April, thousands of **Asian open-billed storks** descend on agricultural land as well, building nests in sugar-palm trees and bamboos and feeding on pira snails.

Coastal areas also attract storks, egrets and herons, and Thale Noi Waterbird Park and the mud flats of Khao Sam Roi Yot are breeding grounds for the large, long-necked **purple heron**. The magnificent **white-bellied sea eagle** haunts the Thai coast, nesting in the forbidding crags around Krabi, Ao Phang Nga and Ko Tarutao and preying on fish and sea snakes. The tiny **edible nest swiftlet** makes its eponymous nest – the major ingredient of the luxury food, bird's-nest soup – in the limestone crags, too (see box, p.673).

The hardy **coconut palm** is also very tolerant of salty, sandy soil, and is equally useful. On islands such as Ko Kood, it's the backbone of the local economy, with millions of coconuts harvested every month for their milk, their oil-producing meat (copra), and their fibrous husks or coir (used for making ropes, matting, brushes and mattress stuffing); the palm fronds are woven into roof thatching and baskets, and the wood has an attractive grain.

Casuarinas (also known as she-oaks or ironwoods) also flourish in sandy soils and are common on beaches throughout Thailand; fast-growing and tall (up to 20m), they are quite often planted as wind breaks. Though its feathery profile makes it look like a pine, it's actually made up of tiny twigs, not needles.

The wildlife

Thailand lies in an exceptionally rich "transition zone" of the Indo-Malayan realm, its forests, mountains and national parks attracting wildlife from both Indochina and Indonesia. In all, Thailand is home to three hundred species of mammal (37 of which are considered to be endangered or vulnerable), while 982 species of bird have been recorded here (49 of them globally threatened).

Mammals

In the major national parks such as Khao Yai, Doi Inthanon and Khao Sok, the animals you're most likely to encounter are **primates**, particularly macaques and gibbons. The latter spend much of their time foraging for food in the forest canopy, while the former often descend closer to the ground to rest and to socialize.

The gibbons are responsible for the distinctive hooting that echoes through the forests. Chief noise-maker is the **white-handed** or **lar gibbon**, a beige- or black-bodied, white-faced animal whose cute appearance, intelligence and dexterity unfortunately make it a popular pet. The poaching and maltreatment of lar gibbons has become so severe that several organizations are now dedicated to protecting them (see box, p.759).

Similarly chatty, macaques hang out in gangs of twenty or more. The **long-tailed** or **crab-eating macaque** lives in the lowlands, near rivers, lakes and coasts as at Ao Phang Nga, Krabi, Ko Tarutao, Ang Thong and Khao Sam Roi Yot. It eats not only crabs, but mussels, other small animals and fruit, transporting and storing food in its big cheek pouch when swimming and diving. The **pig-tailed macaque**, named after its short curly tail, excels at scaling the tall trees of Erawan, Khao Yai, Doi Inthanon and other national parks, a skill which has resulted in many of the males being captured and trained to pick coconuts.

Much more elusive is the **Indochinese tiger**, which lives under constant threat from both poachers and the destruction of its habitat by logging interests, which together have reduced the current population to probably fewer than one hundred; for now Khao Yai and Khao Sok are the two likeliest places for sightings. The medium-sized arboreal **clouded leopard** is also on the endangered list, and is hard to spot anyway as it only comes out to feed on birds and monkeys under cover of darkness, rarely venturing out in moonlight, let alone daylight.

The shy, nocturnal **tapir**, an ungulate with three-toed hind legs and four-toed front ones, lives deep in the forest of peninsular Thailand but is occasionally spotted in daylight. A relative of both the horse and the rhino, it's the size of a pony, with a stubby trunk-like snout and distinctive two-tone colouring to confuse predators: its front half and all four legs are black, its rear half is white.

It's thought there are now as few as two thousand wild **elephants** left in Thailand: small-eared Asian elephants found mainly in Khao Yai and Khao Sok (see box, p.759).

Birds

Because of its location at the zoogeographical crossroads of Southeast Asia, Thailand boasts a huge diversity of **bird** species. The forests of continental Thailand are home to hollow stem characteristic of all varieties of bamboo is a fantastically adaptable material, used by the Thais for constructing everything from outside walls to chairs to water pipes (in hill-tribe villages) and musical instruments; and the bamboo shoot is common in Thai–Chinese cuisine.

Tropical rainforests

Thailand's **tropical rainforests** occur in areas of high and prolonged rainfall in the southern peninsula, most accessibly in the national parks of Khao Sok, Tarutao and Khao Luang. Some areas contain as many as two hundred species of tree within just a couple of acres. Characteristic of a tropical rainforest is the multi-layered series of **canopies**. The uppermost storey sometimes reaches 60m, and these towering trees often have enormous buttressed roots for support; beneath this, the dense canopy of 25–35m is often festooned with climbers and epiphytes such as ferns, lianas, mosses and orchids; then comes an uneven layer 5–10m high consisting of palms, rattans, shrubs and small trees. The forest floor in tropical rainforests tends to be relatively open and free of dense undergrowth, owing to the intense filtering of light by the upper three layers. Again, members of the *Dipterocarpaceae* family are dominant, playing an important role as nesting sites for hornbills, as lookout posts for gibbons – and as timber.

Semi-evergreen and montane forests

Semi-evergreen forests are the halfway house between tropical rainforests and dry deciduous forests and include all lowland and submontane evergreen forests from the plains to about 1000m. They thrive in regions with distinctly seasonal rainfall and fine examples can be found at Khao Yai and Kaeng Krachan national parks, and all along the Burmese border, all of which are potentially good places to observe large mammals, including elephants, gaurs, tigers and bears.

Above 1000m, the canopy of tall trees gives way to hardy **evergreen montane forest** growth such as oaks, chestnuts and laurels, many with twisted trunks and comparatively small leaves. Frequent rainfall means plenty of moss and a dense undergrowth of epiphytes, rhododendrons and tree ferns. Good examples can be seen in Doi Inthanon and Phu Kradung national parks, and in parts of Doi Suthep and Khao Yai national parks.

Mangrove swamps and coastal forests

Mangrove swamps are an important habitat for a wide variety of marine life (including two hundred species of bird, seventy species of fish and fifty types of crab) but, as with much of Thailand's inland forest, they have been significantly degraded by encroachment and large-scale prawn farming. Huge swathes of Thailand's littoral used to be fringed with mangrove swamps, but now they are mainly found only along the west peninsular coast, between Ranong and Satun, though Chanthaburi's Ao Khung Kraben is a notable east-coast exception. On Phuket, the Thachatchai Nature Trail leads you on a guided tour through a patch of mangrove swamp, but an even better way of **exploring the swamps** is to paddle a kayak through the mangrove-clogged inlets and island-lagoons of Ao Phang Nga. Not only do mangrove swamps harbour a rich and important ecosystem of their own, but they also help prevent coastal erosion; in certain areas of the tsunami-hit Andaman coast intact mangrove forest absorbed some of the waves' impact, protecting land and homes from even worse damage.

Nipa palms share the mangrove's penchant for brackish water, and these stubby-stemmed palm trees grow in abundance in the south, though commercial plantations are now replacing the natural colonies. Like most other species of palm indigenous to Thailand, the nipa is a versatile plant that's exploited to the full: alcohol is distilled from its sugary sap, and its fronds are woven into roofs (especially for beach huts and village homes), sticky-rice baskets and chair-backs.

Flora, fauna and environmental issues

Spanning some 1650km north to south, Thailand lies in the heart of Southeast Asia's tropical zone, its northernmost region just a few degrees south of the Tropic of Cancer, its southern border running less than seven degrees north of the Equator. As with other tropical regions, Thailand's climate is characterized by high humidity and even higher temperatures, a fertile combination which nourishes a huge diversity of flora and fauna in a vast range of habitats, from mixed deciduous and dry dipterocarp forests in the mountainous north to wet tropical rainforests in the steamy south. At least six percent of the world's vascular plants are found here, with over fifteen thousand species so far recorded.

The best places to appreciate Thailand's biodiversity are its national parks, the most accessible of which include Khao Yai in the northeast, Doi Inthanon and Doi Suthep in the north, and Khao Sam Roi Yot, Khao Sok and Ko Tarutao in the south. General practical information on national parks is given in Basics (see p.53).

The geography of Thailand

Thailand has a **tropical monsoon climate**. Most rain is brought from the Indian Ocean by the southwest monsoon from May to October, the so-called rainy season. From November to February the northeast monsoon brings a much cooler and drier climate from China: the cold, dry season. However, this northeastern monsoon hits the peninsular east coast after crossing the South China Sea, loading up with moist air and therefore bringing this region's rainiest season in November.

Agriculture plays a significant role in Thailand's economy, and some forty percent of Thais live off the land or the sea. Waterlogged rice paddies characterize the central plains; cassava, tapioca and eucalyptus are grown as cash crops on the scrubby plateau of the northeast; and rubber and palm-oil plantations dominate the commercial land use of the south. Dotted along Thailand's coastline are mangrove swamps and palm forests.

Mixed deciduous and dry dipterocarp forests

An estimated 65 percent of Thailand's forests are **deciduous**, sometimes referred to as monsoon forest because they have to survive periods of up to six months with minimal rainfall, so the trees shed their leaves to conserve water. Deciduous forests are often light and open, with canopies of 10–40m and dense undergrowth. They are dominated by trees of the **Dipterocarpaceae** family, a group of tropical hardwoods prized for their timber and, in places, their resin. **Teak** was also once common in northern deciduous forests, but its solid, unwarpable timber is so sought after that nearly all the teak forests have been felled. Since teak trees take around two hundred years to mature, logging them was banned in Thailand in 1989 and these days most of Thailand's teak comes in from Myanmar.

Bamboo thrives in a monsoon climate, shooting up at a remarkable rate during the wet season, usually in soils too poor for other species; it often predominates in secondary forests, where logging or clearing has previously taken place. The smooth,

Aiming for the more secular environments of the gallery and the private home, National Artist **Pichai Nirand** (b. 1936) rejects the traditional mural style and makes more selective choices of Buddhist imagery, appropriating religious objects and icons and reinterpreting their significance. He's particularly well known for his fine-detail canvases of Buddha footprints, many of which can be seen in Bangkok galleries and public spaces.

Pratuang Emjaroen (b. 1935) is famous for his social commentary, as epitomized by his huge and powerful canvas *Dharma and Adharma; The Days of Disaster*, which he painted in response to the vicious clashes between the military and students in 1973. The 5m x 2m picture depicts severed limbs, screaming faces and bloody gun barrels amid shadowy images of the Buddha's face, a spiked *dharmachakra* and other religious symbols.

Prolific traditionalist **Chakrabhand Posayakrit** (b. 1943) is also inspired by Thailand's Buddhist culture; he is famously proud of his country's cultural heritage, which infuses much of his work and has led to him being honoured as a National Artist. He is best known for his series of 33 *Life of the Buddha* paintings, and for his portraits, including many depicting members of the Thai royal family.

More controversial, and more of a household name, **Thawan Duchanee** (1939–2014) tended to examine the spiritual tensions of modern life. His surreal juxtaposition of religious icons with fantastical Bosch-like characters and explicitly sexual images prompted a group of outraged students to slash ten of his early paintings in 1971 – an unprecedented reaction to a work of Thai art. Nevertheless, Thawan continued to produce allegorical investigations into the individual's struggles against the obstacles that dog the Middle Way, prominent among them lust and violence, but after the 1980s his street cred waned as his saleability mushroomed.

Complacency is not a criticism that could be levelled at **Vasan Sitthiket** (b. 1957), one of Thailand's most outspoken and iconoclastic artists, whose uncompromising pictures are shown at – and still occasionally banned from – large and small galleries around the capital. A persistent crusader against the hypocrisies of establishment figures such as monks, politicians, CEOs and military leaders, Vasan's is one of the loudest and most aggressive political voices on the contemporary art scene, expressed on canvas, in multimedia works and in performance art. His significance is well established and he was one of the seven artists to represent Thailand at the 2003 Venice Biennale, where Thailand had its own pavilion for the first time.

Equally confrontational is fellow Biennale exhibitor, the photographer, performance artist and social activist **Manit Sriwanichpoom** (b. 1961). Manit is best known for his "Pink Man" series of photographs in which he places a Thai man (his collaborator Sompong Thawee), dressed in a flashy pink suit and pushing a pink shopping trolley, into different scenes and situations in Thailand and elsewhere. The Pink Man represents thoughtless, dangerous consumerism and his backdrop might be an impoverished hill-tribe village (*Pink Man on Tour*; 1998), or black-and-white shots from the political violence of 1973, 1976 and 1992 (*Horror in Pink*; 2001).

Women artists tend to be less high profile in Thailand, but in 2007 **Pinaree Sanpitak** (b. 1961) became the first female recipient of the annual Silpathorn Awards for established artists. Pinaree is known for her interest in gender issues and for her recurrent use of a female iconography in the form of vessels and mounds, often exploring the overlap with Buddhist stupa imagery. She works mainly in multimedia; her "Vessels and Mounds" show of 2001, for example, featured installations of huge, breast-shaped floor cushions, candles and bowls.

Among the younger faces on the Thai art scene, **Thaweesak Srithongdee** (b. 1970) blends surrealism and pop culture with the erotic and the figurative, to cartoonlike effect. He is preoccupied with popular culture, as is **Jirapat Tatsanasomboon** (b. 1971), whose work plays around with superheroes and cultural icons from East and West, pitting the *Ramayana*'s monkey king, Hanuman, against Spiderman in *Hanuman vs Spiderman*, and fusing mythologies in *The Transformation of Sita (after Botticelli)*.

wats are often almost indistinguishable from each other, though Bangkok does have a few exceptions, including Wat Benjamabophit, which uses marble cladding for its walls and incorporates Victorian-style stained-glass windows, and Wat Rajabophit, which is covered all over in Chinese ceramics. The most dramatic chedi of the Ratanokosin era was constructed in the mid-nineteenth century in Nakhon Pathom to the original Sri Lankan style, but minus the elephant buttresses found in Sukhothai.

Early Ratanakosin sculptors produced adorned **Buddha images** very much in the Ayutthayan vein. The obsession with size, first apparent in the Sukhothai period, has since plumbed new depths, with graceless concrete statues up to 60m high becoming the norm, often painted brown or a dull yellow. Most small images are cast from or patterned on older models, mostly Sukhothai or Ayutthayan in origin.

Painting has fared much better, with the *Ramayana* murals in Bangkok's Wat Phra Kaeo a shining example of how Ayutthayan techniques and traditional subject matters could be adapted into something fantastic, imaginative and beautiful.

Contemporary

Following the democratization of Thailand in the 1930s, artists increasingly became recognized as individuals, and took to signing their work for the first time. In 1933 the first school of fine art (now Bangkok's Silpakorn University) was established under the Italian sculptor **Corrado Feroci** (later Silpa Bhirasri), designer of the capital's Democracy Monument and, as the new generation experimented with secular themes and styles adapted from the West, Thai art began to look a lot more "**modern**". As for subject matter, the leading artistic preoccupation of the past eighty years has been Thailand's spiritual heritage and its role in contemporary society. Since 1985, a number of Thailand's more established contemporary artists have earned the title **National Artist**, an honour that's bestowed annually on notable artists working in all disciplines, including fine art, performing arts, film and literature.

The artists

One of the first modern artists to adapt traditional styles and themes was **Angkarn Kalayanapongsa** (1926–2012), an early recipient of the title National Artist. He was employed as a temple muralist and many of his paintings, some of which are on show in Bangkok's National Gallery, reflect this experience, typically featuring casts of two-dimensional Ayutthayan-style figures and flying *thep* in a surreal setting laced with Buddhist symbols and nods to contemporary culture.

Taking this fusion a step further, one-time cinema billboard artist, now National Artist **Chalermchai Kositpipat** (b. 1955) specializes in temple murals with a modern, controversial, twist. Outside Thailand his most famous work enlivens the interior walls of London's Wat Buddhapadipa with strong colours and startling imagery. At home his latest project is the unconventional and highly ornate all-white Wat Rong Khun in his native Chiang Rai province (see p.358).

ART GALLERIES AND EXHIBITIONS

Bangkok has a near-monopoly on Thailand's **art galleries**. While the permanent collections at the capital's National Gallery (see p.98) are disappointing, regular exhibitions of more challenging contemporary work appear at the huge, ambitious **Bangkok Art and Cultural Centre** (see p.120); the main art school, Silpakorn University Art Centre (see p.95); the Queen's Gallery (see p.105); and at smaller gallery spaces around the city. The excellent monthly *Bangkok Art Map* (facebook.com/bangkokartmap), an annotated map of the capital's galleries, carries exhibition listings and is available free from galleries. Large-scale art museums in the provinces include the Contemporary Thai Art Centre, part of Silpakorn University's secondary campus in Nakhon Pathom (see p.178), and Chiang Mai University Art Museum (see p.286). For a preview of works by Thailand's best modern artists, visit the virtual Rama IX Art Museum at rama9art.org.

its rulers commissioning some four hundred grand wats as symbols of their wealth and power. Though essentially Theravada Buddhists, the kings also adopted some Hindu and Brahmin beliefs from the Khmers – most significantly the concept of *devaraja* or god-kingship, whereby the monarch became a mediator between the people and the Hindu gods. The religious buildings and sculptures of this era reflected this new composite ideology, both by fusing the architectural styles inherited from the Khmers and from Sukhothai and by dressing their Buddhas to look like regents.

Retaining the concentric layout of the typical Khmer **temple complex**, Ayutthayan builders refined and elongated the prang into a **corncob-shaped tower**, rounding it off at the top and introducing vertical incisions around its circumference. As a spire they often added a bronze thunderbolt, and into niches within the prang walls they placed Buddha images. In Ayutthaya itself, the ruined complexes of Wat Phra Mahathat and Wat Ratburana both include these corncob prangs, but the most famous example is Bangkok's Wat Arun, which, though built during the subsequent Bangkok period, is a classic Ayutthayan structure.

Ayutthaya's architects also adapted the Sri Lankan **chedi** favoured by their Sukhothai predecessors, stretching the bell-shaped base and tapering it into a very graceful conical spire, as at Wat Phra Si Sanphet in Ayutthaya. The **viharns** of this era are characterized by walls pierced by slit-like windows, designed to foster a mysterious atmosphere by limiting the amount of light inside the building. As with all of Ayutthaya's buildings, few viharns survived the brutal 1767 sacking, with the notable exception of Wat Na Phra Mane. Phitsanulok's Wat Phra Si Ratana Mahathat was built to a similar plan – and in Phetchaburi, Wat Yai Suwannaram has no windows at all.

From Sukhothai's Buddha **sculptures** the Ayutthayans copied the soft oval face, adding an earthlier demeanour to the features and imbuing them with a hauteur in tune with the *devaraja* ideology. Early Ayutthayan statues wear crowns to associate kingship with Buddhahood; as the court became ever more lavish, so these figures became increasingly adorned, until – as in the monumental bronze at Wat Na Phra Mane – they appeared in earrings, armlets, anklets, bandoliers and coronets. The artists justified these luscious portraits of the Buddha – who was, after all, supposed to have given up worldly possessions – by pointing to an episode when the Buddha transformed himself into a well-dressed nobleman to gain the ear of a proud emperor, whereupon he scolded the man into entering the monkhood.

While a couple of wats in Sukhothai show hints of painted decoration, religious **painting** in Thailand really dates from the Ayutthayan era. Unfortunately most of Ayutthaya's own paintings were destroyed in 1767, but several temples elsewhere have well-preserved murals, in particular Wat Yai Suwannaram in Phetchaburi. By all accounts typical of late seventeenth-century painting, the Phetchaburi murals depict rows of *thep*, or divinities, paying homage to the Buddha, in scenes presented without shadow or perspective, and mainly executed in dark reds and cream.

Ratanakosin (eighteenth century to the 1930s)

When **Bangkok** emerged as Ayutthaya's successor in 1782, the new capital's founder was determined to revive the old city's grandeur, and the **Ratanakosin** (or Bangkok) period began by aping what the Ayutthayans had done. Since then neither wat architecture nor religious sculpture has evolved much further.

The first Ratanakosin **building** was the bot of Bangkok's Wat Phra Kaeo, built to enshrine the Emerald Buddha. Designed to a typical Ayutthayan plan, it's coated in glittering mirrors and gold leaf, with roofs ranged in multiple tiers and tiled in green and orange. To this day, most newly built bots and viharns follow a more economical version of this paradigm, whitewashing the outside walls but decorating the pediment in gilded ornaments and mosaics of coloured glass. Tiered temple roofs still taper off into the slender bird-like finials called *chofa*, and naga staircases – a Khmer feature inherited by Ayutthaya – have become almost obligatory. The result is that modern

Sukhothai (thirteenth to fifteenth centuries)

Capitalizing on the Khmers' weakening hold over central Thailand, two Thai generals established the first major Thai kingdom in **Sukhothai** in 1238, and over the next two hundred years its citizens produced some of Thailand's most refined art.

Sukhothai's artistic reputation rests above all on its **sculpture**. More sinuous even than the Srivijayan images, Sukhothai Buddhas tend towards elegant androgyny, with slim oval faces and slender curvaceous bodies usually clad in a plain, skintight robe that fastens with a tassel close to the navel. The sculptors favoured the seated pose, with hands in the *Bhumisparsa Mudra*, most expertly executed in the Phra Buddha Chinnarat image, now housed in Phitsanulok's Wat Si Ratana Mahathat (replicated at Bangkok's Wat Benjamabophit) and in the enormous Phra Sri Sakyamuni, now enshrined in Bangkok's Wat Suthat. They were also the first to represent the **walking Buddha**, a supremely graceful figure with his right leg poised to move forwards and his left arm in the *Vitarkha Mudra*, as seen at Sukhothai's Wat Sra Si.

Rather than pull down the sacred prangs of their predecessors, Sukhothai builders added bots, viharns and chedis to the existing structures, as well as conceiving quite separate **temple complexes**. Their viharns and bots are the earliest halls of worship still standing in Thailand (the Khmers didn't go in for large public assemblies), but in most cases only the stone pillars and their platforms remain, the wooden roofs having long since disintegrated. The best examples can be seen in the historical parks at Sukhothai, Si Satchanalai and Kamphaeng Phet.

Most of the **chedis** are in much better shape. Many were modelled on the Sri Lankan bell-shaped reliquary tower (symbolizing the Buddha's teachings ringing out far and wide), often set atop a one- or two-tiered square base surrounded by elephant buttresses; Si Satchanalai's Wat Chang Lom is a good example. The architects also devised the **lotus-bud chedi**, a slender tower topped with a tapered finial that was to become a hallmark of the Sukhothai era; in Sukhothai both Wat Mahathat and Wat Trapang Ngoen display classic examples.

Ancient Sukhothai is also renowned for the skill of its potters, who produced **ceramic ware** known as Sawankhalok, after the name of one of the nearby kiln towns. Most museum ceramics collections are dominated by Sawankhalok ware, which is distinguished by its grey-green celadon glazes and by the fish and chrysanthemum motifs used to decorate bowls and plates; there's a dedicated Sawankhalok museum in Sukhothai.

Lanna (thirteenth to sixteenth centuries)

Meanwhile, to the north of Sukhothai, the independent Theravada Buddhist kingdom of **Lanna** was flourishing. Its art styles – known interchangeably as **Chiang Saen** and Lanna – built on the Dvaravati heritage of Haripunjaya, copying direct from Indian sources and incorporating Sukhothai and Sri Lankan ideas from the south.

The earliest surviving Lanna **monument** is the Dvaravati-style Chedi Si Liam at Wiang Kum Kam near Chiang Mai, built to the pyramidal form characteristic of Mon builders. Also in Chiang Mai, Wat Jet Yot replicates the temple built at Bodh Gaya in India to commemorate the seven sites where the Buddha meditated in the first seven weeks after attaining enlightenment.

Lanna **sculpture** also drew some inspiration from Bodh Gaya, echoing the plumpness of the Buddha image, and its broad shoulders and prominent hair curls. The later works are slimmer, probably as a result of Sukhothai influence, and one of the most famous examples of this type is the Phra Singh Buddha, enshrined in Chiang Mai's Wat Phra Singh. Other good illustrations of both styles are housed in Chiang Mai's National Museum.

Ayutthaya (fourteenth to eighteenth centuries)

From 1351 Thailand's central plains came under the thrall of a new power centred on **Ayutthaya** and ruled by a former prince of Lopburi. Over the next four centuries, the Ayutthayan capital became one of the most prosperous and ostentatious cities in Asia, examples are often accompanied by a small statue of a deer, which refers to the Buddha preaching his first sermon in a deer park.

Srivijaya (eighth to thirteenth centuries)

While Dvaravati's Theravada Buddhists were influencing the central plains and, to a limited extent, areas further to the north, southern Thailand was paying allegiance to the Mahayana Buddhists of the **Srivijayan** civilization. Mahayanists believe that those who have achieved enlightenment – known as **bodhisattva** – should postpone their entry into Nirvana in order to help others along the way, and depictions of these saint-like beings were the mainstay of Srivijayan art.

The finest Srivijayan *bodhisattva* statues were cast in bronze and are among the most graceful and sinuous ever produced in Thailand. Many are lavishly adorned, and some were even bedecked in real jewels when first made. By far the most popular *bodhisattva* subject was **Avalokitesvara**, worshipped as compassion incarnate. Generally shown with four or more arms and with an animal skin over the left shoulder or tied at the waist, Avalokitesvara is also sometimes depicted with his torso covered in tiny Buddha images. Bangkok's National Museum holds the most beautiful Avalokitesvara, the Bodhisattva Padmapani found in Chaiya, but there's a good sandstone example *in situ* at Prasat Muang Singh near Kanchanaburi.

The most typical intact example of a Srivijayan **temple** is the heavily restored Javanese-style chedi at Chaiya's Wat Phra Boromathat, with its highly ornamented, stepped chedi featuring mini-chedis at each corner.

Khmer and Lopburi (tenth to fourteenth centuries)

By the end of the ninth century the **Khmers** of Cambodia were starting to expand from their capital at Angkor into the Dvaravati states, bringing with them the Hindu faith and the cult of the god-king (*devaraja*). They built hundreds of imposing stone **sanctuaries** across their newly acquired territory, most notably within southern Isaan, at Phimai, Phanom Rung and Khao Phra Viharn.

Each magnificent castle-temple – known in Khmer as a **prasat** – was constructed primarily as a shrine for a Shiva lingam, the phallic representation of the god Shiva. They followed a similar pattern, centred on at least one pyramidal or corncob-shaped tower, or **prang**, which represented Mount Meru (the gods' heavenly abode) and housed the lingam. Prangs were surrounded by concentric rectangular **galleries**, whose **gopura** (entrance chambers) at the cardinal points were usually approached by staircases flanked with **naga balustrades**; in Khmer temples, nagas generally appear as symbolic bridges between the human world and that of the gods. Most compounds enclosed ponds between their outer and inner walls, and many were surrounded by a network of moats and **reservoirs**: historians attribute the Khmers' political success in part to their skill in designing highly efficient irrigation systems.

Exuberant **carvings** ornamented almost every surface of the prasat. Usually gouged from sandstone, but frequently moulded in stucco, they depict Hindu deities, incarnations and stories, especially episodes from the *Ramayana*. Towards the end of the twelfth century, the Khmer leadership became Mahayana Buddhist, commissioning Buddhist carvings to be installed alongside the Hindu ones, and often replacing the Shiva lingam with a Buddha or *bodhisattva* image.

The temples built in the former Theravada Buddhist principality of **Lopburi** during the Khmer period are much smaller than those in Isaan; the triple-pranged temple of Phra Prang Sam Yot is typical. Broad-faced and muscular, the classic Lopburi-era Buddha **statue** wears a diadem or ornamental headband – a nod to the Khmers' ideological fusion of earthly and heavenly power – and the *ushnisha* (the sign of enlightenment) becomes distinctly conical rather than a mere bump on the head. Early Lopburi Buddhas also come garlanded with necklaces and ornamental belts. As you'd expect, Lopburi National Museum houses a good selection.

his most famous role, as **Nataraja**, or Lord of the Dance, he is usually shown in stylized standing position with legs bent into a balletic position, and the full complement of arms outstretched above his head. Three stripes on a figure's forehead also indicate Shiva, or one of his followers. In abstract form, he is represented by a **lingam** (once found at the heart of every Khmer temple in the northeast). Primarily a symbol of energy and godly power, the lingam also embodies fertility, particularly when set upright in a vulva-shaped vessel known as a **yoni**. The yoni doubles as a receptacle for the holy water that worshippers pour over the lingam.

Lesser gods

Close associates of Shiva include **Parvati**, his wife, and **Ganesh**, his elephant-headed son. As the god of knowledge and overcomer of obstacles (in the path of learning), Ganesh is used as the symbol of the Fine Arts Department, so his image features on all entrance tickets to national museums and historical parks.

The royal, three-headed elephant, **Erawan**, usually only appears as the favourite mount of the god **Indra**, the king of the gods, with specific power over the elements (particularly rain) and over the east. Other **Hindu gods of direction**, which are commonly found on the appropriate antefix in Khmer temples, include **Yama** on a buffalo (south); **Varuna** on a naga (mythical serpent) or a *hamsa* (west); Brahma (north); and **Isaana** on a bull (northeast).

Lesser mythological figures, which originated as Hindu symbols but feature frequently in wats and other Buddhist contexts, include the **yaksha** giants who ward off evil spirits (like the enormous freestanding ones guarding Bangkok's Wat Phra Kaeo); the graceful half-woman, half-bird **kinnari**; and the ubiquitous **naga**, or serpent king of the underworld, often with as many as seven heads, whose reptilian body most frequently appears as staircase balustrades in Hindu and Buddhist temples.

The schools

In the 1920s art historians and academics began compiling a classification system for Thai art and architecture that was modelled along the lines of the country's historical periods; these are the guidelines followed below. The following brief overview starts in the sixth century, when Buddhism began to take a hold on the country; few examples of art from before that time have survived, and there are no known, earlier architectural relics.

Dvaravati (sixth to eleventh centuries)

Centred around Nakhon Pathom, U Thong and Lopburi in the Chao Phraya basin and in the smaller northern enclave of Haripunjaya (modern-day Lamphun), the **Dvaravati** civilization was populated by Mon-speaking Theravada Buddhists who were strongly influenced by Indian culture.

The only known surviving Dvaravati-era **building** is the pyramidal laterite chedi at Lamphun's Wat Chama Thevi, but the national museums in Bangkok, Nakhon Pathom and Lamphun house quite extensive collections of Buddha **images** from that period. To make the best of the poor-quality limestone at their disposal, Dvaravati sculptors made their Buddhas quite stocky, cleverly dressing the figures in a sheet-like drape that dropped down to ankle level from each raised wrist, forming a U-shaped hemline – a style which they used when casting in bronze as well. Where the faces have survived, they are strikingly naturalistic, distinguished by their thick lips, flattened noses and wide cheekbones.

Nakhon Pathom, thought to have been a target of Buddhist missionaries from India since before the first century AD, has also yielded many **dharmachakra**, originating in the period when the Buddha could not be directly represented. These metre-high carved stone wheels symbolize the cycles of life and reincarnation, and in Dvaravati example. Most Thais are familiar with these exceptional images, all of which have been given special names, always prefixed by the honorific "Phra", and many of which have spawned thousands of miniaturized copies in the form of amulets. Pilgrimages are made to see the most famous originals.

It was in the Sukhothai era that the craze for producing **Buddha footprints** really took off. Harking back to the time when images were allusive rather than representative, these footprints were generally moulded from stucco to depict the 108 auspicious signs or *lakshanas* (which included references to the sixteen Buddhist heavens, the traditional four great continents and seven great rivers and lakes) and housed in a special mondop. Few of the Sukhothai footprints remain, but Ayutthaya- and Ratanakosin-era examples are found all over the country, the most famous being Phra Phutthabat near Lopburi, the object of pilgrimages throughout the year. The feet of the famous Reclining Buddha in Bangkok's Wat Pho are also inscribed with the 108 *lakshanas*, beautifully depicted in mother-of-pearl inlay.

Hindu iconography

Hindu images tend to be a lot livelier than Buddhist ones; there are countless gods to choose from and many have mischievous personalities and multiple inventive incarnations. In Hindu philosophy any object can be viewed as the temporal residence, embodiment or symbol of the deity so you get abstract representations such as the phallic lingam (pillar) for Shiva, as well as figurative images. Though pure Hinduism receded from Thailand with the collapse of the Khmer empire, Buddhist Thais have incorporated some Hindu and Brahmin concepts into the national belief system and have continued to create statues of the three chief Hindu deities – Brahma, Vishnu and Shiva – as well as using many mythological creatures in modern designs.

The Hindu Trinity

Vishnu has always been a favourite: in his role of "Preserver" he embodies the status quo, representing both stability and the notion of altruistic love. He is most often depicted as the deity, but has ten manifestations in all, of which **Rama** (number seven) is by far the most popular in Thailand. The epitome of ideal manhood, Rama is the superhero of the epic story the *Ramayana* – in Thai, the *Ramakien* (see box, p.88) – and appears in storytelling reliefs and murals in every Hindu temple in Thailand; in painted portraits you can usually recognize him by his green face. Manifestation number eight is **Krishna**, more widely known than Rama in the West, but slightly less common in Thailand. Krishna is usually characterized as a flirtatious, flute-playing, blue-skinned cowherd, but he is also a crucial figure in the lengthy moral epic poem, the *Mahabharata*. Confusingly, Vishnu's ninth avatar is the **Buddha** – a manifestation adopted many centuries ago to minimize defection to the Buddhist faith. When represented as **the deity**, Vishnu is generally shown sporting a crown and four arms, his hands holding a conch shell (whose music wards off demons), a discus (used as a weapon), a club (symbolizing the power of nature and time), and a lotus (symbol of joyful flowering and renewal). He is often depicted astride a **garuda**, a half-man, half-bird. Even without Vishnu on its back, the garuda is a very important beast: a symbol of strength, it's often shown "supporting" temple buildings.

Statues and representations of **Brahma** (the Creator) are rare. He too has four arms, but holds no objects; he has four faces (sometimes painted red), is generally borne by a goose-like creature called a *hamsa*, and is associated with the direction north.

Shiva (the Destroyer) is the most volatile member of the pantheon. He stands for extreme behaviour, for beginnings and endings, as enacted in his frenzied Dance of Destruction, and for fertility, and is a symbol of great energy and power. His godlike form typically has four, eight or ten arms, sometimes holding a trident (representing creation, protection and destruction) and a drum (to beat the rhythm of creation). In

The chedi

Upon the Buddha's death, disciples from all over Asia laid claim to his relics, enshrining them in specially constructed towers, known as **chedis** in Thailand. In later centuries, chedis have also become repositories for the ashes of royalty or important monks – and anyone else who could afford to have one built. Each chedi's three main components reflect a traditional symbolism. In theory, the chedi base should be divided into three layers to represent hell, earth and heaven. Above this, the dome usually contains the cube-shaped reliquary, known as a *harmika* after the Sanskrit term for the Buddha's seat of meditation. Crowning the structure, the spire is graded into 33 rings, one for each of the 33 Buddhist heavens.

The mondop and ho trai

Less common wat buildings include the square **mondop**, usually built with a complex, cruciform roof, which houses either a Buddha statue or footprint, or holy texts. One of the most spectacular examples, with an ornate green-and-gold roof and huge doors encrusted with mother-of-pearl, shelters Thailand's holiest footprint of the Buddha, at Wat Phra Phutthabat near Lopburi.

The **ho trai**, or scripture library, is generally constructed on stilts, sometimes over a pond, to protect against termites and fire. You can see particularly good examples of traditional *ho trai* at Wat Rakhang in Bangkok, at Wat Phra Singh in Chiang Mai and at Wat Yai Suwannaram in Phetchaburi.

Buddhist iconography

In the early days of Buddhism, image-making was considered inadequate to convey the faith's abstract philosophies, so the only approved iconography comprised doctrinal **symbols** such as the *Dharmachakra* (Wheel of Law, also known as Wheel of Doctrine or Wheel of Life; see p.739). Gradually these symbols were displaced by **images of the Buddha**, construed chiefly as physical embodiments of the Buddha's teachings rather than as portraits of the man. Sculptors took their guidance from the Pali texts, which ordained the Buddha's most common postures (*asanha*) and gestures (*mudra*).

All three-dimensional Buddha images are objects of reverence, but some are more esteemed than others. Some are alleged to have reacted in a particular way to unusual events, others have performed miracles, or are simply admired for their beauty, their phenomenal size or even their material value – if made of solid gold or jade, for

---

POSTURES AND GESTURES OF THE BUDDHA

Of the **four postures** – sitting, standing, walking and reclining – the **seated Buddha**, which represents him in meditation, is the most common in Thailand. A popular variation shows the Buddha seated on a coiled serpent, protected by the serpent's hood: a reference to the story about the Buddha meditating during the rainy season, when a serpent offered to raise him off the wet ground and shelter him from the storms. The **reclining** pose symbolizes the Buddha entering Nirvana at his death, while the **standing** and **walking** images both represent his descent from heaven.

The most common **hand gestures** include:

Dhyana Mudra (Meditation), in which the hands rest on the lap, palms upwards.

Bhumisparsa Mudra (Calling the Earth to Witness, a reference to the Buddha resisting temptation), with the left hand upturned in the lap and the right-hand fingers resting on the right knee and pointing to the earth (see p.738).

Vitarkha Mudra (Teaching), with one or both hands held at chest height with the thumb and forefinger touching.

Abhaya Mudra (Dispelling Fear), showing the right hand (occasionally both hands) raised in a flat-palmed "stop" gesture.

Art and architecture

Aside from pockets of Hindu-inspired statuary and architecture, the vast majority of historical Thai culture takes its inspiration from Theravada Buddhism, and, though the country does have some excellent museums, to understand fully the evolution of Thai art you have to visit its temples. Artists, sculptors and architects have tended to see their work as a way of making spiritual merit rather than as a means of self-expression or self-promotion, so pre-twentieth-century Thai art history is all about evolving styles rather than individual artists. This section is designed to help make sense of the most common aspects of Thai art and architecture at their various stages of development.

The wat

Buddhist temple complexes, or **wats**, are central to nearly every community in Thailand and, as the main expressions of public architecture and art over the centuries, are likely to loom large in visitors' experiences of the country, too. Wat architecture has evolved in diverse ways, but the names and purposes of the main buildings have stayed constant in Thailand for some fifteen centuries.

Some **general design features** of Thai temples are also distinctive. The Khmers, who had ruled much of the country long before the Thais came onto the scene, built their temples to a cosmological plan, with concentric layers representing earth, oceans and heavens, rising to a central high point (Phanom Rung near Surin is a stunning example of this). Remnants of this layout persisted in Thai temples, including boundary walls – which are sometimes combined with a moat – and the multi-tiered roofs of so many wat buildings.

Furthermore, the Thais come from a tradition of building in wood rather than stone or brick, hence the leaning walls and long, curving roofs that give wats their elegant, tapering lines. On top of this, wat architects have long been preoccupied with light, the symbol of Buddhist wisdom and clarity, covering their buildings with gilt, filigree and vividly coloured glass mosaics.

The bot

The most important wat building is the **bot** (sometimes known as the *ubosot*), where monks are ordained. It usually stands at the heart of the compound, but lay people are rarely allowed inside. There's only one bot in any wat complex, and often the only way you'll be able to distinguish it from other temple buildings is by the eight **sema** or boundary stones which always surround it. Positioned at the four corners of the bot and at the cardinal points of the compass, these *sema* define the consecrated ground and usually look something like upright gravestones, though they can take many forms. They are often carved all over with symbolic Buddhist scenes or ideograms, and sometimes are even protected within miniature shrines of their own. One of the best *sema* collections is housed in the National Museum of Khon Kaen, in the northeast.

The viharn

Often almost identical in appearance to the bot, the **viharn** or assembly hall is the building you are most likely to enter, as it usually contains the wat's principal Buddha image, and sometimes two or three minor images as well. Large wats may have several viharns, while strict meditation wats, which don't deal with the laity, may not have one at all.

a wat or a traditional Thai house, but its ornamentation is supposed to reflect the status of the humans' building, so if that building is enlarged or refurbished, the spirit house should be improved accordingly. And as architects become increasingly bold in their designs, so modernist spirit houses are also beginning to appear, especially in Bangkok where an eye-catching new skyscraper might be graced by a spirit house of glass or polished concrete. **Figurines** representing the relevant guardian spirit and his aides are sometimes put inside, and daily offerings of incense, lighted candles and garlands of jasmine are placed alongside them to keep the *phi* happy – a disgruntled spirit is a dangerous spirit, liable to cause sickness, accidents and even death. As with any religious building or icon in Thailand, an unwanted or crumbling spirit house should never be dismantled or destroyed, which is why you'll often see damaged spirit houses placed around the base of a sacred banyan tree, where they are able to rest in peace.

Masala Kitchen Thanon Sathanee. Small restaurant with a couple of tables on the pavement serving very tasty Indian food such as chicken tikka masala (B90), spinach dahl, naan bread and raita; the owner used to live in Chiang Mai so you can also tuck into the northern curried noodle soup, *khao soi*. 10am–8pm; closed Thurs.

Raan Kopii Next to the station at 25/25–26 Thanon Sathanee ☎ 075 214225. Very popular, updated traditional café: *kopii* with dim sum and main courses (fried rice B50), or espresso, various teas and Western breakfasts. Daily 7am–5pm.

See Far Lifestyle 37 Thanon Phattalung (right by the entrance to Soi 3) ☎ 075 210139. Good, inexpensive restaurant with a varied menu of carefully prepared dishes, specializing in healthy cuisine and local food, such as *tom som plakapong*, a light, refreshing soup of sea bass, mushrooms and cumin, and *kao yook* (B150), a Chinese-style dish of steamed pork with taro found only in Trang. Daily 10.30am–8.30pm.

Wunderbar Thanon Sathanee ☎ 087 624 8728, ⓦ wunderbar-trang.com. Multipurpose farang bar-restaurant that serves a wide selection of drinks (including wine and espressos), Thai food, and burgers (B60), salads, pizzas, breakfasts and other Western standards, as well as platters of cheese, salami, olives and baguettes (B270). Daily roughly 8.30am–9.30pm.

The Trang coast

From Pak Meng, 40km due west of Trang town, down to the mouth of the Trang River runs a 30km-long stretch of lovely beaches, broken only by dramatic limestone outcrops. A paved road roughly parallels this stretch of coast, but otherwise there's surprisingly little development, as the shoreline is technically part of Hat Chao Mai National Park.

Pak Meng and Hat Chang Lang

Although it has a fine outlook to the headlands and islands to the west (with regular boats to the biggest, Ko Hai), the beach at **PAK MENG** is not the most attractive on the coast, becoming a rather muddy strip of sand at low tide. At other times, however, it offers quiet, calm swimming, and there's always the possibility of a meal at one of the many tree-shaded food stalls and restaurants that line the back of the beach.

Immediately south of Pak Meng's beach is the white sand of **Hat Chang Lang**, famous for its oysters, which shelters at its north end the finest luxury hotel in the province, *Anantara Si Kao*.

Hat Chao Mai National Park HQ

The turning for the headquarters is 3km on from Hat Chang Lang • B200 • ☎ 075 213260, ⓦ dnp.go.th

Hat Chao Mai National Park covers 230 square kilometres, including parts of Ko Mook and Ko Kradan, but the park admission fee is only rigidly enforced if you visit its headquarters. From the HQ a short trail leads to the south end of the beach and a viewpoint partway up a karst pinnacle, from which you can see Ko Mook and occasionally dugongs in the bay below. At headquarters there's a simple café as well as accommodation.

Hat Yong Ling and Hat Yao

About 5km south of the national park HQ, beyond Kuantunku, the pier for Ko Mook, is **Hat Yong Ling**. This quiet and attractive convex beach, which shelters a national park ranger station, is probably the nicest along this stretch of coast, with a large cave which you can swim into at high tide or walk into at low tide. Immediately beyond comes **Hat Yao**, which runs in a broad 5km white-sand strip, backed by casuarina trees and some simple restaurants.

(B700–750), Ko Tarutao and Ko Bulon Lae (both B650), including an a/c minibus to Pak Bara (departing 9am) and the boat trip.

By share-taxi Share-taxis for Pak Bara, Satun and Krabi

congregate at the old bus station on Thanon Huay Yod, on the north side of town (about 500m north of the junction with Thanon Wisetkul).

GETTING AROUND

By rental car Avis (☎02 251 1131–2, ⍟avisthailand .com) and Budget (☎075 572159, ⍟budget.co.th), both at the airport.

By motorbike Motorbikes can be rented at *Sri Trang Hotel* (see below), on Thanon Rama VI (B250/day).

INFORMATION AND TOURS

Tourist information TAT has a helpful office on Thanon Wisetkul (daily 8.30am–4.30pm, sometimes closed for lunch on Sat & Sun; ☎075 215867, ✉tattrang@tat.or.th).
Tourist police Thanon Phattalung (Highway 4), about 2km northeast of the centre ☎075 211903 or ☎1155.
Travel agents The best travel agent in town is Trang Island Hopping Tour, directly opposite the station at 28/2 Thanon Sathanee (☎082 804 0583, ⍟trang-island -hopping.com). This well-organized outfit offers a huge range of services, including mainland and island transfers

and tickets, and accommodation booking on any island. The friendly staff are a great source of impartial information on the area, and their office makes a good first stop in town. They also offer one-day boat trips around the islands and day-trips and camping trips to Ko Rok, and inland excursions to waterfalls and caves, as well as trekking, bird-watching, rafting and kayaking. *Wunderbar*, just around the corner (☎075 214563, ⍟wunderbar-trang.com), also acts as a very helpful and clued-up travel agent, especially for island bookings.

ACCOMMODATION

Ban Aothong 25/28–31 Thanon Sathanee ☎075 225611, ✉banaothong@yahoo.com. An overblown facade of multi-tiered roofs and gables announces this upmarket guesthouse that's popular with Thai business-people, with its chunky wooden furniture, half-tester beds and rather kitsch decor. "Standard" double rooms are compact, some with no window, while the slightly pricier "superior" twins have more space, though the bathrooms are still small; all have a/c, hot showers, fridges and cable TV. B750
Koh Teng Hotel 77–79 Thanon Rama VI ☎075 218622 or ☎075 218148. This characterful 1940s Chinese hotel is a little battered and dusty but offers large, mostly clean, basic en-suite rooms with cold showers, some with cable TV and a/c, above a popular restaurant and coffee shop that serves southern Thai and Chinese food and Western breakfasts. Fan B200, a/c B320
Sri Trang Hotel 22 Thanon Sathanee ☎075 218122, ⍟sritranghotel.com. Welcoming, thoroughly updated 1950s hotel offering spacious a/c rooms with some colourful decorative touches, hot water, cable TV, DVD

players and fridges above a cool little café. B890
Thumrin Hotel Thanon Rama VI ☎075 211011–4, ⍟thumrin.co.th. Good-value, very central hotel offering international-standard facilities – a/c, hot water, TV, mini-bar – in a high-rise block above its popular bakery-cum-coffee shop. B900
Thumrin Thana Hotel 69/8 Thanon Huay Yod ☎075 211211, ⍟thumrin.co.th. The best hotel in the town centre, though not in the same league as the *Anantara* on the coast (see p.701). Nearly three hundred spacious, well-equipped rooms, a pool, sauna, fitness centre and massage rooms. B1600
Trang Hotel 134/2–5 Thanon Wisetkul ☎075 218944 or ☎075 218703, ✉tranghotel2012@gmail.com. You can't miss the livid purple facade of this welcoming, moderately priced hotel on the central clock-tower roundabout, and you might want to keep your sunglasses on inside too, where the large, comfortable twin rooms with a/c, hot water, fridge and TV have just been given a makeover in orange, purple and green. B690

EATING AND DRINKING

Trang's streets are dotted with dozens of traditional cafés, which serve up gallons of **kopii** (local filtered coffee) accompanied by various tidbits and light meals. Most famous of these is the local speciality, **muu yaang**, delicious charcoal-grilled pork, which is generally eaten for breakfast. At the excellent **night market**, around the back of the city hall on Thanon Ruenrom, you can try another tasty southern dish, *khanom jiin*, soft noodles topped with hot, sweet or fishy sauces and eaten with crispy greens.

Fatimah Thanon Sathanee. Simple halal restaurant that's especially popular in the evenings. Buffet of southern

curries, tasty *phat thai* (B40), *tom yam*, fried rice, *kopii* and tea. Tues–Sun roughly 9am–9pm.

8

Trang town

TRANG (also known as Taptieng) is gradually developing as a popular jumping-off point for travellers drawn south from the crowded sands of Krabi to the pristine beaches and islands of the nearby coast. The town, which prospers on rubber, oil palms, fisheries and – increasingly – tourism, is a sociable place whose wide, clean streets are dotted with crumbling, wooden-shuttered houses. In the evening, the streets are festooned with colourful lights and, from Thursday to Sunday, the central square in front of the station hosts a lively market, while during the day, many of the town's Chinese inhabitants hang out in the cafés, drinking the local filtered coffee. Trang's Chinese population makes the **Vegetarian Festival** in October or November almost as frenetic as Phuket's (see box, p.623) – and for veggie travellers it's an opportunity to feast at the stalls set up around the temples.

ARRIVAL AND DEPARTURE   TRANG TOWN

By plane Air Asia and Nok Air run daily flights between Bangkok and Trang airport (1hr 30min), which is 3km south of town. On arrival, a/c minibuses bring passengers downtown (B90/person), while on departure, you can charter a tuk-tuk or taxi (about B200/vehicle).

By train Two overnight trains from Bangkok (15–16hr) run down a branch of the southern line to Trang.

By bus Buses arrive at and depart from the new bus terminal on Thanon Phattalung (Highway 4), opposite Robinson department store, about 3km northeast of the centre, including an a/c bus service between Satun and

Phuket four times daily. Shared songthaews (B12) shuttle between here and the train station.

Destinations Bangkok (10 daily; 12hr); Krabi (roughly every 30min; 2hr); Phuket (hourly; 5hr); Satun (roughly hourly; 2hr 30min–3hr).

By minibus A/c minibuses to Pak Meng, Ban Chao Mai, Satun (via Langu), Ko Lanta (including drop-offs as far south as Hat Klong Nin), Nakhon Si Thammarat, Surat Thani and Hat Yai now also use the new bus terminal on Thanon Phattalung. In high season, travel agents such as Trang Island Hopping Tour can arrange through tickets to Ko Lipe

TRANG TOWN

Krabi & Phuket

Tourist Police, Bus Terminal, Phatthalung & Hat Yai

THANON HUAY YOD

THANON WISETKUL

Klong Huai Yong

THANON PHATTALUNG

Pak Meng

THANON THA KLANG

First Andaman Travel

Police Station

Night Market

THANON RATCHADAMNOEN

THANON KANTANG

RATSADA

Clocktower

THANON RAMA VI

Koh Ngai Villa Office

Trang Island Hopping Tour

THANON SATHANEE

THANON WISETKUL

Train Station

TAT

0   100
metres

Kantang & Hat Yao

Airport, Langu, Pak Bara & Satun

ACCOMMODATION
Ban Aothong	6
Koh Teng Hotel	3
Sri Trang Hotel	5
Thumrin Hotel	4
Thumrin Thana Hotel	1
Trang Hotel	2

RESTAURANTS & CAFÉS
Fatimah	2
Masala Kitchen	4
Raan Kopii	5
See Far Lifestyle	1
Wunderbar	3

TRAVEL WARNING

Because of the ongoing **violence** in the deep south (see below), Western governments are currently advising their citizens **not to travel** to or through Pattani, Yala, Narathiwat and Songkhla provinces unless essential; following on from this, insurance companies are refusing to cover travel in the affected areas. The four provinces encompass the city and transport hub of **Hat Yai** and several of the main border crossings to Malaysia: by rail from Hat Yai (and Bangkok) to Butterworth via Padang Besar and to Sungai Kolok; and by road from Hat Yai via Sadao, from Yala via Betong, and down the east coast to Kota Bharu.

The routes to Sungai Kolok, Betong and Kota Bharu pass through particularly volatile territory, with **martial law** declared in Pattani, Yala and Narathiwat provinces; however, martial law is only in effect in certain districts of Songkhla province, and not in Hat Yai itself.

The provinces of **Trang** and **Satun** are not affected, and it's still perfectly possible to continue overland to Malaysia via Satun: by air-conditioned minibus from Satun to Kangar, or by ferry from Thammalang to the Malaysian island of Langkawi (see p.715); or by boat from Ko Lipe to Langkawi (see p.712). For up-to-the-minute advice, consult your government travel advisory (see p.62).

guns against the British colonialists, but having been excluded from power after independence, descended into general banditry and racketeering around Betong. The Thai authorities eventually succeeded in breaking up the bandit gangs in 1989 through a combination of pardons and bribes, but the stability of the region soon faced disruption from another source, a rise in Islamic militancy.

The troubles: 2004 to the present

Armed resistance to the Thai state by **Muslim separatists** had fluctuated at a relatively low level since the 1960s, but in early 2004 the violence escalated dramatically. Since then, there have been thousands of deaths on both sides in the troubles, and barely a day goes by without a fatal incident of one kind or another. The insurgents have viciously targeted Buddhist monks, police, soldiers, teachers and other civil servants, as well as attacking a train on the Hat Yai–Sungai Kolok line and setting off bombs in marketplaces, near tourist hotels and bars and at Hat Yai airport. Increasingly, they have attacked other Muslims who are seen to be too sympathetic to the Thai state.

Often writing the militants off as bandits, the authorities have stirred up hatred – and undermined moderate Muslim voices – by reacting violently, notably in crushing protests at Tak Bai and the much-revered Krue Se Mosque in Pattani in 2004, in which a total of over two hundred alleged insurgents died. Meanwhile, the army has "subcontracted" much of its work to rangers, untrained village militias, thus inflaming the situation further and deepening the ethnic divide. In 2005, the government announced a **serious state of emergency** in Pattani, Yala and Narathiwat provinces, and imposed **martial law** here and in southern parts of Songkhla province. This, however, has exacerbated economic and unemployment problems in what is Thailand's poorest region.

A large part of the problem is that a wide variety of shadowy groups – with names like the Pattani Islamic Mujahideen, the Barisan Revolusi Nasional-Coordinate and Runda Kumpulan Kecil – are operating against the government, generally working in small cells at village level without central control. Rather than religious issues, the most likely causes of their militancy are ethnic grievances: prejudice, lack of opportunity and disempowerment, accompanied by resentment towards not only Thais but also the remote and corrupt Muslim elite. However, it's unclear exactly who they are or what they want, and, faced with such shifting sands, all attempts to broker a ceasefire have failed.

longtail boat and, most importantly, a volleyball net within sight of adult dining areas. Daily 8am–11pm.

AO PHRA-AE (LONG BEACH)
Most of Ao Phra-Ae's most interesting restaurants are along the main road, while down on the beach you get small, mellow bars.

★ **Faim de Loup** On the main road towards the south end of the bay. Very good French bakery, where the croissants, pain au chocolats, fruit tarts and excellent espressos just hit the spot. Also does sandwiches, quiches, potato and sausage salad (B85) and a few plats du jour such as aubergine gratin and salad (B260); free wi-fi, too. Daily 7.30am–5.30pm, sometimes closed on Sun.

Irish Embassy On the main road near the centre of the bay. Very friendly little Irish bar, serving back-home food such as fish and chips and offering quiz nights, TV sports and occasional live music. Daily 4pm–1am.

Klapa Klum Near Lanta Palm bungalows. There are bamboo love-booths and private seating areas at this beachfront bar, plus happy hours (5–8pm), cheap cocktails all night long and weekly on-the-beach parties with international DJs (currently Wed). Daily 5pm–late.

Ozone Bar On the beach, near Somewhere Else bungalows. One of the most famous bars on the beach, especially for its weekly DJ parties (currently Thurs), which usually draw a lively crowd. Daily roughly 11am–late.

Red Snapper On the main road, inland from Lanta Marina bungalows at the southern end of Phra-Ae. Tapas and creative European cuisine using imported meats, such as pork loin with apple chutney and gorgonzola (B310), are the hallmarks of this highly rated, Dutch-run garden restaurant. Sometimes serves daytime sandwiches, too. Daily 5–11pm.

Sayang Beach Resort On the beach, at Sayang Beach Resort. This is a lovely spot for dinner, with tables set out under shoreside casuarinas strung with fairy lights. The kitchen here has a tandoori oven and serves a long menu of authentic Indian dishes, including dhal (B90) and chicken tikka masala (B200), as well as Thai and Western food, plus fresh seafood nightly and a big veggie menu. Daily roughly 10am–10pm.

HAT KHLONG KHONG
Sonya's On the main road, just north of 7-Eleven. Very popular, cheap, garden restaurant with free wi-fi (and pay computers), where you can "build your own" pasta from a wide choice of pastas, sauces, meats and extras. Also has a big selection of Thai food (from B75), Western breakfasts and teas, as well as sandwiches and espresso coffees. Daily 8.30am–9.30pm.

HAT KHLONG NIN
A dozen or so mellow little beachfront bar-restaurants make inviting places to while away a few hours, day or night, with mats and cushions on the sand, tables under the shade of the spiky shoreside pandanus trees, and appropriately chilled sounds.

Cook Kai ⓦ cook-kai.com. Friendly restaurant hung with shell mobiles and lamps, dishing up hearty portions of all the Thai classics, plus famous hotplate dishes such as sizzling squid with garlic and pepper (B190) and a few Western dishes including breakfast. Daily 7.30am–10.30pm.

Jai-Dee North end of the beach, squeezed between the road and the beach. Bar-restaurant with a lovely shady deck and hammocks, internet access and free wi-fi, and a good menu of Thai curries and sandwiches (bacon B80), fresh coffee and breakfasts. Daily 9am–late, kitchen closes 9pm.

AO KANTIANG
Same Same But Different On the beach to the south of Pimalai. Tranquil haven of a bar-restaurant, where the tables and thatched salas are set beneath a tangled growth of shrubs and vines, surrounded by shell-mobiles and driftwood sculptures; it's run by the man behind Ruen Mai restaurant in Krabi, and the mid-priced menu of mainly Thai and seafood dishes is of a similarly high standard. Daily 8am–11pm.

LANTA OLD TOWN (BAN SI RAYA)
Mango House Sophisticated little bar-café all done out in stylish dark wood, which does burgers, salads and sandwiches, as well as wine and freshly roasted coffee. High season daily 8am–8pm.

DIRECTORY

Banks and ATMs Several banks and ATMs in Ban Sala Dan, and there are ATMs beside the road at most of the beaches and in Lanta Old Town, but there are no ATMs or shops at the very southern tip at Ao Mai Phai.

Hospitals Nearly every beach has a clinic; there's a larger health centre in Ban Sala Dan, and the rather basic island hospital is in Lanta Old Town (☎075 697017), though for anything serious you'll need to go to Phuket.

Post offices At the south end of Ban Sala Dan and in Lanta Old Town.

Tourist police On the main road in Ao Phra-Ae (Long Beach; ☎1155).

Travel agent A helpful, clued-up travel agent is Otto Lanta Tour at Otto Bungalows on Hat Khlong Nin (☎083 634 8882, ⓔ ottolantatour@gmail.com; see p.689), who sell plane, train and bus tickets, as well as booking tours and accommodation.

pricey (B2470), are great value as they're on stilts and enjoy glorious bay views from their balconies and glass-fronted interiors, and the furnishings are chic and modern. The plain, cheap fan-cooled wood and bamboo bungalows sit further back. There's also a small cliffside bar affording great views, and a tour agency. Fan B800, a/c B1500

Pimalai Resort and Spa 075 607999, www .pimalai.com. One of Ko Lanta's poshest hotels, at the southern end of Ao Kantiang, spreading over such an extensive area that guests are shuttled around in golf buggies. All rooms are luxuriously and elegantly designed in contemporary style, and there's a delightful spa, two infinity-edge swimming pools, a dive centre and lots of other watersports, tennis courts and free bicycles. However, only the more expensive accommodation gets a sea view (the pool villas and walled beach villas are particularly stunning). In high season, guests are usually transferred direct to the resort by boat, landing at the *Pimalai's* private floating jetty. B11,900

AO KHLONG JAAK

Anda Lanta Resort 075 665018, andalanta.com. Lively, buzzing resort that offers well-furnished, well-maintained a/c bungalows and rooms (all with hot showers, balconies and DVD players), set around the shorefront garden and swimming pool. It's popular with families and has free kayaks and plenty of day-tripping options. B3200

AO MAI PHAI

Baan Phu Lae 081 201 1704, baanphulae.com. Occupying the centre of the bay, this tastefully camp place manages to combine a whiff of Bangkok sophistication with laidback island charm. Its fan-cooled bamboo

bungalows are stylishly simple and nearly all enjoy direct sea views; the a/c rooms high above the shore are less interesting. The Vietnamese-lantern-lit restaurant serves the best food on the beach. Massages, cooking classes and motorbike rental available. Fan B1600, a/c B2000

Bamboo Bay Resort 075 665023, bamboobay .net. At the northern end of the bay, this welcoming and very popular Thai–Danish resort offers 21 concrete bungalows with hot showers, stepped up the cliffside above the headland. Nearly all have great sea views and interiors are spacious and of a high standard. Its *pièce de résistance* is its idyllically sited deck restaurant and bar, which jut out over the rocks just above the water. Wi-fi barely works and only near the restaurant. Fan B1300, a/c B2100

La Laanta Hideaway Resort 075 665066, lalaanta .com. Luxurious bolthole at the far southern end, which is very well liked for its attentive staff and chic, thatched, wooden-floored villas – all with a/c, hot showers, DVD players and low beds – built to a cosy, village-style layout, around two pools and a beachfront garden. Breakfast included. B2800

LANTA OLD TOWN (BAN SI RAYA)

★**Mango House** 086 948 6836, mangohouses .com. The rooms and villas built on stilts over the water here make an attractive and unusual Ko Lanta base. Several century-old wooden buildings, one of them a former charcoal store, have been charmingly converted into accommodation that can sleep between two and six people; interiors are furnished in fishing-village chic, with elegant contemporary bathrooms, DVD players and kitchenette. The big draw though is the large waterside decks, which afford fine views of seven islands. B2500

EATING AND DRINKING

BAN SALA DAN

Many charming old wooden houses built on piles over the water have been turned into attractive jetty restaurants, perfect for whiling away a breezy hour with views of marine activity.

Catfish Named for its cats rather than its fish, and a good place to come for a change from seafood, with a chance to shop for secondhand books. As well as standard Thai food (fried rice B80), there's a wide choice of Western and vegetarian dishes, including falafels (B190), spaghetti, sandwiches, breakfasts, ice cream and espressos. Daily 7.30am–10pm.

Laanta Seafood The oldest restaurant in town and the most highly rated – its seafood, displayed on ice at the front, is great, including *haw mok thalay* (curried seafood soufflé; B140) and local dishes such as *nam prik kung siab*, smoked prawn dip with vegetables. Daily 11am–10pm.

HAT KHLONG DAO

Restaurant tables fill the shoreline in the evening, illuminated with fairy lights and lanterns, which lends a

nice mellow atmosphere. The formula is very similar at most of them, with fresh seafood barbecues the main attraction during the season. Clusters of little beach bars serve cocktails on deckchairs and cushions, often with chill-out music and a campfire to gather round.

Costa Lanta 075 684630 (see p.687). The most sophisticated venue on the beach is a great place for a sundowner, with sea-view daybeds, plump bolsters, cool sounds and lemon-grass martinis. The food, however, doesn't match up to its hefty price tag. Daily 11am–midnight.

Indian Bar Three doors south of Cha-Ba Bungalows. One of the most genial bars on the beach, where the host, dressed as a Hollywood-style American Indian, makes a mean cocktail and does good fire-juggling shows. Claims to open 24hr.

Slow Down 075 684982 (see p.688). Serves up excellent spaghetti bolognese (B180), Swedish specialities such as cold shrimp plate, and Thai food, with set menus available. It's a good place to keep the family happy, with its special kids' menu, cushion seating in a converted (the hotel has a no-under-18s policy) and attentive service. Its 44 a/c rooms occupy chunky, two-storey villas designed in modern-Thai style and set around a tidy beachfront garden of lawns and mature shrubs. There's a gorgeous shorefront saltwater infinity pool, a spa and plenty of activities and day-trips. Breakfast included. The rack rate is one third higher than the internet rate listed here. B13,600

Relax Bay Resort ☎ 075 684194, ⊛ relaxbay.com. On a tiny bay south around the next rocky point (and quite a hike) from *Lanta Marina*, the style of this French-managed place is affordable rustic chic. Accommodation is in forty tastefully simple thatched bungalows, all with large sea-view decks. Also has a luxury safari-style tent on a large deck with a chic outdoor bathroom. There's a pool, a dive centre and yoga classes during high season. Breakfast included. Fan B2150, a/c B5300

Sayang Beach Resort ☎ 075 684156, ⊛ sayangbeach resort.com. Welcoming, family-run place whose thirty a/c bungalows are nicely spaced beneath the palm trees in the expansive shorefront grounds. Some bungalows are designed for families and there's also a beachfront suite. Prices include buffet breakfasts and there's a very good restaurant here too. Daily free transfers to Sala Dan. B2850

Somewhere Else ☎ 081 536 0858. Located in the heart of the liveliest part of Ao Phra-Ae, with bars to the left, right and seaward, this cheap, congenial place on a beachside lawn is one of the main travellers' centres on the beach. Its spacious, unusually designed hexagonal bungalows made of tightly woven bamboo come with pretty bathrooms, some with hot showers. The drawback is that most are close together and lack a sense of privacy, though many have sea views. B400

HAT KHLONG KHONG

★**Bee Bee Bungalows** ☎ 081 537 9932, ⊜ beebee piya02@hotmail.com. A special, friendly place that stands out for its fourteen highly individual huts, each one a charmingly idiosyncratic experiment in bamboo architecture. All are simple but comfortably furnished, given style with batik fabric flourishes, and have fans, mosquito nets and partially open-air bathrooms; some have an upstairs room as well. There's a good bar-restaurant, too, with similarly experimental but lovely wood and thatch *salas*. B600

Lanta Riviera ☎ 075 667043, ⊛ lantariviera.net. There are rows and rows of good, standard-issue, comfortably furnished fan and a/c concrete bungalows here, plus a few rooms in a two-storey building, set among shady beds of shrubs and flowers at the far northern end of the beach. Many of the rooms sleep three so it's popular with families. Also has a pool and jacuzzi near the shore. Fan B800, a/c B1360

Where Else? ☎ 081 536 4870, ⊛ lanta-where-else. com. This charming collection of 22 bungalows has a laidback vibe and lots of personality, though it's more of a party place than *Bee Bee*. The artfully and individually designed bamboo and coconut-wood bungalows all have fans, mosquito nets, hammocks and open-air bathrooms filled with plants, and there are shell mobiles, driftwood sculptures and pot plants all over the place. The pricier bungalows are larger and nearer the sea, and some even have bamboo sunroofs and turrets. B600

HAT KHLONG NIN

Lanta Nature Beach Resort ☎ 075 662560, ⊛ lanta naturebeachresort.com. In the cluster of concrete bungalow operations right on the beach at the southern end of Khlong Nin, this one has rows of cream-and-lilac painted fan and a/c concrete huts, with spacious tiled interiors. There are even bigger, cheaper bungalows in a garden inland, across the road. Fan B1000, a/c B1500

Lanta Paradise ☎ 075 662569, ⊛ lantaparadisebeach resort.com. Though the shorefront concrete bungalows at this friendly spot are packed uncomfortably close together, they feel spacious inside and are well maintained; they lack style and are plain, but are all a/c with hot showers, and there's a pool here too. Breakfast included. B1800

Otto Bungalow ☎ 084 051 7180, ⊜ otto_lanta @hotmail.com. Tightly packed compound right by the road, containing four shorefront A-frame cabins, with thatched roofs, concrete walls, mosquito nets and fans, as well as a variety of a/c rooms, including one in a small converted bus. A place to party into the night, or curse the DJ at 2am from under your pillow. Fan B800, a/c B1500

HAT KHLONG NAM JUD

Lanta Coral Beach ☎ 075 662535, ⊛ lantacoralresort .com. Friendly resort with a lovely, lofty restaurant – especially nice at sunset – up on the rocky point. The twenty good-sized, plain but very clean en-suite bamboo and concrete huts here are scattered over a lawn among the palms (some of which are hung with hammocks); the concrete options, whether fan or a/c, boast hot showers. Fan B600, a/c B1200

The Narima ☎ 075 662668, ⊛ narima-lanta.com. Very quiet but welcoming, elegantly designed, environmentally conscious resort of 32 posh but unadorned thatch-roofed bamboo bungalows set in three rows in a palm-filled garden. The bungalows all have polished wood floors, verandas with sea view, hot showers and fans as well as a/c (but no TV or wi-fi, just paid internet); there's also a three-tiered pool (with kids' level) and a dive centre, and staff rent out jeeps, motorbikes and mountain bikes. Breakfast included. B2500

AO KANTIANG

Lanta Marine Park View ☎ 075 665063, ⊛ lanta marinepark.com. The thirty en-suite bungalows here are ranged up the slope at the northern end of the beach, with steps leading down to the shore. The best of them, though

7

7

RESTAURANTS & CAFÉS	
Catfish	2
Costa Lanta	3
Faim de Loup	6
Laanta Seafood	1
Red Snapper	7
Sayang Beach Resort	5
Slow Down	4

BARS	
Indian Bar	1
Irish Embassy	4
Klapa Klum	3
Ozone Bar	2

ACCOMMODATION	
Cha-Ba Bungalows	7
Costa Lanta	3
Crown Lanta	1
Hans Restaurant	5
Kaw Kwang Beach Resort	2
Lanta LD Beach	10
Lanta Marina Resort	14
Lanta Palm Beach	12
Layana	13
The Noble House	4
Relax Bay Resort	15
Sayang Beach Resort	9
Slow Down	8
Somewhere Else	11
Southern Lanta Resort	6

BAN SALA DAN, HAT KHLONG DAO & AO PHRA-AE

family bungalows and hotel-style rooms. Has an infinity-edged pool, plus snorkel rental and free transfers to and from Sala Dan pier. Fan B650, a/c B1200

The Noble House ☎ 075 668096, ⍈lantanoblehouse .com. Appealingly small-scale, Swiss-run place where the inviting a/c bungalows have big glass windows and hot showers. They're set in facing rows, in a pretty shrub-filled garden, mostly around the little swimming pool. Also has a few a/c hotel rooms at the back of the compound. Buffet breakfast included. B2100

Slow Down ☎ 083 632 1551, ⍈slowdownlanta.se. This Swedish-run resort at the far southern end of the beach, with a very attractive dark blue pool, a kids' pool and a good restaurant, rents out villas and apartments by the week, but also has two hotel rooms (misleadingly called "bungalows"). They're a little dark, but successfully mix Swedish and southern Thai aesthetics, with lots of wood, white walls and wooden-tiled roofs, as well as a/c, hot water, mini-bars and DVD players. B2600

Southern Lanta Resort ☎ 075 684175–7, ⍈southern lanta.com. One of the biggest hotels on the beach, offering dozens of very spacious a/c bungalows set at decent intervals around a garden of shrubs, clipped hedges and shady trees. There's a good-sized swimming pool too. Popular with families and package tourists. Breakfast included. B2000

AO PHRA-AE (LONG BEACH)

Lanta LD Beach ☎ 075 684548, ⍈sandybeachlanta .com. In a grassy lot by the beach, south of *Somewhere Else*, this place offers a fair amount of shade and cheapish en-suite bamboo bungalows with fans and mosquito nets, plus more robust concrete alternatives with either fans or a/c, TVs, fridges and hot water; most have hammocks, and all have small bathrooms and dated but functional decor. Fan B700, a/c B1700

★Lanta Marina Resort ☎ 075 684168, ⍈lanta marina.com. At the far southern end of Ao Phra-ae by a rocky point, this friendly place has 23 shaggily thatched wood-and-split-bamboo bungalows, connected by wooden walkways, which circle a very pretty lawn and flower garden. All the huts have nice beds, well-designed bathrooms, high palm-leaf roofs and fans, and the larger, more expensive ones on the beach have hot showers. B800

Lanta Palm Beach ☎ 075 684406, ⍈lantapalmbeach resort.com. A busy, clean, central and popular spot within stumbling distance of several beach bars. The concrete bungalows and large, bright cottages sit back from the shore a little, within a garden of neat clipped hedges, and come with a/c and hot water. Has internet access and a dive centre. Breakfast included. B2500

★Layana ☎ 075 607100, ⍈layanaresort.com. Located plumb in the middle of the beautiful beach, this is currently the top spot on Ao Phra-ae and one of the best and most liked on the whole island, not least for its calm ambience

Kaw Kwang Beach Resort At the northernmost end of Khlong Dao ☎ 075 668260–1, ⍈lanta-kawkwangresort .com. Welcoming, family-run outfit with good-value (for Lanta) rooms, occupying a large area of beachfront land on Hat Kaw Kwang adjacent to *Crown Lanta*. There are many options here, all with hot showers and TVs, from cheap, decent, old-style en-suite wood and concrete huts among the trees above the shore, to bigger, beachside a/c bungalows, touts who usually transport you to the beach of your choice for free. If you need to use the motorbike sidecar taxi service instead, be warned that drivers will try and charge arrivals way over the normal fares; walk 250m from the pier head to the main road to get a ride at more reasonable rates. Speedboats run between Ban Si Raya at Lanta Old Town and Klongson pier in Trang (3 daily; 30min; B480), which you can book through your resort or Lanta Info (☎081 979 7947; ✉nong@lantainfo.com).

Destinations: Ao Nang, via West Railay (daily; 2hr 30min); Ko Phi Phi Don (2 daily; 1hr 30min); Krabi, via Ko Jum (daily; 2hr 30min); Phuket (1–2 daily; 4hr 30min).

By road The alternative to the ferries is the overland route to Ko Lanta Yai – essential during the rainy season but increasingly popular at any time of year. Access is via Ban Hua Hin on the mainland, 75km south of Krabi, from where a small ferry crosses to Ban Khlong Mark on Ko Lanta Noi, after which there's a 7km drive across to Lanta Noi's southwest tip, then another ferry over the narrow channel to the car-ferry port on Ko Lanta Yai's northeastern coast (though a bridge between Lanta Noi and Lanta Yai is being built); both ferries run approximately every 20min from about 7am to 10pm (B120 in total per car). This is the route used by a/c minibuses from Krabi town (hourly; 2hr; B250–400 depending on which beach you get dropped at, terminates in Lanta Old Town); from Phuket (9 daily; 5hr; B500); from Trang (roughly hourly; 3hr; B300); and by anyone bringing their own vehicle. From Lanta, the Krabi minibuses will make stops at Krabi bus station, airport and then town; on arrival, you'll need to call ☎081 606 3591 to ask them to pick you up at the airport. There's also a daily bus between Ban Hua Hin and Bangkok's Mo Chit bus terminal (12hr), fed by a/c minibuses to and from Ko Lanta Yai, such as the Krabi town minibuses (hourly; 30–50min depending on your pick-up point on Ko Lanta Yai), which any hotel can arrange.

GETTING AROUND

There's no public transport on the island, but motorbikes are widely available for rent and there are jeeps too.

By share-taxi and songthaew A fleet of motorbike sidecar share-taxis, with drivers in numbered vests, and a few white songthaews operate out of Ban Sala Dan and will go pretty much anywhere on the island, though they usually need to be phoned (by staff at hotels or restaurants) for pick-ups from anywhere outside Sala Dan. Lanta has its share of scamming taxi-drivers, so bear in mind the following approximate per-person rates for rides out of Sala Dan: B40 to Hat Khlong Dao, B60 to Ao Phra-Ae, B90 to Hat Khlong Kong, or about B50 between the above; B200 to Ao Mai Phai.

ACCOMMODATION

Ko Lanta Yai is extremely popular during high season (Nov–Feb), when it's worth either booking your first night's accommodation in advance or taking up the suggestions of the bungalow touts who ride the boats from the mainland. A confirmed booking also means you should get free transport from the port to your hotel. **Accommodation pricing** on Ko Lanta is disconcertingly flexible and alters according to the number of tourists on the island: bungalow rates can double between mid-December and mid-January (and some resorts extend their "peak season" to include the whole of January and February), while during the rainy season (May–Oct) rates are vastly discounted.

HAT KHLONG DAO

There are a couple of budget-oriented places to stay on Hat Khlong Dao, but the emphasis is on accommodation for families and others looking for a/c comfort.

Cha-Ba Bungalows ☎075 684118, ✇krabidir.com /chababungalows. There's plenty of kitsch creativity at this welcoming, idiosyncratic complex of bungalows, set among model dinosaurs and Flintstone boulders. The tightly packed bungalows are simple and flimsy, but cute, decorated with loud retro-look fabrics and wallpapers. Fan ones come with hot showers, while the a/c ones also have TVs, fridges and free breakfasts. Fan **B1300**, a/c **B2000**

Costa Lanta ☎075 684630, ✇costalanta.com. You're either going to love or hate this ultra-brutal minimalist grouping of 22 polished-grey concrete boxes, each bungalow consisting of an unadorned bedroom all in grey and white with a mosquito net, a similarly styled bathroom with rain shower and a large terrace. They're set in a broad garden bisected by khlongs, with a big, sleek pool and a striking bar-restaurant. Breakfast included. **B6800**

Crown Lanta ☎075 626999, ✇crownlanta.com. Upmarket, German-managed resort on the island's very northwestern tip, where crown motifs feature heavily on the rooftops. The hotel divides into two zones: standard (with very large balconies) and pool-access rooms near the lobby; up on the hill, villas and another free-form pool, plus a panoramic restaurant, a spa and steps down to a part-sandy, part-rocky private beach. **B7580**

Hans Restaurant ☎075 684152, ✇krabidir.com /hansrestaurant. One of the cheapest places on this beach, with fifteen huts ranged along a narrow, scruffy strip of garden behind the shorefront restaurant, next to the *Royal Lanta* resort in the heart of the beach. Choose between very simple, rickety bamboo bungalows with mosquito nets and bathrooms, and slightly better-furnished wooden versions. High season only. **B700**

7

much as it was a century ago, with its historic charm intact. There's little more to the Old Town than its peaceful main street, which runs right along the coast parallel to Route 4245 and is lined with traditional, hundred-year-old sea- and wind-blasted wooden homes and shops, many of them constructed on stilted jetties over the sea, their first-floor overhangs shading the pavements and plant-filled doorways. The Chinese shrine midway down the street is evidence of the town's cultural mix: Ban Si Raya is home to a long-established Buddhist Chinese–Thai community as well as to Muslims and, in its southern neighbourhood, communities of animist Urak Lawoy *chao ley* ("sea gypsies").

The **Urak Lawoy** *chao ley* (see box, p.602) are thought to have been Ko Lanta's first inhabitants, perhaps as long as five hundred years ago, living along the shoreline during the monsoon season and setting off along the coast again when the winds abated. They have now settled permanently in their own villages on the island, including at **Ban Sang-Ga-U**, 4km to the south of Lanta Old Town; other Urak Lawoy living elsewhere in the Andaman Sea, around Trang and beyond, consider Ko Lanta their capital and will always stop at Sang-Ga-U when making a journey. One of the accessible elements of Urak Lawoy culture is their **music**, an interesting fusion of far-flung influences, featuring violins (from the Dutch East Indies), drums (from Persia) and gongs (from China), as well as singing, dancing and ritual elements. A good time to hear their music is at one of their twice-yearly three-day full-moon **festivals**, or at the Laanta Lanta Festival (see p.682).

As an additional incentive to linger among the wooden architecture of the main street, there are several **shops** selling batik sarongs and souvenirs, plus the charming Hammock House (ⓦjumbohammock.com), whose amazing range of hammocks includes ones woven by people of the endangered Mrabri tribe of northern Thailand (see p.326).

Koh Lanta Community Museum

Across the small grassy park from the pier and parking lot · Daily 9am–3pm · B40

There's an attempt to introduce the cultures of Ban Si Raya's three distinct but peaceable communities at the **Koh Lanta Community Museum**, which is housed in the attractive 1901 wooden building that used to serve as the local district office. Archive photos and one or two English-language captions describe the main occupations for the communities, including fishing and making charcoal from mangrove wood; you can sometimes watch an interesting video in which villagers air their concerns about the recent explosion in tourism on the island and the effect that the influx of incomers and investors is having on traditional lifestyles and livelihoods.

Thung Yee Pheng mangroves

About 1km north of the junction of Route 4245 and the road across from Ao Phra-Ae, take the right turn for a couple of hundred metres · Daily 8am–4pm · B20

This community tourism project allows you to take a short, not very compelling stroll along a 200m boardwalk out into the **mangrove swamps** that line Ko Lanta Yai's east coast. More interesting are the one-hour longtail tours available here (B1000/person, including guide), and you can also hire a two-person kayak to have a look around (B500/2hr, B300 extra for a guide).

ARRIVAL AND DEPARTURE   **KO LANTA YAI**

The principal mainland gateways to Ko Lanta are Krabi, Phuket and Trang, all of which have good long-distance bus services, and **airports**. Trang also has a train station. Flight and minibus through-tickets from Don Muang Airport in Bangkok are offered by Air Asia, via Krabi Airport, and by Nok Air, via Trang Airport.

By boat In high season, there are boats to Ko Lanta Yai from Krabi (B400), via Ko Jum (B400); from Ko Phi Phi (ferry B400, speedboat B600), with connections from Phuket (ferry B700, speedboat B1500); and from Ao Nang (B400) via West Railay (B470). There are also high-season services to Ko Lanta from the Trang islands and Ko Lipe, with connections to Langkawi in Malaysia (see p.702). All of these ferries dock at Ban Sala Dan and are met by bungalow small but lively roadside village covers most necessities, including tours, onward transport, motorbike rental and internet access.

Ao Khlong Jaak and Ao Mai Phai

The road beyond Ao Kantiang to Lanta's southern tip, about 4km away, is steeply undulating and rutted, but is slowly being paved. The next bay south of Kantiang is **AO KHLONG JAAK**, site of some accommodation including the lively *Anda Lanta Resort* (see p.690). Though it's not much more than a trickle, the **waterfall** inland from Ao Khlong Jaak can be reached from the bay by walking along the course of the stream for about two hours. South around the next headland, western Lanta plays its final card in the shape of handsome white-sand **AO MAI PHAI**, a peaceful getaway because of its remote position on the largely unmade road. There's good coral close to shore here, but this makes it too rocky for low-tide swimming, when you'll need to kayak or walk up to Ao Khlong Jaak instead.

Tham Mai Kaew caves

3km southeast of the Khlong Nin junction • 2hr tours Mon–Thurs, Sat & Sun 9am–4pm, Fri 8–10am & 1.30–4pm • B300, including national park entry fee and head torch • ☏ 089 288 8954 • A motorcycle taxi costs about B200 each way from Khlong Dao or Ao Phra-Ae

The myriad chambers at **Tham Mai Kaew caves**, some of which you can only just crawl into, are Ko Lanta's biggest inland attraction. They are filled with stalactites and interesting rock formations, and there's a creepy cave pool too, as well as the inevitable bats. Tours of the cave are given by the local family who first properly explored the cave system in the 1980s; as well as the standard tour they sometimes offer longer cave tours and overnight jungle treks. Most of Thailand's countless caves are underwhelming and certainly not worth B300, but this is one of the better ones, not least because the caretakers have resisted stringing it with electric lights so you're left to wonder both at what you catch with your torch and at what you don't see. Among its star features are crystallized waterfalls, fossils and ammonites embedded in the cave walls and overhangs, stalagmites and stalactites young and old and a tangible sense of there being endless passageways to explore. In the rainy season it's a more slippery, challenging experience, with some wading likely and the option of a dip in the wet-season-only lagoon. Even in the dry season it's moderately arduous and best done in sensible shoes and clothes you're happy to get grubby in; set aside three hours for getting into and out of the caves.

Viewpoint Hill

3km beyond the turn-off to the Tham Mai Kaew caves • Café daily 8am–8pm

Beyond the turn-off to the caves, the eastbound road drops down over the central spine of hills and you pass Viewpoint café, where nearly everyone stops for a drink and a gawp at the stunning panorama. The **view over the east coast** is glorious, encompassing the southeast coast of mangrove-fringed Ko Lanta Noi, dozens of islets – including Ko Bubu and Ko Por – adrift in the milky blue sea, and the hilly profile of the mainland along the horizon.

Lanta Old Town (Ban Si Raya)

ⓦ lantaoldtown.com

The seductively atmospheric little waterfront settlement of **LANTA OLD TOWN**, officially known as **Ban Si Raya**, is Ko Lanta's oldest town. It began life as a sheltered staging post for ships and served as the island's administrative capital from 1901 to 1998. The government offices have since moved to Ko Lanta Noi, and Ban Sala Dan has assumed the role of harbour, island gateway and commercial hub, so Ban Si Raya has been left

7

SNORKELLING TRIPS AND WATERSPORTS ON LANTA

SNORKELLING TRIPS

The best and most popular **snorkelling** is at the islands of **Ko Rok Nai** and **Ko Rok Nok**, 47km south of Ko Lanta; these forested twins are graced with stunning white-sand beaches and accessible waterfalls and separated by a narrow channel full of fabulous shallow reefs.

Also hugely popular is the "**four island**" snorkelling trip that takes in the much nearer islands off Trang – the enclosed emerald lagoon on **Ko Mook** (see p.704), plus nearby **Ko Hai** (Ko Ngai), **Ko Ma** and **Ko Kradan** – but these sites can get very crowded. Another option is the day-trip to **Phi Phi Don**, Phi Phi Leh and Bamboo Island (see p.667). The trips cost around B1500 in a speedboat or B900 in a big boat, including lunch, snorkelling equipment and national park entry fee. For a smaller, more personal experience, contact Sun Island Tours or Freedom Adventures.

DIVING

The **reefs** around Ko Lanta are quieter and in some cases more pristine than those round Phi Phi and Phuket, and excellent for seeing whale sharks. The **diving season** runs from November to April, though a few dive shops continue to run successful trips from May to August. All dive boats depart from Ban Sala Dan, and nearly all dive courses are taught either in Sala Dan or on Hat Khlong Dao, though there are dive shops on every beach.

Some of Lanta's best **dive sites** are located between Ko Lanta and Ko Phi Phi, including the soft coral at **Ko Bidah**, where you get lots of leopard sharks, barracuda and tuna. West and south of Lanta, the **Ko Ha** island group offers four different dives on each of its five islands, including steep drop-offs and an "underwater cathedral" and other caves; visibility is often very good. Much further south, about 56km from Ko Lanta, are **Hin Daeng** and **Hin Muang** (see p.637).

The nearest recompression chambers are located on Phuket (see p.636); check to see that your dive operator is insured to use one of them (see p.52).

KAYAKING

There are several rewarding **kayaking** destinations, rich in mangroves and caves, around Ko Lanta Yai's east coast and around Ko Lanta Noi and its eastern islands, including **Ko Talabeng** and **Ko Bubu**; a few companies also offer kayak-snorkel trips to the four islands described above.

OPERATORS

Freedom Adventures ☎ 084 910 9132, ⌨ freedom -adventures.net. A variety of snorkelling day-trips, as well as all-inclusive overnight camping trips on Ko Rok and Ko Kradan (from B12,000). Book through your resort by phone.

Ko Lanta Diving Centre On the main road into Ban Sala Dan ☎ 075 668065, ⌨ kolantadivingcenter .com. German-run outfit charging B4800 plus B600 National Park fees for two dives, including equipment, B1500 for accompanying snorkellers and B15,650 for the Openwater course.

Lanta Diver On the main road into Ban Sala Dan ☎ 075 684208, ⌨ lantadiver.com. Swedish-owned, PADI Five-star Instructor Development Centre charging from B2900 for two dives, excluding equipment, and B14,300 for the Openwater course.

Lanta GardenHill Tours ☎ 075 684042, ⌨ lanta gardenhilltours.com. One of the main operators of four-island snorkelling trips, which can be booked through any agent on Ko Lanta.

Lanta Kayaking ☎ 081 787 1040. Kayaking trips to Ko Talabeng for B1300, bookable through most travel agents.

Lanta Paddlesports On the main road in Hat Khlong Dao and on several beaches ☎ 043 162159, ⌨ lantapaddlesports.com. Paddleboard lessons, rental and tours, as well as windsurfing, kayaking, surfing and snorkelling trips.

Sun Island Tours ☎ 087 891 6619, ⌨ lantalongtail .com. Various longtail trips to the four islands, around Ko Lanta, and to Lanta's eastern islands (where there's also an overnight camping option), which come very highly rated and cost B1500, excluding national park fees.

Ao Kantiang

The secluded cove of **AO KANTIANG**, some 7km beyond Hat Khlong Nam Jud, is an impressively long curve, backed by jungle-clad hillsides and dominated by one luxury hotel, which keeps the southern half of the beach in pristine condition. Unusually for Lanta, the bay is protected enough to be good for swimming year-round, and there's some coral at the northern end; snorkelling and fishing trips are easily arranged. The

Ao Phra-Ae (Long Beach)

With its lovely long parade of soft, white sand, calm and crystal-clear water that's good for swimming and shady fringe of casuarina trees, **AO PHRA-AE** (also known as **Long Beach**) is strikingly beautiful and the best of Lanta's many long beaches. There's a little more variety and character among the accommodation options here than at Khlong Dao, a couple of kilometres to the north, and quite a development of shops, with ATMs, restaurants and tour agents along the main road. The main stretch of the beach is divided from the southern rocky extremity by a shallow, easily wadeable khlong; *Lanta Marina Resort* marks the southern reaches of the beach and is about half an hour's walk along the beach from *Sayang* at the northern end. Phra-Ae's budget enclave clusters along a network of sandy tracks behind the *Ozone Bar*.

Hat Khlong Khong

The luxuriously long beach at **HAT KHLONG KHONG**, 2km south of Ao Phra-Ae's *Relax Bay Resort*, is peppered with rocks and in most parts only really swimmable at high tide, though the snorkelling is good. Another big draw is the traveller-oriented bungalows, among the most creatively designed places to stay on the island. There are several funky little beach bars too, notably at *Bee Bee Bungalows*.

Hat Khlong Nin

About 4km south of Hat Khlong Khong the road forks at kilometre-stone 13, at the edge of the village of **Ban Khlong Nin**. The left-hand, east-bound arm runs across to Ko Lanta Yai's east coast, via the caves and viewpoint (see p.685). The right-hand fork is the route to the southern beaches and continues southwards along the west coast for 14km to the southern tip.

Just beyond the junction, the little enclave of bungalows, restaurants, bars and tour agents at **HAT KHLONG NIN** lends this beach more of a village atmosphere than the northern beaches. The beach itself is lovely, long and sandy and good for swimming, though the road runs close alongside it. There are several reasonably priced places to stay here, with the cheapest beds in some hotels located in separate little garden compounds on the inland side of the road, and a low-key collection of shoreside bar-restaurants with plenty of character and mellow vibes.

There are minimarkets, ATMs and a clinic at the Ban Khlong Nin junction, and from here you could walk the 3km to the Tham Mai Kaew caves from Khlong Nin in about an hour.

Hat Khlong Nam Jud

Just over 1km south of Hat Khlong Nin, the road passes the two tiny little bays known as **HAT KHLONG NAM JUD**. The northerly one is the domain of *The Narima* (see p.689). A brief scramble around the rocky point to the south, the next tiny cove is rocky in parts but enjoys a swimmable beach and is home to *Lanta Coral Beach* (see p.689).

YOGA AND COOKING CLASSES ON LANTA

YOGA

During high season there are **yoga** classes at *Cha-Ba* bungalows on Khlong Dao (Ⓦkrabidir .com/chababungalows; also meditation classes and yoga and meditation retreats), but the most famous teacher is now at *Oasis Yoga* on Hat Khlong Dao (Ⓦoasisyoga-lanta.com).

THAI COOKING CLASSES

Five-hour **cooking** classes (B2000) are offered by Time for Lime, at the south end of Hat Khlong Dao (Ⓣ075 684590, Ⓦtimeforlime.net).

LANTA FESTIVALS

Every March, Ko Lanta Yai celebrates its rich ethnic heritage at the **Laanta Lanta Festival** (*laanta* meaning roughly "eye-dazzling"), which is held over five days in Lanta Old Town and features both traditional and modern music and entertainments, countless specialist food stalls, and crafts for sale (check ⓦlantaoldtown.com for dates and specifics). Traditional *chao ley* rituals are celebrated on Ko Lanta twice a year, on the full moons of the sixth and eleventh lunar months – usually June and Oct/Nov (see below). Meanwhile, the Chinese shrine in Lanta Old Town is the focus of the island's version of the **Vegetarian Festival** (see p.623), which involves processions, cultural performances and walking on hot coals.

(see box, p.602), most of whom supported themselves by fishing and cultivating the land before the tourist boom brought new jobs, and challenges.

One of those challenges is that the **tourist season** is quite short, with the weather and seas at their calmest and safest from November to April; the main ferries don't run outside that period, and some hotels close, though most do stay open and offer huge discounts. The short money-making window, however, means that accommodation prices on Ko Lanta fluctuate more wildly than many other south Thailand destinations.

The local *chao ley* name for Ko Lanta Yai is *Pulao Satak*, "Island of Long Beaches", an apt description of the string of beaches along the **west coast**, each separated by rocky points and strung out at quite wide intervals. Broadly speaking, the busiest and most mainstream beaches are in the north, within easy reach of the port at **Ban Sala Dan: Hat Khlong Dao** is the family beach and **Ao Phra-Ae** the longer and more beautiful. The middle section has variable sands but some interesting, artsy places to stay, at **Hat Khlong Khong**, **Hat Khlong Nin** and **Hat Khlong Nam Jud**. Southerly **Ao Kantiang** is reliable for swimming year-round and currently marks the end of the made road; beyond here **Ao Khlong Jaak** and **Ao Mai Phai** are a little harder to get to and so feel more remote. Lanta Yai's mangrove-fringed **east coast** has no real tourist development but is both good for kayaking and culturally interesting because of the traditional homes in **Lanta Old Town**. North across the narrow channel from the port at Ban Sala Dan, Lanta Yai's sister island of **Ko Lanta Noi** has Ko Lanta's administrative offices and several small villages but no tourist accommodation. The rest of the Ko Lanta archipelago, which comprises over fifty little islands, is mostly uninhabited.

Ban Sala Dan

During high season, boats from Krabi, Phi Phi and Ko Lipe arrive at the T-shaped fishing port and tourist village of **BAN SALA DAN** (see p.686), on the northernmost tip of Ko Lanta Yai. Pretty much everything you'll need is here, from beachwear shops and minimarkets to banks with currency exchange and ATMs, tour agents and dive shops. The old part of the village, strung out along the north-facing shorefront, retains its charming old wooden houses built on piles over the water, many of which have been turned into attractive restaurants.

Hat Khlong Dao

Long and gently curving **HAT KHLONG DAO** is known as "the family beach", both for its plentiful mid-range accommodation, and for its generous sweep of flat sandy shoreline that's safe for swimming and embraced by protective headlands; there's good snorkelling at the far northwestern end of the beach, off the tiny Kaw Kwang peninsula. Despite being developed to capacity, Khlong Dao is broad enough never to feel overcrowded, the sunsets can be magnificent, and the whole beach is framed by a dramatic hilly backdrop. Though Ban Sala Dan is close by, the beach supports plenty of its own minimarkets and transport outlets, both shoreside and along the main road.

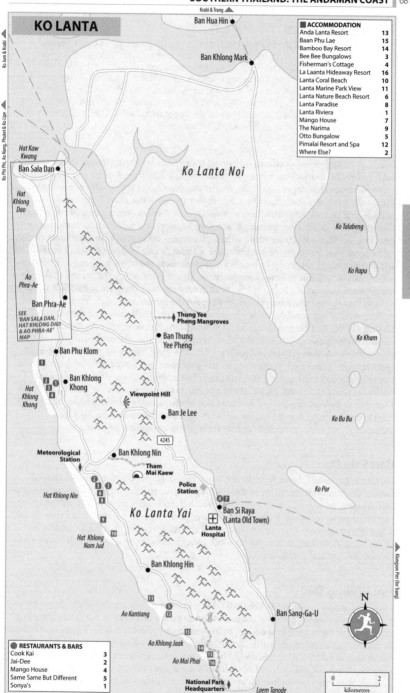

KO LANTA

SEE
'BAN SALA DAN,
HAT KHLONG DAO
& AO PHRA-AE'
MAP

Krabi & Trang

Ban Hua Hin

Ban Khlong Mark

Ko Jum & Krabi

Ko Phi Phi, Ao Nang, Phuket & Ko Lipe

Hat Kaw Kwang

Ban Sala Dan

Hat Khlong Dao

Ao Phra-Ae

Ban Phra-Ae

Ko Lanta Noi

Ko Talabeng

Ko Rapu

7

Thung Yee Pheng Mangroves

Ban Thung Yee Pheng

Ban Phu Klom

Ban Khlong Khong

Viewpoint Hill

Ko Kham

Hat Khlong Khong

Ban Je Lee

Ko Bu Bu

4245

Meteorological Station

Ban Khlong Nin

Tham Mai Kaew

Police Station

Ko Lanta Yai

Ban Si Raya (Lanta Old Town)

Lanta Hospital

Ko Por

Hat Khlong Nin

Hat Khlong Nam Jud

Ban Khlong Hin

Ao Kantiang

Ban Sang-Ga-U

Ao Khlong Jaak

Ao Mai Phai

National Park Headquarters

Laem Tanode

Klongson Pier (for Trang)

N

0 — 2
kilometres

ACCOMMODATION	
Anda Lanta Resort	13
Baan Phu Lae	15
Bamboo Bay Resort	14
Bee Bee Bungalows	3
Fisherman's Cottage	4
La Laanta Hideaway Resort	16
Lanta Coral Beach	10
Lanta Marine Park View	11
Lanta Nature Beach Resort	6
Lanta Paradise	8
Lanta Riviera	1
Mango House	7
The Narima	9
Otto Bungalow	5
Pimalai Resort and Spa	12
Where Else?	2

RESTAURANTS & BARS	
Cook Kai	3
Jai-Dee	2
Mango House	4
Same Same But Different	5
Sonya's	1

have doors onto the veranda to avoid the need for a/c, plus low beds and elegantly simple furniture. The resort has a small pool, a TV and DVD area, a massage service and a restaurant. Minimum stay four nights, seven in peak season. Breakfast included. B5500

AO SI

Ao Si Bungalows ☎ 081 747 2664, ⚲ kohjumonline .com/aosi.html. On Ao Si's northern headland, the woven-bamboo, en-suite bungalows here are built on piles up the side of the cliff and have wrap-around verandas for soaking up the commanding views of the bay and the southern half of the island. No wi-fi. B500

AO TING RAI

OonLee Bungalows ☎ 087 200 8053, ⚲ kohjumoonlee bungalows.com. Small, enthusiastically run and well-liked French–Thai place with sturdy accommodation in various styles stacked up the cliffside. The wooden bungalows have plenty of storage, appealing bathrooms and sea-view verandas; there's a stylish upper-level lounge area and good restaurant, and a bar and massage area at beach level, plus kayaks for rent and free snorkels for guests. *OonLee* offers

lots of organized activities and tours, including guided half-day treks up Khao Ko Pu and fishing trips. B600

Ting Rai Bay Resort ☎ 087 277 7379, ⚲ tingrai.com. Popular spot whose nicely designed wooden bungalows are ranged up the sloping shorefront on stilts, most offering fine views from capacious decks (especially the "honeymoon" ones). Interiors have fans, four-poster style beds, and plenty of attention to detail. The food here is also good. B600

AO LUBOA

Bonhomie Beach Cottages ☎ 086 560 7977, ⚲ bonhomiebeach.com. At the far northern end of the beach, very large, attractively designed en-suite wooden chalets with mosquito nets, many with sea view; price depends on proximity to the sea. B1100

Luboa Hut ☎ 081 388 9241, ⚲ luboahut.com. Friendly establishment with ten en-suite bamboo and wooden bungalows with sea views from their verandas in a well-shaded spot under shoreside trees; many of them are roomy and good quality, some have extra beds or sofas and all have mosquito nets. The owners offer free kayaks and cooking classes. B500

EATING AND DRINKING

LONG BEACH

★**Bo Daeng** For an outstanding Thai meal, at some of the cheapest prices on the island, you should join the (sometimes lengthy) queue here, whose highlights include baked fish, vegetable tempura (B90) and a southern yellow curry (B90), plus Thai desserts, home-baked bread and coconut shakes. Daily 7.30am–9pm.

Freedom Hut Many people round off the night with a drink around the camp fire at this easy-going place, right down at the bottom end of Long Beach. Choose between cocktails, wine and cheapish beer or a snack on the beach. Daily 7.30am–12.30am.

Woodland Lodge Delicious curries – try the Indian curry with prawns (B200) – plenty of choice for vegetarians,

including tasty vegetable tempura (B90), plus Western food, including breakfast and fish and chips. Daily roughly 7am–8.30/9pm.

BAN KO JUM

Ban Ko Jum Seafood ☎ 081 893 6380. The big name in the village is this very popular and very good restaurant, whose tables occupy a scenically sited jetty near the pier, and enjoy fine views across the mangrove channel. Among its big menu of fresh seafood cooked any number of ways (B150–400), the juicy fat prawns barbecued with honey are a standout, and their crab and lobster dishes are famous too. Standards such as *phat thai* (B150) are here too. Daily 9am–10pm.

Ko Lanta Yai

Although **KO LANTA YAI** can't quite compete with Phi Phi's stupendous scenery, the thickly forested 25km-long island has the longest beaches in the Krabi area – and plenty of them. There's decent snorkelling and diving nearby, plus caves to explore, kayaking and other watersports, so many tourists base themselves here for their entire holiday fortnight. The island is especially popular with families, in part because of the local laws that have so far prevented jet-skis, beachfront parasols and girlie bars from turning it into another Phuket, though resort facilities are expanding fast. Lanta is also rapidly being colonized by Scandinavian expats, with villa homes and associated businesses popping up all over the place, at a pace that not all islanders are happy about. The majority of Ko Lanta Yai's ten thousand indigenous residents are mixed-blood descendants of Muslim Chinese–Malay or animist *chao ley* ("sea gypsy") peoples songthaew, passing the airport, either all the way through to Laem Kruat (B100) or changing in Nua Klong.

To/from Ko Phi Phi This service isn't set in stone, but there should be a longtail boat from Ton Sai to the west coast of Ko Jum every afternoon in high season (1hr 30min; B500).

To/from Laem Kruat In the dry season, boats run from Laem Kruat to all three east-coast "village" piers on Ko Jum (45min–1hr; B50–70), from where a motorbike taxi with sidecar (best arranged in advance through your resort) will transfer you to your bungalow, charging from B50 per person. Boats to Ban Ko Pu depart Laem Kruat about every two hours during the day in dry season, while the thrice-daily services to Mutu and Ban Ko Jum are mostly in the afternoon, timed for shoppers and traders to return to the island. In the rainy season you have to travel to Ko Jum by minibus on transport ferries, conveniently never having to change transport. An increasing number of visitors now use this route year-round; some bungalow operators, for example, offer transfers from Krabi airport using this route (about B800/car to Laem Kruat), which continues to Ko Jum.

GETTING AROUND AND SERVICES

Getting around Most bungalows can arrange kayak (about B700/day) and motorbike (about B350/day) rental, while *Bo Daeng* has mountain bikes (B150/day; see below). The main island road is slowly being paved north from Ban Ko Jum, but the track on the west side of Khao Ko Pu remains a bumpy nightmare.

Tourist information For a comprehensive guide to life on the island and pictures of all the bungalow operations, see ⓦ kohjumonline.com.

Clinic The island medical centre is on the road near *Ko Jum Lodge*, beyond the southern edge of Ban Ting Rai.

Exchange There's no ATM on the island, so it's best to bring all the cash you'll need with you. At a pinch, you can change money at Jum Island Travel, next to the pier in Ban Ko Jum, at expensive rates.

ACCOMMODATION

LONG BEACH

Andaman Beach Resort ☏ 089 724 1544, ✉ andaman _kohjum@yahoo.com. You can't miss the steeply roofed concrete bungalows at this friendly, well-run place, painted like gingerbread houses in shocking pink, yellow and other "lucky" colours. Set in a pleasant garden, they're all bright, clean and en suite with mosquito screens and terraces, and are priced according to size and proximity to the beach (rising to B3000 for a big, a/c, beachfront pad with hot water and breakfast). The food's good and reasonably priced, too. B350

Bo Daeng ☏ 081 494 8760. This funky, ultra-cheap and ultra-basic (no wi-fi) travellers' classic is run by a famously welcoming charismatic island *chao ley* family and has legendary food. The rudimentary bamboo huts come with or without private bathrooms – the latter are among the very cheapest on the island, but all have nets and electricity during the evening. Open all year. Shared bathroom B200, en suite B400

Freedom Hut ☏ 084 991 0881 or ☏ 085 655 3020, ⓦ kohjumfreedomhut.com. Large, beautifully simple, thatched bungalows (including a treehouse) in rustic-contemporary style, way off on their own at the southernmost point of the island, with loads of space for hammocks and chairs on the deck. Some have nice outdoor rock bathrooms, and one occupies an unparalleled spot on a tiny rocky promontory, with awesome 360-degree sea views (B3000). B500

Joy Bungalows ☏ 075 618199, ⓦ kohjum-joybungalow .com. This is the longest-running and most famous place to stay on the island, though not necessarily the friendliest. It has a big spread of accommodation set in a very shady grove of trees behind the shorefront, the majority of them smart wooden bungalows in varying sizes and proximity to the sea, plus some cheaper thatched ones and two-bedroom houses. The restaurant has electricity but not the bungalows, so it's paraffin lamps all round at night. B800

New Bungalow ☏ 075 618116, ⓦ kohjumonline.com /new.html. The two-dozen differently styled bungalows at this friendly, long-established place include a few cheapie bamboo ones with and without private bathrooms, some plain, en-suite wooden huts, and a couple of tree-houses (B600) set 5m or so up in the branches by the beach, with idyllic sea views and shared bathrooms. Electricity evenings only and there is no wi-fi. B200

★ **Woodland Lodge** ☏ 081 893 5330, ⓦ woodland -koh-jum.com. Welcoming, helpful and peaceful spot owned by a UK–Thai couple and one of the few places on the island to stay open year-round (with big discounts in the rainy season). Its large, attractive, well-designed bungalows with 24hr electricity are widely set beneath the trees of its shorefront garden and all have good, spacious bathrooms; the doubles have platform beds, mosquito nets, varnished wooden floors and deep shady decks, while the bigger ones are designed for families. B1100

GOLDEN PEARL BEACH

Koh Jum Lodge ☏ 089 921 1621, ⓦ kohjumlodge .com. This French–Thai place is one of the most upscale resorts on the island, with nineteen thatched wooden chalets designed in charming rustic-chic style. Thoughtfully constructed to make the most of the island breezes, they

ACTIVITIES ON KO JUM

Most bungalows can organize **day-trips**, as will tour agencies in Ban Ko Jum, for example to Ko Phi Phi, Bamboo Island and Mosquito Island (about B3500–4000/boat), or around Ko Jum (B2500/boat). Many offer guided hikes up **Khao Ko Pu** (about B1000, including lunch). Ko Jum Divers, at *Ko Jum Beach Villas* at the north end of Long Beach (☎082 273 7603, ⓦkohjum-divers.com), run daily **dive** trips to Ko Phi Phi (B4200), with snorkellers welcome (B2100), and diving courses on offer (fun dive B4600; Openwater B14,200).

At its northern end, Long Beach segues into **GOLDEN PEARL BEACH**, which is about 750m/fifteen minutes' walk north up the beach from *Bo Daeng*, 5km by road from Ban Ko Jum and 1km south of Ban Ting Rai. Like Long Beach, it also has only a few bungalow outfits along its curving shoreline, though these are close by the island road.

Ao Si

Around the rocky headland from Golden Pearl Beach, accessible in ten minutes at low tide or quite a bit further by road, long and beautifully uncluttered **AO SI** is good for swimming. There are a few places to stay, and a big troupe of monkeys makes its home here too. A ten-minute walk through the rubber trees from the uppermost of *Ao Si's* bungalows brings you to Magic Beach, just south of Ao Ting Rai.

Ban Ting Rai, Khao Ko Pu and Ao Ting Rai

The road begins to climb as soon as you leave Golden Pearl Beach, taking you up through the ribbon-like village of **Ban Ting Rai**, pretty with bougainvillaea and wooden houses, and the location of a few small restaurants and noodle shops. At 422m, **Khao Ko Pu**, which rises in the distance, is the island's highest mountain and home to macaques that sometimes come down to forage on the rocks around the northern beaches; guided treks up the eastern flank to the summit take about an hour and reward you with fine 360-degree panoramas encompassing the entire island, the mainland and the outer islands.

The little bay of **AO TING RAI**, sometimes known as **Hat Kidon**, has some nice places to stay and good snorkelling off its shore, with a reef to explore and plenty of fish. At low tide it's too rocky for swimming; you'll need either to pick your way over the rocks, rent a kayak, or walk south 500m along the coastal road, to get to the little sandy crescent known as **Magic Beach**, which is swimmable at any tide. You can walk to Ao Ting Rai from Ao Si in about twenty minutes along the coast road.

Ao Luboa

Ko Jum's peaceful northernmost beach, **AO LUBOA**, feels remote. It's accessed chiefly by a loop in the main island road that circles the northeastern slopes of Khao Ko Pu and terminates at the north end of the bay, though the steeply undulating coast road from Ao Ting Rai can also be walked (about 45min from *OonLee Bungalows*). Like Ao Ting Rai, Ao Luboa's shorefront reef gets exposed at low tide, making it impossible to swim, though at high water things are fine and it's anyway a supremely quiet, laidback beach with just a few bungalows.

ARRIVAL AND DEPARTURE

KO JUM

To/from Krabi & Ko Lanta During high season, usual access to Ko Jum is via the Krabi–Ko Lanta ferry (daily; 1hr 30min from Krabi, currently leaving at 11.30am, or about 45min from Ko Lanta, currently leaving at 8.30am; B400 including transfer to pier). Ko Jum bungalows send longtails out to meet the ferries as they make two stops off the west coast: coming from Krabi, stop one is for the northern "*Ko Pu*" bungalows (on Ao Ting Rai and Ao Luboa), and the second, "Ko Jum", stop is for bungalows on *Ao Si, Golden Pearl* and *Long Beach*. Coming from Krabi town, you need to take a blue

Laem Kruat on the mainland, and a beachfront school. It's about 1km from the village to the southern end of the island's most popular beach, the appropriately named **Long Beach**. Long Beach is connected to **Golden Pearl Beach**, which sits just south of **Ban Ting Rai**, the middle-island village that's about halfway down the west coast. North of Ban Ting Rai, a trio of smaller, increasingly remote beaches at **Ao Si**, **Ao Ting Rai**, and **Ao Luboa** completes the picture. The island's third village, **Ban Ko Pu**, occupies the northeastern tip, about 5km beyond Ban Ting Rai, and has another Laem Kruat ferry pier. Many islanders refer to the north of the island, from Ban Ting Rai upwards, as Ko Pu, and define only the south as Ko Jum. Much of the north is made inaccessible by the breastbone of forested hills, whose highest peak (422m) is Khao Ko Pu.

Very high winds and heavy seas mean that Ko Jum becomes an acquired taste from May through October, so nearly all accommodation and restaurants **close** for that period: the few exceptions are highlighted in the text.

Long Beach and Golden Pearl Beach

LONG BEACH (sometimes known as **Andaman Beach**) is the main backpackers' beach and is indeed long – at around 2.5km – with large chunks of the shoreline still uncultivated, backed by trees and wilderness, and well beyond sight of the island road. From *New Bungalow* towards the southern end it's a twenty-minute walk into Ban Ko Jum village.

7

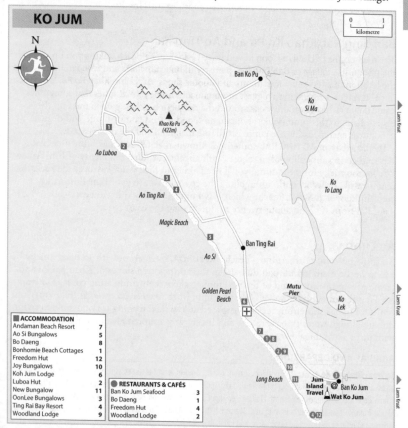

KO JUM

N

0   1
kilometre

Ban Ko Pu

Ko Si Ma

Khao Ko Pu (422m)

Ao Luboa

Laem Kruat

Ko To Lang

Ao Ting Rai

Magic Beach

Ban Ting Rai

Ao Si

Mutu Pier

Golden Pearl Beach

Ko Lek

Laem Kruat

Long Beach

Jum Island Travel

Ban Ko Jum

Wat Ko Jum

Laem Kruat

■ ACCOMMODATION	
Andaman Beach Resort	7
Ao Si Bungalows	5
Bo Daeng	8
Bonhomie Beach Cottages	1
Freedom Hut	12
Joy Bungalows	10
Koh Jum Lodge	6
Luboa Hut	2
New Bungalow	11
OonLee Bungalows	3
Ting Rai Bay Resort	4
Woodland Lodge	9

● RESTAURANTS & CAFÉS	
Ban Ko Jum Seafood	3
Bo Daeng	1
Freedom Hut	4
Woodland Lodge	2

sometimes a long wait, though there's always the option of buying up extra seats or chartering the whole car if you're in a hurry. They are a quick way of getting around and you should get dropped off at the door of your journey's end.

By minibus Inexorably, share-taxis are being replaced by a/c minibuses, which run on almost exactly the same principles at similar prices; on these you'll be more comfortable, with a seat to yourself, and most of the various ranks publish a rough timetable – though the minibuses also tend to leave as soon as they're full.

Brief history

The central area of the Malay peninsula first entered Thai history when it came under the sway of Sukhothai, probably around the beginning of the fourteenth century. Islam was introduced to the area by the end of that century, by which time Ayutthaya was taking a firmer grip on the peninsula. **Songkhla** and **Pattani** then rose to be the major cities, prospering on the goods passed through the two ports across the peninsula to avoid the pirates in the Straits of Malacca between Malaysia and Sumatra. More closely tied to the Muslim Malay states to the south, the Sultanate of Pattani began to **rebel** against the power of Ayutthaya in the sixteenth century, but the fight for self-determination only weakened Pattani's strength. The town's last rebellious fling was in 1902, after which it was definitively and brutally absorbed into the Thai kingdom, while its allies, Kedah, Kelantan and Trengganu, were transferred into the suzerainty of the British in Malaysia.

During World War II the **Communist Party of Malaya** made its home in the jungle around the Thai border to fight the occupying Japanese. After the war they turned their

Highlights

❶ **Ko Hai** A variety of good resorts for all budgets and gorgeous views of the karst islands to the east, especially at sunset. **See p.702**

❷ **Tham Morakhot** Ko Mook's Emerald Cave, with its inland beach of powdery sand at the base of an awesome natural chimney, is best visited by kayak or chartered longtail boat. **See p.704**

❸ **Ko Kradan** Remote island with a long, white, east-facing strand, crystal-clear waters, a reef for snorkellers to explore and a few diverse resorts. See **p.705**

❹ **Ko Sukorn** For a glimpse of how islanders live and a friendly, laidback ambience. **See p.707**

❺ **Ko Tarutao** Huge national park island with mangroves, limestone caves and jungle tracks to investigate, and the most unspoilt beaches in the area along its 26km west coast. **See p.708**

❻ **Hat Pattaya** Though far from undiscovered, Ko Lipe's main beach is a beautiful crescent of white sand as fine as flour that squeaks as you walk along it. **See p.711**

HIGHLIGHTS ARE MARKED ON THE MAP ON P.696

The deep south

The frontier between Thailand and Malaysia carves across the peninsula six degrees north of the equator, but the cultures of the two countries shade into each other much further north. According to official divisions, the southern Thais – the Thai Pak Tai – begin around Chumphon, and as you move further down the peninsula into Thailand's deep south you'll see ever more sarongs, yashmaks and towering mosques, and hear with increasing frequency a staccato dialect that baffles many Thais. Here too, you'll come across caged singing doves outside many houses, as well as strange-looking areas spiked with tall metal poles, on which the cages are hung during regular cooing competitions; and you'll spot huge, hump-backed Brahma bulls on the back of pick-up trucks, on their way to bullfights (in the Thai version, beast is pitted against beast, and the first to back off is the loser).

In Trang and Phatthalung provinces, the Muslim population is generally accepted as being Thai, but the inhabitants of the southernmost provinces – Satun, Pattani, Yala, Narathiwat and most of Songkhla – are ethnically more akin to the Malays: most of the 1.5 million followers of Islam here speak a dialect of Malay and write Yawi, an old modification of Arabic script to reflect Malay pronunciation. To add to the ethnic confusion, the region has a large urban population of Chinese, whose comparative wealth makes them stand out sharply from the Muslim farmers and fishermen.

The touristic interest in the deep south is currently all over on the beautiful **west coast**, where sheer limestone outcrops, pristine sands and fish-laden coral stretch down to the Malaysian border. Along Trang's **mainland coast**, there's a 30km stretch of attractive beaches, dotted with mangroves and impressive caves that can be explored by sea canoe, but the real draw down here is the offshore **islands**, which offer gorgeous panoramas and beaches, great snorkelling and at least a modicum of comfort in their small clusters of resorts. An added attraction is the recently introduced, scheduled boat services which have set up the intriguing possibility of **island-hopping**: it would now be possible to work your way down from Phuket as far as Penang without setting foot on the peninsula. The spread of tourism outwards from Phuket has been inching its way south down this coast for some time, but for now, apart from the tiny, remote but overcrowded honeypot of Ko Lipe, the islands remain largely undeveloped.

ARRIVAL AND GETTING AROUND   THE DEEP SOUTH

As well as the usual bus services, the area covered in this chapter is served by **flights** and **trains** to Trang (see p.698), as well as by **boats** between the islands (see p.702) and from the mainland to the islands.

By share-taxi The deep south has traditionally been the territory of share-taxis, which connect certain towns for

about twice the fare of ordinary buses. The cars leave when they're full, which usually means six passengers, and

The deep south

KO LIPE

Ban Chao Mai

At the south end of Hat Yao is **BAN CHAO MAI** (also called **Ban Hat Yao**), a straggle of houses on stilts, which exists on fishing, especially for crabs. From the harbour, boats run regularly across to Ko Libong, and this is the mainland ferry stop on Tigerline's Lanta–Lipe route. Also on offer are trips by longtail and canoe through the mangroves to the nearby cave of **Tham Chao Mai**, which shelters impressively huge rock pillars and a natural theatre, its stage framed by rock curtains – contact Bang Wit (☎087 463 7628), who speaks English, or ask around in the village for him.

ARRIVAL AND GETTING AROUND — THE TRANG COAST

Air-conditioned **minibuses**, departing roughly hourly but leaving early if already full, run from the bus station in Trang to Pak Meng (45min), as well as via Hat Yao to Ban Chao Mai (1hr), but if you want to explore the whole coastline, you'll need to rent a **motorbike** or **car** in Trang (see p.699).

ACCOMMODATION AND EATING

PAK MENG

Lay Trang Resort ☎075 274027–8, ⒲laytrang .com. The nicest place to stay and eat at Pak Meng, a stone's throw from the pier at the far north end of the beach. Ranged around a large, peaceful garden with lawns and orchids set back from the beach, its bright concrete chalets with huge bathrooms and smart brick rooms come with verandas, hot showers, a/c and TV. Its welcoming, reasonably priced restaurant is nationally famous for its seafood, including *nam prik kung siap* (dried shrimp relish) and *kaeng som* soup with sea bass. B1200

HAT CHANG LANG

★**Anantara Si Kao** ☎075 205888, ⒲anantara.com. The finest luxury hotel in the province, where the low-rise blocks of stylish bedrooms and pool suites, all with large balconies, are set behind a line of casuarina trees. Facilities encompass a beautiful, large pool, Italian and international restaurants, a kids' club, a fitness centre and a spa. Watersports on offer include diving, kayaking and sailing, and there's plenty of other activities, notably cooking and Thai-language lessons and some interesting local tours. The hotel also has its own beach club and restaurant on the main strand on Ko Kradan (see p.705), reached by daily boat transfer. Breakfast included. B5700

HAT CHAO MAI NATIONAL PARK HQ

National park bungalows ⒲dnp.go.th. Fan-cooled, en-suite bungalows and rooms, most with refrigerators, for two to six people, set under the casuarinas at the back of the sandy beach, and a simple café. B800

8

The Trang and Satun islands

Generally blessed with blinding white beaches, great coral and amazing marine life, the islands off the coast of Trang and Satun provinces have managed, mostly with just a handful of resorts on each, to cling onto some of that illusory desert-island atmosphere which better-known places like Phuket and Samui lost long ago. Indeed, islands such as **Ko Hai** and **Ko Kradan** support no permanent settlements other than the bungalow concerns, while on **Ko Tarutao** and **Ko Adang** in the far south, the peace and quiet is maintained by the national parks department; at the other end of the scale, however, nearby **Ko Lipe** is developing at its own merry pace and now boasts over forty resorts, as well as a substantial *chao ley* village (see p.602).

Accommodation on the islands, much of which is mid-priced, is now often fully booked at the very busiest times. Most of the resorts open year-round, though in practice many can't be reached out of season (roughly June–Oct) due to treacherous seas. It's sensible to get in touch ahead of time to check whether the resort you're interested in is open or has vacancies, and in many cases to arrange transfers from Trang; a few of the resorts maintain offices or have agents in Trang town to make this easier.

ISLAND-HOPPING AND TOURS

Access to the Trang and Satun islands from their nearest mainland ports is described in the individual island accounts, but what sets this area apart are the enticing opportunities for **island-hopping**, thanks to regular boat services in the tourist season between Ko Lanta and Ko Lipe, or even between Phuket and Langkawi in Malaysia, which can be booked through any travel agent in the area. (Several companies on Ko Lanta that organize day-trips by speedboat to Ko Hai, Ko Mook and Ko Kradan will drop you off at any of the islands, but the cost will be about the same as with Bundhaya Speedboat, Satun Pakbara Speedboat Club and Tigerline detailed below.) If you just fancy a day exploring some of the islands, any travel agent in Trang can book you on a **boat trip** (roughly mid-Oct to mid-May only) to Ko Kradan for snorkelling, the Emerald Cave on Ko Mook, and other small nearby islands for snorkelling, for around B750/person including packed lunch and soft drinks (excluding the B200 national park fee).

Bundhaya Speedboat ☎074 750248–9, ⓦbundhayaresort.com. Speedboats between Lanta and Lipe (1 daily; about 4hr; B1900) via Ko Hai, Hat Farang on Ko Mook and Ko Bulon Lae. Onward, same-day connections to Langkawi, and to Ko Phi Phi and Phuket.

Satun Pakbara Speedboat Club ☎099 404 0409, ⓦtarutaolipeisland.com. Speedboats between Lanta and Lipe (1 daily; about 4hr; B1900) via Ko Hai, Hat Farang on Ko Mook, Ko Kradan and Ko Bulon Lae. Onward, same-day connections between Lipe and Langkawi, and between Lanta and Ko Phi Phi and Phuket.

Tigerline ☎081 092 8800, ⓦtigerlinetravel.com. Ferries between Phuket and Langkawi (1 daily; about 9hr), via Ko Phi Phi, Ko Lanta, Ko Hai, Hat Farang on Ko Mook (with longtail transfers to Ko Kradan), Ban Chao Mai on the mainland (usually with a change of boat) and Ko Lipe. Hai–Lipe, for example, costs B1600.

Ko Hai (Ko Ngai)

KO HAI (also known as **KO NGAI**), 16km southwest of Pak Meng, is the most developed of the Trang islands, though it's still decidedly low-key and much quieter than Ko Lipe down in Satun. The island's action, such as it is, centres on the east coast, where half a dozen resorts enjoy a dreamy panorama of jagged limestone outcrops, whose crags glow pink and blue against the setting sun, stretching across the sea to the mainland behind. The gently sloping beach of fine, white sand here runs unbroken for over 2km (though at low tide, swimming is not so good at the northern end, which is scattered with dead coral), and there's some good snorkelling in the shallow, clear water off the island's southeastern tip.

ARRIVAL AND DEPARTURE   KO HAI

If you're planning to **fly** into Trang or Krabi airports, contact your resort in advance about transfers. There are also plenty of island-hopping options (see above). Hat Chao Mai National Park maintains a booth at Pak Meng pier, where visitors to Ko Hai will usually be charged B200 entrance fee; hang on to your ticket as this should also cover you if you take a trip to Ko Mook's Emerald Cave.

By ferry The resorts on Ko Hai's east coast currently rely on ferries owned by *Koh Ngai Villa* and *Fantasea* resorts to transfer their guests from Pak Meng (45min–1hr); longtail boats come out to meet the ferries and shuttle passengers to the various resorts up and down the beach. Both ferries depart at around 11.30am; *Villa*'s is the cheaper of the two,

charging B350 from Pak Meng, or B450 including a/c minibus from its office in Trang town (see map, p.698).

By chartered longtail If you miss the ferries, you can charter a longtail boat for around B1300, for example through *Coco Cottage* (see below).

ACCOMMODATION

★Coco Cottage Towards the northern end of the beach ☎087 898 6522, ⓦcoco-cottage.com. Charming, helpful and family-friendly resort in a grassy palm grove,

where most of the chic, thatched, a/c wooden bungalows (both detached and semi-detached) sport verandas and well-designed bathrooms, with outdoor bamboo hot

KO HAI ACTIVITIES

You can rent **snorkelling equipment** and **kayaks** at most of the resorts. All the resorts offer **boat trips** (B1800/boat, maximum six people, at *Ko Hai Seafood*, for example) that take in the Emerald Cave on Ko Mook, nearby islands such as Ko Cheuak and Ko Waen and some snorkelling off Ko Hai.

Towards the southern end of the beach, *Fantasy Resort* has a well-organized **dive shop**, the German-run Rainbow Divers, which specializes in small-group trips and PADI courses (☎075 206962, ⊛rainbow-diver.com; Nov–April).

showers, wooden basins and indoor toilets. Also has a stylish beach bar and a very good restaurant that serves creative Thai food, Thai desserts and espresso coffees. Breakfast included. B3000

Ko Hai Seafood Near the centre of the beach, north of Koh Ngai Villa ☎095 014 1853. Large, well-built, thatched, woven-bamboo bungalows with wall fans, mosquito screens and cold-water bathrooms, in a single row facing the beach across a nice lawn. B1200

Koh Ngai Villa Near the centre of the main beach ☎085 224 8702, ⊛kohngaivilla.com; Trang office opposite the station ☎075 210496. Friendly, old-style beach resort with plenty of space. Simple, well-organized, thatched bamboo bungalows boast verandas, mosquito nets and small toilets, or you could opt for a large room with two double beds in a concrete longhouse or a smart concrete bungalow with a/c, or even a two-person tent (B200, including bedding). Fan B900, a/c B1800

Mayalay Beach Near the centre of the main beach, south of Koh Ngai Villa ☎083 590 7523, ⊛mayalay beachresort.com. Welcoming place with nineteen deluxe, a/c, woven-bamboo bungalows with thatched roofs, day

beds, fridges and capacious hot-water bathrooms. Often open all year round. Breakfast included. B3500

Thanya South end of the beach ☎075 206967, ⊛kohngaithanyaresort.com. A large, very attractive beachside swimming pool with jacuzzis, set on a spacious lawn, is the main draw here. As well as a/c, hot water and fridges, the villas feature verandas, big French windows and lots of polished teak, while the restaurant has a varied menu of Thai food, including some interesting seafood dishes. Breakfast included. B3675

Thapwarin Resort Towards the northern end of the main beach, north of Coco Cottage ☎081 894 3585, ⊛thapwarin.com. Welcoming, shady resort, where you can choose between well-appointed bamboo and rattan cottages with semi-outdoor bathrooms, and large, very smart, beachfront wooden bungalows; all are thatched and have a/c, mini-bars and hot showers (more expensive stilted villas, with bedrooms upstairs and living area downstairs, are also planned). There's a massage spa, beach bar and good restaurant, serving Thai and Western food, including seafood barbecues in the evening. Breakfast included. B3600

Ko Mook

KO MOOK, about 8km southeast of Ko Hai, supports a comparatively busy fishing village on its eastern side, around which – apart from the sandbar that runs out to the very pricey *Sivalai Resort* – most of the beaches are disappointing, reduced to dirty mud flats when the tide goes out. However, across on the island's west coast lies beautiful **Hat Farang**, with gently shelving white sand, crystal-clear water that's good for swimming and snorkelling, and gorgeous sunsets.

Tham Morakhot

Part of Hat Chao Mai National Park • Open mid-Nov to mid-May • B200 admission fee if the park rangers are around

The island's main source of renown is **Tham Morakhot**, the stunning "Emerald Cave" north of Hat Farang on the west coast, which can only be visited by boat, but shouldn't be missed. An 80m swim through the cave – 10m or so of which is in pitch darkness – brings you to a *hong* (see p.648) with an **inland beach** of powdery sand open to the sky, at the base of a spectacular natural chimney whose walls are coated with dripping vegetation. Chartering your own longtail from the boatmen's co-operative on Hat Farang (B800/boat, maximum four people; the boatman will swim with you to guide you through the cave) is preferable to taking one of the big day-trip boats that originate on Lanta or Pak Meng: if you time it right, you'll get the inland beach all to yourself, an experience not to be forgotten. (The boatmen also offer combined trips to Tham

Morakhot, Ko Kradan and Ko Cheuak for B2500/boat.) It's also easy enough to **kayak** there from Hat Farang (from B100/hr from *Sawaddee*), and at low tide you can paddle right through to the inland beach: buoys mark the cave entrance, from where a tunnel heads straight back into the rock; about halfway along, there's a small, right-hand kink in the tunnel which will plunge you briefly into darkness, but you should soon be able to see light ahead from the *hong*. Mid-afternoon is often a good time to paddle off on this trip, after the tour boats have left and providing the tide is right.

ARRIVAL AND DEPARTURE   KO MOOK

In addition to the services mentioned below, there are plenty of island-hopping options (see p.702).

To Hat Farang By far the easiest and quickest way to get to Hat Farang is to book a minibus-and-boat package through a travel agent in Trang (2 daily), which costs B350, including a 30min longtail ride direct to the beach.
To the village Travel agents in Trang also offer a minibus-and-boat package to the village on the east side (B300).

This makes use of the daily public boat at around 11.30am/noon to the village from Kuantunku pier, 8km south of Pak Meng, between Hat Chang Lang and Hat Yong Ling, which often takes a long time to load. (From the village, it's a 30min walk or B50–100 motorbike-taxi ride over to Hat Farang.)

ACCOMMODATION

Most of Hat Farang is unfortunately occupied by the disappointing *Charlie's Resort*, leaving room for only one other resort, *Sawaddee*. However, *Rubber Tree* and *Had Farang* make the best of the attractive, shady slopes behind the beach, while *Ko Mook Riviera Beach Resort* is away on the east side of the island near the village.

Had Farang Bungalows ☎087 884 4785, ⓦfacebook .com/hadfarang. The eighteen bungalows and rooms at this friendly place are mostly basic bamboo and wood affairs, but nearly all are en suite with their own verandas and the restaurant is very good. Also has a few tents with double beds (B400). Fan **B600**, a/c **B1700**
Ko Mook Riviera Beach Resort ☎087 885 7815, ⓦriviera-resorts.com. On the south-facing shore of the sandbar that ends at *Sivalai Resort*, the bright, concrete bungalows at this sustainable, eco-friendly resort all have mosquito-screened French windows directly facing the sea, as well as a/c, satellite TV and DVD player. Bicycles, kayaks and trips to the Emerald Cave and neighbouring islands available. Breakfast and dinner included. **B3800**

Rubber Tree ☎081 606 9358, ⓦmookrubbertree .com. On a well-tended, landscaped slope that's also a working rubber plantation, this friendly resort offers basic thatched fan bungalows with cold-water bathrooms and crisp, white linen, or spacious, smartly designed a/c versions with rubber-wood furniture and hot showers, as well as a good restaurant. Occasionally puts together overnight camping trips to Ko Rok. Breakfast included. Fan **B800**, a/c **B1990**
Sawaddee ☎081 508 0432, ⓔsawaddeeresort64 @yahoo.com; or contact Wunderbar in Trang (see p.700). Laidback, old-style, stilted wooden and concrete bungalows with mosquito nets parallel to the beach, with refurbished en-suite bathrooms, plenty of shade and largely uninterrupted sea views. High season only. **B800**

Ko Kradan

About 6km to the southwest of Ko Mook, **KO KRADAN** is the remotest of the inhabited islands off Trang, and one of the most beautiful, with crystal-clear waters. On this slender, 4km-long triangle of thick jungle, the **main beach** is a long strand of steeply sloping, powdery sand on the east coast, with fine views of Ko Mook, Ko Libong and the karst-strewn mainland, and an offshore reef to the north with a great variety of hard coral; such beauty, however, has not escaped the attention of the day-trip boats from Ko Lanta, who turn the beach into a lunchtime picnic ground most days in high season. From a short way north of the *Anantara* beach club (see p.701), which is located towards the south end of this beach, a path across the island will bring you after about fifteen minutes to **Sunset Beach**, another lovely stretch of fine, white sand in a cove; a branch off this path at *Paradise Lost* leads to a beach on the short south coast, which enjoys good reef snorkelling (also about 15min from the *Anantara* beach club).

ARRIVAL AND DEPARTURE
KO KRADAN

By minibus-and-longtail transfer Agencies such as Trang Island Hopping Tour (see p.699) can arrange minibus-and-longtail transfers from Trang town, via Kuantunku pier (twice daily in season; B450). There are also plenty of island-hopping options (see p.702).

ACCOMMODATION

Kalume ☎093 650 0841, ☜kalumekradan.com. Eco-friendly Italian-run resort on the beach next to *Seven Seas*, with small, basic, thatched bamboo huts with mosquito nets, fans and en-suite bathrooms and smart, large, wooden bungalows with French windows and nice verandas. Good Italian food at the bar-restaurant. **B1500**

Paradise Lost ☎089 587 2409; for further information, go to ☜kokradan.wordpress.com. In the middle of the island, roughly halfway along the path to *Sunset Beach*, is Kradan's best-value accommodation, run by an American and his dogs. Set in a grassy, palm-shaded grove, it offers simple, clean, thatched rattan bungalows with mosquito nets, fans and shared bathrooms or larger, en-suite, wooden affairs (some with hot showers), kayaks, snorkels and good Thai and Western food. **B700**

Seven Seas ☎075 203389–90, ☜sevenseasresorts.com. By far the best of several resorts on the east coast, *Seven Seas* adds a surprising splash of contemporary luxury to this remote spot. Behind a small, black, infinity-edge pool, the large bungalows and rooms with outdoor warm-water bathrooms are stylishly done out in greys and whites, and sport a/c, fridges, TVs and DVD players. There's a spa and a dive shop, and breakfast is included. **B8400**

Ko Libong

The largest of the Trang islands with a population of six thousand, **KO LIBONG** lies 10km southeast of Ko Mook, opposite Ban Chao Mai on the mainland. Less visited than its northern neighbours, it's known mostly for its wildlife, although it has its fair share of golden beaches too. Libong is one of the most significant remaining refuges in Thailand of the **dugong**, a large marine mammal similar to the manatee, which feeds on sea grasses growing on the sea floor – the sea-grass meadow around Libong is reckoned to be the largest in Southeast Asia. Sadly, dugongs are now an endangered species, traditionally hunted for their blubber (used as fuel) and meat, and increasingly affected by fishing practices such as scooping, and by coastal pollution, which destroys their source of food. The dugong has now been adopted as one of fifteen "reserved animals" of Thailand and is the official mascot of Trang province.

Libong is also well known for its migratory **birds**, which stop off here on their way south from Siberia, drawn by the island's food-rich mud flats (now protected by the Libong Archipelago Sanctuary, which covers the eastern third of the island). For those seriously interested in ornithology, the best time to come is during March and April, when you can expect to see brown-winged kingfishers, masked finfoots and even the rare black-necked stork, not seen elsewhere on the Thai–Malay peninsula.

The island's handful of resorts occupies a long, thin strip of golden sand at the fishing village of **Ban Lan Khao** on the southwestern coast. At low tide here, the sea retreats for hundreds of metres, exposing rock pools that are great for splashing about in but not so good for a dip.

ARRIVAL AND DEPARTURE
KO LIBONG

By public longtail Public longtails depart daily year-round from Ban Chao Mai (see p.701) when full (most frequent in the morning and around lunchtime; B40/person), arriving 20min later at Ban Phrao on Ko Libong's

---

KO LIBONG ACTIVITIES

Libong Beach Resort runs **boat trips** to see the dugongs for B1000 per boat. To this you can add on a visit to the bird sanctuary (B1200 in total), plus a cruise around the island (B1500 in total). The resorts can also organize trips to the Emerald Cave on Ko Mook. For **diving**, ask at *Libong Beach Resort*: Yat, a dive master who works on Ko Hai, can usually arrange trips from his home island of Libong.

north side. From here motorbike taxis (B100) transport you to Ban Lan Khao.

By private transfer You can arrange a direct boat transfer from Ban Chao Mai through *Libong Beach Resort* for B900/boat.

ACCOMMODATION

Libong Beach Resort ☎075 225205, ⓦlibong beachresort.com. Friendly resort on the north side of Ban Lan Khao with a wide variety of accommodation set amid lawns and flowers, ranging from small, en-suite concrete and wood bungalows at the back to spacious, bright, stilted, wooden cabins with a/c and nice decks on the beachfront (B2500). Kayak and motorbike rental are available. Fan B700, a/c B1000

Libong Relax Beach Resort ☎091 825 4886,

ⓦlibongrelax.com. Located on an attractive stretch of the beach, all of the bungalows here face directly onto the sea across a narrow, tree-lined lawn and sport some attractive Thai decorative touches. The "Pavilions" have Thai-style roofs, picture windows and large verandas, while the "Cottages" are more functional with smaller verandas; upgrading to a/c also snags you a hot shower. There's a massage hut and the resort can arrange island tours on a motorcycle with a sidecar. Fan B1200, a/c B2000

Ko Sukorn

A good way south of the other Trang islands, low-lying **KO SUKORN** lacks the white-sand beaches and beautiful coral of its neighbours, but makes up for it with its friendly inhabitants and laidback ambience; for a glimpse of how islanders live and work, this is a good place to come.

The lush interior is mainly given over to rubber plantations, interspersed with rice paddies, banana and coconut palms; the island also produces famously delicious watermelons, which are plentiful in March and April. Hat Talo Yai, the main **beach** – 500m of gently shelving brown sand, backed by coconut palms – runs along the southwestern shore.

8

ARRIVAL AND DEPARTURE
KO SUKORN

Transfers from Trang A songthaew-and-boat transfer to Ko Sukorn (B300/person), via the public ferry from Laem Ta Sae, can be arranged through any travel agent in Trang, leaving daily at 11.30am and taking about two and a half hours, or you can arrange a private transfer through the

resorts for about B2000 all-in.

Inter-island transfers *Yataa Island Resort* can organize pricey longtail-boat transfers to or from any of the nearby islands.

ACCOMMODATION

Ko Sukorn Cabana ☎089 724 2326, ⓦsukorncabana .com. This friendly and peaceful place offers stilted, a/c bungalows with attractive bathrooms and large, well-appointed log cabins on a secluded beach to the north of Hat Talo Yai. Kayaks and motorbikes are also available. Breakfast included. B1500

Yataa Island Resort (Sukorn Beach Bungalows) ☎089 647 5550, ⓦsukorn-island-trang.com. Low-key,

quiet resort under new management, where the attractively decorated bungalows and rooms – all a/c and with en-suite hot showers – are set around a lush garden dotted with deckchairs and umbrellas, and there's a small swimming pool and a good restaurant. At the resort, you can also get a good massage, and you're free to paddle around in kayaks. Breakfast included. B1350

KO SUKORN BOAT TRIPS AND OTHER ACTIVITIES

Boat excursions arranged through the resorts include trips out to the islands of Ko Lao Liang and Ko Takieng, which are part of the Mu Ko Phetra National Marine Park, for some excellent snorkelling. These run nearly every day from November to May; at other times of year, the sea is sometimes calm enough but you're usually restricted to fishing trips – and to looking round the island itself, which, at thirty square kilometres, is a good size for exploring. Yataa Island Resort has a handy map that marks all the sights, including the three villages and seafood market, and offers motorbikes (B250/half-day) and mountain bikes (B150/half-day) for rent.

KO LAO LIANG

The beautiful twin islets of **Ko Lao Liang**, with their white-sand beaches, abundant corals and dramatic rock faces, lie to the west of Ko Sukorn. They're deserted apart from a single adventure-sport camp, *Lao Liang Resort* (ⓦ laoliangresort.com; open Nov to April; B1500). All-in costs at the resort comprise camping in deluxe tents on the beach, three meals, including seafood barbecues, and snorkelling gear; kayak rental, rock-climbing, bouldering and snorkelling tours are extra. The resort offers transfers from Trang for B1600 per person return.

Ko Bulon Lae

The scenery at tiny **KO BULON LAE**, 20km west of Pak Bara in Satun province, isn't as beautiful as that generally found in Ko Tarutao National Park just to the south, but it's not at all bad: a 2km strip of fine white sand runs the length of the casuarina-lined east coast, where the two main resorts can be found (open roughly from Nov to April or mid-May), while *chao ley* fishermen make their ramshackle homes in the tight coves of the rest of the island. A reef of curiously shaped hard coral closely parallels the eastern beach, while **White Rock** to the south of the island has beautifully coloured soft coral and equally dazzling fish.

ARRIVAL AND DEPARTURE   KO BULON LAE

From/to Pak Bara Boats for Ko Bulon Lae currently leave Pak Bara (see box below) daily at about 12.30pm (about 1hr; B450). As there's no pier on Bulon Lae, boat arrivals are met by longtails to transfer visitors to shore (B50). Boats return from Bulon Lae to Pak Bara at around 9.30am. There are also island-hopping options (see p.702).

ACCOMMODATION

Bulone ⓣ 081 897 9084 or ⓣ 086 960 0468, ⓦ bulone -resort.net. Friendly, very popular spot in a huge grassy compound under the casuarinas at the north end of the main beach. Airy, en-suite bungalows on stilts come with large verandas and most have a/c, while the restaurant features plenty of vegetarian options and a small selection of tasty Italian favourites. Breakfast included. B3000

Pansand ⓣ 081 693 3667, ⓦ pansand-resort.com; Trang office at First Andaman Travel on Thanon Wisetkul. The oldest and largest resort on the island, on the east-coast beach, where large, smart, peaceful cottages come with verandas, fans, mosquito screens, cold-water bathrooms and plenty of room to breathe. On the beach side of the shady, well-tended grounds, there's a sociable restaurant serving up good seafood and other Thai dishes; boat trips and snorkelling gear are also available. Breakfast included. B1600

Ko Tarutao National Marine Park

B200 admission fee • ⓦ dnp.go.th

The unspoilt **KO TARUTAO NATIONAL MARINE PARK** is probably the most beautiful of all Thailand's accessible beach destinations. Occupying 1400 square kilometres of the Andaman Sea in Satun province, the park covers 51 mostly uninhabited islands. Site of the park headquarters, the main island, **Ko Tarutao**, offers a variety of government-issue accommodation and things to do, while **Ko Adang** to the west is much more low-key and a springboard to some excellent snorkelling. The port of **Pak Bara** (see box below)

TRANSPORT TO AND FROM PAK BARA

The main port for Bulon Lae, Tarutao and Lipe is **PAK BARA**, towards the north end of Satun province. **From Trang**, you can book minibus-and-boat packages to all three islands and there are direct share-taxis to Pak Bara (see p.699); otherwise you'll need to take a Satun-bound bus (2hr–2hr 30min) to the inland town of **Langu** (also served by buses from Phuket via Krabi to Satun) and change there to a red songthaew for the 10km hop to the port. There are also direct a/c minibuses **from Hat Yai** (see p.716), while **from Satun**, frequent buses and a/c minibuses make the 50km trip to Langu, where you'll have to change onto a songthaew.

8

is the main jumping-off point for the park, and houses a **national park visitor centre** (☎074 783485), next to the pier, where you can gather information and book a room on Tarutao or Adang before boarding your boat.

The park's forests and seas support an incredible variety of **fauna**: langurs, crab-eating macaques and wild pigs are common on the islands, which also shelter several unique subspecies of squirrel, tree shrew and lesser mouse deer; among the hundred-plus bird species found here, reef egrets and hornbills are regularly seen, while white-bellied sea eagles, frigate birds and pied imperial pigeons are more rarely encountered; and the park is the habitat of about 25 percent of the world's tropical fish species, as well as dugongs, sperm whales, dolphins and a dwindling population of turtles.

The park amenities on Adang, though not on Tarutao, are officially closed to tourists in the monsoon season from mid-May to mid-November (the exact dates vary from year to year). Accommodation is especially likely to get full around the three New Years (Thai, Chinese and Western), when it's best to book national park rooms in advance (see p.37).

Ko Tarutao

The largest of the national park's islands, **KO TARUTAO** offers the greatest natural variety: mountains covered in semi-evergreen rainforest rise steeply to a high point of 700m; limestone caves and mangrove swamps dot the shoreline; and the west coast is lined with perfect beaches for most of its 26km length. For a different perspective on Ko Tarutao, John Gray's Sea Canoe in Phuket runs multi-day **sea-kayaking** trips that include trips round the island (☎076 254505–6, ⓦjohngray-seacanoe.com).

The west coast

At **Ao Pante**, site of the **park headquarters**, you'll find the only shop on the island, selling basic supplies, as well as a visitor centre. Behind the settlement, the steep, half-hour climb to **To-Boo cliff** is a must, especially at sunset, for the view of the surrounding islands and the crocodile's-head cape at the north end of the bay. A fun ninety-minute trip by boat (B400/boat; contact the visitor centre to book) or kayak can also be made near Ao Pante, up the canal which leads 2km inland from the pier, through a bird-filled mangrove swamp, to **Crocodile Cave** – where you're unlikely to see any of the big snappers, reported sightings being highly dubious.

A half-hour walk south from Ao Pante brings you to the two quiet bays of **Ao Jak** and **Ao Molae**, fringed by coconut palms and filled with fine white sand. Beyond the next headland (a 2hr walk from Ao Pante) lies **Ao Sone** (which gets its name from the

KO TARUTAO
NATIONAL MARINE PARK

casuarina trees that fringe the beach), where a pretty freshwater stream runs past the ranger station at the north end of the bay, a good place for peaceful camping. The main part of the bay is a 3km sweep of flawless sand, with a one-hour trail leading up to **Lu Du Waterfall** at the north end, a ninety-minute trail to **Lo Po Waterfall** in the middle and a **mangrove swamp** at the far south end.

The east coast

On the east side of the island, **Ao Taloh Wow** is a rocky bay with a ranger station, shop and campsite, connected to Ao Pante by a 12km-long road through old rubber plantations and evergreen forest. Beyond Taloh Wow, a 16km-long trail cuts through the forest to **Ao Taloh Udang**, a sandy bay on the south side where you can pitch a tent. Here the remnants of a penal colony for political prisoners are just visible: the royalist plotters of two failed coup attempts against the recently established constitutional regime – including the author of the first English-Thai dictionary – were imprisoned here in the 1930s before returning to high government posts. The ordinary convicts, who used to be imprisoned here and at Ao Taloh Wow, had a much harsher time, and during World War II, when supplies from the mainland dried up, prisoners and guards ganged together to turn to piracy. This turned into a lucrative business, which was not suppressed until 1946 when the Thai government asked the British in Malaysia to send in three hundred troops. Pirates and smugglers still occasionally hide out in the Tarutao archipelago, but the main problem now is illegal trawlers fishing in national park waters.

8

ARRIVAL AND DEPARTURE

KO TARUTAO

From Pak Bara and Ko Lipe The speedboat services between Pak Bara and Ko Lipe (see p.712) will usually call in at Ko Tarutao if requested; Tarutao is about 30min from Pak Bara (B400) and 1hr from Lipe (B500). Boats drop passengers off at Ao Pante on Tarutao; the pier at Ao Pante is sometimes inaccessible at low tide, when longtails (B30) shuttle people to shore.

GETTING AROUND

By truck The visitor centre can arrange transport by road, usually in an open truck, to several of the island's beaches, charging B50/person one-way to Ao Molae, around B400 per vehicle to Ao Sone and B600 per vehicle to Ao Taloh Wow.

By boat Transfers to the same places by boat cost at least twice as much, though you may be tempted by a round-island boat trip for B3000.

By kayak or mountain bike Kayaks and mountain bikes are available at headquarters.

ACCOMMODATION

National park accommodation At park headquarters, the rooms and bungalows (sleeping four people, or available as twin rooms), which are spread over a large, quiet park behind the beach, are for the main part national park standard issue with cold-water bathrooms, but there are also some basic mattress-on-floor four-person rooms in longhouses, sharing bathrooms, as well as a restaurant. There are also bungalows containing en-suite twin rooms and a small restaurant at Ao Molae. HQ B500, Ao Molae B600

Camping There are campsites at Ao Pante, Ao Molae and Ao Taloh Wow. Two-person tents can be rented from Ao Pante for B150/night (plus B50/person for bedding).

Ko Adang

At **KO ADANG**, a wild, rugged island covered in tropical rainforest 40km west of Ko Tarutao, the park station with its accommodation and restaurant is at **Laem Sone** on the southern shore, where the beach is steep and narrow and backed by a thick canopy

SNORKELLING TRIPS AROUND KO ADANG

You can charter **longtail boats** (and rent snorkels and masks, for B50/day) through the rangers for excellent snorkelling trips to nearby islands such as Ko Rawi and Ko Jabang (around B1500–2500 for up to ten people, depending on how far you want to go).

of pines. The half-hour climb to **Sha-do** cliff on the steep slope above Laem Sone gives good views over Ko Lipe to the south, while about 2km west along the coast from the park station, a twenty-minute trail leads inland to the small **Pirate Waterfall**.

ARRIVAL AND DEPARTURE　　　　　　　　　　　　　　　　　　　KO ADANG

By boat To get to Ko Adang, take any boat to Ko Lipe (see p.712), from where a longtail transfer to Adang will cost　B100–200/person.

ACCOMMODATION

National park accommodation At the park station at Laem Sone, there are rooms in bamboo longhouses sleeping three, bungalows of various sizes (2–6 people), and two/three-person tents can be rented (B225/night plus B50/person for bedding). Rooms **B300**, bungalows **B600**

Ko Lipe

Home to a population of around a thousand *chao ley*, tiny **KO LIPE**, 2km south of Ko Adang, is something of a frontier maverick, attracting ever more travellers with one dazzling beach, over fifty private bungalow resorts and a rough-and-ready atmosphere. It's technically a part of Ko Tarutao National Marine Park, but the authorities seem to have given up on the island and don't collect an admission fee from visitors. A small, flat triangle, Lipe is covered in coconut plantations and supports a school and a health centre in the village on the eastern side. By rights, such a settlement should never have been allowed to develop within the national park boundaries, but the *chao ley* on Lipe are well entrenched: Satun's governor forced the community to move here from Phuket and Ko Lanta between the world wars, to reinforce the island's Thai character and prevent the British rulers of Malaya from laying claim to it.

More recently, a huge, diverse influx of tourists – Westerners, Thais, Chinese and Malaysians, families and backpackers – has been enticed here by the gorgeous beach of **Hat Pattaya**, a shining crescent of squeaky-soft white sand with an offshore reef to explore on its eastern side, as well as by the relaxed, anything-goes atmosphere and mellow nightlife. Many of Lipe's *chao ley* have now sold their beachfront land to Thai–Chinese speculators from the mainland, who have increased the island's capacity to over two thousand guest rooms; with the money earned, the *chao ley* have bought the scores of longtail boats that clog up the bay at Hat Pattaya. Lipe's main drag is

8

KO LIPE

● RESTAURANTS & CAFÉS			
Café Lipe	7	Jack's Jungle Resort	2
Daya	5	Pattaya Song	6
Elephant	4	Pooh's	3
Flour Power Bakery	1	Roti Mina	8

■ ACCOMMODATION			
Blue Tribes	11	Mali Resort	4
Cafe Lipe	9	Pattaya Song	8
Castaway	10	Pooh's	5
Daya	6	Porn	1
Idyllic	12	Seaside	7
Koh Lipe Backpackers	3	Varin Village	2

■ BAR	
Navy Club	1

SNORKELLING AND DIVING AROUND KO LIPE

The prime **diving and snorkelling sites** near Ko Lipe are around Ko Adang, Ko Rawi and Ko Dong, just to the north and west in Ko Tarutao National Marine Park, where encounters with reef and even whale sharks, dolphins and stingrays are not uncommon. Further afield to the south, advanced divers head for Eight Mile Rock, a pinnacle that rises to about 14m from the surface, with soft corals, mantas, leopard and whale sharks. A handful of dive shops operate on Lipe, and there are dozens of places offering snorkelling day-trips on *chao ley* longtail boats; snorkellers are liable to pay the park admission fee of B200, though some longtail captains will try to dodge the park rangers.

Koh Lipe Thailand See below. This travel agent offers snorkelling day-trips to the best sites around the islands on the west side of Ko Adang for B550–650/person, including lunch and full snorkelling equipment, or a sunset trip for B450.

Lotus Dive At Pooh's on Walking Street between Sunrise and Hat Pattaya ☎074 750345, ⊛lotusdive .com. Well-regarded dive shop which offers daily trips (B2800 for two dives) and PADI courses (B13,400 for the Openwater). Also does snorkelling trips (B650) and equipment rental (B100/day including fins).

Sabye Sports On the east side of Porn Resort, behind Flour Power Bakery, on Sunset beach ☎089 464 5884, ⊛sabyesports.com. Canadian-run dive shop, Lipe's oldest, which offers daily trips (B3000, including equipment rental, for two dives) and PADI courses (B12,900 for the Openwater). Also offers snorkelling (B2000) and kayaking (B2500) trips and snorkelling equipment rental (B150/day including fins), as well as stand-up paddle-board and wind-surfer rental and accommodation for divers.

8

Walking Street, a paved path lined with tourist businesses between the eastern end of Hat Pattaya and the south end of the village, which lies on east-facing **Sunrise,** an exposed, largely featureless beach that gives access to some good snorkelling around Ko Gra; a few other narrow roads also radiate out from the village. A track runs from *Pattaya Song Resort* at the west end of Pattaya across to **Sunset** beach, a shady, attractive spot with good views of Ko Adang, in around ten minutes.

ARRIVAL AND DEPARTURE
KO LIPE

As well as being one of the hubs for island-hopping boats (see p.702), Ko Lipe is served by **speedboats** from Pak Bara in the north of Satun province and from the Malaysian island of Langkawi. However, services to Lipe seem to change by the year, due to competition between the boat companies and local politicking; in the past, there have been boats from Thammalang near Satun town (see p.714), which may or may not resurface; for up-to-date **transport information**, contact Koh Lipe Thailand (see below). There is no pier on Lipe, so boats usually anchor at a platform off Hat Pattaya, where they're met by **longtails** (B50–100/person to any beach on Lipe); sometimes speedboats will just run ashore at Pattaya, leaving you to jump off onto the beach; in low season, all boats tend to stop at Sunrise Beach, where there's shelter from the southwest monsoon, leaving you with a longtail trip to any of the beaches.

Via Pak Bara Several companies run speedboats (plus occasional ferries) between Pak Bara (see box, p.708) and Ko Lipe in high season (usually at 11.30am & 3.30pm; 1hr 30min; B650). In the rainy season, there's at least one crossing a day, usually heading out at 11.30am.

Via Langkawi Boats operate between Ko Lipe and Langkawi, the large Malaysian island to the southeast, several times a day in high season (1hr; B1000–1400). During the season, a Thai immigration post is set up at the far east end of Lipe's Hat Pattaya to cover this route.

INFORMATION

Koh Lipe Thailand The best travel agent and source of information on the island is Koh Lipe Thailand (Boi's Travel; ☎089 464 5854 or ☎081 541 4489, ⊛kohlipe thailand.com or ⊛thaibeachtravellers.com), which currently has two outlets on Walking Street between Hat Pattaya and the village, with the main, year-round one

hard by the beach (the second, seasonal, shop, further inland towards *Pooh's*, has a book exchange). On offer are all manner of transport tickets (including a/c minibuses in high season to Penang and other popular mainland destinations) plus accommodation bookings (including on the websites).

Currency exchange There are currently no ATMs on Ko Lipe (the nearest is in Pak Bara), but Koh Lipe Thailand, for instance, offers currency exchange and cash advances.

Tourist police Behind the immigration post at the far east end of Hat Pattaya ☎ 1155.

ACCOMMODATION

The majority of Lipe's bungalows are on **Hat Pattaya**, the prettiest but most crowded and expensive beach on the island. *Porn Resort* has **Sunset** beach on the northwest side to itself, while twenty or so resorts have set up shop on **Sunrise**, on the east side near the village. If you turn up on the island and are struggling to find a vacant room, head for one of the Koh Lipe Thailand offices on Walking Street for booking assistance (see opposite).

Blue Tribes East end of Hat Pattaya ☎ 080 546 9464, ⓦ bluetribeslipe.com. Congenial, Italian-run resort and restaurant with very spacious, well-spread and well-designed bungalows and rooms, either in lovely dark wood or in thatched white concrete, sporting large, attractive tiled bathrooms with hot showers, fans, mosquito nets and large verandas; some are two-storey with a balcony and chill-out room/extra bedroom upstairs. Closed mid-May to July. B1700

Café Lipe West of Walking Street, central Pattaya ☎ 086 969 9472, ⓦ cafe-lipe.com. Eco-conscious, solar-powered place in a great location, offering large, old-style bamboo bungalows that are nicely spaced out under a thick canopy of teak and fruit trees. Each has a partly outdoor, cold-water bathroom, fan and mosquito net. Three-night minimum stay. B700

★**Castaway** Sunrise ☎ 083 138 7472, ⓦ castaway -resorts.com. Airy, thatched, mostly two-storey bungalows featuring well-equipped bathrooms with cold rain showers, ceiling fans, big decks, hammocks and a certain amount of style, mostly bestowed by the distinctive red Indonesian hardwood that they're made from. On a sandy patch with a dive shop, a mellow, multi-tiered bar-restaurant and a massage spa; kayaks and snorkels for rent. B3400

Daya West end of Hat Pattaya ☎ 081 542 9866, ⓔ amonrut2010@hotmail.com. *Chao ley*-owned resort with more than thirty colourful, en-suite rooms and bungalows in a large, shady, flower-strewn garden, ranging from simple concrete rooms to clapboard bungalows in a great position on the beach. Kayaks and snorkels available. B600

Idyllic South end of Sunrise ☎ 074 750399, ⓦ idyllicresort.com. This welcoming "concept resort" comes as a big surprise out here in Thailand's far maritime corner, with its angular contemporary architecture in white, grey and wood. Set in an attractive garden, the minimalist rooms boast huge windows, a/c, hot outdoor rain showers, mini-bars and nice touches such as sun hats for guests' use. There are two pools – one infinity-edged and beachside, with a swim-up bar, the other with a jacuzzi – as well as kayaks and other watersports. Breakfast included. B6150

Koh Lipe Backpackers Just east of Daya ⓦ kohlipebackpackers.com. Part of Davy Jones' Locker diving centre, this place offers two eight-bed dorms in plain concrete rooms with thick mattresses, hot showers and lockers, as well as plain, a/c and pricey double bedrooms with en-suite hot-water bathrooms. Dorms B500, doubles B4000

Mali Resort Towards the west end of Hat Pattaya ☎ 077 033020, ⓦ maliresorts.com. At this shady, well-appointed luxury resort, go for one of the Balinese bungalows if you can (from B6800), thatched, dark-wood affairs with big French windows, sizeable verandas and open-air bathrooms, which are spread out around a lovely lawn and beach bar. Breakfast included. B3800

Pattaya Song Far west end of Hat Pattaya ☎ 086 960 0418, ⓦ pattayasongresort.com. Rough-and-ready Italian-run resort, the oldest on the beach (the name means "Pattaya no. 2"), where plain, en-suite clapboard or concrete bungalows are strung out away from the beach (the cheapest, with small bathrooms) or in a lovely location up on a steep promontory with great views of the bay; kayaks for rent. B500

Pooh's On Walking Street between Sunrise and Hat Pattaya ☎ 074 750345, ⓦ poohlipe.com. Well inland behind the popular restaurant, but a good, functional choice if you get stuck for somewhere to stay. The eight concrete single-storey rooms have small terraces, a/c, hot showers and TVs, and there's a dive centre. Breakfast included. B1800

Porn Resort Sunset ☎ 084 691 8743. Popular, attractive and well-run spot in a pleasant, spacious, sloping setting under the trees on the beach. Wood or bamboo bungalows come with verandas, mosquito nets and en-suite bathrooms. Snorkelling equipment for rent. B500

Seaside Near the midpoint of Hat Pattaya ☎ 087 398 7932. Good-value, *chao ley*-owned resort, offering basic but sturdy woven-bamboo bungalows with large bathrooms and mosquito nets, in plenty of space on a grassy patch and mostly under shade, behind the popular *Family* restaurant. B600

Varin Village In the centre of Sunrise Beach ☎ 085 079 9145. No-frills, thatched bamboo bungalows with fans, mosquito nets and en-suite, cold-water bathrooms. Set in rows, they're well spaced out though on a scrappy stretch of lawn with little shade. B600

8

EATING AND DRINKING

There are a couple of beach bars on Sunset, but the east end of Pattaya has the biggest concentration, with low candlelit tables and cushions sprawled on the sand, fire shows and names like *Peace and Love*.

Café Lipe West of Walking Street, central Pattaya (see p.713). Behind a thick screen of foliage this resort restaurant serves up decent veggie choices among its inexpensive Thai dishes, sandwiches and espressos, as well as home-made bread, fruit juices and muesli. Daily 7am–5pm.

Daya West end of Hat Pattaya (see p.713). One of the most popular of half a dozen restaurants that lay out candlelit tables and seafood barbecues on the beach at night. It also offers a long menu of mostly Thai dishes, such as prawn tempura (B120), lots of tofu options for vegetarians, Thai desserts and Western breakfasts. Daily 7am–11pm.

Elephant Walking Street, 100m inland from Pattaya ☏ 088 046 8234. Mellow restaurant and secondhand bookshop, where you can tuck into delicious chicken sandwiches (B180) and burgers made with Australian beef, as well as salads, breakfasts and espressos. Daily 8am–8pm.

★Flour Power Bakery Sunset. At shady, beachfront tables, you can feast on delicious home-made brownies, croissants (B60), baguettes and blueberry pie as well as sandwiches (from B120), spaghetti and Thai dishes including vegetarian options. There are also wines by the glass, cocktails, water refills from their cooler and rental kayaks if you want to burn off the calories. Daily roughly 7am–8pm.

Jack's Jungle Resort About 400m south of Flour Power, on the paved track from Sunset towards the village and Sunrise. It's well worth the walk out to this appealing wooden deck set among trees, for some very tasty Thai food in huge portions and spiced to order, such as chicken *matsaman* curry with rice (B170). Also does wine by the glass, pasta and a few other simple Western dishes. Daily 8am–9.30pm (last orders).

Navy Club Far east end of Hat Pattaya. On the edge of the navy base, this friendly, jerry-built bar and shop with a few wooden benches is the best spot for a quiet, cheap, ice-cold beer watching the sun set. Daily 6/7am till midnight or later, depending on who's in.

Pattaya Song Far west end of Hat Pattaya (see p.713). At tables on the sand here, tuck into very tasty gnocchi bolognese (B240) and other home-made pasta, Thai-style seafood and, in the evenings, authentic pizzas (from B180) and home-baked bruschetta. Daily roughly 8am–10pm.

Pooh's On Walking Street between Sunrise and Hat Pattaya (see p.713). This well-run and welcoming bar-restaurant-bakery is a long-standing institution and a popular hive of activity, with nightly movies. Offers tasty Thai food, including chicken with cashew nuts (B150) and vegetarian dishes, as well as sandwiches, cakes, evening barbecues, DJs and live music, plus a wide choice of breakfasts and espresso coffees. Daily roughly 8.30am–10.45pm.

Roti Mina Walking Street, about 50m inland from Hat Pattaya on the right-hand side ☏ 081 397 7018. Serves all manner of outlandish roti pancakes – raisin and cheese roti, anyone? – as well as the more familiar roti with curry (B100) and banana roti. Also does some classic southern and central Thai dishes. Daily 7am–10pm.

Satun town

Nestling in the last wedge of Thailand's west coast, the remote town of **SATUN** is served by just one road,

Highway 406, which approaches through forbidding karst outcrops. Set in a green valley bordered by limestone hills, the town is leafy and relaxing but not especially interesting, except during its small version of the Vegetarian Festival (see p.623) and its International Kite Festival at the end of February. There's little reason to come here apart from the boat service to and from Langkawi in Malaysia.

National Museum

Soi 5, Thanon Satun Thani, on the north side of the centre • Wed–Sun 9am–4pm • B30

If you find yourself with time on your hands in Satun, it's worth seeking out the **National Museum**. It's memorable, as much as anything else, for its setting, in the graceful **Kuden Mansion**, which was built in British colonial style, with some Thai and Malay features, by craftsmen from Penang, and inaugurated in 1902 as the Satun governor's official residence. The exhibits and audiovisuals in English have a distinctive anthropological tone, but are diverting enough, notably concerning Thai Muslims, the *chao ley* on Ko Lipe, and the **Sakai**, a dwindling band of nomadic hunter-gatherers who still live in the jungle of southern Thailand.

ARRIVAL AND DEPARTURE

SATUN TOWN

By bus Satun's bus station is far to the southeast of the centre on the bypass, but Trang buses usually do a tour of the town centre, stopping, for example, near *On's* on Thanon Bureewanit; incoming buses from Phuket via Krabi, Trang and Langu will set you down on Thanon Satun Thani by the *Wangmai* hotel; and you can book long-distance tickets in advance at the central Baw Khaw Saw office on Thanon Hatthakam Sueksa (for the long journey to

Bangkok, it's worth shelling out a bit extra for the VIP buses that depart around 3–4pm).
Destinations Bangkok (4 daily; 16hr); Phuket (4 daily; 8hr); Trang (hourly; 2hr 30min–3hr).
By minibus A/c minibuses to Langu congregate on Thanon Sulakanukul.
By ferry There are ferries from nearby Thammalang pier to Langkawi in Malaysia (see box below).

GETTING AROUND

By motorbike or car On Kongnual (see below) offers motorbike (B250–300/day) and car rental (B1000–

1500/day).

INFORMATION

On Kongnual 36 Thanon Bureewanit ☎074 724133 or ☎081 097 9783, ✉onmarch13@hotmail.com. From her restaurant, *On's: The Kitchen*, On Kongnual dispenses

helpful tourist information and sells all kinds of transport tickets.

ACCOMMODATION

On's Guest House 36 Thanon Bureewanit ☎074 724133 or ☎081 097 9783, ✉onmarch13@hotmail .com. A variety of rooms in an attractive, modern, Sino-Portuguese-style building above *On's: The Kitchen* restaurant with wooden shutters and coloured-glass

windows. There's a fan-cooled dorm but most have a/c, fridges and satellite TV; bathrooms with hot showers are shared but plentiful. Dorms B250, doubles B450
Rian Thong 4 Thanon Saman Pradit ☎074 711036. Just on the west side of the centre, this is a basic but fairly

8

CROSSING INTO MALAYSIA FROM SATUN

Two or three ferry boats a day cross from Thammalang to the Malaysian island of **Langkawi** (☎074 725294, ⊕langkawi-ferry.com; 1hr 15min; B300). The journey from Satun town to Thammalang is covered by orange songthaews (roughly every 30min; B40) from near the 7-Eleven supermarket on Thanon Sulakanukul, as well as chartered tuk-tuks (B150) and motorcycle taxis (B60–70).

It's also possible to take an a/c minibus to Malaysia's **Kangar** (which has bus connections to Penang and Kuala Lumpur) through Thale Ban National Park (B400; 1 daily in the morning; about 2hr) – contact local fixer On (see above) to book tickets.

decent budget hotel with friendly owners, where some of the large, en-suite rooms with TVs overlook the canal. Fan B240, a/c B350

Satunthanee Hotel Thanon Satun Thani ☎074 711010. This centrally placed, good-value, traditional Chinese hotel offers battered but clean rooms with small bathrooms and TVs, though it suffers from noise from the road and the mosque. Fan B300, a/c B400

Sinkiat Buri Hotel 50 Thanon Apainuratrumluk ☎074 721055–8, ⓦ sinkiathotel.com. The new top hotel in Satun, offering large bedrooms in a minimalist style with lots of dark wood, a/c, rain showers, fridges, flat-screen TVs and good views over the surrounding countryside from the upper floors. Breakfast included. B1400

EATING AND DRINKING

Satun has a slim choice of restaurants, but for a meal in the evening you can't do much better than the lively and popular night market, north of the centre on the west side of Thanon Satun Thani.

Go Ho Thanon Saman Pradit, opposite the Chinese temple ☎074 711018. A cheap, busy, friendly restaurant with leafy pavement tables that serves tasty Thai and Chinese food, including plenty of seafood (according to market price), salads and southern specialities such as *kaeng som* (B120). Mon–Sat 3pm–midnight.

On's: The Kitchen 36 Thanon Bureewanit ☎074 724133 or ☎081 097 9783. Very tasty Thai food, including southern specialities, some interesting fish dishes and handy set menus, such as green curry with prawn patties (*thawt man kung*) and rice for B120. Also offers a wide array of Western food, including good breakfasts, jacket potatoes, pies and espresso coffees. (On's bar, a couple of doors away, *The Living Room*, stays open late, depending on customers.) Daily 8am–10pm.

Hat Yai

8

Travelling to or through **HAT YAI**, the biggest city in the region, is currently **not recommended** because of the troubles in the south (see p.697). To be honest, you're not missing much, but as it's a major transport axis, we've provided a few rudimentary practicalities and a map of the city, in case you get stuck there. The three main Niphat Uthit roads are known locally as *sai neung*, *sai sawng* and *sai saam*.

ARRIVAL AND DEPARTURE   HAT YAI

Travel agency The helpful Cathay Tour (☎074 235044, ⓦ cathaytourthailand.com), a travel agency on the ground floor of the guesthouse of the same name (see opposite), handles onward flight, bus, share-taxi, a/c minibus and ferry bookings, both within Thailand and into Malaysia, as well as offering car and motorbike rental.

By plane About 5km south of town, Hat Yai airport is connected to the downtown area by a/c minibuses (B80) and has Avis (☎02 251 1131, ⓦ avisthailand .com) and Budget (☎074 227268, ⓦ budget.co.th) car rental desks.

By train The train station is on the west side of the centre at the end of Thanon Thamnoon Vithi.

By bus or minibus The bus terminal is southeast of the centre on Thanon Kanchanawanit, while the a/c minibus terminal at Talat Kaset is about 5km west of town, both leaving you with a songthaew ride to the centre.

INFORMATION

Tourist information The TAT office is at 1/1 Soi 2, Thanon Niphat Uthit 3 (daily 8.30am–4.30pm; ☎074 243747, ✉tatsgkhl@tat.or.th).

Tourist police Thanon Niphat Uthit 3, near the TAT office ☎074 246733 or ☎1155.

ACCOMMODATION

Cathay Guest House 93/1 Thanon Niphat Uthit 2 ☎074 243815. This friendly place in the heart of town has long been Hat Yai's main travellers' hub, and the café acts as a sociable meeting place; the rooms have fans and en-suite cold-water bathrooms but are rather run-down. B240

Centara Hotel 3 Thanon Sanehanusorn ☎074 352222, ⓦcentarahotelsresorts.com. Luxury hotel in a good location next to the Central Department Store, featuring contemporary-styled rooms with a spa, fitness centre, sauna, swimming pool and Thai, Chinese and Japanese food at its several restaurants. B1500

Lee Gardens Plaza Hotel 29 Thanon Prachatipat ☎074 261111, ⓦleeplaza.com. Characterless but good-value and central upmarket option with great views of the city from its four hundred comfortable a/c rooms. Facilities include a fitness centre, a rooftop pool and a 33rd-floor panoramic restaurant. Breakfast included. B1350

8

MEDITATING BUDDHA, WAT YAI SUWANNARAM, PHETCHABURI

Contexts

History

As long as forty thousand years ago, Thailand was inhabited by hunter-gatherers who lived in semi-permanent settlements and used tools made of wood, bamboo and stone. By the end of the last Ice Age, around ten thousand years ago, these groups had become farmers, keeping chickens, pigs and cattle, and – as evidenced by the seeds and plant husks which have been discovered in caves in northern Thailand – cultivating rice and beans. This drift into an agricultural society gave rise to further technological developments: the earliest pottery found in Thailand has been dated to 6800 BC, while the recent excavations at Ban Chiang in the northeast have shown that bronze was being worked at least as early as 2000 BC. By two thousand years ago, the peoples of Southeast Asia had settled in small villages, among which there was regular communication and trade, but they had split into several broad families, differentiated by language and culture. At this time, the ancestors of the Thais, speaking proto-Thai languages, were still far away in southern China, whereas Thailand itself was inhabited by Austroasiatic speakers, among whom the Mon were to establish the region's first distinctive civilization, Dvaravati.

Dvaravati and Srivijaya

The history of **Dvaravati** is ill-defined to say the least, but the name is applied to a distinctive culture complex which shared the **Mon** language and **Theravada Buddhism**. This form of religion may have entered Thailand during the third century BC, when the Indian emperor, Ashoka, is said to have sent missionaries to Suvarnabhumi, "land of gold", which seems to correspond roughly to mainland Southeast Asia.

From the discovery of monastery boundary stones (*sema*), clay votive tablets and Indian-influenced Buddhist sculpture, it's clear that Dvaravati was an extensive and prosperous Buddhist civilization that had its greatest flourishing between the sixth and ninth centuries AD. No strong evidence has turned up, however, for the existence of a single capital – rather than an empire, Dvaravati seems to have been a collection of city-states. Nakhon Pathom, Lopburi, Si Thep and Muang Sema were among the most important Dvaravati sites, and their concentration around the Chao Phraya valley would seem to show that they gained much of their prosperity, and maintained religious and cultural contacts with India, via the **trade route** from the Indian Ocean over the Three Pagodas Pass.

Although they passed on aspects of their heavily Indianized art, religion and government to later rulers of Thailand, these Mon city-states were politically fragile and from the ninth century onwards succumbed to the domination of the invading Khmers

6800 BC	**3rd century BC**	**6th–9th centuries AD**
Date of earliest pottery found in Thailand	Theravada Buddhism probably first enters Thailand	Dvaravati civilization flourishes

from Cambodia. One northern outpost, the state of **Haripunjaya**, centred on Lamphun, which had been set up on the trade route with southern China, maintained its independence until the thirteenth century.

Meanwhile, to the south of Dvaravati, the shadowy Indianized state of Lankasuka had grown up in the second century, centred on Ligor (now Nakhon Si Thammarat) and covering an area of the Malay peninsula which included the important trade crossings at Chaiya and Trang. In the eighth century, it came under the control of **Srivijaya**, a Mahayana Buddhist city-state on Sumatra, which had strong ties with India and a complex but uneasy relationship with neighbouring Java. Thriving on seaborne trade between Persia and China, Srivijaya extended its influence as far north as Chaiya, its regional capital, where discoveries of temple remains and some of the finest stone and bronze statues ever produced in Thailand have borne witness to the cultural vitality of this crossroads empire. In the tenth century the northern part of Lankasuka, under the name **Tambralinga**, regained a measure of independence, although it seems still to have come under the influence of Srivijaya as well as owing some form of allegiance to Dvaravati. By the beginning of the eleventh century, however, peninsular Thailand had come under the sway of the Khmer empire, with a Cambodian prince ruling over a community of Khmer settlers and soldiers at Tambralinga.

The Khmers

The history of central Southeast Asia comes into sharper focus with the emergence of the **Khmers**, vigorous empire-builders whose political history can be pieced together from the numerous stone inscriptions they left. The Khmers of **Chenla** – to the north of Cambodia – seized power in the latter half of the sixth century during a period of economic decline in the area. Chenla's rise to power was knocked back by a punitive expedition conducted by the Srivijaya empire in the eighth century, but was reconsolidated during the watershed reign of **Jayavarman II** (802–50), who succeeded in conquering the whole of Kambuja, an area which roughly corresponds to modern-day Cambodia. In order to establish the authority of his monarchy and of his country, Jayavarman II had himself initiated as a *chakravartin*, or universal ruler, the living embodiment of the **devaraja**, the divine essence of kingship – a concept which was adopted by later Thai rulers. Taking as the symbol of his authority the phallic lingam, the king was thus identified with the god Shiva, although the Khmer concept of kingship and thus the religious mix of the state as a whole was not confined to Hinduism: elements of ancestor worship were also included, and Mahayana Buddhism gradually increased its hold over the next four centuries.

It was Jayavarman II who moved the Khmer capital to **Angkor** in northern Cambodia, which he and later kings, especially after the eleventh century, embellished with a series of prodigiously beautiful temples. Jayavarman II also recognized the advantages of the lakes around Angkor for irrigating rice fields and providing fish, and thus for feeding a large population. His successors developed this idea and gave the state a sound economic core with a remarkably complex system of **reservoirs** (*baray*) and water channels, which were copied and adapted in later Thai cities.

In the ninth and tenth centuries, Jayavarman II and his imperialistic successors, especially **Yasovarman I** (889–900), confirmed Angkor as the major power in Southeast

8th century	802–50	Late 9th century
Srivijaya gains sway over southern Thailand	Reign of Khmer king Jayavarman II, founder of Angkor	Khmers begin to push into Thailand

Asia. They pushed into Vietnam, Laos and southern China, as well as into northeastern Thailand, where the Khmers left dozens of Angkor-style temple complexes, as seen today at Prasat Phanom Rung and Prasat Hin Phimai. To the west and northwest, Angkor took control over central Thailand, with its most important outpost at Lopburi, and even established a strong presence to the south on the Malay peninsula. As a result of this expansion, the Khmers were masters of the most important trade routes between India and China, and indeed nearly every communications link in the region, from which they were able to derive huge income and strength.

The reign of **Jayavarman VII** (1181–1219), a Mahayana Buddhist who firmly believed in his royal destiny as a *bodhisattva*, sowed the seeds of Angkor's downfall. Nearly half of all the surviving great religious monuments of the empire were erected under his supervision, but the ambitious scale of these building projects and the upkeep they demanded – some 300,000 priests and temple servants of 20,000 shrines consumed 38,000 tonnes of rice per year – along with a series of wars against Vietnam, exhausted the economy.

In subsequent reigns, much of the life-giving irrigation system around Angkor turned into malarial swamp through neglect, and the rise of the more democratic creed of Theravada Buddhism undermined the divine authority which the Khmer kings had derived from the hierarchical Mahayana creed. As a result of all these factors, the Khmers were in no position to resist the onslaught between the thirteenth and fifteenth centuries of the vibrant new force in Southeast Asia, the Thais.

The earliest Thais

The earliest traceable history of the **Thai people** picks them up in southern China around the fifth century AD, when they were squeezed by Chinese and Vietnamese expansionism into sparsely inhabited northeastern Laos and neighbouring areas. The first entry of a significant number of Thais onto what is now Thailand's soil seems to have happened in the region of Chiang Saen, where it appears that some time after the seventh century the Thais formed a state in an area then known as **Yonok**. A development which can be more accurately dated and which had immense cultural significance was the spread of Theravada Buddhism to Yonok via Dvaravati around the end of the tenth century, which served not only to unify the Thais but also to link them to Mon civilization and give them a sense of belonging to the community of Buddhists.

The Thais' political development was also assisted by **Nan-chao**, a well-organized military state comprising a huge variety of ethnic groups, which established itself as a major player on the southern fringes of the Chinese empire from the beginning of the eighth century. As far as can be gathered, Nan-chao permitted the rise of Thai *muang* or small principalities on its periphery, especially in the area immediately to the south known as **Sipsong Panna**.

Thai infiltration continued until, by the end of the twelfth century, they seem to have formed the majority of the population in Thailand, then under the control of the Khmer empire. The Khmers' main outpost, at Lopburi, was by then regarded as the administrative capital of a land called "Syam" (possibly from the Sanskrit *syam*, meaning swarthy) – a mid-twelfth-century bas-relief at Angkor Wat, portraying the troops of Lopburi preceded by a large group of self-confident Syam Kuk mercenaries, shows that the Thais were becoming a force to be reckoned with.

Mid-12th century	1181–1219	1238
Bas-relief at Angkor Wat depicting Thai mercenaries, a new force to be reckoned with in the region	Reign of Jayavarman VII, perhaps the greatest and certainly the most ambitious of the Khmer kings	The Thais seize the Khmer outpost of Sukhothai

Sukhothai

By the middle of the thirteenth century, the Thais, thanks largely to the decline of Angkor and the inspiring effect of Theravada Buddhism, were poised on the verge of autonomous power. The final catalyst was the invasion by Qubilai Khan's Mongol armies of China and Nan-chao, which began around 1215 and was completed in the 1250s. Demanding that the whole world should acknowledge the primacy of the Great Khan, the Mongols set their hearts on the "pacification" of the "barbarians" to the south of China, which obliged the Thais to form a broad powerbase to meet the threat.

The founding of the first Thai kingdom at **Sukhothai**, now popularly viewed as the cornerstone of the country's development, was in fact a small-scale piece of opportunism which almost fell at the first hurdle. At some time around 1238, the princes of two small Thai principalities in the upper Chao Phraya valley joined forces to capture the main Khmer outpost in the region at Sukhothai. One of the princes, **Intradit**, was crowned king, but for the first forty years Sukhothai remained merely a local power, whose existence was threatened by the ambitions of neighbouring princes. When attacked by the ruler of Mae Sot, Intradit's army was only saved by the grand entrance of Sukhothai's most dynamic leader: the king's 19-year-old son, Rama, held his ground and pushed forward to defeat the opposing commander, earning himself the name **Ramkhamhaeng**, "Rama the Bold".

When Ramkhamhaeng came to the throne around 1278, he saw the south as his most promising avenue for expansion and, copying the formidable military organization of the Mongols, established control over much of the Chao Phraya valley. Over the next twenty years, largely by diplomacy rather than military action, Ramkhamhaeng gained the submission of most of modern-day Thailand; local rulers entered into a complex system of tribute-giving and protection – the political system that persisted in Thailand until the end of the nineteenth century – either through the pressure of the Sukhothai king's personal connections or out of recognition of his superior military strength and moral prestige. To the east, Ramkhamhaeng extended his sphere of influence as far as Vientiane in Laos; by marrying his daughter to a Mon ruler to the west, he obtained the allegiance of parts of southern Burma; and to the south his vassals stretched down the peninsula at least as far as Nakhon Si Thammarat. To the north, Sukhothai concluded an alliance with the parallel Thai states of Lanna and Phayao in 1287 for mutual protection against the Mongols – though it appears that Ramkhamhaeng managed to pinch several *muang* on their eastern periphery as tribute states.

Meanwhile **Lopburi**, which had wrested itself free from Angkor some time in the middle of the thirteenth century, was able to keep its independence and its control of the eastern side of the Chao Phraya valley. Having been first a major cultural and religious centre for the Mon, then the Khmers' provincial capital, and now a state dominated by migrating Thais, Lopburi was a strong and vibrant place mixing the best of the three cultures, as evidenced by the numerous original works of art produced at this time.

Although Sukhothai extended Thai influence over a vast area, its greatest contribution to the Thais' development was at home, in cultural and political matters. A famous **inscription** by Ramkhamhaeng, now housed in the Bangkok National Museum, describes a prosperous era of benevolent rule: "In the time of King Ramkhamhaeng

1278	1281	1287
Ramkhamhaeng "the Bold" comes to the throne of Sukhothai	With the conquest of the Dvaravati outpost of Haripunjaya, King Mengrai unifies the north as the Thai state of Lanna	Alliance between the Thai states of Sukhothai, Lanna and Phayao

this land of Sukhothai is thriving. There is fish in the water and rice in the fields … [The King] has hung a bell in the opening of the gate over there: if any commoner has a grievance which sickens his belly and gripes his heart … he goes and strikes the bell … [and King Ramkhamhaeng] questions the man, examines the case, and decides it justly for him." Although this plainly smacks of self-promotion, it seems to contain at least a kernel of truth: in deliberate contrast to the Khmer god-kings, Ramkhamhaeng styled himself as a **dhammaraja**, a king who ruled justly according to Theravada Buddhist doctrine and made himself accessible to his people. To honour the state religion, the city's temples were lavishly endowed: as original as Sukhothai's political systems were its religious **architecture and sculpture**, which, though bound to borrow from existing Khmer and Sri Lankan styles, show the greatest leap of creativity at any stage in the history of art in Thailand. A further sign of the Thais' new self-confidence was the invention of a new **script** to make their tonal language understood by the non-Thai inhabitants of the land.

All this was achieved in a remarkably short period of time. After the death of Ramkhamhaeng around 1299, his successors took their Buddhism so seriously that they neglected affairs of state, and by 1320 Sukhothai had regressed to being a kingdom of only local significance.

Lanna

Almost simultaneous with the birth of Sukhothai was the establishment of a less momentous but longer-lasting kingdom to the north, called **Lanna**. Its founding father was **Mengrai**, chief of Ngon Yang, a small principality on the banks of the Mekong near modern-day Chiang Saen. Around 1259 he set out to unify the squabbling Thai principalities of the region, first building a strategically placed city at Chiang Rai in 1262, and then forging alliances with Ngam Muang, the Thai king of Phayao, and with Ramkhamhaeng of Sukhothai.

In 1281, after ten years of guileful preparations, Mengrai conquered the Mon kingdom of Haripunjaya based at Lamphun, and was now master of northern Thailand. Taking advice from Ngam Muang and Ramkhamhaeng, in 1292 he selected a site for an impressive new capital of Lanna at **Chiang Mai**, which remains the centre of the north to the present day. Mengrai concluded further alliances in Burma and Laos, making him strong enough to successfully resist further Mongol attacks, although he was eventually obliged to bow to the superiority of the Mongols by sending them small tributes from 1312 onwards. When Mengrai died after a sixty-year reign in 1317, supposedly struck by a bolt of lightning, he had built up an extensive and powerful kingdom. But although he began a tradition of humane, reasonable laws, probably borrowed from the Mons, he had found little time to set up sound political and administrative institutions. His death severely destabilized Lanna, which quickly shrank in size and influence.

It was only in the reign of **Ku Na** (1355–85) that Lanna's development regained momentum. A well-educated and effective ruler, Ku Na enticed the venerable monk Sumana, from Sukhothai, to establish an ascetic Sri Lankan sect in Lanna in 1369. Sumana brought a number of Buddha images with him, inspiring a new school of art that flourished for over a century, but more importantly his sect became a cultural force that had a profound unifying effect on the kingdom. The influence of Buddhism was

1299	**1317**	**1351**
With the death of Ramkhamhaeng, Sukhothai begins its decline	Mengrai dies after being struck by lightning	Ramathibodi founds Ayutthaya

further strengthened under **Tilok** (1441–87), who built many great monuments at Chiang Mai and cast huge numbers of bronze seated Buddhas in the style of the central image at Bodh Gaya in India, the scene of the Buddha's enlightenment. Tilok, however, is best remembered as a great warrior, who spent most of his reign resisting the advances of Ayutthaya, by now the strongest Thai kingdom.

Under continuing pressure both from Ayutthaya and from Burma, Lanna went into rapid decline in the second quarter of the sixteenth century. For a short period after 1546, Chiang Mai came under the control of Setthathirat, the king of Lan Sang (Laos), but, unable to cope with Lanna's warring factions, he then abdicated, purloining the talismanic Emerald Buddha for his own capital at Luang Prabang. In 1558, Burma decisively captured Chiang Mai, and the Mengrai dynasty came to an end. For most of the next two centuries, the Burmese maintained control through a succession of puppet rulers, and Lanna again became much as it had been before Mengrai, little more than a chain of competing principalities.

Ayutthaya

While Lanna was fighting for its place as a marginalized kingdom, from the fourteenth century onwards the seeds of a full-blown Thai nation were being sown to the south at **Ayutthaya**. The city of Ayutthaya itself was founded on its present site in 1351 by U Thong ("Golden Cradle") of Lopburi. Taking the title **Ramathibodi**, he soon united the principalities of the lower Chao Phraya valley, which had formed the western provinces of the Khmer empire. When he recruited his bureaucracy from the urban elite of Lopburi, Ramathibodi set the **style of government** at Ayutthaya – the elaborate etiquette, language and rituals of Angkor were adopted, and, most importantly, the conception of the ruler as *devaraja*. The king became sacred and remote, an object of awe and dread, with none of the accessibility of the kings of Sukhothai: when he processed through the town, ordinary people were forbidden to look at him and had to be silent while he passed. This hierarchical system also provided the state with much-needed manpower, as all freemen were obliged to give up six months of each year to the Crown either on public works or military service.

The site chosen by Ramathibodi turned out to be the best in the region for an international port, and so began Ayutthaya's rise to prosperity, based on its ability to exploit the upswing in **trade** in the middle of the fourteenth century along the routes between India and China. Flushed with economic success, Ramathibodi's successors were able to expand their control over the ailing states in the region. After a long period of subjugation, Sukhothai became a province of the kingdom of Ayutthaya in 1438, six years after Boromraja II had powerfully demonstrated Ayutthaya's pre-eminence by capturing the once-mighty Angkor, enslaving large numbers of its subjects and looting the Khmer royal regalia. (The Cambodian royal family were forced to abandon the palace and to found a new capital near Phnom Penh.)

Although a century of nearly continuous warfare against Lanna was less decisive, success generally bred success, and Ayutthaya's increasing wealth through trade brought ever greater power over its neighbouring states. To streamline the functioning of his unwieldy empire, **Trailok** (1448–88) found it necessary to make reforms to its administration. His **Law of Civil Hierarchy** formally entrenched the inequality of

1432	**1477**	**1511**
Ayutthaya captures and loots Angkor	The eighth world council of Theravada Buddhism is held in Chiang Mai	The first Western power, Portugal, begins trading with Ayutthaya

Ayutthayan society, defining the status of every individual by assigning him or her an imaginary number of rice fields – for example, 25 for an ordinary freeman and 10,000 for the highest ministers of state. Trailok's legacy is found in today's unofficial but fiendishly complex status system, by which everyone in Thailand knows their place.

Ramathibodi II (1491–1529), almost at a loss as to what to do with his enormous wealth, undertook an extensive programme of public works. In the 1490s he built several major religious monuments, and between 1500 and 1503 cast the largest standing metal image of the Buddha ever known, the Phra Si Sanphet, which gave its name to the temple of the royal palace. By 1540, Ayutthaya had established control over most of the area of modern-day Thailand.

Burmese wars and European trade

In the sixteenth century recurring tensions with Burma led **Chakkraphat** (1548–69) to improve his army and build brick ramparts around the capital. This was to no avail however: in 1568 the Burmese besieged Ayutthaya with a huge army, said by later accounts to have consisted of 1,400,000 men. The Thais held out until August 8, 1569, when treachery within their own ranks helped the Burmese break through the defences. The Burmese looted the city, took thousands of prisoners and installed a vassal king to keep control.

The decisive character who broke the Burmese stranglehold twenty years later and re-established Ayutthaya's economic growth was **Naresuan** (1590–1605), who defied the Burmese by amassing a large army. The enemy sent a punitive expedition, which was conclusively defeated at Nong Sarai near modern-day Suphanburi on January 18, 1593, Naresuan himself turning the battle by killing the Burmese crown prince. Historians have praised Naresuan for his personal bravery and his dynamic leadership, although the chronicles of the time record a strong streak of tyranny – in his fifteen years as king he had eighty thousand people killed, excluding the victims of war. A favoured means of punishment was to slice off pieces of the offender's flesh, which he was then made to eat in the king's presence.

The period following Naresuan's reign was characterized by a more sophisticated engagement in **foreign trade**. In 1511 the Portuguese had become the first Western power to trade with Ayutthaya, and Naresuan himself concluded a treaty with Spain in 1598; relations with Holland and England were initiated in 1608 and 1612 respectively. For most of the seventeenth century, European merchants flocked to Thailand, not only to buy Thai products, but also to gain access to Chinese and Japanese goods on sale there. The role of foreigners at Ayutthaya reached its peak under **Narai** (1656–88), but he overstepped the mark in cultivating close links with Louis XIV of France, who secretly harboured the notion of converting Ayutthaya to Christianity. On Narai's death, relations with Westerners were cut back.

Despite this reduction of trade and prolonged civil strife over the succession to the throne whenever a king died – then, as now, there wasn't a fixed principle of primogeniture – Ayutthaya continued to flourish for much of the eighteenth century. The reign of **Borommakot** (1733–58) was particularly prosperous, producing many works of drama and poetry. Furthermore, Thai Buddhism had by then achieved such prestige that Sri Lanka, from where the Thais had originally imported their form of religion in the thirteenth century, requested Thai aid in restoring their monastic orders in 1751.

1558	**1569**	**1590–1605**
The Burmese decisively capture Chiang Mai	The Burmese take Ayutthaya and install a vassal king	Reign of the warrior king Naresuan, who sends the Burmese packing

However, immediately after the death of Borommakot the rumbling in the Burmese jungle to the north began to make itself heard again. Alaunghpaya of Burma, apparently a blindly aggressive country bumpkin, first recaptured the south of his country from the Mon, and then turned his attentions to Ayutthaya. A siege in 1760 was unsuccessful, with Alaunghpaya dying of wounds sustained there, but the scene was set. In February 1766 the Burmese descended upon Ayutthaya for the last time. The Thais held out for over a year, during which they were afflicted by famine, epidemics and a terrible fire that destroyed ten thousand houses. Finally, in **April 1767**, the walls were breached and the city taken. The Burmese razed everything to the ground and tens of thousands of prisoners were led off to Burma, including most of the royal family. The king, Suriyamarin, is said to have escaped from the city in a boat and starved to death ten days later. As one observer has said, the Burmese laid waste to Ayutthaya "in such a savage manner that it is hard to imagine that they shared the same religion with the Siamese". The city was abandoned to the jungle, but with remarkable speed the Thais regrouped and established a new seat of power, further down the Chao Phraya River at Bangkok.

The early Bangkok empire

As the bulk of the Burmese army was obliged by war with China to withdraw almost immediately, Thailand was left to descend into banditry. Out of this lawless mess several centres of power arose, the most significant being at Chanthaburi, commanded by **Phraya Taksin**. A charismatic, brave and able general who had been unfairly blamed for a failed counterattack against the Burmese at Ayutthaya, Taksin had anticipated the fall of the besieged city and quietly slipped away with a force of five hundred men. In June 1767 he took control of the east-coast strip around Chanthaburi and very rapidly expanded his power across central Thailand.

Blessed with the financial backing of the Chinese trading community, to whom he was connected through his father, Taksin was crowned king in December 1768 at his new capital of Thonburi, on the opposite bank of the river from modern-day Bangkok. One by one the new king defeated his rivals, and within two years he had restored all of Ayutthaya's territories. More remarkably, by the end of the next decade Taksin had outdone his Ayutthayan predecessors by bringing Lanna, Cambodia and much of Laos under his sway. During this period of expansionism, Taksin left most of the fighting to Thong Duang, an ambitious soldier and descendant of an Ayutthayan noble family, who became the *chakri*, the military commander, and took the title **Chao Phraya Chakri**.

However, by 1779 all was not well with the king. Being an outsider, who had risen from an ordinary family on the fringes of society, Taksin became paranoid about plots against him, a delusion that drove him to imprison and torture even his wife and sons. At the same time he sank into religious excesses, demanding that the monkhood worship him as a god. By March 1782, public outrage at his sadism and dangerously irrational behaviour had reached such fervour that he was ousted in a coup.

Chao Phraya Chakri was invited to take power and had Taksin executed. In accordance with ancient etiquette, this had to be done without royal blood touching the earth: the king was duly wrapped in a black velvet sack and struck on the back of the neck with a sandalwood club. (Popular tradition has it that even this form of

1767	1768	1782–1809
Ayutthaya is razed to the ground by the Burmese	Taksin crowned king at the new capital, Thonburi	Reign of Rama I, founder of the current Chakri dynasty

execution was too much: an unfortunate substitute got the velvet sack treatment, while Taksin was whisked away to a palace in the hills near Nakhon Si Thammarat, where he is said to have lived until 1825.)

Rama I

With the support of the Ayutthayan aristocracy, Chakri – reigning as **Rama I** (1782–1809) – set about consolidating the Thai kingdom. His first act was to move the capital across the river to Bangkok, a better defensive position against any Burmese attack from the west. Borrowing from the layout of Ayutthaya, he built a new royal palace and impressive monasteries, and enshrined in the palace wat the Emerald Buddha, which he had snatched back during his campaigns in Laos.

As all the state records had disappeared in the destruction of Ayutthaya, religious and legal texts had to be written afresh and historical chronicles reconstituted – with some very sketchy guesswork. The monkhood was in such a state of crisis that it was widely held that moral decay had been partly responsible for Ayutthaya's downfall. Within a month of becoming king, Rama I issued a series of religious laws and made appointments to the leadership of the monkhood, to restore discipline and confidence after the excesses of Taksin's reign. Many works of drama and poetry had also been lost in the sacking of Ayutthaya, so Rama I set about rebuilding the Thais' literary heritage, at the same time attempting to make it more cosmopolitan and populist. His main contribution was the *Ramakien*, a dramatic version of the Indian epic *Ramayana*, which is said to have been set to verse by the king himself – with a little help from his courtiers – in 1797. Heavily adapted to its Thai setting, the *Ramakien* served as an affirmation of the new monarchy and its divine links, and has since become the national epic.

In the early part of Rama I's reign, the Burmese reopened hostilities on several occasions, the biggest attempted invasion coming in 1785, but the emphatic manner in which the Thais repulsed them only served to knit together the young kingdom. Trade with China revived, and the king addressed the besetting problem of manpower by ordering every man to be tattooed with the name of his master and his town, so that avoiding royal service became almost impossible. On a more general note, Rama I put the style of government in Thailand on a modern footing: while retaining many of the features of a *devaraja*, he shared more responsibility with his courtiers, as a first among equals.

Rama II and Rama III

The peaceful accession of his son as **Rama II** (1809–24) signalled the establishment of the **Chakri dynasty**, which is still in place today. This Second Reign was a quiet interlude, best remembered as a fertile period for Thai literature. The king, himself one of the great Thai poets, gathered round him a group of writers including the famous Sunthorn Phu, who produced scores of masterly love poems, travel accounts and narrative songs.

In contrast, **Rama III** (1824–51) actively discouraged literary development – probably in reaction against his father – and was a vigorous defender of conservative values. To this end, he embarked on an extraordinary redevelopment of Wat Pho, the oldest temple in Bangkok. Hundreds of educational inscriptions and mural paintings, on all manner of secular and religious subjects, were put on show, apparently to preserve traditional culture against the rapid change which the king saw corroding the country.

1782	1809–24	1824–51
A grandiose new capital, Bangkok, is established, modelled on Ayutthaya	The Chakri dynasty is consolidated with the reign of Rama II	Rama III's reign

In foreign affairs, Rama III faced a serious threat from the vassal states of Laos, who in 1827 sent an invading army from Vientiane, which got as far as Saraburi, only three days' march from Bangkok. The king's response was savage: having repelled the initial invasion, he ordered his army to destroy everything in Vientiane apart from Buddhist temples and to forcibly resettle huge numbers of Lao in Isaan. In 1834, the king went to war in Cambodia, in a tug of war with Vietnam for control of the land in between; after fourteen years of indecisive warfare, Cambodia lay devastated but in much the same servile position – as one Vietnamese emperor described it, "an independent country that is slave of two".

More significant in the long run was the danger posed by the increase in Western influence that began in the Third Reign. As early as 1825, the Thais were sufficiently alarmed at British colonialism to strengthen Bangkok's defences by stretching a great iron chain across the mouth of the Chao Phraya River, to which every blacksmith in the area had to donate a certain number of links. In 1826 Rama III was obliged to sign a limited trade agreement with the British, the **Burney Treaty**, by which the Thais won some political security in return for reducing their taxes on goods passing through Bangkok. British and American missions in 1850 unsuccessfully demanded more radical concessions, but by this time Rama III was seriously ill, and it was left to his far-sighted and progressive successors to reach a decisive accommodation with the Western powers.

Mongkut and Chulalongkorn

Rama IV (1851–68), commonly known to foreigners as **Mongkut** (in Thai, *Phra Chom Klao*), had been a Buddhist monk for 27 years when he succeeded his brother. But far from leading a cloistered life, Mongkut had travelled widely throughout Thailand, had maintained scholarly contacts with French and American missionaries and, like most of the country's new generation of leaders, had taken an interest in Western learning, studying English, Latin and the sciences. He had also turned his mind to the condition of Buddhism in Thailand, which seemed to him to have descended into little more than popular superstition; indeed, after a study of the Buddhist scriptures in Pali, he was horrified to find that Thai ordinations were probably invalid. So in the late 1830s he set up the rigorously fundamentalist Thammayut sect (the "Order Adhering to the Teachings of the Buddha") and as abbot of the order he oversaw the training of a generation of scholarly leaders for Thai Buddhism from his base at Bangkok's Wat Bowonniwet, which became a major centre of Western learning and is still sponsored by the royal family.

When his kingship faced its first major test, in the form of a threatening British mission in 1855 led by **Sir John Bowring**, the Governor of Hong Kong, Mongkut dealt with it confidently. Realizing that Thailand was unable to resist the military might of the British, the king reduced import and export taxes, allowed British subjects to live and own land in Thailand and granted them freedom of trade. Of the **government monopolies**, which had long been the mainstay of the Thai economy, only that on opium was retained. After making up the loss in revenue through internal taxation, Mongkut quickly made it known that he would welcome diplomatic contacts from other Western countries: within a decade, agreements similar to the Bowring Treaty

1826	**1851–68**	**1855**
The signing of the Burney Treaty, a trade agreement with Britain	Reign of Rama IV (Mongkut)	The Bowring Treaty exacts further trade concessions for the British

had been signed with France, the US and a score of other nations. Thus by skilful diplomacy the king avoided a close relationship with only one power, which could easily have led to Thailand's annexation.

While all around the colonial powers were carving up Southeast Asia among themselves, Thailand suffered nothing more than the weakening of its influence over Cambodia, which in 1863 the French brought under their protection. As a result of the open-door policy, foreign trade boomed, financing the redevelopment of Bangkok's waterfront and, for the first time, the building of paved roads. However, Mongkut ran out of time for instituting the far-reaching domestic reforms which he saw were needed to drag Thailand into the modern world.

The modernization of Thailand

Mongkut's son, **Chulalongkorn**, took the throne as Rama V (1868–1910) at the age of only 15, but he was well prepared by an education which mixed traditional Thai and modern Western elements – provided by Mrs Anna Leonowens, subject of *The King and I*. When Chulalongkorn reached his majority after a five-year regency, he set to work on the reforms envisaged by his father. One of his first acts was to scrap the custom by which subjects were required to prostrate themselves in the presence of the king, which he followed up in 1874 with a series of decrees announcing the gradual abolition of slavery. The speed of his financial and administrative reforms, however, proved too much for the "**Ancients**" (*hua boran*), the old guard of ministers and officials inherited from his father. Their opposition culminated in the Front Palace Crisis of 1875, when a show of military strength almost plunged the country into civil war, and, although Chulalongkorn skilfully defused the crisis, many of his reforms had to be quietly shelved for the time being.

An important administrative reform that did go through, necessitated by the threat of colonial expansionism, concerned the former kingdom of Lanna. British exploitation of teak had recently spread into northern Thailand from neighbouring Burma, so in 1874 Chulalongkorn sent a commissioner to Chiang Mai to keep an eye on the prince of Chiang Mai and make sure that he avoided any collision with the British. The commissioner was gradually able to limit the power of the princes and to begin to integrate the region into the kingdom.

In the 1880s prospects for reform brightened as many of the "Ancients" died or retired. This allowed Chulalongkorn to **restructure the government** to meet the country's needs: the Royal Audit Office made possible the proper control of revenue and finance; the Department of the Army became the nucleus of a modern armed services; and a host of other departments was set up, for justice, education, public health and the like. To fill these new positions, the king appointed many of his younger brothers, who had all received a modern education, while scores of foreign technicians and advisers were brought in to help with everything from foreign affairs to rail lines.

Throughout this period, however, the Western powers maintained their pressure on the region. The most serious threat to Thai sovereignty was the **Franco–Siamese Crisis** of 1893, which culminated in the French, based in Vietnam, sending gunboats up the Chao Phraya River to Bangkok. Flouting numerous international laws, France claimed control over Laos and made other outrageous demands, which Chulalongkorn had no option but to concede. In 1907 Thailand was also forced to acknowledge French

1863	1868–1910	1874
The French bring Cambodia under their protection	Reign of Rama V (Chulalongkorn)	Beginning of the abolition of slavery in Thailand

control over Cambodia, and in 1909 three Malay states fell to the British (while Thailand retained a fourth Muslim state, Pattani). In order to preserve its independence, the country ceded control over huge areas of tributary states and forwent huge sums of tax revenue. But from the end of the Fifth Reign, the frontiers were fixed as they are today.

By the time of the king's death in 1910, Thailand could not yet be called a modern nation-state – Bangkok still did not have complete control over the outermost regions, and corruption and nepotism were grave problems, for example. However, Chulalongkorn had made remarkable advances, and, almost from scratch, had established the political institutions to cope with twentieth-century development.

The end of absolute monarchy

Chulalongkorn was succeeded by a flamboyant, British-educated prince, **Vajiravudh**, who was crowned Rama VI (1910–25). The new king found it difficult to shake the dominance of his father's appointees in the government, who formed an extremely narrow elite, comprised almost entirely of members of Chulalongkorn's family. In an attempt to build up a personal following, Vajiravudh created, in May 1911, the **Wild Tigers**, a nationwide paramilitary corps recruited widely from the civil service. However, in 1912 a group of young army lieutenants, disillusioned by the absolute monarchy and upset at the downgrading of the regular army in favour of the Wild Tigers, plotted a **coup**. The conspirators were easily broken up before any trouble began, but this was something new in Thai history: the country was used to in-fighting among the royal family, but not to military intrigue from men from comparatively ordinary backgrounds.

Vajiravudh's response to the coup was a series of modernizing **reforms**, including the introduction of compulsory primary education and an attempt to better the status of women by supporting monogamy in place of the widespread practice of polygamy. His huge output of writings invariably encouraged people to live as modern Westerners, and he brought large numbers of commoners into high positions in government. Nonetheless, he would not relinquish his strong opposition to constitutional democracy.

When **World War I** broke out in 1914, the Thais were generally sympathetic to the Germans out of resentment over their loss of territory to the French and British. The king, however, was in favour of neutrality, until the US entered the war in 1917, when Thailand followed the expedient policy of joining the winning side and sent an expeditionary force of 1300 men to France in June 1918. The goodwill earned by this gesture enabled the Thais, between 1920 and 1926, to negotiate away the unequal treaties that had been imposed on them by the Western powers. Foreigners on Thai soil were no longer exempted from Thai laws, and the Thais were allowed to set reasonable rates of import and export taxes.

Prajadhipok

Vajiravudh's extravagant lifestyle – during his reign, royal expenditure amounted to as much as ten percent of the state budget – left severe financial problems for his successor. Vajiravudh died without leaving a son, and as three better-placed

1893	**1910–25**	**1912**
Gunboats up the Chao Phraya: the Franco–Siamese Crisis obliges Thailand to give up its claims to Laos and Cambodia	Reign of Rama VI (Vajiravudh)	The first of many coup attempts in modern Thailand

contenders to the Crown all died in the 1920s, **Prajadhipok** – the seventy-sixth child and last son of Chulalongkorn – was catapulted to the throne as Rama VII (1925–35). Young and inexperienced, he responded to the country's crisis by creating a Supreme Council of State, seen by many as a return to Chulalongkorn's absolutist "government by princes".

Prajadhipok himself seems to have been in favour of constitutional government, but the weakness of his personality and the opposition of the old guard in the Supreme Council prevented him from introducing it. Meanwhile a vigorous community of Western-educated intellectuals had emerged in the lower echelons of the bureaucracy, who were increasingly dissatisfied with the injustices of monarchical government. The final shock to the Thai system came with the Great Depression, which from 1930 onwards ravaged the economy. On June 24, 1932, a small group of middle-ranking officials, led by a lawyer, Pridi Phanomyong, and an army major, Luang Phibunsongkhram, staged a **coup** with only a handful of troops. Prajadhipok weakly submitted to the conspirators, or "Promoters", and 150 years of absolute monarchy in Bangkok came to a sudden end. The king was sidelined to a position of symbolic significance and in 1935 he abdicated in favour of his 10-year-old nephew, **Ananda**, then a schoolboy living in Switzerland.

To the 1957 coup

The success of the 1932 coup was in large measure attributable to the army officers who gave the conspirators credibility, and it was they who were to dominate the constitutional regimes that followed. The Promoters' first worry was that the French or British might attempt to restore the monarchy to full power. To deflect such intervention, they appointed a government under a provisional constitution and espoused a wide range of liberal Western-type reforms, including freedom of the press and social equality, few of which ever saw the light of day.

The regime's first crisis came early in 1933 when **Pridi Phanomyong**, by now leader of the government's civilian faction, put forward a socialist economic plan based on the nationalization of land and labour. The proposal was denounced as communistic by the military, Pridi was forced into temporary exile and an anti-communist law was passed. Then, in October, a royalist coup was mounted which brought the kingdom close to civil war. After intense fighting, the rebels were defeated by Lieutenant-Colonel **Luang Phibunsongkhram** (or Phibun), so strengthening the government and bringing Phibun to the fore as the leading light of the military faction.

Pridi was rehabilitated in 1934 and remained powerful and popular, especially among the intelligentsia, but it was Phibun who became prime minister after the decisive **elections of 1938**, presiding over a cabinet dominated by military men. Phibun encouraged a wave of nationalistic feeling with such measures as the official institution of the name Thailand in 1939 – Siam, it was argued, was a name bestowed by external forces, and the new title made it clear that the country belonged to the Thais rather than the economically dominant Chinese. This latter sentiment was reinforced with a series of harsh laws against the Chinese, who faced discriminatory taxes on income and commerce.

1925–35	1932	1935–46
Reign of Rama VII (Prajadhipok)	A coup brings the end of the absolute monarchy and introduces Thailand's first constitution	Reign of Rama VIII (Ananda), mostly in absentia

World War II

The outbreak of **World War II** gave the Thais the chance to avenge the humiliation of the 1893 Franco–Siamese Crisis. When France was occupied by Germany in June 1940, Phibun seized the opportunity to invade western Cambodia and the area of Laos lying to the west of the Mekong River. In the following year, however, the threat of a Japanese attack on Thailand loomed. On December 8, 1941, almost at the same time as the assault on Pearl Harbor, the Japanese invaded the country at nine points, most of them along the east coast of the peninsula. The Thais at first resisted fiercely, but realizing that the position was hopeless, Phibun quickly ordered a ceasefire. Meanwhile, the British sent a force from Malaysia to try to stop the Japanese at Songkhla, but were held up in a fight with Thai border police. The Japanese had time to establish themselves, before pushing down the peninsula to take Singapore.

The Thai government concluded a military alliance with Japan and declared war against the US and Great Britain in January 1942, probably in the belief that the Japanese would win the war. However, the Thai minister in Washington, Seni Pramoj, refused to deliver the declaration of war against the US and, in cooperation with the Americans, began organizing a resistance movement called **Seri Thai**. Pridi, now acting as regent to the young king, furtively coordinated the movement under the noses of the occupying Japanese, smuggling in American agents and housing them in a European prison camp in Bangkok.

By 1944 Japan's final defeat looked likely, and Phibun, who had been most closely associated with them, was forced to resign by the National Assembly in July. A civilian, Khuang Aphaiwong, was chosen as prime minister, while Seri Thai became well established in the government under the control of Pridi. At the end of the war, Thailand was forced to restore the annexed Cambodian and Lao provinces to French Indochina, but American support prevented the British from imposing heavy punishments for the alliance with Japan.

Postwar upheavals

With the fading of the military, the election of January 1946 was for the first time contested by organized political parties, resulting in Pridi becoming prime minister. A new constitution was drafted and the outlook for democratic, civilian government seemed bright.

Hopes were shattered, however, on June 9, 1946, when King Ananda was found dead in his bed, with a bullet wound in his forehead. Three palace servants were tried and executed, but the murder has never been satisfactorily explained. Public opinion attached at least indirect responsibility for the killing to Pridi, who had in the past shown anti-royalist feeling. He resigned as prime minister, and in April 1948 the military made a decisive return: playing on the threat of communism, with Pridi pictured as a Red bogeyman, Phibun took over the premiership.

After the bloody suppression of two attempted coups in favour of Pridi, the main feature of Phibun's second regime was its heavy involvement with the US. As communism developed its hold in the region, with the takeover of China in 1949 and the French defeat in Indochina in 1954, the US increasingly viewed Thailand as a bulwark against the Red menace. Between 1951 and 1957, when its annual state

1939	1941	1946
The country's name is changed from Siam to the more nationalistic Thailand	The Japanese invade, and Thailand forms an alliance with them	Rama VIII is mysteriously shot dead; the present king, Rama IX (Bhumibol), accedes

budget was only about $200 million a year, Thailand received a total $149 million in American economic aid and $222 million in military aid. This strengthened Phibun's dictatorship, while enabling leading military figures to divert American money and other funds into their own pockets.

In 1955, his position threatened by two rival generals, Phibun experienced a sudden conversion to the cause of democracy. He narrowly won a general election in 1957, but only by blatant vote-rigging and coercion. Although there's a strong tradition of foul play in Thai elections, this is remembered as the dirtiest ever: after vehement public outcry, **General Sarit**, the commander-in-chief of the army, overthrew the new government in September 1957.

To the present day

Believing that Thailand would prosper best under a unifying authority – an ideology that still has plenty of supporters today – Sarit set about re-establishing the monarchy as the head of the social hierarchy and the source of legitimacy for the government. Ananda's successor, **King Bhumibol** (Rama IX), was pushed into an active role while Sarit ruthlessly silenced critics and pressed ahead with a plan for economic development. These policies achieved a large measure of stability and prosperity at home, although from 1960 onwards the international situation worsened. With the Marxist Pathet Lao making considerable advances in Laos, and Cambodia's ruler, Prince Sihanouk, drawing into closer relations with China, Sarit turned again to the US. The Americans obliged by sharply increasing military aid and by stationing troops in Thailand.

The Vietnam War

Sarit died in 1963, whereupon the military succession passed to **General Thanom**, closely aided by his deputy prime minister, **General Praphas**. Neither man had anything of Sarit's charisma and during a decade in power they followed his political philosophies largely unchanged. Their most pressing problem was the resumption of open hostilities between North and South Vietnam in the early 1960s – the **Vietnam War**. Both Laos and Cambodia became involved on the side of the communists by allowing the North Vietnamese to supply their troops in the south along the Ho Chi Minh Trail, which passed through southern Laos and northeastern Cambodia. The Thais, with the backing of the US, quietly began to conduct military operations in Laos, to which North Vietnam and China responded by supporting anti-government insurgency in Thailand.

The more the Thais felt threatened by the spread of communism, the more they looked to the Americans for help – by 1968 around 45,000 US military personnel were on Thai soil, which became the base for US bombing raids against North Vietnam and Laos, and for covert operations into Laos and beyond.

The effects of the **American presence in Thailand** were profound. The economy swelled with dollars, and hundreds of thousands of Thais became reliant on the Americans for a living, with a consequent proliferation of corruption and prostitution. What's more, the sudden exposure to Western culture led many to question traditional Thai values and the political status quo.

1957–63	**1973**	**1976**
Successful coup-maker and military strongman, General Sarit, brings Thailand ever closer to the US	Bloody student demonstrations bring the downfall of Sarit's successor, General Thanom	The brutal suppression of further student demos ushers the military back in

The democracy movement and civil unrest

At the same time, poor farmers were becoming disillusioned with their lot, and during the 1960s many turned against the Bangkok government. At the end of 1964, the **Communist Party of Thailand** and other groups formed a **broad left coalition** that soon had the support of several thousand insurgents in remote areas of the northeast. By 1967, the problem had spread to Chiang Rai and Nan provinces, and a separate threat had arisen in southern Thailand, involving **Muslim dissidents** and the Chinese-dominated **Communist Party of Malaya**.

Thanom was now facing a major security crisis, especially as the war in Vietnam was going badly. In 1969 he held elections which produced a majority for the government party but, still worried about national stability, the general got cold feet. In November 1971 he reimposed repressive military rule, under a triumvirate of himself, his son Colonel Narong and Praphas, who became known as the "Three Tyrants". However, the 1969 experiment with democracy had heightened expectations of power-sharing among the middle classes, especially in the universities. **Student demonstrations** began in June 1973, and in October as many as 500,000 people turned out at Thammasat University in Bangkok to demand a new constitution. King Bhumibol intervened with apparent success, and indeed the demonstrators were starting to disperse on the morning of October 14, when the police tried to control the flow of people away. Tensions quickly mounted and soon a full-scale riot was under way, during which over 350 people were reported killed. The army, however, refused to provide enough troops to control the situation, and later the same day, Thanom, Narong and Praphas were forced to resign and leave the country.

In a new climate of openness, **Kukrit Pramoj** (see p.128) managed to form a coalition of seventeen elected parties and secured a promise of US withdrawal from Thailand, but his government was riven with feuding. Meanwhile, the king and much of the middle class, alarmed at the unchecked radicalism of the students, began to support new, often violent, right-wing organizations. In October 1976, the students demonstrated again, protesting against the return of Thanom to Thailand to become a monk at Wat Bowonniwet. Supported by elements of the military and the government, the police and reactionary students launched a massive assault on Thammasat University. On October 6, hundreds of students were brutally beaten, scores were lynched and some even burnt alive; the military took control and suspended the constitution.

General Prem

Soon after, the military-appointed prime minister, **Thanin Kraivichien**, imposed rigid censorship and forced dissidents to undergo anti-communist indoctrination, but his measures seem to have been too repressive even for the military, who forced him to resign in October 1977. General Kriangsak Chomanand took over, and began to break up the insurgency with shrewd offers of amnesty. His power base was weak, however, and although Kriangsak won the elections of 1979, he was displaced in February 1980 by **General Prem Tinsulanonda**, who was backed by a broad parliamentary coalition.

Untainted by corruption, Prem achieved widespread support, including that of the monarchy. Parliamentary elections in 1983 returned the military to power and legitimized Prem's rule. Overseeing a period of strong foreign investment and rapid

1980–88	1991	1992
Period of Premocracy, General Prem's hybrid of military rule and democracy	The military launch a coup, protesting the corruption of the recently democratically elected government	Mass demonstrations lead to bloodshed – and the return of democracy

economic growth, the general maintained the premiership until 1988, with a unique mixture of dictatorship and democracy sometimes called **Premocracy**: although never standing for parliament himself, Prem was asked by the legislature after every election to become prime minister. He eventually stepped down (though he remains a powerful privy councillor and very close to the king) because, he said, it was time for the country's leader to be chosen from among its elected representatives.

The 1992 demonstrations and the 1997 constitution

The new prime minister was indeed an elected MP, **Chatichai Choonhavan**, a retired general with a long civilian career in public office. He pursued a vigorous policy of economic development, but this fostered widespread corruption, in which members of the government were often implicated. Following an economic downturn and Chatichai's attempts to downgrade the political role of the military, the armed forces staged a bloodless **coup** on February 23, 1991, led by Supreme Commander Sunthorn and General Suchinda, the army commander-in-chief, who became premier.

When Suchinda reneged on promises to make democratic amendments to the constitution, hundreds of thousands of ordinary Thais poured onto the streets around Bangkok's Democracy Monument in **mass demonstrations** between May 17 and 20, 1992. Hopelessly misjudging the mood of the country, Suchinda brutally crushed the protests, leaving hundreds dead or injured. Having justified the massacre on the grounds that he was protecting the king from communist agitators, Suchinda was forced to resign when King Bhumibol expressed his disapproval in a ticking-off that was broadcast on world television.

Elections were held in September, with the **Democrat Party**, led by Chuan Leekpai, a noted upholder of democracy and the rule of law, emerging victorious. Chuan was succeeded in turn by Banharn Silpa-archa – nicknamed by the local press "the walking ATM", a reference to his reputation for buying votes – and General Chavalit Yongchaiyudh. The most significant positive event of the latter's tenure was the approval of a **new constitution** in 1997. Drawn up by an independent drafting assembly, its main points included: direct elections to the senate, rather than appointment of senators by the prime minister; acceptance of the right of assembly as the basis of a democratic society and guarantees of individual rights and freedoms; greater public accountability; and increased popular participation in local administration. The eventual aim of the new charter was to end the traditional system of patronage, vested interests and vote buying.

Tom yam kung: the 1997 economic crisis

In February 1997 foreign-exchange dealers began to mount speculative attacks on the **baht**, alarmed at the size of Thailand's private foreign debt – 250 billion baht in the unproductive property sector alone, much of it accrued through the proliferation of prestigious skyscrapers in Bangkok. Chavalit's government defended the pegged exchange rate, spending $23 billion of the country's formerly healthy foreign-exchange reserves, but at the beginning of July was forced to give up the ghost – the baht was floated and soon went into freefall. Thailand was forced to seek help from the **IMF**, which in August put together a $17-billion **rescue package**, coupled with severe austerity measures.

1997	1997	2001
A landmark new constitution aims to end corruption and guarantee individual rights and freedoms	Tom yam kung: Thailand is ravaged by economic crisis	Thaksin Shinawatra, loved and hated in roughly equal measure, wins the general election

In November, the inept Chavalit was replaced by Chuan Leekpai, who immediately took a hard line in following the IMF's advice, which involved maintaining cripplingly high interest rates to protect the baht and slashing government budgets. Although this played well abroad, at home the government encountered increasing hostility from its newly impoverished citizens – the downturn struck with such speed and severity that it was dubbed the **tom yam kung crisis**, after the searingly hot Thai soup. Chuan's tough stance paid off, however, with the baht stabilizing and inflation falling back, and in October 1999 he announced that he was forgoing almost $4 billion of the IMF's package.

Thaksin

The general election of January 2001 was the first to be held under the 1997 constitution, which was intended to take vote-buying out of politics. However, this election coincided with the emergence of a new party, **Thai Rak Thai** ("Thai Loves Thai"), formed by one of Thailand's wealthiest men, **Thaksin Shinawatra**, an ex-policeman who had made a personal fortune from government telecommunications concessions.

Thaksin duly won the election, but instead of moving towards greater democracy, as envisaged by the new constitution, he began to apply commercial and legal pressure to try to silence critics in the media and parliament. As his standing became more firmly entrenched, he rejected constitutional reforms designed to rein in his power – famously declaring that "democracy is only a tool" for achieving other goals.

Thaksin did, however, maintain his reputation as a reformer by carrying through nearly all of his election promises. He issued a three-year loan moratorium for perennially indebted farmers and set up a one-million-baht development fund for each of the country's seventy thousand villages. To improve public health access, a standard charge of B30 per hospital visit was introduced nationwide.

Despite a sharp escalation of violence in the Islamic southern provinces in early 2004 (see p.697), Thaksin breezed through the February 2005 election, becoming the first prime minister in Thai history to win an outright majority at the polls but causing alarm among a wide spectrum of Thailand's elites. When Thaksin's relatives sold their shares in the family's Shin Corporation in January 2006 for $1.7 billion, without paying tax, tens of thousands of mostly middle-class Thais flocked to Bangkok to take part in protracted demonstrations, under the umbrella of the **People's Alliance for Democracy (PAD)**. After further allegations of corruption and cronyism, in September Thaksin, while on official business in the United States, was ousted by a military **coup**.

... and the spectre of Thaksin

Thaksin set up home in London, but his supporters, now the People's Power Party (PPP), won the December 2007 general election. In response, the PAD – its nationalist and royalist credentials and its trademark **yellow shirts** (the colour of the king) now firmly established – restarted its mass protests. Meanwhile, there was a merry-go-round of tribunals and court cases, including the conviction of Thaksin *in absentia* for corruption.

Matters came to a head in November and December 2008: the PAD seized and closed down Bangkok's Suvarnabhumi airport; the ruling People's Power Party was declared illegal by the courts; and **Pheu Thai** (sometimes "Peua Thai"; meaning "For

2004	2006	2010
The violence in the Islamic southern provinces sharply escalates	While in the US, Thaksin is ousted in a military coup and goes into exile	Red-shirted supporters of Thaksin set up a month-long protest camp in Bangkok, before being dispersed by force

Thais"), the PPP's swift reincarnation, found itself unable to form a new coalition government. Instead, led by the Eton- and Oxford-educated **Abhisit Vejjajiva**, the Democrat Party jumped into bed with the Bhumjaithai Party, formerly staunch supporters of Thaksin, to take the helm.

This in turn prompted Thaksin's supporters – now **red-shirted** and organized into the **UDD** (United Front for Democracy against Dictatorship) – to hold mass protest meetings. In March 2009, Thaksin claimed by video broadcast that Privy Council President, Prem Tinsulanonda, had masterminded the 2006 coup and Abhisit's appointment as prime minister, and called for the overthrow of the *amat* (elite).

Amid a clampdown by the Democrat government on free speech, including heavy-handed use of Article 112, the *lèse majesté* law, much more violent protests took place early the following year. Calling on Abhisit to hold new elections, thousands of red shirts set up a heavily defended camp around the **Ratchaprasong** intersection in central Bangkok in early April. On May 19, Abhisit sent in the army to break up the camp by force; altogether 91 people died on both sides in the two months of protests.

Mass popular support for Thaksin, however, did not wane, and in the general election of May 2011, Pheu Thai – now led by his younger sister, **Yingluck Shinawatra** – romped home with an absolute majority.

Thailand's first woman prime minister, Yingluck proposed an amnesty bill for all those involved in the political turmoils of the last ten years, which would have included wiping out Thaksin's corruption convictions, thus allowing him to return to Thailand. However, in late 2013 this prompted further mass protests on the streets of Bangkok: led by Suthep Thaugsuban, who resigned his seat as a Democrat Party MP, thousands of nationalists – no longer wearing yellow shirts, but now blowing whistles as their trademark – occupied large areas of the city centre for several months, in an attempt to provoke the military into staging a coup. In May 2014, this duly happened, and was Thailand's twelfth successful **coup d'état** in the period of constitutional monarchy since 1932 (not to mention seven failed attempts). The army chief, **General Prayut Chan-ocha**, installed himself as prime minister, at the head of a military junta known as the National Council for Peace and Order (NCPO). Political gatherings were banned, politicians, journalists, academics and activists were detained (most temporarily) and censorship of the media was tightened (which in turn fostered broad self-censorship).

In January 2015, Yingluck Shinawatra was banned from politics for five years and may face a lengthy prison term. The NCPO has set up a committee to draft a new constitution, with the aim of reducing the powers of elected politicians, but at the time of writing, it's unclear when new elections will be held. Meanwhile, the 87-year-old king, now the world's longest-running head of state, is in failing health; and Thailand is expected to take a leading role in the formation of the ASEAN Economic Community, an integrated single market that's optimistically scheduled for the end of 2015.

2011	2013	2014
Thaksin's sister, Yingluck, wins the general election with an outright majority	Mass anti-government protests on the streets of Bangkok	Thailand's twelfth military coup since 1932

Religion: Thai Buddhism

Over 85 percent of Thais consider themselves Theravada Buddhists, followers of the teachings of a holy man usually referred to as the Buddha (Enlightened One), though more precisely known as Gautama Buddha to distinguish him from lesser-known Buddhas who preceded him. Theravada Buddhism is one of the two main schools of Buddhism practised in Asia, and in Thailand it has absorbed an eclectic assortment of animist and Hindu elements.

Islam is the biggest of the minority religions in Thailand, practised by between five and ten percent of the population. Most Muslims live in the south, especially in the deep-south provinces of Yala, Pattani and Narithiwat, along the Malaysian border, whose populations are over eighty percent Muslim. The separatist violence in this region (see p.697) has caused great tension between local Buddhist and Muslim communities, which have traditionally co-existed peacefully; it has not, however, obviously affected inter-faith relationships elsewhere in Thailand. The rest of the Thai population comprises Mahayana Buddhists, Hindus, Sikhs, Christians and animists.

The Buddha: his life and beliefs

Gautama Buddha was born as **Prince Gautama Siddhartha** in Nepal, in the seventh century BC according to the calculations for the Thai calendar, though scholars now think it may have been a century or two later. At his birth, astrologers predicted that he would become either a famous king or a celebrated holy man, depending on which path he chose. Much preferring the former, the prince's father forbade the boy from leaving the palace grounds, and set about educating Gautama in all aspects of the high life. Most statues of the Buddha depict him with elongated earlobes, which is a reference to this early pampered existence, when he would have worn heavy precious stones in his ears.

The prince married and became a father, but at the age of 29 he flouted his father's authority and sneaked out into the world beyond the palace. On this fateful trip he encountered successively an old man, a sick man, a corpse and a hermit, and thus for the first time was made aware that pain and suffering were intrinsic to human life. Contemplation seemed the only means of discovering why this was so – and therefore Gautama decided to leave the palace and become a **Hindu ascetic**.

For several years he wandered the countryside leading a life of self-denial and self-mortification, but failed to come any closer to the answer. Eventually concluding that the best course of action must be to follow a "Middle Way" – neither indulgent nor overly ascetic – Gautama sat down beneath the famous riverside bodhi tree at **Bodh Gaya** in India, facing the rising sun, to **meditate** until he achieved enlightenment. For 49 days he sat cross-legged in the "lotus position", contemplating the causes of suffering and wrestling with temptations that materialized to distract him. Most of these were sent by **Mara**, the Evil One, who was finally subdued when Gautama summoned the earth goddess **Mae Toranee** by pointing the fingers of his right hand at the ground – the gesture known as **Calling the Earth to Witness**, or *Bhumisparsa Mudra*, which has been immortalized by thousands of Thai sculptors. Mae Toranee wrung torrents of water from her hair and engulfed Mara's demonic emissaries in a flood, an episode that's also commonly reproduced, especially in temple murals.

Temptations dealt with, Gautama soon came to attain **enlightenment** and so become a Buddha. As the place of his enlightenment, the **bodhi tree** (*bodhi* means "enlightenment" in Sanskrit and Pali; it's sometimes also known as the bo tree, in Thai *ton po*) has assumed special significance for Buddhists: not only does it appear in many Buddhist paintings, but there's often a real bodhi tree (*Ficus religiosa*, or sacred fig) planted in temple compounds as well. In addition, the bot is nearly always built facing either a body of water or facing east (preferably both).

The Buddha preached his **first sermon** in the deer park at Sarnath in India, where he characterized his doctrine, or **Dharma**, as a wheel. From this episode comes the early Buddhist symbol the **Dharmachakra**, known as the Wheel of Law, which is often accompanied by a statue of a deer. Thais celebrate this first sermon with a public holiday in July known as **Asanha Puja**. On another occasion 1250 people spontaneously gathered to hear the Buddha speak, an event remembered in Thailand as **Makha Puja** and marked by a public holiday in February.

For the next forty-odd years the Buddha travelled the region converting non believers and performing miracles. One rainy season he even ascended into the **Tavatimsa heaven** (Heaven of the 33 Gods) to visit his mother and to preach the doctrine to her. His descent from this heaven is quite a common theme of paintings and sculptures, and the **Standing Buddha** pose of numerous Buddha statues comes from this story.

The Buddha "died" at the age of eighty on the banks of a river at Kusinari in India – an event often dated to 543 BC, which is why the **Thai calendar** is 543 years out of synch with the Western one, so that the year 2016 AD becomes 2559 BE (Buddhist Era). Lying on his side, propping up his head on his hand, the Buddha passed into **Nirvana** (giving rise to another classic pose, the **Reclining Buddha**), the unimaginable state of nothingness which knows no suffering and from which there is no reincarnation. Buddhists believe that the day the Buddha entered Nirvana was the same date on which he was born and on which he achieved enlightenment, a triply significant day that Thais honour with the **Visakha Puja** festival in May.

Buddhists believe that Gautama Buddha was the five-hundredth incarnation of a single being: the stories of these five hundred lives, collectively known as the **Jataka**, provide the inspiration for much Thai art. Hindus also accept Gautama Buddha into their pantheon, perceiving him as the ninth manifestation of their god Vishnu.

The spread of Buddhism

After the Buddha entered Nirvana, his **doctrine** spread relatively quickly across India, and probably was first promulgated in Thailand in about the third century BC, when the Indian emperor Ashoka (in Thai, Asoke) sent out missionaries. His teachings, the *Tripitaka*, were written down in the Pali language – a then-vernacular derivative of Sanskrit – in a form that became known as **Theravada**, or "The Doctrine of the Elders".

By the beginning of the first millennium, a new movement called **Mahayana** (Great Vehicle) had emerged within the Theravada school, attempting to make Buddhism more accessible by introducing a pantheon of **bodhisattva**, or Buddhist saints, who, although they had achieved enlightenment, postponed entering Nirvana in order to inspire the populace. Mahayana Buddhism spread north into China, Korea, Vietnam and Japan, also entering southern Thailand via the Srivijayan empire around the eighth century and parts of Khmer Cambodia in about the eleventh century. Meanwhile, Theravada Buddhism (which the Mahayanists disparagingly renamed "Hinayana" or "Lesser Vehicle") established itself most significantly in Sri Lanka, northern and central Thailand and Burma.

Buddhist doctrine and practice

Central to Theravada Buddhism is a belief in **karma** – broadly speaking, the belief that every action has a consequence – and **reincarnation**, along with an understanding that craving is at the root of human suffering. The ultimate aim for a Buddhist is to get off the cycle of perpetual reincarnation and suffering and instead to enter the blissful state of non-being that is **Nirvana**. This enlightened state can take many lifetimes to achieve so the more realistic goal for most is to be reborn slightly higher up the karmic ladder each time. As Thai Buddhists see it, animals are at the bottom of the karmic scale and monks at the top, with women on a lower rung than men.

Living a good life, specifically a life of "pure intention", creates good karma and Buddhist doctrine focuses a great deal on how to achieve this. Psychology and an understanding of human weaknesses play a big part. Key is the concept of *dukka* or **suffering**, which holds that craving is the root cause of all suffering or, to put it simplistically, human unhappiness is caused by the unquenchable dissatisfaction experienced when one's sensual, spiritual or material desires are not met. The concepts concerning suffering and craving are known as the **Four Noble Truths** of Buddhism. The route to enlightenment depends on a person being sufficiently detached from earthly desires so that *dukka* can't take hold. One acknowledges that the physical world is impermanent and ever changing, and that all things – including the self – are therefore not worth craving. A Buddhist works towards this realization by following the **Eightfold Path**, or **Middle Way**, that is by developing a set of highly moral personal qualities such as "right speech", "right action" and "right mindfulness". Meditation is particularly helpful in this.

A devout Thai Buddhist commits to the **five basic precepts**, namely not to kill or steal, to refrain from sexual misconduct and incorrect speech (lies, gossip and abuse) and to eschew intoxicating liquor and drugs. There are **three extra precepts** for special *wan phra* holy days and for those laypeople including foreign students who study meditation at Thai temples: no eating after noon, no entertainment (including TV and music) and no sleeping on a soft bed; in addition, the no-sexual-misconduct precept turns into no sex at all.

Making merit

Merit-making in popular Thai Buddhism has become slightly skewed, so that some people act on the assumption that they'll climb the karmic ladder faster if they make bigger and better offerings to the temple and its monks. However, it is of course the purity of the intention behind one's **merit-making** (*tham buun*) that's fundamental.

Merit can be made in many ways, from giving a monk his breakfast to attending a Buddhist service or donating money and gifts to the neighbourhood temple, and most **festivals** are essentially communal merit-making opportunities. Between the big festivals, the most common days for making merit and visiting the temple are **wan phra** (holy days), which are determined by the phase of the moon and occur four times a month. The simplest **offering** inside a temple consists of lotus buds, candles and three incense sticks (representing the three gems of Buddhism – the Buddha himself, the Dharma or doctrine, and the monkhood). One of the more bizarre but common merit-making activities involves **releasing caged birds**: worshippers buy tiny finches from vendors at wat compounds and, by liberating them from their cage, prove their Buddhist compassion towards all living things. The fact that the birds were free until netted earlier that morning doesn't seem to detract from the ritual. In riverside and seaside wats, fish or even baby turtles are released instead.

For an insightful introduction to the philosophy and practice of Thai Buddhism, see ⓦ thaibuddhism.net. A number of Thai temples welcome foreign students of Buddhism and meditation (see p.51).

The monkhood

It's the duty of Thailand's 200,000-strong **Sangha** (monkhood) to set an example to the Theravada Buddhist community by living a life as close to the Middle Way as possible and by preaching the Dharma to the people. The life of a monk (*bhikkhu*) is governed by 227 precepts that include celibacy and the rejection of all personal possessions except gifts.

Each day begins with an alms round in the neighbourhood so that the laity can donate food and thereby gain themselves merit, and then is chiefly spent in meditation, chanting, teaching and study. As the most respected members of any community, monks act as teachers, counsellors and arbiters in local disputes, and sometimes become spokesmen for villagers' rights. They also perform rituals at cremations, weddings and other events, such as the launching of a new business or even the purchase of a new car. Many young boys from poor families find themselves almost obliged to become either a *dek wat* (temple boy) or a **novice monk** because that's the only way they can get accommodation, food and, crucially, an education. This is provided free in exchange for duties around the wat, and novices are required to adhere to ten rather than 227 Buddhist precepts.

Monkhood doesn't have to be for life: a man may leave the Sangha three times without stigma, and in fact every Thai male (including royalty) is expected to **enter the monkhood** for a short period, ideally between leaving school and marrying, as a rite of passage into adulthood. Thai government departments and some private companies grant their employees paid leave for their time as a monk, but the custom is in decline as young men increasingly have to consider the effect their absence may have on their career prospects. Instead, many men now enter the monkhood for a brief period after the death of a parent, to make merit both for the deceased and for the rest of the family. The most popular time for temporary ordination is the three-month Buddhist retreat period – **Pansa**, sometimes referred to as "Buddhist Lent" – which begins in July and lasts for the duration of the rainy season. (The monks' confinement is said to originate from the earliest years of Buddhist history, when farmers complained that perambulating monks were squashing their sprouting rice crops.)

Monks in contemporary society

Some monks extend their role as village spokesmen to become influential activists: Wat Tham Krabok near Lopburi and Wat Nong Sam Pran in Kanchanaburi are among a growing number of temples that have established themselves as successful drug rehabilitation centres; monks at Wat Phra Bat Nam Pu in Lopburi run a hospice for people with HIV/AIDS as well as a famously hard-hitting AIDS-awareness museum; monks at Wat Phai Lom near Bangkok have developed the country's largest breeding colony of Asian open-billed storks; and the monks at Wat Pa Luang Ta Bua Yannasampanno in Kanchanaburi (see p.201) have hit the headlines with their tiger sanctuary. Other monks, such as the famous nonagenerian Luang Pho Khoon of Wat Ban Rai in Nakhon Ratchasima province, have acquired such a reputation for giving wise counsel and bringing good fortune to their followers that they have become national gurus and their temples now generate great wealth through the production of specially blessed amulets and photographs.

Though the increasing involvement of many monks in the secular world has not met with unanimous approval, far more disappointing to the laity are those monks who **flout the precepts** of the Sangha by succumbing to the temptations of a consumer society, flaunting Raybans, Rolexes and Mercedes (in some cases actually bought with temple funds), chain-smoking and flirting, even making pocket money from predicting lottery results and practising faith-healing. With so much national pride and integrity riding on the sanctity of the Sangha, any whiff of a deeper scandal is bound to strike deep into the national psyche. Cases of monks involved in drug dealing, gun running, even rape and murder have prompted a stream of editorials on the state of the Sangha and the collapse of spiritual values at the heart of Thai society. The inclusivity of the monkhood – which is open to just about any male who wants to join – has been highlighted as a particularly vulnerable aspect, not least because donning saffron robes has always been an accepted way for criminals, reformed or otherwise, to repent of their past deeds.

Interestingly, back in the late 1980s, the influential monk Phra Bodhirak (Photirak) was defrocked after criticizing what he saw as a tide of decadence infecting Thai Buddhism. He now preaches his ascetic code of anti-materialism through his breakaway **Santi Asoke** sect, famous across the country for its cheap vegetarian restaurants, its philosophy of self-sufficiency and for the simple blue farmers' shirts worn by many of its followers.

Women and the monkhood

Although the Theravada Buddhist hierarchy in some countries permits the ordination of **female monks**, or *bhikkhuni*, the Thai Sangha does not. Instead, Thai women are officially only allowed to become **nuns**, or *mae chii*, shaving their heads, donning white robes and keeping eight rather than 227 precepts. Their status is lower than that of the monks and they are chiefly occupied with temple upkeep rather than conducting religious ceremonies.

However, the progressives are becoming more vocal, and in 2002 a Thai woman became the first of several to break with the Buddhist authorities and get **ordained** as a novice *bhikkhuni* on Thai soil. Thailand's Sangha Council, however, still recognizes neither her ordination nor the temple, Watra Songdhammakalyani in Nakhon Pathom, where the ordination took place. The Watra (rather than Wat) is run by another Thai *bhikkhuni*, Dhammananda Bhikkhuni, the author of several books in English about **women and Buddhism** and of an informative website, ⊛thaibhikkhunis.org.

Hindu deities and animist spirits

The complicated history of the area now known as Thailand has made Thai Buddhism a confusingly syncretic faith, as you'll realize when you enter a Buddhist temple compound to be confronted by a statue of a Hindu deity. While regular Buddhist merit-making insures a Thai for the next life, there are certain **Hindu gods and animist spirits** that many Thais – sophisticated Bangkokians and illiterate farmers alike – also cultivate for help with more immediate problems; and as often as not it's a Buddhist monk who is called in to exorcize a malevolent spirit. Even the Buddhist King Bhumibol employs Brahmin priests and astrologers to determine auspicious days and officiate at certain royal ceremonies and, like his royal predecessors of the Chakri dynasty, he also associates himself with the Hindu god Vishnu by assuming the title Rama IX – Rama, hero of the Hindu epic the *Ramayana*, having been Vishnu's seventh manifestation on earth.

If a Thai wants help in achieving a short-term goal, like passing an exam, becoming pregnant or winning the lottery, he or she will quite likely turn to the **Hindu pantheon**, visiting an enshrined statue of Brahma, Vishnu, Shiva or Ganesh, and making offerings of flowers, incense and maybe food. If the outcome is favourable, the devotee will probably come back to show thanks, bringing more offerings and maybe even hiring a dance troupe to perform a celebratory *lakhon chatri*. Built in honour of Brahma, Bangkok's Erawan Shrine is the most famous place of Hindu-inspired worship in the country.

Spirits and spirit houses

Whereas Hindu deities tend to be benevolent, **spirits** (or *phi*) are not nearly as reliable and need to be mollified more frequently. They come in hundreds of varieties, some more malign than others, and inhabit everything from trees, rivers and caves to public buildings and private homes – even taking over people if they feel like it.

So that these *phi* don't pester human inhabitants, each building has a special **spirit house** (*saan phra phum*) in its vicinity, as a dwelling for spirits ousted by the building's construction. Usually raised on a short column to set it at or above eye level, the spirit house must occupy an auspicious location – not, for example, in the shadow of the main building. It's generally about the size of a dolls' house and designed to look like

this complex portrait of court intrigue and rather partisan take on Thai-Burmese relations, director Chatrichalerm Yukol brought in Francis Ford Coppola to edit a shortened version for Western audiences. He followed it with the most expensive Thai film to date, at a reported cost of B700 million, **The Legend of King Naresuan** (*Tamnan Somdej Phra Naresuan*, 2007), telling the story of King Naresuan, a national hero who ruled Thailand from Ayutthaya in the sixteenth century. Capturing a strong nationalist and royalist mood in certain sections of Thai society, the film has been turned into a series, with the sixth and final episode coming out in 2015. Garnering the bizarre "P" rating in the new Thai film classification system (meaning that a film has to be promoted, and all Thais are encouraged to watch it, because of its supposed cultural merit), the third and fourth episodes in the series were the two top-grossing films of 2011. The series has been shot at the purpose-built Prommitr Film Studios just outside Kanchanaburi, whose period sets are now open to the public.

Prachya Pinkaew's martial arts action flick **Ong Bak** (2003) was such a huge box-office hit around the world that its star **Tony Jaa** – who performed all his own extraordinary stunts – was appointed Cultural Ambassador for Thailand. Director and star teamed up again in the similarly testosterone-fuelled **Tom Yum Goong** (2005), in which Tony Jaa's fight skills lead him to Australia on the trail of a stolen elephant. Two sequels to *Ong Bak* have been made up to now, and one sequel to *Tom Yum Goong*.

At the other end of the spectrum, Thai art house also went international with the success of **Apichatpong Weerasethakul**'s challenging **Tropical Malady** (*Sud Pralad*, 2004), which won the Jury Prize at Cannes in 2004. Part gay romance, part trippy jungle ghost story, it was for some a pioneering experiment in Thai storytelling, to others an inaccessible bore. His *Syndromes and a Century* (*Sang Sattawat*, 2006) was Thailand's first film to be entered in competition at the Venice Film Festival but failed to impress the Thai censors who, among other reasons, banned it for its depiction of a guitar-playing Buddhist monk. Apichatpong responded by joining a protest against the introduction of a new, reactionary film-ratings system, but to no avail. His *Uncle Boonmee (who can Recall his Past Lives)*, a dreamy, quasi-realist exploration of Thai belief in *phii* (spirits), won the Palme d'Or at Cannes in 2010 but achieved only a limited release back in Thailand. Other experimental directors to look out for include **Thanska Pansittivorakul** and **Thanwarin Sukhaphisit**.

Neil Pettigrew

Books

We have included publishers' details for books that may be hard to find outside Thailand, though some of them can be ordered online through ⓦdcothai.com, which sells e-books on ⓦebooks.dco.co.th. Other titles should be available worldwide. Titles marked ★ are particularly recommended. There's a good selection of Thai novels and short stories in translation, available to buy as e-books, on ⓦthaifiction.com.

TRAVELOGUES

Carl Bock *Temples and Elephants* (Orchid Press, Bangkok). Nineteenth-century account of a rough journey from Bangkok to the far north, dotted with vivid descriptions of rural life and court ceremonial.

Karen Connelly *Touch the Dragon*. Evocative and humorous journal of an impressionable Canadian teenager, sent on an exchange programme to Den Chai in northern Thailand for a year.

Charles Nicholl *Borderlines*. Entertaining adventures and dangerous romance in the "Golden Triangle" form the core of this slightly hackneyed traveller's tale, interwoven with stimulating and well-informed cultural diversions.

James O'Reilly and Larry Habegger (eds) *Travelers' Tales:* *Thailand*. Absorbing anthology of contemporary writings about Thailand, by Thailand experts, social commentators, travel writers and first-time visitors.

Steve Van Beek *Slithering South* (Wind and Water, Hong Kong). An expat writer tells how he single-handedly paddled his wooden boat down the entire 1100km course of the Chao Phraya River, and reveals a side of Thailand that's rarely written about in English.

Tom Vater *Beyond the Pancake Trench: Road Tales from the Wild East*. Adventures, insights and encounters on the margins of twenty-first-century Thailand. Also covers Cambodia, Laos, Vietnam and India.

CULTURE AND SOCIETY

Michael Carrithers *The Buddha: A Very Short Introduction*. Accessible account of the life of the Buddha, and the development and significance of his thought.

★ **Philip Cornwel-Smith and John Goss** *Very Thai*. Why do Thais decant their soft drinks into plastic bags, and how does one sniff-kiss? Answers and insights aplenty in this intriguingly observant, fully illustrated guide to contemporary Thai culture. Look out also for Cornwel-Smith's forthcoming *Very Bangkok*.

James Eckardt *Bangkok People*. The collected articles of a renowned expat journalist, whose encounters with a varied cast of Bangkokians – from construction-site workers and street vendors to boxers and political candidates – add texture and context to the city.

Sandra Gregory with Michael Tierney *Forget You Had a Daughter: Doing Time in the "Bangkok Hilton" – Sandra Gregory's Story*. The frank and shocking account of a young British woman's term in Bangkok's notorious Lard Yao prison after being caught trying to smuggle 89g of heroin out of Thailand.

Roger Jones *Culture Smart! Thailand*. Handy little primer on Thailand's social and cultural mores, with plenty of refreshingly up-to-date insights.

★ **Erich Krauss** *Wave of Destruction: One Thai Village and Its Battle with the Tsunami*. A sad and often shocking, clear-eyed account of what Ban Nam Khem went through before, during and after the tsunami. Fills in many gaps left unanswered by news reports at the time.

Elaine and Paul Lewis *Peoples of the Golden Triangle*. Hefty, exhaustive work illustrated with excellent photographs, describing every aspect of hill-tribe life.

Father Joe Maier *Welcome to the Bangkok Slaughterhouse: The Battle for Human Dignity in Bangkok's Bleakest Slums* and *The Open Gate of Mercy*. Catholic priest Father Joe shares the stories of some of the Bangkok street kids and slum-dwellers that his charitable foundation has been supporting since 1972 (see p.58).

Trilok Chandra Majupuria *Erawan Shrine and Brahma Worship in Thailand* (Tecpress, Bangkok). The most concise introduction to the complexities of Thai religion, with a much wider scope than the title implies.

Cleo Odzer *Patpong Sisters*. An American anthropologist's funny and touching account of her life with the prostitutes and bar girls of Bangkok's notorious red-light district.

★ **Phra Peter Pannapadipo** *Little Angels: The Real-Life Stories of Twelve Thai Novice Monks*. A dozen young boys, many of them from desperate backgrounds, tell the often poignant stories of why they became novice monks. For some, funding from the Students Education Trust (see p.58) has changed their lives.

Phra Peter Pannapadipo *Phra Farang: An English Monk in Thailand*. Behind the scenes in a Thai monastery: the

frank, funny and illuminating account of a UK-born former businessman's life as a Thai monk.

★**Pasuk Phongpaichit and Sungsidh Piriyarangsan** *Corruption and Democracy in Thailand*. Fascinating academic study, revealing the nuts and bolts of corruption in Thailand and its links with all levels of political life, and suggesting a route to a stronger society. Their sequel, a study of Thailand's illegal economy, *Guns, Girls, Gambling, Ganja*, co-written with Nualnoi Treerat, makes equally eye-opening and depressing reading.

Denis Segaller *Thai Ways*. Fascinating collection of short pieces on Thai customs and traditions written by a long-term English resident of Bangkok.

Pira Sudham *People of Esarn*. Wry and touching, potted life stories of villagers who live in, leave and return to the poverty-stricken northeast, compiled by a northeastern lad turned author.

Phil Thornton *Restless Souls: Rebels, Refugees, Medics and Misfits on the Thai–Burma Border*. An Australian journalist brings to light the terrible and complicated plight of the Karen, thousands of whom live as refugees in and around his adopted town of Mae Sot on the Thai–Myanmar border.

Richard Totman *The Third Sex: Kathoey – Thailand's Ladyboys*. As several *kathoey* share their life stories with him, social scientist Totman examines their place in modern Thai society and explores the theory, supported by Buddhist philosophy, that *kathoey* are members of a third sex whose transgendered make-up is predetermined from birth.

Tom Vater and Aroon Thaewchatturat *Sacred Skin*. Fascinating, beautifully photographed exploration of Thailand's spirit tattoos, *sak yant*.

William Warren *Living in Thailand*. Luscious gallery of traditional houses, with an emphasis on the homes of Thailand's rich and famous; seductively photographed by Luca Invernizzi Tettoni.

Daniel Ziv and Guy Sharett *Bangkok Inside Out*. This A–Z of Bangkok quirks and cultural substrates is full of slick photography and sparky observations but was deemed offensive by Thailand's Ministry of Culture, so some Thai bookshops won't stock it.

HISTORY

Anna Leonowens *The English Governess at the Siamese Court*. The mendacious memoirs of the nineteenth-century English governess that inspired the infamous Yul Brynner film *The King and I*; low on accuracy, high on inside-palace gossip.

Chang Noi *Jungle Book: Thailand's Politics, Moral Panic and Plunder 1996–2008* (Silkworm Books, Chiang Mai). A fascinating, often humorous, selection of columns about Thailand's political and social jungle, by "Little Elephant", an anonymous foreign resident, which first appeared in *The Nation* newspaper.

Michael Smithies *Old Bangkok*. Brief, anecdotal history of the capital's early development, emphasizing what remains to be seen of bygone Bangkok.

John Stewart *To the River Kwai: Two Journeys – 1943, 1979*. A survivor of the horrific World War II POW camps along the River Kwai returns to the region, interlacing his wartime reminiscences with observations on how he feels 36 years later.

William Warren *Jim Thompson: the Legendary American of Thailand*. The engrossing biography of the ex-intelligence agent, art collector and Thai silk magnate whose disappearance in Malaysia in 1967 has never been satisfactorily resolved.

Thongchai Winichakul *Siam Mapped*. Intriguing, seminal account of how Rama V, under pressure on his borders from Britain and France at the turn of the twentieth century, in effect colonized his own country, which was then a loose hierarchy of city-states.

★**David K. Wyatt** *Thailand: A Short History*. An excellent treatment, scholarly but highly readable, with a good eye for witty, telling details. Good chapters on the story of the Thais before they reached what's now Thailand, and on more recent developments. The same author's *Siam in Mind* (Silkworm Books, Chiang Mai) is a wide-ranging and intriguing collection of sketches and short reflections that point towards an intellectual history of Thailand.

ART, ARCHITECTURE AND FILM

Jean Boisselier *The Heritage of Thai Sculpture*. Expensive but accessible, seminal tome by influential French art historian.

★**Susan Conway** *Thai Textiles*. A fascinating, richly illustrated work which draws on sculptures and temple murals to trace the evolution of Thai weaving techniques and costume styles, and to examine the functional and ceremonial uses of textiles.

★**Sumet Jumsai** *Naga: Cultural Origins in Siam and the West Pacific*. Wide-ranging discussion of water symbols in Thailand and other parts of Asia, offering a stimulating mix of art, architecture, mythology and cosmology.

Bastian Meiresonne (ed) *Thai Cinema* (ⓦasiexpo.com). Anthology of twenty short essays on Thai cinema up to 2006, published to accompany a film festival in France, including pieces on art house, shorts and censorship. In French and English.

Steven Pettifor *Flavours: Thai Contemporary Art*. Takes up the baton from Poshyananda (see below) to look at the newly invigorated art scene in Thailand from 1992 to 2004, with profiles of 23 leading lights, including painters, multimedia and performance artists.

★**Apinan Poshyananda** *Modern Art In Thailand*. Excellent introduction which extends up to the early 1990s, with very readable discussions on dozens of individual artists, and lots of colour plates.

Dome Sukwong and Sawasdi Suwannapak *A Century of Thai Cinema*. Full-colour history of the Thai film industry and the promotional artwork (billboards, posters, magazines and cigarette cards) associated with it.

★ **Steve Van Beek** *The Arts of Thailand*. Lavishly produced and perfectly pitched introduction to the history of Thai

architecture, sculpture and painting, with superb photographs by Luca Invernizzi Tettoni.

William Warren and Luca Invernizzi Tettoni *Arts and Crafts of Thailand*. Good-value large-format paperback, setting the wealth of Thai arts and crafts in cultural context, with plenty of attractive illustrations and colour photographs.

NATURAL HISTORY AND ECOLOGY

Ashley J. Boyd and Collin Piprell *Diving in Thailand*. A thorough guide to 84 dive sites, plus general introductory sections on Thailand's marine life, conservation and photography tips.

★ **Boonsong Lekagul and Philip D. Round** *Guide to the Birds of Thailand*. Unparalleled illustrated guide to Thailand's birds. Worth scouring secondhand sellers for.

Craig Robson *A Field Guide to the Birds of Thailand*. Expert

and beautifully illustrated guide to Thailand's top. bird species, with locator maps.

Eric Valli and Diane Summers *The Shadow Hunters*. Beautifully photographed photo-essay on the bird's-nest collectors of southern Thailand, with whom the authors spent over a year, together scaling the phenomenal heights of the sheer limestone walls.

LITERATURE

Alastair Dingwall (ed) *Traveller's Literary Companion: Southeast Asia*. A useful though rather dry reference, with a large section on Thailand, including a book list, well-chosen extracts, biographical details of authors and other literary notes.

M.L. Manich Jumsai *Thai Ramayana* (Chalermnit, Bangkok). Slightly stilted, abridged prose translation of King Rama I's version of the epic Hindu narrative, full of gleeful descriptions of bizarre mythological characters and supernatural battles. Essential reading for a full appreciation of Thai painting, carving and classical dance.

★ **Chart Korbjitti** *The Judgement* (Howling Books). Sobering modern-day tragedy about a good-hearted Thai villager who is ostracized by his hypocritical neighbours. Contains lots of interesting details on village life and traditions, and thought-provoking passages on the stifling conservatism of rural communities. Winner of the S.E.A. Write Award in 1982.

★ **Rattawut Lapcharoensap** *Sightseeing*. This outstanding debut collection of short stories by a young Thai-born author now living overseas highlights big, pertinent themes – cruelty, corruption, racism, pride – in its neighbourhood tales of randy teenagers, bullyboys, a child's friendship with a Cambodian refugee, a young man who uses family influence to dodge the draft.

Nitaya Masavisut (ed) *The S.E.A. Write Anthology of Thai Short Stories and Poems* (Silkworm Books, Chiang Mai). Interesting medley of short stories and poems by Thai writers who have won Southeast Asian Writers' Awards, providing a good introduction to the contemporary literary scene.

Kukrit Pramoj *Si Phaendin: Four Reigns* (Silkworm Books, Chiang Mai). A kind of historical romance spanning the four reigns of Ramas V to VIII (1892–1946). Written by former prime minister Kukrit Pramoj, the story has become a modern classic in Thailand, made into films, plays and TV dramas, with heroine Ploi as the archetypal feminine role model.

S.P. Somtow *Jasmine Nights*. An engaging and humorous rites-of-passage tale, of an upper-class boy learning what it is to be Thai. *Dragon's Fin Soup and Other Modern Siamese Fables* is an imaginative and entertaining collection of often supernatural short stories, focusing on the collision of East and West.

★ **Khamsing Srinawk** *The Politician and Other Stories*. A collection of brilliantly satiric short stories, full of pithy moral observation and biting irony, which capture the vulnerability of peasant farmers in the north and northeast, as they try to come to grips with the modern world. Written by an insider from a peasant family, who was educated at Chulalongkorn University, became a hero of the left, and joined the communist insurgents after the 1976 clampdown.

Atsiri Thammachoat *Of Time and Tide* (Thai Modern Classics). Set in a fishing village near Hua Hin, this poetically written novella looks at how Thailand's fishing industry is changing, charting the effects on its fisherfolk and their communities.

Klaus Wenk *Thai Literature – An Introduction* (White Lotus, Bangkok). Dry, but useful, short overview of the last seven hundred years by a noted German scholar, with plenty of extracts.

THAILAND IN FOREIGN LITERATURE

Dean Barrett *Kingdom of Make-Believe*. Despite the clichéd ingredients – the Patpong go-go bar scene, opium smuggling in the Golden Triangle, Vietnam veterans – this

novel about a return to Thailand following a twenty-year absence turns out to be a rewardingly multi-dimensional take on the farang experience.

★**Mischa Berlinski** *Fieldwork*. Anthropology versus evangelism, a battle played out over an imaginary hill tribe in the hills of Chiang Rai by a fascinating cast of characters, as wrily and vividly told by its narrator.

Botan *Letters from Thailand*. Probably the best introduction to the Chinese community in Bangkok, presented in the form of letters written over a twenty-year period by a Chinese emigrant to his mother. Branded as both anti-Chinese and anti-Thai, this 1969 prize-winning book is now mandatory reading in school social studies' classes.

Pierre Boulle *The Bridge Over the River Kwai*. The World War II novel that inspired the David Lean movie and kicked off the Kanchanaburi tourist industry.

John Burdett *Bangkok 8*. Riveting Bangkok thriller that takes in Buddhism, plastic surgery, police corruption, the *yaa baa* drugs trade, hookers, jade smuggling and the spirit world.

Alex Garland *The Beach*. Gripping cult thriller (later made into a film, shot partly on Ko Phi Phi Leh) that uses a Thai setting to explore the way in which travellers' ceaseless quest for "undiscovered" utopias inevitably leads to them despoiling the idyll.

Andrew Hicks *Thai Girl*. A British backpacker falls for a reticent young beach masseuse on Ko Samet but struggles with age-old cross-cultural confusion in this sensitive attempt at a different kind of expat novel.

Michel Houellebecq *Platform*. Sex tourism in Thailand provides the nucleus of this brilliantly provocative (some would say offensive) novel, in which Houellebecq presents a ferocious critique of Western decadence and cultural colonialism, and of radical Islam too.

Christopher G. Moore *God of Darkness*. Thailand's best-selling expat novelist sets his most intriguing thriller during the economic crisis of 1997 and includes plenty of meat on endemic corruption and the desperate struggle for power within family and society.

Darin Strauss *Chang & Eng*. An intriguing, imagined autobiography of the famous nineteenth-century Siamese twins (see p.183), from their impoverished Thai childhood via the freak shows of New York and London to married life in small-town North Carolina. Unfortunately marred by lazy research and a confused grasp of Thai geography and culture.

FOOD AND COOKERY

Vatcharin Bhumichitr *The Taste of Thailand*. Another glossy introduction to this eminently photogenic country, this time through its food. The author runs a Thai restaurant in London and provides background colour as well as about 150 recipes adapted for Western kitchens.

Jacqueline M. Piper *Fruits of South-East Asia*. An exploration of the bounteous fruits of the region, tracing

their role in cooking, medicine, handicrafts and rituals. Well illustrated with photos, watercolours and early botanical drawings.

★**David Thompson** *Thai Food* and *Thai Street Food*. Comprehensive, impeccably researched celebrations of the cuisine with hundreds of recipes, by the owner of the first Thai restaurant ever to earn a Michelin star.

TRAVEL GUIDES

Oliver Hargreave *Exploring Phuket & Phi Phi: From Tin to Tourism*. Fascinating, thoroughly researched guide to the Andaman coast's big touristic honeypots; especially good on Phuket's history.

★**Thom Henley** *Krabi: Caught in the Spell – A Guide to Thailand's Enchanted Province* (Thai Nature Education, Phuket). Highly readable features and observations on the attractions and people of south Thailand's most beautiful

region, written by an expat environmentalist.

Dawn F. Rooney *Ancient Sukhothai*. Lively and beautifully photographed full-colour guide to the ruins of the northern plains: Sukhothai, Si Satchanalai and Kamphaeng Phet.

William Warren *Bangkok*. An engaging portrait of the unwieldy capital, weaving together anecdotes and character sketches from Bangkok's past and present.

Language

Thai belongs to one of the oldest families of languages in the world, Austro-Thai, and is radically different from most of the other tongues of Southeast Asia. Being tonal, Thai is very difficult for Westerners to master, but by building up from a small core of set phrases, you should soon have enough to get by. Most Thais who deal with tourists speak some English, but once you stray off the beaten track you'll probably need at least a little Thai. Anywhere you go, you'll impress and get better treatment if you at least make an effort to speak a few words.

Distinct dialects are spoken in the north, the northeast and the south, which can increase the difficulty of comprehending what's said to you. **Thai script** is even more of a problem to Westerners, with 44 consonants and 32 vowels. However, street signs in touristed areas are nearly always written in Roman script as well as Thai, and in other circumstances you're better off asking than trying to unscramble the swirling mess of letters and accents. For more information on transliteration into Roman script, see the box in this book's introduction.

Probably the best pocket dictionary is Paiboon Publishing's (⦿paiboonpublishing.com) *Thai-English, English-Thai Dictionary* (also available as a CD and as an app), which lists words in phonetic Thai as well as Thai script, and features very useful examples of the Thai alphabet in different fonts.

The best **teach-yourself course** is the expensive *Linguaphone Thai* (including eight CDs and an alphabet book), which also has a shorter, cheaper beginner-level *PDQ* version (with four CDs or available as a downloadable coursebook and audio files). *Thai for Beginners* by Benjawan Poomsan Becker (book with CDs or app; Paiboon Publishing) is a cheaper, more manageable textbook and is especially good for getting to grips with the Thai writing system. For a more traditional textbook, try Stuart Campbell and Chuan Shaweevongse's *The Fundamentals of the Thai Language*, which is comprehensive, though hard going. The **website** ⦿thai-language.com is an amazing free resource, featuring a searchable dictionary with over sixty thousand entries, complete with Thai script and audio clips, plus lessons and forums; you can also browse and buy Thai language books and learning materials. There are also plenty of **language classes** available in Thailand (see p.70).

Pronunciation

Mastering **tones** is probably the most difficult part of learning Thai. Five different tones are used – low, middle, high, falling, and rising – by which the meaning of a single syllable can be altered in five different ways. Thus, using four of the five tones, you can make a sentence from just one syllable: "mái mài mâi maˇi" meaning "New wood burns, doesn't it?" As well as the natural difficulty in becoming attuned to speaking and listening to these different tones, Western efforts are complicated by our habit of denoting the overall meaning of a sentence by modulating our tones – for example, turning a statement into a question through a shift of stress and tone. Listen to native Thai speakers and you'll soon begin to pick up the different approach to tone.

The pitch of each tone is gauged in relation to your vocal range when speaking, but they should all lie within a narrow band, separated by gaps just big enough to differentiate them. The **low tones** (syllables marked `), **middle tones** (unmarked syllables), and **high tones** (syllables marked ´) should each be pronounced evenly and with no inflection. The **falling tone** (syllables marked ˆ) is spoken with an obvious drop in pitch, as if you were sharply emphasizing a word in English. The **rising tone** (marked ˇ) is pronounced as if you were asking an exaggerated question in English.

As well as the unfamiliar tones, you'll find that, despite the best efforts of the transliterators, there is no precise English equivalent to many **vowel and consonant sounds** in the Thai language. The lists below give a simplified idea of pronunciation.

VOWELS

a as in dad
aa has no precise equivalent, but is pronounced as it looks, with the vowel elongated
ae as in there
ai as in buy
ao as in now
aw as in awe
ay as in pay
e as in pen

eu as in sir, but heavily nasalized
i as in tip
ii as in feet
o as in knock
oe as in hurt, but more closed
oh as in toe
u as in loot
uu as in pool

CONSONANTS

r as in rip, but with the tongue flapped quickly against the palate – in everyday speech, it's often pronounced like "l"
kh as in keep
ph as in put

th as in time
k is unaspirated and unvoiced, and closer to "g"
p is also unaspirated and unvoiced, and closer to "b"
t is also unaspirated and unvoiced, and closer to "d"

GENERAL WORDS AND PHRASES

GREETINGS AND BASIC PHRASES

When you speak to a stranger in Thailand, you should generally end your sentence in *khráp* if you're a man, *khâ* if you're a woman – these untranslatable politening syllables will gain goodwill, and are nearly always used after *sawàt dii* (hello/goodbye) and *khàwp khun* (thank you). *Khráp* and *khâ* are also often used to answer "yes" to a question, though the most common way is to repeat the verb of the question (precede it with *mâi* for "no"). *Châi* (yes) and *mâi châi* (no) are less frequently used than their English equivalents.

Hello	sawàt dii
Where are you going?	pai năi? (not always meant literally, but used as a general greeting)
I'm out having fun/ I'm travelling	pai thîaw (answer to pai năi, almost indefinable pleasantry)
Goodbye	sawàt dii/la kàwn
Good luck/cheers	chôhk dii
Excuse me	khăw thâwt
Thank you	khàwp khun
It's nothing/ it doesn't matter	mâi pen rai
How are you?	sabai dii reŭ?
I'm fine	sabai dii
What's your name?	khun chêu arai?
My name is...	phŏm (men)/diichăn (women) chêu...

I come from...	phŏm/diichăn maa jàak...
I don't understand	mâi khăo jai
Do you speak English?	khun phûut phasăa angkrìt dâi măi?
Do you have...?	mii...măi?
Is...possible?	...dâi măi?
Can you help me?	chûay phŏm/ diichăn dâi măi?
(I) want...	ao...
(I) would like to...	yàak jà...
(I) like...	châwp...
What is this called in Thai?	nîi phasăa thai rîak wâa arai?

GETTING AROUND

Where is the...?	...yùu thîi năi?
How far?	klai thâo rai?
I would like to go to...	yàak jà pai...
Where have you been?	pai năi maa?
Where is this bus going?	rót nîi pai năi?
When will the bus leave?	rót jà àwk mêua rai?
What time does the bus arrive in...?	rót theŭng...kìi mohng?
Stop here	jàwt thîi nîi
here	thîi nîi
there/over there	thîi nâan/thîi nôhn

right	khwăa
left	sái
straight	trong
north	neŭa
south	tâi
east	tawan àwk
west	tawan tòk
near/far	klâi/klai
street	thanŏn
train station	sathàanii rót fai
bus station	sathàanii rót mae
airport	sanăam bin
ticket	tŭa
hotel	rohng raem
post office	praisanii
restaurant	raan ahăan
shop	raan
market	talàat
hospital	rohng pha-yaabaan
motorbike	rót mohtoesai
taxi	rót táksîi
boat	reua
bicycle	jàkràyaan

ACCOMMODATION AND SHOPPING

How much is...?	...thâo rai/kìi bàat?
I don't want a plastic bag, thanks	mâi ao thŭng khráp/khâ
How much is a room here per night?	hăwng thîi nîi kheun lá thâo rai?
Do you have a cheaper room?	mii hăwng thùuk kwàa măi?
Can I/we look at the room?	duu hăwng dâi măi?
I/We'll stay two nights	jà yùu săwng kheun
Can you reduce the price?	lót raakhaa dâi măi?
Can I store my bag here?	fàak krapăo wái thîi nîi dâi măi?
cheap/expensive	thùuk/phaeng
air-con room	hăwng ae
ordinary room	hăwng thammadaa
telephone	thohrásàp
laundry	sák phâa
blanket	phâa hòm
fan	phát lom

GENERAL ADJECTIVES

alone	khon diaw
another	ìik...nèung
bad	mâi dii
big	yài
clean	sa-àat
closed	pìt
cold (object)	yen

cold (person or weather)	năo
delicious	aròi
difficult	yâak
dirty	sokaprok
easy	ngâi
fun	sanùk
hot (temperature)	ráwn
hot (spicy)	phèt
hungry	hĭu khâo
ill	mâi sabai
open	pòet
pretty	sŭay
small	lek
thirsty	hĭu nám
tired	nèu-ay
very	mâak

GENERAL NOUNS

Nouns have no plurals or genders, and don't require an article.

bathroom/toilet	hăwng nám
boyfriend or girlfriend	faen
food	ahăan
foreigner	fàràng
friend	phêuan
money	ngoen
water/liquid	nám

GENERAL VERBS

Thai verbs do not conjugate at all, and also often double up as nouns and adjectives, which means that foreigners' most unidiomatic attempts to construct sentences are often readily understood.

come	maa
do	tham
eat	kin/thaan khâo
give	hâi
go	pai
sit	nâng
sleep	nawn làp
walk	doen pai

NUMBERS

zero	sŭun
one	nèung
two	săwng
three	săam
four	sìi
five	hâa
six	hòk
seven	jèt
eight	pàet
nine	kâo
ten	sìp
eleven	sìp èt

twelve, thirteen...	sìp săwng, sìp săam...
twenty	yîi sìp/yiip
twenty-one	yîi sìp èt
twenty-two,	yîi sìp săwng,
twenty-three...	yîi sìp săam...
thirty, forty, etc	săam sìp, sìi sìp...
one hundred,	nèung rói, săwng rói...
two hundred...	
one thousand	nèung phan
ten thousand	nèung mèun
one hundred thousand	nèung săen
one million	nèung lăan

TIME

The most common system for telling the time, as outlined below, is actually a confusing mix of several different systems. The State Railway and government officials use the 24-hour clock (9am is *kâo naalikaa*, 10am *sìp naalikaa*, and so on), which is always worth trying if you get stuck.

1–5am	tii nèung–tii hâa
6–11am	hòk mohng cháo–sìp èt
	mohng cháo
noon	thîang
1pm	bài mohng
2–4pm	bài săwng mohng–
	bài sìi mohng
5–6pm	hâa mohng yen–
	hòk mohng yen
7–11pm	nèung thûm–hâa thûm

midnight	thîang kheun
What time is it?	kìi mohng láew?
How many hours?	kìi chûa mohng?
How long?	naan thâo rai?
minute	naathii
hour	chûa mohng
day	wan
week	aathít
month	deuan
year	pii
today	wan níi
tomorrow	phrûng níi
yesterday	mêua wan níi
now	diăw níi
next week	aathít nâa
last week	aathít kàwn
morning	cháo
afternoon	bài
evening	yen
night	kheun

DAYS

Sunday	wan aathít
Monday	wan jan
Tuesday	wan angkhaan
Wednesday	wan phút
Thursday	wan pháréuhàt
Friday	wan sùk
Saturday	wan săo

FOOD AND DRINK

BASIC INGREDIENTS

kài	chicken
mŭu	pork
néua	beef, meat
pèt	duck
ahăan thalay	seafood
plaa	fish
plaa dùk	catfish
plaa mèuk	squid
kûng	prawn, shrimp
hŏy	shellfish
hŏy nang rom	oyster
puu	crab
khài	egg
phàk	vegetables

VEGETABLES

makĕua	aubergine
makĕua thêt	tomato
nàw mái	bamboo shoots
tùa ngâwk	bean sprouts
phrík	chilli
man faràng	potato

man faràng thâwt	chips
taeng kwaa	cucumber
phrík yùak	green pepper
krathiam	garlic
hèt	mushroom
tùa	peas, beans or lentils
tôn hŏrm	spring onions

NOODLES

ba mìi	egg noodles
kwáy tiăw (sên yài/	white rice noodles
sên lék)	(wide/thin)
khanŏm jiin nám yaa	noodles topped with
	fish curry
kwáy tiăw/ba mìi haêng	rice noodle/egg
	noodles fried with
	egg, small pieces
	of meat and a few
	vegetables
kwáy tiăw/ba	rice noodle/egg
mìi nám (mŭu)	noodle soup, made
	with chicken broth
	(and pork balls)

kwáy tiăw/ba mìi rât nâ (mŭu)	rice noodles/egg noodles fried in gravy-like sauce with vegetables (and pork slices)
mìi kràwp	crisp fried egg noodles with small pieces of meat and a few vegetables
phàt thai	thin noodles fried with egg, bean sprouts and tofu, topped with ground peanuts
phàt siyú	wide or thin noodles fried with soy sauce, egg and meat

RICE

khâo	rice
khâo man kài	slices of chicken served over marinated rice
khâo mŭu daeng	red pork with rice
khâo nâ kài/pèt	chicken/duck served with sauce over rice
khâo niăw	sticky rice
khâo phàt	fried rice
khâo kaeng	curry over rice
khâo tôm	rice soup (usually for breakfast)

CURRIES AND SOUPS

kaeng phèt	hot, red curry
kaeng phánaeng	thick, savoury curry
kaeng khîaw wan	green curry
kaeng mátsàman	rich Muslim-style curry, usually with beef and potatoes
kaeng karìi	mild, Indian-style curry
hàw mòk thalay	seafood curry soufflé
kaeng liang	peppery vegetable soup
kaeng sôm	tamarind soup
tôm khà kài	chicken, coconut and galangal soup
tôm yam kûng	hot and sour prawn soup
kaeng jèut	mild soup with vegetables and usually pork

SALADS

lâap	spicy ground meat salad
nám tòk	grilled beef or pork salad
sôm tam	spicy papaya salad
yam hua plee	banana flower salad
yam néua	grilled beef salad
yam plaa mèuk	squid salad
yam sôm oh	pomelo salad
yam plaa dùk foo	crispy fried catfish salad

yam thùa phuu	wing-bean salad
yam wun sen	noodle and pork salad

OTHER DISHES

hâwy thâwt	omelette stuffed with mussels
kài phàt bai krapao	chicken fried with holy basil leaves
kài phàt nàw mái	chicken with bamboo shoots
kài phàt mét mámûang	chicken with cashew nuts
kài phàt khĭng	chicken with ginger
kài yâang	grilled chicken
khài yát sài	omelette with pork and vegetables
kûng chúp paêng thâwt	prawns fried in batter
mŭu prîaw wăan	sweet and sour pork
néua phàt krathiam phrík thai	beef fried with garlic and pepper
néua phàt nám man hâwy	beef in oyster sauce
phàt phàk bûng fai daeng	morning glory fried in garlic and bean sauce
phàt phàk ruam	stir-fried vegetables
pàw pía	spring rolls
plaa nêung páe sá	whole fish steamed with vegetables and ginger
plaa rât phrík	whole fish cooked with chillies
plaa thâwt	fried whole fish
sàté	satay
thâwt man plaa	fish cake

THAI DESSERTS (*KHANŎM*)

khanŏm beuang	small crispy pancake folded over with coconut cream and strands of sweet egg inside
khâo lăam	sticky rice, coconut cream and black beans cooked and served in bamboo tubes
khâo niăw daeng	sticky red rice mixed with coconut cream
khâo niăw thúrian/ mámûang	sticky rice mixed with coconut cream and durian/mango
klûay khàek	fried banana
lûk taan chêum	sweet palm kernels served in syrup
săngkhayaa	coconut custard
tàkôh	squares of transparent jelly (jello) topped with coconut cream

DRINKS (*KHREÛANG DEÙM*)

bia	beer
chaa ráwn	hot tea
chaa yen	iced tea
kaafae ráwn	hot coffee
kâew	glass
khúat	bottle
mâekhŏng	Thai brand-name
(or anglicized Mekong)	rice whisky
klûay pan	banana shake
nám mánao/sôm	fresh, bottled or fizzy
	lemon/orange juice
nám plào	drinking water
	(boiled or filtered)
nám sŏdaa	soda water
nám taan	sugar
kleua	salt
nám yen	cold water
nom jeùd	milk
ohlíang	iced black coffee
thûay	cup

ORDERING

I am vegetarian/vegan	**Phŏm (male)/diichăn (female) kin ahăan mangsàwirát/jeh**
Can I see the menu?	**Khăw duù menu nóy?**
I would like…	**Khăw…**
with/without…	**Sài/mâi sài…**
Can I have the bill please?	**Khăw check bin?**

Glossary

Amphoe District.

Amphoe muang Provincial capital.

Ao Bay.

Apsara Female deity.

Avalokitesvara Bodhisattva representing compassion.

Avatar Earthly manifestation of a deity.

Ban Village or house.

Bang Village by a river or the sea.

Bencharong Polychromatic ceramics made in China for the Thai market.

Bhumisparsa mudra Most common gesture of Buddha images; symbolizes the Buddha's victory over temptation.

Bodhisattva In Mahayana Buddhism, an enlightened being who postpones his or her entry into Nirvana.

Bot Main sanctuary of a Buddhist temple.

Brahma One of the Hindu trinity – "The Creator". Usually depicted with four faces and four arms.

Celadon Porcelain with grey-green glaze.

Changwat Province.

Chao ley/chao nam "Sea gypsies" – nomadic fisherfolk of south Thailand.

Chedi Reliquary tower in Buddhist temple.

Chofa Finial on temple roof.

Deva Mythical deity.

Devaraja God-king.

Dharma The teachings or doctrine of the Buddha.

Dharmachakra Buddhist Wheel of Law (also known as Wheel of Doctrine or Wheel of Life).

Doi Mountain.

Erawan Mythical three-headed elephant; Indra's vehicle.

Farang Foreigner/foreign.

Ganesh Hindu elephant-headed deity, remover of obstacles and god of knowledge.

Garuda Mythical Hindu creature – half man, half bird; Vishnu's vehicle.

Gopura Entrance pavilion to temple precinct (especially Khmer).

Hamsa Sacred mythical goose; Brahma's vehicle.

Hanuman Monkey god and chief of the monkey army in the *Ramayana*; ally of Rama.

Hat Beach.

Hin Stone.

Hinayana Pejorative term for Theravada school of Buddhism, literally "Lesser Vehicle".

Ho trai A scripture library.

Indra Hindu king of the gods and, in Buddhism, devotee of the Buddha; usually carries a thunderbolt.

Isaan Northeast Thailand.

Jataka Stories of the Buddha's five hundred lives.

Khaen Reed and wood pipe; the characteristic musical instrument of Isaan.

Khao Hill, mountain.

Khlong Canal.

Khon Classical dance-drama.

Kinnari Mythical creature – half woman, half bird.

Kirtimukha Very powerful deity depicted as a lion-head.

Ko Island.

Ku The Lao word for prang; a tower in a temple complex.

Laem Headland or cape.

Lakhon Classical dance-drama.

Lak muang City pillar; revered home for the city's guardian spirit.

Lakshaman/Phra Lak Rama's younger brother.

Lakshana Auspicious signs or "marks of greatness" displayed by the Buddha.

Lanna Northern Thai kingdom that lasted from the thirteenth to the sixteenth century.

Likay Popular folk theatre.

Longyi Burmese sarong.

Luang Pho Abbot or especially revered monk.

Maenam River.

Mahathat Chedi containing relics of the Buddha.

Mahayana School of Buddhism now practised mainly in China, Japan and Korea; literally "the Great Vehicle".

Mara The Evil One; tempter of the Buddha.

Mawn khwaan Traditional triangular or "axe-head" pillow.

Meru/Sineru Mythical mountain at the centre of Hindu and Buddhist cosmologies.

Mondop Small, square temple building to house minor images or religious texts.

Moo/muu Neighbourhood.

Muang City or town.

Muay thai Thai boxing.

Mudra Symbolic gesture of the Buddha.

Mut mee Tie-dyed cotton or silk.

Naga Mythical dragon-headed serpent in Buddhism and Hinduism.

Nakhon Honorific title for a city.

Nam Water.

Nam tok Waterfall.

Nang thalung Shadow-puppet entertainment, found in southern Thailand.

Nielloware Engraved metalwork.

Nirvana Final liberation from the cycle of rebirths; state of non-being to which Buddhists aspire.

Pak Tai Southern Thailand.

Pali Language of ancient India; the script of the original Buddhist scriptures.

Pha sin Woman's sarong.

Phi Animist spirit.

Phra Honorific term – literally "excellent".

Phu Mountain.

Prang Central tower in a Khmer temple.

Prasat Khmer temple complex or central shrine.

Rama/Phra Ram Human manifestation of Hindu deity Vishnu; hero of the *Ramayana*.

Ramakien Thai version of the *Ramayana*.

Ramayana Hindu epic of good versus evil: chief characters include Rama, Sita, Ravana, Hanuman.

Ravana see Totsagan.

Reua hang yao Longtail boat.

Rishi Ascetic hermit.

Rot ae/rot tua Air-conditioned bus.

Rot thammadaa Ordinary bus.

Sala Meeting hall, pavilion, bus stop – or any open-sided structure.

Samlor Three-wheeled passenger tricycle.

Sanskrit Sacred language of Hinduism; also used in Buddhism.

Sanuk Fun.

Sema Boundary stone to mark consecrated ground within temple complex.

Shiva One of the Hindu trinity – "The Destroyer".

Shiva lingam Phallic representation of Shiva.

Soi Lane or side road.

Songkhran Thai New Year.

Songthaew Public transport pick-up vehicle; means "two rows", after its two facing benches.

Takraw Game played with a rattan ball.

Talat Market.

Talat nam Floating market.

Talat yen Night market.

Tambon Subdistrict.

Tavatimsa Buddhist heaven.

Tha Pier.

Thale Sea or lake.

Tham Cave.

Thanon Road.

That Chedi.

Thep A divinity.

Theravada Main school of Buddhist thought in Thailand; also known as Hinayana.

Totsagan Rama's evil rival in the *Ramayana*; also known as Ravana.

Tripitaka Buddhist scriptures.

Trok Alley.

Tuk-tuk Motorized three-wheeled taxi.

Uma Shiva's consort.

Ushnisha Cranial protuberance on Buddha images, signifying an enlightened being.

Viharn Temple assembly hall for the laity; usually contains the principal Buddha image.

Vipassana Buddhist meditation technique; literally "insight".

Vishnu One of the Hindu trinity – "The Preserver". Usually shown with four arms, holding a disc, a conch, a lotus and a club.

Wai Thai greeting expressed by a prayer-like gesture with the hands.

Wang Palace.

Wat Temple.

Wiang Fortified town.

Yaksha Mythical giant.

Yantra Magical combination of numbers and letters, used to ward off danger.

Small print and index

A ROUGH GUIDE TO ROUGH GUIDES

Published in 1982, the first Rough Guide – to Greece – was a student scheme that became a publishing phenomenon. Mark Ellingham, a recent graduate in English from Bristol University, had been travelling in Greece the previous summer and couldn't find the right guidebook. With a small group of friends he wrote his own guide, combining a highly contemporary, journalistic style with a thoroughly practical approach to travellers' needs.

The immediate success of the book spawned a series that rapidly covered dozens of destinations. And, in addition to impecunious backpackers, Rough Guides soon acquired a much broader readership that relished the guides' wit and inquisitiveness as much as their enthusiastic, critical approach and value-for-money ethos.

These days, Rough Guides include recommendations from budget to luxury and cover more than 120 destinations around the globe, as well as producing an ever-growing range of ebooks.

Visit **roughguides.com** to find all our latest books, read articles, get inspired and share travel tips with the Rough Guides community.

Rough Guide credits

Editors: Emma Gibbs, Ann-Marie Shaw and Olivia Rawes
Layout: Nikhil Agarwal
Cartography: Deshpal Dabas
Picture editor: Lisa Jacobs
Proofreader: Jan McCann
Managing editor: Keith Drew
Assistant editor: Payal Sharotri
Production: Jimmy Lao

Cover design: Nicole Newman, Lisa Jacobs and Nikhil Agarwal
Photographers: Martin Richardson and Karen Trist
Editorial assistant: Freya Godfrey
Senior pre-press designer: Dan May
Programme manager: Gareth Lowe
Publishing director: Georgina Dee

Publishing information

This ninth edition published October 2015 by
Rough Guides Ltd,
80 Strand, London WC2R 0RL
11, Community Centre, Panchsheel Park,
New Delhi 110017, India
Distributed by Penguin Random House
Penguin Books Ltd,
80 Strand, London WC2R 0RL
Penguin Group (USA)
345 Hudson Street, NY 10014, USA
Penguin Group (Australia)
250 Camberwell Road, Camberwell,
Victoria 3124, Australia
Penguin Group (NZ)
67 Apollo Drive, Mairangi Bay, Auckland 1310,
New Zealand
Penguin Group (South Africa)
Block D, Rosebank Office Park, 181 Jan Smuts Avenue,
Parktown North, Gauteng, South Africa 2193
Rough Guides is represented in Canada by Tourmaline
Editions Inc. 662 King Street West, Suite 304, Toronto,
Ontario M5V 1M7
Printed in Singapore

MIX
Paper from
responsible sources
FSC
www.fsc.org   **FSC™ C018179**

Help us update

We've gone to a lot of effort to ensure that the ninth
edition of **The Rough Guide to Thailand** is accurate
and up-to-date. However, things change – places get
"discovered", opening hours are notoriously fickle,
restaurants and rooms raise prices or lower standards. If
you feel we've got it wrong or left something out, we'd like
to know, and if you can remember the address, the price,
the hours, the phone number, so much the better.

Please send your comments with the subject line
"Rough Guide Thailand Update" to @ mail@uk
.roughguides.com. We'll credit all contributions and send
a copy of the next edition (or any other Rough Guide if you
prefer) for the very best emails.
Find more travel information, connect with fellow
travellers and plan your trip on ⓦ roughguides.com.

Acknowledgements

The authors jointly would like to thank Emma, Annie, Olivia, Keith and Lisa at Rough Guides; and staff at tourist offices
throughout Thailand.

Ron Emmons Thanks to Paul Gray for tips on the Central
Plains and Northeast regions, and to Emma Gibbs for her
sharp-eyed editing. Thanks also to those generous people
who shared their time and local expertise to bring me
up-to-date with recent developments: Tan and Michel
Hermann in Sukhothai; Noom in Lopburi; Dennis Compton;
Evelien and Chalee in Kanchanaburi; Jimmy at Birdland
in Sangkhlaburi; Dave Coughlin in Mae Sot; Thanaphat
Kinglek (Tony) and Siraphat Thongsiri in Khao Yai; Wicha
Littidej in Nang Rong; Brent and Tun in Ubon Ratchathani;
Phajongkit Laoraowirodge in Khon Kaen; Julian Wright in
Nong Khai; Toy in Sang Khom, and Pat in Loei.

Paul Gray Big thanks to Anne Bachmann, Mike Barraclough
and Steve Epstein in Chiang Mai; Kanokros Sakdanares
and Marion Walsh in Bangkok; Fhu and Ung in Nan; Wat in
Chiang Khong; Tom in Phetchaburi; Suda in Chumphon;

Rashi, Bambi, Jorge and Andy on Ko Samui and Ko Pha
Ngan; Matt Bolton on Ko Tao; Ekkachai in Trang; On in
Satun; and Tuppadit Thaiarry and all the staff at Avis. Thanks
for their love and forbearance during a difficult time to
Gade and Stella Gray, who make everything possible. I'd like
to dedicate my work on this book to my dad, Bill Gray, who
was there for me over several editions of this guide, giving
much-needed support, encouragement and advice.

Phillip Tang Thank you Géraldine Galvaing for the
spontaneous trips from Bang Sue to Baan Phu Lae and
the magic of night temples and mango smoothies.
Thanks to the new Thai friends and to Sutassa Vareetip
for suggestions. Big thanks to Emma Gibbs for her hard
work, patience and guidance in editing, and Keith Drew for
having me on board. Special warm thanks to Lisa N'paisan
and Vek Lewis for keeping the home fires homely.

ABOUT THE AUTHORS

Ron Emmons (⊕ronemmons.com) has been based in Chiang Mai, Thailand, since the 1980s. He has contributed to several updates of the *Rough Guide to Thailand*, is co-author of the *Rough Guide to Vietnam* and has updated guidebooks on various Southeast Asian destinations for National Geographic, Frommer's and DK Books. He is the author and photographer of *Portrait of Thailand* and *Walks along the Thames Path*, as well as a collection of travelogues, *Searching for Shangri-La*. His travel articles and images appear regularly in international publications.

Paul Gray After twenty years of toing and froing, Paul has recently settled down in Thailand. He is author of the *Rough Guide to Bangkok* and co-author of the *Rough Guide to Thailand's Beaches & Islands*, as well as the *Rough Guide to Ireland*, and has edited and contributed to many other guidebooks, including an update of his native Northeast for the *Rough Guide to England*.

Phillip Tang has spent two decades travelling around Thailand and Asia. He has also contributed to travel guides to China, Japan and Korea, as well as books on Latin America, such as the *Rough Guide to Peru* and the *Rough Guide to South America on a Budget*. More at ⊕phillíptang.co.uk.

Readers' updates

Thanks to all the readers who have taken the time to write in with comments and suggestions (and apologies if we've inadvertently omitted or misspelt anyone's name):

Angelika Becker, Hiroko Canning, Lucie Cluver and Rich, Steven Flintham, John Garratt, Eva Grimbergen, Alessa Hardwick, Dan Jacobs, Alan McEvoy, Monica Mackaness, Gabriel Martinez, Jo Murphy, Silke Nelis and Nicolaas, Chris Pitt, Barry Rice, Liz Talliss, Alina Vasile, Suzanne Verheij

Photo credits

All photos © Rough Guides except the following:
(Key: t-top; c-centre; b-bottom; l-left; r-right)

p.1 Sergio Pessolano/Getty Images
p.2 Pete Atkinson/Getty Images
p.4 Igor Prahin/Getty Images (tr)
p.9 Gavin Gough/Getty Images (tr); Mark Horn/Getty Images (br)
p.11 Tumjang/Getty Images (br)
p.12 Markus Braun/Alamy
p.13 Constantinos Pliakos/Alamy (tl); Luca Tettoni/SuperStock (b)
p.15 SuperStock (br)
p.16 Richard Powers/Corbis (t); Terry Whittaker/Alamy (bl)
p.17 Martin Puddy/Corbis (b)
p.18 SuperStock (tl); Anders Ryman/Alamy (tr); Luca Tettoni/SuperStock (b)
p.19 Katja Kreder/SuperStock (c)
p.20 Henry Westheim/Alamy (t); Jack Barker/Alamy (cl)
p.21 StockShot/Alamy (t); Andy Selinger/SuperStock (bl); Luca Tettoni (br)
p.22 SuperStock (l); Otto Stadler/SuperStock (c)
p.77 Visions Of Our Land/Getty Images
p.93 Gavin Gough/Getty Images (t); Art Kowalsky/Alamy (br)
p.175 SuperStock
p.189 Kevin Levesque/Alamy (t); Matteo Colombo/Getty Images (br)
p.257 Raspu/Getty Images (tl); Pakorn Lopattanakij/Alamy (b)

pp.268–269 Teradat Santivivut/Getty Images
p.295 Dave Stamboulis/Robert Harding Picture Library
p.313 Simon Reddy/Alamy (t); Chris Hellier/Alamy (b)
p.333 epa/Alamy (t); Jack Barker/Alamy (bl)
p.357 Paul Kingsley/Alamy (b)
p.379 Karen Trist/Dorling Kindersley
p.407 David Henley/Dorling Kindersley (t)
p.475 Mick Shippen/4Corners (bl); Steve Vidler/SuperStock (br)
pp.504–505 Jim Doberman/Getty Images
p.557 Dave Stamboulis/SuperStock (bl); Simon Reddy/Alamy (br)
p.641 Richard Taylor/Corbis (tl); Travelscape Images/Alamy (b)
p.671 Travel Pix Collection/AWL Images (b)
pp.692–693 Michael Christopher Brown/Corbis
p.695 SuperStock
p.703 Lee Dalton/Alamy (b)

Front cover and spine Wat Mahatat, Sukhothai Historical Park © Tuul/Robert Harding Picture Library
Back cover Ko Tub © Bruno Morandi/Getty Images; Two leaf monkeys, Phetchaburi © Prasit Chansareekorn/Getty Images; Wat Phra That Hariphunchai © Suttipong Sutiratanachai/Getty Images

Index

Maps are marked in grey

Map symbols

The symbols below are used on maps throughout the book

International boundary		Cave		Telephone office
Provincial boundary		Waterfall		Airline office
Chapter division boundary		Spring		Hospital/clinic
Expressway		Rocks		Post office
Pedestrianized road		Lighthouse		Embassy/consulate
Road		Viewpoint		Toilet/restrooms
One-way street		Ruins/archeological site		Market
Steps		Wildlife park		Landmark hotel
Unpaved road		Gate		Temple
Path		Arch		Mosque
Railway		Statue		Hindu temple
Ferry route		Airport		Chinese temple/pagoda
River/canal		Transport stop		Stadium
Wall		Point of interest		Church
Cable car & station		National park (country map)		Building
Footbridge		Ranger station		Christian cemetery
Bridge		Museum		Swamps/marshes
Border crossing		Bank/ATM		Park/forest
Peak		Internet access		Beach
Mountain		Tourist information		

Listings key

- Accommodation
- Restaurant/café
- Bar/club/drinking
- Shop

City Arts and Cultural Centre and Historical Centre
THANON INTHRAWARAROT
Three Kings Monument
THANON RATCHDAMNOEN
Suan Dork Gate
Wat Phra Singh
Wat Chedi Luang
THANON RATCHAMANKA
Yoga Tree
THANON BOON RUANGRIT
THANON ARAK
THANON SAMLARN
THANON PHRA POKKLAO
JHABAN

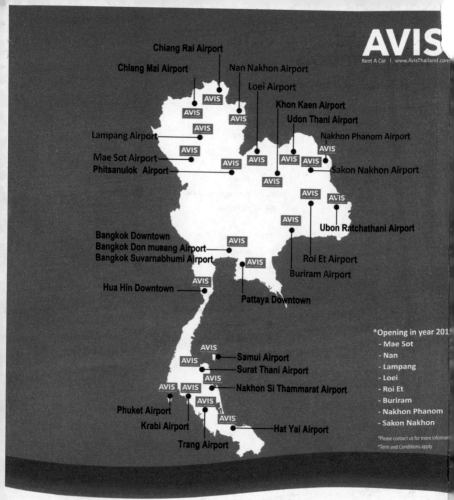

Available at all Airport Locations, Call us Now!

Call Center: **02 251 1131**

www.AvisThailand.com